Medium/Heavy Duty Truck Engines, Fuel & Computerized Management Systems

FIFTH EDITION

Sean Bennett

CENGAGE
Learning·

Australia • Brazil • Japan • Korea • Mexico • Singapore • Spain • United Kingdom • United States

Medium/Heavy Duty Truck Engines, Fuel & Computerized Management Systems: Fifth Edition

Medium/Heavy Duty Truck Engines, Fuel & Computerized Management Systems: Fifth Edition
Sean Bennett

For product information and technology assistance, contact us at
Cengage Learning Customer & Sales Support, 1-800-354-9706

For permission to use material from this text or product,
submit all requests online at **cengage.com/permissions**
Further permissions questions can be emailed to
permissionrequest@cengage.com

This book contains select works from existing Cengage Learning resources and was produced by Cengage Learning Custom Solutions for collegiate use. As such, those adopting and/or contributing to this work are responsible for editorial content accuracy, continuity and completeness.

Compilation © 2016 Cengage Learning

ISBN: 978-1-3370-4034-1

Cengage Learning
20 Channel Center Street
Boston, MA 02210
USA

Cengage Learning is a leading provider of customized learning solutions with office locations around the globe, including Singapore, the United Kingdom, Australia, Mexico, Brazil, and Japan. Locate your local office at:
www.international.cengage.com/region.

Cengage Learning products are represented in Canada by Nelson Education, Ltd.

For your lifelong learning solutions, visit **www.cengage.com/custom.**

Visit our corporate website at **www.cengage.com.**

CONTENTS

PREFACE

Five years of experience with selective catalytic reduction (SCR) technology has brought us to the point we can declare it to be a major success. So successful, in fact, that many large fleets have accelerated equipment renewal schedules to get rid of the pre-2010 generations of tractors with their high cut-percentage EGR systems that compromise both fuel economy and engine longevity. This has led to a recent mini-boom in Class 8 tractor sales, underscoring the fact that the inconveniences (and extra cost) of using DEF have been more than compensated for by its advantages.

INNOVATIONS OVER THE NEXT FEW YEARS

With regard to technical innovations in the diesel engine industry, the immediate future appears to be settled when compared with the first decade of this millennium, when every successive bout of EPA standards heralded entirely new engine, fuel, and emissions management technologies. There will not be any major changes in the diesel fuel systems used by engine manufacturers in the foreseeable future, and common rail (CR) fueling is expected to continue its current dominance. In 2013, Paccar reengineered its large-bore MX-Series engines to replace EUP fueling with a Delphi Lucas CR system, which is covered in this edition.

Many of the changes we will see in the industry heading toward 2020 will be in the methods used to communicate with truck chassis and powertrain data buses. The use of telematics is expected to increase, and this has initiated some debate over who has ownership of, and access to, data exchanged over vehicle communication buses. While it can be argued that highway safety enforcement agencies have a legitimate right to access truck running data using telematics, the security of current wireless data exchange is low level and if compromised, could be abused if it fell into the wrong hands. These issues have delayed the mandatory implementation of electronic onboard (data) recorders (EOBRs)—but that hasn't deterred many of our largest fleets from voluntarily adopting EOBR because of its numerous logistic and maintenance advantages.

FREIGHT EFFICIENCY

Most engine-related changes set to take place over the next five years are not likely to be hardware-related. As we head toward the Obama Administration's 2017 and 2018 standards on commercial vehicle fuel efficiency and reduced greenhouse gas emissions (GHGs), it is certain that engine management software will be tweaked; still, the real changes are expected to occur in the areas of tractor-trailer aerodynamics and freight efficiency. The term *freight efficiency* has been a catchphrase in trucking since 2007: by definition, it is fuel consumed per ton hauled. To meet the 2017 and 2018 standards, the entire vehicle will come under scrutiny, with the objective of maximizing overall efficiency. This is shifting focus off the diesel engine and onto such things as trailer length, maximum permissible cargo weight, vehicle aerodynamics, and tire rolling friction.

STRUCTURE OF THIS EDITION

Consistent with the fourth edition, this text uses a generic approach to teaching fuel systems rather than dedicating a stand-alone chapter to each manufacturer's system. Because diesel CR fuel systems are used by all but one of the major engine original equipment manufacturers (OEMs), the approach in this edition is to address this technology in two generic chapters that appear in the second section of the book. This content is later enhanced with OEM-specific content in dedicated chapters in the third section.

TRUCK VERSUS OFF-HIGHWAY DIESELS

My personal technical background is trucks. However, because this book has over the years been adopted by many diesel programs that cater to heavy-equipment, agricultural, marine, and stationary diesel engines, a broader-based approach has been used since the publication of the first edition. Although this has not changed the book title, it has meant including engine and fuel system technology that has never been used in truck applications—or may be regarded as obsolete by the truck community. In this fifth edition, although I have abbreviated or eliminated coverage of some of the older hydromechanical systems, materials on a couple of key hydromechanical fuel systems have been retained to accommodate the learning outcomes of those programs using the book for non-truck programs, and for the requirements of certification testing. It should be added that the port-helix pump-line-nozzle (PLN) fuel system continues to be used on a majority of trailer reefer systems produced today, and they are both EPA and CARB compliant because of their specified power ratings.

HANDS-ON LEARNING

An objective of this book is to keep it 100% current with the changes mandated for commercial diesel engines meeting EPA Tier 4 emissions, and to do so recognizing that mechanical technicians tend to learn by doing rather than by reading. Although the emphasis is vocational, with the objective of mastering hands-on repair technology, understanding how and why systems function is crucial to developing skilled technicians. Truck and diesel technology program graduates will ultimately target a broad spectrum of employers with diverse needs. The technical skill sets required by small fleets, major fleets, independent garages, construction sites, and OEM dealerships vary enormously, and while the fleet technician may never do anything more involved than servicing engines, OEM technicians will diagnose, recondition, and test engines on a regular basis. The challenge to college diesel programs—and this textbook—is to meet those diverse requirements in a single package.

CLIMATE CHANGE AND SUSTAINABILITY

Because issues of climate change and sustainability are now integrated into the syllabi of some learning institutions, I was asked to address the impact of diesel engines on the environment in the previous edition. Because EPA and CARB diesel emissions requirements have been covered in detail from the first edition of this textbook onward, my feeling is that this objective has already been met and there is no need to add a chapter dedicated solely to that subject matter.

Regardless of politics, there is no doubt that the generation reaching adulthood today has to contend with a world that has been significantly environmentally damaged by those generations that preceded them. The damage has been committed sometimes knowingly, sometimes more innocently.

It is vital that all persons today are provided with an awareness of their personal footprint on the world, not just in terms of talking the talk but also in walking the walk. When a technician uses his knowledge to overwrite the fueling algorithm in an engine in order to produce 5% more horsepower, the difference in increased emissions of that one engine may produce an insignificant global impact. However, when this type of illegal practice becomes commonplace, the effect can be severe. As you acquire skills as a truck technician, you will soon be in a position to use that expertise to influence the environment in a small way. It is important that you use knowledge to protect your world and that of your children.

IMPORTANCE OF FEEDBACK

One of my roles as textbook writer is to listen and respond to feedback from a network of instructors and industry specialists, coast to coast. It is not always easy, because sometimes the suggestions are contradictory and a truck diesel specialist is likely to have opinions different from those of an agricultural equipment specialist. Over the years, I have made a point of visiting truck, diesel, heavy-equipment, and agricultural colleges and speaking directly to the instructor teams in schools spread over four continents; this has turned out to be one of my most valuable sources of feedback.

Over the years, Bernie Andringa of Skagit Valley College, Mount Vernon, Washington, has been one of my most diligent reviewers, and his detailed annotations and suggestions have been featured in this book since the second edition, so once again I owe some special thanks to him. I would also like to credit an ex-colleague of mine from Centennial College, John Murphy, who, in addition to making many valuable suggestions, proofread the content on spark-ignition systems that appears in the natural gas chapter of this book. Finally, I'd like to thank my enduring editor, Sharon Chambliss, for putting up with me project after project: as textbooks have changed over the years, morphing into e-books with an ever-expanding suite of support materials, the crucial role of a savvy editor cannot be emphasized enough.

Sean Bennett, October 2015
Feedback and comments are welcomed: email@seanbennett.org

Supplements

WORKBOOK TO ACCOMPANY

MEDIUM/HEAVY DUTY TRUCK ENGINES, FUEL & COMPUTERIZED MANAGEMENT SYSTEMS

FIFTH EDITION

SEAN BENNETT

WORKBOOK

The Student Workbook reinforces the foundations provided by the textbook with a special emphasis on some of the hands-on competencies required of entry-level diesel technicians. Some chapters contain up to seven job sheets and these are structured to help students make the connection between the theoretical concepts introduced in the textbook and actual shop floor practice. Each job sheet is correlated with relevant NATEF tasks. In addition, the Student Workbook contains study tips, practice questions, and online tasks to stress the increasing important of networking in both learning and workplace environments.

INSTRUCTOR RESOURCES CD

Carefully prepared, the Instructor Resources CD brings together several time-saving tools that allow for effective, efficient instruction. The Instructor Resources CD contains the following components:

- **PowerPoint®** lecture slides, which present the highlights of each chapter.
- An **Image Gallery**, which offers a database of hundreds of images in the text. These can easily be imported into the PowerPoint® presentations.
- An **Answer Key** file, which provides the answers to all end-of-chapter questions and Review Questions in the Student Workbook.
- **NATEF Correlations**, in which the current NATEF Medium/Heavy Truck Standards are correlated to the chapter of the core text and all relevant Workbook job sheets.
- **End-of-Chapter Review Questions**, which are provided in MS Word format.

INSTRUCTOR COMPANION WEBSITE

The Instructor Companion Website, found on cengagebrain.com, offers the following components to help minimize instructor preparation time and engage students:

- **PowerPoint®** lecture slides, which present the highlights of each chapter.
- An **Image Gallery** that offers a database of hundreds of images in the text. These can easily be imported into the PowerPoint® presentations.
- An **Answer Key** file, which provides the answers to all end-of-chapter questions and Review Questions in the Student Workbook.
- **NATEF Correlations**, in which the current NATEF Medium/Heavy Truck Standards are correlated to the chapter of the core text and all relevant Workbook job sheets.
- **End-of-Chapter Review Questions**, which are provided in MS Word format.

Cengage Learning Testing Power by Cognero is a flexible, online system that allows you to:

- Author, edit, and manage test bank content from multiple Cengage Learning solutions.
- Create multiple test versions in an instant.
- Deliver tests from your LMS, your classroom, or wherever you want.

MINDTAP FOR *MEDIUM-/HEAVY-DUTY TRUCK ENGINES, FUEL, & COMPUTERIZED MANAGEMENT SYSTEMS*

MindTap is a personalized teaching experience with relevant assignment that guide students to analyze, apply, and improve thinking, allowing you to measure skills and outcomes with ease.

- *Personalized Teaching:* Becomes your own with a Learning Path that is built with key student objectives. Control what students see and when they see it; match your syllabus exactly by hiding, rearranging, or adding your own content.
- *Guide Students:* Goes beyond the traditional "lift and shift" model by creating a unique learning path of relevant readings, multimedia, and activities that move students up the learning taxonomy from basic knowledge and comprehension to analysis and application.
- *Measure Skills and Outcomes:* Analytics and reports provide a snapshot of class progress, time on task, engagement, and completion rates.

DIESEL ENGINES FIFTH EDITION UPDATES

Features of this edition:

- Full color with a completely fresh art manuscript.
- Significantly revised telematics content, with updated contents on EOBR, I2V, V2I, V2V, and geofencing.
- Updating of trends in the trucking industry, including the impact of Right-to-Repair legislation and HD-OBD requirements.
- Enhanced coverage of engine temperature management hardware and software.
- Detailed coverage of the conversion of PC-11 engine oil to EPA MY 2017 CK-4 and FA-4 category lube oils.
- Enhanced coverage of input circuit diagnostics required for EPA MY 2013.
- Information on interpreting 2015 dash warning icons and emission-status icons.
- Greatly expanded J1939 and CAN coverage that includes 2014 updates addressing proprietary CAN buses, gateways between J1939 and OEM CANs, and bus diagnostics.
- Updated coverage on 2014 DLCs, including auto-baud detect capable (ABDC) communication adapters (CAs), green J1939 nine-pin connectors, and J1962 DLCs.
- Expanded coverage of Cummins's XPI common rail (CR) system.
- Expanded coverage of Detroit Diesel's ACRS fuel system.
- Significantly expanded coverage of natural gas (NG) fuel systems, with focus on the latest Cummins Westport ISL-G and ISX-G engines; coverage of both NG SI (coil-over-plug) ignition systems and NG diesel pilot ignition; coverage of NG safety handling and refueling procedures, including service procedure safety requirements.
- Ultracapacitor (UC) principles and coverage of UC cranking-assist technology.
- Coverage of how DDEC (J1939) interfaces with Daimler chassis buses (CAN 2), explaining the role played by the CPC, MCM, SAMs, and gateway modules in the system.
- Expanded coverage of Paccar engine management that includes both the MX EUP (2010–2013) and MX CR (post-2013) fuel systems featuring Delphi CR.
- Significantly increased coverage of emissions aftertreatment systems, including diagnostics, hardware removal and replacement, and system failure analysis; coverage of single-canister DOC, SCR, and DPF hardware being implemented for EPA 2017.
- An outline of the legal and environmental consequences of diesel emission systems tampering (hardware and software) and the individual (technician) and employer responsibilities and liabilities.

ACKNOWLEDGMENTS

INDIVIDUALS

Ray Amlung, Cummins Engineering, Columbus, IN

Bernie Andringa, Skagit Valley College, Mount Vernon, WA

Jim Bardeau, Centennial College, Toronto

Kabeer Barudin, Harper Detroit Diesel, Toronto

Bev Blaine, Cummins Ontario, Toronto

Darrin Bruneau, Canadore College, North Bay, ON

Chris Carlin, Lincoln College of Technology, Grand Prairie, TX

Wayne Carpenter, Baker College, Owosso, MI

Mike Cerato, Centennial College, Toronto

Howard Chesneau, Fuel Quality Services, GA

George Clark, Centennial College, Toronto

Dave Coffey, Caterpillar Engines, Peoria, IL

David Conant, Lincoln College of Technology, Nashville, TN

Dennis Conrad, SUNY, Alfred, NY

Christopher Conto, New York Network, SUNY, Albany, NY

Joshua Cooley, Schenectady, NY

Cameron Cox, SAIT, Calgary, Alberta

Jeff Curtis, Bellingham Technical College, Bellingham, WA

George Czata, Harper Detroit Diesel, Toronto

Ken DeGrant, Dearborn Group, IN

Pat Dillard, Cummins Training, Atlanta, GA

Enzo DiPietroantonio, Cummins Eastern Canada, Toronto

Owen Duffy, Centennial College, Toronto

Craig Fedder, Navistar International Trucks, Chicago, IL

David Fehling, Association of Diesel Specialists, Kansas City, MO

Donald Fetherolf, Mack Trucks Incorporated, Allentown, PA

Scott Furr, Cummins Atlantic, Charlotte, NC

James Gregory, SUNY, Cobleskill, NY

DeShaun Gunter, Universal Technical Institute, Rancho Cucamonga, CA

Douglas Hammond, SUNY, Cobleskill, NY

Terry Harkness, Toromont Caterpillar, Toronto

Sergio Hernandez, Palomar College, San Marcos, CA

Brian Humphries, PetroCan Suncor Engineering, Toronto

Bob Huzij, Cambrian College, Sudbury, Ontario

Matthew Jones, Lincoln College of Technology, Indianapolis, IN

Vincent Jones, Universal Technical Institute, Irving, TX

Serge Joncas, Volvo Training, Toronto

Gord King, Fanshawe College, London, Ontario

Brittany Kisstler, SUNY, Cobleskill, NY

Marty Kubiak, Detroit Diesel, Detroit, MI

Nick Lasch, SUNY, Cobleskill, NY

Bobby Leatherman, Lincoln College of Technology, Nashville, TN

Patrick Leitner, Freightliner NE Training Center, NJ

George Liidemann, Centennial College, Toronto

Sam Lightowler, Toronto Transit Commission, Toronto

Jim Lonnie, Caterpillar, Peoria, IL

Roger Look, Caterpillar, Peoria, IL

Ben Macaro, Cummins Eastern Canada, Toronto

James Mack Berks Career, Leesport, PA

Bob Marshall, University of Northern Ohio, Lima, OH

Brad Martin, Detroit Diesel Corporation, London, Ontario

Tony Martin, Kinross Fort Knox, Fairbanks, AK

Stacie Masullo, Altamont, NY

Kerry Matthews, Cummins Atlantic, Charlotte, NC

Alan McClelland Centennial College, Toronto

Timothy Meyer, Cummins Fuels Division, Columbus, IN

Don Mitchell, Case Corporation, Moline, IL

John Montgomery, Volvo-Mack Trucks, Toronto

Jason Montini, Lincoln College, South Nashville, TN

John Murphy, Centennial College, Toronto

Stephen Pang, Toronto Transit Commission, Toronto

George Parsons, Sault College, Sault Ste. Marie, Ontario

Bob Pattangale, Robert Bosch LLC, Chicago, IL

Steve Paul, Kenworth of Toronto, Toronto

Mike Perreira, Cummins Ontario, Toronto

Douglas L. Potter, Rochester, NY

Rachel Qin, S&R Communications, Toronto

Martin Restoule, Algonquin College, Ottawa, Ontario

Jack Rosebro, Perfect Sky, Carpinteria, CA

Ken Riley, Toromont Caterpillar Training Department, Toronto

Sara Saplin, Wards Forest Media, NY

Fred Schmidt, Donaldson Company, Minneapolis, MN

Donny Seyer, Seyer Automotive, Wheatridge, CO

Craig Smith, Volvo-Mack Trucks, St. John's, Newfoundland

Darren Smith, Centennial College, Toronto
Angelo Spano, Centennial College, Toronto
Lori Staples, New York Networks, SUNY, Albany, NY
Dan Sullivan, Sullivan Solutions, Durham, NC
Stefanie Thiel, Mahle Gruppe, Stuttgart, Germany
Al Thompson, Centennial College and Toronto ATS
Bruce Thornton, BOCES, Albany, NY
Pierre Valley, Centennial College, Toronto
Garry Vannederynan, Orion Bus, Oriskany, NY

David Vasquez, Universal Technical Institute, Rancho Cucamonga, CA
George Vass, Volvo Trucks Training, Toronto
Cedrick D. White, Vatterott Memphis, TN
David Wilson, Cummins Northeast LLC, Albany, NY
Jim Wilson, Robert Bosch LLC, Chicago, IL
Brian D. Whitmire, Lincoln College of Technology, Indianapolis, IN
Gus Wright, Centennial College, Toronto
Gilles Ybarro, Université Laval, Quebec

ORGANIZATIONS AND CORPORATIONS

Association of Diesel Specialists, Kansas City, MO
Ballard Power Systems, Burnaby, British Columbia
Caterpillar Engines, Peoria, IL
Centennial College, Toronto
Cummins Eastern Canada, Toronto, Ontario
Cummins Engine Company, Columbus, IN
Cummins Northeast, Albany, NY
Daimler Trucks North America, Portland, OR
Davco Manufacturing, Saline, MI
Delphi Fuel Division, Troy, MI
Denso Corporation, Aichi, Japan
Detroit Diesel Corporation, Detroit, MI
Donaldson Corporation, Minneapolis, MN
Freightliner LLC, Portland, Oregon
Harper Detroit Diesel, Toronto
Hino Toyota, Bloomfield Hills, MI
Hutchison Center, University of Alaska, Fairbanks
Imperial Oil, Toronto, Ontario
Institution of Mechanical Engineers, London, England
International Trucks, Chicago, IL
Isuzu America, Cerritos, CA
Jacobs Manufacturing, Bloomfield, CT
Kent Moore, Warren, MI
Kenworth of Ontario, Toronto

Lincoln Technical Institute, West Orange, NJ
Mack Trucks Canada, Toronto
Mack Trucks Incorporated, Greensboro, NC
Mahle Gruppe, Stuttgart, Germany
Mercedes-Benz, Montvale, NJ
Metropolitan Transit Authority, Brooklyn, NY
Mid-Ontario Freightliner, Toronto
Nashville Auto-Diesel College, Nashville, TN
New York Networks, SUNY, Albany, NY
Robert Bosch America LLC, Farmington Hills, MI
Society of Automotive Engineers, Warrendale, PA
Stanadyne Corporation, Windsor, CT
State University of New York, Cobleskill, NY
Sullivan Training Systems, Raleigh, NC
Superflow Corporation, Colorado Springs, CO
Technology and Maintenance Council, ATA, Alexandria, VA
Toromont Caterpillar, Toronto
Toronto Transit Commission, Toronto
Universal Technical Institute (UTI), Scottsdale, AZ
University of Northwestern Ohio, Lima, OH
Vibratech TVD, Springfield, NY
Volvo Trucks, Greensboro, NC
Westport Innovations Incorporated, Vancouver, British Columbia
Williams Controls Incorporated, Portland, OR

SECTION

1

DIESEL ENGINE FUNDAMENTALS

Section 1 begins with an introduction to the trucking industry and its technology. This chapter is followed by chapters on tools and safety; study of these is recommended before progressing to actual shop procedures. However, the section is mainly devoted to introducing the diesel engine, beginning with its operating fundamentals and historical development and then examining it on a system-by-system basis. Chapter 14 deals with engine service techniques and is important for the novice technician because it addresses some key entry-level skills. Chapter 15 provides some tips on diesel engine disassembly and reassembly procedures, and the final chapter in the section presents engine run-in and dynamometer testing.

1

INTRODUCTION

OBJECTIVES

After studying this chapter, you should be able to:

- Describe the overall objectives of this textbook.
- Describe some of the recent technological advances that have changed trucks in the past decade.
- Define the role of the trucking industry in North America.
- Outline the role of the contemporary truck technician.
- Understand the role the truck technician is expected to play in the delivery of customer service.
- Outline popular customer service trends in the truck OEM industry.
- Discuss the potential impact of HD-OBD and "Right-to-Repair" legislation enacted in Massachusetts and pending in many other states on the truck repair industry.
- Describe the qualifications required to practice as a truck or bus technician.
- List some of the professional associations to which truck technicians may belong and identify the benefits of each.
- Define engines by displacement.
- Identify the major engine OEMs and the market share of each.
- Describe green diesel technology and its impact on the immediate future of commercial vehicles.
- Learn to identify the equipment you are working on.

KEY TERMS

American Trucking Association (ATA)

Association of Diesel Specialists (ADS)

broker

California Air Resources Board (CARB)

chief executive officer (CEO)

electronic engine management

electronic onboard recorder (EOBR)

electronic service tool (EST)

Environmental Protection Agency (EPA)

Federal Motor Carrier Safety Alliance (FMCSA)

freight efficiency

heavy-duty onboard diagnostics (HD-OBD)

high-intensity kaizen event (HIKE)	National Automotive Technicians Education Foundation (NATEF)	Right-to-Repair legislation	telematics
hours of service (HOS)		service information systems (SIS)	total quality management (TQM)
hydromechanical management	National Institute for Automotive Service Excellence (NIASE, ASE)	Six Sigma	triage
information technology (IT)	original equipment manufacturer (OEM)	small bore	TRIZ
kaizen		Society of Automotive Engineers (SAE)	ultra-low sulfur (ULS)
large bore	policy adjustment	Technology and Maintenance Council (TMC)	vehicle identification number (VIN)
medium bore	Recommended Practices (RPs)		W. Edwards Deming
multiplexing			

INTRODUCTION

The primary objective of this textbook is to provide a basic understanding of the truck diesel engine and its fuel management circuits to the extent required by truck, bus, and heavy equipment technicians. Much of the book deals with electronically managed engines, but reduced coverage of older hydromechanical systems has been retained because mechanically managed engines are still in operation, especially in off-highway applications. In addition, hydromechanically managed engines remain a secondary requirement of some curriculum and certification task competencies. The technology addressed in this textbook focuses on principles of operation, the objective being to help the technician understand the systems rather than address the detail of the procedure required to repair them. Some repair detail appears in the e-resource that accompanies this book, but students and technicians should develop the habit of using online service information systems whenever possible.

Most engine **original equipment manufacturers (OEMs)** mandate that technicians be certified to diagnose and repair their engines and the computerized systems that manage them. Certification requires that the technician attend proprietary courses. These product-specific courses usually last a week or less and deliver the information and procedures required to diagnose and repair one specific engine series. Because of the delivery time constraints, product-specific courses seldom touch on the principles of operation. This textbook is very concerned with why and how components and systems function and less concerned with reproducing procedure and specifications that are best obtained from OEM literature and training courses.

SHIFT TOWARD THE GREEN DIESEL

The focus of this book is the diesel engine and its hydromechanical and electronic fuel management systems. Because of the increasingly aggressive statutory noxious-emissions controls required for commercial highway diesel engines and, more recently, their off-highway counterparts, diesel engines have undergone some radical changes in recent years. First, industry experienced a shift away from the **hydromechanical management** systems during the late 1980s. By the late 1990s, industry accepted that commercial diesel engines required management by computer, which we generally refer to as **electronic engine management**. During the period between 2004 and 2010, the changes to highway diesel engines were even more dramatic, as the industry was forced to adopt a full suite of emission control devices.

The drive toward producing a clean diesel engine has led to significant changes in the type of fuels used, more precise computerized control of combustion, and extensive exhaust gas aftertreatment devices. The recent *green* state initiative has led many states to adopt California's CARB standards: significantly, the number of states involved in this movement increases annually; these states now account for over half of the gross domestic product (GDP) of the United States. However, the EPA has recently ruled that states other than California are not permitted to set their own standards, resulting in a lawsuit by the 17 "green" states against the EPA, contending that if California can have "clean air," why not them? This issue is discussed in more detail in Chapter 47 of this book.

MULTIPLEXING

Computer-controlled or electronically managed engines and other chassis systems are universal today because they fail less often, make vehicles much easier to drive, require less maintenance, and produce better fuel mileage. Trucks today use a technology known as **multiplexing**, which allows the engine, transmission, brakes, and other chassis systems to talk to each other and makes possible high-tech chassis features such as yaw control and antirollover electronics. These antirollover systems may require up to eight chassis controllers working together in a collision avoidance event taking place in less than a second of real time. In addition to the powertrain network, multiplexing has evolved so that most truck OEMs are using proprietary communications buses that link to the powertrain bus.

CARB AND EPA

The **California Air Resources Board (CARB)** and the federal **Environmental Protection Agency (EPA)** led the drive toward emission control standards that made the "dirty" diesel engines of a generation ago a thing of the past. As each new set of emission control standards is introduced, so also are new and exciting technological advances that make the diesel engine today a work in progress. Though the tendency may not be to embrace these changes, we have come to accept them. In anticipation of the introduction of **ultra-low sulfur (ULS)** fuel in 2007, engine manufacturers were reporting in 2004 that fuel economy could be impacted by up to 5%. By the time ULS legislation was effected in October 2006, engine performance technology had advanced so that the actual hit on fuel economy turned out to be 0% to 1% negative, depending on the application. Since 2010, most engine OEMs have been able to improve fuel economy despite the addition of emission control hardware, some of which requires fuel to be injected into the aftertreatment circuit.

Moving Toward 2020

The core features of the 2010 EPA-compliant diesel engine will not change that much during the second decade of this century. Off-road diesel engines over 70 horsepower (52 kW) have been subject to the same stringent EPA emission standards as their on-highway counterparts since 2011. Hydromechanical fuel systems with limited or no engine emission controls will continue to be used in smaller on-highway engines (reefer units) and in low- or nonregulated areas such as marine and stationary applications for the foreseeable future.

The diesel industry is now looking to the federal administration's objectives of increased fuel efficiency and reduced CO_2 dump scheduled for 2017 and 2018, with phased implementation up to 2020. Reduction of CO_2 emission and better fuel economy are both about using less hydrocarbon fossil fuel. These objectives have altered the trucking industry's definition of fuel economy and disposed of the term *miles per gallon*. This term may be appropriate for comparing the performance of one family automobile versus another, but is meaningless when applied to the business of hauling freight. Today, fleets are likely to use the term **freight efficiency**, which is defined as "fuel consumed per ton hauled." It means that OEMs will look at the performance of the entire rig in terms of fuel usage, evaluating everything from tires to aerodynamics. There is a move to make low rolling resistance (LRR) tires mandatory by 2017.

Aerodynamics

As the trucking industry approaches 2020, many fleets are pre-empting mandatory changes to commercial vehicle aerodynamics because the average return on investment due to fuel saved is just 11 months. Aerodynamic devices recognized by SmartWay include:

- Roof fairings
- Bumper aerodynamics
- Fuel tank cowling
- Side extenders, panels, and skirts
- Undercarriage flow devices
- Trailer and van body boat tails

OBJECTIVES OF THIS BOOK

This textbook attempts to make engine and fuel management technology easy to understand for the technician specializing in truck service and repair. As each year passes, the role of the truck technician changes with the technology. Technician skills today emphasize diagnostic abilities followed by ability to do a remove/replace procedure. That can be tough on novice technicians. Diagnosis is usually regarded as a higher-level skill. A generation ago the individual responsible for diagnosis in a truck shop was widely experienced, usually with many years of field practice. In the real world of today's truck shop, the technician is required to perform less disassembly/reconditioning and much more troubleshooting and diagnosis. Most diagnosis of current diesel engines is performed using online **service information systems (SIS)**, so the technician must possess first-rate computer skills. In fact, to get the most out of the approach this book uses toward diesel technology, it helps if the student has access to one of the OEM SIS data hubs.

CORE SKILLS

Computers are part of the way of life in the modern truck shop. They are used to diagnose engine malfunctions, program customer and proprietary data to engine control modules (ECMs), and track every aspect of working life in a business. A heavy emphasis is placed on computer literacy throughout this book. Change in the trucking industry is exponential. The specific systems addressed by this textbook will become obsolete within a relatively short time. However, the technical skill sets addressed in its pages should become the building blocks for a career that will necessarily have to adapt to change as each innovation is introduced. **Figure 1-1** shows a 2010 Kenworth T700 with a multiplexed chassis, and **Figure 1-2** is a left-side view of a 2013 electronically controlled Cummins engine.

FIGURE 1-1 2010 Kenworth chassis.

FIGURE 1-2 Left side view of a 2013 Cummins ISX 15-liter engine.

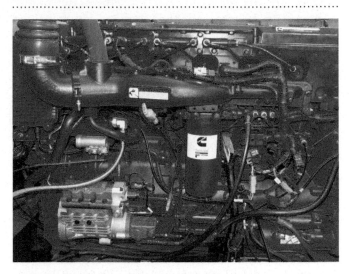

ROLE OF THE TRUCKING INDUSTRY AND THE TRUCK TECHNICIAN

The trend in the trucking industry in North America is for it to grow by the year. In many ways, new truck sales provide a barometer of how the economy is doing in any given year. The saying "If you got it, a truck brought it" is true for most of the consumer items we purchase. Even if that item was transported by train, boat, or plane for a portion of its journey, trucks would have played a role in pickup and delivery at stages of the journey. Total freight annual volumes hauled by truck are one of the best indicators of the health of the economy.

Millions of people are directly and indirectly employed by the trucking industry. Trucks must be designed, built in factories, marketed, and then operated and maintained. The role of the technician in this industry is a small but crucial one. If all the truck technicians in the United States withheld their labor for 2 weeks, a large percentage of the economy would shut down. The trucking industry, in addition to employing mechanical technicians to maintain and repair equipment, employs drivers, dispatchers, warehouse personnel, people to market services, and people to manage operations.

CAREERS IN TRUCKING

For some truck technicians, practicing as a technician will be just one of the career roles they play in the industry. A **chief executive officer (CEO)** of a major truck OEM who retired in the 1990s described his years with the company beginning when he started as a janitor, apprenticed as a mechanic, practiced as a technician, and progressed with the company as a service manager, sales manager, and production operations manager. He moved through upper management and finally achieved the CEO position. While this is unlikely to be the objective of most aspiring truck technicians, one study indicated that within 5 years of achieving certification status, 50% of truck technicians no longer worked as hands-on technicians. Most were employed in other positions in the trucking industry. There are many opportunities in management, sales, training, field service operations, and information systems that the qualified truck technician can explore.

Many truck technicians have no desire to do anything but repair trucks. They will, over time, become the experts the industry needs to maintain the ever more sophisticated equipment on our highways. There are engine specialists in the truck garages of North America who know and understand a given engine model better than the engineers who designed it. Over a period of time, they learn to diagnose every rattle and burp the engine can produce.

THE TRUCK TECHNICIAN OF THE TWENTY-FIRST CENTURY

For a technician to effectively work on modern electronically managed engines, considerable general experience, knowledge of mechanical principles, and product-specific training are required. Persons choosing a career as a truck technician in North America usually begin by attending a 1- or 2-year college program, followed by a period of hands-on training culminating in professional examinations conducted by the **National Institute for Automotive Service Excellence (NIASE or ASE)**, the **Association of Diesel Specialists (ADS)**, or other licensing agencies. In Canada, most provinces mandate both the structure and duration of apprenticeship (3 to 5 years), and then license technicians by on-the-job standards of competency and their ability to pass certification examinations.

COST-DRIVEN CHANGE

In recent years, many labor-intensive procedures (such as the out-of-chassis overhaul of major components) have been moved out of the truck garage to remote and often offshore remanufacturing centers. Remanufacturing centers are often located in a jurisdiction where labor rates are low and the remanufacturing processes can be subdivided, allowing lesser skilled but specialist workers to perform most of the labor. This is a result of the service and repair industry becoming highly cost conscious.

A 2005 MIT study estimated that more than 6% of the GNP of the United States (some $820 billion) was required annually to repair the damage caused by mechanical wear in general. Reducing this kind of dollar expenditure by fractions of a percent can represent massive savings. Every aspect of the repair procedure is analyzed for efficiency and cost-effectiveness. The truck engine technician of a generation ago who may have diagnosed, disassembled, reconditioned, and tested an engine is probably responsible today only for the diagnosis. That expert is followed by someone of lesser experience who removes and replaces the engine on a rebuilt/exchange basis. The rebuild facility will often be located in a jurisdiction where labor costs are lower; frequently, this means in another country.

TELEMATICS

Another factor that has powerfully influenced change in the trucking industry is the improvement in communications technology resulting in increasing use of **telematics**. *Telematics* is the long-distance transmission of data. Combinations of microwave and satellite telecommunications are used by many fleet operators to track vehicle location and communicate with onboard electronic systems. In other words, the various computer-controlled systems that are networked on the chassis are also communicating with remote devices.

EOBRs

Telematics can also be used for purposes of highway safety enforcement by the **Federal Motor Carrier Safety Alliance (FMCSA)** to track data such as driver **hours of service (HOS)**. Currently any driver cited for a greater than 10% HOS violation can be required to have an **electronic onboard recorder (EOBR)** installed in any vehicle he drives, but the FMCSA is aiming have to these devices installed in all linehaul commercial vehicles.

SKILLS REQUIRED

The changes the industry has undergone during the **information technology (IT)** revolution have produced a need for a different type of truck and a different kind of truck technician. The modern truck is a network of networks in itself. Chassis computers share information over a data backbone to optimize vehicle operation and make the vehicle safer. For instance, the response capability of the various system computers networked to a chassis data bus greatly exceeds that of the human driver in the event of a pending vehicle rollover. **Figure 1–3** shows some of the many computer-controlled subsystems on a modern truck. Today's truck technician requires the following skills:

- Computer literacy
- Language comprehension accuracy
- Hands-on mechanical competence
- Ability to adapt to frequent technological change
- Ability to distill information in order to produce diagnoses

There is no doubt that the technician of today is required to know much more than the technician of a generation ago. A technician is

FIGURE 1–3 Chassis computer-controlled systems used on a modern truck.

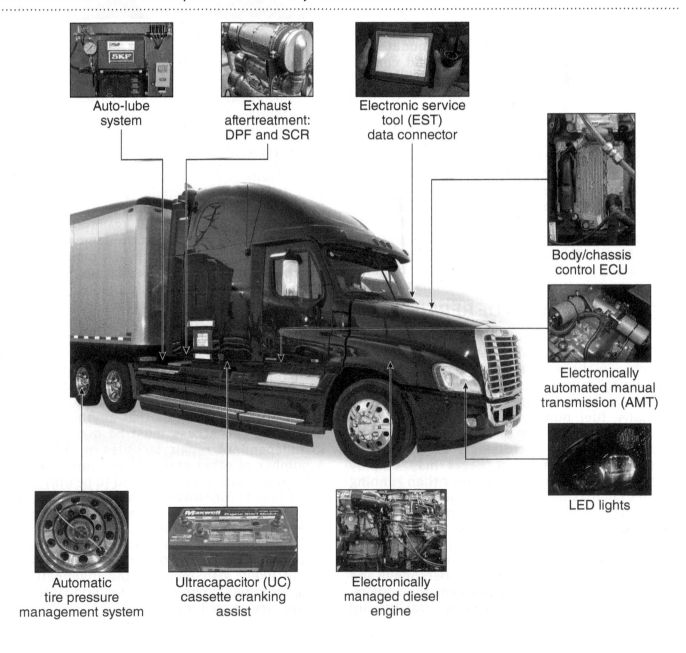

Auto-lube system

Exhaust aftertreatment: DPF and SCR

Electronic service tool (EST) data connector

Body/chassis control ECU

Electronically automated manual transmission (AMT)

LED lights

Automatic tire pressure management system

Ultracapacitor (UC) cassette cranking assist

Electronically managed diesel engine

FIGURE 1–5 One of two modules used to manage a 2013 DD15 engine.

publications is to join as a technician member. The TMC publishes bulletins such as the *TMC Fleet Advisor, Transport Topics,* and other technical periodicals. Once a year the TMC publishes a compendium of **Recommended Practices (RPs)** titled *Recommended Maintenance Practices Manual.* This is an essential reference for truck technicians because it benchmarks standards of accepted practice in the industry. Coverage is bumper to bumper. Check out the TMC at http://tmc.truckline.com. The address is:

American Trucking Association
Technology and Maintenance Council
950 N. Glebe Road, Suite 210
Arlington, VA, 22203-4181
Phone: (703) 838-1763

AUTOMOTIVE ENGINEERING Published monthly by the **Society of Automotive Engineers (SAE)** and sent to all of its members, *Automotive Engineering* (http://aei-online.org) covers the whole automotive spectrum from an engineering/technological perspective focusing on innovation. Most innovations in the truck, bus, and heavy equipment industries are covered.

AUTOMOTIVE NEWS *Automotive News* (http://www.autonews.com) covers the whole automotive industry (including trucks), mostly from the sales perspective. It tracks the monthly and yearly sales data for all vehicles, including each category of truck by class size.

COMMERCIAL CARRIER JOURNAL (CCJ) *Commercial Carrier Journal* (http://www.ccjdigital.com) is published monthly and covers the trucking industry from the service and maintenance perspective. It is highly recommended as a means of keeping up to date with the changes in truck technology as they happen.

DIESEL PROGRESS *Diesel Progress* (http://www.dieselprogress.com) covers the diesel engine industry from the smallest to the largest engines. It is a great magazine for the engine and fuels specialist. Most new diesel engine technologies are profiled in *Diesel Progress* ahead of production. It is one of the best ways to keep informed of upcoming emissions legislation, buying trends, and emerging technology.

FLEET ADVISOR *Fleet Advisor* (http://www.truckline.com) is the TMC monthly newsletter and covers a broad range of issues relevant to the trucking industry. It publishes reports from the truck-driver, technical, legal, and business perspectives of the industry. It announces the Recommended Practices (RPs) under discussion and invites participation from TMC members.

TRANSPORT TOPICS *Transport Topics* (http://www.ttnews.com) is the weekly newspaper published by the American Trucking Association, and its mandate is to cover any item of interest to trucking in North America. It is especially useful for keeping track of safety and emissions standards enforcement.

THE TRAILBLAZER This TMC technical journal summarizes the contents of the biannual TMC meetings, and thus is an excellent tool for keeping on top of emerging trends in truck technology. It is available by subscription only, but can often be found unopened in lunchrooms of truck service facilities. **Figure 1–6** shows a selection of periodicals that can help keep truck technicians up to date.

OEM Service Information Systems

OEM service literature is written with the objective of sequencing a procedure and seldom makes for entertaining reading. However, many OEMs have their own in-house magazines to keep their employees current, and the technical service bulletins (TSBs) of today are usually presented in a more readable format than they were 10 years ago because OEMs realize their importance as an information tool. Many

FIGURE 1–6 A selection of publications designed to keep truck technicians up to date with innovations.

OEMs also provide learning packages deliverable in either CD-ROM or online formats. These are usually interactive and often are directed toward in-house certification at their conclusion. Often self-directed learning packages are integrated with the OEM online service information systems so technicians can certify on a specific system and learn at whatever pace they feel like. Technicians should never forget that self-development tends to be rewarding and has a way of stimulating interest. Those who do not bother, stagnate.

EXPERIENCE

For the technician, there is no substitute for the hands-on experience of tackling a procedure. Employers should ensure, after investing in sending a technician to a 1-week course training for a specific procedure, that the technician be given the opportunity to practice the newly learned skills at the first opportunity. If 6 months slip by between the training course and the hands-on application that the techniques target, much of the learned content will have been forgotten.

Be an Observer

Apprentice technicians should make a practice of using their eyes and ears a lot. They should watch successful technicians and learn from them: how they organize their work area, how they strategize each task they undertake, how they test the results of a repair procedure, and how they approach and deal with customers. Novice truck technicians have a steep learning curve to adjust to, and during the process it will be important to learn how to think. There is little room for impulse, guesswork, or carelessness in working with today's technology, and the consequences of a mistake can be very costly.

Policy Adjustments

It would take a self-righteous truck technician indeed to claim that he or she has never made a mistake. Errors do happen on the truck shop floor. While making mistakes may be part of life, in service facilities it is essential that they be limited. Mistakes are costly to business practice and to the shop's reputation. They are known as **policy adjustments** by those administrating billing. When you are unfortunate enough to make a mistake, regard it as a learning experience that should stick in your mind, never to be repeated. Technicians who make frequent mistakes will probably be required to seek employment in a different industry.

CUSTOMER SERVICE AND PROFESSIONALISM

A generation ago, few truck diesel technicians had to concern themselves with what is today known as *customer service*. Most large operations had personnel on their payroll to deal with customer service issues and, in fact, many technicians worked with the expectation that the customer adapt to their way of working—certainly never the other way around. The catchphrase back then was *take it or leave it*. Many service facilities had signs directed at customers expressly forbidding them access to the working area of service garages, usually citing insurance regulations. Things have changed.

W. EDWARDS DEMING

The pioneer of modern customer service philosophy was an American, **W. Edwards Deming**. Deming's ideas on customer service initially met with little acceptance in North America, but he had an easier time convincing the Japanese. In his lifetime, Deming acquired near-hero status in Japan. Japanese companies adopted his teachings and used them to step into the world arena and establish Japan as a major economic force. By applying Deming's teachings to production technology and customer service, the Japanese auto industry has established itself in a position of global dominance. Emerging automobile manufacturers in countries such as Korea, China, and India have modeled their industries on the Japanese example.

Total Quality Management

W Edwards Deming is credited with coining the phrase **total quality management (TQM)**. Many companies today claim to use TQM. It is best described as an overarching corporate philosophy that views customer service as the very reason for that company being in business and includes every employee as a stakeholder. In other words, every person within a corporation is regarded as a member of a team, and every member of the team contributes significantly to the image that the organization projects. The notion that every person in a company has an essential role to play was alien to many North American and European organizations in the 1970s and 1980s, which maintained strictly hierarchical structures in which those at the base of the pyramid tended to be little valued. The Japanese exploited this and essentially, among their many imports to North America, reimported the teachings of W. Edwards Deming.

It should be noted that more than half of the main players in the truck manufacturing industry claim to practice some form of TQM, including the company with the largest market share, which has set many of the trends of the industry over the past 2 decades, forcing the rest to either keep up or lose market share. TQM has been dismissed as a trend by some, and indeed many companies have treated Deming's teachings as a sort of smorgasbord, picking and choosing techniques and other items they feel might result in an increase in business profitability and omitting those they feel might cost them money. This is a case of missing the point. Nevertheless, TQM has influenced the way in which all companies do business.

Kaizen

We first used this Japanese word a little earlier in the chapter to describe a model of continuous personal self-improvement. However, Japanese manufacturing has used this "continuous improvement" ideal on a much broader scale. Imported Japanese automobiles were often derided during the 1960s with accusations of low quality, probably with some justification. A gradual reversal took place during the 1970s and into the 1980s. Japanese manufacturers built a solid base by listening to customer concerns and constantly correcting shortcomings. Listening to and responding to customer complaints laid the building blocks of the modern Japanese auto industry, based around kaizen production cycles.

Today, we more often than not associate Japanese-manufactured products with good quality backed by excellent customer service support. It matters little to the buying public that many of these "Japanese" products are now manufactured in America by American workers. As a nation, we have come to associate the product of Japanese companies with superiority because of their emphasis on customer service and quality.

Keeping Customers Happy

Many truck facilities are offering extended service hours—often at 24-hour, 7-day-a-week facilities. As soon as one operation offers this type of service in a given area, others must too if they are to compete effectively. In addition, service operations are recognizing the crucial role played by their technicians in delivering customer service. Many are training their personnel in this area, offering seminars with titles such as "How to Communicate with Customers" and "Handling the Difficult Customer." Operations that used to discourage customers from even entering the service garage are now welcoming customers, encouraging them to talk to the technician performing the work, and providing them with waiting facilities more in keeping with a hotel lobby than with what used to be associated with a truck service garage.

Honesty

The working environment in a modern truck shop can be difficult for the novice technician. A truck owner/operator with 20 years in the business is likely to have learned a thing or two about the equipment he or she operates and can easily intimidate a first-year apprentice truck technician. It is essential to underline the fact that one of the core premises of TQM is honesty. Technicians will find that, in dealing with customers, the relationship will always be made easier when the approach is open and sincere. Until recently, two of the worst traits of the automotive garage were the fact that many customers felt that they were being talked down to or that their repairs were misrepresented either to inflate a bill or disguise a lack of competence in diagnosing a problem. Using an honest approach will probably not reduce the number of policy-adjusted (write-off time) work orders, but it will have the effect of increasing the number of repeat customers.

Professionalism

All technicians should develop a sense of professionalism. You will never witness a doctor or dentist criticizing the handiwork of a colleague who previously worked on the body or mouth in question, although there are surely cases where there is justification to do just that. Unfortunately, it is all too common to hear a technician deriding the abilities of whoever previously worked on a piece of equipment. This is simply unprofessional and reflects as badly on the person doing the criticizing as well as the person supposedly at fault. Actually, it reflects badly on the whole industry. Mistakes happen. Remember that what goes around comes around. Accept that and the fact that the even very best technicians can have bad days, commit errors, and have lapses in concentration. Technicians should make a practice of learning from their own mistakes and those of their colleagues and actively work to improve the level of professionalism in the industry.

SIX SIGMA

If you have made a visit to any Caterpillar or Cummins dealership recently, you will have noticed more than a few posters advocating Six Sigma practices. **Six Sigma** was developed by Motorola Corporation as a corporate means of eliminating defects. In Six Sigma, a *defect* is defined as a "unit that is not a member of the intended population," so it is not entirely clear whether a defect might include employees who fail to pull their weight. The concept was pioneered by Bill Smith at Motorola in 1986; since its introduction, Motorola claims to have saved more than $17 billion. Six Sigma has become an element of many companies' production improvement initiatives, including Honeywell (Allied Signal), Raytheon, Cummins, and Caterpillar.

Key Concepts of Six Sigma

Six Sigma identifies the following six key concepts:

- Quality: the attributes a customer expects from a product

- Defect: failure to deliver what a customer wants
- Process capability: what a company's systems and processes can deliver
- Variation: what a customer sees and feels about a product
- Stability: process of managing consistent, predictable processes to improve what a customer sees and feels
- Design for Six Sigma: adapting to meet customer needs (external) and process capability (internal)

Caterpillar practices Six Sigma in all its manufacturing facilities and most of its dealerships. It borrows from martial arts the colors of belts to represent status; for instance, master black belts, black belts, green belts, and yellow belts represent diminishing levels of status within the Six Sigma hierarchy. Master black belts devote all their time to Six Sigma analysis and promotion, and black belts report to the master black belts; at a lower level, yellow belts are mere rookies in the system.

Fundamentally, Six Sigma is about teamwork, as is TQM. Six Sigma stratifies the team a little more than TQM does. However, if employees can be motivated to buy into the program, it has been proven to produce improvement, so the key is establishing employee motivation. As a society we embrace trends and catchphrases and maybe with good reason: any program that promises some change for the better is likely to result in some improvement, even if short-lived. Recently, Six Sigma has been integrated with the TRIZ methodology for problem solving and product design.

TRIZ

TRIZ is another much-used term in the workplace these days; if your employer suddenly installs an employee suggestion box and then sincerely attempts to get you to use it, it may be due to TRIZ. The acronym **TRIZ** is derived from the Russian phrase for "theory of inventive problem solving." The fundamental principles of TRIZ tell us that:

- If you have a problem, somebody someplace has already solved it (or a similar one). Being inventive means finding that solution and adapting it to your problem.
- Compromises should not be accepted, because they reduce effectiveness. In other words, compromises should be eliminated

wherever and whenever possible—a concept that might be difficult to accept in North America where compromise is the norm.

HIKE

High-intensity kaizen event or **HIKE** is used by a number of truck fleets, including Swift Transport, with its corporate office located in Phoenix, Arizona. Swift has made HIKE part of its culture, and HIKE shows up in all phases of Swift's corporate profile. Take a look at its website for a firsthand look at how Swift presents its image to the world. HIKE depends largely on teamwork and responding to employee suggestions for improving efficiency.

A simple example of how HIKE is implemented at Swift Transport is the use of a technician-driven wireless parts ordering system in combination with a radio-equipped parts runner to avoid having highly paid technicians waiting in line for service at a parts counter.

TRIAGE

One tangible result of the truck service industry's drive to improve customer service and boost efficiency has been to introduce triage bays in truck shops. By definition, **triage** is the sorting of commodities into a sequence by either quality or urgency. Truck shops use triage bays where an expert technician performs a preliminary diagnosis so that the actual repair can be channeled to the appropriate technician or area of the service facility. Because the preliminary assessment is made by a technician rather than a service writer, the language that appears on the work order is likely to more accurately detail the nature of the repair required. In some Cummins dealerships, all vehicles are triaged by connecting to and reading the data bus, even if the work order stipulates nothing more than a simple oil change.

CUSTOMER SERVICE SUMMARY

Throughout their careers, most truck technicians will have to participate in both small and big ways in customer service initiatives. You might feel like dismissing some of these as trends that will die a natural death. The core truth is that as a technician you will, in effect, be selling your expertise in the marketplace—and if you are selling anything, you need a buyer. The salespersons and companies that are selling your skills probably regard their skills in marketing just as highly as you might regard your technical skills. So, when it comes to understanding and practicing customer service, you have no choice. The best mechanical technician in the world cannot survive in the marketplace if no one is willing to pay for those skills.

QUALIFICATIONS AND CAREERS FOR THE TRUCK TECHNICIAN

Truck technicians should regard ASE certification as essential in today's employment environment. Certification raises the status of technicians, establishing them as professionals. While ASE certification is important, so are those OEM certifications that qualify a technician for a specific overhaul procedure or recommended practice. Technicians should never turn down opportunities for professional development, and should value the certificates and diplomas awarded for taking them.

ASE MASTER TECHNICIAN

Certification for truck technicians in the United States is managed by the National Institute for Automotive Service Excellence (NIASE), usually abbreviated ASE. These tests may now be taken on paper twice a year (May or November) or on computer at more than 200 secure, proctored test sites year round. At the time of this writing, costs for taking the computerized tests are slightly higher and candidates should note that each individual test is timed. The ASE tests for truck technicians were recently updated; in 2014, ASE tests for truck technicians were as follows:

T1	Gasoline Engines	60 questions
T2	Diesel Engines	55 questions
T3	Drivetrains	40 questions
T4	Brakes	50 questions
T5	Suspension Steering	50 questions
T6	Electrical System	50 questions
T7	Heating, Ventilation, and Air Conditioning	40 questions
T8	Preventive Maintenance	50 questions
L2	Electronic Diesel Engine Diagnosis Specialist	45 questions

FIGURE 1–7 Logo used by an ASE certified training program.

To qualify for Master Technician (MT) status, technicians must pass six ASE tests: T2, T3, T4, T5, T6, and T7. To maintain certification, retesting must be taken every 5 years. Retests have only half the number of questions and are designed to ensure that technicians remain up to date. The ASE L2 test addresses electronically controlled diesel engines exclusively and is built around a generic, composite engine. Before tackling the L2 test, students should get on the ASE website and download the *L2 Reference Guide*. Training and competency standards for vocational technical colleges, high school, and university-based automotive technology learning programs are managed by the **National Automotive Technicians Educations Foundation (NATEF)**. **Figure 1–7** shows the insignia used by an ASE/NATEF-certified program.

The ASE address is:

National Institute for Automotive Service Excellence

101 Blue Seal Drive, SE, Suite 101

Leesburg, VA 20175

Phone: (703) 669-6600

Web: http://www.asecert.org, http://www.ase .org

WARNING:

ASE certification examinations are intended to test your performance skills. Performance skills cannot be learned from textbook study alone. Before undertaking any ASE certification, make sure you have some hands-on knowledge or you will be wasting money.

OTHER CERTIFICATIONS

In Canada, technicians must be licensed to practice in most provinces. Licensing requires undertaking a structured apprenticeship with employers signing off on a range of competencies,

followed by a provincially administered examination that qualifies technicians for Red Seal status. The duration of a truck technician apprenticeship in Canada is typically 4 years, and it is mandatory to be either a qualified technician or a registered apprentice before working on any highway vehicle.

In Australia, technician training and certification of automotive, truck, off-road equipment and diesel technicians is managed by each state: there is a higher level of industry involvement and some larger companies manage in-house apprenticeship training.

Most engine OEMs require technician certification on each engine series they manufacture. Usually this requires some online study, a 1-week hands-on training course, and some written and practical competency testing. In most cases, OEM engine certification programs are designed with the assumption that technicians taking the courses are experienced, because basic concepts are not taught.

PROFESSIONAL ASSOCIATIONS

The Society of Automotive Engineers (SAE) has governed most of the standards in the automotive industry, whether it is for a standard screw thread, the viscosity of a lubricant, or the electronic protocols required to integrate two separate computer-controlled systems on a vehicle. The SAE regulates the industry from both an engineering and technical perspective and produces a vast and comprehensive amount of literature on every subject relevant to vehicles. Most of these are accessible in hard copy, through the Internet, and on CD-ROM. Membership in the SAE is inexpensive and opens access to detailed information on just about every technical aspect of any vehicle. The address for the SAE is:

Society of Automotive Engineers

400 Commonwealth Drive

Warrendale, PA 15096

Phone: (800) STS-9596

Web: http://www.sae.org

The Technology and Maintenance Council (TMC) division of the **American Trucking Association (ATA)** sets standards and practices in the industry. You can join the TMC as a student or technician member and receive continual technical updates and participate in feedback on its development of Recommended Practices. Since its formation in 2003, the technicians' wing of the TMC has supported technician professional development and hosted technical skills competitions at its annual meetings. The TMC *Recommended Practices Manual* should be available in every truck shop; most of the procedures and practices are consensually agreed to by OEM and member experts. The TMC newsletter *Fleet Advisor* is sent to all TMC members monthly. The TMC contact information was given a little earlier in this chapter.

PROPRIETARY ASSOCIATIONS

Many OEMs have in-house professional associations whose objective is educating technicians, keeping them current, and maintaining high professional standards. The oldest of these is probably the Detroit Diesel Corporation (DDC) Guild. Membership is available for technicians working in DDC service dealerships. Its testing is designed to challenge the technician to keep up to date with DDC technology, and membership offers a number of benefits. The current DDC Guild platform is online-based and known as G2. Most OEMs today offer high-quality in-house certification programs, usually run online.

DEFINING ENGINES BY DISPLACEMENT

In this textbook, our focus is primarily on highway engines used in truck and bus chassis. However, many of the engines referenced are also used in a range of other applications, which include:

- Off-highway mechanical drive mobile
- Off-highway hydrostatic drive mobile
- Marine motive power
- Land-based genset
- Marine genset
- Land-based auxiliary power

Because this textbook is used in programs that do not address highway equipment, it is necessary to define terms such as **small bore**, **medium bore**, and **large bore** when referring to a diesel engine so that no confusion results. It should be stressed that these are loose definitions and each OEM will probably have opinions that vary somewhat.

- Small bore: diesel engines with displacements between 5.9 and 8 liters
- Medium bore: diesel engines with displacements between 8 and 12 liters
- Large bore: diesel engines with displacements between 12 and 16 liters

In reality, these definitions only apply to the way we refer to engine displacement in the trucking industry. If our perspective were that of a railway locomotive diesel engine specialist, then a 16-liter engine would be considered small bore. It should also be recognized that as diesel engine technology develops, especially as it applies to power over weight, in many cases the small-bore engine (by our definition) is often taking on tasks that required a medium-bore engine a generation ago. And while fleets will often spec a 13-liter engine into a Class 8 highway tractor, most **brokers** (owner-operators) would tell you that they would not consider an engine under 15 liters displacement.

ENGINE OEMS AND MARKET SHARE

In 2006, Caterpillar held the dominant share of the lucrative Class 8 truck engine market with 28.3% (http://wardsauto.com) of total sales, but things have changed significantly since then. In 2007, Caterpillar announced that in 2010 it would withdraw from competing in the on-highway truck arena to focus on its off-highway markets. Overnight, this fractioned Caterpillar truck engine sales, leaving the highway sector of the market up for grabs.

Although Caterpillar continued to supply a small number of engines to on-highway markets after 2007, and ceased production of on-highway diesel engines to the United States and Canada in 2010, it continued to supply on-highway engines to all other markets throughout the world. Caterpillar unveiled an on-highway vocational truck in 2011. This was a joint Navistar and Caterpillar endeavor powered by a Navistar-modified Caterpillar C15 engine. Caterpillar's withdrawal from the on-highway sector opened the door for Cummins to take over. Here is how on-highway truck engine sales (United States and Canada) were divvied up in 2012 (source: http://statistica.com):

Cummins	42%
Navistar	17%
Mack	11%
Detroit Diesel	10.5%
Volvo	8%
Paccar	6%
Hino (Toyota)	3.5%
Mercedes Benz	0.5%

HEALTH, SAFETY, AND A GREEN ENVIRONMENT

There is nothing more important than maintaining a safe and healthy shop environment. Health and safety are examined in Chapter 2 of this book, and if you are embarking on a course of study as a truck technician, you will notice that safety issues are emphasized up front. It is crucial for technicians beginning careers in the trucking industry to understand the consequences of unsafe practices. Unsafe practices can mean doing something that results in an immediate bodily injury to the perpetrator or someone in the work area ... or it can cause a problem that is not so immediate, such as not using hearing protection and not experiencing compromised hearing until 30 years have passed.

A GREEN WORLD

In recent years, there has been increasing emphasis on *green* technologies. This term may be used to describe the remediation of any practice that has the potential to harm the environment. For instance, the engine emissions technology incorporated into all current commercial vehicles exists today only because its predecessors were judged to have damaged the environment and those that live in it.

"Green" has become a catchphrase that can sell products, so the term gets used more often than it should. That said, the diesel engine of today may not be truly green, but it does pollute significantly less than its forerunners of just 10 years ago. For the immediate future, further greening of the diesel is going to focus on fuel efficiency, and the federal government is in a process of defining how to evaluate this from a compliance perspective.

ALTERNATE-FUEL AND HYBRID DRIVE

Because of our dependence on petroleum products imported from unstable and often unfriendly countries, there has been much increased experimentation and adoption of alternate-fuel and hybrid drive technologies. Although most of these currently use modified diesel powerplants, there is no argument that they lower emissions and reduce fuel consumption. In addition, some of these new drive technologies make a lot of sense, especially in

FIGURE 1–8 Diesel electric hybrid transit bus operated by the MTA in New York City; these are an increasingly common sight in many North American urban areas today.

inner-city, stop-start applications such as transit buses and courier pickup and delivery vehicles. For this reason, there is greater emphasis on these "greener" technologies in this textbook. **Figure 1–8** shows an increasingly common sight in our metropolitan areas today: a diesel electric, hybrid-powered transit bus.

TECH TIP:

The average age of the U.S. Class 8 fleet tractor in 2014 was 6.6 years.

VIN

We identify all vehicles on the road by **vehicle identification number (VIN)**. It is critically important to locate the VIN on any vehicle you are working on. Although some OEMs will do some of this work for you—that happens the moment you connect an **electronic service tool (EST)** to the data bus—others require that you enter this number to access service information and diagnostic fields.

The VIN is a 17-alphanumeric-character identification code that identifies every major chassis subsystem, including such things as the year of manufacture, manufacturing plant, and key options. Most of the major systems on a chassis can be identified by the VIN. In some cases, the

OEM software may require that only part of the VIN be entered to access service literature and diagnostic routines—for instance, the final eight digits.

Get used to knowing exactly what you are working with. When you have not personally filled in the work order data, the first thing you should verify is that the VIN has been input correctly. Whenever you have to reference the vehicle for parts, warranty, or any kind of service info, the VIN is required. **Figure 1-9** shows the VIN sticker on one type of commercial vehicle. It is usually located in more than one place on the chassis.

FIGURE 1-9 VIN sticker.

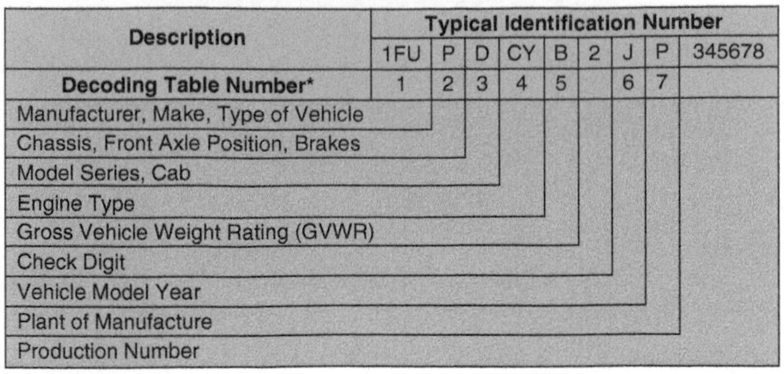

Description	Typical Identification Number							
	1FU	P	D	CY	B	2	J	P	345678
Decoding Table Number*	1	2	3	4	5		6	7
Manufacturer, Make, Type of Vehicle								
Chassis, Front Axle Position, Brakes								
Model Series, Cab								
Engine Type								
Gross Vehicle Weight Rating (GVWR)								
Check Digit								
Vehicle Model Year								
Plant of Manufacture								
Production Number								

SUMMARY

- The objective of this textbook is to provide the truck technician with an understanding of the operating principles of modern heavy- and medium-duty diesel engines and their fuel management systems.
- There is a heavy emphasis on the electronically controlled engines that power most current highway trucks.
- Truck, bus, and heavy equipment technicians are still required to work on hydromechanically managed engines because such engines are used in legacy equipment, engines producing less than 70 horsepower (52 kW), and as yet unregulated applications. Most reefer engines output less than 70 horsepower.
- It is important for the truck technician to have a good understanding of customer service trends prevalent in the industry.
- Truck technicians become certified by passing ASE examinations in the United States, provincial certification in Canada, and state-managed apprenticeships in Australia.
- Because of the rapid changes in technology, the truck technician should regard education,

both self-driven and formal, as an ongoing process.
- Practicing truck technicians should consider membership in both professional and proprietary organizations, because they provide an easy means of remaining up to date with the trends of the industry.
- For many, becoming a truck technician is just the first step of a career in the trucking industry, which grows at an accelerated rate even during times of recession.
- The truck technician of today must come to terms with electronic vehicle management systems, shop data-tracking systems, and communications technology.
- The *clean* diesel engine of today exists because its predecessors played a major role in fouling the atmosphere.
- Alternative-fuel and hybrid-drive commercial vehicles exist not because they are better than diesel power, but because they help reduce our reliance on imported petroleum and lower emissions.

REVIEW EXERCISES

1. Log on to the Internet and search http://www.asecert. org, http://www.diesel.net, and http://www.dieselnet. com. Explore the websites of some of the major truck engine OEMs. Select a company that has an e-mail query page and solicit information on one of its products.

2. Log on to the TMC website and bookmark it into your favorites.

3. Find out what it takes to become a TMC technician member. If you qualify, consider joining.

4. Contact the ASE online or by mail and request electronic or hard-copy information on its testing criteria and locations.

5. Investigate the role of the trucking industry in your community. Contact a local trucking association and request data on the business activities of its members.

6. Obtain copies of *Diesel Progress*, the *CCJ*, and other trade publications. Remember that many publications make electronic versions available and accessible via the Internet.

7. Contact some OEMs in the automotive and truck manufacturing fields and ask them about their customer service philosophy. A lack of response can sometimes be as informative as a response.

8. Select one of the major OEMs and make a list of its Class 5, 6, 7, and 8 chassis lines and the engine options it makes available.

9. Locate the VIN from a commercial truck and identify the vehicle type and the engine used.

10. Research online the latest developments in the joint Cummins and Peterbilt SuperTruck endeavor. Make a list of the technologies being explored by the SuperTruck team.

2

HAND AND SHOP TOOLS, PRECISION TOOLS, AND UNITS OF MEASUREMENT

OBJECTIVES

After studying this chapter, you should be able to:

- Identify the hand tools commonly used by truck technicians and describe their function.
- Categorize the various types of wrenches used in shop practice.
- Identify different types of torque wrenches.
- Calculate torque specification compensation when a linear extension is used.
- Describe the precision measuring tools used by the engine and fuel system technician.
- Outline the operating principles of a standard micrometer and name its components.
- Read a standard micrometer.
- Outline the operating principles of a metric micrometer and name its components.
- Read a metric micrometer.
- Understand how a dial indicator is read.
- Define *TIR* and how it is determined.
- Understand how a dial bore gauge operates.
- Outline the procedure for setting up a dial bore gauge.
- Perform accurate measurements using a dial bore gauge.
- Describe the shop tools generally provided by an employer.
- Describe some typical shop hoisting equipment and its application.
- Identify and describe the correct use of common fasteners.
- Describe the nature and use of chemical adhesives and sealants.
- Understand how to convert English and metric measurements.

KEY TERMS

bar	chain hoist	dividers	Industrial Fastener Institute (IFI)
boom hoist	dial bore gauge	electronic digital caliper (EDC)	inside diameter (id)
calipers	dial indicator		

inside micrometer	scissor jack	tensile strength	units of atmosphere (atms)
micrometer	spreader bar	torque-to-yield	
outside diameter (od)	stiction	total indicated runout (TIR)	
outside micrometer	telescoping gauge		

INTRODUCTION

This chapter is intended to provide a guide to tools for novice truck technicians. The tools are loosely divided into the categories of hand tools, precision measuring tools, and shop tools (**Figure 2–1**). There is also a guide to the contents of a truck technician's toolbox; however, the rookie technician should invest in only a minimum number of tools before obtaining employment, and then develop a tool collection with the job requirements in mind.

Some guidance in standard-to-metric conversion units is also provided. The modern truck technician is usually expected to work on engines engineered on metric systems using specifications generally presented in standard or English values, so it helps to be familiar with both systems.

HAND TOOLS

The technician will need to possess a basic set of hand tools. Although some basic guidelines are provided later in this chapter, the tools selected and their quality will largely be determined by the nature of the work. Hand tools vary considerably in price, so before spending large sums of money, the technician should determine whether the expenditure is justified by the amount of use the tools will get. Most better-quality hand tools carry lifetime warranties; however, this may not cover a tool that wears out, so it is good to question the extent of the warranty offered. Diesel technicians seldom wear out tools; the main problem is usually loss. Because of the high price of hand tools, most technicians learn to check the contents of their toolboxes carefully after completing each job. Most loss of tools is usually the result of carelessness on the part of the technician. Thousands of wrenches are lost every week because they are left on a truck, bus, or car chassis.

COMBINATION WRENCHES

Most technicians usually own a couple of sets of combination wrenches, including the common sizes. A combination wrench is manufactured with a box end and an open end, both of the same nominal size (**Figure 2–2A**). Most truck diesel technicians should only consider better-quality combination wrenches that are guaranteed for life. A wide range of prices exists between lower-quality wrenches, which tend to

FIGURE 2–1 A technician's tool cabinet.

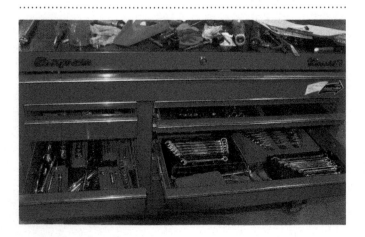

FIGURE 2–2 Wrenches: A. Open-end; B. and C. Combination; D. Box-end.

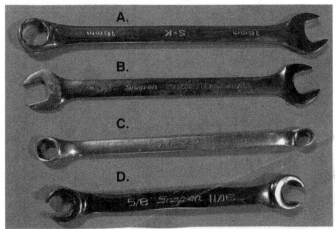

be heavy and clumsy (but often are as strong as the best quality) and the best quality, which are light and smooth to handle. It is useful to own a set of top-quality combination wrenches in sizes up to $\frac{3}{4}$" (19 mm) because these are able to access fasteners on engines that heavier, clumsier wrenches cannot access. Less expensive but fully warranted wrenches can be considered for use on sizes larger than $\frac{3}{4}$" (19 mm). There are many cheaper, poor-quality wrenches on the market, many of them imported. These are seldom guaranteed. Poor-quality wrenches are dangerous and should be used by no technician.

OPEN-END WRENCHES

Open-end wrenches have open jaws on either side of the wrench, usually with different sizes at either end and slightly offset (**Figure 2–2B**). The wrench should be of sufficient quality that the jaws do not spread when force is applied, and the jaws should not be so bulky as to restrict access to difficult-to-get-at fasteners. Such wrenches may damage softer fasteners (such as brass pipe nuts) because their design permits them to impart force to only two of the six flats of a hex nut.

BOX-END WRENCHES

A box-end wrench surrounds the fastener and may be of hexagonal or double-hexagonal design (**Figure 2–2C**). As most bolts and nuts are of a hexagonal design, the hex box-end wrench will grip more securely; however, it will be less versatile where access is restricted, as it can only fit on the fastener in 6 radial positions through a rotation rather than the 12 radial positions of the double-hex, box-end wrench.

LINE WRENCHES

The appropriate wrench to work on the pipe nuts used in hydraulic and fuel injection components is a line wrench, shown in **Figure 2–2D**. It has the appearance of a box-end wrench with a small section removed so that it fits through the pipe to enclose the pipe nut. The line wrench should be used in place of the open-end wrench to avoid damaging pipe nuts. A line wrench can also be known as a *flare nut wrench* or *crowsfoot wrench*.

ADJUSTABLE WRENCHES

The adjustable wrench consists of a rigid jaw integral with the handle and an adjustable jaw

moved by a worm adjuster screw. The truck technician should probably own a couple of these and then resolve to use them as little as possible. Their advantage is versatility and their ability to (sometimes) grip a worn fastener. Their disadvantage is that they cause wear because the adjustable jaw never fits tightly to the flats on a hex fastener and it tends to round them out. Never apply excessive force to an adjustable wrench.

SOCKET WRENCHES

Diesel technicians will require complete socket sets in $\frac{1}{4}$", $\frac{3}{8}$", and $\frac{1}{2}$" drive sizes and may consider a $\frac{3}{4}$" drive. What constitutes a complete set of sockets varies a little by manufacturer, but typically $\frac{1}{4}$" drive sets are provided with sockets up to $\frac{1}{2}$" (12 mm), $\frac{3}{8}$" drives up to $\frac{3}{4}$" (19 mm), and $\frac{1}{2}$" drives up to $1\frac{1}{4}$" (30 mm). Sockets may be of the hex or double-hex design and enclose the fastener. The socket may be hand-rotated by a ratchet or flex bar and power-rotated by a pneumatically powered wrench or impact wrench.

Impact sockets are manufactured of softer alloys than those designed to be driven manually, to prevent fracture. Technicians should purchase good-quality sockets because the consequence of a failed socket is personal injury. Deep sockets permit access to a nut in which a greater length of the bolt or stud is exposed. A crowsfoot socket is essentially an open-end wrench that can be turned by a ratchet; it grips two of the six flats of a nut and is probably mostly used for final torquing of a difficult-to-access nut. A *line socket* is the socket counterpart to the line wrench. It grips four of the six flats of a nut; its main use is to deliver final torque to a pipe nut.

RATCHETS AND BREAKER/FLEX BARS

Reversible ratchets used in conjunction with sockets are tools much used by any technician. They are used to rapidly turn fasteners by hand and should be of good quality because the consequence of failure is personal injury. However, they are not designed to accommodate high torque loads. The ratchet spur wheel is locked to one direction of rotation by a single or double cog. The spur and cog cannot be observed because they are enclosed in the ratchet head, but this determines the ultimate strength of the tool.

INTRODUCTION

This chapter is intended to provide a guide to tools for novice truck technicians. The tools are loosely divided into the categories of hand tools, precision measuring tools, and shop tools (**Figure 2–1**). There is also a guide to the contents of a truck technician's toolbox; however, the rookie technician should invest in only a minimum number of tools before obtaining employment, and then develop a tool collection with the job requirements in mind.

Some guidance in standard-to-metric conversion units is also provided. The modern truck technician is usually expected to work on engines engineered on metric systems using specifications generally presented in standard or English values, so it helps to be familiar with both systems.

HAND TOOLS

The technician will need to possess a basic set of hand tools. Although some basic guidelines are provided later in this chapter, the tools selected and their quality will largely be determined by the nature of the work. Hand tools vary considerably in price, so before spending large sums of money, the technician should determine whether the expenditure is justified by the amount of use the tools will get. Most better-quality hand tools carry lifetime warranties; however, this may not cover a tool that wears out, so it is good to question the extent of the warranty offered. Diesel technicians seldom wear out tools; the main problem is usually loss. Because of the high price of hand tools, most technicians learn to check the contents of their toolboxes carefully after completing each job. Most loss of tools is usually the result of carelessness on the part of the technician. Thousands of wrenches are lost every week because they are left on a truck, bus, or car chassis.

COMBINATION WRENCHES

Most technicians usually own a couple of sets of combination wrenches, including the common sizes. A combination wrench is manufactured with a box end and an open end, both of the same nominal size (**Figure 2–2A**). Most truck diesel technicians should only consider better-quality combination wrenches that are guaranteed for life. A wide range of prices exists between lower-quality wrenches, which tend to

FIGURE 2–2 Wrenches: A. Open-end; B. and C. Combination; D. Box-end.

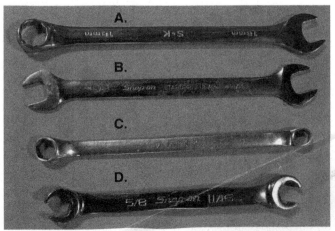

FIGURE 2–1 A technician's tool cabinet.

be heavy and clumsy (but often are as strong as the best quality) and the best quality, which are light and smooth to handle. It is useful to own a set of top-quality combination wrenches in sizes up to ¾" (19 mm) because these are able to access fasteners on engines that heavier, clumsier wrenches cannot access. Less expensive but fully warranted wrenches can be considered for use on sizes larger than ¾" (19 mm). There are many cheaper, poor-quality wrenches on the market, many of them imported. These are seldom guaranteed. Poor-quality wrenches are dangerous and should be used by no technician.

OPEN-END WRENCHES

Open-end wrenches have open jaws on either side of the wrench, usually with different sizes at either end and slightly offset (**Figure 2–2B**). The wrench should be of sufficient quality that the jaws do not spread when force is applied, and the jaws should not be so bulky as to restrict access to difficult-to-get-at fasteners. Such wrenches may damage softer fasteners (such as brass pipe nuts) because their design permits them to impart force to only two of the six flats of a hex nut.

BOX-END WRENCHES

A box-end wrench surrounds the fastener and may be of hexagonal or double-hexagonal design (**Figure 2–2C**). As most bolts and nuts are of a hexagonal design, the hex box-end wrench will grip more securely; however, it will be less versatile where access is restricted, as it can only fit on the fastener in 6 radial positions through a rotation rather than the 12 radial positions of the double-hex, box-end wrench.

LINE WRENCHES

The appropriate wrench to work on the pipe nuts used in hydraulic and fuel injection components is a line wrench, shown in **Figure 2–2D**. It has the appearance of a box-end wrench with a small section removed so that it fits through the pipe to enclose the pipe nut. The line wrench should be used in place of the open-end wrench to avoid damaging pipe nuts. A line wrench can also be known as a *flare nut wrench* or *crowsfoot wrench*.

ADJUSTABLE WRENCHES

The adjustable wrench consists of a rigid jaw integral with the handle and an adjustable jaw moved by a worm adjuster screw. The truck technician should probably own a couple of these and then resolve to use them as little as possible. Their advantage is versatility and their ability to (sometimes) grip a worn fastener. Their disadvantage is that they cause wear because the adjustable jaw never fits tightly to the flats on a hex fastener and it tends to round them out. Never apply excessive force to an adjustable wrench.

SOCKET WRENCHES

Diesel technicians will require complete socket sets in ¼", ⅜", and ½" drive sizes and may consider a ¾" drive. What constitutes a complete set of sockets varies a little by manufacturer, but typically ¼" drive sets are provided with sockets up to ½" (12 mm), ⅜" drives up to ¾" (19 mm), and ½" drives up to 1¼" (30 mm). Sockets may be of the hex or double-hex design and enclose the fastener. The socket may be hand-rotated by a ratchet or flex bar and power-rotated by a pneumatically powered wrench or impact wrench.

Impact sockets are manufactured of softer alloys than those designed to be driven manually, to prevent fracture. Technicians should purchase good-quality sockets because the consequence of a failed socket is personal injury. Deep sockets permit access to a nut in which a greater length of the bolt or stud is exposed. A crowsfoot socket is essentially an open-end wrench that can be turned by a ratchet; it grips two of the six flats of a nut and is probably mostly used for final torquing of a difficult-to-access nut. A *line socket* is the socket counterpart to the line wrench. It grips four of the six flats of a nut; its main use is to deliver final torque to a pipe nut.

RATCHETS AND BREAKER/FLEX BARS

Reversible ratchets used in conjunction with sockets are tools much used by any technician. They are used to rapidly turn fasteners by hand and should be of good quality because the consequence of failure is personal injury. However, they are not designed to accommodate high torque loads. The ratchet spur wheel is locked to one direction of rotation by a single or double cog. The spur and cog cannot be observed because they are enclosed in the ratchet head, but this determines the ultimate strength of the tool.

A *breaker bar* (also known as a *flex bar*, *power bar*, and *Johnson bar*) has a grip bar and pivoting drive square to engage with a socket in the same way a ratchet does; they are available in $\frac{1}{4}$", $\frac{3}{8}$", $\frac{1}{2}$", $\frac{3}{4}$", and 1" sizes. A breaker/flex bar can be used to release fasteners that require considerably more force than could be safely applied to a ratchet; however, the use of "helpers" such as a pipe over the handle should be avoided.

TORQUE WRENCHES

Torque wrenches measure resistance to turning effort (**Figure 2–3**). The objective of torquing fasteners is to ensure that a specified clamping force between two components is achieved. However, an estimated 90% of the force applied to a torque wrench is required to overcome the friction of the fastener thread surface area, with about 10% contributing to clamping force (**Figure 2–4**).

Most technicians possess at least one torque wrench—and probably do not use it as much as they should. In assembling engine and fuel system components, every fastener should be torqued to specification. Studies indicate that when technicians fail to use torque wrenches,

they overtorque fasteners to values 50% to 100% over the specification. This action can damage fasteners and distort components, including cylinder blocks and heads.

Four general types of torque wrench are used:

- Flex beam
- Dial gauge
- Click or sensory
- Electronic (with audible beep)

The torque wrenches commonly used today in engine repair facilities are the sensory or click type and the electronic type: in both, when the selected torque value is attained, the wrench produces an audible click or beep. Diesel technicians are often required to torque large numbers of fasteners to the same specification, such as when torquing cylinder heads to a cylinder block; it makes sense to use a click- or electronic-type torque wrench when performing this type of procedure.

Stiction

Stiction is stationary friction. Referencing Figure 2–4, the student can see that starting to turn a bolt requires a lot more force than keeping it turning. The tighter the bolt is torqued, the greater the stiction, and this can affect torque readings. Lubricating bolts can help, but the type of lubricant (lube) used is important. This means that the lube suggested by the service literature should always be used. This can range from nothing at all to engine lube to locking adhesives. Failure to observe these recommendations can result in either high or low clamping pressures.

Care of Torque Wrenches

Click-type torque wrenches should always be backed off to a zero reading after use, and their calibration should be routinely checked. Electronic torque wrenches should be switched off after use, and calibration should be routinely checked. Dial-type torque wrenches have circular dial scales with a needle that indicates the applied torque value. These tend to be more useful when torquing sequences of fasteners at different torque values; dial-type torque wrenches are usually more expensive than click-type torque wrenches. Beam-type torque wrenches use a flexible, medium alloy steel shaft (beam) that deflects when torque is applied; a needle pointer indicates the applied torque effort. These tend to be the most expensive, but have good accuracy and seldom require calibration if properly stored and cared for. However, it

FIGURE 2–3 Sensory (click-type) torque wrench.

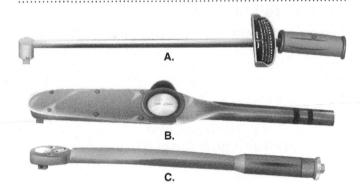

A.

B.

C.

FIGURE 2–4 Torque to overcome friction.

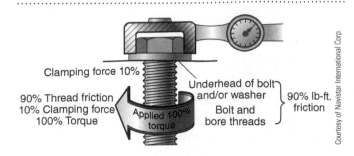

Clamping force 10%

90% Thread friction
10% Clamping force
100% Torque

Applied 100% torque

Underhead of bolt and/or washer

Bolt and bore threads

90% lb-ft. friction

Courtesy of Navistar International Corp.

FIGURE 2–5 Torque setting scale on a typical click-type torque wrench.

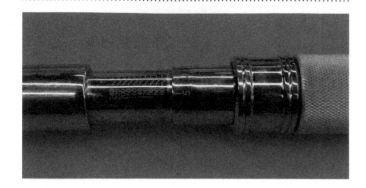

should be noted that the needle pointer is vulnerable to abuse.

Technicians should probably own a $\frac{3}{8}$" and $\frac{1}{2}$" drive torque wrench of the click or electronic type. The torque wrench calibration should be checked annually with a torque wrench tester. Torque specifications are provided by original equipment manufacturers (OEMs) in order to obtain reasonably consistent clamping pressures between mated components. Torque values for fuel injection and engine component fasteners are usually factored for lubricated threads.

TECH TIP:

Sensory or click-type torque wrenches are set by internal spring tension to a specified torque value, either by rotating the handle or by a dial and latch. On torque wrenches that use spring tension to define torque, the spring tension should be relieved after use, as shown in **Figure 2–5**. In other words, store the torque wrench with the torque specification set at zero or the tool will have to be recalibrated more often.

Torque Wrench Extensions

Torque wrenches are mainly used with sockets, line sockets, or crowsfoot jaw wrenches. Torque readings are a product of the length of the handle measured in feet or inches and the force applied to the handle. For example, a 2-foot (ft.)-long torque wrench when applied with 10 pounds (lb) of force would produce 20 lb-ft. of torque. To express any torque value specified in lb-ft. in lb-in., simply multiply by 12. So, 20 lb-ft. is equivalent to 240 lb-in. When a standard extension (one that is at right angles to the plane of the wrench) is used with a torque wrench, no

torque reading adjustment is required. If a linear extension (one on the same linear plane as the wrench) is used, the mechanical advantage is increased, and the torque reading should be adjusted using the following formula:

$$TS = \frac{T \times L^1}{(L^1 + L^2)}$$

where

T = torque in lb-ft.
TS = torque scale in lb
L^1 = torque wrench frame length in inches
L^2 = torque wrench extension length in inches

So, if a torque specification is 50 lb-ft. and an 18" torque wrench is to be used in conjunction with a 12" linear extension, the following calculation should be used to determine what the correct reading on the torque wrench scale should be:

$$TS = \frac{T \times L^1}{(L^1 + L^2)} = \frac{50 \times 18}{(18 + 12)}$$
$$TS = \frac{900}{30}$$
$$T = 30 \text{lb-ft}$$

Torque wrenches may be calibrated in the standard or metric systems: pound-feet or Newton-meters.

1 lb-ft. = 1.356 Newton-meters

1 Newton-meter = 0.7375 lb-ft.

Torque-to-Yield Bolts

Torque-to-yield bolts are designed to stretch to their yield point as they are tightened. They are often used where more precise clamping load forces are required, so they are typically seen on cylinder heads, connecting rods, and crankshaft main bearings. As a torque-to-yield bolt is tightened, it is stretched to its elastic limit, so it is designed for one-off use. When service literature on a repair procedure indicates that a bolt should be discarded and replaced with a new one, usually a torque-to-yield fastener is used.

TECH TIP:

Reusing old torque-to-yield bolts can result in costly engine failures. Observe the service literature procedure and replace them.

Tightening Torque-to-Yield Fasteners

Tightening of torque-to-yield fasteners is usually performed progressively using a combination of torque and turning angle. The first step is to torque the fastener or set of fasteners to a low specification so that an even clamping load is applied to the mating components. This is usually followed by a second pass at an incrementally higher torque value. After this, each fastener is turned a specified number of degrees measured with a protractor or template placed over the fastener hex; this may occur in two or three additional steps. For example, each fastener might be turned 90 degrees, followed by an additional 45 degrees. Torque-to-yield ensures a more accurate and even clamping force. The tools used for torque-to-yield fasteners are:

- Protractors with a movable pointer
- Electronic (measure the turn angle with more precision)

HAMMERS

Mechanical technicians mostly use ball peen hammers in various different weights. The specified weight of a hammer is the head weight, which starts at $\frac{1}{2}$ lb and should go up to about 4 lb in weight. While there is no place for the carpenter's claw hammer in the technician's toolbox, a 4-lb (2-kg) cross peen hammer can be a useful addition, and the engine specialist should also own a 5-lb (2.5-kg) rubber mallet and a couple of soft-faced or fiberglass hammers.

Safety glasses should be worn whenever using any striking tool. The impact faces of hammers should be inspected regularly and discarded when the face becomes damaged. Properly heat-treated hammers should possess highest hardness at the contact face and be relatively soft behind it to buffer the shock loads. Hammer handles are also important—a hammer should not be used if its handle is damaged. The handle may be made of hickory or fiberglass, in which case it is susceptible to damage; or of steel and integral with the head with a rubber-cushioned grip. Examples of hammers and mallets are shown in **Figures 2–6** and **2–7.**

WARNING:
Never strike a hammer with another hammer. The hardened impact surfaces can shatter and cause serious injury.

PLIERS

Most technicians will require a large selection of pliers, which are used for gripping and cutting.

FIGURE 2–6 Types of hammers: A. Brass soft face; B. Ball peen; C. Cross peen or blacksmith.

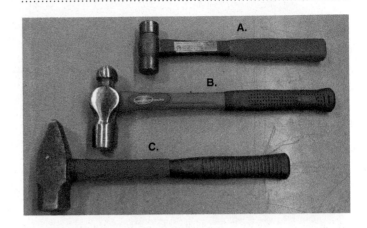

FIGURE 2–7 Soft-face mallets.

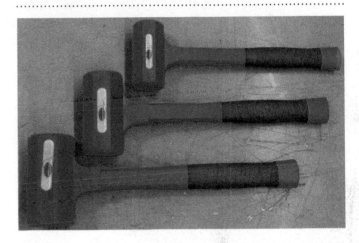

Pliers used for working on electrical circuits should have insulated handles. Each type of pliers is named; some examples are needle nose, slip joint, lineman, and sidecutter. **Figure 2–8** shows a typical pair of lineman pliers.

SCREW EXTRACTORS

Fasteners occasionally fail when the fastener head shears. When methods such as welding a

FIGURE 2–8 A typical set of lineman pliers.

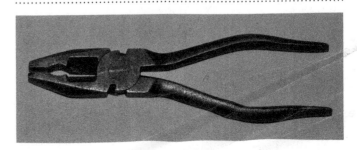

FIGURE 2–9 A screw extractor set.

FIGURE 2–10 Screw pitch gauge set.

nut onto a fastener that has had its hex head sheared off have failed, a screw extractor must be used. First, the fastener must be drilled as centrally as possible to 75% of its depth and half its diameter; then the appropriately sized screw extractor must be inserted. Two types exist. The *taper square screw extractor* is designed to bite into and grab the bore of the drilled hole; it can be progressively driven into the hole if the edges round out. The *left-hand twist screw extractor* works by tapping its way into the drilled hole in the fastener as it is turned counterclockwise. **Figure 2–9** shows a typical set of screw extractors.

STUD EXTRACTORS

Stud extractors may be used to extract a fastener only when the fastener is not sheared flush. Two types are used. The *collet type* fits over the exposed length of the stud and locks to the stud as it is rotated counterclockwise. The *wedge type* consists of a splined circular wedge that locks to the stud as it is rotated. Wedge-type stud extractors should only be used with hand tools, as they are driven eccentrically.

TAPS AND DIES

Taps and dies are designed to cut threads in both standard and metric specifications. Taps cut internal threads in bores; quite often the technician will use a tap to repair damaged threads. Three types are used:

1. Taper tap: used to cut threads to a virgin bore
2. Plug tap: used to finish-cut or repair threads

3. Bottom tap: used to cut the final threads in a blind hole

Dies cut external threads. Most are designed with graduated teeth and a taper, enabling them to cut threads to a shaft. It is important to use an appropriate cutting medium. Again, technicians are more likely to use these to repair damaged threads. In fact, most toolbox-quality taps and dies should not be used to cut virgin threads in hardened steels, especially if the fastener is critical.

Thread Chasers

A *thread chaser* is a die designed for the sole purpose of repairing minor damage to an existing thread. It cuts in much the same way a die does, but it is not designed to cut new threads.

Thread Pitch Gauges

Thread pitch gauges are designed to measure the thread pitch (angle) and number of threads per inch (tpi) of any thread pattern. They are used to determine which tap, die, or fastener is appropriate. **Figure 2–10** shows a typical pack of screw pitch gauges.

REAMERS

Reamers are rotary cutting tools that enlarge an existing hole to an exact dimension. They are used where a greater degree of accuracy is required than a drill is capable of delivering. Reamers are available in several types: adjustable reamers can be set to cut holes through a range of dimensions, and spiral-fluted taper reamers are designed to be driven by air or electric power tools and enlarge a hole accurately to a specific size.

TABLE 2–1 Recommended Cutting Fluid Processes

Metal	Drilling	Reaming	Tapping
Mild steel	Soluble oil/water	Lard	Lard
Middle alloy	Soluble oil/water	Lard	Lard
Cast iron	Dry	Dry	Lard
Brass	Dry	Water	Dry
Copper	Soluble oil/water	Soluble oil/water	Soluble oil/water
Aluminum	Kerosene	Kerosene	Soluble oil/water

DRILL BITS

Drill bits are driven by an electric or pneumatic power tool. Twist drills must be machined to the correct cutting pitch (angle); normally this is done by grinding on a fine abrasive wheel. The *point angle* of a drill bit is the combined angle of the dressed cutting edges, usually about 120 degrees for drilling most steels and cast irons. This will produce a cutting pitch of about 30 degrees. The point angle is increased when harder steels must be drilled. The two cutting edges of the twist drill must be angled identically from the center point of the drill and have the same radial dimension; a slight difference will result in a larger hole than the drill shank specification. Drills sharpened by hand seldom produce exactly sized holes. Drill speeds should be adjusted for the material being cut and the size of the hole.

HACKSAWS

Most technicians will be required to use a hacksaw from time to time. A hacksaw is designed specifically to cut metals. A hacksaw should have a rigid frame, and the blade selected should have the appropriate number of teeth per inch (tpi) for the metal to be cut; generally, the harder the metal, the more tpi required. Metal thickness is also a factor and a rule of thumb is that at least two teeth must be in contact with the material to be cut. Better-quality hacksaw blades tend to be cost effective, as they last until they wear out, whereas cheaper blades tend to break. Inspect the blades and replace them when dulled or missing teeth are evident.

A hacksaw should be used with a light but firm grip. An even horizontal stroke with no rocking will produce the fastest cutting rates. A relaxed, calm approach to the cutting task has a way of producing fast results, whereas those who attempt to power their way through often end up breaking blades and losing their tempers.

CUTTING FLUIDS

Soluble oil is machinist's oil mixed with water according to the manufacturer's recommendations. Remember that engine oil is not soluble and cannot be used as a substitute. See **Table 2–1**.

PRECISION MEASURING TOOLS

Following are some examples of precision measuring instruments used in a typical truck service garage. Precision measuring tools tend to be high-cost items. They are sometimes provided by employers, but technicians who frequently use a specific tool may wish to purchase their own.

ELECTRONIC DIGITAL CALIPERS

Electronic digital calipers (EDCs) are a great addition to the toolbox. EDCs are an invaluable tool for the diesel technician who works extensively in the engine and fuel areas. These dimensional measuring tools will perform inside, outside, and depth measurements to half a thousandth or 0.0005-inch accuracy. EDCs perform with good accuracy and have the advantage of being easier to read than micrometers. Additionally, they will perform metric to standard linear conversions at the push of a button. **Figure 2–11** shows some of the uses of an EDC.

MICROMETERS

Some truck servicing operations require precise measurements of both outside and inside diameters, such as the diameter of a shaft and the bore of a hole. The **micrometer** is the common

FIGURE 2–11 Various uses of a set of digital calipers.

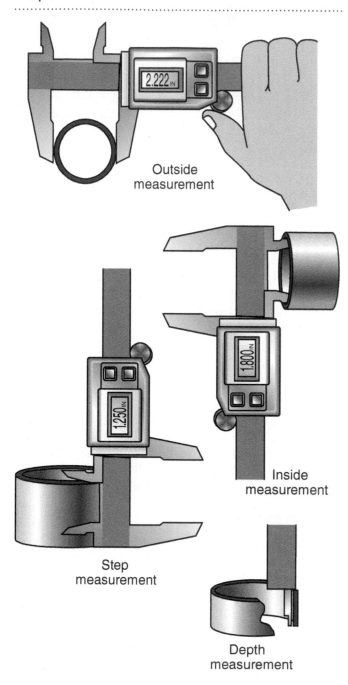

Outside measurement

Step measurement

Inside measurement

Depth measurement

FIGURE 2–12 Nomenclature and components of (A) an outside and (B) an inside micrometer.

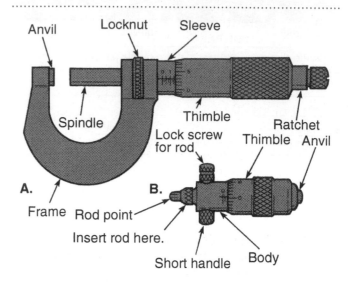

Anvil Locknut Sleeve

Spindle

Thimble

Lock screw for rod

A. Frame Rod point

Insert rod here.

Short handle

Ratchet Thimble Anvil

B.

Body

On both outside and inside micrometers, the thimble is revolved between the thumb and the forefinger. Only very light pressure is required when bringing the measuring points into contact with the surfaces being measured. It is important to remember that the micrometer is a delicate instrument and that even slight excessive pressure will result in an incorrect reading.

Reading an Inch-Graduated Outside Micrometer

Standard micrometers are made so that each full turn of the thimble moves the spindle 0.025 in. (twenty-five thousandths of an inch). This is accomplished by using 40 threads per inch on the thimble. The sleeve index line is marked with sleeve numbers 1, 2, 3, and so on up to 10. Each sleeve number represents 0.100 inch, 0.200 inch, 0.300 inch, and so on. The sleeve on the micrometer contains sleeve graduations that represent 1 inch in 0.025-in. (twenty-five thousandths of an inch) increments. Each of the thimble graduations represents 0.001 in. (one thousandth of an inch). In one complete turn, the spindle moves through 25 graduations or 0.025 in. (twenty-five thousandths of an inch). Inch-graduated micrometers come in a range of sizes: 0 to 1 inch, 1 inch to 2, 2 inches to 3, 3 inches to 4, and so on. The most commonly used micrometers are calibrated in increments of one-thousandth of an inch.

To read a micrometer, first read the last whole sleeve number visible on the sleeve index line. Next, count the number of full sleeve graduations past the number. Finally, count

instrument for taking these measurements. Both outside and inside micrometers are calibrated and read in the same manner and are both operated so that the measuring points exactly contact the surfaces being measured.

The components of a micrometer include the frame, anvil, spindle, locknut, sleeve, sleeve numbers, sleeve long line, thimble marks, thimble, and ratchet (**Figure 2–12**). Micrometers are calibrated in either inch or metric graduations.

the number of thimble graduations past the sleeve graduations. Add these together for the measurement. These three readings indicate tenths, hundredths, and thousandths of an inch, respectively. For example, a 2- to 3-in. micrometer that has taken a measurement is described in **Figure 2–13**.

1. The largest sleeve number visible is 4, indicating 0.400 in. (four-tenths of an inch).
2. The thimble is three full sleeve graduations past the sleeve number. Each sleeve graduation indicates 0.025 in., so this indicates 0.075 in. (seventy-five thousandths of an inch).
3. The number 12 thimble graduation is lined up with the sleeve index line. This indicates 0.012 in. (twelve thousandths of an inch).
4. Add the readings from steps 1, 2, and 3. The total of the three is the correct reading. In our example:

Sleeve	0.400 in.
Sleeve graduations	0.075 in.
Thimble graduations	0.012 in.
Total	0.487 in.

5. Now add 2 inches to the measurement, because this is a 2- to 3-inch micrometer. The final reading is 2.487 inches.

Reading an Outside Micrometer with a Vernier Scale

In cases in which a measurement must be within 0.0001 in. (one ten-thousandth of an inch), a micrometer with a Vernier scale should be used. This micrometer is read in the same way as a standard micrometer. However, in addition to the three scales found on the typical micrometer, this type has a Vernier scale on the sleeve. When taking measurements with this micrometer (sometimes called a *mike*), read it in the same way as you would a standard mike. Then, locate the thimble graduation that aligns precisely with one of the Vernier scale lines (**Figure 2–14**). Only one of these lines will align exactly. The other lines will be misaligned. The Vernier scale number that aligns with the thimble graduation is the 0.0001-in. (one ten-thousandth of an inch) measurement.

Reading a Metric Outside Micrometer

A metric micrometer is read in the same manner as the inch-graduated micrometer except that the graduations are in the metric system of measurement.

Readings are obtained as follows:

- Each number on the sleeve of the micrometer represents 5 mm or 5/1,000 of a meter (**Figure 2–15A**).

FIGURE 2–13 The three steps in reading a micrometer.

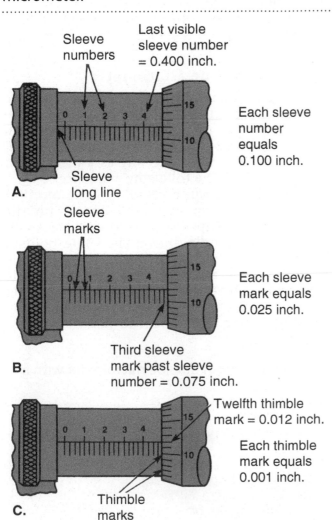

Sleeve numbers

Last visible sleeve number = 0.400 inch.

Sleeve long line

Each sleeve number equals 0.100 inch.

A.

Sleeve marks

Each sleeve mark equals 0.025 inch.

Third sleeve mark past sleeve number = 0.075 inch.

B.

Twelfth thimble mark = 0.012 inch.

Each thimble mark equals 0.001 inch.

Thimble marks

C.

FIGURE 2–14 Measuring ten-thousandths of an inch using a micrometer with a Vernier scale.

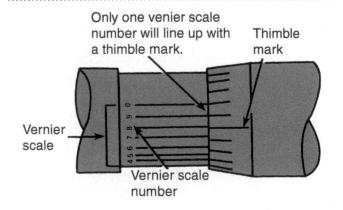

Only one venier scale number will line up with a thimble mark.

Thimble mark

Vernier scale

Vernier scale number

FIGURE 2–15 Reading a metric micrometer.

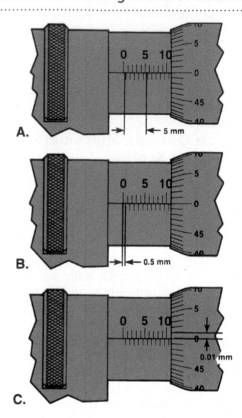

A.

B.

C.

FIGURE 2–16 The reading shown on this metric micrometer is 7.28 mm.

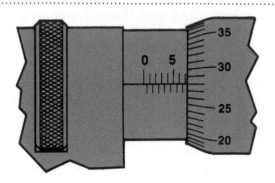

- Each of the 10 equal spaces between each number, with index lines alternating above and below the horizontal line, represents 0.5 mm or five-tenths of a millimeter. One revolution of the thimble changes the reading one graduation on the sleeve scale or 0.5 mm (**Figure 2–15B**).
- The beveled edge of the thimble is divided into 50 equal divisions with every fifth line numbered (0, 5, 10, ... 45). Because one complete revolution of the thimble advances the spindle 0.5 mm, each graduation on the thimble advances the spindle 0.5 mm; each graduation on the thimble is equal to 1/50 of 0.5 mm or one hundredth of a millimeter (**Figure 2–15C**).

As with the inch-graduated micrometer, the three separate readings are added together to obtain the total reading (**Figure 2–16**):

- Read the largest number on the sleeve that has been exposed by the thimble. In the illustration it is 5, which means the first number in the series is 5 mm.
- Count the number of lines past the number 5 that the thimble has exposed. In the example,

this is 4, and because each graduation is equal to 0.5 mm, 4 graduations equal 4×0.5 or 2 mm. This, added to the figure obtained in step 1, gives 7 mm.

- Read the graduation line on the thimble that coincides with the horizontal line of the sleeve scale and add this to the total obtained in step 2. In the example, the thimble scale reads 28 or 0.28 mm. This, added to the 7 mm from step 2, gives a total reading of 7.28 mm.

Using an Outside Micrometer

Using digital display micrometers has become popular in recent years. These are no more accurate but virtually eliminate interpretation errors. **Figure 2–17** shows a digital micrometer. It is used in the same way as a mechanical micrometer. Use the following sequence.

To measure small objects using an **outside micrometer**, grasp the micrometer with the right hand and slip the object to be measured between the spindle and anvil. While holding the object against the anvil, turn the thimble using the thumb and forefinger until the spindle contacts the object. Never clamp the micrometer tightly. Use only enough pressure on the thimble to allow the component to just fit between

FIGURE 2–17 An outside micrometer with a digital display.

FIGURE 2–18 Slip the micrometer and adjust the thimble until it just begins to grab.

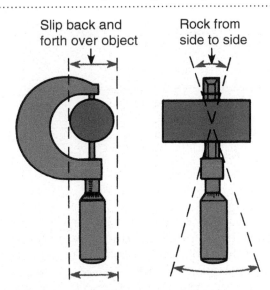

Slip back and forth over object

Rock from side to side

FIGURE 2–19 Obtaining a precise measurement with an inside micrometer.

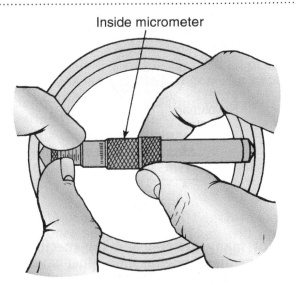

Inside micrometer

the anvil and the spindle. If the micrometer is equipped with a ratchet screw, use it to tighten the micrometer around the object for final adjustment. For a correct measurement, the object must just slip while adjusting the thimble. It is important to slide the mike back and forth over the work until you feel a very light resistance, while at the same time rocking the mike from side to side to ensure that the spindle cannot be closed any further (**Figure 2–18**). These steps should be taken with any precision measuring device to ensure accurate measurements.

Measurements will be reliable if the mike is calibrated correctly. To calibrate a micrometer, close the mike over a micrometer standard. If the reading differs from that of the known micrometer standard, then the mike requires adjustment.

Reading an Inside Micrometer

Inside micrometers (**Figure 2–19**) are used to measure bore sizes. They are frequently used with outside mikes to reduce the chance of error. To use an inside mike, place it inside the bore or hole and extend the measuring surfaces until each end touches the bore surface. If the bore is large, it might be necessary to use an extension rod to increase the measuring range. Extension rods come in various lengths. The inside micrometer is read in the same manner as an outside micrometer.

To obtain a precise measurement in either inch or metric graduations, hold the anvil firmly against one side of the bore and rock the inside mike back and forth and side to side. This

ensures that the mike fits in the center of the work with the correct amount of resistance. As with the outside micrometer, this procedure will require a little practice until you get a feel for the correct resistance and fit of the mike. After taking a measurement with the inside mike, use an outside mike to take a comparison measurement. This reduces the chance of errors and helps ensure an accurate measurement.

SHOP TALK

Follow these tips for taking care of a micrometer:

- Always clean a micrometer before using it.
- Do not touch the measuring surfaces.
- Store the micrometer properly. The spindle face should not contact the anvil face, or a change in temperature might spring the micrometer.
- Clean the mike after use. Wipe it clean of any oil, dirt, or dust using a lint-free cloth.
- Do not drop the mike. It is a sensitive instrument and must be handled with care.
- Check the calibration weekly. If the mike is dropped at any time, check it immediately.

DIAL INDICATORS

Dial indicators are used to measure travel or movement in values of thousandths to one hundred thousandths of an inch. Metric dial indicators are calibrated to read in tenths to thousandths of a millimeter. Dial indicators are

FIGURE 2–24 Cylinder bore data recording chart for a six-cylinder engine. Note the locations for taking longitudinal and transverse measurements.

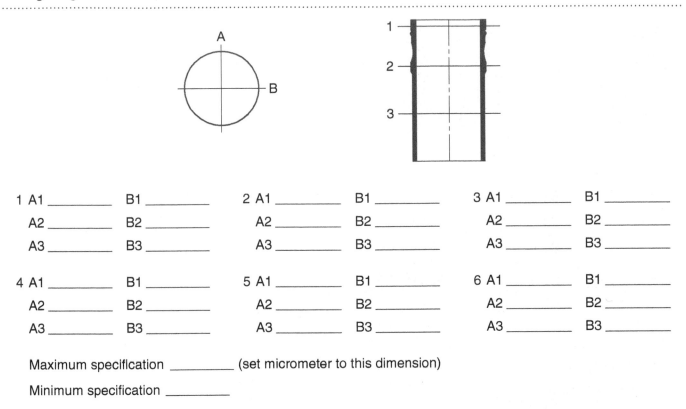

1 A1 _____	B1 _____	2 A1 _____	B1 _____	3 A1 _____	B1 _____
A2 _____	B2 _____	A2 _____	B2 _____	A2 _____	B2 _____
A3 _____	B3 _____	A3 _____	B3 _____	A3 _____	B3 _____
4 A1 _____	B1 _____	5 A1 _____	B1 _____	6 A1 _____	B1 _____
A2 _____	B2 _____	A2 _____	B2 _____	A2 _____	B2 _____
A3 _____	B3 _____	A3 _____	B3 _____	A3 _____	B3 _____

Maximum specification _____ (set micrometer to this dimension)

Minimum specification _____

least one full revolution (on a typical indicator, this will be 100 thousandths). Remove the dial bore gauge. Lock the jam nut on the adjustable guide. It does not matter if the adjustable guide moves slightly as the jam nut is engaged. Next, insert the dial bore gauge back into the mike. Make sure the dial bore indicator turns through approximately one rotation of travel, then zero the indicator and lock the setting. Having set the dial bore gauge, remove and reinstall it a couple of times to check the measurement.

Each time the dial bore gauge is installed into the mike it should read exactly zero. When it does, the zero corresponds to the *maximum* permitted bore specification. This means that *any* positive reading on the indicator is out of spec. This also means that for recording the data, every in-spec reading in a within-spec bore should be a minus reading.

Making Bore Measurements

If making measurements to determine the serviceability of cylinder liners, they should be made in the following locations:

1. Top of the ring belt sweep
2. Bottom of the ring belt sweep

3. Midway between measurement 2 and the bottom of the liner

These locations are shown in Figure 2–24. To make a bore measurement, gently hold the dial bore gauge between two fingers on the grip of the handle above the indicator. Allow the measuring sled to pivot in the bore using the dial bore handle to sweep the device through an arc. Watch the needle as the dial bore gauge moves through each sweep, and look for the stroke-over point—in other words, the point at which the needle reverses.

Recording the Measurements

This is where technicians should keep things as simple as possible. Think in terms of relative thousandths. Avoid recording the specification and complete the chart as discussed earlier. On this engine, the OEM defines the specification tolerance as 4.8744 inch to 4.8768 inch. First, round these values to the nearest half-thousandths of an inch. Now record the following specs onto the bore chart shown in Figure 2–24:

- Minimum specified bore size: 4.8745" (or 4.874½")
- Maximum specified bore size: 4.8770"

FIGURE 2–25 Completed cylinder bore data recording chart using the method outlined in this chapter: Note the out-of-spec data on #3 cylinder.

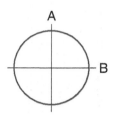

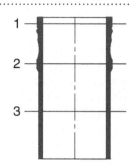

1 A1 -1 B1 $-\frac{1}{2}$ 2 A1 -1 B1 $-1\frac{1}{2}$ 3 A1 $\boxed{+1\frac{1}{2}}$ B1 $\boxed{+1}$

   A2 $-1\frac{1}{2}$ B2 $-1\frac{1}{2}$ A2 $-1\frac{1}{2}$ B2 -2 A2 $-\frac{1}{2}$ B2 $-\frac{1}{2}$

   A3 -2 B3 -2 A3 -2 B3 -2 A3 -1 B3 $-1\frac{1}{2}$

4 A1 $-\frac{1}{2}$ B1 -1 5 A1 $-\frac{1}{2}$ B1 $-\frac{1}{2}$ 6 A1 $-\frac{1}{2}$ B1 -1

   A2 $-1\frac{1}{2}$ B2 -1 A2 -1 B2 $-1\frac{1}{2}$ A2 -1 B2 -1

   A3 -2 B3 -2 A3 $-1\frac{1}{2}$ B3 -2 A3 $-1\frac{1}{2}$ B3 -2

Maximum specification ____4.877"____ (set micrometer to this dimension)

Minimum specification ____4.874 $\frac{1}{2}$"____

The specification window within which this cylinder sleeve should measure is 0.0025", usually expressed as 2½ thousandths inch. Observe the way in which the bore chart shown in **Figure 2–25** has been completed, and note the out-of-spec cylinder.

> ## TECH TIP:
> *Always* use a bore chart when measuring bore to specification. It is the only effective means of organizing the stream of data generated from making at least six measurements per cylinder on an inline six-cylinder engine.

DEPTH GAUGES

Depth gauges may be of the micrometer or dial gauge type. In each case, the instrument consists of a block to which either a micrometer assembly or a dial indicator mechanism is attached. The micrometer depth gauge is read opposite from the standard micrometer: When the spindle is flush with the block (that is, when it is in its most retracted position), the micrometer reads zero. As the thimble is rotated, the plunger extends beyond the flush position on the block to produce readings on the sleeve calibration scale. The calibration scales on both standard and metric depth micrometers are read in the same way as regular micrometers. The dial-type depth gauge is simply a dial indicator mounted on a block. It is read in a manner similar to a dial indicator.

COMBINATION SQUARE

The combination square consists of a right-angle square, a protractor, and a center gauge assembled on a steel ruler. A good-quality, precision combination square may be used as a square, protractor, center gauge, depth gauge, height gauge, level, straightedge, and ruler. It is a valuable addition to the technician's toolbox.

TELESCOPING GAUGES (SNAP GAUGES)

Telescoping gauges are used to measure internal dimensions. They have no integral calibration and must be used in conjunction with a standard outside micrometer. In other words, they are a comparison measuring instrument. A set of telescoping gauges is usually capable of measuring dimensions from ½" up to 6". The gauge has the appearance of a T; the T bar is equipped with a spring-loaded plunger, which, when released by the locking handle, expands to the dimension to be measured because it is spring-loaded. The gauge may then be locked by the locking handle and removed from the bore; an outside micrometer is then used to measure the T bar dimension.

The diesel engine rebuilder should generally attempt to avoid the use of telescoping gauges. Because it is an indirect measuring instrument, the chances of making inaccurate measurements increase. Telescoping gauges should not be used to measure cylinder bores, first because of the potential to make inaccurate measurements, and second because it takes much longer than using a dial bore gauge. The best use of telescoping gauges is for tasks such as measuring connecting rod big and small ends (which are shown in Chapter 15 of this book).

SMALL-HOLE GAUGES

Small-hole gauges, like telescoping gauges, are comparison measuring instruments used to measure small cylindrical bores in conjunction with an outside micrometer. In the typical small-hole gauge, a tapered spindle is rotated by a handle to spread split ball halves, moving them outward to contact the bore walls being measured. The gauge is adjusted for minimal drag in the bore, then measured with an outside micrometer. A typical application of a split ball gauge would be the measuring of valve guide bores.

PLASTIGAGE

Plastigage™ is used to check friction-bearing clearances. It consists of a cylindrical plastic thread enclosed in an envelope calibrated in the dimensions that the Plastigage is designed to measure. To measure bearing-to-shaft clearance, a small strip should be cut and placed across the width of the bearing shell. Next, the cap should be torqued to specification, which results in flattening the Plastigage. The cap is then removed and the width to which the Plastigage has been flattened should be measured against the calibration scale on the envelope. The wider the flattened dimension of the Plastigage, the narrower the bearing clearance. Plastigage is used to measure rod and main bearing clearance on engines. When crankshaft main journal clearance is

measured, the engine must be inverted so that the weight of the crankshaft is fully supported by the cylinder block and not by the main caps. Chapter 7 goes into detail on the step-by-step procedure of using Plastigage.

Plastigage is available in four size ranges, but in diesel engine technology the following are generally used:

Green: clearance range	0.001" to 0.003"
Red: clearance range	0.002" to 0.006"
Blue: clearance range	0.004" to 0.009"

Carefully remove Plastigage from the shaft when the measurement is complete. A Plastigage test strip that is flattened irregularly indicates journal taper.

DIVIDERS AND CALIPERS

Dividers are used for measuring dimensions between lines or points and scribing reference points and arcs. **Calipers** are designed with internally or externally arced legs to perform internal and external measurements. Dividers and calipers are comparison measuring instruments that require the use of a calibrated measuring instrument such as a micrometer or ruler to produce a specific dimension.

PRECISION STRAIGHTEDGE

A precision straightedge is manufactured from a middle alloy carbon steel. It should be encased in a protective wood or plastic cover and hung vertically when stored. A precision straightedge is used for such tasks as measuring cylinder block deck wear and warpage in conjunction with a set of thickness gauges. **Figure 2–26** shows a machinist's straightedge being used on a cylinder block deck.

THICKNESS GAUGES (FEELER GAUGES)

Thickness gauges are precisely machined blades of tool steel usually packaged in sets. They are available in standard and metric dimensions and tend to be one of the most used items in the technician's toolbox. Thickness gauges are used for adjusting valve lash; checking connecting rod endplay; checking backlash on gear sets; checking ring end gap; and, when used with a precision straightedge, checking cylinder head and cylinder block warpage and wear.

FIGURE 2–26 Machinist's straight edge being used on a cylinder block deck.

Go/no-go gauges are feeler gauges that are stepped to enable a more precise setting of a lash dimension. The outboard dimension is lower by either 0.001 or 0.002 inch than the inboard or stepped ledge of the blade. When using go/no-go gauges, the outboard step defines the specified dimension while the inboard step defines the "no-go" dimension. The go/no-go thickness gauges reduce the variable element of "feel" when adjusting valve lash. Some OEMs recommend their use and technicians less familiar with setting valves may find that doing so results in improved lash setting consistency. The technician should be aware that thickness gauges wear with frequent use and should be measured from time to time with a micrometer. Individual blades in a thickness gauge set can be easily replaced. **Figure 2–27** shows a set of thickness gauges.

TRUCK TECHNICIAN'S TOOLBOX

Technicians should equip their toolboxes in keeping with the type of work they will be performing. Tools are costly and a comprehensive collection takes years to assemble, so technicians should spend wisely, especially during the early years of a career. Figure 2–1 showed a typical tool cabinet. The following information might help as a guideline for some of the tools required on the shop floor. Begin with the safety items:

FIGURE 2–27 Set of thickness gauges.

- Safety glasses (make a practice of wearing these while at work: see Chapter 3)
- Hearing protection muffs and plugs
- Uncured leather gloves (use for heavy lifting)
- Latex gloves (these provide the hands with protection against oil and grease)
- ¼" drive ratchet
- ⅜" drive ratchet
- ½" drive breaker/flex bar
- ½" drive ratchet
- ¾" drive ratchet
- ¾" drive breaker/flex bar

- Sockets: Purchasing in sets is usually more economical. See **Table 2–2**.
- Allen sockets—an assortment of sizes
- ½" drive torque wrench—click or dial type to 250 ft.-lb (swivel/flex head useful for engine work in tight locations)
- ⅜" drive torque wrench—preferably dial type to 120 in.-lb
- ¾" and 1" drive torque wrenches—usually provided by shops
- 4:1 torque multiplier—usually provided by shops
- Combination wrenches—standard: ⁵⁄₃₂"–1¼"; metric: 4 mm–30 mm
- Open- and box-end wrenches—standard: ⁵⁄₃₂"–1¼"; metric: 4 mm–30 mm

Note that purchasing wrenches in sets, rather than individually, is usually significantly more economical.

- Allen keys—standard and metric sets
- Screwdrivers—purchase in sets: slotted, Phillips, TORX (to #30)
- Digital multimeter (DMM)—2½- or 3½-digit resolution: Consider purchasing a rubber holster to protect the tool, such as the one shown in **Figure 2–28**.
- Circuit test light
- Circuit testing clips and cables
- Breakout Ts
- Breakout boxes—specialty diagnostic breakout boxes are usually provided by shops
- Electronic service tools (ESTs)—usually provided by shops; avoid investing in costly ESTs and software because they rapidly become obsolete
- Coolant hydrometer (not a recommended instrument)

FIGURE 2–28 A typical DMM shown in rubber protective holster.

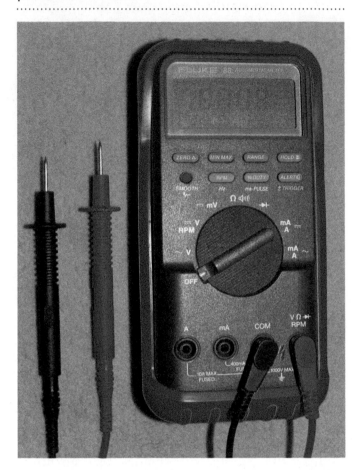

- Refractometer (for coolant and battery electrolyte)—usually provided by shops. Ensure that it is calibrated for electrolyte, ethylene glycol (EG), and propylene glycol (PG).
- 4-lb cross peen hammer (optional)
- 1½-lb ball peen hammer (wood handle)

TABLE 2–2 Ratchet Drives and Socket Sizes

	Double Hex	Hex	Hex Deep	Soft Impact
¼" drive		4 mm–12 mm ⁵⁄₁₆"–½"	4 mm–12 mm ⁵⁄₁₆"–½"	
⅜" drive	10 mm–19 mm ⅜"–¾"	10 mm–19 mm ⅜"–¾"	10 mm–19 mm ⅜"–¾"	
½" drive	½"–¹⁵⁄₁₆" 12 mm–19 mm	½"–1¼" 12 mm–24 mm	½"–⁵⁄₁₆" 12 mm–19 mm	½"–1¼" 12 mm–24 mm
¾" drive		⅞"–1½" 20 mm–30 mm		

- $1\frac{1}{2}$-lb nylon/rubber head
- Hacksaw: Selecting a good-quality frame with high rigidity and using the best blades can pay off in saved frustration and sweat
- Prybar set—to 18" size (length)
- Cold chisel set—to 1"
- Set of punches—to 1"
- Brass drift—1" × 8"
- Mild steel drift—1" × 12"
- Stud extractor set wheel, stud extractor collar
- Nut splitter
- Bolt cutter
- Seal and bearing drivers—normally provided by shops
- Lineman pliers 8" and 12"
- Terminal crimpers—bent nose electronic pliers
- Specialty terminal crimpers/connector disassembly tools—usually provided by shops
- Wire strippers—needle nose pliers
- Sidecutters
- Tin snips—straight cut
- Slip joint/waterpump pliers—12", 24", 36"
- Vise grips (Never let anyone kid you that these are the tools of an amateur; there are thousands of valid uses for them in the truck shop)
- 10" pipe jaw/10" straight jaw/8" needle nose vise grips
- 18" pipe wrench
- Adjustable wrenches—6", 8", 12"
- $\frac{1}{2}$" chuck pneumatic drill
- High-speed (HS) drill bits to $\frac{3}{8}$" size
- $\frac{3}{8}$" drive air ratchet
- $\frac{1}{2}$" drive impact gun (see Figure 2–32)
- Pneumatic chisel/hammer
- Truck tire air chuck
- Tire gauge to 150 psi–1 MPa
- Air blower nozzle
- Air hose—often provided by shops (see Figure 2–32)
- Hand primer pump coupled into #8 hydraulic hose and fittings
- Variable-focus flashlight
- Soldering gun
- Telescoping mirror
- Telescoping magnet
- 0–1" micrometer
- 0–1" depth micrometer
- 0–25 mm micrometer
- 0–25 mm depth micrometer
- Micrometer sets exceeding 1" are provided by shops
- 6"–150 mm Vernier caliper—digital preferred
- 12" tape measure

- Dial bore gauge—telescoping gauges (usually provided by shops)
- Stethoscope—usually provided by shops
- Infrared thermometer—usually provided by shops
- Fluorescent trouble light—often provided by shops
- Heavy-duty hand tools—wrenches sized over $1\frac{1}{4}$" or 30 mm, $\frac{3}{4}$" and 1" drive sockets, and other heavy-duty specialty tools are normally provided by shops
- Roller cabinet—many shallow drawers are preferable to fewer deep ones
- Top box—also consider a side cabinet for shop manuals and fluid containers
- Creeper— rovided by shops

SHOP TOOLS

Shop tools are those tools generally provided by the employer. Tools that are too large to fit into a toolbox, high in cost, or highly specialized to a specific procedure should be provided by the service garage.

SLEDGEHAMMERS

Sledgehammers are designed so that the weight of the head (and perhaps the length of the arms holding the hammer) defines the force imparted. Sledgehammers have a variety of functions in the truck shop and, while they are unlikely to be called on in engine reconditioning, they may be required in some of the procedures required to remove components from a chassis. They are usually manufactured in 8, 12, and 16 lb weights. Before using a sledgehammer, the handle should be inspected for damage and the head-to-handle securement checked. When swinging a sledgehammer, the hand grip should be firm but relaxed and the weight of the head allowed to define the amount of force delivered. On no account should the operator attempt to amplify this force with muscle power, as it usually results in missing the target. If the force is insufficient to achieve the objective, select a heavier hammer.

TECH TIP:

The neck of a sledgehammer handle is vulnerable when its operator misses the target. Help protect the neck of the sledgehammer handle against accidental damage by binding it with a split section of appropriately sized rubber coolant hose.

FIGURE 2-29 Press and bearing clamp used to install bearing on shaft.

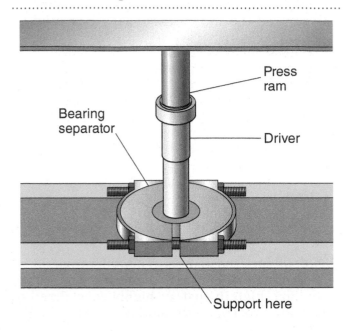

Bearing separator

Press ram

Driver

Support here

PRESSES

Most service garages will have at least one power press. Extreme caution is required when operating a power press: components should be properly supported, and mandrels/drivers should be used when required. Arbor presses are hand actuated. Whenever pressing components using any kind of power press, always consider both the consequences of component slippage and where separated components will fall. Personal safety and the safety of those working in the vicinity must always be considered. **Figure 2-29** shows a press driving a bearing onto a shaft.

SCISSOR JACKS

Scissor jacks are designed to quickly raise one end of a truck to heights of up to 8 feet above the shop floor. Clevises on the jack fit under each frame rail, and the truck is raised by an air-actuated piston. Scissor jacks are an invaluable shop tool, but they must be safely used. Ensure that the lift clevises are positioned at a safe location on the frame rails and make allowance for the relative movement between the truck and jack during raising and lowering. When the truck has been raised, engage the mechanical stops and make sure that the weight is supported on them and not the power piston. Also check the weight of the vehicle to be lifted and the load

capacity of the scissor jack. It is good practice to double-block a raised truck by providing two mechanical supports. Chock the wheels on the end of the chassis not being raised after the unit has been raised to the desired height. Do *not* attempt to do this before hoisting, because the vehicle must be allowed to roll unhindered during the lift.

LIFT AND HOISTS

Raising a heavy-duty truck trailer on a lift system requires special care. Adapters and hoist plates must be positioned correctly on multiple posts and rail-type lifts to prevent damage to the underbody of the vehicle. There are specific lift points to use where the weight of the vehicle is evenly supported by the adapters or hoist plates. The correct lift points may be found in the vehicle service literature. Before operating any lift or hoist equipment, carefully read the manufacturer's literature and understand all the operating and maintenance instructions.

INDEPENDENT POST LIFT SYSTEMS

Independent post lift systems have become commonplace in truck shops in recent years. These consist of "portable" hydraulic (or mechanical jack screw) lift posts that can be positioned under a truck, bus, or trailer chassis and phased to lift the vehicle level. Various systems are available using between 2 and 6 posts. Lift and lower of each post is phased using a hard-wire or wireless system. Great care should be exercised when using these systems! Make sure you receive some basic training in the use of post lift devices before using one yourself. An example is the wireless Gray WPLS-160 shown in **Figure 2-30**, for which post lift and lower phasing is mastered by a computerized control console.

"A" FRAME HOISTS

"A" frame hoists are often large enough to pass over the top of a truck and use a block-and-tackle (chain falls) lift mechanism. They can be used to lift components such as an engine or a cab from the chassis. They may also be capable of hoisting one end of the chassis, but extreme caution should be exercised because of the tendency of anything lifted by chains to swing. The hoist mechanism should be inspected annually, whether or not local regulations require the inspection.

FIGURE 2–30 A typical truck hoist system using four independent posts wirelessly connected.

Courtesy of Gray USA Corp.

FIGURE 2–31 Hydraulic boom hoist (often known as a cherry picker).

BOOM HOISTS

A **boom hoist** is a portable, hydraulically actuated, one-arm crane that has many uses in the truck and bus garage. They are available in a variety of sizes and load-carrying ratings. The pickup arm is usually adjustable in length; the longer the adjustment arm setting, the less the load lift potential. If the load-carrying ability is exceeded, the boom hoist will topple. They are commonly known by their slang name *cherry picker*. **Figure 2–31** shows a boom hoist set to lift an engine.

TRANSMISSION AND CLUTCH JACKS

Transmission and clutch jacks are usually hydraulically actuated and designed to fit under the truck frame and support the transmission/clutch. It is important to ensure that transmissions are securely chained to the jack, especially when the mass of the unit is top heavy such as in triple countershaft units. When it is expected that the jack must support the transmission stationary, such as when removing an engine from a chassis, ensure that the transmission jack load is supported mechanically. Clutch jacks should be used when installing heavy-duty clutches: a $15\frac{1}{2}$-in. clutch pack can weigh

somewhere around 175 lb (80 kilograms [kg]) and should never be handled without some kind of assistance.

SPREADER BARS

A **spreader bar** is a rigid bar, usually adjustable in length, used for lifting engines out of a chassis. The spreader bar should be adjusted to the length of the engine; it can then be attached to the engine at three or four points. The bar should be close to level before a lift is attempted. Chains should be installed so that the chain length is at a minimum with the spreader bar clear of the engine. The chains should be attached to the engine by means of hooks to lifting eyes located on either the cylinder head or cylinder block assembly. Never fit lifting eyes to the rocker housing fasteners. Some engines have just two permanently fitted lifting eyes. It is usually safe to lift these engines using the spreader bar on a two-point lift.

LOAD ROTOR

The load rotor is alternate to the spreader bar when it comes to hoisting an engine: it permits a limited ability to tilt the load during the lift. Load rotors consist of a ratcheting chain block with a single chain equipped with hooks at either end. The hooks fit to the engine lift eyes and the load rotor chain block locks the chain, permitting a different length of chain on either side of the block. This feature often permits the chains to be fitted to the engine and clear the upper engine components.

CHAINS

Chains are rated by working load limit—a value that is normally equivalent to about 25% of the **tensile strength** of the chain material. Many jurisdictions require that chains be inspected annually. Additionally, technicians should visually inspect all chains before using them. The saying that every chain is only as strong as its weakest link bears true. Truck diesel engines can weigh more than a ton and while relying on a chain to support this kind of weight, the technician should try to avoid working under the load. Apart from inspecting the **chain hoists** and checking their load rating, the technician should check the hooks, lifting eyes, lifting eye fasteners, and connecting links.

SLINGS

Slings may have to be used to hoist engines from the chassis in some applications. These are normally manufactured from synthetic fibers or braided steel wire. Again, the load capacity must be checked and the sling integrity inspected. Avoid using steel cable slings unless also using the engine lift eyes.

AIR TOOLS

Air tools are extensively used in any truck service location. Some of the air tools are owned by technicians; others are provided by the shop. Technicians working around pneumatic equipment sometimes forget that it can be dangerous. It makes sense to wear eye protection and be aware that dusts driven into the air by pneumatic tools can cause breathing problems. Most shops provide heavy-duty pneumatic tools such as 1" drive air guns. A $\frac{1}{2}$" drive impact wrench such as that shown in **Figure 2–32** will be one of the most frequently used tools in the truck technician's cabinet. The engine technician primarily uses this for disassembly. Buying a good-quality air gun and properly maintaining it by keeping it moisture-free and oiled (observe the oiler and filter in Figure 2–32) will help ensure that it functions well for a number of years.

TECH TIP:

Purchase a good-quality ½-inch drive air impact wrench and, with a little care, it should last for many years. Low-cost impact guns are generally a poor investment for a truck technician who uses one daily.

FIGURE 2–32 Typical setup for a ½-inch drive impact gun.

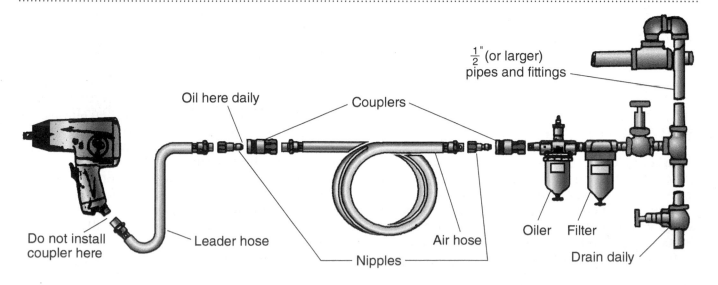

$\frac{1}{2}$" (or larger) pipes and fittings

Oil here daily

Couplers

Do not install coupler here

Leader hose

Nipples

Air hose

Oiler   Filter

Drain daily

CAUTION:

A pneumatic air gun should never be used to final torque any engine fastener. While torque wrenches can be used to disassemble engines, using them for reassembly can generally be regarded as an undesirable practice.

OXYACETYLENE EQUIPMENT

Technicians use oxyacetylene for heating and cutting probably on a daily basis. Less commonly, this equipment is used for brazing and welding. Technicians using oxyacetylene stations require some basic instruction in the safety requirements and handling of this equipment. A more detailed explanation of oxyacetylene handling and safety is provided in Chapter 3 of this book. Despite the fact that oxyacetylene equipment is used by every technician, the novice technician is seldom provided with adequate instruction. At least consult the section in Chapter 3 before using this equipment, and also get some hands-on instruction.

STEAM AND HIGH-PRESSURE WASHERS

Hot water, high-pressure washers have generally replaced the steam cleaners more commonly used a decade ago. Hot water, high-pressure washers are safer and usually require less maintenance than steam washers. The technician should be aware of the potential for damage when using any type of high-temperature, high-pressure washers; eye protection and gloves should be worn when operating this equipment. Environmental regulations in most jurisdictions mandate that the runoff from this type of cleaning operation not be permitted to directly enter sewage systems. Power wash runoff should be filtered through a water separator system, and the separator tanks should be pumped out regularly. Heavy fines may be imposed when sewage is contaminated with oil and road dirt washed off trucks, buses, and their engines.

PULLERS

Shops usually have a selection of general-use and specialty pullers that can be power- or mechanically actuated. Ensure that puller jaws and legs are capable of handling the force to which they will be subject. Safety glasses should always be worn when operating pullers. They are often used in conjunction with a bearing puller clamp. A typical bearing puller clamp is shown in Figure 2–29 where it is used in conjunction with a press.

BUSHING DRIVERS

A bushing driver consists of a mandrel, which should fit tightly in the bushing bore with the shoulder having an identical **outside diameter (od)** to the bore that the bushing is pressed into. This should enable bushings to be removed and installed without damaging either the bushing or the bore to which it is fitted. Bushings may be installed using direct mechanical force, such as a hammer or slide hammer, or by using hydraulic or pneumatic power drivers. Always wear safety glasses when using bushing drivers. Some bushings must be reamed for final fit after installation.

GLASS BEAD BLASTERS/ SANDBLASTERS

Most shops rebuilding engines are equipped with a glass bead blaster or sandblaster. Usually these are encased in an enclosed housing and powered pneumatically. They are an ideal method of cleaning up components, especially when the components are coated with high-tack adhesives or gasket remains that can be difficult to remove. In enclosed housing glass bead blasters, protective gloves are integral with the unit and in most cases they can only be actuated when the component is placed inside and the cover sealed. Armored glass permits the object being blasted to be observed. Technicians should consider using hearing protection, as these units are capable of producing high noise levels.

TECH TIP:

Following any bead or sandblasting procedure, all the beading material must be completely removed from the components treated. Special attention must be paid to bolt holes, oil galleries, and bearing surfaces.

TACHOMETERS

Tachometers measure rotational speed. Mechanical tachometers consist of a pickup button that directly contacts the rotating component (it should be held close to its axis) and produces a direct rpm (revolutions per minute) reading. Electronic tachometers use a sensor that reads a magnetic strip and reports the rpm digitally. Electronic tachometers should be capable of producing mean (average) readings when reading rotational speed on components whose rpm is fluctuating.

FASTENERS

Mobile equipment on our roads today uses both standard and metric threads; metric fasteners are common but not universal even in late model applications (**Figure 2-33**). For a number of years, though, engine and major chassis components have used metric fasteners almost exclusively (diameter and pitch are measured in millimeters), so do not expect to see too many engines that use standard fasteners.

Most fasteners used on a truck are hex head fasteners (usually nonflanged); most metric fasteners are also nonflanged. Hardened flat washers are used under the bolt head, between the clamped components and the hex nut, to distribute the load: this prevents localized stress. The washers are cadmium or zinc plated and have a

hardness rating of 38 to 45 Rockwell "C" hardness (HRC). Some fasteners, often those smaller than $1/2$-inch diameter, have integral flanges that fit against the clamped surfaces. These flanges eliminate the requirement for washers.

FASTENER GRADES AND CLASSES

Fasteners are divided into grades established by the SAE or the International Fastener Institute (IFI). Fastener grades indicate the tensile strength of the fastener; the higher the number (or letter), the stronger the fastener. Bolt (capscrew) grades can be identified by the number and pattern of radial lines/dashes/dots forged on the bolt head (**Figure 2-34**).

Hex nut (and locknut) grades can also be identified by the number and pattern of axial lines and dots on various surfaces of the nut (**Figure 2-35**). Nearly all of the bolts used on the heavy-duty vehicle are grades 5 and 8, but some OEMs use special spec variants of both grades, which are identified using a coding qualifier such as that shown in **Figure 2-36**. Matching grades of hex nuts are used with grade 5 bolts; grade 8, grade C, or grade G (flanged) hex nuts are used with grade 8 bolts.

Every fastener manufacturer is required by law to register its headmarking logo with the **Industrial Fastener Institute (IFI)** for purposes of identification and maintenance of

FIGURE 2-33 SAE and metric thread bolts.

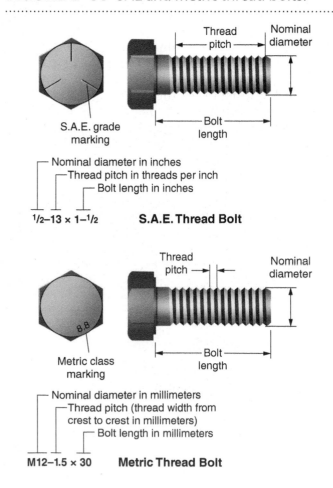

Nominal diameter in inches
Thread pitch in threads per inch
Bolt length in inches

$1/2$–13 × 1–$1/2$ **S.A.E. Thread Bolt**

Nominal diameter in millimeters
Thread pitch (thread width from crest to crest in millimeters)
Bolt length in millimeters

M12–1.5 × 30   **Metric Thread Bolt**

FIGURE 2-34 Bolt (capscrew) identification.

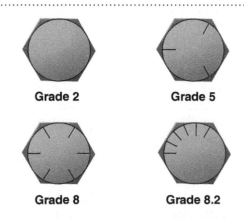

Grade 2   Grade 5

Grade 8   Grade 8.2

Note: Grade 2 bolts have no grade markings; grade 2 bolts are rarely used on trucks.

These grade markings are used on plain hex-type and flanged bolts (capscrews). In addition to the grade markings, the bolt head must also carry the manufacturer's trademark or identification.

FIGURE 2–35 Hex nut identification.

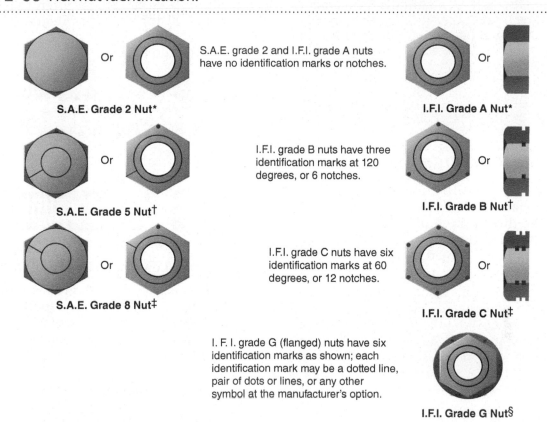

S.A.E. grade 2 and I.F.I. grade A nuts have no identification marks or notches.

S.A.E. Grade 2 Nut*

I.F.I. Grade A Nut*

I.F.I. grade B nuts have three identification marks at 120 degrees, or 6 notches.

S.A.E. Grade 5 Nut†

I.F.I. Grade B Nut†

I.F.I. grade C nuts have six identification marks at 60 degrees, or 12 notches.

S.A.E. Grade 8 Nut‡

I.F.I. Grade C Nut‡

I. F. I. grade G (flanged) nuts have six identification marks as shown; each identification mark may be a dotted line, pair of dots or lines, or any other symbol at the manufacturer's option.

I.F.I. Grade G Nut§

* Strength compatible with grade 2 bolt.
† Strength compatible with grade 5 bolt.
‡ Strength compatible with grade 8 or grade 8.2 bolt.
§ Flanged locknut, strength compatible with grade 8 or grade 8.2 bolt.

FIGURE 2–36 Bolt classes can be identified by the numbers forged on the head of the bolt.

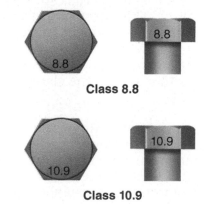

Class 8.8

Class 10.9

Note: In addition to the grade markings, the bolt head must also carry the manufacturer's trademark or identification.

manufacturing standards. All graded fasteners are also required by law to meet certification standards for size, tensile strength, chemical composition, and hardness.

TECH TIP:

A grade 5 bolt or nut is identified when the radial marks or dots are more than 60 degrees (1 hex flat). A grade 8 bolt or higher is identified when the radial marks or dots are spaced 60 degrees (1 hex flat) or less apart. Study Figure 2–35 and make sure you can interpret fastener gradings at a glance. An absence of radial marks or dots identifies a grade 2 bolt, which is generally unsuitable for use in truck applications. In the case of SAE grade 5 or grade 8 fasteners, only two marks or dots may be used, depending on the manufacturer.

CAUTION:

While most technicians have no difficulty identifying grade 5 and grade 8 bolts/capscrews, many get confused when attempting to identify their equivalent nuts: remember the 60-degrees or less (grade 8), MORE than 60-degrees rule explained in the preceding Tech Tip. Be especially careful not to confuse the crimp marks used on lock nuts with grade identification (ID) marks.

UNF AND UNC THREADS

United National Fine (UNF) (previously SAE) and United National Coarse (UNC) (previously USS) designate the thread pitch of fasteners. Thread pitch is classified as threads per inch (TPI) in fasteners. UNF and UNC threads are usually known respectively as "fine" and "coarse" threads.

METRIC FASTENERS

Fasteners with metric threads are divided into classes adopted by the American National Standards Institute (ANSI). The higher the class number, the stronger the fastener. Bolt classes can be identified by the numbers forged on the head of the bolt. Hex nut (and locknut) classes can be identified by the lines or numbers on various surfaces of the nut (**Figure 2–37**). Class 8 hex nuts are always used with class 8.8 bolts; class 10 hex nuts with class 10.9 bolts. **Figure 2–38** shows grade C fasteners with prevailing torque

FIGURE 2–37 Identification markings on Class 8 and Class 10 nuts.

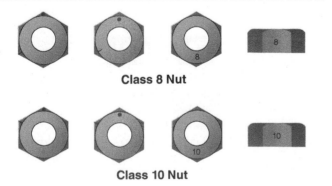

Class 8 Nut

Class 10 Nut

FIGURE 2–38 Grade C fastener assembly with a prevailing torque locknut.

Grade 8 Hex Head Bolt

Grade 8 Low-Profile Hex Head Bolt

Grade C Prevailing Torque Locknut

locknuts. Threads can be measured with a screw pitch gauge.

TIGHTENING FASTENERS

When a capscrew or bolt is tightened to its specified torque, or a nut is tightened to its torque value on a bolt, the shank of the capscrew or bolt stretches slightly. This stretching (tensioning) results in a preload. OEM-specific torque values are calculated to provide enough clamping force on bolted components and the correct tension on the fastener to maintain the clamping force.

Friction and Clamping Force

Use of a torque wrench to tighten fasteners will help prevent overtensioning. Overtensioning causes permanent stretching of the fasteners, which can result in breakage of components or fasteners. When torquing a fastener, typically 80 to 90% of the turning force is used to overcome thread, cap, and nut face friction; only 10 to 20% results in capscrew or bolt clamping force. About 40 to 50% of the turning force is needed to overcome the friction between the underside of the capscrew head or nut and the washer. Another 30 to 40% is needed to overcome the friction between the threads of the capscrew and the threaded hole or the friction between the threads of the nut and bolt.

All metals are elastic to some extent, which means they can be stretched and compressed to a certain point. This elastic, spring-like property is what provides the clamping force when a bolt is threaded into a tapped hole or when a nut is tightened. As the bolt is stretched, clamping force is created due to bolt tension. Like a spring, the more a bolt is stretched, the tighter it becomes. However, a bolt can be stretched too far, which will result in shear. At this point, the bolt can no longer safely clamp the load it was designed to support.

Fastener Elasticity

Elasticity means that a bolt can be stretched a certain amount, and each time the stretching load is reduced, the bolt will return to its original, normal size. In other words, it is reusable. However, if a bolt is stretched beyond its yield point, it permanently deforms. A bolt will continue to stretch a little more each time it is used, just like a piece of taffy that is stretched until it breaks (**Figure 2-39**).

Importance of Correct Torque Procedure

Proper use of torque avoids exceeding the yield point of a bolt. Torque values are calculated with at least a 25% safety factor below yield point. Some fasteners, however, are intentionally torqued just barely into a yield condition, although not quite enough to create the classic Coke-bottle shape of a necked-out bolt. This type of fastener, which is known as a torque-to-yield (TTY) bolt, uses close to 100% of its tensile strength, compared to around 75% on a regular fastener when both are torqued to specification. TTY bolts are normally required to be template torqued; this requires using incrementally increasing torque values using a torque wrench, with final torque turning through a specified number of degrees. TTY fasteners, however, should not be reused unless otherwise specified.

Effect of Lubricants

The torque required to tighten a fastener is reduced when friction is reduced. If a fastener is dry (unlubricated) and plain (unplated), thread friction is high. If a fastener is wax coated or oiled or has a zinc phosphate coating or cadmium plating, friction forces are reduced. Each of these coatings and combinations of coatings has a different effect. Using zinc-plated hardened flat washers under the bolt (capscrew) head and nut reduces friction. Dirt or other foreign material on the threads or clamping surfaces of the fastener or component can increase friction to the point that the torque specification is met before any clamping force is produced.

Even though varying conditions affect the amount of friction, a different torque value cannot be given for each. To ensure that they are always torqued accurately, most OEMs recommend that all fasteners be lubricated with oil (unless specifically instructed to install them dry), and then torqued to the values for lubricated- and plated-thread fasteners. When locking compound or antiseize compound is recommended for a fastener, the compound acts as a lubricant, and oil is not required.

Overtorquing Fasteners

Be careful not to strip bolt threads when using power wrenches. It is easy to turn a bolt beyond its yield point within a split second. Impact wrenches are the worst offenders. Some friction is required to prevent a nut from spinning. When a nut is lubricated, there is insufficient friction to stop the impact wrench from hammering the nut beyond the bolt yield point and/or stripping the threads.

Do not run a nut full speed onto the bolt threads with an impact gun. Instead, run it up slowly until it contacts the work, and then note the socket position and observe how far it turns. Smaller air-powered speed wrenches do not produce the aggressive turning force of impact wrenches and are safer to use. Follow this procedure with a torque-modulated air wrench as well.

WASHERS AND LOCK WASHERS

A rule of thumb on lock washers is that if the fastener assembly did not come with one, do not add one. Lock washers are extremely hard and tend to break under severe pressure. Use locknuts with hard, flat washers. Properly torqued, this type of fastener should never loosen—even when lubricated (**Figure 2-40**).

FIGURE 2-39 This bolt has been torqued beyond its yield point.

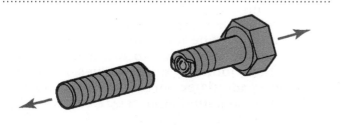

FIGURE 2–40 Washers used to lock fasteners to prevent them coming loose.

Plain   Spring   External   Internal
         lock   tooth lock   tooth lock

As a general rule, when using flat washers, the radius (rounded) side should face the head of the bolt. Note that there is a difference between UNF (SAE) and UNC (USS) flat washers: UNF washers fit tighter to the shank of the bolt and have a reduced skirt radius. UNC flat washers fit looser to the shank of the bolt, and have a larger skirt diameter.

> ### TECH TIP:
> When installing flat washers, the radius (rounded) side should always face the bolt cap.

FASTENER REPLACEMENT

When selecting and installing replacement fasteners, keep the following points in mind:

- When replacing fasteners, use only identical bolts, washers, and nuts; they should be the same size, strength, and finish as originally specified.
- When replacing graded (or metric class) bolts and capscrews, use only fasteners that have the manufacturer trademark or identification on the bolt head; do not use substandard bolts.
- When using nuts with bolts, use a grade (or class) of nut that matches the bolt.
- When installing nonflanged fasteners, use hardened steel flat washers under the bolt (capscrew) head and under the hex nut or locknut.
- For bolts 4 inches (100 mm) or less in length, make sure that at least $1\frac{1}{2}$ threads and no more than $\frac{5}{8}$-inch (16 mm) bolt length extends through the nut after it has been tightened. For bolts longer than 4 inches (100 mm), allow a minimum of $1\frac{1}{2}$ threads and a maximum of $\frac{3}{4}$-inch (19 mm) bolt length protrusion.
- Never hammer or screw bolts into place. Align the holes of the mating components so that the fastener surfaces are flush with the washers, and the washers are flush with the clamped surfaces.
- When installing fasteners into threaded aluminum or plastic components, start the fasteners by hand to ensure that cross-threading does not damage the threads.
- Do not use lock washers (split or toothed) next to aluminum surfaces.
- When installing studs that do not have an interference fit, install them with thread locking compound.
- When installing components mounted on studs, use free-spinning (nonlocking) nuts and helical spring (split) lock washers or internal-tooth lock washers. Avoid using locknuts because they tend to loosen the studs during removal. Do not use flat washers.
- Do not use lock washers and flat washers in combination (against each other); each defeats the other's purpose.
- Use stainless steel fasteners against chrome plating, unpainted aluminum, or stainless steel.

Figure 2–41 is a comprehensive ASTM bolt head marking guide.

> ### SHOP TALK
> If a torque-to-yield bolt is replaced with a new bolt of identical grade but torqued to a value found in a standard torque chart, the clamping force produced will be at least 25% less.

> ### CAUTION:
> A fastener without strength markings must be assumed to be at the lowest common denominator of ratings (grade 2) and not suitable for use in vehicle applications. A fastener with no manufacturer's logo is probably from Asia and likely to be of lower quality; there are many of these in circulation, so technicians should be very aware!

Fastener Tightening

When tightening fasteners, remember the following procedures:

- Clean all fasteners, all threads, and all surfaces before installing them.
- To ensure they are torqued accurately, fasteners should be lubricated with oil (unless specifically instructed to install them dry), and then torqued to the values for lubricated- and plated-thread fasteners. When locking compound or antiseize compound is

FIGURE 2–41 Bolt head identification chart.

Grade Marking	Specification	Material	Nominal Size Dia. In.	Proof Load PSI (MPs)	Tensile Strength Min. PSI (MPa)	Bolt Rockwell Hardness		Nut Rockwell Hardness	
						Min.	Max.	Min.	Max.
	ASTM A307 Grade A SAE J429 Grade 1	Low carbon steel	¼ thru 1½	33,000	60,000	B70	B100	—	—
	SAE J429 Grade 2	Low carbon steel	¼ thru ¾ over ¾ to 1½	55,000 33,000	74,000 60,000	B80	B100	—	C32
	ISO SAE J1199 Property Class 5.8	Low or medium carbon steel	M5 thru M24	55,100 (380)	75,400 (520)	B82	B95	—	C32
	ASTM A449 Type 1 SAE J429 Grade 5	Medium carbon steel, quenched and tempered	¼ thru 1 over 1 to 1½	85,000 74,000	120,000 105,000	C25 C19	C34 C30	—	C32 C32
	ISO/DIN SAE J1199 Property Class 8.8	Medium carbon steel, quenched and tempered	M3 thru M16 M17 thru M36	84,100 (580) 87,000 (600)	116,000 (800) 120,350 (830)	C20 C23	C30 C34	—	C32
	SAE J429 Grade 5.1 (SEMS)	Low or medium carbon steel, quenched and tempered with assembled washer	No. 6 thru 5/8	85,000	120,000	C25	C40	—	—
	ISO SAE J1199 Property Class 9.6	Medium carbon steel, quenched and tempered	M1.6 thru M16	94,250 (650)	130,500 (900)	C27	C36	—	C32
	SAE J429 Grade 7	Medium carbon allow steel, quenched and tempered, roll threaded after heat treatment	¼ thru 1½	105,000	133,000	C28	C34	—	—
	ASTM A354 Grade BD Bowma-Torq®/Grade 8 SAE J429 Grade 8	Medium carbon alloy steel, quenched and tempered	¼ thru 1½	120,000	150,000	C33	C39	C24	C36
	SAE J429 Grade 8.2	Low carbon boron martensite steel, fully killed, fine grain, quenched and tempered	¼ thru 1	120,000	150,000	C35	C42	—	—
	ISO SAE J1199 Property Class 10.9	Medium carbon alloy steel, quenched and tempered	M6 thru M36	120,350 (830)	150,800 (1040)	C33	C39	C26	C36
	ISO Property Class 12.9	Medium carbon alloy steel, quenched and tempered	M1.6 thru M36	140,650 (970)	176,900 (1220)	C38	C44	C26	C36
	Bowmalloy®	Proprietary medium carbon alloy steel, quenched and tempered	¼ thru 1½	156,000	180,000 Min. 2,000,000 Max.	C38	C42	C26	C36

*Manufacturer's identification symbols are required per ASTM, ISO, or SAE.

Courtesy of Navistar International Corp.

recommended for a fastener, the compound acts as a lubricant, and oil is not needed.
• Hand turn fasteners so they contact before using a torque wrench to tighten them to their final torque values.

• Tighten the nut, not the bolt head, when possible. This gives a truer torque reading by eliminating bolt body friction.
• Always use a torque wrench to tighten fasteners, and use a slow, smooth, even pull on

the wrench. Do not use a short, jerky motion, or inaccurate readings can result.

- When reading a bar-type torque wrench, look straight down at the scale. Viewing from an angle can give a false reading.
- Only pull on the handle of the torque wrench.
- Do not allow the beam of the wrench to touch anything.
- Tighten bolts and nuts incrementally. Typically, this should be to one-half specified torque, to three-fourths torque, to full torque, and then to full torque a second time.
- Never overtorque fasteners; overtightening causes permanent stretching of fasteners, which can result in breakage of parts or fasteners.
- If specific torque values are not given for countersunk bolts, use the torque value for the corresponding size and grade of regular bolt.
- Follow the torque sequence when provided to ensure that clamping forces are even and mating parts and fasteners are not distorted.

FASTENER FAILURES

Most fastener failures can be attributed to human error concerning application and/or assembly. The consequences of fastener failure on transportation equipment can be fatal. The following are the most common reasons:

- Overtorquing
- Mismatched graded fasteners
- Reuse of a fastener (especially nuts)
- Use of too long a bolt
- Compression of clamped materials
- Improperly installed washers

Reuse of Fasteners

The Industrial Fastener Institute has conducted detailed studies on the loss of strength in reused fasteners. A key conclusion is that a reused nut is more likely to fail. Threads on a nut are manufactured to be slightly softer than those on the bolt so that they deform slightly to form into the contour of the bolt threads when torqued. While the IFI recommends that both the nut and bolt be replaced in any critical application, it emphasizes that nuts are a poor reuse risk. Some facts:

- The first thread of a USS nut supports 38% of the total load on a bolt
- The second thread supports 25% of the total bolt load
- The third thread supports 18% of the total bolt load

FIGURE 2–42 Steps in the installation of a helical screw repair coil: A. Drill out the damaged threads using the correct sized drill bit. B. Tap new threads into the hole using the specified tap. The thread depth should exceed the depth of the hole. C. Install the proper sized coil insert on the mandrel provided in the installation kit. Bottom it against the tang. D. Lubricate the insert and thread it into the hole until flush with the surface. Use a punch or chisel to break off the tang.

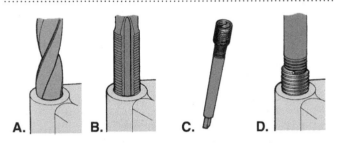

A.   B.   C.   D.

- Therefore, more than 80% of the total bolt load is supported by the first three threads on the nut

Thread Repair

A common fastening problem is stripped threads. This is usually caused by high torque or by cross-threading. Threads can sometimes be replaced by using threaded inserts. Several types of threaded inserts are available; the helically coiled insert is the most popular (**Figure 2–42**). To install this and similar thread reconditioning inserts, proceed as follows:

1. Establish the size, pitch, and length of the thread required. Refer to the insert manufacturer's instructions for the correct size drill for the thread tap to be used for the repair.
2. Drill out the damaged threads with the specified drill. Clean out the drill swath and chips from the hole.
3. Tap new threads in the hole using the specified tap. Lubricate the tap while threading the hole. Back out the tap every quarter turn or so. When the hole is threaded to the required depth, remove the tap and all metal cuttings from the hole.
4. Select the appropriate size insert and screw it onto the special installing mandrel or tool. Make sure that the tool engages with the tang of the insert. Screw the insert into the hole by turning the installing tool clockwise. Lubricate the thread insert with engine oil if it is installed

in cast iron (do not lubricate if installing into aluminum). Turn the thread insert into the tapped hole until it is flush with the surface or one turn below. Remove the installer.

Screw/Stud Removers and Extractors

Stud removers are used to install and remove studs. They have a hardened, grooved eccentric roller or jaws that grip the stud tightly when turned. Stud removers/installers may be turned by a socket wrench drive handle.

Extractors are used on screws and bolts that have sheared below a surface. Twist drills, fluted extractors, and hex nuts are included in a screw extractor set (see Figure 2–9). This type of extractor lessens the tendency to expand a screw or stud that has been drilled out by providing gripping contact through the full length of the stud.

Thread Locking Compound Application

When applying a thread locking compound, follow the safety precautions given on the locking compound container. Then proceed as follows:

1. Clean the male and female threads of the fasteners, removing dirt, oil, and other contaminants. If the area around the fastener is contaminated, clean with solvent, and then allow everything to air dry for 10 minutes. Be sure solvent is completely evaporated before applying thread adhesive.
2. Apply a small amount of locking compound from the container to the circumference of three or four fastener threads.
3. Install and immediately torque the nut. Retorquing the nut is not possible after installation without destroying the adhesive locking bond.

CAUTION:

Thread locking compounds are powerful adhesives. They are color coded. Use only the color code recommended by the OEM.

SHOP TALK

To disassemble fasteners that have been held together with a thread locking compound, it may be necessary to heat the bond line to 400°F (205°C) before removing the nut. Every time fasteners held by locking compounds/adhesives are disassembled, replace them. If mating components are damaged by overheating, replace them.

ADHESIVES AND CHEMICAL SEALING MATERIALS

Chemical adhesives and sealants may provide added holding force and sealing ability when two components are joined. Sealants are applied to threads where fluid contact is frequent. Chemical thread retainers are either aerobic (cures in the presence of air) or anaerobic (cures in the absence of air). When using a chemical adhesive or sealant, follow the manufacturer's instructions. Note that some adhesives molecularly bond to the surface of metals, destroying the material on removal. Some can be harmful on contact with skin. In almost all cases, the material safety data sheet (MSDS) for these products is published on the company's website.

SEALANTS

The following list briefly describes some common shop sealants:

- High tack. Available as a paste or aerosol spray. Rapidly cures and can be used to hold gaskets in place while clamping two components together. Every toolbox should be equipped with some.
- RTV silicone (room temperature vulcanized silicone). Cheap and outlasts paper gaskets. Uses acid to cure, which is corrosive, and for this reason should not really be used in any chassis applications. Having said this, it is more commonly used than any other shop sealant.
- Nonacidic vehicle silicone. RTV silicone that uses a nonacidic desiccant. Designed to replace gaskets, not to glue them into position. These usually take longer to cure, may be system specific, and are usually coded by color—for example, high temperature for exhaust manifolds and turbos, transmissions, wheel ends, etc. Apply a single bead about $1/4$ inch or less dead center along one side of the mating face. Circle around the bolt holes. Do not apply too much. Mate up wet; do not allow cure time.
- Rubber gasket dressing. This should be applied to reuse rubber gaskets. It tacks them into position while mating up components.
- Rubber gasket maker. Rubber compound that cures slowly but can actually be put into service immediately due to its high integrity. When fully cured, it is very difficult to remove and can actually destroy thinner

steels. Rated for high temperature and may be good for problem leaks.

- Weatherstrip adhesive. Designed to adhere weatherstripping. Should not be used for anything else. Can be extremely difficult to remove, especially when applied to aluminum or carbon fibers.

Thread Lock Compounds

Thread lock compounds are usually manufactured in liquid and gel forms. Several manufacturers produce thread sealants. Although there are no rules about this, most manufacturers usually abide by the following color codes:

- Red. The highest strength adhesive and sealant. Usually red locking compound functions effectively at high temperatures. Powerful enough to damage some metals on removal. Use in small quantities.
- Blue. A good multipurpose adhesive and sealant rated at medium strength.
- Green. A medium-strength adhesive and sealant with wicking capability; this allows it to run down threads and create a better seal.
- Purple. A low-strength thread adhesive that seals threads effectively.

THE METRIC SYSTEM AND ENGLISH/METRIC CONVERSION

The metric system has been authorized by an act of Congress in the United States and by federal legislation in Canada. The metric system is used by most countries in the world, and has been generally adopted by industry for use in the United States as a replacement for the standard system. For example, every truck diesel engine engineered in the United States since 1980 has been a metric engine. However, the specifications reproduced in service literature are usually presented in both standard and metric systems with the consequence that most mechanical technicians are forced to have an understanding of both. Some OEMs such as Caterpillar have published specifications using only the metric system for a generation. (It should be noted that the British replaced the "English" system of weights and measures with the metric system more than 40 years ago.)

The metric system is a decimal system, the meter being the basis of all measures, whether of length, surface, capacity, volume, or weight. The meter measures 39.37 inches and is theoretically one ten-millionth of the distance from the equator to either the North or the South Pole. The unit of weight is the gram (15.432 grains), and is the weight of a cubic centimeter of water at its greatest density at about 39°F.

Multiples of the units are expressed by the Greek prefixes *deca*, *hecto*, *kilo*, *mega*, and *giga*, indicating, respectively, tens, hundreds, thousands, millions, and billions. Decimal parts of the units are indicated by the Latin prefixes *deci*, *centi*, *milli*, *micro*, *nano*, and *pico*, meaning, respectively, tenth, hundredth, thousandth, millionth, thousand millionth, and billionth.

METRIC WEIGHTS AND MEASURES

Listings of the commonly used metric weights and measures as well as a conversion table for common metric measurements to standard units follow. Note that *gr* indicates U.S. grains and should not be confused with metric grams.

Metric Weights

Milligram	($1/1000$ gm)	= 0.0154 gr
Centigram	($1/100$ gm)	= 0.1543 gr
Decigram	($1/10$ gm)	= 1.5432 gr
Gram		= 15,432 gr
Decagram	(10 gm)	= 0.3527 oz
Hectogram	(100 gm)	= 3.5274 oz
Kilogram	(1000 gm)	= 2.2046 lb
Myriagram	(10,000 gm)	= 22.046 lb

Metric Dry Measures

Milliliter	($1/1000$ L)	= 0.061 cu. in.
Centiliter	($1/100$ L)	= 0.6102 cu. in.
Deciliter	($1/10$ L)	= 6.1022 cu. in.
Liter		= 0.908 qt
Decaliter	(10 L)	= 9.08 qt
Hectoliter	(100 L)	= 2.838 bu
Kiloliter	(1000 L)	= 1.308 cu. yd

Metric Liquid Measures

Milliliter	($1/1000$ L)	= 0.0338 fl. oz
Centiliter	($1/100$ L)	= 0.338 fl. oz

Deciliter	($\frac{1}{10}$ L)	= 0.845 gill
Liter		= 1.0567 qt
Decaliter	(10 L)	= 2.6418 gal
Hectoliter	(100 L)	= 26.417 gal
Kiloliter	(1000 L)	= 264.18 gal

Metric Measures of Length

Millimeter	($\frac{1}{1000}$ m)	= 0.0394 in.
Centimeter	($\frac{1}{100}$ m)	= 0.3937 in.
Decimeter	($\frac{1}{10}$ m)	= 3.937 in.
Meter		= 39.37 in.
Decameter	(10 m)	= 393.7 in.
Hectometer	(100 m)	= 328.1 ft
Kilometer	(1000 m)	= 0.62137 mi
	(1 mile = 1.6093 km)	
Myriameter	(10,000 m)	= 6.2137 mi

Metric Surface Measures

Centare	(1 sq. m)	= 1550 sq. in.
Are	(100 sq. m)	= 119.6 sq. yd
Hectare	(10,000 sq. m)	= 2.471 acre

METRIC TO STANDARD CONVERSION FORMULAE

The following formulae can be used to translate metric values to standard and vice versa.

Linear Measurements

Centimeters × 0.3937 = in.
Meters = 39.37 in.
Kilometers = 0.621 mi
Kilometers × 3280.89 = ft
Square centimeters × 0.155 = sq. in.

Volume and Mass Measurements

Cubic centimeters × 0.06102 = cu. in.
Cubic meters × 35.3144 cu. ft
Liters × 0.2642 = gal (231 cu. in.)
Kilograms × 2.2046 lb
Kilograms per square millimeter × 1422.3 = lb per sq. in.
Kilograms per square centimeter × 14,223 = lb per sq. in.

Torque Conversion

1 lb-ft. = 1.355 Newton-meters (N·m)
1 N·m = 0.738 lb-ft

Temperature Conversion

$$\text{Degrees Fahrenheit} = \frac{9 \times C}{5} + 32$$

$$\text{Degrees Celsius} = \frac{5 \times (F - 32)}{9}$$

PRESSURE CONVERSIONS

Fuel injection test instruments are often calibrated in **units of atmosphere (atms)**. Technicians should become familiar with the process of converting units of pressure into the metric and standard systems. This is an easy way:

Atmospheric pressure @ sea level = 14.7 psi = 101.3 kPa = 1 unit of atmosphere or 1 atms

Remembering the following is not as mathematically accurate as the previous equivalent, but it is a fast method of converting pressure values that is accurate enough for quick conversions:

15 psi = 100 kPa = 1 atms

So, to convert 45 psi to kPa:

$$\frac{45}{15} = 3 \text{ units of atmosphere or 3 atms}$$

3 atms = 100 kPa = 300 kPa

In Europe, a unit of pressure measurement known as a **bar** is used. Be familiar with bar, because Bosch uses this unit for specifications in the many diesel fuel systems it manufactures. One bar is equivalent to 105 Newtons per square meter, which is not precisely equivalent to one atmosphere. Although units of bar and atms are often used as if they were exactly equivalent, this is not so, and where precise values are required they should not be confused. Some fuel injection comparator equipment is calibrated in bar.

1 atms = 14.7 psi = 101.3 kPa = 1.033 bar
= 29.92" Hg = 407.19" H$_2$O

Power Conversion

1 hp = 550 lb-ft per second = 0.746 kW
= 42.4 Btus per minute

WORKPLACE ORGANIZATION

There is no one thing that turns customers away from a service facility faster than a dirty, cluttered shop. Keeping the workplace clean and organized is the responsibility of every technician. Just as important is the way a technician maintains order within his or her personally owned toolbox. The consequence of not keeping a personal toolbox organized is to misplace costly tools and not realize they are missing until the next time they have to be used. Whenever possible, use the tool manufacturer's storage cases and mounting hardware (see **Figure 2–43** and **Figure 2–44**), because it helps identify a missing component at a glance.

TOOLBOX DRAWER ORGANIZERS

Drawer organizers cost little compared to the price of a single wrench and will repay the investment you make in them many times over. Their primary benefit is that a technician can immediately identify exactly what tool is missing. The reason truck drivers often have collections of Snap-on wrenches is not because they have stolen them but because technicians have left them in the engine compartment or elsewhere in the cab and on the chassis.

EXHAUST EXTRACTION PIPING

A key piece of shop equipment is the exhaust extraction system. In a truck shop, this consists of overhead piping and duct work. Failure to use the exhaust extraction pipes presents health and safety problems, which are the subject of Chapter 3. Breathing diesel exhaust fumes, especially those produced by truck engines built before 2007, is a health hazard. Observing a few simple rules can minimize this hazard:

- When starting an engine up outside before bringing it into the service shop, warm the engine for 5 minutes before moving the truck. You may be able to reduce this time with newer trucks, but try to avoid driving a truck that is producing visible smoke into the shop.

FIGURE 2–43 Heavy-duty puller set stored in the wall mountings supplied by the tool manufacturer, so that a missing component can identified at a glance.

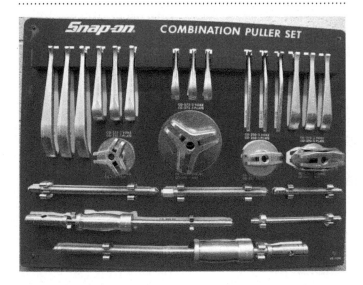

FIGURE 2–44 Proper storage of a dial bore gauge set, which protects the tool and allows a missing component to be identified immediately.

- When preparing to remove a truck from the shop following service work, install the exhaust extraction pipe over the stack(s) before attempting to start the engine. This way you can build the air pressure and warm the engine before moving the vehicle.

The exhaust extraction pipes are stainless steel or galvanized flex pipes designed to fit over the vertical stacks on the truck. An extraction pump helps pull the diesel exhaust out of the shop. **Figure 2–45** shows a network of exhaust extraction pipes in a truck shop.

FIGURE 2–45 Exhaust extraction flex pipes in a truck shop.

SUMMARY

- The actual contents of a truck technician's toolbox will be determined by the type of work performed. However, 80% of the contents are probably common among all truck technicians.
- Cheaper tools are often bulkier and more prone to breakage.
- The personal safety of the user is always on the line when hand tools are being used, so it makes sense for the professional to invest in reliable tools.
- The apprentice technician should acquire a mastery of precision measuring tools before using them in work; this is best done by practice using the instruments to measure actual engine components.
- Reading both standard and metric micrometers becomes much easier when the technician understands exactly how they are constructed and calibrated.
- A standard micrometer must be rotated through 40 complete revolutions from the point at which the spindle contacts the anvil producing a zero reading to the point at which it reads 1". Each complete revolution of the thimble therefore represents 0.025".
- A metric micrometer must be rotated through 50 complete revolutions from the point at which the spindle contacts the anvil producing a zero reading to the point at which it reads 25 mm. Each complete revolution of the thimble therefore represents 0.5 mm.

- Diesel engine technicians should be familiar with setting up and using dial bore gauges.
- Shop hoisting apparatus should be routinely inspected by qualified personnel and by the technician before using it. This may be a legal requirement in some jurisdictions.
- The technician must check out shop power equipment before each use.
- The technician should know how to identify SAE, IFI, and ISO fastener grades and understand the importance of selecting the correct grade for the job being performed. The engine technician must also understand that many specialty fasteners used on engines have special metal properties and should not be replaced by generic SAE, IFI, or ISO fasteners.
- The technician should get used to both standard and metric systems and be prepared to work in both, because both are widely used in the industry. Formulae need not be remembered, but the technician should get used to rapidly converting values from each system.
- Technicians who take the trouble to organize their personal tools will benefit from the resulting minimization of tool losses.
- A key piece of shop equipment is the exhaust extraction system. To be effective at preventing harmful fumes from being discharged into a closed, indoor environment, it must be used properly.

REVIEW QUESTIONS

1. When the spindle contacts the anvil on a standard 0–1" micrometer, it should read:
   a. 0
   b. 0.001"
   c. 0.025"
   d. 1"

2. How many complete rotations must the thimble of a standard micrometer be turned to travel through a reading of zero to a reading of 1 inch?
   a. 25
   b. 40
   c. 50
   d. 100

3. How many complete rotations must the thimble of a metric micrometer be turned to travel through a reading of zero to a reading of 25 mm?
   a. 25
   b. 40
   c. 50
   d. 100

4. When the thimble of a metric micrometer is turned through one full revolution, the dimension between the anvil and the spindle has changed by:
   a. 0.1 mm
   b. 0.5 mm
   c. 2.5 mm
   d. 0.5 mm

5. When using a dial indicator to check the concentricity of a flywheel housing, during a single rotation of the flywheel the reading on the positive side of the zero on the dial peaks at 0.003 while the reading on the negative side peaks at 0.006. What is the TIR?
   a. 0.003"
   b. 0.006"
   c. 0.009"
   d. 0.018"

6. Which of the following precision measuring instruments would be required to measure a valve guide bore?
   a. Dial indicator
   b. Inside micrometer
   c. Split ball gauge and micrometer
   d. Dial bore gauge

7. If 300 kPa is converted to pounds per square inch, the result would be closest to which of the following values?
   a. 15 psi
   b. 30 psi
   c. 45 psi
   d. 300 psi

8. To which of the following values would 1.5 mm be closest?
   a. 0.0625"
   b. 0.125"
   c. 0.250"
   d. 1.50"

9. Convert 550° Fahrenheit into Celsius.
   a. 240
   b. 288
   c. 385
   d. 550

10. A wrench with box and open ends at either end, both of the same nominal dimension, is known as a(n):
    a. torque wrench.
    b. combination wrench.
    c. box-end wrench.
    d. adjustable wrench.

11. Which of the following is used to identify an SAE grade 8 bolt?
    a. 3 radial strokes on the capscrew head
    b. 5 radial strokes on the capscrew head
    c. 6 radial strokes on the capscrew head
    d. 8 radial strokes on the capscrew head

12. If a 12" linear extension is used on a torque wrench with a 24" bar, the reading on the torque wrench scale required to produce an actual torque value of 250 lb-ft would be:
    a. 36 lb-ft
    b. 120 lb-ft
    c. 167 lb-ft
    d. 323 lb-ft

13 Convert 250 lb-ft to Newton-meters and select the closest value from the following answers.
    a. 167 N·m
    b. 340 N·m
    c. 410 N·m
    d. 500 N·m

14. Convert 600 hp into kW and select the closest value from the following answers.
    a. 350 kW
    b. 450 kW
    c. 550 kW
    d. 650 kW

15. The cutting fluid recommended for use when cutting threads in mild steel is:
    a. soluble oil and water.
    b. lard.
    c. dry.
    d. kerosene.

16. When drilling into cast iron, the correct method calls for the procedure to be performed:
    a. with kerosene.
    b. with lard.
    c. preheated.
    d. dry.

17. A bolt designed so that the shoulder has a small interference fit with the bore it is to be fitted to is called a(n):
    a. SAE #5.
    b. SAE #8.
    c. body bound bolt.
    d. Huck fastener.

18. The working load of a chain is normally what percentage of the rated tensile strength of the chain material?
    a. 10%
    b. 25%
    c. 50%
    d. 75%

19. Which Plastigage color code should be selected to measure a main bearing clearance that the manufacturer specifies must be between 0.0023 and 0.0038?
    a. Red
    b. Green
    c. Blue

20. After Plastigage checking a main bearing, using red Plastigage, the measuring strip has not been deformed. Technician A states that the bearing clearance must be greater than 0.006". Technician B states that a strip of green-coded Plastigage must be used to perform the measurement. Who is correct?
    a. Technician A only
    b. Technician B only
    c. Both A and B
    d. Neither A nor B

Prerequisite: Chapter 2

PERSONAL AND SAFETY AWARENESS

OBJECTIVES

After studying this chapter, you should be able to:

- Identify the basic personal safety equipment required in a truck service environment.
- Outline the importance of wearing the appropriate clothing and footwear on the shop floor.
- Explain the importance of using eye protection in the shop environment.
- Describe two methods used to protect hearing.
- Understand how to lift heavy objects in the safest manner and the importance of using power lift equipment whenever possible.
- Explain the function of OSHA.
- Identify the four categories of fire and the fire extinguishers required to put them out.
- Explain the legislation pertaining to an employee's Right to Know.
- Interpret the acronyms WHMIS and MSDS.
- Interpret the emergency and first-aid policies used in a service garage.
- Understand the importance of basic training in first-aid and fire suppression techniques.
- Explain the safety requirements of handling oxyacetylene gases and heating, cutting, and welding processes.
- Describe the safety devices used on oxygen and acetylene cylinders.
- List the federal agencies responsible for administering hazardous waste disposal and shop and personal safety in the United States and Canada.

KEY TERMS

backfire

compressed air

corrosive

flammable

flashback

Hazard Communication Regulation

inflammable

material safety data sheets (MSDS)

Occupational Safety and Health Administration (OSHA)

oxyacetylene

personal protective equipment (PPE)

radioactive

reactive

Resource Conservation and Recovery Act (RCRA)

Right-to-Know legislation

toxic

Workplace Hazardous Materials Information Systems (WHMIS)

PERSONAL PROTECTIVE EQUIPMENT

Ownership of **personal protective equipment (PPE)** is important—but not as important as developing the habit of using it properly. The following are some tips.

EYE PROTECTION

In some shops, the wearing of safety glasses is mandatory. It should be in all. Although most technicians probably own at least one pair of safety glasses, they tend not to be worn nearly enough. For the person who does not regularly use eyeglasses, wearing safety glasses is only an irritation for the first few days, after which they will not be noticed. Part of the problem is that many technicians purchase, or are provided with, safety glasses of the poorest quality, which tend to be uncomfortable and actually impair vision. A technician who will spend $50 on a wrench that might be used four times a year balks at spending the same amount on a good-quality pair of safety glasses worn every day. Be smart: Purchase a good-quality pair of safety glasses and get used to wearing them all the time. **Figure 3–1** shows a face shield and safety glasses.

EYEWASH STATIONS

Batteries contain a sulfuric acid solution. This and other potentially dangerous chemicals are a fact of life in most truck shops, so it is essential

FIGURE 3–1 The various eye protection devices available for use on the shop floor include safety glasses and face shields.

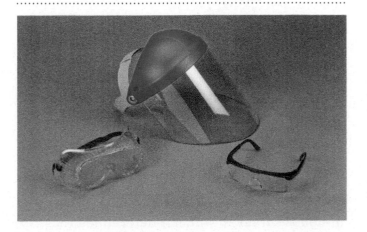

FIGURE 3–2 A typical shop eyewash station.

to have functional eyewash stations located strategically throughout the facility. **Figure 3–2** shows one type of eyewash station.

HEARING PROTECTION

Two types of hearing protection are available: internally worn plugs made of a sponge or wax fiber, and the external type that have the appearance of ear muffs. The latter tend to be uncomfortable and can be dangerous if they work too effectively. The noise levels in truck service facilities vary considerably, but in most noise is not consistently at levels that will result in hearing damage. The technician should own hearing protection devices and use them on an as-necessary basis. Some machining procedures require the use of hearing protection. When operating a chassis dynamometer or entering an engine test cell, hearing protection must be worn; in fact, using both internal and external hearing protection is recommended. **Figure 3–3** shows a set of hearing muffs and malleable ear plugs.

SAFETY FOOTWEAR

Legal requirements aside, anyone working in an automotive, truck, or heavy equipment service facility should wear safety footwear, preferably

FIGURE 3–3 Hearing protection.

boots so that the ankle is properly protected. These boots should have a steel toe and heel. Poor-quality safety shoes are extremely uncomfortable and may in themselves end up damaging the feet they are supposedly protecting. Purchase footwear that breathes and is capable of adapting to the shape of the wearer's foot; this usually means leather. Synthetic materials may suffice for the amateur mechanic who wears them once a week, but not the professional who wears them daily.

Safety boots should be approved by Underwriters Laboratories (UL), denoted by an accreditation label. In addition, technicians working around hybrid diesel-electric mobile equipment should wear electric shock resistant (ESR) footwear, which is designated by an orange omega on a white rectangle.

CLOTHING

Generally, technicians are to some extent exposed to **oxyacetylene** and various electric welding processes. Anyone exposed to working around heat and flame should be aware of the dangers of many synthetic fibers when ignited:

WARNING:

Most synthetic fibers treated with fire retardant will ignite and burn vigorously when exposed to flame for a prolonged period. Make a practice of not wearing synthetic fibers at work.

when they burn, they melt and fuse to the skin. It is good practice to wear cotton clothing and coveralls. Synthetic fibers treated with fire retardant tend not to breathe and can be uncomfortable in hot weather.

GLOVES AND BARRIER CREAMS

Gloves are not particularly comfortable when performing engine work because those that properly protect the hands from grease and oil tend not to breathe. However, given their potential to protect the hands, technicians should consider using gloves when working on engines. Many service shops make a variety of gloves available for their technicians. Most technicians find it difficult to work effectively with intricate components while wearing any of the gloves currently on the market. Those gloves that least compromise the sense of touch also seem to be the ones that rip most easily and do not breathe. Considering that the truck technician comes into contact with many potentially harmful fluids, the wearing of gloves is probably justified.

Barrier creams are wax-based hand creams that provide some protection; however, most of these dissolve when in contact with solvents. Barrier creams work to help clean up hands rather than protect them from harmful liquids. Perhaps the technician is best advised to be aware of the potential harm in the fluids and materials in the workplace and practice good personal hygiene. For instance, because diesel fuel has been identified as a carcinogen, it is good practice, after coming into contact with it, to wash thoroughly with soap and water. The same applies to used engine oil and all types of antifreeze solution.

BACK PROTECTION

Most technicians start young and seldom think much about the physical abuse to which they will subject their bodies. While truck technicians usually have an assortment of lifting apparatus available to them, many do not use them enough. Lifting a 15½" clutch assembly would be heavy work if it had to be done in a weight room. A clutch pack lacks the convenient hand grips provided with barbells, and the mass is concentrated in the center. Performing this feat in the cramped conditions under a truck is an invitation to back problems. One major OEM performed an in-house survey in which it determined that 50% of its service personnel had taken some time off

FIGURE 3–4 Use your leg muscles, never your back, when lifting a heavy load.

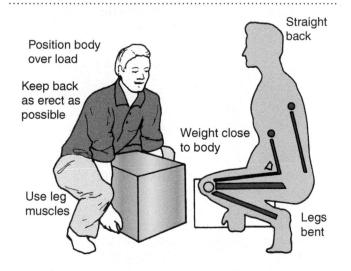

work due to a back-related problem before they had reached the age of 30 years. Back problems are a fact of many technicians' lives.

Bad lifting habits are developed young and reinforced by the fact that it takes some years before a problem develops. The best strategy is avoidance.

Lift smart! Lift with the legs rather than the back and do not lift heavy weights in confined spaces. There is always a jack or hoist that can make the job easier. One national chain of hardware stores provides its employees with flexible back braces. These employees wear the braces as part of their uniform. A back brace spreads the focal point of the load being lifted over a larger area of the back, so it makes a whole lot of sense for anyone exposed to routine heavy lifting to wear one. If there were a single factor that could threaten the technician's ability to work through a career, it would be problems related to the back. **Figure 3–4** demonstrates the correct technique for lifting.

BREATHING PROTECTION

The truck engine technician should be aware of the atmosphere in the shop and wear a protective mask when necessary. The environment of the truck shop is not generally unhealthy, but is mostly defined by the type of work being performed. Exhaust-fume extraction pipes should always be fitted to vehicles when they have to run on the shop floor, and engines should be warm when moving vehicles in and out of the garage. It goes without saying that

extra precautions are required when painting, sand blasting, servicing brakes and clutches, and performing other operations.

WORKPLACE HAZARDS AND SAFETY REGULATIONS

Again, it should be stressed that the environment of the typical truck service garage is not usually an unhealthy one. The environmental hazards associated with a trucking operation are generally determined by the specific nature of the business conducted. However, every truck technician should make safe practice part of his or her working routine. Repairing trucks requires the use of an extensive array of equipment. Apprentice technicians should make it their business to learn how to safely operate shop equipment. This often involves asking questions of those who do know how. If an apprentice technician just pretends to know how to operate a piece of equipment, the result can be fatal. Note the universal safety symbols shown in **Figure 3–5**: They are mostly common sense, but make sure you recognize them and know what they mean.

DRIVING TRUCKS

Licensing and insurance requirements vary by state and province. Before driving a truck on a highway, technicians should ensure that they are appropriately qualified and fully insured. Trucks brought in for repair must be moved from the yard into the shop in any case, so apprentice technicians usually get their first experience of driving a truck as *yard jockeys*. There is nothing especially difficult about driving a truck, but it is not a car, and a lesson or two from a driver trainer can help develop good driving habits. Certain vehicles should be handled with some caution. An example would be a garbage packer with bucket fork hydraulics. Whenever the hydraulics have to be actuated to access components on a chassis, ensure that someone familiar with the system provides some instruction in the procedure.

When road-testing trucks, technicians should be aware of the fact that the handling characteristics of a tractor uncoupled from a trailer are quite different from those of the tractor/trailer combination. The weight distribution of an uncoupled tractor is uneven, being focused over the steering axle; this results in comparatively little weight over the driven rear axle(s).

FIGURE 3–5 Generic safety symbols.

 This symbol indicates *prohibited action*

 Do not overtorque: do not use pipes or lever extensions

 No hammering

 No prying

 Do not strike hard objects

 No impact/power drive

 Do not step in or on drawers

 Do not open multiple drawers

 Do not pull to move

 This symbol indicates *mandatory action*

 Mandatory ear protection

 Mandatory face shield

 Mandatory mask

 Mandatory respirator

 Mandatory protective clothing

 Mandatory protective gloves

 Mandatory eye protection

 Must read instructions before use

 This symbol indicates a *hazard alert*
Red background—danger
Orange background—warning
Yellow background—caution

 Vibration hazard

 Risk of explosion

 Overhead/overload hazard

 Risk of electric shock

 Risk of fire

 Risk of entanglement

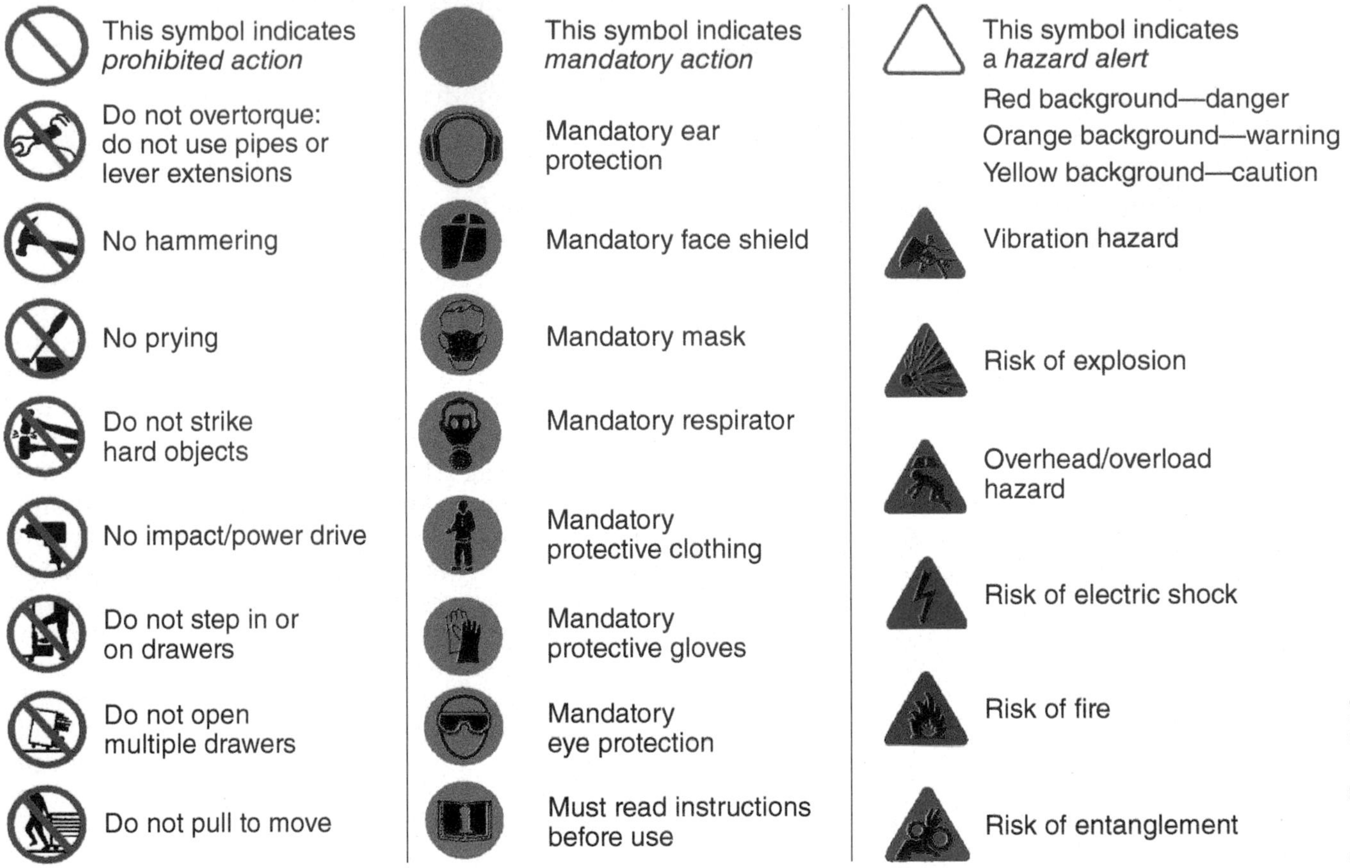

Courtesy of Snap-on Tools Company

When bobtailing—that is, driving an uncoupled tractor on a highway—special care should be exercised at all times, especially when the road surface is wet, icy, or snow covered.

HOISTS, CHAINS, SLINGS, AND JACKS

Any lifting apparatus should be inspected by a qualified person on an annual basis; this may be statutorily mandated in some jurisdictions. Never take risks with visibly damaged lifting apparatus. A minor leak in a jack lift ram may be the first step in a seal blowout. Tag and report any defective equipment. A nick in a chain link or a couple of frayed strands in a braided wire sling should be sufficient to remove the device from service and tag it for assessment by a qualified inspector.

FIRES

Some basic fire suppression training will equip an individual with the skills required first to assess the extent of a fire, and next to handle a fire extinguisher. Fire departments and firefighting equipment suppliers will provide training at the most basic level in how to assess the seriousness of a fire and how to extinguish small fires safely. At least a percentage of employees in a service facility should be trained in basic fire safety. In shops with a health and safety committee, one of the functions of such a committee is to identify potential fire hazards and rectify them. The objective of training in basic firefighting techniques is not to take over the role of the fire departments, but rather to do everything possible in a safe manner to control a fire until the arrival of fully trained firefighters.

All shops must be equipped with a variety of fire extinguishers. A fire extinguisher is categorized by the type of fire it is capable of extinguishing. There are four categories of fire:

Class A—Combustible materials such as wood, paper, textiles. Extinguished by cooling, quenching, and oxygen deprivation.

Class B—Flammable liquids, oils, grease, fuels, and paints. Extinguished by smothering (oxygen deprivation).

Class C—Fires that occur in the vicinity of electrical equipment, perhaps caused by a current overload. Extinguished by shutting down power switches and smothering with a nonconducting liquid or gas.

Class D—Combustible metals such as magnesium and sodium. Extinguished by smothering with an inert chemical powder.

The corresponding types of fire extinguishers and the fire categories they are designed to suppress are:

Soda-acid—Consists of bicarbonate of soda and sulfuric acid. Used for Class A fires only. Not a suitable fire extinguisher for a garage.

Water—Consists of pressurized water. Used for Class A fires only. Not a suitable fire extinguisher for a garage.

Carbon dioxide—Consists of compressed carbon dioxide. Used for Class B and C fires; not so effective for Class A fires. This type of fire extinguisher has uses in the shop beyond putting fires out; it provides a safe means of killing a runaway engine without damaging it.

Dry chemical—Consists of mostly sodium bicarbonate. Used for Class A, B, C, and D fires. Most shops should be equipped with dry chemical fire extinguishers. They are best used by directing the stream at the base of the fire and then upward.

CAUTION:

Fire suppression in any shop or industrial facility is a job for a trained expert. A technician should always tackle any firefighting with a safety-first approach.

EMERGENCIES

Emergencies are going to arise from time to time in the workplace, and it makes sense to ensure that every employee has a clear idea of how to react. If the nature of the emergency is medical, then whatever first-aid policy is in effect should be followed, and part of this policy is at what point outside aid is sought. First-aid kits and eyewash stations should be clearly identified, and a shop procedure for periodically checking the contents should be in place. Lists of emergency telephone numbers that include fire, medical emergency, and police should be posted. All employees should be made aware of the fire drill procedure, both in written form and by occasional test drills.

FIRST-AID TRAINING

Many employers offer training courses in basic first-aid procedures; these courses are usually of short duration, but it makes a lot of sense to have a workforce trained in how to react to a medical emergency. The role of the individual administering the first aid is primarily one of assessment. Most people do not require a first-aid course to teach them how to apply an adhesive strip on a cut, but knowledge of how to assess the extent of an injury and how to sequence the steps required to enlist external or expert assistance can save lives. It is wise for at least a percentage of any workforce to be capable of performing cardiopulmonary resuscitation (CPR). Larger operations equipped with more sophisticated medical apparatus such as defibrillators should attempt to ensure that there is always someone on the premises who is properly trained to use that equipment.

USE OF FLAMMABLE SOLVENTS FOR CLEANING FLOORS

The generally illegal practice of using solvents to clean floors is actually widespread. The potential for environmental damage is great even when the shop floor drain-off is passed through separator tanks before discharge to public sewage systems. Pouring solvent onto an oil-soaked concrete floor does effectively lift oil and grease, which when power-washed into drain systems floats on top. It only takes a spark from a torch to ignite this mixture. The resultant danger in a service facility is amplified by the range of trucks that may be present, many of which may be hauling hazardous materials.

When floors are cleaned, ensure that the cleaning agent is both environmentally and workplace safe. Most service facilities should identify trucks entering the shop with potentially hazardous loads.

GENERAL SHOP CLEANLINESS

Apart from the fact that they appear to the outsider to be totally unprofessional, dirty and cluttered shop floors are dangerous. Larger shops usually employ cleaning personnel, so cleanliness tends to be less of a problem. In smaller service garages, cleanliness should be the responsibility of each technician. It is common sense to clean up after completing a job; better said, cleanup is part of the job. Apart from the obvious danger of a cluttered shop floor, customers are inclined to see a dirty shop facility as a backyard, substandard operation, even if the output quality of the work is satisfactory.

MAINS ELECTRICAL SUPPLY

Most service garages use mains electrical supply at three pressures: 110–120 volts (V), 220 V, and 450–600 V. In most jurisdictions, truck technicians are not expected to service this equipment and in some cases may be prohibited from doing so. It is not an objective of this book to cover any mains pressure electrical systems, but merely to underline the danger of working around high-voltage equipment.

Dynamometers, welding equipment, hot tank heaters, and machine shop equipment often use 450–600 V-AC circuits. Welding equipment, machine shop equipment, drill presses, high-intensity lighting, and so on use single- or three-phase feeds. When a problem occurs, allow a properly qualified person to repair the problem and avoid taking personal risks. Service technicians should also understand the potential dangers of 110 V-AC systems. The use of extension cords should be avoided when practical: Use permanent, fixed electrical outlets when possible. All shop electrical tools and trouble lights should be properly grounded. Take care not to run extension cords through puddles of water, and routinely inspect for indications of insulation failure.

VENTILATION

In most jurisdictions, it is mandatory to have a shop exhaust system, a network of flexible exhaust pipes connected to an air pump whose function it is to safely expel exhaust gas from the building. Uncombusted and incompletely combusted diesel fuels are known carcinogens (cancer-causing agents), and the inhalation of fumes produced by a running engine should be avoided. Today's truck engines burn fairly clean once they are at operating temperature, so it is good practice to at least warm up the engine of a truck for 5 minutes before driving it from the yard into the shop. Whenever an engine has to be run inside the shop, always connect the shop exhaust pipe(s), even when starting and warming the engine before removing the truck.

OSHA

All workplaces in the United States and Canada are protected by **Right-to-Know legislation**, and most companies have an implicit role in ensuring that their employees are fully aware of any harmful substances, hazardous chemicals, or potentially dangerous practices. In the United States, Right-to-Know legislation is covered by the federal **Hazard Communication Regulation** and administered by OSHA. **OSHA**, or the **Occupational Safety and Health Administration**, is also the federal organization that establishes rules for safe work practices. All workplaces are required to observe OSHA regulations, and technicians should also be somewhat familiar with them; they are posted in most places of work.

In both the United States and Canada, employers have an obligation to ensure that their employees properly understand **Workplace Hazardous Materials Information Systems (WHMIS)** and specifically the **material safety data sheets (MSDS)** that accompany any potentially hazardous substance. As the burden is on employers to prove that this training has been provided, in most cases they offer WHMIS training on a regular basis and track it by testing and awarding certificates.

CATEGORIES OF HAZARDOUS SUBSTANCES

The technician should understand the terms that describe dangerous substances. The same terms are used on trailer and tanker safety placards, and they may determine whether a vehicle can be safely brought into a shop to be worked on.

- **Flammable**: identifies any materials that can be combusted. Includes substances that may be slightly flammable as well as explosives.
- **Inflammable**: means capable of inflammation, so it is synonymous with *flammable*.
- **Corrosive**: materials of high acidity or alkalinity that may dissolve other substances and destroy human or animal tissue.
- **Toxic**: materials that may cause death or illness if consumed, inhaled, or absorbed through the skin.
- **Reactive**: materials that may become chemically reactive if they come into contact with other materials, resulting in toxic fumes, combustion, or explosion.
- **Radioactive**: any substance that emits measurable levels of radiation. When containers of highly radioactive substances have to be brought into a shop environment, they should be tested by qualified personnel with the appropriate equipment.

HAZARDOUS WASTE DISPOSAL

In the United States, the disposal of hazardous waste is covered by federal legislation called the **Resource Conservation and Recovery Act (RCRA)**. The RCRA is reinforced by fines heavy enough to put small operations out of business if they fail to comply; jail sentences are also used to reinforce this legislation and punish violators. It is administered by a national response center, the phone number of which appears at the end of this chapter.

COMPRESSED AIR

Compressed air is used in truck shops to power equipment and clean components. Using compressed air presents a potential danger, and the rookie trainee is seldom instructed on how to use it. The typical truck technician usually possesses an assortment of air-powered tools, which are connected by means of pneumatic couplers to a shop air supply. Certain basic rules should be observed and great care should be exercised when using compressed air to clean and air-dry components. Eye protection should always be worn when using any air-driven tools and equipment. Special care should be exercised when using compressed air to hydrostatically test components.

CAUTION:

Compressed air is potentially dangerous and must be treated with respect. Hydrostatic testing must always be performed in exact accordance with the manufacturer's testing guidelines.

ELECTRIC ARC WELDING SAFETY

It is not an objective of this book to teach arc welding techniques, but it is important that diesel technicians recognize the damage potential when welding on vehicle chassis, especially a chassis that is substantially electronic. Each OEM has its own set of guidelines for welding on chassis, but the following guidelines issued by Caterpillar (RENR9343-04) are typical:

1. Turn the ignition key off.
2. Disconnect the negative terminal from the battery pack.
3. Disconnect all the electronic components from the wiring harnesses, including ECMs, actuators, and sensors.
4. Protect the wiring harness from weld spatter and debris.
5. Connect the welding ground clamp as close as possible to the area to be welded. This reduces the chances of welding current arcing damage to engine bearings and electrical components.

CAUTION:

Never use an electrical component or ECM housing as a welding ground.

OXYACETYLENE SAFETY

Truck and bus technicians use oxyacetylene for heating and cutting probably on a daily basis; less commonly, this equipment is used for brazing and welding. Technicians using this equipment require some basic instruction in its safety requirements and handling. The following information should be known by every person using oxyacetylene equipment.

Acetylene

Acetylene is an unstable gas produced by immersing calcium carbide in water. It is stored in a compressed state and dissolved in acetone at pressures of approximately 250 psi (1.72 MPa). Acetylene cylinders are fabricated in sections and seam welded; next a paste of cement, lime silica, and asbestos is baked within the cylinder, forming a honeycomb structure. The cylinder is then charged with liquid acetone, which floods the honeycomb structure and is itself capable of absorbing acetylene. The base of the acetylene cylinder is concave and has two or more fusible plugs threaded into two apertures. The fusible plugs are made of a lead base alloy and are designed to melt at around 212°F (100°C), so if the cylinder is exposed to heat, the fusible plugs are designed to melt and permit the acetylene to escape and avoid exploding the cylinder.

Acetylene regulators and hose couplings use a left-hand thread. The regulator gauge working pressure should *never* be set at a value exceeding 15 psi (100 kPa). Acetylene becomes extremely unstable at pressures higher than 15 psi. The acetylene cylinder should always be used in the upright position; using the cylinder in a horizontal position will result in the acetone draining into the hoses. **Figure 3–6**

shows an oxyacetylene station set up for a cutting torch.

Oxygen

Oxygen cylinders are forged in a single piece, no part of which is less than ¼" (6 mm) in thickness; the steel used is armor-plate quality, high-carbon steel suitable for pressure vessels. Oxygen is contained in the cylinder at a pressure of 1 ton per square inch (138 bar), so the design is consistent with those for high-pressure vessels with radial corners; they are periodically hydrostatic tested at 3300 psi (228 bar). The safety device on an oxygen cylinder is a rupture disc designed to burst if cylinder pressure exceeds its normal value, such as when exposed to heat. Oxygen regulator and hose fittings use a right-hand thread.

It should be noted that oxygen cylinders tend to pose more problems than acetylene when exposed to fire. They should be stored in a designated place when not in use (this should be identified to the fire department during an inspection) and not left randomly on the shop floor.

FIGURE 3–6 Oxyacetylene station setup with a cutting torch.

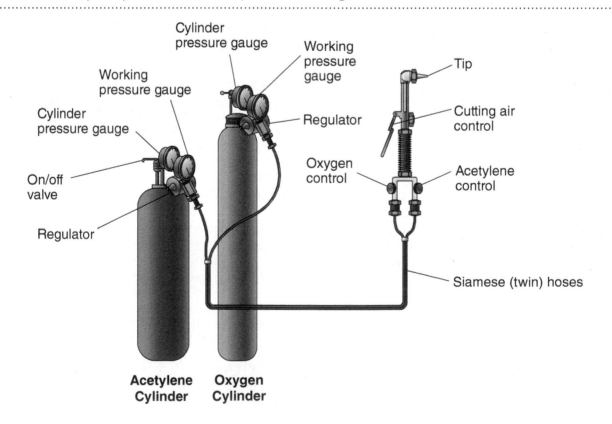

Oxygen is stored in the cylinders at a pressure of 2200 psi (152 bar). The hand wheel-actuated valve forward-seats to close the flow from the cylinder and back-seats when the cylinder is opened; it is important to ensure, therefore, that the valve is fully opened when in use. The consequence of not fully opening the valve is leakage past the valve threads.

Regulators, Gauges, Hoses, and Fittings

A *regulator* is a device used to reduce the pressure at which gas is delivered: it sets the working pressure of the oxygen or fuel. Both oxygen and fuel regulators function similarly in that they increase the working pressure when turned clockwise. They close off the pressure when backed out counterclockwise.

Pressure regulators are usually equipped with two gauges. The cylinder pressure gauge indicates the pressure in the cylinder. The working pressure gauge indicates the working pressure and this should be trimmed to the required value while under flow. The hoses used with oxyacetylene equipment are usually color coded: green is used to identify the oxygen hose and red identifies the fuel hose. The hose connects the regulator assembly with the torch. Hoses may be single or paired (siamese). Hoses should be routinely inspected and replaced when defective.

Fittings couple the hoses to the regulators and the torch. Each fitting consists of a nut and gland. Oxygen fittings use a right-hand thread and fuel fittings use a left-hand thread. The fittings are machined of brass, which has a self-lubricating characteristic. Never lubricate the threads on oxyacetylene fittings.

TECH TIP:

Acetylene fuel fittings use a left-hand thread, so they cannot be connected to oxygen fittings.

CAUTION:

Lubricating the brass fittings used on oxyacetylene equipment is unnecessary and can cause an explosion.

Backfire

Backfire is a condition in which the fuel ignites within the nozzle of the torch, producing a popping or squealing noise; it often occurs when the torch nozzle overheats. Extinguish the torch and clean the nozzle with tip cleaners. Torches may be cooled by immersing in water briefly with just the oxygen valve open.

Flashback

Flashback is a much more severe condition than backfire. It takes place when the flame travels backward into the torch to the gas-mixing chamber and upstream. Causes of flashback are inappropriate pressure settings (especially low pressure settings) and leaking hoses/fittings. When a backfire or flashback condition is suspected, close the cylinder valves immediately, beginning with the fuel valve. Flashback arresters are usually fitted to the torch and limit the extent of damage when a flashback occurs.

Torches and Tips

Torches should be ignited by first setting the working pressure setting under flow for both gases, then opening the fuel valve only and igniting the torch using a flint spark lighter. Set the acetylene flame to a clean burn (no soot), then open the oxygen valve to set the appropriate flame. When setting a cutting torch, set the cutting oxygen last. When extinguishing the torch, close the fuel valve first, then the oxygen; finally, the cylinders should be shut down and the hoses purged.

Welding, cutting, and heating tips may be used with oxyacetylene equipment. Consult a welder's manual to determine the appropriate working pressures for the tip/process to be used. There is a tendency to set gas working pressure high. Even when using the large heating tip often described as a rosebud, the working pressure of both the acetylene and the oxygen should usually be set at no more than 7 psi (50 kPa); check the recommendations of the heating tip manufacturer. When using handheld cutting torches, the pressure for the oxygen can be set at values up to 40 psi (275 kPa), while the acetylene pressure should typically be set at 5 psi (35 kPa).

Eye Protection

Safety requires that a No. 4 to No. 6 grade filter lens be used whenever using an oxyacetylene torch. The flame radiates ultraviolet light, which can damage eyesight.

SAFETY HOTLINES

Chemical Emergency Preparedness Hotline
CERCLA (SARA Title III)   1-800-535-0202
Chemical Transportation Emergency Center
(CHEMTREC) 24-Hour   1-800-424-9300
CMA Chemical Referral Center   1-800-CMA-8200
EPA, Small Business Hotline   1-800-368-5888
EPA RCRA, Superfund, Hazardous
Waste Hotline—Office of Solid
Waste and Emergency
Response   1-800-424-9346
National Response Center (Report chemical releases, radiological
incidents)   1-800-424-8802
National Safety Council   312-527-4800
NIOSH (National Institute of Occupational
Safety and Health)   1-800-356-4674
OSHA, Health Standards   202-523-7075
Safe Drinking Water Hotline   1-800-426-4791
Substance Identification   1-800-848-6538
United States Department of Transportation
Hotline   202-366-4488

Figure 3–7 shows some of the WHMIS safety symbols used to identify potentially hazardous products. Most are common sense, but a couple of them may trick technicians. Try to memorize these. Once again, the message is to work smart: Identify substances before you use them!

FIGURE 3–7 Symbols used on WHMIS labels.

Class A
—compressed gas

Class B
—flammable and combustible material

Class C
—oxidizing material

Class D1
—poisonous and infectious material: materials causing immediate and serious toxic effects

Class D2
—poisonous and infectious material: material causing other toxic effects

Class D3
—poisonous and infectious material: biohazardous infectious material

Class E
—corrosive material

Class F
—dangerously reactive material

SUMMARY

- Every technician should own and use personal safety attire.
- Because of the high risk of eye injury in the typical service garage, technicians should develop the habit of wearing safety glasses, even when it is not mandatory.

- Novice technicians should be aware that their chances of suffering a back injury during their working life are greater than for any other type of injury; they should develop and use safe lifting techniques starting at the beginning of their careers.

- A clean, well-organized shop floor will always produce lower accident rates than cluttered, dirty facilities.
- The objectives of first-aid and basic fire suppression training are to teach employees

how to respond until expert intervention is available.
- Every technician should be fully aware of the danger potential of oxyacetylene equipment and be instructed in how to use it safely.

REVIEW EXERCISES

1. Using an actual service garage, perform a fire safety report, noting the location of fire extinguishers, where oxyacetylene gases are stored, and potential fire hazards.

2. Access OSHA on the Internet and note the contents of its information package.

3. Make a list of all emergency services in the local area and how to access them.

4. Using an actual service garage, perform a plant safety inspection, noting the condition of hoisting apparatus, electrical wiring and breakers, and any potential dangers.

5. List 10 clothing and equipment items that play a role in personal safety on the shop floor.

6. Explain why the cylinder valve on a compressed oxygen cylinder should be in either the fully open or the fully closed position. State the maximum setting pressure on an acetylene regulator and explain why it is important to observe that limit.

7. Outline the internal construction of an acetylene cylinder.

8. Describe the operation of the cylinder safety devices on both oxygen and acetylene cylinders.

REVIEW QUESTIONS

1. Materials that have either high acidity or alkalinity are described as:
   a. flammable.
   b. toxic.
   c. radioactive.
   d. corrosive.

2. Materials that may emit toxic fumes or explode when brought into contact with other materials are described as:
   a. reactive.
   b. toxic.
   c. radioactive.
   d. corrosive.

3. Which of the following is required to have a left-hand thread?
   a. Oxygen cylinder fitting
   b. Acetylene cylinder fitting
   c. Cutting nozzle fitting

4. Which of the following would be the most serious condition when operating oxyacetylene cutting equipment?
   a. Flashback
   b. Backfire
   c. Popping

5. Which of the following grades of eye protection filter would be recommended when performing oxyacetylene cutting?
   a. 2
   b. 5
   c. 10
   d. 13

6. Which type of fire extinguisher would effectively snub a runaway engine without itself causing any damage?
   a. Foam
   b. Carbon dioxide
   c. Dry chemical powder
   d. Water

7. The reason the exhaust pipe of an engine run inside the shop must always be connected to the shop exhaust system is to protect:
   a. the employees.
   b. paintwork on the trucks.
   c. paintwork within the building.
   d. the ozone layer

8. What is a carcinogen?
    a. A cancer-causing agent
    b. A respiratory illness
    c. A fire hazard
    d. A skin irritant

9. Where should the ground clamp be placed when preparing to perform electric arc welding on a chassis?
    a. On the front bumper
    b. On the rear cross member
    c. As far from the weld as possible
    d. As close to the weld as possible

10. Technician A states that the location of oxygen bottles on the shop floor does not matter so long as the fire department is aware of where acetylene bottles are stored. Technician B states that the safety device on an oxygen bottle is a rupture disc. Who is correct?
    a. Technician A only
    b. Technician B only
    c. Both A and B
    d. Neither A nor B

4

ENGINE BASICS

OBJECTIVES

After studying this chapter, you should be able to:

- Define the terms that describe basic engine operation.
- Outline the roles played by each subsystem in the engine.
- Describe the seven subcircuits that the engine has been divided into for study purposes.
- Calculate engine displacement using the appropriate formula.
- Outline the differences among square, undersquare, and oversquare engines.
- Apply the term *mean effective pressure* to an engine operating cycle.
- Identify the differences between a naturally aspirated engine and a manifold boosted engine.
- Explain the term *volumetric efficiency* and apply it to cylinder breathing efficiencies.
- State how Boyle's and Charles's laws apply to engine operation.
- Describe how friction and inertia factors affect engine operation.
- Explain how the heat energy of a fuel is converted to kinetic energy.
- Define *rejected heat* and explain the thermal efficiency factors in a diesel engine.
- Outline in detail the diesel four-stroke cycle.
- Outline in detail the diesel two-stroke cycle.
- Outline in detail the Otto four-stroke cycle.
- Explain why it is desirable for any engine to produce peak cylinder pressure at 10 to 20 degrees ATDC on the power stroke during any speed or load phase of operation.
- Define the term *scavenging* and apply it to both the diesel four-stroke cycle and two-stroke cycle.
- Outline the basic characteristics of a diesel fuel.

KEY TERMS

after top dead center (ATDC)

Atkinson cycle

before top dead center (BTDC)

bore

bottom dead center (BDC)

Boyle's law

British thermal unit (Btu)

calorific value

Charles's law

clearance volume

combustion pressure

compression ignition (CI)

compression pressure

compression ratio

cylinder volume

diesel cycle

diesel engine

direct injection (DI)

engine

engine displacement

fire point

friction	joule	Otto cycle	stroke
heat energy	kinetic energy	oversquare engine	swept volume
heat engine	manifold boost	ratio	thermal efficiency
ignition lag	mean effective pressure (MEP)	rejected heat	top dead center (TDC)
indirect injection (IDI)		spark ignited (SI)	undersquare engine
inertia	Miller cycle	square engine	volumetric efficiency
internal combustion engine	naturally aspirated (NA)	static friction	

INTRODUCTION

This chapter begins by introducing some basic engine terminology. Before technicians can properly understand how an engine functions, they have to become familiar with some of the language used to describe its operation. After introducing the basic terminology, the text goes on to describe the diesel cycle, two-stroke diesel cycle, and Otto cycle. At the end of the chapter, some more complex terms that build on the first batch of basic terms are discussed. The engine terminology introduced in this chapter is used repeatedly throughout the textbook; many of the terms are expanded on in later chapters.

KEY ENGINE TERMS

The terms explained here are the building blocks required to understand engine technology. Mostly the technically correct terms are used in this textbook, but remember that the terminology used on the shop floor might differ. When referencing manufacturers' service literature, a basic understanding of the key terms that are introduced in this chapter is expected. The following text simply interprets many of the words that are later used to describe the various engine cycles and key events within those cycles.

BASIC DEFINITIONS

The following terms have to be understood before the basics of engine technology can be grasped. The good news is that you probably are familiar with many of them. Be careful, though: These definitions may be slightly different from those you are familiar with.

ENGINE. A machine that converts one energy form to another form of energy.

HEAT ENGINE. An engine that converts the potential **heat energy** of a combustible fuel into mechanical work. The diesel is a heat engine that functions by converting the heat energy of diesel fuel into mechanical work at its flywheel.

INTERNAL COMBUSTION ENGINE. A heat engine in which the combustion of fuel is contained within a cylinder. Differentiated from a steam engine in which the fuel is combusted outside of the engine.

DIESEL ENGINE. An internal combustion engine in which the cylinder fuel air charge is ignited by the heat of compression.

KINETIC ENERGY. The energy of motion. When a heat engine attempts to convert the energy available in a fuel to mechanical work, some heat losses result. Kinetic energy describes that percentage of the potential energy of the fuel that actually gets converted to usable mechanical energy.

TOP DEAD CENTER (TDC). The uppermost point of the piston travel in an engine cylinder.

BOTTOM DEAD CENTER (BDC). The lowest point of piston travel in the engine cylinder.

BEFORE TOP DEAD CENTER (BTDC). Any point of piston travel through its upstroke.

AFTER TOP DEAD CENTER (ATDC). A point of piston travel through its downstroke.

BORE. The diameter of a cylinder. Bore is expressed as the piston sectional area over which cylinder pressures act. The bore dimension in an engine cylinder is identified in **Figure 4-1**.

STROKE. The distance through which a piston travels from BDC to TDC. Stroke is established

FIGURE 4–1 Bore and stroke.

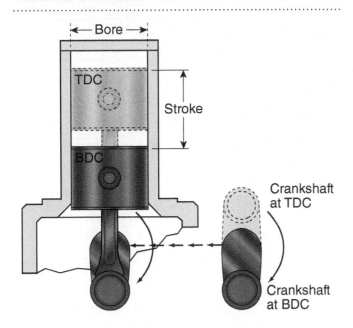

Examples:

Navistar International MaxxForce 13

Engine displacement calculation data: six-cylinder engine, bore 126 mm, stroke 166 mm

Engine displacement = 126 × 126 × 166 × 0.7854 × 6

= 12,419,134 cubic millimeters

= 12.4 liters (rounded)

Caterpillar ACERT Post-2007 C15

Engine displacement calculation data: six-cylinder engine, bore 5.4", stroke 6.75"

Engine displacement = 5.4 × 5.4 × 6.75 × 0.7854 × 6

= 927.54 cubic inches

= 928 cubic inches (rounded)

by the crank throw offset; that is, the distance from the crankshaft centerline to the throw centerline multiplied by 2 equals the stroke dimension. Figure 4–1 identifies the bore and stroke dimensions in an engine cylinder.

SWEPT VOLUME. The volume displaced by the piston in the cylinder as it moves from BDC to TDC. It can be calculated if both stroke and bore are known.

CLEARANCE VOLUME. The remaining volume in an engine cylinder when the piston is at the top of its travel or TDC. Clearance volume influences actual compression temperatures and cylinder breathing efficiencies. The clearance volume on older indirect injection (IDI) diesel engines was considerable, but it is much less on today's direct-injected (DI) engines.

CYLINDER VOLUME. The total volume in the cylinder when the piston is at BDC: swept volume plus clearance volume.

ENGINE DISPLACEMENT. The swept volume of all the engine cylinders expressed in cubic inches or cubic centimeters/liters.

Displacement = bore × bore × stroke × 0.7854
× number of cylinders

> **TECH TIP:**
>
> To convert liters to cubic inches or cubic inches to liters, use the following simple formulae in which 61 is either multiplied or divided into the value to be converted:
>
> MaxxForce 13 = 12.4 liters × 61 = 756.4
> = 756 cubic inches (rounded)
>
> Caterpillar C15 = 928 cubic inches ÷ 61 = 15.213
> = 15.2 liters (rounded)

SQUARE ENGINE. An engine in which the cylinder bore diameter is exactly equal to the piston stroke dimension. When bore and stroke values are expressed, bore always appears before stroke.

OVERSQUARE ENGINE. An engine in which the cylinder bore diameter is larger than the stroke dimension. A majority of spark-ignited, gasoline-fueled engines fall into this category, though this could change as direct-injected, gasoline-fueled engines become popular.

UNDERSQUARE ENGINE. An engine in which the cylinder bore diameter is smaller than the stroke dimension. Most high-compression diesel engines are undersquare, as shown by the displacement that was calculated earlier.

COMPRESSION IGNITION (CI). CI is the acronym commonly used to describe any diesel engine in which the fuel charge is ignited by heat generated on the compression stroke.

SPARK IGNITED (SI). An engine in which the air–fuel charge is ignited by a timed electrical spark. When diesel engine platforms are converted to run on natural gas (NG), they require an SI system.

DIRECT INJECTION (DI). Either a CI or an SI engine in which the fuel charge is injected directly into the engine cylinder rather than to a precombustion chamber or part of the intake manifold. Almost all current diesel engines use DI, as does a new generation of gasoline-fueled, SI engines.

INDIRECT INJECTION (IDI). A CI or an SI engine in which the fuel charge is introduced outside the engine cylinder to a precombustion chamber, cylinder head intake tract, or intake manifold.

RATIO. The quantitative relationship between two values expressed by the number of times one contains the other. The term is commonly used in automotive technology to describe the drive/driven relationships of two meshed gears, the mechanical advantage of levers, and the cylinder compression ratio.

COMPRESSION RATIO. A measure of the cylinder volume when the piston is at BDC versus the cylinder volume when the piston is at TDC. Compression ratios in diesel engines fall between 14:1 and 24:1. Current, high-speed, turbocharged truck and bus diesel engines have compression ratios typically between 16:1 and 17:1. **Figure 4–2** shows a diesel engine with a compression ratio of 17:1.

COMPRESSION PRESSURE. The actual cylinder pressure developed on the compression stroke. Actual compression pressures developed range from 350 psi (2.41 MPa) to 700 psi (4.82 MPa) in CI engines. The higher the compression pressure, the more heat developed in the cylinder. Truck diesel engines typically produce compression pressures of ±600 psi.

COMBUSTION PRESSURE. The peak pressure developed during the power stroke. In today's electronically controlled truck diesel engines, combustion pressures may peak at up to five times the compression pressure.

FIGURE 4–2 Diesel engine compression ratio.

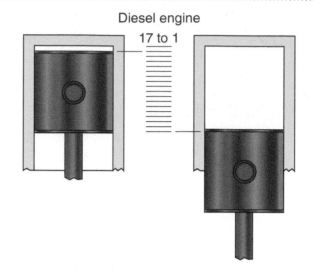

Diesel engine
17 to 1

NATURALLY ASPIRATED (NA). Describes an engine whose only means of inducing air (or air–fuel mixture) into its cylinders is the low cylinder pressure created by the downstroke of the piston.

MANIFOLD BOOST. Describes the extent of charge pressure above atmospheric delivered to the cylinders in a turbocharged engine. Most current truck and bus diesel engines are boosted; that is, they are turbocharged.

VOLUMETRIC EFFICIENCY. A measure of an engine's breathing efficiency. It is usually defined as the ratio between the volume of actual fresh air taken into the cylinder before the intake valve(s) close versus the cylinder swept volume. However, properly expressed, volumetric efficiency is a ratio of *masses*, not volumes. If the example of a liquid filling a pump cylinder is used to explain volumetric efficiency, it is the weight of liquid drawn into the pump cylinder in a cycle versus the maximum weight of the liquid the cylinder could contain. In a diesel engine, the fluid being charged to the cylinder is air, which happens to be compressible. This means that in a turbocharged engine volumetric efficiency can often exceed 100%. Therefore, another way of defining the term is to say that it is the amount of air charged to the engine cylinder in an actual cycle versus the amount it would contain if it were at atmospheric pressure. Volumetric efficiency is usually expressed in percentage terms.

FIRE POINT. The temperature at which a flammable liquid gives off sufficient vapor for continuous combustion to take place. This is also known as *ignition temperature.* The fire point or ignition temperature of a diesel fuel is specified by a cetane number (CN), which is explained in some detail in Chapter 17.

THE DIESEL CYCLE

A *cycle* is a recurring sequence of events. The **diesel cycle** is usually described by the four strokes of the pistons made as an engine is turned through two revolutions. A complete cycle of a diesel engine requires 2 full rotations, and this translates into 720 crankshaft degrees. Each of the four strokes that make up the cycle involves moving a piston either from the top of its travel to its lowest point of travel or vice versa; each stroke of the cycle therefore translates into 180 crankshaft degrees. The four strokes that make up the four-stroke cycle are intake, compression, power, and exhaust (**Figure 4–3**). The diesel cycle by definition is a four-stroke cycle. Two-stroke cycle compression ignition engines exist but, correctly, these should be qualified as two-stroke cycle diesel engines.

DIRECT-INJECTION, COMPRESSION IGNITION ENGINE

The events that make up the four-stroke cycle diesel engine take place in sequence as follows.

1. Intake Stroke

The piston is drawn from TDC to BDC with the cylinder head intake valve(s) held open. The downstroke of the piston creates lower-than-atmospheric pressure in the cylinder and in a naturally aspirated engine, this induces a charge of fresh, filtered air into the cylinder. Because most current truck and bus engines are turbocharged, the cylinder will actually be filled with charged air (i.e., at a pressure above atmospheric) when the intake valve(s) open and the piston travels downward. The actual cylinder charge depends on the manifold boost value (extent of turbo-boost; this varies with how the engine is operated).

The *air* that is taken into the cylinder is a mixture of gaseous elements: approximately four-fifths nitrogen and one-fifth oxygen. The oxygen is required to combust the fuel. Note that the fuel is not introduced into the cylinder until later in the cycle. By pressurizing the air charge using a turbocharger, more oxygen can be forced into each engine cylinder. All diesel engines are designed for lean burn operation; that is, the cylinder will be charged with much more air than is required to combust the fuel. Volumetric efficiency in most phases of engine operation will usually exceed 100% in turbocharged engines, usually by substantial amounts.

There are some emissions disadvantages of having excess air in the engine cylinder, so most

FIGURE 4–3 The four-stroke diesel cycle.

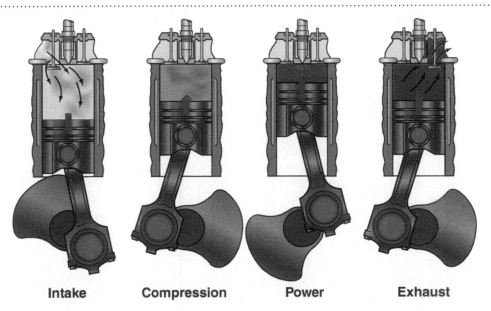

Intake   Compression   Power   Exhaust

FIGURE 4–4 A. Intake stroke: Turbo-boosted air is charged to the engine cylinder. B. Compression stroke: Piston is driven upward, compressing the air charge. C. Power stroke: Fuel is injected to the cylinder, ignites, and the resulting gas expansion drives the piston downward. D. Exhaust stroke: Piston is driven upward, displacing the end gas through the exhaust valves.

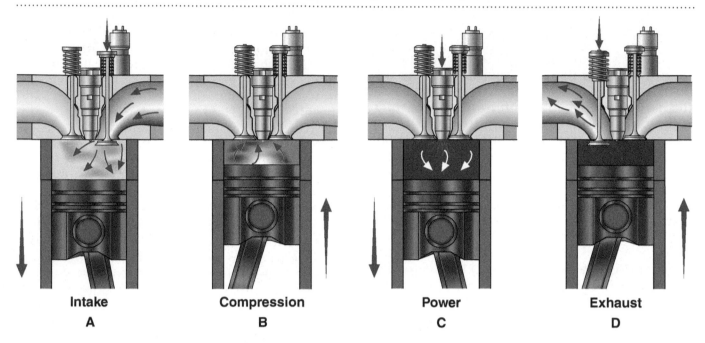

Intake	Compression	Power	Exhaust
A	B	C	D

modern diesel engines recycle a percentage of exhaust gas back into the engine to reduce the amount of oxygen in the cylinder during some operating modes. Another way of reducing the amount of oxygen in the cylinder during combustion is to delay the closing of the intake valve on the compression stroke. This is called *variable valve timing (VVT)* and it has the effect of lowering the compression ratio. **Figure 4–4A** demonstrates the intake stroke on a modern diesel engine.

2. Compression Stroke

The piston is now driven from BDC to TDC with the intake and exhaust valves closed, compressing the charge of air in the cylinder and in doing so, heating it. Compression pressures in diesel engines vary from 400 psi (2750 kPa) to 800 psi (5500 kPa). The actual amount of heat generated from these compression pressures also varies, but it usually substantially exceeds the minimum ignition temperature values of the fuel. Compression ratios used to achieve the compression pressure required of diesel engines generally vary from a low of 14:1 to a high of 25:1. However, in modern turbocharged,

highway diesel engines, compression ratios are typically around 16:1 to 17:1. **Figure 4–4B** illustrates the compression stroke on a modern diesel engine.

3. Expansion or Power Stroke

Shortly before completion of the compression stroke, atomized fuel is introduced directly into the engine cylinder by a multi-orifii (multiple-hole) nozzle assembly. The fuel exits the injector nozzle in the liquid state in droplets appropriately sized for combustion in a DI engine. Once exposed to the heated air charge in the cylinder, these liquid droplets are first vaporized and then ignited. The ignition point is usually designed to occur just before the piston is positioned at TDC, with the objective of peaking the gas pressure acting on the piston during the expansion stroke at 10 to 20 degrees ATDC. However, because this is the objective at all engine speeds and loads, it is difficult to achieve it uniformly with hydromechanical fuel systems. Noxious emissions requirements of newer electronically managed engines often mean that the power stroke may not be managed to produce optimum mechanical efficiency, because of the requirement to remain within legal emission specifications. **Figure 4–4C** illustrates the power stroke in a typical diesel engine.

In managing the power stroke, it is desirable to have little pressure acting on the piston at TDC. Cylinder gas pressure should peak at 15 to 20 degrees ATDC when throw leverage exists but is close to minimum. As gas pressure acts on the piston and forces it through its stroke, the cylinder pressure will decrease, but as it does throw leverage increases, reaching its maximum when the angle between the connecting rod and crank throw is at 90 degrees. This relationship between pressure and throw leverage helps to transmit the energy produced in the engine cylinder as smoothly as possible to the flywheel. **Figure 4–5** maps the key events of the compression and power strokes in the diesel cycle.

4. Exhaust Stroke

Somewhere after 90 degrees ATDC during the expansion stroke, most of the heat energy that can be converted to kinetic energy has been converted and the exhaust valve opens. The products of cylinder combustion are known as *end gas*. The exhausting of combustion end gases occurs in four distinct phases and the process begins during the latter portion of the power stroke (see **Figure 4–4D**):

1. Pressure differential—At the moment the exhaust valves open during the latter portion of the power stroke, pressure is higher in the cylinder than in the exhaust manifold. High-pressure end gas in the cylinder will therefore flow to the lower pressure zone in the exhaust manifold. This phase is also known as *gas blowdown.*

2. Inertial—Next the piston comes to a standstill at BDC, at the completion of the power stroke. However, gas inertia established during the pressure differential phase will result in the end gases continuing to flow from the cylinder to the exhaust manifold while the piston is in a stationary and near-stationary state of motion.

3. Displacement—As the piston is forced upward through its stroke, it positively displaces combustion end gases above it.

4. Scavenging—Toward the end of the exhaust stroke, as the exhaust valve begins to close, the intake valve begins to open with the piston near TDC. The scavenging phase takes place during valve overlap and can be highly effective in expelling end gases and providing some piston crown cooling. The efficiency of the scavenging process is greatest with turbocharged engines. **Figure 4–6** shows the events of the two breathing strokes, intake and exhaust.

FIGURE 4–5 Events of the compression and power strokes.

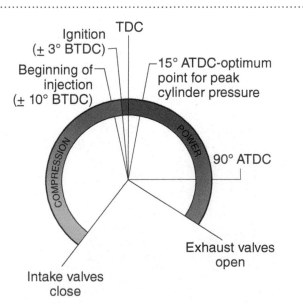

FIGURE 4–6 Events of the intake and exhaust strokes.

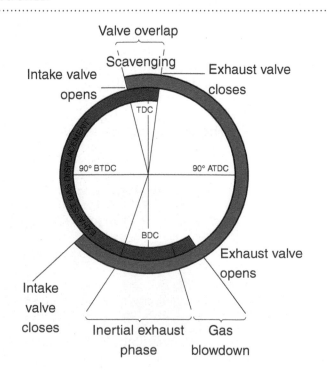

THE TWO-STROKE CYCLE DIESEL ENGINE

Although two-stroke cycle diesel engines have not been able to meet on-highway Environmental Protection Agency (EPA) emissions requirements for more than two decades, there are a surprising number of these engines still running, both on and off our roads, in marine and heavy equipment applications. For this reason, diesel technicians should have a basic understanding of two-stroke cycle operating principles. However, if you wish to study two-stroke cycle diesel in more detail, refer to earlier editions of this textbook.

In the two-stroke cycle diesel engine, the intake and exhaust strokes are eliminated, meaning that in 360 degrees of rotation, each engine cylinder has fired. Theoretically, the two-stroke cycle diesel engine should develop twice as much power as a four-stroke cycle engine of the same displacement, but in reality this is not achieved, mainly due to reduced cylinder breathing efficiency. Some of the on-highway, two-stroke cycle engines still in existence today are managed electronically, but even these are disappearing fast. Refer to **Figure 4–7** to follow the explanation of the two-stroke cycle in the next sections.

TWO-STROKE CYCLE CONSTRUCTION

The physical characteristics of the two-stroke cycle engine differ from those of the four-stroke cycle diesel engine mainly because cylinder breathing must take place in less than one-fifth of the time. All the valves in the cylinder head,

usually four per cylinder, are exhaust valves. After combustion, the cylinder end gases must be expelled; to enable this, air must be pumped through the cylinder from an air box charged by a Roots blower, which is sometimes aided by a turbocharger. In on-highway applications, because of widely variable speed and load variations, engine breathing requires the use of a Roots blower. A *Roots blower* is a positive displacement pump that works efficiently at all rotational speeds. Its disadvantage is that it is gear driven and leeches some engine power.

A turbocharger may completely replace the Roots blower in applications such as a genset designed to run at continuously high output, resulting in sufficient exhaust gas heat to efficiently drive the turbine to scavenge the cylinders. In on-highway applications, though, a Roots blower must be used and a turbocharger is used in addition to the blower. The cylinder liners are machined with ports designed to be exposed when the piston is in the lower portion of its downstroke. When these ports are exposed to the air box by the downward traveling piston, the cylinder is charged with air for scavenging and breathing. The ports are usually canted (angled) to encourage a vortex (cyclonic) airflow dynamic.

TWO-STROKE CYCLE EVENTS

The two-stroke cycle sequence begins with the piston at BDC when cylinder *scavenging* takes place. At this moment the piston has fully exposed the canted intake ports and the exhaust valves are fully opened. Air from the air box rushes into the cylinder and displaces the combustion end gases, spiraling them upward to exit through the exhaust valves. Air from the

FIGURE 4–7 The two-stroke diesel cycle.

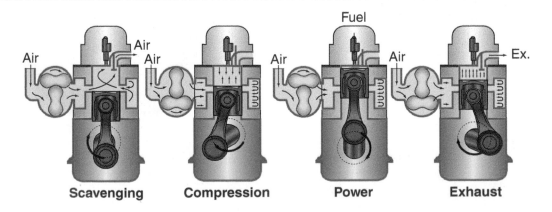

Scavenging   **Compression**   **Power**   **Exhaust**

FIGURE 4–8 Two-stroke diesel cycle events.

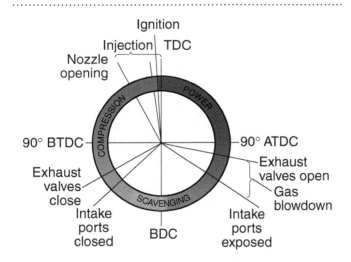

air box continues to charge the cylinder until the piston reverses and its upward travel closes off the intake ports; the exhaust valves close almost simultaneously. Every upward stroke of the piston is therefore a compression stroke. **Figure 4-8** maps the events of the two-stroke cycle diesel engine.

SCAVENGING EFFICIENCY

If all the end gases were effectively expelled, only air would be compressed during the compression stroke. However, scavenging efficiency is a problem with these engines, and any end gases remaining in the cylinder after the exhaust valves close will dilute the incoming air charge. A few degrees before TDC, the fueling of the cylinder begins directly into the engine cylinder. After a short delay, ignition occurs and expanding combustion gases act on the piston and drive it downward through the power stroke. Every downward stroke of the piston is a power stroke. Shortly before the liner intake ports are exposed by the piston, the exhaust valves open, beginning the exhaust process, which must take place quickly and in two stages: pressure differential and scavenging.

THE OTTO CYCLE

Every technician should have a clear understanding of the **Otto cycle**, which is the engine cycle used in most SI (spark-ignited) gasoline-fueled engines. The first stroke of the cycle is

appropriately called the *induction stroke*. A charge of air–fuel mixture is induced into the engine cylinder by the low pressure created by the downstroke of the piston in the engine cylinder as it moves from TDC to BDC. The air–fuel charge is usually mixed outside the engine cylinder, either by a carburetor located upstream from the intake plenum or by injectors located at the intake tract of the cylinder head. More recent gasoline-fueled engines may be direct-injected, in which case air only is induced into the cylinder during the intake stroke. In the more common indirect injected engines, when the piston stops at BDC and the intake valve closes, the cylinder contains all of the ingredients—that is, the fuel and air—required for the subsequent power stroke.

The mixture of fuel and air is compressed on the second stroke of the cycle, which is known as the *compression stroke*. Compression ratios must be somewhat lower on indirect injected SI engines because the compression ignition of the more volatile fuel used (gasoline) must be avoided. Compression ratios on gasoline engines have crept upward over the years. Something around 8:1 to 10:1 is typical. This produces compression pressures around 150 psi (10 bar). The cylinder charge is ignited just before completion of the compression stroke. Compression ratios and the resulting compression pressures may be higher with direct-injected, gasoline-fueled engines because the issue of unwanted compression ignition is avoided.

The power stroke can produce peak combustion pressures approximately five times the compression pressure. Gasoline fuels are chemically more complex than diesel fuels and must be formulated with a mixture of fractions (hydrocarbon compounds derived from crude petroleum) that ignite in a sequential chain reaction, expanding to apply pressure to the piston evenly through the power stroke. As with the diesel engine, the cylinder pressure and the crank throw angle must be phased to transfer the power smoothly and evenly to the flywheel. At some point after the piston has passed 90 degrees ATDC on the power stroke, the exhaust valves open and begin a four-phase exhaust process more or less identical to that of the four-stroke cycle diesel engine, with the exception of the scavenging phase, which must be held short to prevent the discharge of unburned air–fuel mixture (the incoming charge) into the exhaust system.

Thermal efficiencies tend to be lower in Otto cycle engines than in diesel engines, making

10 degrees and 20 degrees ATDC, when there is some but nevertheless a small amount of throw leverage. As the piston is forced down through the power stroke, the gas pressure acting on the piston diminishes, but as it does throw leverage increases. Ideally, this relationship between cylinder pressure and crank throw leverage should be managed in a way that results in consistent torque delivery from an engine cylinder through the power stroke until the throw forms a 90-degree angle with the connecting rod: This occurs a little before true 90 degrees ATDC.

BOYLE'S LAW   (Robert Boyle, U.K., 1627–1691). States that the absolute pressure that a given quantity of gas at constant temperature exerts against the walls of a container is universally proportional to the volume occupied. In other words, assuming a constant temperature, the pressure of a specific quantity of gas depends on the volume of the vessel it is contained in. So, to use an example of this law as it applies to a diesel engine, it means that a constant-temperature mass of gas (air) in a cylinder, as its volume is reduced by moving the piston, will exert pressure on the cylinder walls because the number of molecules will remain the same, but they will have less room to move in, thereby causing the pressure rise.

CHARLES'S LAW   (Jacques Charles, France, 1746–1823). States that an increase in temperature in gases produces the same increase in volume if the pressure remains constant. In other words, heating a gas must result in an increase in volume if the pressure is to remain unchanged. Using the Celsius scale, it can be proved that the volume of a gas increases by 0.003663 of its volume at zero degrees Celsius for every one degree of temperature rise. On the Fahrenheit scale, the volume increases by 0.002174 for every one degree of temperature rise above 32°F. If one graphed this equation negatively, it would show that a point would be reached at which the gas would have no volume; the vibration of the molecules would cease and the gas would contain no heat energy and would cease to exist as a substance. This would occur at absolute zero or −460°F (−273°C). To conclude, if the volume of a gas is changed by increasing its temperature while keeping its pressure constant, then its volume will increase proportionally with temperature rise.

The first law of thermodynamics. States that heat energy and mechanical energy are naturally convertible. This is predicated by the law of conservation of energy, which states that energy can neither be created nor destroyed. This means that the total energy available remains constant. However, energy can change its form. Heat energy can be changed into mechanical energy (the operating principle of any internal combustion engine) or vice versa. Similarly, heat energy can be changed into electrical energy and vice versa.

The second law of thermodynamics. States that heat will not flow from a cool body to a warmer body without some kind of assistance, but that it will flow from a warm body to a cooler body. If the objective is to force heat from a cool body to a hot body, such as in an air conditioning system, some form of external assistance must be applied.

FRICTION.   Force is required to move an object over the surface of another. Friction is the resistance to motion between two objects in contact with each other. Friction is factored by both load and surface condition. Smooth surfaces produce less friction than rough surfaces, and if a lubricant such as water or oil is added, friction diminishes. Lubricants coat and separate two surfaces from each other and reduce friction, but the lubricant itself provides some resistance to movement, which is known as *viscous (fluid) friction*. A friction bearing such as a crankshaft main bearing provides a sliding friction dynamic, whereas ball bearings provide a rolling friction dynamic that usually offers less resistance to motion.

STATIC FRICTION.   Describes the characteristic of an object at rest to attempt to stay that way. For example, the engine piston at its travel limit stops momentarily before the crankshaft and connecting rod reverse its movement. When the piston is momentarily stopped, the crankshaft must overcome the static friction of the stationary piston, which places both the connecting rod and a portion of the crankshaft under tension. This tensile loading of the connecting rod and crankshaft is amplified as rotational speed increases.

INERTIA.   Describes the tendency of an object in motion to stay in motion or, conversely, an object at rest to remain that way. *Kinetic inertia* describes the characteristic of an object in motion to stay in motion. For example, an engine piston moving in one direction must be stopped at its travel limit, and its kinetic inertia must be absorbed by the crankshaft and connecting rod. The inertia principle is used by the engine vibration damper and the flywheel: the inertial mass represented by the flywheel would have to be greatest in a single-cylinder, four-stroke cycle engine. As the number of cylinders increases, the inertial mass represented by the flywheel can be reduced due to the greater mass of rotating components and the higher frequency of power strokes.

Joule's heat efficiency (James Prescott Joule, U.K., 1818–1889). Joule established the relationship between the units of heat and work that could be done. The unit **joule** is named for him. This relationship is used to describe the potential energy of a fuel and is known as *Joule's mechanical heat equivalent.*

1 Btu of potential heat energy = 778 lb.-ft of mechanical energy

1 J (joule) of potential heat energy = 1 lb.-ft of mechanical energy

1 J = 1 Newton/meter (N·m) = 0.7374 lb.-ft

CALORIFIC VALUE. The potential heat energy of a fuel. A heat engine attempts to convert the potential heat energy of a fuel into kinetic energy; the thermal efficiency of the engine is a measure of how successful this conversion is. The calorific value of fuels is measured in Btu (English system) or joules and calories (metric system).

BRITISH THERMAL UNIT (BTU). A Btu is a measure of heat energy. One Btu is the amount of heat required to raise the temperature of 1 pound of water 1 degree Fahrenheit.

THERMAL EFFICIENCY. A measure of the combustion efficiency of an engine calculated by comparing the heat energy potential of the fuel (calorific value) with the amount of usable mechanical work produced. Today's electronically controlled diesel engines can have maximum thermal efficiency values exceeding 40%, but typical real-world thermal efficiencies may be a little lower, as shown in **Figure 4–9**.

REJECTED HEAT. The percentage of the heat potential of the fuel that is not converted into useful work by an engine. If a diesel engine operating at optimum efficiency can be said

FIGURE 4–9 How the potential energy of diesel fuel is released in a diesel engine.

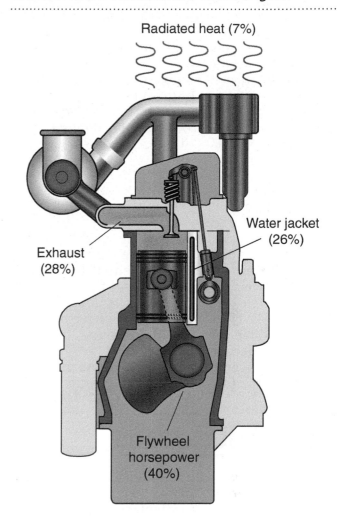

Radiated heat (7%)

Water jacket (26%)

Exhaust (28%)

Flywheel horsepower (40%)

to have a thermal efficiency of 40%, then 60% of the calorific value of the fuel has to be discharged as *rejected heat*. Half of the rejected heat is typically transferred to the engine hardware to be dissipated to the atmosphere by the engine cooling system, and the other half exits in the exhaust gas. A turbocharger makes use of rejected heat by compressing the intake air forced into the engine cylinders, thereby increasing the thermal efficiency of the engine. Figure 4–9 shows how the potential energy of the fuel (100%) is released in a typical diesel engine during a real-world performance cycle: 40% is converted into useful mechanical energy delivered to the flywheel. The remainder of that potential heat energy, totaling 60%, is released as rejected heat. The rejected heat is dispersed as radiated heat (7%) to engine coolant (26%), and into the exhaust (28%).

SUMMARY

- Most diesel engines are rated by their ability to produce power and torque. The tendency is to rate gasoline-fueled auto engines by their total displacement.
- Diesel engines have high compression ratios, so they tend to be undersquare.
- Almost every medium- and large-bore highway diesel engine is manifold boosted—that is, it is turbocharged.
- The most common diesel cycle is a four-stroke cycle consisting of four separate strokes of the piston occurring over two revolutions; a complete engine cycle is therefore extended over 720 degrees.
- The two-stroke diesel cycle enables every downstroke of a piston to be a power stroke, so in theory, it has the potential to produce more power per engine pound than the four-stroke cycle. In practice, this is unobtainable. Two-stroke cycle diesel engines have not been EPA certifiable for on-highway use for more than two decades.
- MEP is the average pressure acting on the piston through the four strokes of the cycle. Usually the intake and exhaust strokes are discounted, so MEP is equal to the average pressure acting on the piston through the compression stroke subtracted from the average pressure acting on the piston through the power stroke.
- Ideally, engine fueling should be managed to produce peak cylinder pressures at somewhere around 10 to 20 degrees ATDC, when the relative mechanical advantage provided by the crank throw position is low. This means that as cylinder pressure drops through the power stroke, throw mechanical advantage increases, peaking when the rod-to-throw angle is at 90 degrees and providing a smooth unloading of force to the engine flywheel.
- An engine attempts to convert the potential heat energy of a fuel into useful mechanical energy. The degree to which it succeeds is rated as the engine's *thermal efficiency*.
- The portion of the heat energy of a fuel that is not converted to kinetic energy is known as *rejected heat*. Rejected heat must be dissipated to the atmosphere by means of the engine cooling and exhaust systems.

REVIEW QUESTIONS

1. A popular six-cylinder Navistar diesel engine has a bore of 120 mm and a stroke of 155 mm. What is the engine displacement?
   a. 9.4 liters
   b. 10.5 liters
   c. 12.4 liters
   d. 13.6 liters

2. Which of the following accurately describes engine displacement?
   a. Total piston swept volume
   b. Mean effective pressure
   c. Peak horsepower
   d. Peak torque

3. Engine breathing in the two-stroke cycle is usually referred to as:
   a. inertial.
   b. scavenging.
   c. exhaust displacement.

4. The tendency of an object in motion to stay in motion is known as:
   a. kinetic energy.
   b. dynamic friction.
   c. inertia.
   d. mechanical force.

5. When a modern diesel engine is running at optimum efficiency, the percentage of rejected heat would typically be:
   a. 20%.
   b. 40%.
   c. 60%.
   d. 80%.

6. What percentage of the potential heat energy of the fuel does the modern diesel engine convert to kinetic energy when the engine is operating close to optimum efficiency?
   a. 20%
   b. 40%
   c. 60%
   d. 80%

7. In which of the four strokes of the cycle is the cylinder pressure at its highest in a running diesel engine?
   a. Intake
   b. Compression
   c. Power
   d. Exhaust

8. Where does scavenging take place in a four-stroke cycle diesel engine?
   a. BDC after the power stroke
   b. TDC after the compression stroke
   c. Valve overlap
   d. 10 to 20 degrees ATDC on the power stroke

9. Ideally, where should peak cylinder pressure occur during the power stroke?
   a. TDC
   b. 10 to 20 degrees ATDC
   c. 90 degrees ATDC
   d. At gas blowdown

10. Which of the seven subcircuits of the engine deals with the camshaft, valvetrains, and mechanical actuation of injectors and fuel pumping apparatus?
   a. Powertrain
   b. Feedback assembly
   c. Lubrication circuit
   d. Engine housing circuit

11. A Cummins ISB engine has a displacement of 6.7 liters. Convert this to cubic inches.
   a. 365 cubic inches
   b. 409 cubic inches
   c. 444 cubic inches
   d. 530 cubic inches

12. A 2007 Caterpillar ACERT C13 engine has an actual total cylinder swept volume of 12.5 liters. Convert this to cubic inches.
   a. 454 cubic inches
   b. 555 cubic inches
   c. 610 cubic inches
   d. 762 cubic inches

13. A 2011 six-cylinder, Paccar MX 360 engine has a bore of 130 mm and stroke of 162 mm. Calculate the displacement of this engine.
   a. 11.1 liters
   b. 11.9 liters
   c. 12.9 liters
   d. 14 liters

14. A six-cylinder engine has a bore of 4.875" and a stroke of 6.5". Calculate the total displacement and express it in cubic inches.
   a. 530 cubic inches
   b. 610 cubic inches
   c. 728 cubic inches
   d. 855 cubic inches

15. A Volvo six-cylinder engine has a bore of 144 mm and a stroke of 165 mm. Calculate the total displacement and express it in liters.
   a. 11.1 liters
   b. 12.7 liters
   c. 14.8 liters
   d. 16.1 liters

16. When running an engine at idle speed, which would typically be the optimum location to peak the cylinder pressure?
   a. 20 degrees BTDC
   b. 10 degrees BTDC
   c. TDC
   d. 15 degrees ATDC

17. When running an engine at rated speed and load, which would typically be the optimum location to peak the cylinder pressure?
   a. 30 degrees BTDC
   b. 15 degrees BTDC
   c. TDC
   d. 15 degrees ATDC

18. At which point in the engine cycle does the crank throw leverage peak?
   a. TDC
   b. Around 15 degrees ATDC
   c. Just before 90 degrees ATDC
   d. BTDC

19. Which law states that all energy forms are convertible?
   a. The first law of thermodynamics
   b. The second law of thermodynamics
   c. Boyle's law
   d. Charles's law

20. The energy of motion is known as:
   a. inertia.
   b. kinetic energy.
   c. thermal energy.
   d. potential energy.

21. A six-cylinder engine has a bore of 5.69 inches and a stroke of 6.5 inches. Calculate the total displacement and express it in liters.
   a. 11.1 liters
   b. 12.7 liters
   c. 14.8 liters
   d. 16.1 liters

22. A six-cylinder engine has a bore of 4.875" and a stroke of 6.5". Calculate the total displacement and express it in liters.
   a. 10.3 liters
   b. 11.9 liters
   c. 12.5 liters
   d. 12.8 liters

Prerequisite: Chapter 4

HISTORY OF THE HEAT ENGINE

OBJECTIVES

After studying this chapter, you should be able to:

- Identify some of the key players in the history of technology.
- Outline the development of the diesel engine chronologically.
- Outline a brief account of Watt's, Carnot's, Diesel's, and Cummins's achievements.
- Describe the first heat engine and the first jet engine.
- List some inventors of key motive power achievements.
- Identify the builder of the world's first automobile.
- Recognize the significant events that contributed to the evolution of the modern truck engine.
- Recount the role of Henry Ford in revolutionizing industrial process.
- Describe how an Indiana farm boy became known as the "father of the highway diesel engine."
- Outline the significant role that Vernon Roosa played in simplifying diesel fuel injection.
- Identify the inventors of the first electronic digital computer.
- Define the acronym *ENIAC*.
- Identify the inventor of the World Wide Web and its importance to us today.

KEY TERMS

aeolipile	digital computer	latent heat	reaction turbine
Carnot cycle	heat engine	power	World Wide Web

INTRODUCTION

The modern vehicle has reached a stage of technological development in which an operator rarely has to consider exactly what happens when the ignition circuit is switched and energizes the series of other circuits that make it run. It is an action that many of us perform several times a day in a world in which a person may travel more in a single day than our forebearers of just 200 years ago did in a lifetime.

The modern vehicle is a result of humanity's pursuit of constant improvement. We may be able to identify the individual credited with the invention of the diesel engine, but it should always be remembered that he had the cumulative practical and technical achievements of all those who preceded him as a starting base for his research. The first diesel engines were crude and unreliable machines. In a hundred or so years, the observations, research, and sometimes lifelong efforts of thousands of engineers, technicians, and designers, most of whom are "nameless," have resulted in the technical excellence of the modern, highly reliable diesel engine.

Thousands of components are integral in the modern truck chassis, each with roles in various mechanical, hydraulic, pneumatic, electrical, and electronic circuits. Each had to be invented, manufactured, and systematically improved to its present stage of development. Every invention will surely be further improved as each year goes by—and as each year goes by, the rate of improvement accelerates. Consider the truck manufactured just 20 years ago and match its performance head-to-head with today's version. Aside from subjective considerations such as appearance, the contemporary vehicle will in most cases significantly outperform its predecessors just as surely as the 2030 model will outperform today's model.

PROGRESSIVE DEVELOPMENT

In inventing the diesel engine, Rudolph Diesel took a significant step forward in the progress of technology as applied to the modern truck. There were significant steps both before and after him. The argument has been made that the invention of the Otto cycle and diesel engines was inevitable after the theoretical foundation provided by the French scientist Beau de Rochas, but it would be difficult to make the argument that Diesel's engine of 1892 was not a pretty significant event.

This chapter identifies some of the individuals in the history of technology whose accomplishments were important to the development of both the **heat engine** (any machine that converts the heat energy of a fuel to mechanical outcomes) and the modern diesel engine. In examining the history of technology until fairly recent times, it was usually possible to match an accomplishment with the name of the inventor. Today, the thrust toward technological advance is something that large corporations must finance, and "inventions" are usually the work of dozens of individuals and are owned by the funding company.

Within this list of innovators, there are people who may be described as mathematicians, scientists, engineers, chemists, technicians, physicists, and diesel mechanics, with many different levels of education but certainly with one label in common: They were *inventors*. Most inventions result from an individual's refusal to accept the impossible.

In many ways, the history of technology is the history of modern humans. Take any current truck, put it on an empty asphalt parking lot, and completely disassemble it. Disassemble every component and subcomponent until further disassembly is impossible. There will be 100,000 or so manufactured components that will seem to have little obvious connection to a truck. Think about how each of those components was designed and manufactured and how each evolved. How many countries were sourced for the raw materials? How many individuals were involved in the manufacture? Now think about the number of people through the ages who were involved in the evolution of that truck. Start with the invention of the wheel. There is no chance that the first wheel was even remotely as round as a wheel on a vehicle today; the progressive efforts of thousands of minds helped make that happen.

TECHNOLOGY IS RATIONAL

Everything in technology is rational. In other sciences such as physics or astronomy, the more people learn, the more they discover they do not know. There are no mysteries in technology, just challenges that take a little longer to figure out. So when next stymied with a troubleshooting problem on an engine, technicians must remember that the cause will be rational. They should make it a challenge to discover the cause and then explain it in terms that make sense to them. Technicians should think a little about what James Watt and Rudolf Diesel did and then refuse to accept that the concept of the unexplained can exist in technology.

FIGURE 5-9 Line drawing of Diesel's 1893 engine.

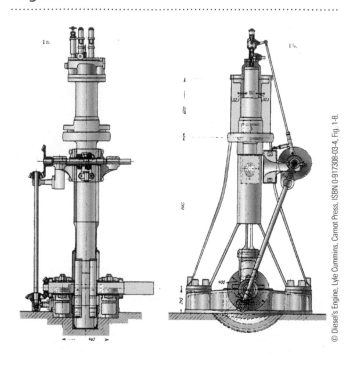

© Diesel's Engine, Lyle Cummins, Carnot Press, ISBN 0-917308-03-4, Fig. 1-8.

translate into any personal happiness: He suffered from bouts of depression and alcoholism and in 1913 mysteriously disappeared from the deck of a ship traveling from Dresden to London in what may have been a suicide.

ROBERT BOSCH (1861–1942): GERMANY

Noted for:

The invention of the spark plug

The invention of the magneto

The invention of high-pressure oil injection for diesel engines

Robert Bosch was educated in the United States, where he worked with Thomas Edison and his colleague, Siegmund Bergmann. Bosch returned to Stuttgart, Germany, where he founded Bosch GmbH in 1886, a firm that has grown to be the world's largest auto parts manufacturer. While continuing to develop the company that bore his name, Bosch was active as an engineer and inventor, primarily in the auto electrical field. However, in 1927 he overcame a problem that had stunted the progress of the diesel engine for a number of years, namely that of introducing the fuel charge to a high-compression diesel engine. Bosch devised his port-helix metering, high-pressure liquid

injection pump to overcome the problem of precise fueling of diesel engines running at higher speeds. His system and competitors' copies of it remain in use today with surprisingly few modifications and electronic management.

HENRY FORD (1863–1947): UNITED STATES

Noted for:

Inventing the assembly line procedure

Establishing the Ford Motor Company

The son of Irish immigrants, Ford dropped out of school before he turned 15 years old. He worked as a machinist's apprentice in Detroit and later set up his own machine shop on his father's farm, which evolved into an automobile building company. He also worked for a time as the chief engineer for the Edison Company in Detroit. Henry Ford is not known primarily for technical innovation, but for the fact that he revolutionized the factory component assembly procedure, introducing what is now known as the *assembly line method*. He established the Ford Motor Company in 1903, and in 1908 the Model T appeared. By 1913, mass production enabled him to sell it for $500. His business philosophy was to reduce unit cost and maximize sales.

HARRY RICARDO (1885–1974): UNITED KINGDOM

Noted for:

The Ricardo combustion chamber—side valve design

Fuel research and theories of ignition, combustion, and detonation

The indirect-injected diesel engine

Stratified charge combustion

Smoke emission controls

Ricardo was born in London and studied as a mechanical engineer at Cambridge University. Although he is best known for the spark ignition (SI) engine side valve combustion chamber that bears his name, Ricardo is important in the history of diesel technology for his research on the nature of combustion in the diesel engine; many of his conclusions are still embodied in practice to this day. During the Second World War, Ricardo worked extensively on controlling smoke emission from engines powering British tanks, which was making them conspicuous to enemy gunners. He was the pioneer of emissions technology and his work on diesel fuel combustion dynamics still has relevance today.

HANS LIST (1896–1996): AUSTRIA

Noted for:

Researching the scavenging of two-stroke cycle engines

Developing high-speed, direct-injected diesel engines

Authoring *The Internal Combustion Engine* (1935)

List was born in Graz, Austria, in 1896, the son of a railway design engineer. He studied thermodynamics at the Graz Technical University and wrote his PhD thesis on the control of diesel engines. When he was 50 years old, List started a consultancy engineering firm called AVL in his hometown of Graz, which rapidly became world renowned in addressing the combustion dynamics of diesel engines. Many current high-speed, direct-injected diesel engines had at least some of their engineering undertaken by List's AVL GmbH.

CLESSIE CUMMINS (1888–1968): UNITED STATES

Noted for:

Inventing the mechanically actuated, liquid fuel injector

Entering the first diesel-powered car in the Indianapolis 500

Building the Cummins engine company

Being known as the "father" of the truck engine

Inventing the engine compression brake

Inventing the Cummins cycle engine—a four-stroke, three-barrel design

Clessie Cummins was the first of five children born to an Indiana farmer/cooper (barrel maker). He attended 13 different schools because his parents moved around. He left school after completing grade 8, and he remained contemptuous of formal education throughout his life. Cummins began his working life employed as a chauffeur for an Indiana banking family called the Irwins. He turned the Irwins' garage into a machine shop and, with the financial help of his

FIGURE 5–10 Cummins 6 BHP, four-stroke cycle engine of 1919.

employers, introduced his first diesel engine to the marketplace in 1919: a 6 BHP, single-cylinder, kerosene-fueled engine (**Figure 5–10**).

Over the next few years, he and his company became associated with a number of publicity stunts, all of which had the objective of furthering Cummins's firm conviction that the diesel engine was the engine of the future. The first of these was staged in 1930 when a 1925 Packard, powered by a 50 BHP, four-cylinder Cummins U–model, drove 792 miles from Indianapolis to the New York auto show on $1.38 of fuel. The following year he set the speed record for a diesel engine-powered car in Daytona Beach (**Figure 5–11**) using a U–model engine now rated at 86 BHP @1,700 rpm of 101.4 mph; by 1934, Cummins had increased this record to 138 mph using a Model H engine powering a Duesenberg. Cummins also entered Cummins-powered Duesenbergs in the Indianapolis 500,

FIGURE 5–11 Cummins at Daytona Beach in 1931.

Clessie Lyle Cummins
Daytona Beach, Florida, 1931

- Vernon Roosa proved that diesel engines could be effectively managed with a light-weight, simple, and low-cost fuel injection pump.

- Computer technology opened the door for the comprehensive engine management systems used on today's engines.
- The Internet has transformed the way people learn, communicate, and transact business.

REVIEW QUESTIONS

1. Who invented the first heat engine?
   a. Otto
   b. da Vinci
   c. Hero
   d. Diesel

2. Which of the following properly describes the first heat engine?
   a. Internal combustion
   b. Two-stroke cycle
   c. Four-stroke cycle
   d. Reaction turbine

3. Who invented the term *horsepower*?
   a. Papin
   b. Watt
   c. Stephenson
   d. Diesel

4. Who built the world's first useful steam engine?
   a. Savery
   b. Newcomen
   c. Watt
   d. Carnot

5. Who designed the first centrifugal governor?
   a. da Vinci
   b. Watt
   c. Bosch
   d. Diesel

6. In what year did Diesel patent his compression ignition engine?
   a. 1864
   b. 1892
   c. 1896
   d. 1912

7. Who patented the first high-pressure liquid fuel injection pump for a diesel engine?
   a. Otto
   b. Diesel
   c. Ricardo
   d. Bosch

8. Who is known as the "father of the highway diesel engine?"
   a. Diesel
   b. Bosch
   c. Cummins
   d. Roosa

9. What are the U.S. inventors Eckert and Mauchly known for?
   a. The first electronic digital computer
   b. The first turbocharger
   c. The first internal combustion engine
   d. The first dry cell battery

10. The world's first automobile was built by:
    a. Trevithick.
    b. Watt.
    c. Carnot.
    d. Cugnot.

Prerequisite: Chapter 4

POWER

OBJECTIVES

After studying this chapter, you should be able to:

- Understand the language of power as it applies to commercial diesel engines.
- Define the terms *torque* and *power* and describe what is required to produce each in an engine.
- Construct the formulae required to calculate power equations.
- Calculate brake power using actual engine data.
- Interpret a simple fuel map.
- Convert BHP to kW.
- Calculate indicated power using the PLANC formula.
- Define the term *brake specific fuel consumption (BSFC)* and relate it to a truck diesel engine fuel map.
- Interpret OEM torque and power graphs and check their mathematical accuracy.
- Understand how load is expressed as percentage of power output.
- Interpret the term *B-life* in relation to power output.
- Relate engine brake power to the actual power requirements of a highway rig and its load.

KEY TERMS

B-life

brake horsepower (BHP)

brake specific fuel consumption (BSFC)

dynamometer

energy

force

horsepower

indicated power (IP)

kilowatt (kW)

load

mechanical efficiency

potential energy

power

rated power

rated speed

rejected heat

Society of Automotive Engineers (SAE) power

specific fuel consumption (SFC)

thermal efficiency

torque

torque rise

torque rise profile

torsionals

work

INTRODUCTION

In the 1,600 years between Hero and Watt (see Chapter 5), many heat engines were designed and built, but not one achieved better than 1% thermal efficiency and most a lot less. *Thermal efficiency* relates to how effectively the potential heat energy of a fuel is converted into usable mechanical energy. James Watt began a process of analyzing all the factors that contribute to an engine's ability to perform work and wrote the language and mathematics to describe it. It is important that the diesel technician acquire a basic understanding of power production. Although it is possible to operate diagnostic equipment such as **dynamometers** simply by matching specifications to readouts on test instruments, the technician will not be capable of properly analyzing test data without understanding some of the language and technology of power.

MEASURING POWER

The intent of this chapter is to simplify some of the concepts of power. Technicians can further develop their knowledge in this area by consulting more advanced reference texts and doing some online research. When it comes to understanding power, both standard and metric measurement systems are used by industry. In reality, however, in rating the power of engines, it is far more likely that the term **horsepower** will be used rather than its metric equivalent *kilowatts*. The best solution is for the technician to become familiar with both standard and metric systems. Despite the fact that every diesel engine a technician is likely to encounter in a modern truck was engineered using the metric system, engine original equipment manufacturers (OEMs) most often publish power analysis specifications using only the standard system. This means that technicians should first begin to understand power using the standard system.

DEFINITIONS AND FORMULAE

To understand the basics of power, it is first necessary to understand the language used to describe it. The term *power* is very often misused, which adds to the difficulty in understanding it. We begin by introducing a series of definitions and then work toward developing them into the formulae required to calculate power. It is important that the contents of this section be properly understood before tackling the latter chapters on engine dynamometers and power analysis.

ENERGY

Energy is best defined as the capacity for producing work. Energy exists in a number of forms; kinetic, potential, electrical, thermal, chemical, and nuclear are its common forms. *Kinetic energy* is the energy of motion, and any body in a state of motion is described as possessing kinetic energy. Air in its compressed state and contained in a reservoir has the potential for creating motion and is therefore described as having *potential energy*. A compressed spring does also, so it too has potential energy.

First Law of Thermodynamics

The first law of thermodynamics tells us that energy can be neither created nor destroyed; however, the way in which energy manifests itself can be changed. In an internal combustion engine, the potential heat energy of a fuel is released as the fuel is combusted. This produces gas expansion, resulting in pressure that acts on a piston and drives the piston through its power stroke. In this way, the heat potential of the fuel produces kinetic energy. Not all of the potential heat energy of the fuel can be successfully converted to kinetic energy. The energy released by combusting fuel in an engine cylinder that cannot be converted to kinetic energy is called **rejected heat**. Rejected heat has to be dissipated to atmosphere.

EFFECTS OF HEAT ENERGY

Heat is easily converted into mechanical energy, and this can happen in many ways. The sun's heat raises millions of tons of water vapor high into the atmosphere daily, so all the mechanical energy of falling water, whether as rain or snow in rivers or glaciers, stems directly from the sun's heat. The term *heat engine* is used to describe a wide range of engines that convert the heat potential of fuels into mechanical energy. Included in the category of heat engines are rocket engines, steam engines, jet turbines, gasoline, and diesel engines.

FORCE

Force is generally defined in terms of the effects it produces, although it should always be remembered that force can be exerted with no result. If force is applied to a body at rest, it may be sufficient to cause the body to move; however, it might not. In other words, you can apply a lot of force to an object, but unless the object is moved, no work results. Using the standard system, force is measured in pounds. In the Système Internationale (SI) metric system, the Newton (N) is the unit by which force is measured.

1 N = force that produces acceleration of 1 meter/second on a mass of 1 kg

How Force Is Produced in an Engine

In a diesel engine, force is represented by cylinder pressure. Cylinder pressure results from combusting fuel in the engine cylinder. This force acts on the sectional area of the piston crown and is transmitted to rotary motion by acting on the crank throw. In other words, it produces **torque**. *Torque* is twisting force and because it is classified as force it does not necessarily result in any work being accomplished. If you can recall attempting to ride your tricycle up a steep hill when you were 3 years old, there would have come a point when you simply could not apply enough force to the pedals (producing torque at the drive wheel) to keep moving. In a diesel engine, the amount of force is controlled by the amount of fuel delivered to the engine cylinders. This is because of the excess air factor in a diesel.

WORK

Work is accomplished when the application of force produces a result. When the definition is applied to an engine, work is accomplished when force acting on the piston results in piston travel. In the following formula, standard values are always listed first:

Work   =   Force   × Distance
(watt-second/joules) (pounds/Newtons) (feet/meters)

To use a non-engine analogy to define work, if two persons of identical weight run exactly 100 meters, each has accomplished the same amount of work.

ENGINE TORQUE

Torque is turning effort. In a typical engine, the force acting on the piston is transmitted to a crankshaft throw. The throw is a lever. The farther offset it is from the crankshaft centerline, the more leverage it can exert. Torque is the product of force applied to the crank throw. The

ability to produce torque in an engine is directly related to cylinder pressure. Because of this, we can say that peak torque will always occur when cylinder pressures are at their highest.

A bicycle is also an engine. The power source is the rider. A bicycle has a crankshaft driven by a pair of throws called pedals, offset 180 degrees. Peak torque is realized whenever muscle force acting on the pedals is at a maximum. High torque is required to propel a bicycle and the weight of its rider up a steep hill, so gear selection must be made so that the required torque is within the capabilities of its power source, the cyclist.

Torque = Force (pounds/Newtons) × Leverage (feet/meters)

POWER

Power is the rate of doing work. If two sprinters of equal weight run 100 meters, each will have accomplished the same amount of work. However, if one runs this distance in 20 seconds and the other in 10 seconds, the latter has twice the power.

$$\text{Power (watts)} = \frac{\text{Work (joules)}}{\text{Time (seconds)}}$$

Horsepower

James Watt coined the term *horsepower* before he developed his steam engine. Steam engines before Watt had at best 1% thermal efficiencies. That meant that only 1% of the heat potential of the fuel combusted was converted into useful mechanical energy. It also meant that the draft horse was more often the engine of choice. In fact, the draft horse was used widely enough in those days that most people had at least an idea of what the animal was capable of. Watt closely observed the horse at work with a mathematician's eye and came to this conclusion: A medium-sized draft horse could raise a 330-pound weight through a distance of 100 feet in 60 seconds.

Horsepower Formula

Subsequent observation has concluded that this is actually about 50% more than the average draft horse could sustain over a working day, but Watt obviously did not observe the performance of the horse for a prolonged period. Truly, a draft horse can only produce about ½ horsepower continuously, but that does not matter today.

The foregoing data, expressed as a formula, are used to calculate horsepower:

$$330 \text{ lb} \times 100 \text{ ft.} = 33,000 \text{ lb-ft./min.}$$
$$= 550 \text{ lb-ft. per second}$$
$$= HP$$
$$1 \text{ HP} = 33,000 \text{ lb-ft. work in 1 minute}$$
$$= \frac{33,000}{60} \text{ lb-ft.} = 550 \text{ lb-ft. 1 second}$$

Importance of Time

Power is always related to time—it is simply the rate of doing work. A cyclist in competition will usually select a gear ratio that permits the pumping out of power strokes at the fastest rate manageable, knowing that each downstroke of a pedal from top dead center (TDC) to bottom dead center (BDC) translates into an actual distance on the road. If a race were to be held among a group of runners of identical weight, every runner who completed the race would have accomplished the same amount of work. The work accomplished by each runner would be the act of transporting his or her mass over a defined distance. However, one of the runners will have won the race by crossing the finish line ahead of the other runners. This runner has accomplished the race distance in the least amount of time and can be said to have demonstrated the most power.

POWER CALCULATIONS

In a diesel engine, as with the cyclist, the number of power strokes per second, in conjunction with the actual torque value, determines brake power. A dynamometer is a tool for testing engine power. It applies a resistance to turning effort and measures it; it therefore measures *torque*. When torque is factored with *time* (engine rpm), the brake power can be calculated. This is usually an automatic function of an engine dynamometer.

Brake Power

Brake power is power measured at the flywheel of an engine. It is always lower than indicated power (calculated power) because of the amount of power consumed by the engine in overcoming internal friction and pumping losses—usually about 10%. The term is used to describe actual engine power over calculated power. Almost always, diesel engine OEMs rate the power of their engines using brake power, which is expressed as **brake horsepower (BHP)**.

Calculating Brake Power

Despite the fact that industry in both Canada and the United States has embraced the metric system, most of us still think using the standard system of weights and measurements. In the trucking industry especially, we have been especially reluctant to adopt the metric system. That means that manufacturers sell (in engine ratings) and express brake power as horsepower.

$$\text{Brake Horsepower} = \frac{\text{Force} \times \text{Distance} \times \text{Time}}{33,000 \text{ lb} \times 1 \text{ ft.} \times 1 \text{ min.}}$$

Distance must take into account the fact that an internal combustion engine rotates and, therefore, the distance factor is not linear but circular (torque); to accommodate this, pi (π) (3.1416) is used to construct the equation, which is simplified as follows:

$$2\pi = 2 \times 3.1416 = 6.2832$$
$$33,000 \div 6.2832 = 5252.10084$$
$$\text{or, for calculation purposes, 5252}$$

In the first brake power formula, the values time and distance are multiplied by each other and by the force value. In a diesel engine, force is expressed as *torque*. However, time and distance are commonly expressed as one value, *revolutions per minute (rpm)*. So, for practical purposes, the brake power formula that is used becomes:

$$\text{Brake Horsepower Power} = \frac{\text{Torque (lb-ft.)} \times \text{rpm (time)}}{5252}$$

$$\text{Brake Power (kW)} = \frac{\text{Torque (N.m)} \times \text{rpm}}{9429}$$

This formula can be used to calculate brake horsepower providing that the torque value and rotational speed values are known (**Figure 6–1**). For instance, a Cummins ISX can be specified to produce a peak torque value of 2,050 lb-ft. at 1,200 rpm. To calculate the amount of power this engine produces at this speed and torque:

$$\text{BHP} = \frac{2050 \text{ lb-ft.} \times 1200 \text{ rpm}}{5252}$$
$$= 468 \text{ BHP}$$

Using the metric system, brake power is measured in watts, so, using the formula explained earlier in this section:

$$1 \text{ Newton-meter} = 1 \text{ joule}$$
$$1 \text{ joule per second} = 1 \text{ watt}$$

Because engine brake power has such a close relationship with speed, a sure way of

FIGURE 6–1 Mack MP10 (16-liter) power and torque graph.

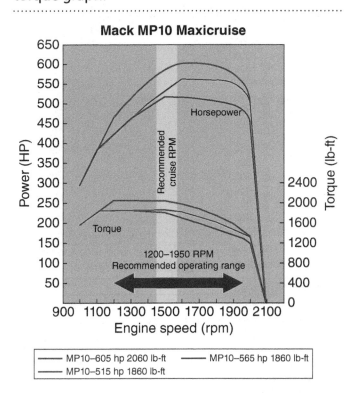

FIGURE 6–2 Simple fuel map showing torque rise and BSFC curve.

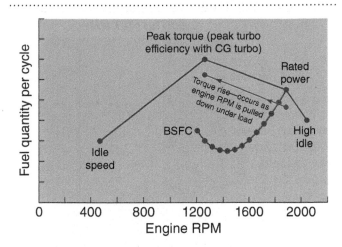

As mentioned before, truck, heavy equipment, and bus diesel engines are usually classified by rating their actual or brake power in horsepower (BHP), but most OEMs also provide a **kilowatt (kW)** power rating. In all cases, power is measured at the flywheel (see **Figure 6–2** and **Figure 6–3**). The brake power of the engine measured at the chassis wheels, such as would be displayed by a chassis dynamometer, would be somewhat less. There are other methods of reckoning power values, some of which are listed later in this chapter.

increasing power is simply to allow the engine to turn faster. In the days of hydromechanical engines, the simple act of increasing governed engine rpm would usually increase engine power—though possibly at the expense of such factors as specified idle and peak torque rpm.

Now you know enough of the math of power output to pick up a calculator and be able to check the accuracy of OEM power graphs such as the one reproduced in Figure 6–1: Pick any point on the torque curve, match it to the rpm directly below it, and use the formula just shown; the result should be close to that shown on the power band (at the same rpm) of the graph.

CONVERSIONS

1 lb-ft.	= 1.356 Nm
1 Nm	= 0.737 lb-ft.
1 HP	= 0.746 kW = 746 watts
1 kW	= 1.341 HP
1 HP	= 2,454 Btu per hour
1 metric HP	= 4,500 kilogram/meters per minute
	= 0.9863 HP

INDICATED POWER (IP)

Indicated power is calculated power. It is useful for comparison purposes, but obviously it is not as reliable an indicator of true power as brake power. The following formula is used to calculate indicated power:

P MEP (<u>P</u>ressure)

L <u>L</u>ength of stroke

A Piston cross-sectional <u>a</u>rea

N <u>N</u>umber of power strokes per minute

C Number of engine <u>c</u>ylinders

$$IP = \frac{PLANC}{33,000}$$

Example:
A four-stroke cycle, six-cylinder diesel engine with a bore of 5.0 inches and a stroke of 5.5 inches is run at a speed of 2,000 rpm. The mean effective pressure (MEP) obtained from an indicator diagram is specified as 200 psi. Calculate the indicated horsepower of the engine. First, use

Torque Rise Profile

The term **torque rise profile** comes from the graphic representation of the upper portion of the fuel map often shown by engine OEMs on their sales literature. This has been simplified in Figure 6–2. Torque rise profile is perhaps best understood as being the *desired* engine-operating range. For a truck with a mechanical transmission, this is important because it defines the upper and lower rpm shift limits. An engine described as high torque rise when compared with the same engine with identical rated power but low torque rise:

- May result in poor fuel efficiency given a heavy driver's boot
- Requires a transmission with fewer gear ratios and/or less shifting
- Is described by truck drivers as being "more powerful"

Torque rise is often expressed as a percentage of rated speed. In other words, an engine with a nominal rated speed of 2,000 rpm and torque rise of 35% would produce peak torque at 1,300 rpm. This is what is shown in Figure 6–1. Diesel engine governing is discussed more in detail later in Chapter 20, but this should help to begin with. The graph shown in Figure 6–2 shows a performance curve that would be considered a high torque rise engine by today's standards of fuel economy.

Fuel Map Performance

Generally, a fleet truck engineered for a linehaul highway application today requires fuel map programming (or governing, in older engines) for fuel economy and, therefore, to the disappointment of the driver, lacks a high torque rise characteristic. Sure enough, the driver may be shifting gears a little more often while getting up to a cruise speed, but once there, it is desirable to operate the engine as efficiently as possible—that is, in the sweet spot rpm of the torque rise profile. This is usually somewhere close to the midpoint between peak torque rpm and rated rpm. However, a dump truck hauling aggregates in a constant stop-start application would require a much wider engine-operating rpm range—in other words, a high torque rise engine.

Torque Rise Programming

Terms like *high torque rise* and *low torque rise* are used less often today because there are so many options for programming engine operation according to the expected conditions. A diesel engine programmed with low torque rise for fuel economy in a linehaul application can usually be reprogrammed for high torque rise performance with no hardware changes. One key for making this possible is the variable-geometry turbocharger.

In the days of hydromechanical and early generation electronically controlled diesel engines, the two primary variations on an engine described as high torque rise over the conventional version of the same engine had to do with:

- Fuel system management
- Turbocharger geometry

The features that defined the high torque rise engine were:

1. The fuel injected per cycle at peak torque was designed to significantly exceed that injected per cycle at rated speed.
2. The turbocharger geometry was tailored to provide a constant rate of airflow per minute from the peak torque rpm (base of the torque rise profile) through to the **rated speed** (peak BHP rpm). This meant that the mass of airflow delivered to the engine cylinder per cycle was greatest at peak torque when the engine was turning at a lower rpm, meaning that there was more *time* to get that boosted air into the cylinder.

In the days before programmable engine management and the common use of variable-geometry turbochargers, making significant changes to the torque rise profile on a diesel engine usually meant costly fuel system recalibration and the replacement of the turbocharger.

SPECIFIC FUEL CONSUMPTION

Specific fuel consumption (SFC) is the fuel consumed per unit of work produced. This datum, described as **brake specific fuel consumption (BSFC)**, is often diagrammed into power/fuel map/performance graphs to demonstrate fuel efficiency through the torque rise of the engine. If the data are constructed around brake power values (and they usually are when truck engine data are displayed), the specific fuel consumption is labeled as BSFC. When the data are constructed around indicated power specifications, the term *indicated specific fuel consumption* (IFSC) is used. A hypothetical BSFC is shown in Figure 6–2, mainly to get across the idea that in diesel engines, as rpm increases, fuel consumption increases with it; this explains why maximum engine rpms have tended to go down over recent years.

LOAD

Load is usually defined as the ratio of power developed to the normal **rated power** at a specific rpm of an engine and is expressed as a percentage. In some instances, *load* is used to express the ratio of torque developed to that of peak torque and, again, this is expressed as a percentage. This can be observed when using most OEM software during diagnostic testing. When performing dynamometer testing, after the rated power/speed value is established, the load data can be useful in establishing whether abnormalities exist in the fuel map.

INTERPRETING OEM FUEL MAPS

Each engine OEM has differing methods of graphically representing power on a graph. However, you should now have the key tools to interpret these graphs. Figure 6–3, **Figure 6–4**, and **Figure 6–5** show how Caterpillar, Detroit Diesel, and Navistar International use graphical data to sell their engines: The performance

FIGURE 6–4 Detroit Diesel Series DD15 (15-liter) performance curves.

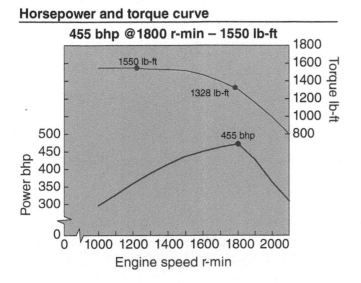

FIGURE 6–5 Navistar N13 (13-liter) power and torque curves.

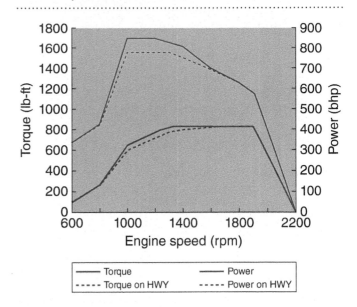

curves depicted are all late-model versions of the engines. As with Figure 6–1, you can do the math shown here to verify the data shown in the graphs.

B-LIFE AND POWER

Today, technicians who work in the trucking industry sooner or later will come across the terms *B10* and *B50-life* in relation to engine longevity. **B-life** is explained in more detail in Chapter 49, but for now B-ratings can be defined as the projection in percentages of engines that will fail at various mileage intervals. In the trucking industry, the miles are linehaul miles (truck vocational and off-highway engines use engine hours), so if an engine series has a B10 rating of 550,000 miles, according to OEM data, 10% of the samples are failing at that mileage. If the same engine had a B50 rating of 725,000, then 50% of the sample engines have failed by the time they have run 725,000 miles.

So, how do B-ratings relate to power? Before the age of computerized engine management, it was widely believed that running diesel engines continuously at close to their full power and load ratings reduced B-life. However, with electronic management of diesel engines came audit trails that proved the opposite. Given appropriate servicing and preventive maintenance, diesel engines that are worked hard tend to last longer, provided that the work they are doing is "continuous." What is now known to have a negative impact on B-life is the operation of diesel engines inconsistently alternating between periods of high power/load request and low power/load request.

ENGINE CONFIGURATION, ENGINE SPEED, AND TORSIONAL FORCES

The number of cylinders in any engine will define the geometric interval (expressed in crank degrees) between firing pulses. This plus the factor of engine speed will define the actual time interval between the engine's firing pulses. Because the pressure developed in engine cylinders is seldom exactly synchronized with the throw vector angle of the crankshaft (see Chapter 4), there is usually a fractional acceleration of the crankshaft above mean crankshaft speed at each firing pulse, followed by a fractional slowdown just prior to the next firing pulse. These torsional forces (sometimes called **torsionals**) are amplified at slower engine rpm levels when the time interval between each power stroke is greatest, and can affect the driven components in the drivetrain.

RUN-SLOW, GEAR-FAST

Today's diesel engines, which are designed for fuel economy combined with low emissions, tend to wind out at much lower rpm levels than those of a generation ago. This type of engine programming is referred to as *run-slow, gear-fast* governing. Operating engines this way increases the real-time interval between power pulses, and the resulting torsionals can be a problem especially when the engine is being worked hard. Note the flat, wide band torque specs in the 2013 Cummins ISX power graph in **Figure 6–6**.

As a rule, prolonged running with high cylinder pressures at the *lower* rpm levels within the torque curve should be avoided. Most electronic engines cannot be lugged down (the programming will not permit it), but with some high torque rise engines, there may be consequences to high load operation in the lower portion of the torque rise curve. These consequences can involve premature drivetrain component

FIGURE 6–6 One of many power and torque curve options that can be spec'd to a Cummins ISX (15-liter) engine: note the flat, wide band torque lines on the graph.

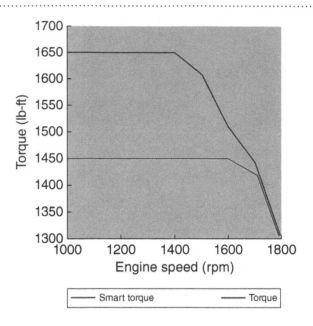

(transmission, drive axle carrier) failures, although a new generation of high absorption rate vibration dampers in clutch discs has helped minimize some of these consequences.

HOW MUCH POWER DO YOU NEED?

Spec'ing out truck engines is a specialty; there are so many variables that they are difficult to outline in a way that is readily understood. Most OEMs have some fairly good software to help make engine spec'ing an easier task for their salespersons, but the best experts in this field are probably those who spec large numbers of trucks for the major fleets. A small spec'ing error can result in millions of dollars lost or saved over the course of a year. **Figure 6–7** shows the power and torque specifications of a post-2013 Paccar MX13 engine.

Diesel technicians seldom have to spec out a truck, but it does not hurt to understand a little about how this is done. Some of the hard math of truck engine spec'ing is simplified here. For our example, we will use a truck hauling an

FIGURE 6–7 Paccar MX13 (13-liter) engine used in Peterbilt and Kenworth applications.

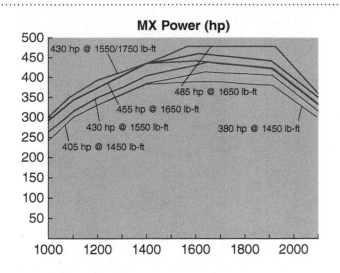

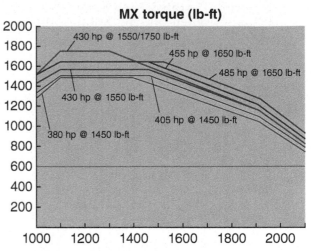

80,000 lb (36,290 kg) load and overlook some of the gearing and aerodynamic complexities that could arise:

- It takes 255 BHP to move the truck down a level asphalt road at 60 mph with no wind.
- On a 1% uphill grade, to maintain the same speed, another 65 BHP will have to be added, so now the engine requires 320 BHP.
- Back on the level highway, if there is a 5 mph headwind, another 16 BHP will have to be added to maintain that road speed of 60 mph. Should the headwind be 10 mph, another 36 BHP has to be added.

- Parasitic losses such as an air-conditioning system (up to 15 BHP) and engine fan (viscous type: averaging 4–6 BHP, on-off type up to 15 BHP but only on 2% of running time) all have to be factored into the BHP requirement for a particular truck.
- So, running up a 3% grade (not that steep a hill) with a 20 mph headwind (not that strong a wind) is going to require a whopping 531 horsepower to maintain the same road speed. Throw in some of the common parasitic losses an engine has to sustain and you can see why some operators, especially brokers, target 600 BHP engines.

SUMMARY

- Energy exists in many forms, including kinetic, potential, electrical, and chemical.
- Energy is the capacity for performing work.
- Force is usually defined in terms of the effects it could produce, despite the fact that the application of force does not necessarily result in work being accomplished.
- Torque is defined as turning effort; that is, it is twisting force and as such may not necessarily result in work accomplished.
- Work is accomplished when force produces a result (movement).
- Power is the rate of producing work; as such, it is always related to time.

- Brake power is power measured at the flywheel of an engine.
- Indicated power is calculated power using the engine specifications and does not factor in friction and pumping losses.
- When engine torque and rpm are known, brake power can be calculated.
- Indicated power can be calculated if mean effective pressure (MEP), stroke, bore, power strokes per minute, and the number of engine cylinders are known.
- Mechanical efficiency is the brake power specification divided by the indicated power specification expressed as a percentage.

- Brake power measured at the flywheel is typically around 10% to 25% more than brake power measured at the drive wheels of a truck.
- Torque rise is desirable in highway diesel engines; it occurs as an engine is pulled down by load from its rated power rpm to its peak torque rpm.

- Load is the ratio of power delivered to rated power at the same rpm, expressed as percentage.
- Running an engine in the lower rpm portion of the torque rise profile, especially high torque rise engines, can create torsional oscillations that can affect the entire drivetrain.

REVIEW QUESTIONS

1. Calculate the brake power of an engine producing 1,150 lb-ft. of torque at the flywheel when it is turning at 2,000 rpm.

2. Use the PLANC formula to calculate the indicated power of a six-cylinder, four-stroke cycle engine run at 1,800 rpm using the following data:
   Stroke: 6.0 inches
   Bore: 5.5 inches
   MEP: 220 psi

3. Which of the following is required to produce peak torque in a diesel engine?
   a. Peak brake power
   b. Peak cylinder pressure
   c. Peak volumetric efficiency
   d. Peak mechanical efficiency

4. In most hydromechanical fuel systems, when maximum engine rpm is increased, the engine brake power potential will also increase.
   a. True
   b. False

5. Which of the following statements helps explain why an engine develops peak brake power at a higher rpm than peak torque?
   a. Cylinder pressures are highest.
   b. More power strokes per second occur.
   c. There is more time for combustion.
   d. Volumetric efficiency is better at high rpm.

6. Which of the following is true of an engine described as having high torque rise when comparing it with its standard version with the same nominal rated power?
   a. It will produce higher brake power.
   b. It will have a higher maximum speed.
   c. It will provide a wider operating rpm range.
   d. It will be more fuel efficient.

7. A group of cyclists all weighing 175 lb (80 kg) and riding on bicycles of equal weight ride a 6.4-mile (10-kilometer) race and all finish it. Which of the cyclists has performed the most work?
   a. The winner
   b. All have performed equal work
   c. The loser

8. Usable power at the flywheel of an engine is known as:
   a. BSFC.
   b. brake power.
   c. indicated power.
   d. torque.

9. When engine power is calculated rather than tested, it is known as:
   a. mean effective pressure.
   b. BSFC.
   c. brake power.
   d. indicated power.

10. Which of the following expresses 1 HP correctly?
    a. 33,000 lb-ft. of work per second
    b. 550 lb-ft. of work per second
    c. 5,252 lb-ft. of work per minute

11. Convert a torque value of 25 lb-ft. into Newton-meters.
    a. 19.8
    b. 21.3
    c. 33.9
    d. 38.1

12. A Cummins ISX 11.9 liter engine, programmed to 330 HP, produces a peak torque value of 1,350 lb-ft. at 1,300 rpm. Convert the torque value to Newton-meters.
    a. 1,007 N·m
    b. 1,275 N·m
    c. 1,830 N·m
    d. 2,225 N·m

13. A Detroit Diesel DD16 is rated at 600 HP. Express this in kilowatts.
    a. 400 kW
    b. 448 kW
    c. 464 kW
    d. 488 kW

14. A Navistar MaxxForce 13 produces 355 kW of power at 1,800 rpm. Convert the kW to an HP value.
    a. 276 HP
    b. 355 HP
    c. 455 HP
    d. 475 HP

15. When comparing truck engine brake power measured at the flywheel to that measured at the drive wheels, which one of the following should be true about brake power?
    a. There is no difference if the transmission and drive carrier are functioning properly.
    b. Power at the wheels exceeds that at the flywheel by 10% to 25%.
    c. Power can only be measured at the drive wheels.
    d. Power at the flywheel exceeds that at the drive wheels by 20% to 25%.

Prerequisite: Chapter 4

ENGINE POWERTRAIN COMPONENTS

OBJECTIVES

After studying this chapter, you should be able to:

- Identify the engine powertrain components.
- Define the role of the piston assembly in the engine powertrain.
- Identify trunk and articulating pistons and list their advantages and disadvantages.
- Describe the characteristics of Monotherm™ and Magnum Monosteel™ pistons and identify the reasons they are becoming the pistons of choice by engine OEMs.
- Outline the advantages of the Mexican hat, open combustion chamber design in modern direct-injected, low-emissions diesel engines.
- Diagnose some typical piston failures and determine the causes.
- Explain how piston rings act to lubricate the cylinder walls and seal the cylinder.
- Identify some commonly used diesel engine piston rings and outline the conditions that enable rings to seal most efficiently.
- Classify piston wrist pins by type.
- Describe the role of connecting rods and outline the stresses to which they are subjected.
- Identify common crankshaft throw arrangements and match to the appropriate cylinder block configurations.
- Outline the forces a crankshaft is subjected to under normal operation.
- Describe the materials, manufacturing, and surface hardening processes of typical heavy-duty crankshafts.
- Outline the causes of abnormal bending and torsional stress to which a crankshaft may be subjected.
- Identify some typical crankshaft failures and their causes.
- Evaluate crankshaft condition visually by precision measuring and electromagnetic flux inspection.
- Describe some common crankshaft reconditioning practices.
- Outline the procedure for an in-chassis, rod, and main bearing rollover.
- Measure friction bearing clearance using Plastigage™.
- Define the term *hydrodynamic suspension*.
- Outline the roles played by the harmonic balancer and flywheel assemblies.
- Describe the principle of operation of a viscous-type harmonic balancer.
- Perform a ring gear removal and replacement on a flywheel.
- Outline the steps required to recondition a flat or pot-type, heavy-duty flywheel.

KEY TERMS

anodizing	crosshead piston	lugging	rod eye
antithrust face	crown	Magnum Monosteel™ (piston)	scraper ring
antithrust side	Ferrotherm™ (piston)	major thrust side	small end
articulating piston	forged steel trunk piston	Mexican hat piston crown	thrust bearing
bearing shell	fractured rods	minor thrust side	thrust face
big end	friction bearing	Monocomp™ (piston)	torsion
broach	gas dynamics	Monotherm™ (piston)	torsional stress
buttress screws	headland piston	Ni-Resist™ insert	trapezoidal ring
cam ground	headland volume	pin boss	trapezoidal rod
composite steel trunk piston	hone	piston pin	trunk-type piston
compressional load	hydrodynamic suspension	Plastigage™	undercrown
compression ring	keystone ring	quiescent	valve pocket
connecting rod	keystone rod	ring belt	wrist pin
cracked rods	lands	ring groove	

INTRODUCTION

This chapter addresses the group of engine components responsible for transmitting the gas pressures developed in engine cylinders to the engine power takeoff mechanism, usually a flywheel. This group of components defined as the *engine powertrain* includes:

- Pistons
- Piston rings
- Wrist pins
- Connecting rods
- Crankshafts
- Friction bearings
- Flywheels
- Vibration dampers

The approach is to take a close look at all of the powertrain components in sequence. The powertrain is actuated by cylinder gas pressure. This pressure acts on the piston and drives it through its stroke. A piston moves linearly. Its linear movement has to be converted into torque. To accomplish this, a connecting rod links the piston assembly to a throw on the crankshaft. The crankshaft throw is offset from the centerline of the crankshaft. As the piston reciprocates in the cylinder bore, the crankshaft rotates. The drive torque imparted to the crankshaft is delivered to a flywheel. The flywheel is bolted to the crankshaft. One of its roles is to act as coupling so that engine torque can be delivered to the drivetrain components and ultimately to the drive wheels. This chapter begins with a close look at pistons.

PISTON ASSEMBLIES

By definition, a *piston* is a circular plug that seals the engine cylinder bore and reciprocates within it. The piston is subject to the gas pressure conditions within the cylinder. It can either:

- Impart force: delivers force when traveling upward on its compression stroke
- Receive force: combustion pressures act on it during the powerstroke

The piston assembly consists of the piston, piston rings, and a wrist pin. Piston rings seal the cylinder and lubricate the cylinder walls. The wrist pin is installed through a boss in the piston; it connects the piston to the connecting rod.

PISTON TERMINOLOGY

A diesel engine piston is shown in **Figure 7–1** along with the terminology used to describe it. The type of piston shown is a forged steel trunk piston used in many current diesels. However, there are four general categories of pistons used in diesel engines, which are discussed a little later. Following the callouts in Figure 7–1, you should be able to make sense of the description that follows.

FIGURE 7–1 Piston terminology.

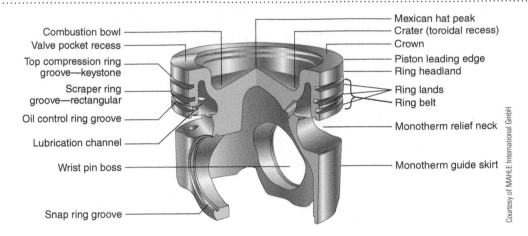

Combustion bowl
Valve pocket recess
Top compression ring groove—keystone
Scraper ring groove—rectangular
Oil control ring groove
Lubrication channel
Wrist pin boss
Snap ring groove

Mexican hat peak
Crater (toroidal recess)
Crown
Piston leading edge
Ring headland
Ring lands
Ring belt
Monotherm relief neck
Monotherm guide skirt

Courtesy of MAHLE International GmbH

Piston Crown

The upper face of the piston is called the **crown**, and it is exposed directly to the cylinder chamber and, therefore, the effects of combustion. Diesel engine pistons absorb up to 20% of the (rejected) heat of the combustion gases. A piston's ability to rapidly dissipate heat is essential, especially when aluminum pistons are used. High-output, turbocharged engines often have piston cooling jets that spray lubricating oil on the underside of the piston to help remove heat. Piston crown temperatures are always high, and the rings assist in cooling by conducting some of this heat to the cylinder walls. The crown geometry (shape) has much to do with the gas dynamics (swirl and squish) produced during the compression stroke. This determines the fuel-air mixing characteristics as well as the ignition location within the cylinder. The Mexican hat piston crown design shown in Figure 7–1 is common in low-emissions, direct-injected (DI) truck engines.

The circumferential edge of the piston around the crown is known as its *leading edge*. Most modern diesel engines have low clearance volumes. This means that at top dead center (TDC), the piston rises in the cylinder bore to a height that recesses are required in the crown to accommodate cylinder valve protrusion. These recesses are known as **valve pockets**.

Piston Materials

It cannot be emphasized enough how critical it is for a piston to efficiently transfer heat. In some cases, diesel engine combustion temperatures can exceed the melting point of the piston material. This only occurs for fractions of a second, but it means that pistons play a role as a sort of heat siphon. Actual piston temperatures depend on the piston material. In current diesel engines, pistons are usually manufactured from aluminum and iron-based alloys. However, some original equipment manufacturers (OEMs) have experimented with ceramic sections and composites. Today's heavy-duty diesel engines tend to use various composite steel alloys in a single-piece construction. Some facts:

- Combustion temperatures rise to transient spikes of 3630°F (2000°C).
- Aluminum melts at 1220°F (660°C).
- Cast iron melts at 2800°F (1540°C).
- Composite steel alloys can sustain up to 5000°F (2800°C)

Two basic piston designs are used in current commercial and off-highway diesel engines:

- Trunk-type pistons
- Articulating pistons

TRUNK-TYPE PISTONS

Trunk-type pistons are single-piece pistons consisting of a crown and integral skirt. There are three categories of trunk-type pistons used in diesel engines today:

- Aluminum trunk pistons
- Forged steel trunk pistons
- Composite steel trunk pistons

ALUMINUM TRUNK PISTONS

Until the 1990s, most commercial diesel engines used single-piece pistons manufactured from aluminum alloys. They continue to be used today in light-duty engine applications. The reason for using single-piece aluminum pistons almost exclusively in those earlier diesel engines was primarily to minimize piston weight. One of the key aluminum alloying substances was a small percentage of silicon that considerably toughened the aluminum.

The low melting temperature of aluminum, combined with a lack of toughness when compared with forged steels or cast irons, requires most aluminum trunk pistons to use a ring groove insert for at least the top compression ring groove. The insert is usually a **Ni-Resist™ insert**, a nickel-bearing, iron alloy with great resistance to high temperatures and wear, but also with a coefficient of heat expansion nearly identical to that of aluminum. The Ni-Resist insert is molecularly bonded to the aluminum piston. **Figure 7–2** is an image of an aluminum trunk piston; note the location of the Ni-Resist insert.

Heat treatment also improves the performance of aluminum as a piston material. In some small-bore diesels manufactured since 2000, hypereutectic (an alloying process) aluminum pistons are used to provide greatly increased wear resistance. Another method of increasing the toughness and high-temperature performance of aluminum (without compromising its primary advantage of light weight) is the ceramic fiber reinforced (CFA) process introduced on smaller-bore diesels. The CFA process eliminates the requirement for a Ni-Resist insert because it reinforces the piston at the top of the ring belt, extending up into the top of the crown. This allows placement of the top compression ring close to the leading edge and reduces headland volume (see Figure 7–1). High location of the top compression ring is almost a requirement for low-emissions diesels. Another fiber reinforcement manufacturing practice known as squeeze cast, fiber reinforced (SCFR) is used by some manufacturers to toughen the crown area of the piston. This is an alumina fiber manufacturing process.

CAM GROUND Aluminum pistons are light in weight and have a high coefficient of heat transfer,

FIGURE 7–2 Aluminum trunk-type piston and ring terminology.

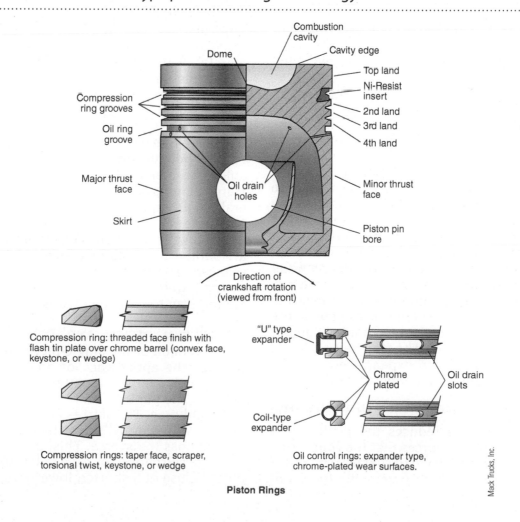

Piston Rings

which means they get rid of any heat they are subjected to rapidly. Aluminum also has a high coefficient of heat expansion and contraction, so they are usually **cam ground** when used in diesel engines. A cam ground piston is slightly elliptical (oval) when cold. As the piston heats, the greater mass of material around the **pin boss** expands more than the thinner skirt area between the pin bosses. The idea is that at running temperatures, the piston should expand to a circular shape. The disadvantage of cam ground pistons is that they should be warmed to operating temperature before being subjected to high cylinder pressures. Failure to properly warm cam ground pistons before loading an engine can overstress the piston rings and piston lands. Aluminum trunk pistons are shaped to beef up the piston where it is most vulnerable, so apart from the reinforcement at the pin boss, they also have increased mass at the crown, as shown in Figure 7–2.

TOUGHENING TREATMENTS Aluminum trunk pistons may also be toughened up by surface and alloying treatments to improve their wear characteristics. Some common methods are:

- Tin plating (tinning can also be used to repair scores on pistons)
- **Anodizing** (applying an electrolytic-generated oxide coating)
- Chrome plating (usually of the crown)
- Squeeze cast, fiber reinforced (more than just a surface treatment; this process increases the structural integrity of the piston)

WRIST PINS AND RING BELT Piston wrist pins, when not full floating, are usually press-fit to the piston boss and float on the rod eye. Heating the piston to 200°F (95°C) in boiling water facilitates pin assembly. Aluminum trunk pistons are prone to piston slap, especially during engine warmup. *Piston slap* is the tilting action of the piston when the piston is thrust-loaded by cylinder combustion pressure. It can be minimized by tapering the piston so that the outside diameter at the lower skirt slightly exceeds the outside diameter over the ring belt region. The ring belt region is exposed to more heat and expands more as the piston heats to operating temperatures.

Advantages of Aluminum Trunk Pistons

- Light weight. This reduces the piston mass and also the inertia forces that the connecting rod and crankshaft have to sustain. The result is that tensile stressing (stretching forces) of the connecting rod and crankshaft are significantly lower, permitting the use of lighter weight components throughout the engine powertrain.
- Cooler piston crown temperatures. The ability of aluminum alloy pistons to rapidly dissipate combustion heat results in lower crown operating temperatures, especially when oil cooling jets are targeted at the piston **undercrown**. The undercrown is the reverse side of a piston crown.
- Quieter. Engines using aluminum alloy trunk-type pistons generally produce less noncombustion-related noise than comparatively configured and sized engines with articulating piston assemblies.

Steel Trunk Pistons

Although **forged steel trunk pistons** were used half a century ago in drag racing applications, they are a relatively new introduction to diesel engine technology. They first appeared on some versions of the Cummins ISX in 2002, but they have since been adopted by almost all engine OEMs to meet 2004/2007/2010 emissions standards. Since 2010, steel alloy trunk-type pistons have become the most common found in some medium- and large-bore commercial diesel engines. It is unlikely that diesel engine piston materials will change significantly in the foreseeable future.

The steel trunk piston design adopted by most diesel engine OEMs originates from piston design specialist Mahle, but more recently, Federal Mogul has made its versions available. The brand name used for the Mahle steel trunk pistons is **Monotherm™**, and the Federal Mogul equivalents are known as **Magnum Monosteel™** pistons. In this textbook, we will use the term *steel trunk pistons* unless either a Monotherm or Monosteel piston is being referenced. There are small design and manufacturing differences in each. **Figure 7–3** shows a Monotherm forged steel trunk piston.

MONOTHERM DESIGN AND CONSTRUCTION The Mahle version of the single-piece steel trunk piston has the appearance of an aluminum trunk piston with a large circumferential slot cut away between the pin boss and the ring belt to reduce mass and drag. The skirt is designed to guide the piston over its thrust sides and is recessed across the pin boss transverse. This, plus the fact that a separate skirt does not have to be supported, permits the use of a shorter, lower-weight wrist pin.

CHAPTER 7 ENGINE POWERTRAIN COMPONENTS **119**

FIGURE 7–3 A forged steel trunk Monotherm piston.

FIGURE 7–4 Magnum Monosteel steel truck piston. Note the aperture cut away from the skirt to reduce piston mass and drag.

Federal-Mogul Corporation

It also allows the piston pin boss support area to be increased, making the design well suited to engines producing high cylinder pressures. Mahle claims that its pistons can sustain peak cylinder pressures exceeding 3,500 psi (250 bar).

The Monotherm's micro-alloyed steel construction provides high enough strength to permit much less material to be used. The result is a tough steel piston of about the same weight of the older aluminum trunk pistons used in large-bore truck engines. Monotherm pistons also feature a bushingless wrist pin bore. The pin boss is phosphate treated over the pin bearing bore. Figure 7–1 and Figure 7–3 both show forged steel trunk pistons typical of those used in a majority of current, high-horsepower highway diesel engines.

Monosteel Design and Construction

The Federal Mogul version of the steel trunk piston is shown in **Figure 7–4**. It differs in appearance from the Monotherm piston in that an aperture is cut into a full skirt to reduce the mass and contact drag. The aperture reduces the total skirt area by around 40% without compromising its ability to guide the piston. The earliest use of the Monosteel trunk piston was in the post-2007 Caterpillar C7 engine, but since 2014 they are being used in large-bore diesel engines.

Monosteel pistons are manufactured in two sections that are friction welded; in this way,

cast and forged sections are joined. The enclosed crown cooling gallery shown in **Figure 7–5** allows for large-volume oil flow, thus providing the piston with high temperature resistance. Magnum Monosteel pistons are electroplated with chrome

FIGURE 7–5 Sectional view of a Magnum Monosteel piston showing the high-flow oil cooling gallery.

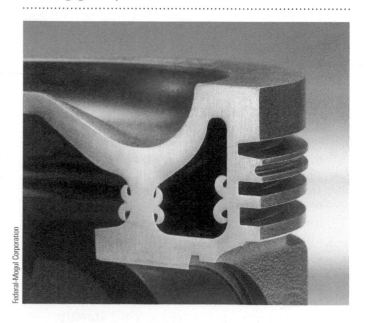

Federal-Mogul Corporation

for thermal protection and help resist acidic corrosion from exhaust gases.

Advantages of Steel Trunk Pistons

The problem of piston slap in aluminum trunk pistons has been overcome with the steel trunk design. Steel alloy pistons expand much less than aluminum trunk pistons when heated from cold to operating temperatures because iron expands much less than aluminum. This means they can be manufactured with a much tighter fit to the liner bore.

The lubricating oil cooling gallery integrated into steel trunk-type pistons is enclosed, allowing for higher oil feed and flow-back volumes. The oil feed to the underside of the piston is delivered by a spray cooling jet. In most cases, the connecting rods used with forged steel trunk pistons are not rifle drilled with a lubrication passage. This means that the piston and wrist pin depend almost entirely on the oil spray cooling jet for lubrication and cooling, emphasizing the importance of precision in setting up the jet.

The reasons that so many engine OEMs have adopted forged steel trunk pistons over the past few years are primarily based on the increased cylinder combustion pressures in late model engines, engine longevity considerations, and emissions requirements. Following is a list of these reasons:

- Reduction of headland volume. **Headland volume** is the volume in the cylinder above the top compression ring and below the crown leading edge. This volume tends to be less affected by cylinder turbulence and the effects of cylinder scavenging, so it collects dead-end gas. Headland volume can be minimized by placing the top compression ring as close as possible to the crown leading edge. Because the tensile strength of forged steel is much greater than that of the aluminum alloy trunk piston and requires no groove insert, the upper ring groove can be located close to the crown leading edge. Steel trunk-type pistons place the top compression ring just slightly under the leading edge of the piston, minimizing headland volume.
- Thermal expansion factors. *Thermal expansion* is simply how the piston material responds to heat. Forged steel has a much lower coefficient of heat expansion than aluminum, so a cam ground design is not required in steel trunk pistons. Also, due to lower expansion response to heat, piston-to-liner clearances can be lower, reducing the vulnerability of the piston to damage by high cylinder pressures at cold startup.

- Longevity. Micro-alloyed forged steel coated with phosphate provides a much longer service life than equivalent aluminum trunk pistons.
- Light weight. Monotherm pistons are as light in weight as aluminum trunk pistons but have the strength to sustain the increasingly high cylinder pressures of modern diesel engines. Some forged steel trunk pistons are specified to sustain cylinder pressures exceeding 3,500 psi (250 bar). The light weight also provides the potential for high engine speeds, though as yet no engine OEMs are introducing this; development of higher diesel engine speeds is currently inhibited by emissions controls and regulations.

Composite Steel Trunk Pistons

More recently, **composite steel trunk pistons** have been introduced. These are a variation of the forged steel trunk-type pistons in that the crown and skirt sections of the piston are manufactured separately: The two sections are then screwed together using a proprietary process. The piston crown section is manufactured from a high-temperature steel, then screwed into a steel skirt assembly. Mahle-manufactured versions of these pistons are known as **Monocomp™**. **Figure 7–6** shows a composite steel trunk piston; study it closely to see where the two sections are joined.

FIGURE 7–6 Composite steel trunk piston.

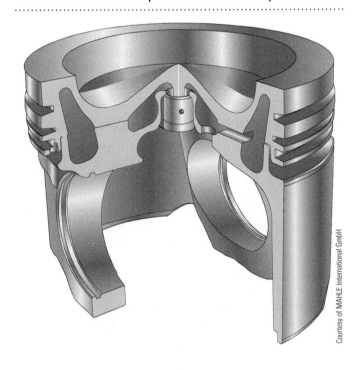

Courtesy of MAHLE International GmbH

ARTICULATING PISTONS

Articulating pistons were adopted by most medium- and heavy-duty diesel engines during the 1990s and up to 2004, usually in their high-power output models. **Figure 7–7** shows a Mack Trucks three-ring articulating piston assembly (which was used in its E-Tech engines up until 2007) in which the crown has been raised slightly from the skirt assembly. More recently, the use of articulating pistons in diesel engines has all but ceased as OEMs have opted to use new-generation steel and composite steel trunk-type pistons. Two types of articulating piston assemblies are used in commercial diesel engines:

- Crosshead pistons—Differentiated by the use of a semifloating wrist pin bolted to the connecting rod.
- Full articulating pistons—Use a full-floating wrist pin that permits pivot on the connecting rod eye, crown, and skirt assemblies.

Crosshead Pistons

The Detroit Diesel Corporation (DDC) used **crosshead pistons** for many years. The crosshead piston is a two-piece piston assembly consisting of a crown and a skirt linked by a semifloating wrist pin which is itself bolted to the connecting rod. Because this design allowed both the crown and skirt assemblies some degree of independent movement (each could pivot on the wrist pin), the assembly can be said to articulate. The key difference between the crosshead and a true articulating piston is that crosshead wrist pins are bolted directly to the connecting rods. In other words, the wrist pins used on crosshead pistons are semifloating rather than full floating.

Full Articulating Piston

The articulating piston consists of a crown, usually manufactured of forged steel or cast-iron alloy, and a separate skirt, usually (but not always) manufactured of aluminum alloy. **Figure 7–8** shows an articulating piston assembly. A full-floating wrist pin permits both the crown and skirt to pivot independently while also linking them to the connecting rod eye. The true articulating piston assembly always uses a free-floating wrist pin and therefore shares bearing surface with both the pin boss and the connecting rod eye. This requires a heavier wrist pin and helps to disadvantage the articulating piston with higher weight. Mahle's **Ferrotherm™** articulating pistons were used by a number of diesel engine OEMs in their medium- and large-bore highway engines. **Figure 7–9** shows the crown of a Ferrotherm piston.

ADVANTAGES OF ARTICULATING PISTONS The crown assembly used in articulating pistons is manufactured from either forged steel or a cast-iron alloy. Both forged steel and cast-iron

FIGURE 7–7 Articulating piston assembly.

Mack Trucks, Inc.

FIGURE 7–8 Articulating piston assembly.

FIGURE 7–9 The crown of an articulating piston assembly.

materials are suitable for the high pressures and temperatures they are directly exposed to. The skirt can be made out of a lighter material, usually an aluminum alloy. Two-piece articulating piston assemblies were widely adopted during the early 1990s, despite their heavier weight than the aluminum trunk pistons they replaced, because of the following reasons:

- Greater longevity. The industry was progressing to greatly increased engine life and the forged steel crown assembly was tougher and much more durable than aluminum.
- Reduced piston slap. This reduced both noise and wear but also provided better performance during the phase from cold start to engine operating temperature.
- More durable crown assembly. Because of the higher combustion pressures, temperatures, and emissions standards required of high-efficiency, low-emissions diesel engines entering the 1990s, using an aluminum alloy crown material was insufficient.
- Reduced headland volume. Another significant reason diesel engine OEMs adopted articulating pistons despite the extra weight penalty was the ability to raise the top piston ring and locate it close to the piston leading edge. The cylinder volume above the top compression ring and below the piston

leading edge is less affected by cylinder turbulence and scavenging, so it tends to collect dead gas, which is not good when it comes to minimizing emissions. This dead gas zone is known as headland volume, and using articulating pistons was the industry's first attempt at minimizing it. The tensile strength of the aluminum alloy trunk piston and its requirement for a Ni-Resist insert was insufficient to locate the upper ring groove close enough to the crown leading edge. Some OEMs refer to pistons with reduced headland volume as **headland pistons**. However, this term is not relevant today because all diesel engine pistons use reduced headland volume to minimize smoking and improve fuel economy.

DISADVANTAGES A major disadvantage of articulating pistons compared to the aluminum trunk design is significantly increased weight, which increases tensional loading on the powertrain. This requires the use of beefed-up engine cylinder block and powertrain components, especially the connecting rods and crankshaft. This weight penalty proved to be a major factor in the demise of articulating pistons in many diesel engines, which were thus replaced by tougher and lighter steel trunk-type pistons.

PISTON THRUST FACES

As cylinder gas pressure acts on a piston, there is a tendency for it to cock (pivot off a vertical centerline) in the cylinder bore because it pivots on the wrist pin. This action creates thrust surfaces on either side of the piston. The major thrust face is on the inboard side of the piston as its throw rotates through the power stroke. The minor thrust face is on the outboard side of the piston as its throw rotates through its power stroke. Take a close look at Figure 7–2 in which the piston thrust faces are identified. The major thrust face is sometimes simply called the **thrust face**, whereas the minor thrust face is called the **antithrust face**. It is important for the diesel technician to identify the thrust faces of a piston for purposes of failure analysis, which we will explore in the final chapters in this book. On a steel trunk-type piston such as the Monotherm, only the thrust faces are skirted, with the objective of guiding the piston true in the bore while reducing the weight of the piston.

COMBUSTION CHAMBER DESIGNS

In DI diesel engines, the physical shape of the piston crown determines what happens to gas in the cylinder on the compression and power strokes. Indirect-injected (IDI) diesel engines were used in a few small-bore and automotive diesel engine applications up until 2001, but none are currently manufactured: today, IDI can be regarded as an obsolete technology. The commercial vehicle diesel technician is only likely to have encountered IDI technology in the now-obsolete Caterpillar precombustion chambers used with their poppet nozzles.

High Turbulence

DI engines use an open combustion chamber principle. In an open combustion chamber, the injector is usually located in the cylinder head and positioned over the piston crown. The shape of the piston crown therefore defines the type of combustion chamber. Because the mixing of the fuel charge with air takes place within the engine cylinder, the **gas dynamics** (swirl and turbulence) are critical in determining the mixing efficiency and the actual location where ignition occurs. Because the piston is the only moving component in the cylinder after the intake valves close, the geometry (shape) of the piston crown is critical in defining the gas dynamics. Aggressive crown geometry, such as more pronounced **recesses** and protrusions, result in more aggressive turbulence.

For many years, diesel engine designers attempted to maximize cylinder turbulence, but this changed in the early 1990s. A high-turbulence or aggressive-gas dynamic can be a big help when the atomized droplets of fuel are large, because gas movement in the cylinder can help rip them into smaller droplets. However, today we have the technology to produce much higher injection pressures that result in smaller droplets of injected fuel, so high turbulence is no longer a requirement.

Quiescent Dynamics

As fuel injection pressures have increased, the need for high-turbulence cylinder gas movement has lessened. High turbulence can actually disadvantage emissions because clusters of fuel droplets can be thrown outside the primary flame front, ignite late, and produce unwanted afterburn. So, as diesel engine designers got more serious about reducing emissions, the objective was to produce less swirl and turbulence. This gave birth to the term **quiescent** gas dynamics. The word *quiescent* comes directly from the word *quiet,* so its meaning is pretty clear. For a generation of diesel engines, quiescent combustion dynamics became common. However, beginning with the 2007 model year emissions, there has been a trend to increase cylinder turbulence once again, especially in diesel engines capable of multipulse fuel injection. A full explanation of combustion dynamics and multipulse fuel injection appears later in Chapter 17. Most DI engines use one of three basic piston crown designs.

Mexican Hat

The **Mexican hat piston crown** design is by far the most common, and the title perfectly describes its shape. The central area of the piston crown is recessed below the piston leading edge, forming a crater (also known as a *toroidal recess*). Rising from the center of the crater is a cone-shaped protrusion (see Figure 7–1 and Figure 7–2). This aggressive cone shape is engineered to produce the required amount of turbulence through the compression stroke and gas movement through the power stroke. In most cases, the fuel injector is positioned directly above the center of the cone so that it directs atomized fuel toward the crater, where the swirl effect is greatest.

Both the bowl depth and cone height of Mexican hat piston crowns determine how much gas movement is generated. Deep bowl designs produce greater turbulence and are often used with fuel systems with lower peak injection pressures. When engine OEMs describe their engines as having quiescent gas dynamics, it means that they are designed to produce relatively low turbulence and, almost always, higher fuel injection pressures. Another reason diesel engine OEMs frequently use Mexican hat pistons is that diesel fuel droplets can be directed into the crater and be relied on to ignite before contacting the crown material. This provides a low risk of fuel burnout scorching on the piston crown directly below the injector and lengthens service life.

Mann Type (or "M" Type)

The Mann-type piston crown is named after the German company that first designed it. It is usually used with older trunk-type pistons and consists of a spherical recess or bowl located directly under the injector, though not necessarily in the center of the piston crown. Depending on the depth of the recess, the Mann-type combustion chamber generally produces high turbulence but is more vulnerable to localized burnout in the bowl. M-type piston crown geometry is not common today even on Mann-engineered engines such as some of the Navistar MaxxForce lineup.

Dished

The dished piston crown has a slightly concaved to almost flat design that produces low turbulence when compared with the previous types. You will see this in some current small-bore and older IDI diesel engines using a cylinder head located in the precombustion chamber.

PISTON COOLING

The size of the piston, peak cylinder pressures, and whether the engine is turbocharged all determine what type of piston cooling is required. Within the same engine family, you may find that engines with lower horsepower specifications do not use cooling jets and those with higher horsepower trim do. Because combustion temperatures may peak at values that exceed the melting temperature of the cylinder materials (especially where aluminum is used), it is essential that any heat not converted to usable energy either be exhausted directly or dissipated into the cylinder materials. A percentage of cylinder heat is always transferred through the piston assembly.

Three methods are used to cool pistons. Engines may use one or combinations of these piston cooling methods:

1. Shaker—Oil is delivered through the connecting rod to a cell or gallery in the underside of the crown; this oil is distributed by the motion of the piston, after which it drains to the crankcase.
2. Circulation—Oil is delivered through the connecting rod rifling, through the wrist pin, and subsequently circulated through a series of grooves machined into the underside of the piston crown. It then drains back into the crankcase.
3. Spray—A stationary jet cylinder block mounted below the cylinder liner and fed by a lubricating oil gallery is directed at the underside of the piston, often into a circular cooling gallery (see Figure 7–5). This oil cools the piston crown and may also lubricate the wrist pin. The jet must be precisely aimed on installation to be effective. This is usually accomplished using a transparent perspex (thermoplastic resin) template that fits over

FIGURE 7–10 Spray nozzle targeting.

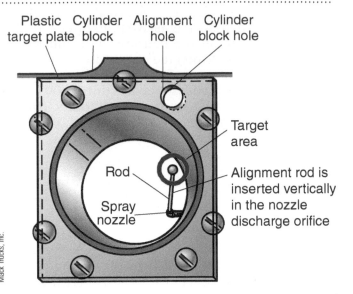

Plastic target plate   Cylinder block   Alignment hole   Cylinder block hole

Target area

Rod

Spray nozzle

Alignment rod is inserted vertically in the nozzle discharge orifice

Mack Trucks, Inc.

the fire ring groove on the cylinder block deck and an aim rod inserted in the jet orifice; a direction or target window is scribed in the perspex template and the aim rod must be positioned within the window as shown in **Figure 7–10**. The spray cooling method is used in a majority of current diesel engines.

CAUTION:

A slightly misaligned piston cooling jet can destroy an engine by torching the piston it is supposed to cool. Always check the cooling jet spray window and pay special attention to avoid making contact with a cooling jet when installing piston/rod assemblies. Because aluminum melts at much lower temperatures than steel, cooling of aluminum pistons is more critical than with forged steel trunk or articulating pistons. However, a slightly misaimed piston cooling jet can cause rapid failure, especially in some newer engines that rely entirely on cooling jets to lubricate and cool the piston.

Some Facts

- The rate of heat flow is approximately three times greater in aluminum than in cast iron. Therefore, aluminum will dissipate the heat it is exposed to much more quickly than cast irons and steels.
- Weight of aluminum is 0.097 lb per cubic inch.
- Weight of forged steel or cast iron is 0.285 lb per cubic inch.

PISTON FIT PROBLEMS

- Excessive piston-to-bore clearance results in the piston knocking against the cylinder wall; this is especially noticeable with aluminum trunk pistons when the engine is cold.
- Too little piston clearance causes piston scoring and scuffing (localized welding) as the film of lube oil on the cylinder wall is scraped off.

PISTON RINGS

The function of piston rings is to seal the piston in the cylinder bore. Most pistons require rings to effectively seal, and those that do not are usually found in automobile racing applications using special piston materials and, more importantly, run at high rpm that permit little *time* for cylinder leakage. Rings have three important functions:

1. Sealing: They are designed to seal compression and combustion gases within the engine cylinder.
2. Lubrication: They are designed to apply and regulate a film of lubricant to the cylinder walls.
3. Cooling: Rings provide a path for heat to be transferred from the piston to the cylinder walls.

Piston rings are located in circumferential recesses in the piston known as **ring grooves**. Ring grooves are located between **lands**. Check out Figure 7–1 and Figure 7–2, paying special attention to the ring area.

ROLES OF PISTON RINGS

Piston rings may be broadly categorized as compression and oil control rings. **Compression rings** are responsible for sealing the engine cylinder and play a role in helping to dissipate piston heat to the cylinder walls. The term **scraper ring** is used to describe rings below the top compression ring that play a role in sealing cylinder gas as well as managing the oil film on the cylinder wall. Oil control rings are responsible for lubricating the cylinder walls and also provide a path to dissipate piston heat to the cylinder walls.

Ring Materials

Piston rings are designed with an uninstalled diameter larger than the cylinder bore, so that when they are installed, radial pressure is applied to the cylinder wall. Until recently, most piston compression rings were manufactured from cast-iron alloys and tended to be more brittle than today's versions. Today, most piston rings have metal properties more similar to stainless steel than cast iron. This makes them much less likely to fracture, and many are highly flexible. The open graphite structure of the cast-iron rings gave them desirable self-lubricating properties but a not-so-desirable shorter service life. In most current diesels, these have given way to much tougher and more flexible rings that often show little evidence of wear at engine overhaul. The wall section of the piston in which the set of rings is located is known as the **ring belt**.

RING ACTION

The major sealing force of piston rings is high-pressure gas. Piston rings have a small side clearance. The result of this minimal side clearance is that when cylinder pressure acts on the upper sectional area of the ring, three things happen to make it seal:

1. Pressure forces the ring downward into the land.
2. Forcing the ring into the land enables cylinder pressure to get behind the ring.
3. When cylinder pressure gets behind the ring between it and the groove wall, it gets driven outward into the cylinder wall, creating the seal.

The lower-right side of **Figure 7–11** explains ring action in diagram form. Make sure you understand this. What this tells us is that cylinder sealing efficiencies increase with cylinder pressure. The higher the cylinder pressure, the better rings seal the cylinder.

Number of Rings

The number of rings used is determined by the engine manufacturer, and the factors are bore size, engine speed, and engine configuration. Time is probably the major factor in determining the number of compression rings. The slower the maximum running speed of the engine, the greater the total number of rings, because there is more time for gas blowby to occur. Most current truck and bus medium- and large-bore diesel engines have rated speeds that are in the 2,000-rpm range. Engine OEMs commonly use a three-ring configuration of two compression rings and a single oil control ring. Go back a

FIGURE 7–11 Piston ring geometry and action.

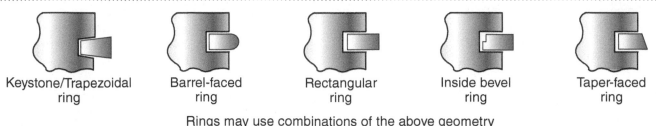

Keystone/Trapezoidal ring   Barrel-faced ring   Rectangular ring   Inside bevel ring   Taper-faced ring

Rings may use combinations of the above geometry

Compression Ring Types

Straight joint   Angle joint   Step joint

Types of Ring Joints

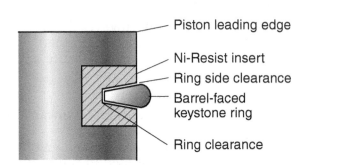

- Piston leading edge
- Ni-Resist insert
- Ring side clearance
- Barrel-faced keystone ring
- Ring clearance

Ring Geometry Terminology

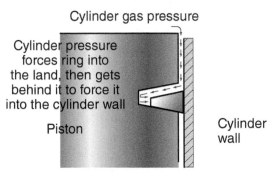

Cylinder gas pressure

Cylinder pressure forces ring into the land, then gets behind it to force it into the cylinder wall

Piston   Cylinder wall

Compression Ring Action

little in time, and you might have seen a greater number of rings. Four- and five-ring configurations are sometimes still seen, but usually in offshore, off-highway products.

Gas Blowby

The top compression ring gets the greatest sealing assist from cylinder pressures. Gas blowby from the top compression ring passes downward to seal the second compression ring, and so on. Gas that blows by all the rings enters the crankcase, so crankcase pressure values are often used as an indication of the overall health of an engine. As a rule of thumb, gas pressure diminishes by around 50% beyond the top compression ring. Because the cylinder is sealed by rings, some cylinder leakage past the ring belt is inevitable, but the limiting factor is time. When an engine is operated at 2,000 rpm, one full stroke of a piston takes place in 15 milliseconds, so there is, quite simply, insufficient time for significant cylinder leakage to take place.

Gas blowby is likely to be more pronounced when the engine is lugged. *Lugging* is a running condition in which cylinder pressures are peaking below peak torque rpm and there is more time for cylinder leakage. It should be noted that all the piston rings play a role in controlling the oil film on the cylinder wall, including the top compression ring. The role all the rings play in terms of cylinder wall oil control becomes increasingly more important as emissions standards get tougher and are more rigorously enforced: Excess oil on cylinder walls is combusted.

PISTON RING TYPES

There are many different types of piston rings, categorized by function and geometry. Refer to Figure 7–9 during the following explanation.

Compression Rings

The primary role of compression rings is to seal cylinder compression and combustion pressures.

FIGURE 7–12 Comparison of plasma-filled ring face and chrome-plated keystone rings.

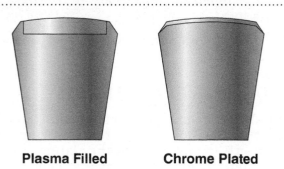

Plasma Filled **Chrome Plated**

Their secondary role is to assist in managing the oil film applied to the cylinder wall. There are many different designs, and a variety of materials are used. Malleable and cast irons have generally given way to highly alloyed steels containing molybdenum, silicon, chromium, vanadium, and other alloys. Most current diesel engine piston rings lack the brittleness of the older cast-iron rings. In fact, most can be substantially deformed without fracturing. Compression rings are usually coated by tinning, plasma, and chrome cladding to reduce friction. **Figure 7–12** shows an example of Caterpillar plasma-filled and chrome-plated compression rings.

Some ring coatings are break-in coatings designed to facilitate run-in. These temporary coatings wear off and end up in the crankcase lube, which is something that should be taken into account when interpreting oil sample analyses. Sometimes the upper compression ring is known as the *fire ring*, but more often this term is used to describe the cylinder seal at the top of the liner that is often integral with the cylinder head gasket.

Combination Compression and Scraper Rings

Combination compression and scraper rings are designed both to assist in sealing combustion gases that have blown by the ring above it and to assist in controlling the oil film on the cylinder wall. Manufacturers that use this term are referring to a ring or rings located in the intermediate area of the ring belt, under the top compression ring and above the oil control ring(s).

Oil Control Rings

Oil control rings are designed to control the oil film on the cylinder wall, which has to be achieved with some precision. Too much oil on the cylinder wall will end up in the combustion chamber, while too little will result in scoring and scuffing of the cylinder wall. The action of first applying and then wiping lubricant from the cylinder wall is also responsible for removing heat from the cylinder and transferring it to the engine lube. Most oil control rings use circumferential scraper rails forced into the cylinder wall by a circumferential expander, usually a coiled spring. They are sometimes known as *conformable* rings, because they will flex to conform to a moderately distorted liner bore.

PISTON RING GEOMETRY

Ring geometry describes the physical shape of the piston rings. Figure 7–9 shows some examples of ring geometry used in diesel engines today. Most piston rings use combinations of the characteristics outlined here. Following are some examples.

Keystone or Trapezoidal Rings

Keystone or **trapezoidal rings** are wedge-shaped and fitted to a wedge-shaped ring groove. The design is commonly used for the top compression ring because its shape allows gas pressure exerted on its upper sectional area to easily get behind the ring and act on its inner circumference to load it into the cylinder wall. Keystone rings also inhibit the buildup of carbon deposits due to the angled scraping action caused by the relative motion of the ring within its groove. This makes them less susceptible to sticking. They also function effectively as they wear. Keystone rings have become the ring of choice among diesel engine designers, as shown in the examples of pistons and rings in this chapter.

Rectangular Rings

The sectional shape of the ring is rectangular. Commonly used in the past when the ring material of choice was cast iron, this ring design is loaded evenly (that is, with relatively little twist) into the cylinder wall when subjected to gas pressure, resulting in lower unit sealing pressures but greater longevity. Some pistons that use a keystone top compression ring use a rectangular second or third compression ring, as seen in Figure 7–1.

Barrel Faced

The outer face is "barreled" with a radius (rounded), usually with the objective of increasing its service life. There is no sharp edge to bite into the cylinder wall when the ring subjected to gas pressure twists within the groove. Keystone rings are often barrel faced. Figures 7–9 and 7–10 show examples of barrel-faced keystone rings.

Inside Bevel

A peripheral recess is machined into the inner circumference of the ring to facilitate cylinder gas getting behind the ring and causing it to twist within the groove. When a ring twists within its groove, the result is usually high unit-sealing pressures; that is, the ring is allowed to bite into the cylinder wall to maximize the seal. A ring with an inside bevel is shown in Figure 7–9.

Taper Faced

The design is much the same as the rectangular ring, with the exception that the outer face is angled, giving it a sharp lower edge. Once again, this enables the ring to achieve high unit-sealing pressures; that is, to bite into the cylinder wall when loaded with cylinder gas pressure. A taper-faced ring is shown in Figure 7–9.

Channel Section

This design is used exclusively for oil control rings. They usually consist of a channel-sectioned or grooved ring with a number of slots to permit oil to be both applied and removed from the cylinder walls. Often an expander ring is used in conjunction with this design to improve its conformability. *Conformability* refers to a ring's ability to adapt to minor variations in the liner bore. The expander ring is a coiled or trussed spring installed to a groove behind the face rails. See the channel-section oil control rings shown in the lower-right corner of Figure 7–2.

RING JOINT GEOMETRY

Piston rings must be designed so that when heated to operating temperatures, the ring does not expand so much that the joint edges come into contact: This would buckle the ring. A ring must also be capable of sealing with some efficiency when cold and cylinder pressures are low. Three types of joint design are used:

1. Straight. The split edges of the ring abut. This design has the disadvantage of affording the most potential for gas blowby at the ring joint, especially when cold. It is, however, the most commonly used.
2. Stepped. This design uses an L-shaped step at the joint, which overlaps and affords the least potential for cylinder leakage at the ring joint.

3. Angled. The ring is faced with complementary angles at the abutting joint and, because of an angled overlap, seals efficiently at the ring joint.

Figure 7–9 shows some examples of ring joint geometry.

INSTALLING PISTON RINGS

Rings should be installed to the piston using the correct installation tool. Stretching rings over the piston by hand can crack the plating and cladding materials. Also, try to avoid using generic, multipurpose ring expanders. This is one case where the engine OEM's special tool is usually the best bet; examples of OEM ring expanders are shown in **Figure 7–13** and **Figure 7–14**. *Never* install a piston ring in which the coating appears cracked or chipped. Most rings must be correctly installed and that means they usually have an up side. OEM instructions should be consulted to avoid installing a ring upside down. Most rings are marked, either by using a dot to indicate the upside or by writing "top" on the upside; always check the OEM service literature to avoid making costly errors.

TECH TIP:

Most piston rings have an up side that is often not easy to see at a glance. Check the OEM instructions for installing rings and identify the means each uses to identify the up side of its rings.

FIGURE 7–13 One type of ring expander.

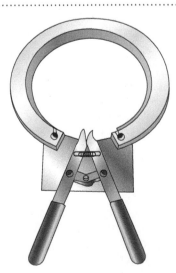

FIGURE 7–14 Another type of ring expander, these should be used to prevent damage to rings during installation.

Ring End Gap

The ring end gap is checked by installing a new ring into the cylinder bore into the ring belt sweep and measuring with thickness gauges. The specification is usually 0.003" to 0.004" per 1 inch of cylinder diameter (0.3–0.4 mm per 100 mm). When checking ring end gap, do so by installing a cold ring into a cold liner; the effect is to make the end gap appear large. When installing a new ring into a used cylinder liner/bore, measure ring end gap at the lowest point of the ring belt swept area (tightest section). Remember that, as with most engine specifications, the specs for ring end gap are established for performance at engine operating temperature, and a warm ring will expand to almost close the gap. Never use a ring that measures out of specification. In certain cases where the OEM permits, ring end gap can be adjusted by filing, but note that this practice is almost never acceptable on current large-bore diesel engine piston rings.

Ring Gap Spacing or Stagger

Observe OEM instructions. The gaps are usually offset by dividing the number of rings into 360 degrees, so if there were three rings, the stagger would be 120 degrees offset. However, there are other ways of doing this. **Figure 7–15** and **Figure 7–16** demonstrate two different OEM methods: one using a three-ring piston and the other a four-ring piston. It is not recommended that ring gaps be placed directly over the thrust or antithrust faces of the piston.

FIGURE 7–15 Ring stagger and pressure balance.

Top compression
- Full keystone
- Plasma

Intermediate compression
- Full keystone
- Taper face

Oil control
- One-piece chrome
- Spring expander

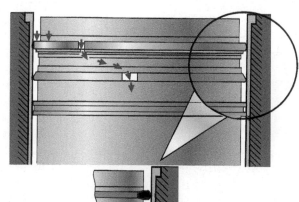

Courtesy of Navistar International Corp.

FIGURE 7–16 Ring stagger.

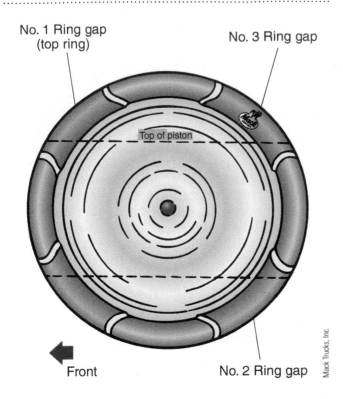

No. 1 Ring gap (top ring)

No. 3 Ring gap

Top of piston

Front

No. 2 Ring gap

Mack Trucks, Inc.

Ring Side Clearance

Ring side clearance is the installed clearance between the ring and the groove it is fitted to. The dimension is measured using thickness gauges. **Figure 7–17** shows the ring side

FIGURE 7–17 Oil ring side clearance.

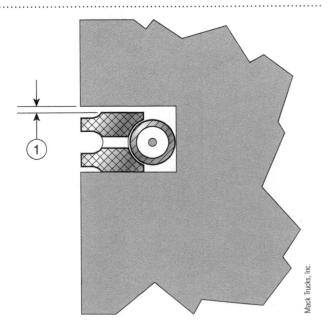

Mack Trucks, Inc.

clearance dimension. This dimension must be within specification for the ring to seal properly.

PISTON AND CYLINDER WALL LUBRICATION

Oil control rings are designed to maintain a precisely managed film of oil on the engine cylinder wall. On the downstroke of the piston, when not loaded by cylinder pressure, lubricating oil is forced into the lower part of the ring groove while the ring is contacting the upper ledge of the land. When the piston changes direction to travel upward, the ring is forced into the lower land of the ring groove, allowing the lubricating oil to pass around the ring to be applied to the liner wall. While the action of simultaneously applying and scraping oil from the cylinder walls ensures that the applied film thickness is minimal, all engines will burn some oil. In the latest generation of low-emissions engines, the amount of burned oil is minimal. This is due both to the ring design and the properties of CJ-4 and later lube oils.

WRIST PINS

The main function of **wrist** or **piston pins** is to connect the piston assembly with the connecting rod eye or small end. In the two-piece, articulating piston assembly, they also link the crown with the skirt, allowing both the crown and skirt to pivot independently. A wrist pin has to be tough enough to transmit loading to (compression stroke) and from (power stroke) the piston assembly while also acting as a pivot point between the connecting rod and piston. The highest expected cylinder pressures determine whether the pin is solid or bored through. Because the weight of the wrist pin adds to the piston total weight, it is designed to be as light as possible while sustaining the loads it is subjected to. This is one of the reasons that forged steel trunk pistons have replaced articulating pistons: The wrist pin can be reduced in length and weight because of the elimination of the separate skirt.

Maximum engine speed and peak cylinder pressures determine actual wrist pin design and material. In most cases, wrist pins are manufactured from mild steel and surface hardened, but middle alloy steels are used in some heavy-duty applications to reduce weight and increase flexibility. Their bearing surfaces are lubricated by engine oil in two ways:

- Directed upward through a rifle bore in the connecting rod. This method was used in most engines until recently.
- Sprayed upward by a piston cooling jet targeted at a gallery entry port. This method is used on some steel trunk pistons.

Full-floating piston pins are fitted to both the rod eye and the piston boss with minimal clearance, usually between 0.0001" and 0.001" (0.0025 mm and 0.0250 mm). Some newer piston bosses are bushingless.

Piston Pin Retention

All full-floating piston pins require a means of preventing the pin from exiting the pin boss and contacting the cylinder walls. Snaprings and plugs are used. When installing the internal snaprings used by most engine OEMs, it is important to observe the installation instructions. These usually require that the split joint be installed perpendicular to the piston (on a vertical plane to piston travel), either up or down depending on the manufacturer, but usually down. Snaprings are subject to inertia, which increases proportionally with piston speed. When snaprings are installed with the split joint at right angles to the direction of piston travel, they have been known to separate from their retention groove in the pin boss, causing an engine failure. Semi-floating wrist pins such as those used in crosshead piston assemblies are bolted directly to the connecting rod. In older DDC two-stroke cycle engines, a press-fit, sealing cap is used; this component should be vacuum leak tested when assembled. Failure of this cap to seal will result in wrist pin lubricant bleeding to the cylinder walls, and air box pressures may charge the crankcase.

ASSEMBLING PISTON AND RINGS

When clamping a piston/connecting rod assembly in a vise, use brass jaws or a generous wrapping of rags around the connecting rod. The slightest nick or abrasion may cause a stress point from which a failure could develop. It is also important to handle rings with the specified tools during reassembly. Overflexing of piston rings during assembly can damage the surface coatings of the rings, while the ring ends can score an aluminum piston during installation. Some root causes of piston and ring failures are identified in Chapter 50.

REUSING PISTON ASSEMBLIES

It is not common to reuse piston assemblies with aluminum alloy trunk-type pistons, but it is becoming more common with some of the latest pistons that use forged steels. Attempt to observe OEM-recommended practice, but realize that routine replacement of pistons at an engine overhaul may not always be justified. For engines under warranty, always check to see whether piston replacement is covered. If the technician is planning to reuse a piston, here are some common practices:

- Clean crystallized carbon out of the ring groove using a correctly sized ring groove cleaner; or, if a used top compression ring can be broken (many cannot, use a grinder!), file it square and use this. Then visually assess the condition of the groove.
- The ring groove is correctly measured with a new ring installed square in the cylinder bore using thickness gauges. A typical maximum clearance spec would be 0.006" (0.150 mm), but once again, always observe the OEM's specification.
- Ring end gap is measured by inserting the ring by itself into the cylinder bore and measuring gap with thickness gauges. Typically, ring end gaps are 0.003" to 0.004" (0.075 to 0.100 mm) per 1" (2.5 cm) of cylinder diameter, so for a 5" cylinder bore end gaps would typically measure between 0.015" and 0.020". Remember, check OEM specifications and *always* measure new rings before installation.

Piston Thrust and Antithrust Side Identification

The piston thrust side is that half of the piston divided at the wrist pin pivot on the inboard side of the crank throw during the downstroke. For a typical engine that rotates clockwise viewed from the front, the major thrust side is the right side of the piston observed from the rear of the engine. The opposite side is known as the **antithrust side**. The terms **major thrust side** and **minor thrust side** are also used. Refer to Figure 7–2 and make sure this is understood: it could be key to effective troubleshooting later.

CONNECTING RODS

Connecting rods (also known as *conn rods*) transmit the force developed in the cylinder, acting on the piston to the throw on the crankshaft

FIGURE 7–18 Connecting rod terminology.

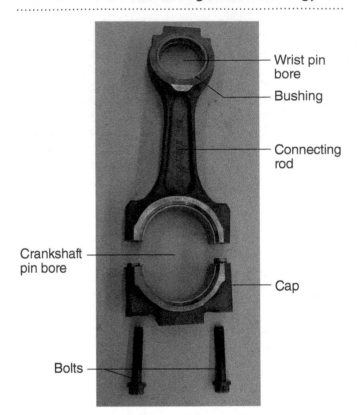

FIGURE 7–19 Cracked rod showing the mating faces: A. Disassembled; B. Assembled.

A.

B.

(**Figure 7–18**). The end of the conn rod that links to the piston wrist pin is known as either the **rod eye** or the **small end**, while the end that links it to the crankshaft throw is known as the **big end**. Both the rod eye and big end have bearing surfaces. In this way, the linear force that acts on the piston and drives it through its stroke can be converted to rotary force or torque by the crank throw, which rotates around the centerline of the crankshaft. Conn rods used with crosshead-type pistons have no rod eye bearing and instead have a saddle that bolts directly to the wrist pin; upper bearing action is therefore provided by the piston pin boss bearing. Most commercial diesel engines use two-piece conn rods. The rod is usually forged in one piece, the big end cap being subsequently separated, faced, and fastened (bolted) for machining.

CRACKED RODS

For many years, **cracked rod** technology has been used in auto racing applications, but it has now become common in diesel engines. Some diesel OEMs refer to this as **fractured rod** technology. Cracked rods have a big end that is machined in one piece. After machining,

the rod big end is fractured. Depending on the materials used, the fracture process may take place at room temperature, or the rod may be frozen to subzero temperatures. Fracturing requires a diametric separation through the rod big end. This produces rod and rod cap mating faces that appear rough but form a perfect final fit alignment. Providing they are assembled properly, cracked rods make the procedure of checking rod sideplay after assembly unnecessary. Most diesel engine OEMs are using cracked rods in at least some of their engines (**Figure 7–19**).

CONNECTING ROD CONSTRUCTION

Most rods use an I-beam section design, but round section has also been used. The majority are rifle drilled from big to small ends to carry lubricant from the crank throw up to the wrist pin for purposes of both lubrication and cooling. **Trapezoidal** or **keystone rods** have become commonplace because they reduce bending stresses on the wrist pin by increasing the loaded sectional area, which is ideal for diesels with high cylinder pressures. Keystone rods have a wedge-shaped rod eye or small end. Conn rods are subjected to two types of

FIGURE 7–20 Wrist pin bushing removal.

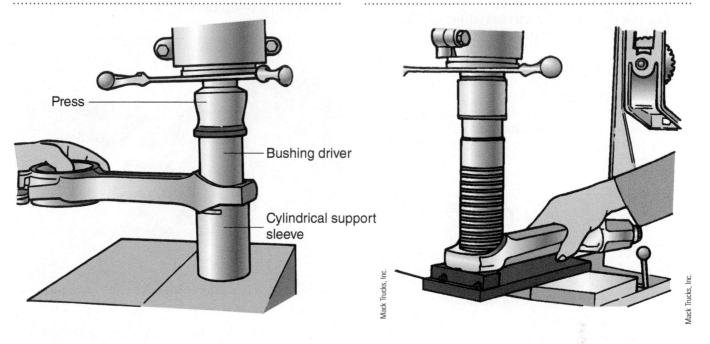

Mack Trucks, Inc.

loading: compressional and tensional. The conn rods shown in **Figure 7–20**, **Figure 7–21**, and **Figure 7–22** all use a keystone small end. Conn rods have complex metal properties due to the punishment they sustain under normal

FIGURE 7–21 Connecting rod fixture.

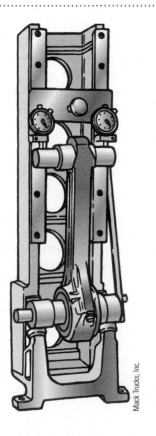

Mack Trucks, Inc.

FIGURE 7–22 Burnishing a wrist pin bushing.

Mack Trucks, Inc.

operation. They are required to have some elasticity, be lightweight, and have the ability to absorb the compressional and tensional loads of the piston.

COMPRESSIONAL LOADING

During the compression and power strokes of the cycle, the connecting rod is subjected to **compressional loads**. Another way of saying compression is "squeezing." The extent of compressional loading on a rod can be calculated knowing the cylinder pressure and the piston sectional area values. Commercial diesel engine connecting rods seldom fail due to compressional overloading of conn rods, and when they do, it is coincidental with another failure such as hydraulic lock. Hydraulic lock is usually the result of a cylinder head gasket failure that has permitted coolant to leak into the cylinder.

TENSIONAL LOADING

Tensional loading is stretching force. At the completion of each stroke, the piston actually stops in the cylinder at either TDC or bottom dead center (BDC). This reversal of motion occurs nearly 70 times per second in each connecting rod when an engine is run at 2,000 rpm. The greater the mass of the piston assembly, the greater the inertial forces and therefore the greater the tensile stress the rod and crank throw are subject to. This stress can be extreme in engines using heavy articulating piston assemblies. Tensile loading on connecting rods increases with engine rpm and the resulting piston speed increase. When an engine is oversped, the increased tensile loading on the conn rod can result in a tensile failure.

Offset Big End Caps

Many OEMs offset (from horizontal) the mating faces of the two halves of the big end. Doing this ensures that the rod cap fasteners do not have to sustain the full tensile loading of the rod. The conn rod shown in the rod fixture in Figure 7–20 uses an offset big end.

> ## TECH TIP:
> One way of checking for a marginally bent conn rod is to remove the cylinder heads and check the height of each piston in the cylinder in its TDC position. In cases of a severely bent conn rod, the engine will not rotate.

CONNECTING ROD INSPECTION

1. Remove the bearing bushings using a press as shown in Figure 7–20, then install the big end cap and torque to specification.
2. Measure the big and small end bores with snap or telescoping gauges used in conjunction with an outside micrometer. Big end concentricity is critical and stretch is a result of tensile loading of the rod.
3. Rods should be checked for straightness and twisting in a mechanical rod fixture (Figure 7–21) or electronic rod gauge fixture.
4. The oil passage in the bore should be blown out with compressed shop air and, if necessary, cleaned with a nylon bristle rifle brush.
5. Finally, the conn rod should be electromagnetic flux tested for cracks. This process involves magnetizing the rod using an electromagnet designed for the purpose and then coating it with a fine magnetic flux, either dry or in a solution. A crack will interrupt the magnetic field, and the flux will concentrate at the flaw. When the magnetic flux is suspended in solution, it is coated in white pigment so that small cracks may be observed using black light (ultraviolet). Any components that have been magnetic flux tested should be demagnetized before being reused.
6. When conn rod eye bushings are replaced, the newly installed bushings should be sized with a burnishing **broach** as demonstrated in Figure 7–22.

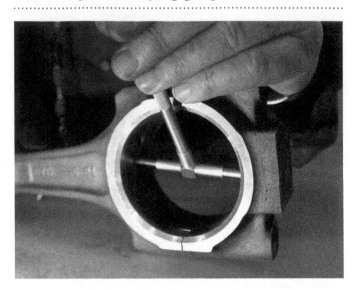

FIGURE 7–23 Measuring conn rod big end bore using a telescoping gauge.

Conn rods should be handled with a great amount of care. When assembling the rod to the piston, a brass jaw vise and light clamping pressure should be used. Slight nicks and scratches on conn rods create stress focal points that can lead to a separation failure. Most diesel engine OEMs suggest that conn rods be electromagnetic flux tested *every* time they are removed from the engine. The cost of magnetic flux examination is small compared to the damage potential of a rod failure. When a conn rod fails in a running engine, the result is often a rod driven through the cylinder block casting. OEMs recommend that connecting rods that fail the inspection procedure be replaced. When reconditioning engines, bear in mind that removing material from a conn rod changes its weight and therefore alters the dynamic balance of the engine. **Figure 7–23** shows the procedure used to measure connecting rod big end bore using a telescoping gauge.

Replacing Rods

As reconditioning of rods is not widely practiced when rebuilding today's diesel engines, conn rods should be inspected according to the procedures outlined by the manufacturer and if rejected, replaced. When replacing rods, they should be weight matched according to OEM technical service instructions. Because most truck and bus diesels are relatively slow running compared with gasoline engines, some OEMs permit flexibility here, but the consequence of replacing a conn rod with one of either greater or lesser weight is an unbalanced engine. Manufacturers usually code conn rods to a weight class; typically, each weight class will have a window of about 1.4 ounces (40 grams). When replacing defective conn rods, always match the weight codes.

Rod Cap Fasteners

Most OEMs require that rod cap fasteners be replaced at each reassembly. Moreover, they should be replaced with the correct OEM fastener and not cross-matched to an SAE-graded bolt. Thread deformation and stretching make these bolts a poor reuse risk, considering the consequences of fastener failure at the rod cap. The actual chances of failure are low, but remember, the consequences of a conn rod failure are severe. If the work is being performed for a customer, recommend that the fasteners be replaced and leave the decision to reuse the fasteners to the customer. If you are a betting person, the odds are more favorable when reusing fasteners with an offset mating big end.

Connecting Rod Bearings

Most engine OEMs use a single-piece bushing, press-fit to the rod eye, and two-piece friction **bearing shells** at the big end. Rod eye bearings should be removed using an appropriately sized mandrel or driver (see Figure 7–20) and an arbor or hydraulic press. Using a hammer and any type of driver that is not sized to the rod eye bore is not recommended because the chances of damage are high. New one-piece bushings should be installed using a press and mandrel, ensuring that the oil hole is properly aligned, and then sized using a broach or **hone** as shown in Figure 7–22. Split big end bearings should also be installed respecting the oil hole location, and the throw journal-to-bearing clearance should be measured. Bearing shells and rod eye bushings should both be installed to a clean dry bore: remove any packing protective coating from the bearings by washing them in solvent, followed by compressed air drying.

> ### TECH TIP:
> Rod sideplay must be checked after a rod cap has been torqued to the rod. Cocking of the rod cap to rod fit can cause an engine to bind and damage the crankshaft by scoring the web cheeks. In applications in which cracked rods are used, this check is unnecessary, as a perfect fit of rod cap to rod can be assumed. Snapping the assembly fore and aft on the journal should produce a clacking noise, indicating sideplay.

REMOVING AND INSTALLING PISTONS

A piston assembly normally refers to an assembled piston, piston rings, and connecting rod. This is sometimes known as a *piston pack;* some OEMs include the cylinder liner within their definition of *piston pack.* Most highway commercial diesel engines are designed to enable an in-chassis overhaul if required: This means that piston assemblies can be pulled from an engine without removing the crankshaft. In some engines, the dimensions of the conn rod big end prevent removal through the cylinder liner; in this case, the piston pack and liner must be removed as an assembly. Before removing pistons, always consult the OEM service literature. Note that in some off-highway diesel engines, the piston assembly cannot be removed from above, meaning that an in-chassis overhaul is not possible. An appropriate ring compressor such as that shown in Chapter 15 must be used when installing piston packs into an engine cylinder bore.

CRANKSHAFTS AND BEARINGS

A *crankshaft* is a shaft with offset throws or journals to which piston assemblies are connected by means of conn rods. **Figure 7–24** shows some typical crank throw configurations, but note that in the case of the V-configured engines, OEMs may use different numbering sequences than that shown here. For instance, in its V-engines Detroit Diesel numbers cylinders sequentially by left and right bank: 1L, 2L, 3L, 4L, 1R, 2R, 3R, 4R. When rotated, the offset crank throws convert the linear, reciprocating movement of the pistons in the cylinder bores into rotary motion at the crankshaft. Crankshafts are supported by friction bearings at main journals

FIGURE 7–24 Crank throw configurations.

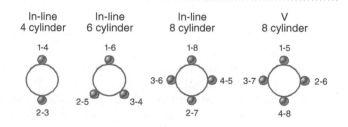

and require pressurized lubrication at all times that the engine is run to enable their **hydrodynamic suspension** within the bearing bores.

HYDRODYNAMIC SUSPENSION

Hydrodynamic suspension is the supporting of a rotating shaft on a fluid wedge of constantly changing, pressurized engine oil. In this way, direct shaft main journal-to-bearing bore contact is avoided; an oil film protects the friction bearing shell when the engine is stationary or cold cranked. Friction bearings are also used at the crank throw/conn rod big end. The lubrication required for these bearings is supplied from oil passages routed through the crankshaft and oil holes located at each journal. Offsetting the oil hole angle from the crankshaft axis generally drives a thicker wedge of oil onto which the crankshaft main is rolled as it turns, so most OEMs do this.

CRANKSHAFT FORCES

Crankshafts are designed for dynamic balance and use counterweights to oppose the unbalancing forces generated by the pistons. These forces tend to diminish as the number of cylinders in an engine increases, and companion throws (geometrically paired) contribute to a counterbalancing effect. Crankshafts are subjected to two types of force: bending forces and torsional forces.

BENDING FORCES

Bending stress occurs between the supporting main journals between each power stroke. Crankshafts are engineered to withstand the considerable bending forces that result from subjecting a crank throw to the compression and combustion pressures developed in the cylinder. This normal bending stress takes place between the main journals at any time the crank throw between them is loaded by cylinder pressure; therefore, it peaks when engine cylinder pressures peak.

TORSIONAL FORCES

Torsion is twisting. **Torsional stresses** are the twisting vibrations that a crank is subject to that occur at high speed. Crankshaft torsional vibration occurs because a given crank throw while under compression (that is, driving the piston assembly attached to it upward on the compression stroke) slows to a speed marginally less than average crank speed. Subsequently, the same throw, on receiving power stroke forces, accelerates to a speed marginally greater than average crank speed. These twisting vibrations or oscillations take place at high frequencies, and crankshaft design, materials, and hardening methods must take them into account.

Torsional stresses on a crankshaft tend to peak at crank journal oil holes at the flywheel end of the shaft. These torsional oscillations are amplified when an engine is run at slower speeds with high cylinder pressures because the real-time duration between cylinder firing pulses is extended. This type of running (lower speed/high load) is known as **lugging**. However, most current diesel engines are designed to run at up to 30% lower speeds and output 30% more torque than those of a generation ago. These engines produce higher torsional oscillations that are projected through the drivetrain, making the proper matching transmissions and final drive carriers essential.

CRANKSHAFT CONSTRUCTION

Figure 7–25 is a technician's guide to crankshaft terminology. Understanding these terms is critical when measuring and machining crankshafts. Most diesel engine crankshafts are made of steel forgings, but exceptionally special cast-iron alloys have been used. All crankshafts are tempered (heat treated) to provide a tough core with the required flexing characteristics to withstand the bending and torsional punishment they are subject to. Most diesel engine OEMs use proprietary processes to forge crankshafts, and they maintain some secrecy about the details of the process. An understanding of journal hardening procedures is important as the reconditionability of the crankshaft depends on this.

Journal Surface Hardening Methods

Though OEMs often use proprietary terms to describe the following processes, there are basically three methods of surface hardening main and rod journals:

- Flame hardening. Used on plain carbon and sometimes middle alloy steels. Flame hardening consists of the direct application of heat followed by quenching with oil or water. The result is relatively shallow surface hardening; the actual hardness depends on the carbon and other alloy content of the steel. Note: Flame is sometimes used as protection in

FIGURE 7–25 Crankshaft terminology.

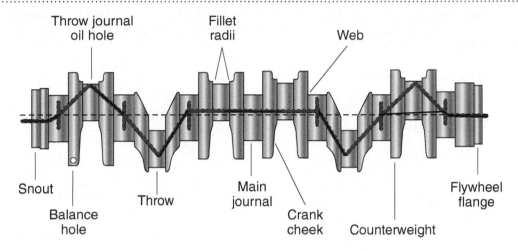

Throw journal oil hole

Fillet radii

Web

Snout

Balance hole

Throw

Main journal

Crank cheek

Counterweight

Flywheel flange

- - - - Crankshaft centerline

induction hardening treatment ovens because it prevents crankshaft exposure to air (specifically *oxygen*) during the tempering process.

- Nitriding. Used on alloy steels. Nitriding involves higher temperatures than flame hardening, and the surface hardens to a greater depth—around 0.025" (0.65 mm).
- Induction hardening. Area to be hardened is enclosed by an applicator coil through which alternating current (AC) is pulsed, heating the surface; tempering is achieved by blast air or liquid quenching. This process results in hardening to depths of up to 0.085" (1.75 mm), providing a much wider wear and machinability margin than the preceding methods. Most current diesel crankshafts are surface hardened by this method and sometimes during the process, flame is used in the induction oven to prevent air exposure to the crankshaft when it is at a cherry-red temperature and therefore vulnerable to oxidation.

Removing Crankshaft from Cylinder Block

The cylinder block should be in an engine stand and in an inverted position. Once the main bearing caps and any other obstructions have been removed, a rigid crankshaft yoke should be fitted to the hoist. The yoke prongs should be fitted with rubber hose (to prevent damage to the journals) and linked to a pair of throws in the center of the crankshaft (for weight balance). **Figure 7–26** demonstrates how a yoke connects the crankshaft to a hoist.

Torque Twist Control Devices

In an effort to reduce engine weight, engine OEMs have used tougher, lighter alloys in cylinder block manufacture. This makes a cylinder block more susceptible to torque twist flexing when the engine is under extreme loads or there are sudden changes in load. OEMs have attempted to limit cylinder block torque flexing by installing bolster plates across the lower cylinder block flange and transverse bolts known as **buttress screws** into the main caps. When buttress screws

FIGURE 7–26 Crankshaft removal from cylinder block.

Mack Trucks, Inc.

are used, the main cap is fastened through a vertical plane in the usual manner—but also transversely by buttress screws. If removing a main cap on a diesel engine after removing the cap screws is difficult, check on the outside of the cylinder block for buttress screws. Buttress screws have to be removed before a buttressed main cap can be removed.

CRANKSHAFT FAILURES

A certain small percentage of crankshaft failures will result from manufacturing and design problems. Design problems are usually revealed shortly after an engine series is introduced and are quickly remedied by the OEM because it does not wish to have an engine tagged with a basic engineering fault likely to produce failures. Because research, development, and testing of new engine series are so thorough in today's engines, when crankshaft failures occur, the cause will most likely be attributable to one of the categories listed next.

Bending Failures

Abnormal bending stresses occur when:

- Main bearing bores are misaligned. Any kind of cylinder block irregularity causes abnormal stress over the affected crankshaft area.
- Main bearings fail or become irregularly worn.
- Main caps are broken or loose.
- Standard specification main bearing shells are installed where an oversize is required.
- Flywheel housing is eccentrically (relative to the crankshaft) positioned on the cylinder block. This produces a broken-back effect on the drivetrain. The condition usually results from a failure to (dial) indicate a flywheel housing on reinstallation.
- Crankshaft is not properly supported either out of the engine before installation or while replacing main bearings in-chassis. The latter practice is more likely to damage the block line bore, but may deform the crankshaft as well.

Bending failures tend to initiate at the main journal fillet and extend through to the throw journal fillet at 90 degrees to the crankshaft axis.

Torsional Failures

Excessive torsional stress can result in fractures occurring from a point in a journal oil hole extending through the fillet at a 45-degree angle or circumferential severing through a fillet. In an inline six-cylinder engine, the #5 and #6 journal oil holes tend to be more vulnerable to torsional failure when the crankshaft is subjected to high torsional loads.

Causes of crankshaft torsional failures are:

- Loose, damaged, or defective vibration damper or flywheel assembly.
- Unbalanced engine-driven components: fan pulleys and couplings, fan assembly, idler components, compressors, and power take-offs (PTOs).
- Engine overspeed. Even fractional engine overspeeding will subject the crankshaft to torsional stresses that it was not engineered for and may initiate a failure. It should be remembered when performing failure analysis that the event that caused the failure and the actual failure may be separated by a considerable time span.
- Unbalanced cylinder loading. A dead cylinder or fuel injection malfunction of over- or underfueling a cylinder(s) can result in a torsional failure.
- Defective engine mounts. This can produce a "shock-load" effect on the powertrain.

Spun Bearing(s)/Bearing Seizure

Spun bearings are lubrication-related failures caused by a lack of oil in one or all of the crank journals. The bearing is subjected to high-friction loads and surface-welds itself to the affected crank journal. This may result in a spun bearing in which the bearing friction welds itself to the journal and rotates with the journal in the bore or alternatively continues to scuff the journal to destruction. When a crankshaft fractures as a result of bearing seizure, the surface of the journal is destroyed by excessive heat, and it fails because it is unable to sustain the torsional loading. Causes of spun bearings and bearing seizure are:

- Misaligned bearing shell oil hole.
- Improper bearing-to-journal clearance. Excessive clearance will result in excessive bearing oil throw-off, which starves journals farthest from the supply of oil. Insufficient bearing clearance can be caused by overtorquing, use of oversize bearing shells where a standard specification is required, and cylinder block line bore irregularities.
- Sludged lubricating oil causing restrictions in oil passages.
- Contaminated engine oil. Fuel or coolant in lube oil will destroy its lubricity.

Etched Main Bearings

Etched main bearings are caused by the chemical action of contaminated engine lubricant. Chemical contamination of engine oil by fuel, coolant, or sulfur compounds can result in high acidity levels that can corrode all metals. However, the condition is usually first noticed in engine main bearings. It may result from extending oil change intervals beyond that recommended. Etching appears initially as uneven erosion pock marks or channels.

CRANKSHAFT INSPECTION

Most truck and bus engine OEMs recommended that a crankshaft be magnetic flux tested at every out-of-chassis overhaul. Essentially, this process requires that the component to be tested be magnetized and then coated with minute iron filings. When AC is pulsed though the shaft, the magnetic lines of force that result will bend into a crack or nick, causing the iron filings to collect in the flaw.

Magnafluxing

Magnafluxing a crankshaft requires that it be magnetized using a circumferential electromagnet. Fine magnetic particles are coated in white pigment and suspended in fluid, allowing them to be sprayed over the crankshaft where they concentrate over any flaw that breaks up the magnetic field force lines. Minute flaws can be identified by inspection with an ultraviolet or black light. Any component that has been magnetized for a magnetic flux examination must be demagnetized before it is reused. It should be noted that most small cracks observed by magnetic flux inspections are harmless. The following cracks require crankshaft replacement:

- Circumferential fillet cracks
- 45-degree cracks extending into critical fillet areas or journal oil holes

TECH TIP:

Most small cracks observed when magnetic flux testing crankshafts are harmless. However, beware of fillet cracks and cracks extending into oil holes.

Visual Inspection

Evidence of failures in these locations *requires* the replacement of the crankshaft; the consequence of not doing so could be total destruction

of the engine. Following magnetic flux inspection, the crankshaft thrust surfaces should be checked for wear and roughness. It is usually only necessary to polish or dress these areas using the appropriate crank machining equipment and using the methods described later in this section. Also, the front and rear main seal contact areas should be checked for wear; wear sleeves, interference fit to the seal race, are available for most engines and can be easily installed without specialized tooling. Most crankshafts in current medium- and large-bore highway diesel engines require no special attention during the life of the engine.

Crankshaft Measuring Practices

Specifications listed here are *typical* maximums. The OEM service literature should always be consulted when determining the serviceability of a specific crankshaft.

To measure crankshaft main bearings, the crankshaft should be placed in V-blocks or a crankshaft lathe, then indicated with a dial indicator as shown in **Figure 7–27**. Rod journals should be measured across axes 90° apart in three places, usually at either end and in the center of the journal, and the results matched to OEM specification. Using a measuring chart is

FIGURE 7–27 Indicating a crankshaft main using a dial indicator.

the preferred method of organizing the data and retaining it.

- *Journal out of roundness:* 0.001"–0.002" (0.025–0.050 mm)
- *Journal taper:* 0.0015" (0.0375 mm)
- *Bent crankshaft:* Check in V-blocks with a dial indicator while smoothly rotating by hand—out-of-service (OOS) specifications differ widely due to differing crankshaft materials and lengths.

Polishing Crankshafts

The objective of polishing a crankshaft is to remove minor main and throw journal scratches, scores, and nicks from a crankshaft that has been measured and gauged to be within the OEM specifications. The use of oversized bearings would not normally result from a polishing procedure because no significant amount of journal surface material should be removed.

The crankshaft should be mounted to the appropriate lathe mandrels with the journal oil holes plugged with flush port caps and rotated at low speed in a crank grinding lathe in the normal engine rotation direction. A long, narrow strip of low-abrasive emery cloth (the type sold in rolls) wetted with diesel fuel or kerosene should be applied for short periods to the journals requiring the polishing, and frequent inspection should be performed. When polishing the throw journals, the rotation will be eccentric, so a longer strip of emery cloth should be used.

The crankshaft thrust faces may also have to be similarly dressed. This procedure is a little trickier, and the emery cloth should be wrapped around an oversized, flat wood tongue depressor. Care should be exercised whenever hands have to be placed near rotating machinery. Thrust face scoring may require dressing by grinding, but before performing this procedure check on the availability of oversized thrust washers/bearings.

Reconditioning Crankshafts

While it should be made very clear that most diesel engine OEMs do not approve of the reconditioning of crankshafts, the practice is widespread. In most cases, the reconditioning procedures attempt not to compromise the original surface hardening, but where the damage is severe, such as in the example of a spun bearing, journal damage is sustained below the surface hardening. Although journal surfaces can be rehardened, this practice is not common. The reconditioning methods are simply outlined here and the

technician should remember that the industry consensus is that they are bad practice and poor economics in the long term. There are four basic methods of crankshaft reconditioning:

1. Grinding to an undersize dimension. This may require that oversize bearings, not always supplied by the engine OEM, be available.
2. Metallizing surface followed by grinding to the original size.
3. Chroming surface to the original size.
4. Submerged arc welding buildup followed by grinding to the original size.

ROD AND MAIN BEARINGS

There are probably engineers who devote their entire careers to the study and development of the **friction bearings** used in diesel engines. It makes sense for the diesel technician to have a basic appreciation of bearing construction (**Figure 7–28**) and to be able to diagnose characteristic failures. Most diesel engine manufacturers make available excellent bearing failure analysis charts and booklets. These use high-definition color photography and examples of actual failures that make diagnosing failures a cinch. Some examples of classic bearing failures are shown in Chapter 49 (Failure Analysis) of this book.

FIGURE 7–28 Construction of a typical bearing.

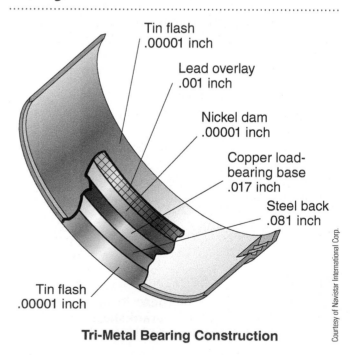

Tri-Metal Bearing Construction

CONSTRUCTION AND DESIGN

Two basic designs are used in current applications:

1. Concentric wall—uniform wall thickness
2. Eccentric wall—wall thickness is greater at the crown than the parting faces; also known as deltawall bearings

Materials

Rod and main friction bearings consist of a steel base or backing plate, onto which is layered copper, lead, tin, aluminum, and sintered combinations of metals, often with a zinc or tin outer protective coating. Friction bearings are designed to have a degree of embedability. This means that the outer face of the bearing must be soft enough to permit small abrasives to penetrate the outer shell, known as the *overlay*, to a depth at which they will cause a minimum amount of scoring to the crank journals that rotate in the bearing. **Figure 7–29** shows a copper-bonded friction bearing favored by Caterpillar.

BEARING CLEARANCE

The engine OEM's specification must be precisely observed. Bearing clearance is measured with Plastigage using the methods shown in **Figure 7–30** and **Figure 7–31**. Most manufacturers make several oversizes (of bearings) to

FIGURE 7–30 Checking bearing clearance using Plastigage.

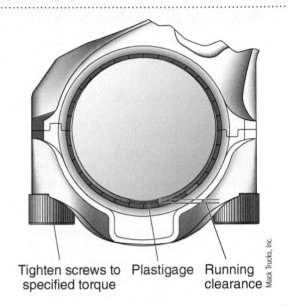

Tighten screws to specified torque   Plastigage   Running clearance

Mack Trucks, Inc.

accommodate a small amount of crankshaft journal wear or machining. It is important not to assume that a new engine will always have standard-size bearings. Typical bearing clearances in highway diesel engine applications run from 0.002" to 0.004" (0.050 mm to 0.100 mm). The ability to maintain hydrodynamic suspension

FIGURE 7–29 Copper-bonded bearing construction.

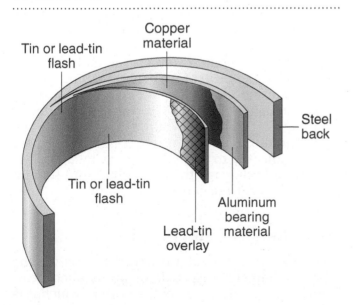

Tin or lead-tin flash

Copper material

Steel back

Tin or lead-tin flash

Lead-tin overlay

Aluminum bearing material

FIGURE 7–31 Correct method of locating Plastigage.

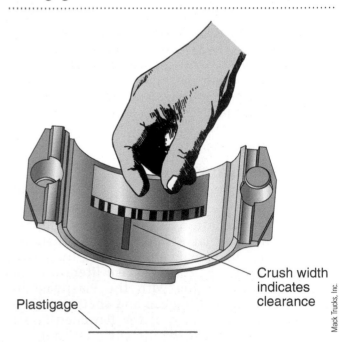

Crush width indicates clearance

Plastigage

Mack Trucks, Inc.

TABLE 7–1 Plastigage™ Code Identification

Part Number	Color	Standard Dimension Window	Metric Dimension Window
HPG1	Green	0.001–0.003 inch	0.025–0.76 mm
HPR1	Red	0.002–0.006 inch	0.051–0.152 mm
HPB1	Blue	0.004–0.009 inch	0.102–0.229 mm
HPY1	Yellow	0.009–0.020 inch	0.230–0.510 mm

of the crankshaft diminishes with increased bearing clearances. When bearing clearance increases above specification, a drop in oil pressure results that may indicate the need for an in-chassis bearing rollover. Increased bearing clearance also increases oil throw-off, and this may result in excessive lube being thrown up onto the cylinder walls.

The technician should not attempt to measure bearing clearance when the engine is in-chassis, because the results will have little validity. This is because of the flexibility of crankshafts when not fully supported at each main bearing. The engine should be upside down and level so that there is no weight load acting on the retaining cap of the bearing being measured.

The bearing clearance specifications should be referenced first. Sometimes bearing clearances are expressed in ten-thousandths of an inch because they are engineering specs. In this case, round the value to the nearest half-thousandths (0.0005") and work in units of thousandths. For instance, an OEM clearance spec of 0.0027" can be expressed as 2½ thousandths. Next, select the Plastigage color code capable of measuring between the specified parameters. **Plastigage™** is malleable plastic thread that easily deforms to conform to whatever clearance space is available when compressed between a bearing and a journal. The crushed width can then be measured against a scale on the Plastigage packaging. The lower the clearance, the wider the Plastigage strip will be flattened.

Using Plastigage

A short strip of Plastigage should be cut and placed across the center of the bearing in line with the crankshaft. The bearing cap with the bearing shell in place should then be installed and torqued to specification in the incremental steps outlined in the service literature. Do not rotate the engine with the Plastigage in place. Next, the bearing cap and shell should be removed and the width of the flattened Plastigage checked against the dimensional gauge on the Plastigage packaging. If clearance is within specifications, carefully remove the Plastigage from the journal before reinstalling the cap and shell assembly.

Selecting the Correct Plastigage Strip

Plastigage is manufactured in four sizes, each color-coded for the range of clearances that size is capable of measuring. **Table 7–1** identifies each Plastigage color-coded size window in both standard and metric dimensions. Although most diesel OEMs still display their specifications using standard measurements, some display in both standard and metric, and one uses metric-only specifications.

TECH TIP:

Always ensure that all Plastigage residue is removed from a bearing after measuring. Use a mild solvent and never an abrasive object to perform this.

CRANKSHAFT ENDPLAY

One of the main bearings is usually flanged to define crank endplay; this is known as the **thrust bearing** and it is available in several sizes to accommodate some thrust surface wear as well as some thrust face dressing in the crankshaft. Alternatively, split rings known as *thrust washers* may be used to control crank endplay. Endplay specifications would typically be in the 0.008" to 0.012" (0.2 mm to 0.3 mm) range. Use a dial indicator to measure. Use a lever that is not going to damage the crankshaft and force it fore and aft for measurement.

BEARING RETENTION

Bearings are retained primarily by *crush:* the outside diameter of a pair of uninstalled bearing shells slightly exceeds the bore to which it is

FIGURE 7–32 Bearing spread and crush.

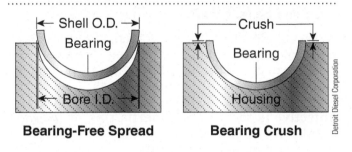

Bearing-Free Spread　　**Bearing Crush**

Detroit Diesel Corporation

FIGURE 7–33 Upper and lower bearing shells.

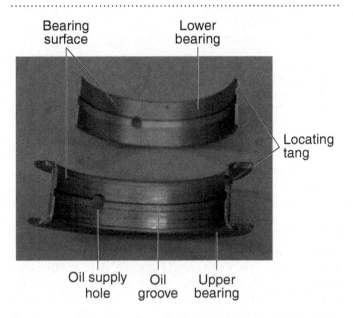

installed (**Figure 7–32**). This creates radial pressure that acts against the bearing halves and provides good heat transfer. The bearing halves are also slightly elliptical to allow the bearing to be held in place during installation. This provides what is known as *bearing spread* (see Figure 7–32). Tangs in bearings (**Figure 7–33**) are inserted into notches in the bearing bore to minimize longitudinal movement, prevent bearing rotation, and align oil holes.

BEARING REMOVAL AND INSTALLATION

Service literature should always be consulted and the OEM's procedures observed. This operation is very straightforward when performed out of chassis because the crankshaft is removed when installing the cylinder block side bearing shell, and the technician is working above the engine with perfect visibility and accessibility for the remainder of the procedure.

Bearing Rollover

Many novice truck technicians will get their first experience of engine work by performing what is known as an in-chassis bearing rollover—a simple procedure, but one that can be messy, especially on a hot engine that may drip oil for hours. The procedure is practiced more often than necessary on today's engines because a slight drop in oil pressure is often mistakenly attributed to bearing wear. Many service facilities offer bearing rollover "specials," usually early in the spring season when temperatures begin to warm and coincide with a slight reduction in oil pressure. It is not unusual today, when performing a bearing rollover, to remove a set of bearings in near-perfect condition. This is a testament to the quality of today's bearings (and other factors) compared to those of a generation ago.

In chassis, main bearings are rolled out using a capped dowel (often "homemade" by machining a bolt) inserted into the journal oil hole. Ensure that the dowel cap does not exceed the thickness of the bearing because if it does, it will destroy the journal. Next, rotate the crank to roll the bearing out, tang side first. Using a screwdriver or similar method will almost certainly result in scratch and score damage to the journal. New bearing halves are installed clean, dry, and with as little handling as possible. If a new bearing is coated with a protective film of grease or light wax, this should be removed using a bristle brush and solvent (do not use a solvent that has any residual oil component, such as Varsol™), followed by air drying.

The backing should be installed clean, dry, and preferably without finger contact—trace quantities of lubricant, moisture, or dirt will reduce its ability to transfer heat. The facing may be lightly coated with clean engine lubricant applied by finger. Most engine OEMs recommend avoiding the use of any type of grease, such as white lube (lithium-based grease) or other engine assembly lubes, on the bearing face, because these reduce the ability of the engine lubricant to hydrodynamically support the crankshaft on startup and may, in the crankcase, interact with the additives in the engine oil. After performing any procedure that involves the draining of lubricant from the oil galleries and passages that supply the bearings, it is good practice to prime the engine lubrication circuit using a remote pump before cranking.

Bedplate Main Bearings

Some small-bore engines (usually of offshore origins) have introduced a lower cylinder block

TECH TIP:

When resistance to rotating the engine is experienced during a bearing rollover, it may help to loosen the fan belts. Just remember to reset the fan belt tension when the bearing rollover is completed.

bedplate. The bedplate replaces a set of main bearing caps with a single casting plate that bolts to the engine cylinder block. This design can enable a lighter cylinder block to withstand higher resistance to acceleration and deceleration torsionals. It goes without saying that the bedplate design is not conducive to an in-chassis overhaul.

VIBRATION DAMPERS

Vibration damper and *harmonic balancer* both refer to the same component, but vibration damper is used by most diesel engine OEMs so it is used in this text. A vibration damper is mounted on the free end of the crankshaft, usually at the front of the engine. Its function is to reduce the amplitude of vibration and add to the flywheel's mass in establishing rotary inertia. In other words, its primary function is to reduce crankshaft torsional vibration (there is a full explanation of crankshaft torsional vibration earlier in this chapter in the section on crankshafts).

VIBRATION DAMPER CONSTRUCTION

A typical vibration damper consists of a damper drive or housing and inertia ring (**Figure 7–34** and **Figure 7–35**). The housing is coupled to the crankshaft and, using springs, rubber, or a viscous medium, drives the inertia ring: The objective is to drive the inertia ring at *average* crankshaft speed. Vibration dampers therefore have three main components:

1. Drive member: bolted to the crankshaft
2. Drive medium: either a fluid (silicone gel) or solid rubber
3. Driven member: an inertia ring

Two types of vibration dampers are used in current diesel engines:

1. Viscous drive type
2. Solid rubber drive type

Viscous Drive Operating Principle

Viscous drive-type vibration dampers are more common in truck and bus diesels. The drive member is bolted to the crankshaft and consists of an annular hollow housing. Within the hollow housing, the inertia ring is suspended in and driven by silicone gel. Because the drive member is bolted to the crankshaft snout, it is subject to the torsional oscillations occurring at the front of the crankshaft. When the drive member rotates, it rotates the drive medium (silicone gel) and inertia ring with it. Because the inertia ring contains most

FIGURE 7–34 Sectional views of vibration dampers.

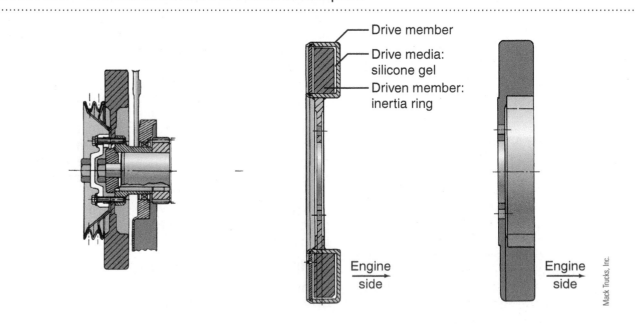

FIGURE 7–35 Sectional view of a viscous vibration damper.

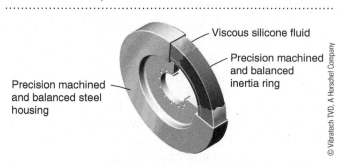

Viscous silicone fluid

Precision machined and balanced inertia ring

Precision machined and balanced steel housing

© Vibratech TVD, A Horschel Company

FIGURE 7–36 Front view of a post-2010 Mack Trucks MP-8 engine showing the location of its viscous-type vibration damper.

of the mass (weight) of the vibration damper, it will rotate at *average* crankshaft speed and not be subject to the torsionals occurring at the front of the crankshaft. Because the speeds of the drive member and inertia ring differ, shearing action will take place in the drive medium, which is the silicone gel. This shearing action of the viscous fluid film between the drive housing and the inertia ring affects the damping action.

Replacing Viscous Vibration Dampers

Most OEMs recommend the replacement of the vibration damper at each major overhaul, but this is seldom observed due to the expense. Practice has shown these components to frequently exceed OEM-projected expectations, but some risk is involved. The consequences of not replacing the damper when scheduled can be costly, as it can result in a failed crankshaft. Inside a viscous vibration damper, the shearing action of the silicone gel produces friction, which is released as heat. This leads to eventual breakdown of the silicone gel, a result of prolonged service life or old age. Drive housing damage is another common reason for viscous damper failure, and this is probably caused by careless maintenance practices in most cases: the slightest ding is sufficient reason to replace a vibration damper. **Figure 7–36** shows the location of the viscous-type vibration damper used on a Mack Trucks MP-8 engine.

Solid Rubber Vibration Dampers

Solid rubber-type vibration dampers are less often used on today's heavy truck diesel engines because they tend to be less effective at dampening torsionals on modern high-torque, lower-speed engines. This type consists of a drive hub bolted to the crankshaft: a rubber ring is bonded both to the drive hub and the outer inertia ring, which contains most of the mass. The rubber ring therefore acts both as the drive and the damping medium. The elasticity of rubber enables it to function as a damping medium, but the internal friction generates heat, which eventually hardens the rubber and renders it less effective and vulnerable to shear failures.

INSPECTING VIBRATION DAMPERS

Because the critical functional element in a vibration damper is its drive medium, either silicone gel or the rubber, it is difficult to inspect. Typical service facilities lack the equipment to check the operating or dynamic effectiveness of these devices. However, if an engine balance irregularity is suspected and the OEM-projected service life is known to have been exceeded, the damper should be replaced. If the service life has not been exceeded, there are some external checks that the technician may perform to help diagnose the condition:

1. Visually inspect the damper assembly. Any dents or signs of warpage in either viscous or solid rubber drive dampers are reason to reject the component.
2. Using a dial indicator, rotate the engine manually, and check for damper housing radial and axial runout to the OEM specification. This is usually a low tolerance specification (especially on the viscous type), usually 0.005" (0.127 mm) or less.
3. Check for indications of fluid leakage in the viscous type, initially with the damper in place. Trace evidence of leakage justifies replacement of the damper.

4. If the damper checks out okay using the preceding tests, remove it from the engine. By hand, shake the damper; any clunking or rattle is reason to replace it.

5. Next, using a gear hot plate or component heating oven, heat the damper to its operating temperature, usually close to the engine coolant operating temperature, around 180°F (90°C)—this may produce evidence of a leak in viscous dampers. The slightest leak is reason to replace the damper.

6. A final strategy is to mount the damper in a lathe using a suitable mandrel. It should be run up through the engine operating rpm range and monitored using a balance sensor and strobe light.

CAUTION:

Recommend that a viscous-type vibration damper be replaced at engine overhaul regardless of its external appearance. Explain that this is an OEM recommendation. If the customer declines, he has made the decision, not the technician. A failed vibration damper can cause crankshaft failure.

FLYWHEELS

The engine flywheel in the typical commercial diesel engine is normally mounted at the rear of the engine. It has three basic functions:

1. To store kinetic energy (the energy of motion) in the form of inertia and both help smooth out the power pulses in the engine and establish an even crankshaft rotational speed.

2. To provide a mounting for engine output: it is the PTO device to which a clutch or torque converter is bolted.

3. To provide a means of rotating the engine by cranking motor during startup.

As an energy storage device, the flywheel plays a major role in dampening the torsional vibrations that act on the crankshaft during engine operation, and its mass helps rotate the engine between firing pulses. Flywheel mass (weight) depends on a number of factors, such as whether the engine is a two- or four-stroke cycle, the number of engine cylinders, and the engine operating rpm range. Because the number of crank angle degrees between power strokes is half that on a two-stroke cycle compared to a four-stroke cycle of the equivalent number of cylinders, generally less flywheel mass is required.

- Six-cylinder, two-stroke cycle—frequency of power strokes: 60 crank angle degrees
- Six-cylinder, four-stroke cycle—frequency of power strokes: 120 crank angle degrees

The flywheel therefore stores potential energy in the form of inertia. Engines designed to be run at consistently high rotational speeds require less flywheel mass, and it should be noted that a heavy flywheel will inhibit rapid response to acceleration demand. While a four-stroke cycle, single-cylinder diesel engine is unlikely to power any modern truck, it is worth taking a look at such an engine (you can still find some old single-cylinder Lister engines on farms) and noting its flywheel mass, a dominant characteristic of its appearance.

TYPES OF FLYWHEELS

The flywheels (and flywheel housings) used on all North American-built trucks are categorized by the SAE by size, shape, and bolt configuration. This allows engines to be easily coupled to different OEM clutches and transmissions. Two basic geometric shapes are used: the *flat face* design and the *pot* design. **Figure 7–37** shows a flat face truck flywheel. Most trucks equipped with current medium-and large-bore highway diesel engines use one of two SAE flywheel sizes:

SAE #4—accommodates a 15½" clutch assembly

SAE #5—accommodates a 14" clutch assembly

FIGURE 7–37 Sectional view of a flywheel.

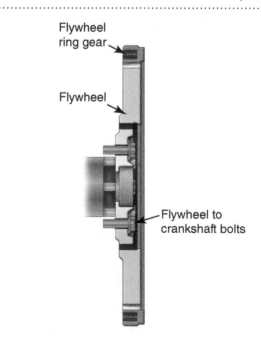

Flywheel ring gear

Flywheel

Flywheel to crankshaft bolts

FLYWHEEL CONSTRUCTION

Flywheels used on most truck and bus diesel engines are machined from cast iron or cast steel. Rim velocities are factored by the rotational speed (engine rpm) and the clutch diameter. However, rim stresses seldom generate metallurgical failures in commercial diesel engine flywheels, due to their relatively low rotational speeds. Stresses tend to peak at the juncture of the hub with the rim, an area that is subject to torsional as well as centrifugal loads, but failures are rare.

RING GEAR REPLACEMENT

A ring gear is shrunk-fit to the outer periphery of the flywheel. This is the means of transmitting cranking torque to the engine by the starter motor during startup. A worn or defective ring gear is removed from the flywheel by first removing the flywheel from the engine and then using an oxyacetylene torch to partially cut through the ring gear, working from the outside on a single tooth. This is in most cases sufficient to expand the ring gear so that the removal can be completed using a hammer and chisel. Care should be taken to avoid heating the flywheel any more than absolutely necessary or damaging the flywheel itself by careless use of the oxyacetylene flame. A hacksaw and chisel may also do the job.

Installing a New Ring Gear

To install a new ring gear, place the flywheel on a flat, level surface, and check that the ring gear seating surface is free from dirt, nicks, and burrs. Ensure that the new ring gear is the correct one and, if its teeth are chamfered on one side, that they will face the cranking motor pinion after installation. Next, the ring gear must be expanded using heat so that it can be shrunk to the flywheel. Most OEMs specify a specific heat value because ring gears are heat treated, and overheating will damage the tempering and substantially reduce the hardness. A typical temperature specification would be around 400°F (200°C), but this may be as high as the 600°F (315°C) recommended by Caterpillar (see Figure 7–37).

Because of its size, the only practical method of heating a ring gear for installation is to use a rosebud-type (high gas flow) oxyacetylene heating tip. To ensure that the ring gear is heated evenly to the specified temperature and especially to ensure that it is not overheated, the use of a temperature-indicating crayon such as Tempilstick is recommended. When the ring gear has been heated evenly to the correct temperature,

FIGURE 7–38 Rear view of a post-2010 Cummins ISX; note the flywheel housing and flywheel.

it will usually drop into position and almost instantly contract to the flywheel. Handle a hot ring gear with blacksmith tongs. **Figure 7–38** is a rear view of a post-2010 Cummins ISX showing the flywheel housing and flywheel.

RECONDITIONING AND INSPECTING FLYWHEELS

Flywheels are commonly removed from engines for reasons such as clutch damage, leaking rear main seals, or leaking cam plugs, and care should be taken when both inspecting and reinstalling the flywheel and the flywheel housing. Flywheels should be inspected for:

- Face warpage
- Heat checks
- Scoring
- Intermediate drive lug alignment and integrity
- Axial and radial runout (using dial indicators, straight edges, and thickness gauges)

Damaged flywheel faces may be machined using a flywheel resurfacing lathe to OEM tolerances: typical maximum machining tolerances range from 0.060" to 0.090" (1.50 mm to 2.30 mm). It is important to note that when resurfacing pot-type flywheel faces, the pot face must have the same amount of material ground away as the flywheel face; the consequence of machining only the flywheel clutch face is to have an inoperable clutch.

SUMMARY

- For purposes of study, the engine powertrain comprises those engine components responsible for delivering the power developed in the engine cylinders to the power takeoff mechanism, usually a flywheel.
- Aluminum trunk-type pistons were widely used in medium- and large-bore diesel engines until the late 1980s, because of their light weight and ability to rapidly transfer heat. They are still used today, but mostly in light-duty diesel engines.
- Aluminum alloy trunk-type pistons used in diesel engines support the top compression ring with an Ni-Resist insert. They are also cam ground and tapered due to the way they expand in operation.
- Two-piece, articulating piston assemblies replaced aluminum trunk pistons and until model year 2007 were the piston design favored by engine OEMs.
- Articulating pistons usually consist of a forged steel crown and aluminum alloy skirt. The two pieces are coupled to the wrist pin, which affords each some independent movement.
- Today, diesel engine OEMs favor forged or composite steel trunk pistons in their high-output engines. The Mahle versions of these are known as Monotherm and Monocomp pistons; the Federal Mogul version is known as a Monosteel piston.
- Steel trunk pistons use high-strength alloy steels and reduced skirt contact area to reduce mass and piston drag.
- The Mexican hat piston crown, open combustion chamber is the most common in today's low-emissions, direct-injected diesel engines.
- Engine oil is used to help cool pistons in three ways: shaker, circulation, and spray jet methods.
- Piston rings seal when cylinder pressure acts on the exposed sectional area of the ring, which first forces it down into the land, and then gets behind it to load the ring face into the cylinder wall. This means that the efficiency with which piston rings seal a cylinder increases proportionally with cylinder pressure.
- Gases that manage to pass by the piston rings and enter the crankcase are known as blowby gases.
- The keystone ring design is commonly used for the top compression ring in today's highway diesel engines.
- Oil control rings are designed to apply a film of oil to the cylinder wall on the upstroke of the piston and to "scrape" it on the downstroke. All the piston rings play a role in controlling the oil film on the cylinder.
- Full-floating wrist pins have a bearing surface with both the piston boss and the connecting rod eye. Crosshead pistons articulate but have a semifloating wrist pin that bolts directly to the rod small end.
- Full-floating wrist pins are retained in the piston boss by snaprings. DDC two-stroke cycle engines use press-fit caps to seal the pin boss between the piston pin and the air box.
- Connecting rods are subjected to compressional and tensional loads in normal service operation. Most connecting rods will survive the life of the engine, but they should be dimensionally and crack inspected at each overhaul.
- Crankshafts must be designed to withstand considerable bending and torsional stress.
- Most medium- and large-bore highway diesel engines use induction-hardened crankshafts.
- Engine OEMs often do not approve of reconditioning failed crankshafts; however, the practice is widespread despite the risk of a subsequent failure.
- Friction bearings used in crankshaft throw and main journals are retained by crush.
- Vibration dampers consist of a drive member, drive medium, and inertia ring.
- The viscous-type damper is the most commonly used on today's truck and bus diesels. The hollow drive ring is bolted directly to the crankshaft, and the inertia ring is suspended in gelled silicone. The shearing action of the silicone drive medium between the drive ring and the inertia ring effects the damping.
- The flywheel stores kinetic energy in the form of inertia to help smooth out the power pulses delivered to the engine powertrain.
- The SAE categorizes flywheels by size and shape.

REVIEW QUESTIONS

1. Which of the following engine conditions would be the likely cause of a tensile failure of a connecting rod?
   a. Engine overspeed
   b. High cylinder pressures
   c. Prolonged lug down
   d. Prolonged engine idling

2. Which of the following is a disadvantage of an articulating piston assembly when compared to an aluminum alloy trunk piston?
   a. Piston slap control
   b. Highest possible location of an upper ring groove
   c. Service life
   d. Increased tensile loading on the connecting rods

3. Where would a Ni-Resist insert be located?
   a. Upper ring belt, aluminum trunk piston
   b. Upper ring belt, crosshead piston
   c. Steel trunk piston, pin boss
   d. Lower ring belt, articulating piston

4. Under which of the following conditions would a piston ring seal more effectively?
   a. High engine temperatures
   b. Low engine temperatures
   c. High cylinder pressures
   d. Low cylinder pressures

5. A crankshaft has a fracture failure that appears to have initiated at a throw journal oil hole. Which of the following would be the most likely cause?
   a. A broken main cap
   b. Excessive cylinder pressure
   c. A failed vibration damper
   d. A spun rod bearing

6. Which of the following journal surface hardening methods would provide the highest machinability margin?
   a. Flame hardening
   b. Nitriding
   c. Shot peening
   d. Induction hardening

7. Rod and main journal bearing clearances are properly measured with:
   a. tram gauges.
   b. dial indicators.
   c. Plastigage.
   d. snap gauges.

8. What type of piston is favored by diesel engine OEMs in post-2007 products?
   a. Forged steel trunk
   b. Aluminum trunk
   c. Two-piece articulating
   d. Two-piece crosshead

9. When observing a disassembled engine, the outer crown edges of all six pistons show signs of melting and erosion. This could be caused by:
   a. advanced timing.
   b. a dribbling injector.
   c. retarded timing.
   d. fuel with high sulfur content.

10. Which of the following types of pistons use bushingless pin bosses?
    a. Ferrotherm
    b. Monotherm
    c. Crosshead
    d. Aluminum alloy

11. What would be the consequence of a misdirected piston oil cooling jet?
    a. Fuel in lube
    b. Torched piston
    c. Low oil pressure
    d. Overheated engine lube

12. Technician A states that keystone rings are most common in current diesel engines. Technician B states that keystone connecting rods have a wedge-shaped big end. Who is correct?
    a. Technician A only
    b. Technician B only
    c. Both A and B
    d. Neither A nor B

13. What should be used to install piston rings onto a piston?
    a. The thumb and index finger
    b. A ring contractor
    c. A ring expander
    d. Snaping pliers

14. Which of the following operating modes would be more likely to result in a compressional failure of a connecting rod?
    a. Prolonged low idle running
    b. Hydraulic lock caused by head gasket failure
    c. Prolonged high idle running
    d. Overspeeding engine

15. Which of the following would be the more likely outcome of running an engine with a failed vibration damper?
    a. Increased fuel consumption
    b. Increased cylinder blowby
    c. Crankshaft failure
    d. Camshaft failure

16. Into what area of a Mexican hat combustion chamber are the injected droplets of fuel directed?
    a. Center of the cone protrusion
    b. Crater
    c. Piston leading edge
    d. Upper compression ring

17. The upper face of a piston assembly is called the:
    a. skirt.
    b. boss.
    c. trunk.
    d. crown.

18. Technician A states that a cam ground piston is circular when cold and expands to an elliptical shape at operating temperature. Technician B states that the reason the cam ground piston is elliptical when cold is to accommodate the thermal expansion of the greater mass of material at the piston boss as it is raised to operating temperature. Who is correct?
    a. Technician A only
    b. Technician B only
    c. Both A and B
    d. Neither A nor B

19. The piston crown design most commonly used by OEMs in today's highway diesel engines is the:
    a. Mexican hat.
    b. Mann type.
    c. dished.
    d. barrel face.

20. Which term is used to describe the cylinder volume between the piston upper compression ring and its leading edge?
    a. Dead volume
    b. Headland volume
    c. Toroidal recess
    d. Clearance volume

21. Which of the following is true of a CFA piston?
    a. The ring belt reinforcement insert extends up into the leading edge of the piston.
    b. It is a type of Ni-Resist insert.
    c. It is used only on articulating pistons.
    d. The ring belt operates at higher temperatures.

22. When crankshaft thrust surfaces are reground, which of the following would be true?
    a. Undersize thrust bearings are required.
    b. Oversize thrust bearings are required.
    c. The thrust washers must be shimmed.
    d. The thrust washers must be machined to a smaller dimension.

23. Technician A states that main bearing shells are usually interchangeable and may be installed in either the upper or lower position. Technician B states that the main bearing shell with an oil hole must always be installed in the main bearing cap. Who is correct?
    a. Technician A only
    b. Technician B only
    c. Both A and B
    d. Neither A nor B

24. Excessive clearance at the crankshaft main bearings could result in which of the following conditions?
    a. Aerated oil
    b. Fluctuating oil pressures
    c. High oil pressure
    d. Low oil pressure

25. Technician A states that the type of vibration damper most commonly used on truck diesel engines is the viscous type. Technician B states that the inertia ring drive medium on a viscous-type vibration damper is a rubber compound. Who is correct?
    a. Technician A only
    b. Technician B only
    c. Both A and B
    d. Neither A nor B

8

ENGINE FEEDBACK ASSEMBLY

OBJECTIVES

After studying this chapter, you should be able to:

- Identify the engine feedback assembly components.
- Describe the role of the engine timing geartrain in managing engine functions.
- Describe the procedure required to time an engine geartrain.
- Define the role of the camshaft in a typical diesel engine.
- Interpret the terminology used to describe camshaft geometry.
- Inspect a camshaft for wear and damage, selecting the appropriate tools.
- Outline the procedure required to remove and replace a set of block camshaft bearings.
- Identify the role valvetrain components play in running an engine.
- List the types of tappet/cam followers used in diesel engines.
- Inspect a set of push tubes or rods and evaluate their serviceability.
- Describe the role of the rocker assembly in the engine feedback assembly.
- Define the role of cylinder head valves and interpret the terminology used to describe them.
- Outline the procedure required to recondition a set of cylinder head valves, identifying valve margin and other critical wear/machining tolerances.
- Describe how valve rotators operate.
- Define the role of valve seat inserts and outline the servicing procedure.
- Perform a valve lash adjustment on a diesel engine using OEM specifications.
- Perform basic failure analysis on diesel engine cylinder valves.
- Outline the consequences of either too much or too little valve lash.
- Create a valve polar diagram.

KEY TERMS

base circle (BC)	double overhead	interference angle	overhead camshaft
cam geometry	camshaft (DOHC)	keeper	(OHC)
cam profile	follower	lifter	pallet
camshaft	helical gear	outer base circle	periphery
companion cylinders	hunting gears	(OBC)	ramps
concept gear	inner base circle (IBC)	overhead adjustment	rocker

INTRODUCTION

The feedback assembly of an engine is the engine's mechanical management apparatus. It includes timing and accessory drive gearing, the camshaft, tappets, **valve** and unit injector trains, rockers, and fuel pumping mechanisms. Its components are driven by, and often timed to, the engine crankshaft. The drive mechanism for medium- and heavy-duty highway diesel engine feedback assemblies is almost always a gearset. In lighter duty engines, pulleys and belts, chains, and sprockets may be used as drives.

TIMING GEARS

Diesel engine timing gears can be located at either the front or rear of the longitudinally mounted engines that power most commercial trucks and the transverse-mounted engines that power most buses. Although timing geartrains are more commonly located in the front of diesel engines, many post-2007 commercial diesel engines have adopted rear-mounted timing geartrains. Timing gears are responsible for driving the camshaft and most of the engine accessories on a diesel-powered truck engine.

The geartrain is enclosed in a housing that permits engine oil lubrication of the rotating components. Some larger engines may locate the timing geartrain in the rear or both front and rear. The gear ratios dictate the rotational speed and maintain a fixed location between the driven components in any given moment of engine operation. Camshafts may be mounted within the engine cylinder block or overhead, meaning that it is cradle mounted on the cylinder head. A typical front-of-engine timing gearset driving an **overhead camshaft (OHC)** is illustrated in **Figure 8–1**.

Timing gears are lubricated in two ways:

- Splash: Gear teeth rotate through the lubricant in the oil sump, pick up oil, and transfer it to other gears in the timing train before draining back to the sump.
- Bearing spill: Oil used to lubricate the shaft support bearing spills to the timing gear housing, where it is circulated before returning to the oil sump.

TIMING GEAR CONSTRUCTION

Diesel engine gears are cast or forged alloys that are heat tempered and then surface hardened by a flame, nitriding, carburizing, or induction-hardening process. The gear teeth are milled in manufacture to spur and helical designs; combinations of both are used in the geartrains of some current engines. The noise produced by

FIGURE 8–1 A pre-2010 Detroit Diesel Series 60 timing geartrain. This OHC engine uses a timing geartrain in the front of the engine.

FIGURE 8–2 A typical timing gear cover used on an engine with a cylinder block-located camshaft.

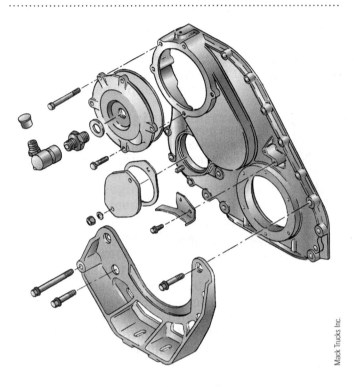

Mack Trucks Inc.

the geartrain is a factor and, for this reason, helical cut gears tend to be more common. **Helical gears** have the advantage of increased tooth contact area, lowering unit forces. The **spur gear** design offers the advantage of much lower thrust loads. Timing gears are commonly press-fitted to the shafts that they drive and are positioned on the shaft by means of keys and keyways. **Figure 8–2** shows a typical timing gear cover used on an engine with a cylinder block-mounted camshaft.

TIMING GEAR INSPECTION, REMOVAL, AND INSTALLATION

Visual inspection should be sufficient to determine the condition of timing gears. Indications of cracks, pitting, heat discoloration, or lipping of the gear teeth usually require its replacement. Press and tapered friction fit gears require the use of a mechanical, pneumatic, or hydraulic puller to remove the gear from the shaft. When the shaft and gear can be removed from the engine, a shop air-over-hydraulic press may be used—make sure that the usual safety precautions are observed and that care is taken to

support the components on separation. When a gear has to be separated from a shaft while on the engine, a mechanical bolt puller or portable hydraulic press is usually required; while using puller tools, ensure that they are mounted in such a way that it will not damage either the cylinder block or other gears. Note that some timing gears cannot be removed from a shaft (usually denoted by having a single part number): in these instances, the shaft and gear must be replaced as a single assembly.

Installing a Camshaft Gear

Install the new gear to the shaft by heating to the original equipment manufacturer's (OEM's) specified temperature. To heat the gear to the prescribed temperature, use a thermostatically regulated oven or hot plate. If a bearing hot plate is used, ensure that it is large enough to fit the entire surface area of the gear. Typical specified temperatures are around 300°F (150°C). The consequence of overheating a gear will be to destroy the heat treatment/tempering and possibly the surface hardening, resulting in premature failure. A heat-indicating crayon such as **Tempilstick™** may be used to determine the exact temperature. At the required temperature, the gear can be dropped over the shaft and allowed to air-cool. Use of a power press to install interference-fit gears to shafts should be generally avoided, as damage to the shaft may result; a hand-actuated arbor press is less likely to inflict damage. The engine geartrain must be timed according to the OEM procedure to ensure that the relative positions of the camshaft and critical accessory drives are correct and balanced. As noted earlier, some current engines locate the engine timing geartrain at the rear of the engine. **Figure 8–3** shows the rear-of-engine timing gear rotation on a Volvo D16 engine. It is similar to that of its sibling, the current Mack Trucks MP-10 engine.

Figure 8–4 shows a cutaway view of the rear gearset used in a Mack Trucks post-2010 MP-8 engine; **Figure 8–5** shows a similar arrangement used in a post-2010 Detroit Diesel DD13.

A number of gears are used in the engine geartrain, especially when a **single overhead camshaft (SOHC)** or **double overhead camshaft (DOHC)** assembly has to be driven. If the camshaft is to be rotated in the same direction of rotation as the crankshaft, an idler gear must act as an intermediary between the crankshaft and camshaft gears. There is no requirement that the camshaft be turned in the same direction as the cause noise and damage. The ISX engine uses two concept gears. The lower concept gear acts as an idler gear and uses seven coaxial springs. The upper concept gear, located on the injector camshaft, uses four coaxial springs and drives the valve/brake camshaft.

Timing OHC Concept Gears

The procedure used to time an ISX geartrain is briefly outlined in the following sequence. Refer to Figure 8–6 while going through the procedure:

1. Pin the crankshaft and wedge both of the camshafts. This effectively locks both camshafts and the crankshaft into position. The locking wedges and crankshaft pin are Cummins special tools and they must be used.

2. First install the lower concept gear, shaft, and retainer plate, making sure that the thrust bearing is behind the gear. Install the gear shaft bolts, followed by the gear fasteners, and torque to specifications.

3. The lower gear cover and seal can now be installed and torqued to specifications. Next, the vibration damper should be installed.

4. Both cam noses should have been cleaned with solvent, leaving no oil residue. The two cam gears should be installed loosely (so they can be moved) on each cam nose. The injector cam concept gear should be installed with two gear screws backed out with the gear teeth aligned. Both cam gears should be snug on the camshaft nose tapers but not so snug that they cannot be rotated.

5. Place a 0.010" feeler gauge between the teeth of the adjustable idler gear and its mesh point with the injector cam concept gear. Now, using hand pressure only, move the adjustable idler gear into mesh toward the center of the engine so there is no air gap on either side of the feeler gauge. Both cam gears may rotate slightly while performing this step. This sets the lash between the adjustable idler gear and the injector camshaft concept gear. Lash at the lower idler concept gear is set by the spread of the lower idler concept gear teeth, which are constrained by the crank gear.

6. While holding the adjustable idler gear, torque the idler shaft fasteners to specification, and remove the feeler gauge.

7. Next, torque the injector cam concept gear fasteners to specification, followed by the valve cam gear fasteners. Remove the camshaft wedges and the crankshaft pin.

Lubricate the engine geartrain with whatever lubricant is normally used in the engine.

CAMSHAFTS

The **camshaft** in most commercial diesel engines is gear-driven by the crankshaft through one revolution per complete cycle of the engine. In a four-stroke cycle engine, to complete a full cycle the engine must be turned through 2 revolutions or 720 degrees, during which the camshaft would turn one revolution. Camshaft speed is therefore one-half engine speed. In a two-stroke cycle engine, the full cycle is completed in a single rotation or 360 degrees; camshaft speed and crankshaft (engine) speed are therefore geared so they are equal.

CAM PROFILE

The camshaft in a diesel engine actuates the **valvetrains** (the term **train** can describe any components that ride the cam profile and are actuated by it). In many diesel engines, the injection pumping apparatus, such as unit pumps and mechanically or electronically actuated unit injectors, are also cam actuated. The camshaft is supported at its journals by bushings or bearings that are in most cases pressure lubricated. **Cam geometry** refers to the physical shape of the cams; the term **cam profile** is also used. The profile outside the base circle will actuate the trains riding the cam and convert the rotary movement of the camshaft into reciprocating motion. Overhead camshafts are becoming more common in current truck diesel engines: Cummins ISX, Navistar Maxx-Force 13 and 15, and the current Volvo and Mack families of engines are examples. Valvetrain timing and unit injection pump or unit injector stroke are determined by cam geometry and the camshaft gear timing to the engine crankshaft. **Figure 8–7** shows the sequence of camshaft-actuated events.

CONSTRUCTION AND DESIGN

Middle alloy steels are used with hardened journals and cams. Hardening is usually by nitriding or other hard-facing processes, followed by finish grinding. Diesel engine camshafts are not usually reconditioned; resurfacing of the journals is possible, but most camshaft failures are cam lobe-related. Camshafts are supported by bearing journals within a longitudinal bore

FIGURE 8–7 Camshaft timing events.

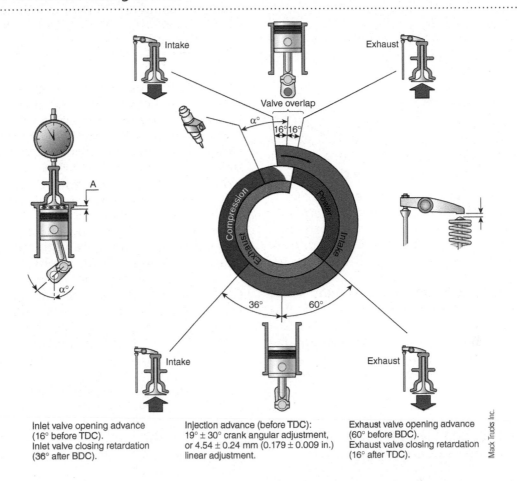

Intake

Exhaust

Valve overlap

α° 16° 16°

Compression

Power

Exhaust

Intake

A

α°

36° 60°

Intake

Exhaust

Inlet valve opening advance (16° before TDC). Inlet valve closing retardation (36° after BDC).

Injection advance (before TDC): 19° ± 30° crank angular adjustment, or 4.54 ± 0.24 mm (0.179 ± 0.009 in.) linear adjustment.

Exhaust valve opening advance (60° before BDC). Exhaust valve closing retardation (16° after TDC).

Mack Trucks Inc.

in the cylinder block or on a pedestal arrangement in the cylinder head in the case of an overhead cam.

Base and Outer Base Circle

Cams are eccentrics machined to convert rotary motion to linear movement. The smallest radius of a cam concentric with the camshaft centerline is known as the **base circle (BC)** or **inner base circle (IBC)**. The largest radial dimension from the camshaft centerline is known as the **outer base circle (OBC)**. The shaping of the profile that connects cam IBC with its OBC is described as *ramping*. A cam may be designed so that the larger percentage of its **periphery** (circumference) is IBC; in this case, the train that it is responsible for actuating will be unloaded for most of the cycle. Cams used to actuate engine cylinder valves use an IBC design. **Figure 8–8** shows a typical cylinder block-mounted camshaft assembly.

Alternatively, cams may be designed so that most of their periphery is OBC, in which case the train that the cam actuates will be loaded for most of the cycle. Cummins TP injectors and

FIGURE 8–8 Camshaft, bushings, and timing gear housing from an engine with a cylinder block-mounted camshaft.

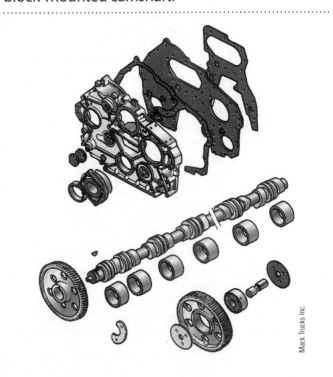

Mack Trucks Inc.

FIGURE 8–9 Camshaft terminology.

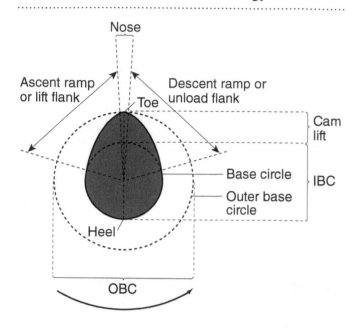

some types of electronic unit pump (EUP) fueled engines use mostly OBC cam profiles. **Figure 8–9** explains some cam terminology as it applies to a cam whose profile is mostly IBC.

REMOVING AND INSTALLING THE CAMSHAFT FROM THE ENGINE

The procedure for removing the camshaft from a cylinder head-mounted OHC is relatively straightforward, usually only requiring the cam caps to be released from the cam pedestals. When a camshaft has to be removed from a cylinder block, the tappet/follower assemblies will not permit the camshaft simply to be withdrawn while the engine is in an upright position. If the engine cannot be inverted, such as when removing the camshaft from an engine in-chassis, the tappet/follower mechanisms must be raised sufficiently so that they do not obstruct the camshaft as it is withdrawn. Most engine OEMs provide special tools to perform this procedure—usually magnets on a shaft that lift the follower after which the shaft is locked to the train bore in the cylinder head. All the followers must be raised in this fashion so that the cam lobes and journals do not interfere with them as the camshaft is withdrawn from the block.

When the correct tools are not available, the OEM special tools may be improvised by using coat hanger wire (mechanic's wire is not usually substantial enough) to first hook the follower and then lift it by bending the wire at the top. When withdrawing or installing the camshaft from a cylinder block bore, it is important that it never be forced, because the result will almost certainly be damage to the camshaft or its support bearings. In certain engines, protrusions of powertrain components, such as the crank web and crank throw, may interfere with the camshaft eccentrics, requiring that the engine be rotated at intervals while the camshaft is being removed and installed. **Figure 8–10** shows a

FIGURE 8–10 Camshaft configuration used to actuate both valve and injector trains.

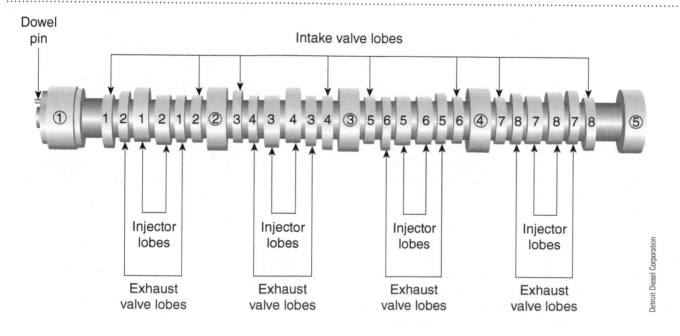

Detroit Diesel Corporation

FIGURE 8–11 A camshaft mounted on V-blocks.

camshaft used to actuate both valve and injector trains.

CAMSHAFT INSPECTION

If possible, place the camshaft in V-blocks to inspect it, as shown in **Figure 8–11**.

1. Visual: Pitting, scoring, peeling of lobes and scoring, wear, blueing of journals. Check the drive gear keyway for distortion and key retention ability. Any visible deterioration of the hard surfacing on the journal or cam profile indicates a need to replace the camshaft. The inspection can be by touch; a fingernail stroked over a suspected hard-surfacing failure can identify hard-surfacing failure in its early stages better than the eye.

2. Mike the cam profile heel-to-toe dimension and check to OEM specifications. Mike the base circle dimension and check to specifications. Subtract the IBC dimension from the heel-to-toe dimension to calculate the cam lift dimension. Check to specifications. Cam lift can also be measured using a dial indicator with the camshaft mounted in V-blocks, as shown in **Figure 8–12**: Zero the dial indicator on the cam IBC and rotate the camshaft to record the lift. Ensure that a dial indicator with sufficient total travel to measure the expected lift is used. When checking the cam lift dimension with the camshaft in-engine using a dial indicator, the measurement may not exactly coincide with the parameters required by the OEM, even when the cam profile is in sound condition, due to the lie of the camshaft in the support journals.

3. Check for cam lobe surface wear using a straightedge and thickness gauges sized to the maximum wear specification.

4. Install the camshaft in V-blocks (Figure 8–11) and check for shaft bending using a dial indicator. It is unusual for camshafts to bend in normal service. Bending of a camshaft is usually caused by the failure of another engine component.

Failure to meet the OEM specifications in any of the foregoing categories indicates that

FIGURE 8–12 Indicating a cam profile using a dial indicator.

the camshaft should be replaced. The technician should be aware that the smallest indication of a hard-surfacing failure on the cam profile requires little time to advance to a total failure. Probably the most important inspection is the visual inspection that initiates this listed sequence.

CAMSHAFT BUSHINGS/BEARINGS

The camshaft is supported by pressure-lubricated friction bearings at the main journals. The camshaft is subjected to loading whenever a cam is actuating the train that rides its profile. This loading can be considerable, especially when engine compression brake hydraulics and fuel injection pumping apparatus are actuated by the camshaft. Cam bushings are normally routinely replaced during engine overhaul, but if they are to be reused they must be measured with a dial bore gauge (**Figure 8–13**) or telescoping gauge and micrometer to ensure that they are within the OEM reuse specifications.

Interference-fit, cylinder block-located camshaft bushings are removed in sequence, usually starting at the front and working to the back of the cylinder block. The correct sized bushing driver (mandrel) and slide hammer should be used. Cam bearing split shells are retained either by cam cap crush (overhead camshafts) or lock rings. Interference-fit cam bushings are installed using the same driver tools used to remove them. Care should be taken to properly align the oil holes: When installing bushings to a cylinder block in-chassis, where access and visibility are restricted, painting the oil hole location on the bushing rim with a shop paintstick or correction whiteout may help align the bushing before driving it. Ensure that the correct bushing is driven into each bore.

FIGURE 8–13 Measuring cam bushing bore.

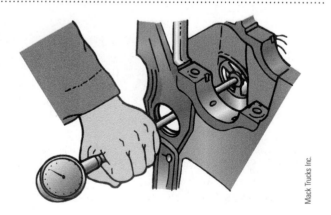

Mack Trucks Inc.

Bushings and their support bores vary dimensionally, and bushings rarely survive being driven into a bore and then removed. *Bearing clearance* is the camshaft bushing dimension measured with a dial bore gauge or telescoping gauge and micrometer minus the camshaft journal dimension measured with a micrometer. Prolonged use of certain types of engine compression brakes can be especially hard on camshaft bearings.

CAMSHAFT ENDPLAY

Camshaft endplay is defined either by free or captured thrust washers/plates. Thrust loads are not normally excessive unless the camshaft is driven by a helical toothed gear (see **Figure 8–14**), in which instance there is more likely to be wear at the thrust faces. Endplay is best measured with a dial indicator: The camshaft should be gently levered longitudinally rearward, then forward, and the travel measured and checked to specifications.

Camshaft Position Sensors

Camshaft position sensors (CPSs) are used in all current engines. They function to signal shaft speed and position data to the engine control module (ECM). CPSs may use either an

FIGURE 8–14 Helical camshaft drive gear; this requires more control of thrust forces to limit endplay.

inductive pulse generator or a Hall-effect signaling principle. The operating principles of camshaft position sensors are studied in some detail in Chapter 34. A typical inductive pulse generator CPS signals a frequency value, and an irregular tooth on the chopper wheel at the #1 cylinder location is commonly used to signal TDC.

VALVE AND INJECTOR TRAINS

While a camshaft rotates, the trains it actuates move linearly. Valve and injector trains transmit the effects of cam geometry to the cylinder valves and injector assemblies. Followers ride the cam profiles to actuate the trains. The linear movement of the train is converted to rotary motion once again at the rocker. It is this rocking action that opens and closes valves and provides fuel injection pumping force in many engines. Rockers may be used in both cylinder block-mounted camshaft engines (shown in **Figure 8–15**) and those with overhead camshafts.

FOLLOWERS

Tappet, *lifter*, and *follower* may all mean the same thing depending on which OEM is using the term. These terms describe components that usually are positioned to directly ride, or at least be actuated by, a cam profile. The term **tappet** has a broader definition and is sometimes used to describe what is more often referred to as a **rocker** lever. In this text, the term cam

FIGURE 8–15 Typical valvetrain assembly.

Mack Trucks Inc.

follower or *lifter* is used to describe a component that rides the cam profile, and the term *rocker* is used to describe the means of actuating valves. The function of cam followers is to reduce friction and evenly distribute the force imparted from the cam's profile to the train it is responsible for actuating. While some light-duty diesel engines use hydraulic lifters, medium- and heavy-duty diesel engines using cylinder block-mounted camshafts use two categories of followers; those using overhead camshafts use either direct-actuated rockers or roller-type cam followers.

Solid Lifters

Lifters are manufactured from cast iron and middle alloy steels and are usually located in guide bores in the cylinder block so they ride the cam profile over which they are positioned. Pushrods or push tubes are fitted to lifter sockets. The critical surface of a solid lifter is the face that directly contacts the cam profile. This face must be durable and may either be chemically hardened, cladded with a toughened alloy, or have a disc of special alloy steel molecularly bonded to the face.

LIFTER INSPECTION Solid lifters should be carefully inspected, primarily for thrust face wear, at engine overhaul. Stem and socket wear should also be checked. The guide bores in the cylinder block should be measured using digital calipers or a telescoping gauge and micrometer. Sleeving lifter guide bores is a relatively simple procedure that involves boring to an interference fit to the new sleeve outside diameter. Always check that the lifters do not drag or cock in newly sleeved guide bores.

Roller-Type Cam Followers

Roller-type cam follower assemblies can sustain much higher forces, so they are commonly used in engines that use the camshaft to actuate injector pumping apparatus. They are used with both OHC and cylinder block-mounted camshafts. Roller-type cam followers usually consist of a roller supported by a pin mounted to a clevis. The clevis can either be cylindrical and mounted in a cylinder block guide bore, or be a pivot arm fitted to either the cylinder block or cylinder head.

ROLLER CAM FOLLOWER INSPECTION In the case of some OHC designs, a roller-type cam follower assembly and the rocker arm are integral. An example is the OHC design used to actuate

FIGURE 8–16 Roller-cam follower actuated valvetrain.

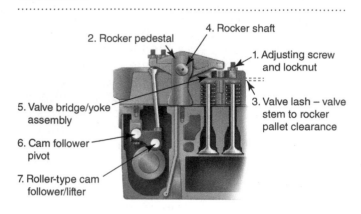

the DDC Series 60 and 50 parallel port valve and electronic unit injector (EUI) configuration. Roller-type cam followers more evenly distribute whatever loading they are subjected to and thus outlast solid followers. The roller faces are usually chemically hard surfaced. Roller contact faces should be inspected for pitting, scoring, and indications of hard-surfacing disintegration. The roller assembly should also be checked for axial and radial runout. **Figure 8–16** shows a Caterpillar valvetrain actuated by a roller-type cam follower.

PUSHRODS AND TUBES

Engines using cylinder block-mounted camshafts require a means of transmitting the effects of cam action to the rocker assemblies in the cylinder head. Push tubes and pushrods act as intermediaries in the train and are located between the cam followers and rocker assemblies. Because they are subjected to shock loads that increase proportionally with engine rpm, they are manufactured from alloyed steels, both to sustain these loads and to keep the weight of the actuation train to a minimum.

The hollow push tube is more commonly used than solid pushrods, especially in cases where the camshaft is mounted low in the cylinder block, and they are required to be fairly long. A typical push tube is a cylindrical, hollow steel shaft fitted with a solid ball or socket at either end. Balls and sockets form bearing surfaces at the follower and rocker. The bearing contact surfaces are usually lubed by engine oil. This is especially important at the rocker end, as the rocker moves through an arc while the push tube moves linearly. Balls and sockets are usually chemically hard surfaced. Push tubes

are preferred over solid pushrods because the tubular shape provides nearly as high section modulus (shape characteristic related to rigidity) as a solid cylindrical rod and nearly as much strength with less weight. Pushrods are cylindrical and solid. They are used mostly in applications that permit them to be short and relatively low in weight, such as in old Detroit Diesel two-stroke cycle engines.

Inspecting Push Tubes

Both pushrods and push tubes seldom fail under normal operation, but when they fail there are two main causes:

1. Inaccurate valve lash or injector adjustments
2. Engine overspeeding

Ball and socket wear should first be checked visually. Reject them if there is evidence of hard-surface flaking or disintegration. Next, check:

1. Ball/socket-to-tube integrity: Test by dropping onto a concrete floor from a height of 2". A separating ball will always ring flat. *Never* reuse a push tube with a separating ball or socket.
2. Straightness: Roll the push tube on a known true flat surface, such as a (new) toolbox deck. The slightest bend (wobble as it is rolled) is reason to reject a push tube.

> ### CAUTION:
> It does not make economic sense to ever straighten a push tube or pushrod. The failure will recur—it is only a question of when. Even as a "temporary" repair, it makes little sense, as the consequences of push tube failure can be much more expensive than the cost of replacing it.

ROCKER ARMS

Rockers are levers. They transfer camshaft motion to the valves and mechanically actuated injectors. They are used in both in-block camshaft and overhead camshaft configurations. **Figure 8–17** shows a rocker assembly used on a Detroit Diesel OHC, 4-valves per cylinder engine, with mechanically actuated electronic unit injectors (EUIs).

In a rocker assembly, the rocker pivots on a rocker shaft. When a cam **ramps** off its base circle, it acts on the train that rides the cam profile and "rocks" the rocker arm, thereby actuating the

FIGURE 8–17 Rocker assembly used on a Detroit Diesel OHC, 4-valves per cylinder engine, with mechanically actuated electronic unit injectors.

FIGURE 8–18 Rocker shaft assembly on a cylinder block-located camshaft engine.

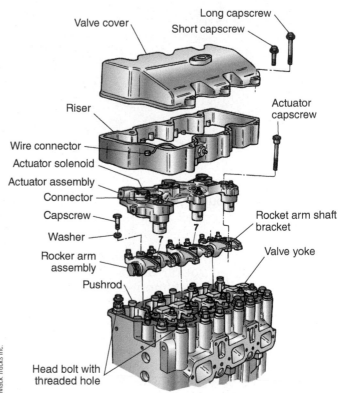

Mack Trucks Inc.

components on the opposite side of the rocker arm (either valves or unit injectors). Lubricating oil is normally ducted through the rocker shaft to supply each rocker arm. **Figure 8–18** shows an exploded view of the rocker shaft assembly on an engine with a cylinder block camshaft equipped with a Jacobs-type engine brake (see Chapter 13).

ROCKER RATIO

Rocker ratio may be used to amplify the cam lift dimension to increase valve or unit injector plunger travel. This requires that the distance from the centerline of the rocker shaft pivot bore to the pushrod side be less than its distance to the valve or unit injector side. Rocker ratio expresses the mechanical advantage obtained over the actual cam lift dimension. A rocker ratio of 1:2 would convert a cam lift dimension of 1" into 2" of valve opening travel. In the case of a rocker with equal distance on either side of the centerline (center of pivot), the rocker ratio would be 1:1, meaning equal cam and valve lift.

Inspecting Rockers

The rocker arms should be inspected for wear at the push tube end cup or ball socket, the pivot bore (usually a bushing), and the **pallet** end. The pallet end of a rocker is the bearing surface that contacts and actuates the valve stem or valve bridge. If the hard surfacing at either end of a rocker shows signs of deteriorating, the rocker arm should be replaced. The pivot bore bearing/bushing can be replaced if it shows signs of wear, as can the adjusting screw ball. The rocker shafts should be checked for straightness and wear at the rocker bearing race.

FIGURE 8–19 Rocker assembly mounting brackets.

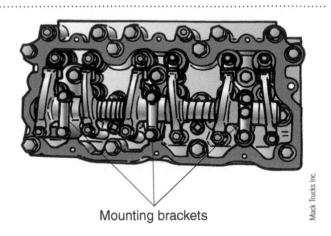

Mounting brackets

Mack Trucks Inc.

Figure 8–19 shows an overhead view of a pedestal-mounted rocker shaft assembly actuated by a cylinder block-mounted camshaft.

Valve Bridges

Engines using OHCs along with a 4-valve design typically use one cam-actuated rocker to actuate the exhaust valves and another rocker to actuate the intake valves: Each rocker mechanically acts on a **valve bridge** that simultaneously opens a pair of valves. **Figure 8–20** shows an overhead view of a Volvo D12 engine with mechanically actuated EUIs and valve bridges that enable a single rocker to actuate a pair of valves.

FIGURE 8–20 Rocker assembly used on a Volvo VDE12 OHC engine seen from the left side. Note the use of valve bridges used to actuate the cylinder valves and the mechanically actuated EUIs.

FIGURE 8–21 Overhead right-side view of the rocker assembly in a post-2010 Volvo D16 engine that uses an OHC and rockers to actuate the valves and center-located EUI.

A valve bridge can also be called a *valve yoke* or *crosshead* depending on the OEM. **Figure 8–21** shows a Volvo D16 engine that uses a 4-valve design with an electronic unit injector centrally located over the cylinder head. **Figure 8–22** shows a cutaway of the similarly designed Mack Trucks MP-8. Note how the bridges are used to allow a single rocker to actuate a pair of valves.

FIGURE 8–22 Cutaway view of the rocker assembly in a post-2010 Mack Trucks MP-8 engine equipped with an OHC. The engine uses a 4-valve design and bridge-actuated valves; the EUI is centrally located over the engine cylinder.

Pallet Links

Because a rocker moves radially and whatever it actuates moves linearly, the "bearing" or pallet end of the rocker may be subject to some friction, especially when considerable actuation force is required, as with a mechanically actuated fuel injector. It makes sense to use a link between the rocker pallet and the injector tappet. These links may also be known as *injector links*. They may clip onto the rocker pallet or be inserted into a bore in the injector tappet. They should be inspected for wear at overhaul.

CYLINDER HEAD VALVES

Cylinder head valves provide the means of admitting air into, and discharging exhaust out of, the engine cylinders. Although any movement of cylinder valves in current engines is due to cam profile, the timing of engine valve movement depends on whether the engine is equipped with a compression brake or uses variable valve timing (VVT). With a VVT or engine brake equipped engine, the engine management electronics can manage valve lift and influence timing, sometimes within a wide window. The location of the valves, the lift, and valve timing can influence cylinder gas dynamics. *Cylinder gas dynamics* refers to the movement of gases in the cylinder during both combustion and exhaust strokes.

VALVE DESIGN AND MATERIALS

Cylinder head valves are mushroom-shaped, poppet-type valves. The stems are fitted to cylindrical guides in the cylinder head and loaded by a spring or springs to seal to a seat. A disc-shaped, spring retainer locks the spring(s) in position. **Split locks**, also known as **keepers**, are fitted to a peripheral groove at the top of the valve stem to hold the spring retainer in position. Valves can be vulnerable to high cylinder temperatures when they are in an open position—that is, not seated. This is because they rely on transferring heat through seat contact. Thermal failure occurs when valves overheat. Exhaust valves are more vulnerable to thermal failure than intake valves because they open when cylinder temperatures are at their highest. As a consequence, the valve head is manufactured using different alloys from the stem: The two sections are then inertia welded. *Inertia welding* is a type of friction welding that requires spinning the stem at high velocity and pressure until a

FIGURE 8–23 Valve terminology.

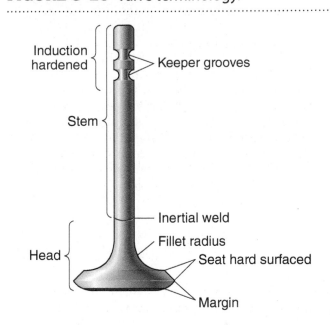

molecular bond is created. Refer to **Figure 8–23** while studying this section: It identifies all the critical valve components and terminology.

Intake Valves

Intake valves are manufactured from a variety of middle alloy steels. Intake valves do not have to sustain the high temperatures that exhaust valves are exposed to. However, they are actuated at high speeds and must have some degree of flexibility. The flexibility is required so that at high engine speeds, when valve closing velocity is at its highest, the valves do not hammer out their seats. Although most diesel engine designers use a valve seat angle of 45 degrees due to greater toughness, some choose to use 30-degree cut seats on just the intake valves. This takes advantage of the superior breathing efficiency of 30-degree seat angles over 45-degree seat angles.

Exhaust Valves

Running temperatures of exhaust valves are much higher than those of intake valves. When the exhaust valve is first opened during the latter portion of the power stroke, flame quench has just taken place and cylinder temperatures are just past their peak. Only about 20% of the heat the valve is subjected to can be dissipated through the stem, so the exhaust valve must sustain high temperatures for the duration of the exhaust process until it seats.

Exhaust valves are manufactured using special ferrous alloys. They may be cladded (coated) at the head and often use chromium, nickel, manganese, tungsten, cobalt, and molybdenum to improve flexibility, toughness, and heat resistance. Exhaust valves are cooled primarily by dissipating heat to the valve seats, and secondarily by intake air at the valve overlap and through the stem-to-guide contact area. Inertia welding is commonly used to manufacture exhaust valves using separate alloys for the stem and head. In this way, the stem can be made out of an alloy with sufficient material hardness, while the head can be manufactured from an alloy with extreme heat resistance and flexibility. The separate stem and head are then molecularly joined by a friction-welding process that requires spinning the stem at high velocity and pressure. Examine Figure 8–23 to see the location where the stem and head are joined on a typical inertia weld valve.

Valve Breathing Efficiency

Given identical lifts, valves machined with 45-degree seats have lower breathing efficiencies than those with 30-degree seats. Valve seats with 45-degree seats are widely used in highway diesel applications simply because they tend to have greater longevity. They can sustain greater dynamic loads, high seating forces, and high temperatures because they have more mass behind the seat. Valves machined with 30-degree seats tend to run hotter than those with 45-degree seats because they have less mass at their periphery. They also have less distortion resistance and lower unit seating force. To get around this problem, some engine OEMs use a 30-degree valve seat angle on their intake valves and a 45-degree seat angle on the exhaust valves.

VALVE OPERATION

Current diesel engine valves rely on maximizing the seat contact area for cooling purposes and, as a consequence, **interference angles** are seldom machined. An interference angle requires that the valve be machined at 0.5 to 1.0 degree more acute angle than the seat. This results in the valve biting into its seat with high unit pressure. Interference angle also breaks up carbon formations on the valve seat, but at the cost of reducing the valve-to-seat contact area. This can create a problem when transferring valve heat. A majority of current diesel engines use valve rotators to minimize carbon buildup on the seat and to promote even wear. An interference angle is not usually machined to valves using valve rotators, but the DDC Series 60 is a notable exception.

Valve Rotators

Valve rotators use a ratchet principle or a ball and coaxial spring to fractionally rotate the valve each time it is actuated. Valve rotation should be checked after assembly by marking an edge of the stem and guide with a marker pen and then tapping the valve stem with a light nylon hammer a number of times. The valve should visibly rotate each time the stem is struck with the nylon hammer.

Valve Harmonics

Cylinder head valves are seated by a spring or pair of springs. When a pair of springs is used, they are often oppositely wound to help cancel the coincidence of vibration harmonies that may contribute to valve flutter or float. **Valve float** can occur at higher engine speeds when valve spring force is insufficient (valve operating velocities are highest) and may cause asynchronous (out-of-time) valve closures. Springs are a critical component of the valvetrain assembly; their importance is increased as engine rpm increases and reduces the real-time periods between opening and closing.

INSPECTING VALVE SPRINGS AND RETAINERS

1. Once the cylinder head has been removed from the cylinder block, the valves may be removed using either a lever-type valve spring compressor, as shown in **Figure 8–24**,

FIGURE 8–24 Removing or installing a valve from a cylinder head using a lever-type valve spring compressor.

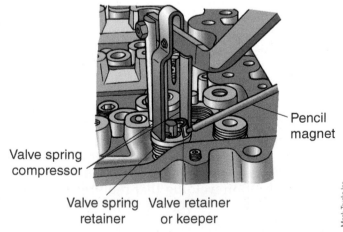

Pencil magnet

Valve spring compressor

Valve spring retainer   Valve retainer or keeper

Mack Trucks Inc.

FIGURE 8–25 Removing or installing a valve from a cylinder head using a C-clamp valve spring.

or a C-clamp style, shown in **Figure 8–25**. Check the keepers and the valve keeper grooves for wear. Inspect the retainers.

2. Measure the spring vertical height and compare to specifications. Minor differences do not matter.
3. Test valve spring tension using a tension gauge (**Figure 8–26**). The valve spring tension should be within 10% of the original tension specification. If not, replace the valve spring.
4. Check the spring(s) for abrasive wear at each end.
5. Check that the spring is not cocked, using a straightedge.
6. Check valve spring operation with the valve installed in the cylinder head. Remember that as the cylinder head valve seat material is ground away, the spring operating height is lengthened, reducing spring tension. Valve protrusion and recession must be checked to specification, as shown in **Figure 8–27** and **Figure 8–28**.

VALVE SERVICING

The rocker assembly, including engine brake and VVT actuators, should be removed from the cylinder head(s). Use a valve spring compressor (shown previously in Figure 8–24) to remove

FIGURE 8–26 Valve spring tension tester.

FIGURE 8–27 Valve protrusion and recession dimensions.

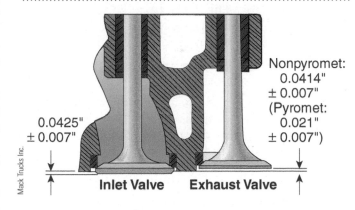

0.0425"
± 0.007"

Nonpyromet:
0.0414"
± 0.007"
(Pyromet:
0.021"
± 0.007")

Inlet Valve   **Exhaust Valve**

Mack Trucks Inc.

FIGURE 8–28 Measuring valve protrusion with a depth micrometer.

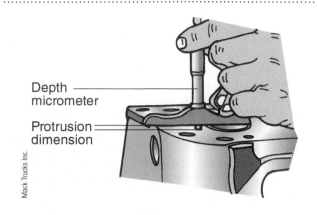

Depth micrometer

Protrusion dimension

Mack Trucks Inc.

valves from the cylinder head. The valves should be tagged by location. Valves should first be cleaned on a buffer wheel, taking great care not to remove any metal. A glass bead blaster may be used to remove carbon deposits from the seat face, fillet, and head, but avoid blasting the stem.

Valve inspection should begin with visually checking for dishing, burning, cracks, and pits; evidence of any of these conditions requires that the valve be replaced. Check the valve fillet for cracks and nicks—using a portable magnetic flux crack detector may help here—and again, reject the valve if cracks are evident in this critical area. Next, the valve should be measured. Using a micrometer, mark the valve stem at three points through the valve guide bushing sweep and check to specifications. Valve stem straightness should be checked with a vertical runout indicator.

Valve Margin

Measure the **valve margin** (see Figure 8–23), which is the dimension between the valve seat and the flat face of the valve head mushroom. This specification is critical when machining valves, and it must exceed the minimum specified value after the grinding process has been completed. A valve margin that is lower than the specification will result in valve failures caused by overheating. The split lock keeper grooves (see Figure 8–23) on the valve stem should also be checked for wear, nicks, and cracks.

Valve Dressing/Grinding

Before servicing a set of valves, the previously outlined checks and measurements should be completed. It is pointless to machine valves that have failed in any of the previous categories. First, dress the grinding stone using a diamond dressing tool. Adjust the valve grinder chuck to the specified angle and the carriage stop to limit travel so the stone cannot contact the stem. Run the coolant (soluble machine oil and water solution) and make a single shallow pass. When machining valves, try to make the minimum number of passes to produce a valve seat face surface free of ridging and pitting. The final step should be to check that the valve margin is still within specification.

In cases in which the valve has been loosely adjusted, the stem end may be slightly mushroomed due to hammering from the rocker. Grind a new chamfer, taking care to remove as little material as possible. Too much chamfer will reduce the rocker-to-stem contact area and may damage the rocker pallet. When valves must be replaced, the new valves must be inspected, measured, and sometimes ground using the same procedure as for used valves.

VALVE SEAT INSERTS

Most commercial diesel engines use valve seat inserts rather than integral valve seats machined into the cylinder head. The primary advantage of valve seat inserts is that they can be manufactured from tough, temperature-resistant material and then easily replaced when the cylinder head is serviced. Cast-iron alloys toughened with nickel, chromium, and molybdenum may be used, but the use of alloyed steels, some with stellite cladding, is more common. Valve seat inserts are press-fit to a machined recess in the cylinder head; sometimes they are staked to position (with a punch) after installation. Because most of the heat of the valve must be transferred from the valve to the seat, it is essential that the contact area of the seat and the cylinder head be maximized.

Valve Seat Removal and Installation

Valve seats must be removed using a removal tool consisting of a sectored collet designed to expand into the valve seat, after which it can be either levered out or driven out with a slide hammer. When installing new valve seats, first clean out the seat counterbore using a low-abrasive emery cloth. The new insert should be inserted into the OEM-specified driver, which has a pilot shaft that fits tight to the valve guide bore. Use a hammer to drive the insert into its bore until it bottoms. Next, check the concentricity of the valve seat with the valve guide bore using a dial gauge; this is a critical specification (**Figure 8–29**). In most cases, the seat will have to be ground, even though new seats are finish ground. It is important that the valve grinders be serviced before fitting and machining the valve seats, so that the new seats are machined to be concentric with the guides that will be put in service.

Valve Seat Grinding

Valve seats are ground using a specified grit abrasive stone, and dressed to the appropriate angle, with a pilot shaft that fits to the valve guide. The valve head protrusion or recess dimension specifications must be respected when grinding valve seats; in cases in which the cylinder head deck surface has been machined, undersize valve seat inserts are available from most OEMs. Whenever a cylinder head deck has been machined, the valve stem height, which is dictated by the specific valve seat insert location, must be within specifications to ensure the correct valve spring dynamics.

FIGURE 8–29 Measuring valve seat concentricity with a concentricity gauge.

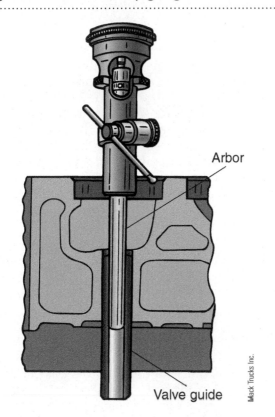

Arbor

Valve guide

Mack Trucks Inc.

VALVE LASH ADJUSTMENT

When valves are properly adjusted, there should be clearance between the pallet end of the rocker arm and the top of the valve stem. Valve lash is required because as the moving parts heat up, they expand, and if clearance were not factored in somewhere in the valvetrain, the valves would remain constantly open by the time an engine reached operating temperature. Actual valve lash values depend on factors such as the length of the push tubes and the materials used in valve manufacture. Exhaust valves are subject to more heat and as a consequence expand more than intake valves when heated to operating temperature. Valve lash specifications for exhaust valves are usually greater than the intake valve lash setting specification.

Maladjusted Valves

Loose valve adjustment will retard valve opening and advance valve closing, decreasing the cylinder breathing time. Actuating cam geometry is designed to provide some "forgiveness" to the train at the valve opening and valve closure to reduce the shock loading. When valves are set loose, the valvetrain is loaded at a point on the cam ramp beyond the intended point. The same occurs at valve closure when the valve is seated. High valve opening and closing velocities subject the valve and its seat to hammering that can result in cracking, failure at the head-to-stem fillet, and scuffing to the cam and its follower.

VALVE ADJUSTMENT PROCEDURE

The following steps outline the valve adjustment procedure on a typical four-stroke cycle, inline six-cylinder diesel engine. Valves should always be adjusted using the OEM's specifications and procedures.

CAUTION:

Shortcutting the engine OEM-recommended valve (and injector) setting can result in engine damage unless the technician knows the engine well. Cam profiles are not always symmetrical, and some engines may have camshaft profiles designed with ramps between the base circle and outer base circle for purposes such as actuating engine compression brakes. Similarly, a valve rocker that shows what appears to be excessive lash when not in its setting position is not necessarily defective.

In order to set valve lash, you should become familiar with the cylinder firing order and companion cylinders on an inline six-cylinder engine. The inline six-cylinder engine is currently the universal commercial diesel engine configuration and all technician certification testing requires the ability to navigate its features and operating principles.

Six-cylinder engine firing order: 1–5–3–6–2–4
Companion cylinders or cylinder throw pairings:
1–6 at TDC
5–2 at 120 degrees BTDC
3–4 at 120 degrees ATDC

CAUTION:

Always check OEM service literature before checking and setting valves. On engines that require the valves and mechanically actuated injectors to be set simultaneously, failure to position the engine in the precise setting location can result in engine damage.

Companion Cylinders

Cylinder throw pairings are called **companion cylinders**. In other words, when #1 piston is at TDC completing its compression stroke, #6 piston (its companion) is also at TDC having just completed its exhaust stroke. If the engine is viewed from overhead with the rocker covers removed, engine position can be identified by observing the valves over a pair of companion cylinders. For instance, when the engine timing indicator (timing marker) indicates that the pistons in cylinders #1 and #6 are approaching TDC and the valves over #6 are both closed (lash is evident), then the point at which the valves over #1 cylinder rock (exhaust closing, intake opening) at valve overlap will indicate that #1 is at TDC having completed its exhaust stroke and #6 is at TDC having completed its compression stroke. This method of orienting engine location is commonly used for valve adjustment.

Adjustment

1. Locate the valve lash dimensions. These are often specified on the engine ID plate on the rocker housing cover or cylinder block. The lash specification for the exhaust valve(s) is usually (but not always) greater than that for the inlet valve.
2. The valves on current diesel engines should usually be set under static conditions and with the engine coolant at 100°F (37°C) or less. Locate the engine timing indicator and the cylinder calibration indexes, 120 degrees apart; depending on the engine, this may be located on a vibration damper, on any pulley driven at engine speed, or on the flywheel.
3. Ensure that the engine is prevented from starting by mechanically or electronically no-fueling the engine. The engine will have to be barred in its normal direction of rotation through two revolutions during the valve-setting procedure, requiring the engine to be no-fueled to avoid an unintended startup.
4. If the engine is equipped with valve bridges or yokes (**Figure 8–30**) that require adjustment, this procedure should be performed before the valve adjustment. To adjust a valve yoke, back off the rocker arm, then loosen the yoke adjusting screw locknut and back off the yoke adjusting screw. Using finger pressure on the rocker arm (or yoke), load the pallet end (opposite to the adjusting screw) of the yoke to contact the valve; next, screw the yoke adjusting screw clockwise until it bottoms on the other valve

FIGURE 8–30 Valve bridge/yoke assembly.

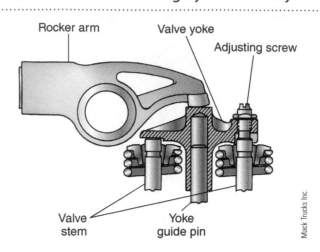

Mack Trucks Inc.

stem. Turn an additional one flat of a nut (60 degrees) as shown in **Figure 8–31**, then lock to position by torquing the jam nut.

CAUTION:

When loosening and tightening the valve yoke adjusting screw locknut, the guide on the cylinder head is vulnerable to bending. Most OEMs recommend that the yoke be removed from the guide and placed in a vise to back off and final-torque the adjusting screw locknut.

5. To verify that the yoke is properly adjusted, insert two similarly sized thickness gauges of 0.010" (0.25 mm) or less between each valve stem and the yoke. Load the yoke with finger pressure on the rocker arm and simultaneously withdraw both thickness gauges; they should produce equal drag as they are withdrawn. If the yokes are to be adjusted, they can be adjusted in sequence as each valve is adjusted. In some engines, valve yokes can only be adjusted with the rocker assemblies removed, because it is impossible to access the yoke to verify the adjustment otherwise.
6. If the instructions in the OEM literature indicate that valves must be adjusted in a specific engine location, ensure that this is observed; the cams that actuate the valves may only have a small percentage of IBC. Setting valves requires the lash dimension between the rocker arm and the valve stem on the rocker arm and the valve yoke to be defined. When performing this procedure, the valve adjusting screw jam nut should be backed off and the adjusting screw backed

FIGURE 8–31 Adjusting a valve bridge/yoke assembly: The procedure on this engine is to bottom the adjusting screw, turn one flat, then torque the jam nut.

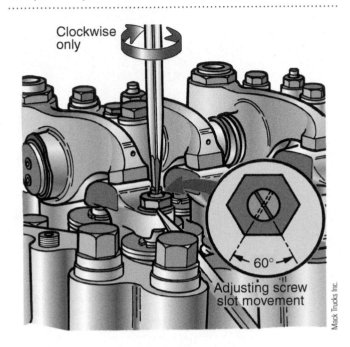

Mack Trucks Inc.

FIGURE 8–32 Adjusting intake valve lash on a Mack Trucks E-Tech engine.

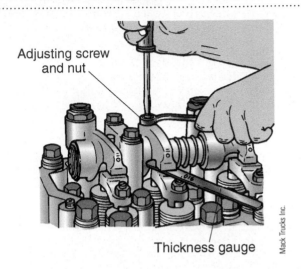

Mack Trucks Inc.

out. Insert the specified size of thickness gauge between the rocker and the valve stem/yoke. Release the thickness gauge. Then turn the adjusting screw clockwise until it bottoms; turn an additional ½ flat of a hex nut (30 degrees). Hold the adjusting screw with a screwdriver and with a wrench, torque the jam nut. Now, for the first time since inserting the thickness gauge, handle

it once again; withdraw the thickness gauge. A light drag indicates that the valve is properly set. If the valve lash setting is either too loose or too tight, repeat the setting procedure. Do *not* set valves too tight. Set all the valves in cylinder firing order sequence, rotating the engine 120 degrees between settings. It is preferable to begin at #1 cylinder and proceed through the engine in firing order sequence. **Figure 8–32** shows this procedure: Note that the feeler gauge is not being held during the adjustment. Sometimes an engine top end set can be done in just two engine locations set one revolution apart. **Figure 8–33** shows the locations for setting valves on a DT466 engine.

FIGURE 8–33 Valve lash adjustment on a Navistar International DT466E. Note that all the valves can be adjusted in just two engine positions.

With	Adjust Valves									
Piston 1 at TDC (compression)	INT 1	EXH 2	INT 3			EXH 6	INT 7		EXH 10	
Piston 6 at TDC (compression)				EXH 4	INT 5			EXH 8	INT 9	INT 11	EXH 12

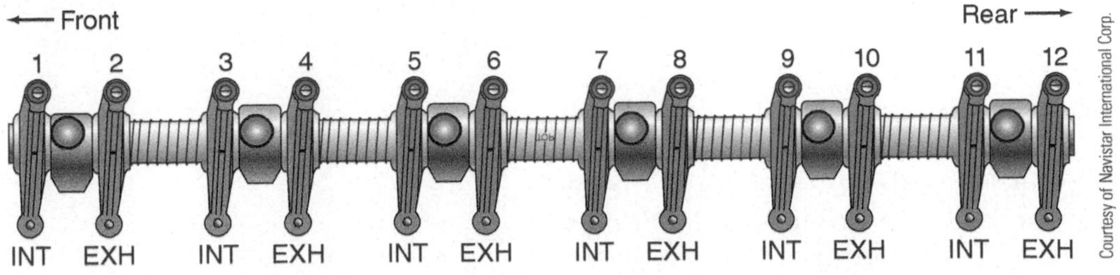

← Front   Rear →

1 2 3 4 5 6 7 8 9 10 11 12

INT EXH   INT EXH   INT EXH   INT EXH   INT EXH   INT EXH

Courtesy of Navistar International Corp.

Barring Engines

When setting valves, you will have to rotate the engine. With today's engines, the technician should use the OEM-approved method specified in its service literature. Manually barring an engine into overhead setting positions can be made easier if a tool such as that shown in **Figure 8–34** is used: This engages with the flywheel ring gear teeth, allowing the engine to be easily rotated with a ½-drive ratchet. These tools are available for several current diesel engines.

VARIABLE VALVE TIMING

Variable valve timing (VVT) refers simply to any means used to vary either the opening or closing of cylinder valves. Highway diesel engines have used engine compression brakes for five decades. Engine brake controls were

FIGURE 8–34 Barring an engine using a toothed barring tool while observing the engine position scale.

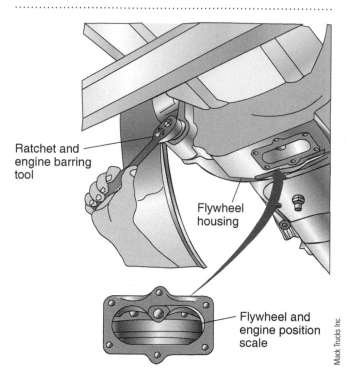

Ratchet and engine barring tool

Flywheel housing

Flywheel and engine position scale

Mack Trucks Inc.

initially hydromechanically controlled and actuated, but since the early 1990s, these have been electronically controlled and hydraulically (engine lube) actuated. More recently, VVT of intake valves has been introduced. **Figure 8–35**

FIGURE 8–35 Caterpillar ACERT C13 variable valve actuator assembly: The VVA fits over the rocker assembly.

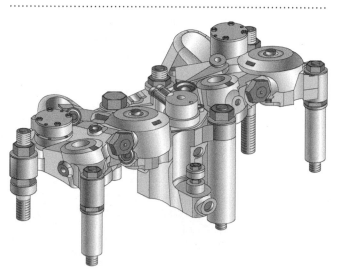

shows the **variable valve actuator (VVA)** assembly used on a Caterpillar C13 engine. Having the ability to manage the moment of intake valve closure permits retarding the beginning of the compression stroke, with the net result that the ECM can determine exactly how much intake gas is admitted to the engine cylinder. This enables a large engine to behave like a smaller engine when the power output requirement is lower, along with a bonus of reducing emissions. VVT is addressed in more detail in later chapters, when discussing specific engines that use it as a combustion and emissions management strategy.

VALVES: CONCLUSION

Valves are normally—but not always—set when the piston is at TDC on the cylinder being set. There are some very critical exceptions to this rule that are addressed in later chapters. When the piston is at TDC on the compression stroke, it can usually be assumed that the valves are fully closed. The procedure for setting valves in an engine is sometimes referred to as **overhead adjustment** or tune-up. In most cases, the valve setting procedure is accompanied by procedures such as injector timing and/or lash setting/train loading.

OTHER FEEDBACK ASSEMBLY FUNCTIONS

The engine feedback assembly in many modern engines is responsible for actuating the pumping of fuel to injection pressure values. Some current and many older engines are fueled by mechanically actuated injectors. These include different types of mechanical unit injectors (MUIs), EUIs, and electronic unit pumps (EUPs). The high-pressure fueling apparatus on all of these engines is actuated by cam profile. Because the means of actuating each type of pumping device is distinct to each OEM system, this area is covered in later chapters dealing with each fuel system.

Injector pumping train components are arranged somewhat similarly to the valvetrains and depend largely on the location of the camshaft and the force required to actuate the pump elements, which can be considerable. For instance, in engines with a block-mounted camshaft, the push tubes used in the injector train must be built to sustain much higher compressional loads than those used in the valve trains.

FIGURE 8–36 View of the top end of a Volvo 16-liter diesel engine showing the OHC and valve arrangement after removal of the rocker assemblies.

Injector actuation trains usually have to be precisely set, because the location of the injector pumping plunger is moved when the train is adjusted. Failure to observe the injector height specification, which is often set with a tram gauge, can affect fuel delivery timing. These critical adjustments are examined later in this book. **Figure 8–36** shows a view from the rear of a Volvo OHC 16-liter engine after removal of the rockers.

CREATING A VALVE POLAR DIAGRAM

If you take a look at Figure 8–7, captioned "Camshaft timing events," earlier in this chapter, you can observe the key cylinder head valve opening and closing events during the diesel cycle. A **valve polar diagram** is a somewhat simplified version of this illustration that can be performed on any engine. It is an especially useful learning tool for entry-level students because it requires that the engine be closely observed through an entire effective cycle. The objective is to map the valve opening and closing events by observing the rockers as an engine is barred over. Students can perform this exercise by first mapping the valves only. Then they can advance to include injector actuation train activity on engines equipped with mechanically actuated injection systems such as those using PT, MUI,

EUI, EUP, and HPI-TP fuel systems. When performing this exercise, you should try to be as precise as possible. You should end up with a diagram similar to that shown in Figure 8–7, but with specifications for the engine on which you are working.

SUMMARY

- The engine feedback components incorporate the engine timing geartrain, the camshaft, valve and unit injector trains, and, in some cases, the injection pumping apparatus. For purposes of study, the actuation mechanisms of the fuel injection components are examined in the sections dealing with specific fuel systems.
- Camshaft drive gears must be precisely timed with the crankshaft-driven, engine geartrain so that the events activated by the engine feedback assembly are synchronized with those in the engine.
- The camshaft drive gear is most often interference-fit to the camshaft and positioned by a keyway.
- Camshaft gears are heat treated when they are fitted to camshafts, so it is essential that they be heated evenly to a precise temperature for fitting to the camshaft. Overheating will result in premature failure.
- Camshafts may be rotated either with, or opposite to, the direction of engine rotation.
- Camshaft gears may use spur or helical cut gear teeth; thrust loads are much higher when helical gears are used, but they are much quieter in operation.
- Gear backlash must be measured using thickness gauges or dial indicators.
- Cam lift on block-located camshafts may be inspected using a dial indicator mounted above the push tube or rod.
- Cam base circle or IBC is that portion of the cam periphery with the smallest radial dimension. Cam OBC is that portion of the cam periphery with the largest radial dimension.
- The critical cam dimensions may be checked on an overhead camshaft or an out-of-engine camshaft with a micrometer. Cam lift can be checked with a dial indicator in a block-mounted camshaft.
- A visual inspection of the camshaft should identify most cam failures, but profile wear may be checked to specification using a straightedge and thickness gauges. The camshaft should be mounted in V-blocks to test for straightness.
- Out-of-engine camshafts should be supported on pedestals, on V-blocks, or hung vertically to prevent damage.
- Most medium- and large-bore diesel engine cam followers are of the solid or roller types; when hydraulic lifters are used in diesel engines, it is in small-bore applications.
- A cam train consists of the series of components it is responsible for actuating.
- Most truck diesel engines with block-mounted camshafts use trains consisting of a follower assembly, push tubes, and rockers.
- OHCs are used in many current diesel engines; when used, the injector and valve trains are actuated indirectly using rocker arms.
- Most valvetrains are adjusted with a lash factor to allow for expansion of the materials as the engine heats to operating temperature.
- Some injection pumping actuation trains are set at zero lash or even a slight load when the actuating cam profile is on its IBC. Injector train settings may have to be precisely set because they help define injection timing.
- Rocker assemblies provide a means of reversing the direction of linear movement of the push tube or follower; in some cases this provides a mechanical advantage.
- Cylinder head valves are used to aspirate or breathe the engine cylinders. They are actuated by the cam geometry and time the air into and end gases out of the engine cylinders.
- Exhaust valves are often manufactured of more highly alloyed steels than intake valves because they must sustain much higher temperatures.
- When reconditioning valves by regrinding, a critical specification is the valve margin.
- Most diesel engines do not use an interference angle to seat valves, because the seating contact surface area is compromised.
- A 45-degree cut valve has higher seating force but lower gas flow than a 30-degree cut valve.
- Valve seats are usually interference-fit to the cylinder head and finish ground concentric to the valve guide bore.

- When setting valve lash, the OEM specifications as to engine position for the valve being adjusted should be observed because the cam geometry on some engines is not clearly divisible into IBC and OBC sections.
- Valve lash should be set using thickness gauges; valves in current engines are set statically and cold.
- Loose valves cause lower cylinder breathing efficiencies and what is known as top end clatter, and may damage cam profiles.
- Valve yokes or bridges do not usually have to be adjusted as part of a routine valve adjustment: It is important that the bridge be properly supported to prevent its pedestal guide from being damaged.
- Variable valve timing is commonly used to control exhaust valves for engine braking and also to delay intake valve closing for purposes of reducing emissions.
- Creating a valve polar diagram is an effective way to map the valve opening and closing events in any engine you choose. You can also map how mechanically actuated injectors are phased into the cycle.

REVIEW QUESTIONS

1. The location on a cam profile that is exactly opposite the toe is referred to as the:
   a. nose.
   b. ramp.
   c. heel.
   d. sole.

2. On a cam profile described as mostly inner base circle, the profiles between IBC and OBC are known as:
   a. cam geometry.
   b. ramps.
   c. ridges.
   d. heels.

3. Which of the following dimensions would be consistent with a typical engine timing gear backlash setting?
   a. 0.002" (0.05 mm)
   b. 0.008" (0.20 mm)
   c. 0.014" (0.36 mm)
   d. 0.024" (0.60 mm)

4. In which direction must a camshaft be rotated on a diesel engine with a crankshaft that is rotated clockwise?
   a. Either clockwise or counterclockwise depending on the engine
   b. Clockwise
   c. Counterclockwise

5. Which tool would be required to measure the cam lift of a cylinder block-mounted camshaft in position?
   a. A dial indicator
   b. An outside micrometer
   c. A depth micrometer
   d. Thickness gauges

6. A camshaft gear is usually precisely positioned on the camshaft using a(n):
   a. interference fit.
   b. key and keyway.
   c. captured thrust washer.
   d. dial indicator.

7. When grinding a valve face to remove pitting, the critical specification to monitor during machining would be the:
   a. shank diameter.
   b. stem.
   c. poppet diameter.
   d. margin.

8. Which of the following operating conditions would be more likely to cause a valve float condition?
   a. Engine lug down
   b. Operating in the torque rise profile
   c. Engine overspeed
   d. Operating in the droop curve

9. When grinding a new set of cylinder valve seats, which of the following should be performed before the machining?
   a. Install the valves.
   b. Install the rockers.
   c. Adjust the valve yokes.
   d. Install the valve guides.

10. The reason for using a pair of oppositely wound valve springs is to:
    a. minimize valve dynamic flutter.
    b. double the closing force of two similarly wound valves.
    c. increase the valve closing velocity.
    d. diminish valve noise.

11. Technician A states that the backlash in timing gearsets can be measured with a dial indicator. Technician B states that if the gear backlash is insufficient, the result can be gear whine. Who is correct?
   a. Technician A only
   b. Technician B only
   c. Both A and B
   d. Neither A nor B

12. Technician A states that helical cut gears are often used in engine timing geartrains because they operate more quietly. Technician B states that shaft thrust loads are much higher when helical cut gears are used. Who is correct?
   a. Technician A only
   b. Technician B only
   c. Both A and B
   d. Neither A nor B

13. Technician A states that when installing an interference-fit gear to a shaft, the gear should not be heated above 400°F. Technician B states that if an oxyacetylene rosebud is not available, an interference-fit gear should be pressed to the shaft using a hydraulic press. Who is correct?
   a. Technician A only
   b. Technician B only
   c. Both A and B
   d. Neither A nor B

14. Technician A states that it is good practice to lubricate the inside bores of camshaft bushings to facilitate camshaft installation. Technician B states that if the cam bushing oil holes are not properly aligned, an immediate camshaft failure could be the result. Who is correct?
   a. Technician A only
   b. Technician B only
   c. Both A and B
   d. Neither A nor B

15. Which of the following methods is used to transfer drive from the crankshaft to the camshaft on most commercial diesel engines?
   a. Belt and pulley
   b. Timing chain and sprocket
   c. Gears
   d. Fluid coupling

16. Technician A states that variable valve timing (VVT) is used on some diesel engines to delay the closing of intake valves on the compression stroke. Technician B states that VVT is used to open the intake valves early during the power stroke. Who is correct?
   a. Technician A only
   b. Technician B only
   c. Both A and B
   d. Neither A nor B

17. What type of cam geometry is required if the objective is to load the train that rides it for most of the cycle?
   a. Mostly OBC profile
   b. Mostly IBC profile
   c. Symmetrical OBC and IBC profiles

18. Technician A states that the camshaft on a two-stroke cycle engine turns through one complete rotation per complete engine revolution. Technician B states that the camshaft on a four-stroke cycle diesel engine rotates through one revolution per two engine revolutions. Who is correct?
   a. Technician A only
   b. Technician B only
   c. Both A and B
   d. Neither A nor B

19. Technician A states that to check cam lift, the camshaft must be removed from the engine to obtain a valid reading. Technician B states that to check for a bent camshaft, the camshaft should be removed from the engine and runout tested in V-blocks. Who is correct?
   a. Technician A only
   b. Technician B only
   c. Both A and B
   d. Neither A nor B

20. Technician A states that valves machined with 45-degree seats breathe with higher efficiencies than those machined with 30-degree seats. Technician B states that valves machined with 30-degree seats run cooler than those machined with 45-degree seats. Who is correct?
   a. Technician A only
   b. Technician B only
   c. Both A and B
   d. Neither A nor B

Prerequisites: Chapters 4, 7, and 8

ENGINE HOUSING COMPONENTS

OBJECTIVES

After studying this chapter, you should be able to:

- Identify the components classified as engine housing components.
- Identify the types of cylinder block used in current truck diesel engines.
- Outline the procedure required to inspect a cylinder block.
- Measure an engine block to specifications using service literature.
- Identify the types of cylinder liners used in diesel engines.
- Explain the procedure required to remove dry, wet, and midstop liners.
- Describe the process required to remove a seized dry liner from a block bore.
- Perform selective fitting of a set of dry liners to a cylinder block.
- Explain how cavitation erosion occurs on wet liners.
- Identify the types of cylinder heads used in truck diesel engines.
- Describe the component parts of a cylinder head.
- Define *component creep* and *gasket yield*.
- Explain the procedure required to measure, test, and recondition a cylinder head.
- Describe the role of the intake and exhaust manifolds.
- Describe the function of the oil pan in the engine.
- Determine the types of oil pan failures that may be repairable by welding.

KEY TERMS

bubble collapse	cylinder block	interference fit	sleeves
buttress screws	cylinder head	liners	sump
cavitation	dry liners	oil pan	template torque
compacted graphite iron (CGI)	exhaust manifold	parent bore	torque-to-yield
crankcase	fire rings	plasma transfer wire arc (PTWA)	wet liners
creep	gasket	scavenging pump	yield point
	intake manifold		

weight—at least until all of the emissions control hardware on the current engine has been weighed. Most diesel engine OEMs today use compacted graphite iron (CGI) in cylinder block construction because of its light weight and ability to withstand much higher forces.

CGI Cylinder Blocks

CGI cylinder blocks (see Figure 9–1) have been a key to reducing engine weight over the past decade. Contemporary high-horsepower diesel engines often weigh less than engines having half their horsepower made just 10 years ago. Almost all OEMs use CGI cylinder blocks on their heavy-duty engines. Among the benefits of CGI are:

- 70% lighter than an equivalent gray cast-iron block
- 200% the fatigue limit of gray
- 40% more rigid than gray cast iron

Plasma Transfer Wire Arc

In the past, Caterpillar has used **plasma transfer wire arc (PTWA)** as a method of reconditioning diesel engines with cast-iron parent bores, but the technology is now used to enable the use of parent bore aluminum cylinder blocks in light- and medium-duty diesels. The PTWA process provides a highly temperature- and wear-resistant surface on either iron or aluminum alloys. The process uses a combination of compressed air and electricity to create a plasma jet with temperatures up to 35,000°F (19,500°C), into which steel wire is fed by a rotating spray gun. This breaks up the melting steel wire into droplets of around 25 microns, which molecularly bond to the liner walls. As the melted steel oxidizes, it forms a crystalline structure known as Wuestite, producing a final cladded thickness of about 150 microns. When PTWA is used on aluminum alloy cylinder blocks, the surface toward which PTWA is targeted must be pretreated. The PTWA process is commonly known as *cladding*. Cladded cylinder blocks cannot be reconditioned without the use of specialized equipment.

CYLINDER BLOCK FUNCTIONS

Although there are some differences among manufacturers, a diesel engine cylinder block must perform some or all of the following:

- Incorporate bores for the piston assemblies.
- Incorporate main bearing bores to mount the crankshaft.
- Incorporate coolant passages/water jacket.
- Incorporate lubricant passages/drillings.
- Incorporate mounting locations for other engine components.

A cylinder block may contain longitudinal bore(s) to mount the camshaft(s). Figure 9–2 shows the bores and passages identified above. **Figure 9–3** shows the location of expansion or cup plugs in a typical six-cylinder engine block. These are usually fitted with a slight interference and retained by a medium-duty adhesive such as blue Loctite.

FIGURE 9–3 Inline 6-cylinder block showing the location of the cup plugs and installation method.

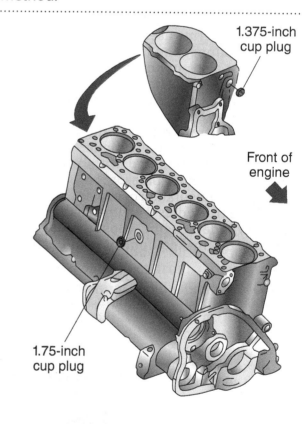

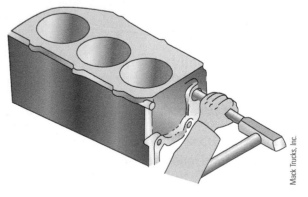

1.375-inch cup plug

Front of engine

1.75-inch cup plug

Mack Trucks, Inc.

CATEGORIES OF CYLINDER BLOCK

Cylinder blocks used in commercial diesel engines can be categorized by type:

- Integral cylinder bore or parent bore
- Cladded surface parent bore
- Wet sleeve/liner
- Dry sleeve/liner
- Combination wet/dry liners

Other factors, such as two-stroke cycle and air cooled, are also reflected in the block design.

INTEGRAL CYLINDER BORE

Most automobile and small-bore engines use integral or parent bore cylinder blocks. Until recently, they were less likely to be seen in commercial diesel engines, especially those of large-bore dimensions. There was a time when an integral cylinder bore was used in a medium-bore application; they were referred to by the derogatory term "throw-away blocks." This came about because it was difficult to bore for sleeves on a rebuild due to the close proximity of the bore's cylinders to one another. However, this has changed by the introduction of induction hardening of iron-based cylinder blocks and specialized cladding processes such as the PTWA described earlier.

The older Caterpillar 3208, Cummins ISB, and MB-900 family of engines (manufactured until 2010) are examples of parent cylinder block assemblies. The initial cost savings in producing a block of this design may be compromised at engine overhaul when the block requires either replacement, a boring/sleeving machining operation, or factory reconditioning. The advantages of parent bore engines are:

- Lower initial cost
- No liner O-rings to fail
- No liner protrusion specs to adhere to on reassembly

Induction-Hardened Parent Bore

In the late 1990s, Freightliner/Mercedes-Benz introduced a parent bore engine in which the cylinder bores were induction hardened. The MB-900 engine families of four- and six-cylinder engines use a unique, helical-striped, induction-hardening feature in the upper ring belt sweep. This is claimed to give the bores considerably extended service life compared with other parent bore engines. In the event the cylinder bores are worn to oversize, they can be bored and sleeved. Mercedes-Benz recommend that only the manufacturer perform sleeving on these engines. This engine became very successful in both on- and off-highway applications, but has not been used for on-highway applications after model year (MY) 2010.

PTWA Parent Bore

The PTWA process described a little earlier has been used for some years as a means of reconditioning diesel engines with cast-iron parent bores, but the technology can be adapted to clad aluminum alloy cylinder block bores. Because OEMs are constantly working to make diesel engines lighter in weight, aluminum cylinder blocks with PTWA bores are already used in light-duty diesel engines, and it is likely only a matter of time before we see aluminum heavy-duty diesel engine cylinder blocks.

WET LINER/SLEEVE

The cylinder block is designed so that the water jacket is in direct contact with the liner in the block bore; the liner must therefore have a wall thickness sufficient to sustain the engine's peak combustion pressures. **Wet liners** transfer heat efficiently into the coolant and are easily replaced at overhaul. Their main disadvantage is that a seal must be maintained for the life of the liner and that an O-ring failure results in coolant contamination of the engine lube.

Cavitation caused by vapor bubble implosion can shorten the life of wet liners, but this is seldom a problem if the coolant chemistry is properly monitored. Despite the fact that a wet liner is constructed from a sizeable mass of cast iron or steel, it is relatively easily flexed. Try installing a telescoping gauge into the bore of a wet liner on the bench and locking it so it grabs into position. Gentle hand pressure is sufficient to flex the liner enough for the telescoping gauge to unseat and drop to the bottom of the liner. Now think about how much flexing could occur when the liner is subject to 3,000 psi (207 bar) of combustion pressure.

How Cavitation Erosion Occurs

Wet liners, when subject to cylinder pressures, which may be as high as 3,000 psi (207 bar), expand outward into the wall of coolant that surrounds them and then contract, creating a sort of lower pressure void or "bubble" whose matter is actually boiled-off coolant vapor. This bubble almost immediately collapses, causing the wall of coolant to collide with the liner exterior wall. The condition repeats itself at high frequency (17 times per second on each liner at 2,000 rpm) and has been tested to produce pressures of up to 60,000 psi (4137 bar). **Bubble collapse** results in cavitation unless the coolant provides protection in the form of a coating on the exterior of the liner wall. Cavitation can be identified by pitting/erosion that usually appears on the liner outside the thrust faces of the piston.

Liner O-Rings

The O-rings used to seal wet liners are made from a variety of rubber-type compounds, and it is important that the OEM installation recommendations be observed. Rubber type means that O-rings may be 100% rubber or be derived entirely from petro chemicals—or any combination of the two. OEM recommendations can include that O-rings be installed dry or coated in coolant, soap, engine oil, and various other substances. The reason is that some O-rings are designed to react to the coating substance and swell, creating a perfect seal. Wet liners are often alloyed so they possess characteristics metallurgically superior to the block casting, which increase service life. One OEM induction hardens the inside bore liner.

Dry Sleeves

A thinner-walled sleeve than the wet liner, the dry sleeve is installed into the block bore usually with a marginally loose fit and retained by the cylinder head. The dry sleeve does not transfer heat as efficiently as the wet liner, but it is easily replaced and does not present coolant sealing problems.

In older applications, **dry liners** were made of cast-iron material almost identical to that of the engine block; these were installed with a fractional interference to maximize heat transfer. Current dry liners tend to be alloyed for superior toughness, and because a liner's ability to transfer heat is dependent on maximizing its surface contact area in the cylinder block bore, they are manufactured with a slightly greater coefficient of heat expansion than cast iron. They are therefore designed to be installed loose so they expand into the block bore when heated, maximizing the contact surface. If this type of liner is installed with an interference fit, they buckle in use, greatly reducing their service life. Precise measuring of the block bore inside diameter (id), the liner outside diameter (od), and selective fitting eases installation and increases

engine longevity. Loose fits of around 0.0015" (0.035 mm) are common.

Combination Wet/Dry Sleeves

The wet/dry sleeve is designed so that the hottest part of the liner at the top is in direct contact with the coolant in the water jacket and the lower portion fits directly to the cylinder block with a fractional loose or interference fit. Consequently, the upper portion in direct contact with the water jacket must have considerably more mass, because it has to contain the cylinder combustion pressures. Wet/dry liners are required to seal the water jacket usually with O-rings. They are also known as *midstop liners*. **Figure 9–4** shows a typical wet/dry liner and counterbore shims: The crevice seal (item 1) is used to seal coolant within the cylinder block water jacket: coolant is in direct contact with the upper section of the midstop liner. **Figure 9–5** is a wet liner, with most of its exterior surface exposed to the cylinder block water jacket. **Figure 9–6** is a photo image of a midstop or wet/dry liner. The crevice seals used in any liners exposed to the water jacket should be lubricated according to OEM instructions. Depending on the type

FIGURE 9–4 Wet/dry liner components.

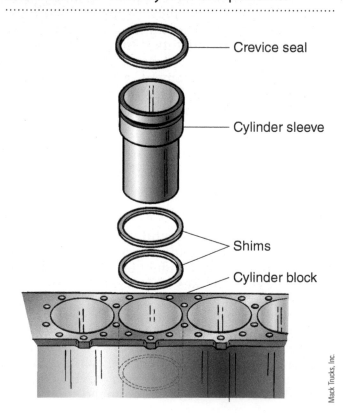

- Crevice seal
- Cylinder sleeve
- Shims
- Cylinder block

Mack Trucks, Inc.

FIGURE 9–5 A typical wet liner.

FIGURE 9–6 A midstop liner.

of rubber compound used for the crevice seal, the instruction may be to install it:

- Dry
- Lubed with ethylene glycol
- Lubed with a proprietary soap solution

Cylinder Sleeve Removal

Sleeves should be removed with a puller and adaptor plate or shoe. The procedure is obviously more simple on wet liners. Dry sleeves often require the use of mechanical (**Figure 9–7**), hydraulic, or air-over-hydraulic pullers. When these fail to extract a seized liner, vertical arc weld runs may break a liner free, but great care has to be exercised because the block may become distorted. To use this method of removing a seized liner, first ensure that every critical engine component is moved well out of the way, then use two vertical-down runs with an E6010/11 electrode at 90 degrees from the piston thrust faces. Shock-cool the welds with cold water and attempt to use the puller again. Avoid fracturing seized liners out of their bores, as this practice almost always results in bore damage. As a last resort, liners can be machined out using a boring jig.

TECH TIP:

Removing pistons from cylinder liners can be made easier by removing the ridge of carbon buildup that forms at the top of the ring belt sweep (**Figure 9–8**). The carbon in the wear ridge can be removed using a flexible knife blade followed by gentle use of emery cloth. Note that on some engines, the piston cannot be drawn through the liner bore during disassembly; these may require the removal of the piston and liner as an assembly or (in some off-highway engines) removal of the crankshaft.

FIGURE 9–7 Pulling a liner using a mechanical puller.

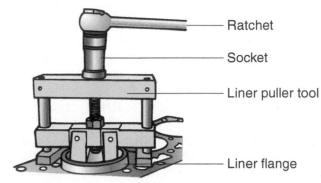

— Ratchet

— Socket

— Liner puller tool

— Liner flange

FIGURE 9–8 Cylinder wear ridge.

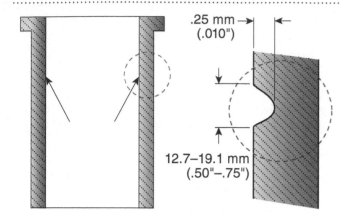

.25 mm → (.010")

12.7–19.1 mm (.50"–.75")

FIGURE 9–9 Installing counterbore shims on a Navistar DT 466E engine.

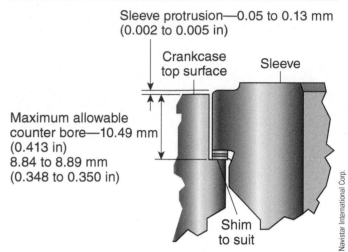

Sleeve protrusion—0.05 to 0.13 mm (0.002 to 0.005 in)

Crankcase top surface

Sleeve

Maximum allowable counter bore—10.49 mm (0.413 in) 8.84 to 8.89 mm (0.348 to 0.350 in)

Shim to suit

Courtesy of Navistar International Corp.

Maximum allowable variation of counterbore between four points—0.025 mm (0.001 in)

Block Serviceability Checks

1. Strip the block completely, including the cup expansion and gallery plugs.
2. Soak in a hot or cold tank with the correct cleaning solution.
3. Check for scaling in the water jacket not removed by soaking. One OEM reports that 0.060" (1.5 mm) scale buildup has the insulating effect of 4" (100 mm) cast iron.
4. Check for excessive erosion around the deck coolant ports and fire ring seats.
5. Electromagnetic flux test the block for cracks at each out-of-chassis overhaul.

Final Inspection and Assembly

1. Check for deck warpage using a straightedge and thickness gauge. A typical maximum specification is approximately 0.004" (0.1 mm), but always reference OEM tolerances.
2. Check the main bearing bore and alignment. Check the engine service history to ensure that the engine has not previously been line bored. A master bar is used to check alignment for a specific engine series. Check that the correct bar has been selected for the engine being tested and then clamp to position by torquing down the main caps minus the main bearings. The master bar should rotate in the cylinder block main bearing line bore without binding. Should it bind, the cylinder block should be line bored.
3. Check the cylinder sleeve counterbore (**Figure 9–9**) for the correct depth and circumference. Counterbore depth should typically not vary by more than 0.001". Counterbore depth can be subtracted from the sleeve flange dimension to calculate sleeve

protrusion. The liner protrusion dimension may be set by shims, shim plates, or liner selective flange depth. When counterbores have to be recut, ensure that the OEM recommended tools are used and that the counterbores are shimmed to specification.
4. Check the cam bore dimensions and install the cam bushings with the correct cam bushing installation equipment: Use drivers with great care, as the bushings may easily be damaged, and ensure that the oil holes are lined up before driving each bushing home.
5. Install the gallery and expansion plugs. These are often interference-fitted and sealed with silicone, thread sealants, and hydraulic dope. **Figure 9–10** shows a Volvo D13 prepped for reassembly with the liners and expansion plugs installed.

PTWA Liner Cladding

The PTWA process, described earlier regarding its application on cast-iron and aluminum alloy parent bores, is also being applied to cylinder liners. PTWA cladded liners can greatly add to cylinder liner longevity, in many cases meaning that liners do not have to be replaced through the life of an engine. It should be noted that when liners are PTWA cladded and the liner internal surface becomes damaged, the liners must be replaced rather than reconditioned.

FIGURE 9–10 A Volvo engine cylinder block fitted with liners.

FIGURE 9–11 Cylinder crosshatch cut with a 200-grit stone on a Volvo D16 engine.

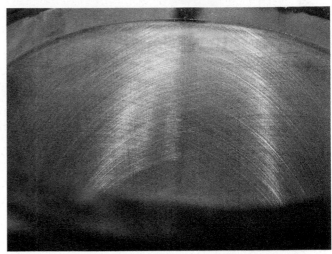

LINER AND SLEEVE RECONDITIONING

Liner and sleeve reconditioning is not a common practice currently, due to the time limit constraints on the technician and projected service life of reconditioned liners. It is probably good practice to advise customers against reconditioning liners, citing the fact that it will probably cost them more in the long term. OEMs make oversize liners when the block bores are damaged and have to be rebored. Two basic methods of liner reconditioning are used.

Glaze Busting

When checked to be within serviceability specs, the liner should be deglazed. Deglazing involves the least amount of material removal. A power-driven (heavy-duty electric drill with accurate rpm control) flex hone or rigid hone with 200- to 250-grit stones can be used for deglazing. The best type of glaze buster is the flex hone, typically a conical (Christmas tree) or cylindrically shaped shaft with flexible branches of carbon/abrasive balls.

PRESERVING CROSSHATCH The objective of glaze busting is to machine away the cylinder ridge above the ring belt travel and reestablish the crosshatch. The drill should be set at 120 to 180 rpm and used in rhythmic reciprocating thrusts: short sequences with frequent stops to

inspect the finish produce the best results. A 60- to 70-degree horizontal crossover angle (some OEMs express this as 120- to 130-vertical crosshatch), 15 to 20 micro-inch (0.00038 to 0.00050 mm) depth crosshatch should be observed (Figure 9–9). When using a spring-loaded hone to deglaze liners, results are produced faster, but there is also more chance of damaging the cylinder liner. **Figure 9–11** shows the crosshatch on a Volvo D16 engine after machining.

Honing

Honing is performed with a rigid hone, powered once again at low speeds by either a drill or overhead boring jig. The typical cylinder hone consists of three legs, which are static set to produce a radial load into the liner wall. The abrasive grit rating of the stones determines the aggressiveness of the tool—200- to 250-grit stones are typical. Overhead boring tools can be programmed to produce the required stroke rate for the specified crosshatch, but if using a hand-held tool, remember that a few short strokes with a moderate radial load tend to produce a better crosshatch pattern than many strokes with a light radial load.

CREATING CROSSHATCH Once again, a 60- to 70-degree horizontal crossover angle, 15 to 20 micro-inch crosshatch should be observed. It should be clearly visible by eye, as shown in Figure 9–9. The honing process is designed to produce the specified crosshatch geometry so that the liner contact surface retains the oil required to enable rings to seal effectively. When installing

FIGURE 9–12 Sealing a wet/dry liner.

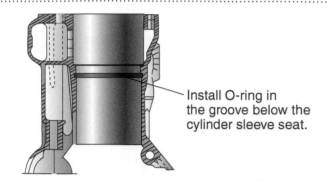

Install O-ring in the groove below the cylinder sleeve seat.

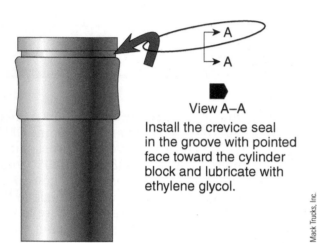

View A–A

Install the crevice seal in the groove with pointed face toward the cylinder block and lubricate with ethylene glycol.

Mack Trucks, Inc.

wet liners, observe the OEM installation procedure. **Figure 9–12** shows a typical method of sealing a wet/dry liner in the cylinder bore.

Selective Fitting of Liners

Selective fitting of liners to block bores is good practice whether or not the block bore has been machined. To selective-fit a set of dry liners to a block, measure the inside diameter of each block bore across the north-south and east-west faces and grade in order of size. Next, get the set of new liners and measure the outside diameter of each, once again grading in order of size. Ensure that *every* measurement falls within the OEM specifications. Then fit the liner with the largest outside diameter to the block bore with the largest inside diameter and so on, down in sequence.

CYLINDER HEADS

Cylinder heads seal the engine cylinders and manage cylinder breathing. In diesel applications, they are usually cast-iron assemblies

FIGURE 9–13 Top and bottom views of a typical cylinder head.

Mack Trucks, Inc.

machined with breathing tracts and ports, cooling and lubrication circuit manifolds, fuel manifolds, and injector bores. The 2011 Paccar MX family of engines uses CGI cylinder heads along with CGI cylinder blocks to reduce weight. Aluminum alloys may be used, but so far this is done only in small-bore, light-duty engines. Cylinder heads may also support rocker assemblies and camshafts when overhead camshaft design is used. Several configurations are used in diesel engines:

1. Multicylinder, single-slab casting
2. Multicylinder, multiple cast units
3. Single cylinder

Cylinder heads usually contain the valve assemblies, breathing ports, injector bores, and coolant and lubricant passages. On older indirect injection (IDI) applications, precombustion chambers were either built in or installed as units in the head. Top and bottom detail views of cylinder heads are shown in **Figure 9–13**, a sectional view of a cylinder head is shown in **Figure 9–14**, and a cutaway view is shown in **Figure 9–15**.

CYLINDER HEAD DISASSEMBLY, INSPECTION, AND RECONDITIONING

Before beginning any disassembly procedure, reference the OEM service literature. When removing variable valve timing and engine brake actuators, there is usually a very specific procedure to observe. The following is a general procedure:

1. Remove the valves with a C-type spring compressor and gently tap each valve with a nylon hammer to loosen the keepers and retainers.
2. Clean the cylinder heads in a soak tank (preferably hot).

FIGURE 9–14 Sectional view of a Mack E-Tech cylinder head.

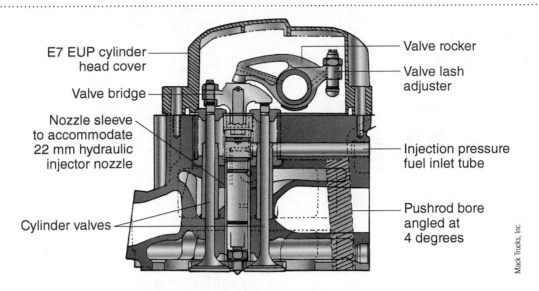

FIGURE 9–15 Cutaway view of a cylinder head.

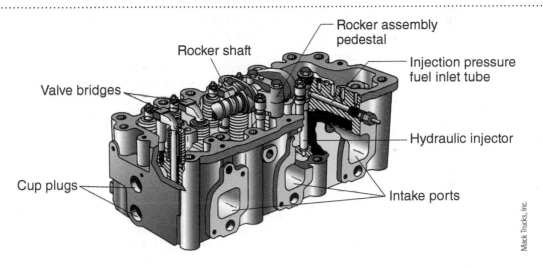

3. Check the cylinder head height dimension. Each OEM has its own preference on where to make the measurement, so check with the service literature. One manufacturer's method is shown in **Figure 9–16**.

4. Dress the head gasket surface with an emery cloth or other fine-grit, noncorrosive abrasive.

5. Electromagnetic flux test the head for cracks. Optionally, dye penetrant testing can be used, but this is messy and inaccurate.

6. Hydrostatic pressure test: Cap and plug the coolant ports, then place the head in a test jig and heat by running hot water through. When hot to the touch, hydrostatically test using shop air at around 100 psi. Areas to watch are valve seats and injector sleeves. When brass injector sleeves are used (usually older engines), perform the hydrostatic test both cold and hot.

7. If the injector sleeves have to be replaced, use the appropriate removal and installation tools and repeat the pressure test after the operation. These are sometimes swaged and sometimes threaded into the injector bore.

8. Check for warpage using a straightedge and an appropriately sized thickness gauge. The specification will vary according to the size of the head.

9. Check valve guide bore to specs with a ball gauge. If in need of replacement, the

FIGURE 9–16 Cylinder head height dimension.

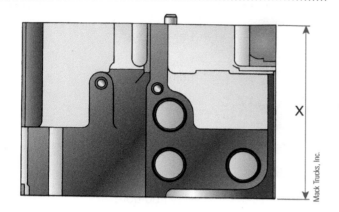

guide must be pressed or driven out with the correct driver or mandrel. Damage to the guide bore may require reaming to fit an oversize guide. Integral guides can be repaired by machining for guide sleeves or knurling. Installation of new guides can be made easier by freezing (dry ice) or use of press-fit lubricant.

10. New guides may require reaming after installation, but some OEMs use cladded guides that should *never* be reamed.

11. Check the valve seats for looseness using a light, ball peen hammer and listening—a loose seat resonates at a much higher pitch. To recondition, select the appropriate mandrel pilot and insert into the guide, then match the valve seat to the mandrel grinding stone. Stellite-faced seats require special grinding stones. Dress the stone to achieve the required seat angle. Interference angles are seldom used in current applications because they compromise the valve's ability to transfer heat to the head. An interference angle is usually not required when valve rotators are used.

12. New valve seats are installed with an **interference fit** and require the use of the correct driver; after installation, the seat is usually knurled or staked in position. Most current diesels use alloy steel seats—cast iron does not require staking of seats. After valve and seat reconditioning, check the valve head height (valve protrusion) with a dial indicator.

13. Valve reconditioning. Clean the valves with a wire wheel or glass bead blaster, then check for stretching, cupping, burning, or pitting. When refacing (dressing) valves,

ensure that the valve margin remains within OEM specifications. Check valve seating using Prussian blue (a/k/a machinist's blue). Lapping is not required if the grinding has been done properly.

14. Check the valve springs for straightness, height, and tension using a right-angle square, tram gauge, and tension gauge.

15. Check valve rotators. Positive rotators (rotocoil) can be checked after hand assembly by tapping the valve open with a nylon hammer after assembly to simulate valve-train action—they should rotate.

CYLINDER HEAD INSTALLATION

Most current cylinder head gaskets are integral, meaning the fire rings and grommets are manufactured integrally with the gasket plate. If not, care should be taken to ensure that the **fire rings** (sealing rings at the liner flange) and grommets are properly positioned while the cylinder head is being installed to the block. The head **gasket** must be properly torqued to ensure that its **yield point** is attained for proper sealing. *Yield point* means that a malleable gasket is crushed to conform to the profile designed to produce optimum sealing. Properly torquing a cylinder head means observing the OEM torque increments and sequencing. An engine cylinder head that is torqued to the correct specification without observing the incremental steps can damage the gasket by deforming it. The objective of torquing cylinder head gaskets is to ensure that the specified clamping force is obtained and the gasket conforms to its engineered yield shape. Cold torquing is required on current engines.

Component Creep

Most head gaskets require no applied sealant and in fact may fail if sealants are used. Head gaskets are designed to seal engine components in a region where both the temperature and pressure are at their highest; they must do this and at that same time accommodate a large amount of component **creep**. *Creep* is the relative movement of clamped engine components due to different coefficients of heat expansion or different mass. Because a cylinder head has much less material than the cylinder block, it will expand more rapidly as it is heated and contract more rapidly as it cools. While doing this, it is clamped to the cylinder

FIGURE 9–17 Cylinder head torque sequence.

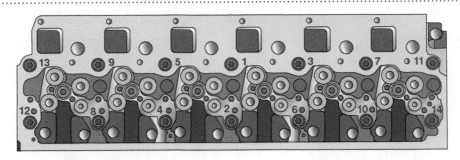

block and must maintain a good enough seal to contain cylinder combustion pressures, which can exceed 3,000 psi. The head gasket is the key to ensuring that this seal is effective under all the operating conditions of the engine. Cylinder head fasteners should be lightly lubed with engine oil before installation. Oil should never be poured into the block threads because a hydraulic lock may result. The torque sequence for a typical cylinder head is shown in **Figure 9–17**.

Incremental Torque Sequence

On inline multicylinder heads, it is usually required that separate heads be aligned with a straightedge across the intake manifold faces before torquing. Failure to observe torquing increments and sequencing can result in cracked cylinder heads, failed head gaskets, and fire rings that will not seal. Because of the large number of fasteners involved, a click-type torque wrench should be used. Many OEMs use **torque-to-yield** fasteners that require a **template torque** method to be used. Torque-to-yield is fully described in Chapter 2 but, simply, this requires setting a torque value first and then turning a set number of degrees beyond that value using a template or protractor. Cylinder head bolts usually should be installed lightly oiled. Excessive quantities of oil should be avoided because the excess can drain into the bolt hole and cause a hydraulic lock.

> ### TECH TIP:
> Installing a cylinder head onto an engine can be made easier by using guide studs inserted into cylinder bolt holes. This reduces the chances of cylinder gasket misalignment occurring during head installation.

ROCKER HOUSING COVERS

Rocker housing or valve covers seal the upper portion of the engine above the cylinder head. Because valve and injector trains have become more complex over the years, the physical size of rocker housing covers has increased, especially on engines equipped with double overhead camshafts, variable valve timing, and engine brakes. Rocker housing covers are the most frequently removed engine component. They have to be removed to access the valves and injectors for purposes of tune-up and injector timing. For this reason, many engine OEMs have adopted the use of multiuse, rubber compound sealing gaskets usually fitted to a captured groove in the rocker housing cover. These gaskets also help damp the top end clatter (noise) produced by the rockers. OEM recommendations for installing these gaskets should be observed, especially if the gaskets will be used more than once. Usually a light coating of engine oil is all that should be applied. Try to avoid using aggressive adhesives such as weatherstrip glue because they ruin rubber gaskets, which tend to be much more costly than their fiber predecessors.

INTAKE AND EXHAUST MANIFOLDS

In current diesel engines, the **intake manifold** is required to deliver both air and recirculated exhaust gas (EGR) to the engine cylinders. The intake manifold is bolted to the cylinder head(s) enclosing the intake tracts. Because of turbocharging, the runners that extend from the intake plenum can be of unequal lengths without compromising engine breathing. EGR mixing

FIGURE 9–18 Sectional view of an inline six-cylinder diesel engine: Note the location of the engine housing components.

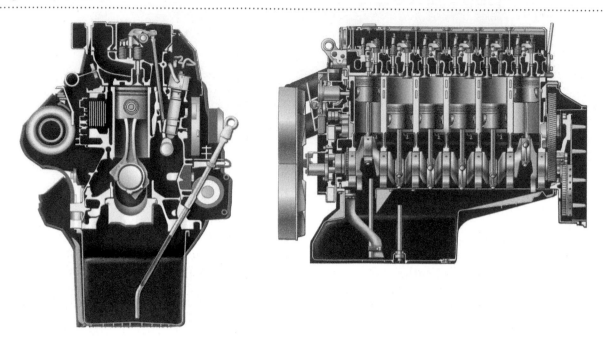

with boost air may take place in the region of the intake manifold plenum.

Intake manifolds can be either wet (coolant ports) or dry. Most current mobile diesel engines use dry intake manifolds. Materials used for intake manifolds are usually aluminum alloy or cast iron, but some OEMs are experimenting with plastics and carbon-based fibers. The gaskets used are usually fiber based and must be able to accommodate a small amount of component creep and the peak boost pressures. Peak manifold boost pressures may be as high as 100 psi on some more recent engines. When a single section cast aluminum manifold is bolted to a multicylinder head configured engine, it is critical that the cylinder heads be aligned with a straightedge before they are torqued down. **Figure 9–18** shows a sectional view of an engine: Identify the location of all of the components studied so far in Chapters 7, 8, and 9.

EXHAUST MANIFOLD

The function of the **exhaust manifold** is to collect cylinder end gases and deliver them to the turbocharger or, in the case of a naturally aspirated engine, directly to the exhaust piping. They are usually manufactured in single or multiple sections of cast iron. The exhaust manifold assembly is bolted to the cylinder head; in engines using multiple heads, it should be aligned before torquing.

Tuned Manifolds

Most current diesel engine exhaust manifolds are described as *tuned*, meaning that exhaust gas is routed to the turbocharger with minimal flow resistance. The gas dynamic of exhaust manifolds is discussed in more detail in Chapter 12. The term *tuned* is applied to any exhaust system designed with at least some accommodation to optimize exhaust gas flow. If the exhaust manifold and piping is properly designed, as each slug of cylinder exhaust is discharged, it will not "collide" with that from another cylinder, but instead be timed to unload into its tailstream.

Minimizing Heat Losses

Because exhaust gas heat can be "recycled" to drive turbochargers, most current exhaust manifolds are designed to minimize heat losses upstream from the turbocharger turbine housing. This may mean that the exhaust tract in the cylinder head and sections of the exhaust manifold are "insulated," usually with stainless steel inserts, to reduce heat losses.

Exhaust Manifold Gaskets

Exhaust manifold gaskets in truck/bus engine applications are usually of the embossed steel type, although occasionally fiber gaskets are used. They must be able to sustain a high degree of component creep along with high temperatures. Embossed steel exhaust manifold gaskets are almost always installed dry and should be used once only. In many cases, the fastening hardware, such as studs, bolts, and nuts, is manufactured from highly alloyed steels to accommodate high temperatures and the high thermal expansion/contraction rates.

OIL PANS OR SUMPS

The **sump** is a reservoir usually located at the base of the engine cylinder block enclosing the crankcase. **Oil pans** are manufactured from cast aluminum, stamped mild steel, laminated steels, and various plastics and synthetic fibers. The oil pan acts as the reservoir used to collect the lubrication oil that gravity causes to drain to the crankcase and from which the oil pump pickup can recycle it through the lubrication circuit. Take a look at the oil pan and its pickup tube in Figure 9–18.

OIL PAN FUNCTIONS

Oil pans can act as a sort of boom box and amplify engine noise, so they are usually designed to minimize sound. Laminated steels are effective at noise damping and with it, provide some desirable toughness to the oil pan. The oil pan also plays a role in dissipating lube oil heat to atmosphere, but the effectiveness of this role obviously has a lot to do with the material from which the pan is manufactured. Aluminum will dissipate heat more effectively than a fiber-reinforced plastic. Also, this heat exchanger role of the oil pan can produce problems when running in midwinter or subarctic conditions and cause gelling and sludging. Some off-highway trucks use a deep oil pan design to accommodate a scavenging pump. **Scavenging pumps** are secondary oil pumps designed to ensure that the engine lubrication circuit is provided with adequate oil when the vehicle is operating on steep grades.

Removing an Oil Pan

Oil pans are usually located in the airflow under the frame rails and are vulnerable to damage from objects on the road—from rocks on rough terrain to small animals on the highway. Most highway diesel engines have oil pans that can be removed from the engine while it is in chassis. It is advisable to drain the oil sump before removing it. Oil pans that seal to the engine block using gaskets can be difficult to remove, especially where adhesives have been used to ensure a seal. A 4-lb (2-kilo) rubber mallet may make removal easier. Avoid driving screwdrivers between the oil pan and its block mating flange, because the result will be damage to the oil pan flange and the cylinder block mating flange.

TECH TIP:

A pneumatic gasket scraper is a great way to remove gasket residue from the engine block oil pan flange face. Care must be taken to avoid gouging the mating surfaces because some pneumatic scrapers can be aggressive. Therefore, avoid using pneumatic gasket scrapers on aluminum, glass fiber, or carbon fiber oil pans.

Oil Pan Inspection

Oil pans that use rubber isolator seals tend not to present removal problems. In fact, sometimes rubber isolator seals can be reused if inspection shows them to be in good condition. After removal, the oil pan should be cleaned of gasket residues and washed with a pressure washer. Inspect the oil pan mating flanges, check for cracks, and test the drain plug threads. Cast aluminum oil pans that fasten both to the cylinder block and to the flywheel housing are prone to stress cracking in the rear due to cylinder block torque twist. Carefully inspect them before returning to service. When torquing aluminum oil pans, always meticulously observe torque sequences and values.

WELDING DAMAGED OIL PANS

Cast aluminum oil pans can be successfully repair-welded without distortion using the tungsten inert gas (TIG) process, providing the cracks are not too large and the oil-saturated area of the crack is ground clean. It is more difficult to execute a lasting repair weld on a stamped steel oil pan, due to the distortion that results. Steel oil pans may rust through, in which case they should be replaced rather than welded. Whenever an oil pan has indications of porosity resulting from corrosion, it should always be replaced. The technician should always be aware of the fact that a failure of the oil sump or its drain plug on the road can result in the loss of the engine. It is generally recommended that plastic composite, fiberglass, and carbon fiber oil pans be replaced rather than repaired.

FLYWHEEL HOUSINGS

Flywheel housings bolt to the rear of the cylinder block. They form the stationary coupling between the engine and transmission. Flywheel housings used in most medium- and heavy-duty truck drivetrains are categorized by Society of Automotive Engineers (SAE) codes. These SAE code designations permit a similarly coded transmission bell housing to couple to the flywheel housing. This is important because it allows transmission OEMs to fit their product to a range of different OEM engines. The flywheel housing encloses the flywheel and clutch pack as it couples the engine and transmission. In some cases, the rear engine mounts may be integral with, or attach to, the flywheel housing. Rear engine mounts may also be located on the transmission bell housing. The starter motor is usually flange-mounted to the front of the flywheel housing. **Figure 9–19** shows the flywheel housing used on a 2010 Mack Trucks MP-8 engine.

Flywheel housings are usually precision located to the engine cylinder block by cylindrical or diamond dowels: Clamping force is provided by fasteners, usually 12 grade 8 bolts. Flywheel housings should be checked for:

- Flange inside diameter radial concentricity. This is an important check; it is covered in some detail in Chapter 15. If it fails to meet specification, it produces a broken-back effect, imparting drive torque to the transmission bell housing that can take out

FIGURE 9–19 Flywheel housing on a 2010 Mack Trucks MP-8 engine.

clutches, clutch shafts, crankshafts, and transmissions.
- Outer flange face runout. This is the mating face to the transmission bell housing. It seldom fails to meet specification, but it should be checked at engine overhaul.

SUMMARY

- The engine cylinder block can be considered the main frame of an engine, as it is the component to which all others are attached.
- Heavy-duty diesel engine cylinder blocks are manufactured from gray cast iron (older engines) or compacted graphite iron (CGI). Some light-duty diesel engines use cast aluminum alloy cylinder blocks, often with bores cladded by a PTWA process.
- Most commercial diesel engines use wet, dry, or wet/dry liners to make engine overhaul easier

and faster and extend engine life. Some small- and medium-bore diesel use parent bores that are induction hardened or steel cladded.
- Dry liners are fitted to the cylinder block fractionally loose or with a fractional interference fit.
- Dry liners do not transfer heat from the engine cylinder to the coolant in the water jacket as efficiently as wet liners.
- Selective fitting of dry liners to cylinder block bores ensures the best liner-to-bore fit.

- Wet liners transfer heat to the water jacket efficiently because they are surrounded by the coolant; however, they must also support combustion pressures.
- Wet liners must seal the water jacket using O-rings.
- Liners are clamped into position by cylinder heads. Therefore, the protrusion of liner flanges is a critical specification.
- Liner protrusion is set by shimming the counterbore or selective spec liner flanges.
- Engine cylinder blocks should be boiled in a tank; have every critical dimension measured, especially deck straightness and line bore; and be magnetic flux tested at every major engine overhaul.
- The cylinder head houses the valvetrain assemblies, the injectors, and the engine breathing passages.
- The engine cylinder block should be pressure tested hydrostatically by first heating through with hot water: Common locations for cracks are the injector bore tubes and the valve seats.

- Cylinder heads must be torqued in sequence to ensure even clamping pressure.
- Torquing cylinder heads in increments is designed to achieve the cylinder head gasket yield point by evenly achieving the required clamping force.
- Cylinder head bolts should be lightly lubed with engine oil before installation.
- The intake manifold is responsible for directing intake air and recirculated exhaust gas into the cylinder head intake tracts.
- Most truck diesel engines use the term *tuned* to describe their exhaust manifolds because they feed the turbine housing of the turbocharger, and the way gas is moved through the manifold is critical for scavenging end gases.
- Gaskets used to seal the engine housing components must be able to accommodate dynamic creep without failing; for this reason, they are almost always single-use items.

REVIEW QUESTIONS

1. Which of the following cylinder block designs would be the most common in medium- and heavy-duty truck diesel engines?
   a. Eight-cylinder, 90-degree V-configuration
   b. Inline six cylinder
   c. Six-cylinder, 60-degree V-configuration
   d. Inline eight cylinder

2. The main reason for bench pressure testing a diesel engine cylinder head is to:
   a. test cylinder gas leakage.
   b. check for air leaks.
   c. check for exhaust leaks.
   d. check for coolant leaks.

3. When selective fitting a set of dry liners to a cylinder block, which of the following statements should be true?
   a. The liner with the largest od is fitted to the bore with the largest id.
   b. The liners are installed with an interference fit.
   c. The liner with the smallest od is fitted to the bore with the largest id.
   d. The liners are installed with a fractionally loose fit.

4. Which of the following is the recommended method of pulling dry liners from a cylinder block?
   a. The arc welding method
   b. A puller and shoe assembly
   c. Heat and shock cool method
   d. Fracture the liner in position

5. Which of the following tools is recommended for checking cylinder block line bore?
   a. Straightedge and thickness gauges
   b. Dial bore gauge
   c. Dial indicator
   d. Master line bore bar

6. When boiling out a cylinder block, why is it critical that all the scale in the water jacket be removed?
   a. Scale is an effective insulator.
   b. Scale may contaminate the engine lubricant.
   c. Scale can accelerate coolant silicate drop-out.
   d. Scale causes cavitation of wet liners.

7. Which of the following tools should be used to check a cylinder block deck for warpage?
   a. Master bar
   b. Dial indicator
   c. Laser
   d. Straightedge and thickness gauges

8. Which of the following tools should be used to check a cylinder head for warpage?
   a. Master bar
   b. Dial indicator
   c. Laser
   d. Straightedge and thickness gauges

9. Technician A states that all the machined surfaces of a cylinder block should be checked to specification with a straightedge and thickness gauges. Technician B states that cylinder blocks should be boiled in a soak tank at every major overhaul. Who is correct?
   a. Technician A only
   b. Technician B only
   c. Both A and B
   d. Neither A nor B

10. When cavitation damage is evident on a set of wet liners, which of the following is more likely to be responsible?
    a. Lubrication breakdown
    b. High cylinder pressures
    c. Coolant breakdown
    d. Cold engine operation

11. When cylinder block counterbores are machined, which of the following would be required?
    a. Oversize fire ring
    b. Shims
    c. Undersize liner flange
    d. Cylinder head resurfacing

12. Technician A states that it is good practice to magnetic flux test a cylinder block for cracks at each major overhaul. Technician B states that before performing a magnetic flux test, the cylinder block should be boiled in a soak tank. Who is correct?
    a. Technician A only
    b. Technician B only
    c. Both A and B
    d. Neither A nor B

13. Most current heavy-duty, diesel engine cylinder blocks are manufactured from:
    a. cast aluminum alloy.
    b. cast-iron alloys.
    c. composite fibers.
    d. compacted graphite iron (CGI).

14. Once a cylinder head gasket fire ring has been torqued to its yield point, it should:
    a. not be reused after removal.
    b. immediately be heated to operating temperature.
    c. deform and no longer seal effectively.

15. Technician A states that all cylinder heads on current engines should be hot torqued after a rebuild procedure. Technician B states that cylinder head bolts should be soaked in engine lubricating oil before installation. Who is correct?
    a. Technician A only
    b. Technician B only
    c. Both A and B
    d. Neither A nor B

10

Prerequisites: Chapters 4, 7, 8, and 9

ENGINE LUBRICATION SYSTEMS

OBJECTIVES

After studying this chapter, you should be able to:

- Outline the function of the main components in a typical diesel engine lubrication circuit.
- List the properties of heavy-duty engine oils, including API CJ-4, CK-4, and FA-4 category lube oils.
- Define the term *hydrodynamic suspension* and describe how this principle is used in a typical diesel engine.
- Interpret the terminology used to classify lubrication oil.
- Interpret API classifications and SAE viscosity grades.
- List some of the properties and ingredients of synthetic engine oils.
- Outline what is meant by *green* engine lubricants.
- Identify the components used in a diesel engine lubricating system.
- Replace and properly calibrate a lube oil dipstick.
- Describe the two types of oil pumps commonly used on diesel engines and outline the operating principles of each.
- Perform the measuring procedures required to determine the serviceability of an oil pump.
- Describe the operation of an oil pressure regulating valve.
- Define the term *positive filtration*.
- Outline the differences between full flow and bypass filters.
- Service a set of oil filters.
- Outline the role of an oil cooler in the lubrication circuit.
- Test an oil cooler core using vacuum or pressure testing.
- Identify the methods used to measure oil pressure in current diesel engines.
- Outline the procedure for taking an engine oil sample for analysis.
- Interpret the results of a laboratory oil analysis.

KEY TERMS

American Petroleum Institute (API)

American Society for Testing Materials (ASTM)

blotter test

boundary lubrication

bundle

bypass filter

bypass valve

centrifugal filter

dry sump

Engine Manufacturers Association (EMA)
fire point
flash point
fluid friction
full flow filter
gerotor
high-temperature, low-shear (HTLS)
hydrodynamic suspension
inhibitors
lamina
lubricity
oil cooler
positive filtration
pour point
proposed category (PC)
relief valve
shear
spectrographic testing
synthetic oil
thick film lubrication
total base number (TBN)
tribology
viscosity

INTRODUCTION

All medium- and large-bore diesel engines currently used on North American highways use a pressurized lubrication system to supply the bearings and moving components with engine oil. Engine oil is the medium used in lubrication circuits, and it is specially formulated to fulfill the lubrication and service life requirements of diesel engines. A modern diesel engine with a not-too-ambitious 1 million highway miles on its odometer will have produced as many power strokes as a human heart beats in five lifetimes. Engine lubricating oil temperatures run somewhat higher than engine coolants, and the actual oil temperature is probably a more reliable indicator of true engine running temperature. The basic components and flow routing required of a diesel engine lubrication system are shown in **Figure 10–1**, and

FIGURE 10–1 Navistar lubrication circuit.

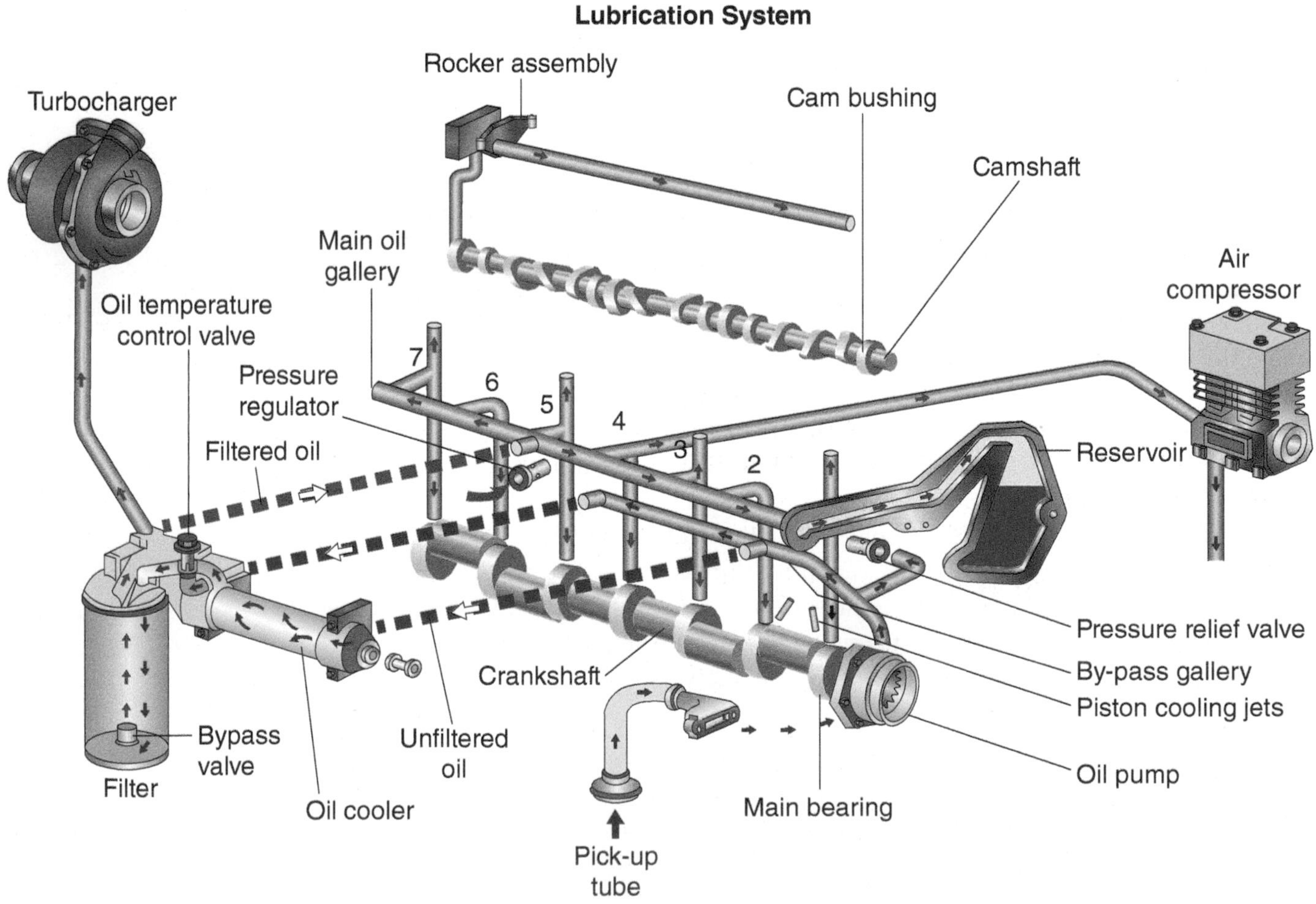
Lubrication System
Rocker assembly
Turbocharger
Cam bushing
Camshaft
Main oil gallery
Air compressor
Oil temperature control valve
Pressure regulator
Filtered oil
7
6
5
4
3
2
Reservoir
Pressure relief valve
By-pass gallery
Piston cooling jets
Oil pump
Crankshaft
Bypass valve
Filter
Unfiltered oil
Oil cooler
Main bearing
Pick-up tube

Courtesy of Navistar International Corp.

FIGURE 10–2 Oil filter pad and cooler circuit.

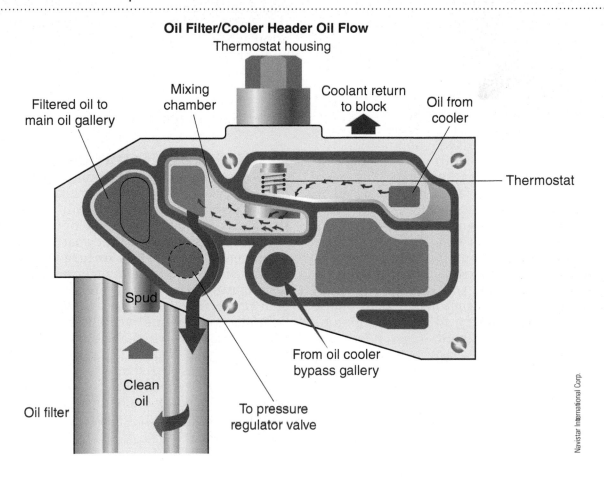

Oil Filter/Cooler Header Oil Flow

Figure 10–2 details the mixing of hot and cool oil through the filter pad assembly. This chapter discusses:

- Functions of a lubrication circuit.
- Lubricants: usually petroleum-based, liquid media used to reduce friction, hydrodynamically support shafts, help seal pistons, and act as a cooling medium.
- Sump: oil storage space enclosing the crankcase but, exceptionally, a remotely located tank in what is referred to as a **dry sump** system.
- Pump: responsible for moving the oil through the lubrication circuit to supply the system oil passages and bearings.
- Filter: commercial diesel engine lubrication systems require multistage filtration systems to remove particulates from the engine oil.
- **Oil cooler**: a heat exchanger that uses engine coolant as its medium. Heat picked up by the engine oil is transferred to the coolant, from which it can be dissipated to atmosphere.
- Piston cooling requirements: spray nozzles.

FRICTION

Friction is a common element in our lives that we simply take for granted. For instance, we can walk up a steep hill without slipping because of high friction between the soles of our feet and the ground surface. We also accept that when that same hill is covered with packed snow, we can ski down it. In the first instance, the coefficient of friction is high, and in the second it is low. Rubber soles have a higher coefficient of friction than skis; packed snow has a lower coefficient of friction than bare earth. Another way of thinking about the coefficient of friction is as a means of rating the aggressiveness of friction surfaces. Lubricants are designed to reduce friction between surfaces that are, or could be, in contact with one another creating wear at the contact points.

ENGINE LUBRICATING OIL

The main functions of a diesel engine lubricating system are:

1. Lubrication. The primary task of an engine oil is to minimize friction and act as a medium to support the **hydrodynamic suspension** of the crankshaft and camshaft.
2. Sealing. Act as a sealant to enable the piston and ring assembly to seal compression and combustion gases away from the crankcase.
3. Cooling medium. Heat generated by combustion and friction must be dissipated to atmosphere via heat exchangers.
4. Cleaning agent. Condensed by-products of combustion gases end up in the engine crankcase and can combine to form harmful liquids (acids) and particulates (sludge).
5. Protection. Maintain an oil film even when subjected to high thrust loads, such as the compressional loading to which a piston/rod assembly is subjected.

Lubricating oils are usually petroleum-based products that are complex mixtures made up of many different fractions. Like gasoline and diesel fuel, engine lubricant is elementally composed of about 85% carbon and 15% hydrogen. The fractioned compounds that make up an engine oil are refined from petroleum and asphalt bases and subsequently mixed.

Increasingly, engine OEMs recommend the use of **synthetic oils**, which are gaining acceptance as commercial diesel engine lubricants. There is little argument as to the superior qualities of synthetic lubes, and the acceptance of extended drain intervals by most diesel engine OEMS has contributed to the cost-effectiveness of synthetics.

The theoretical action of an engine oil is to form a film between moving surfaces so that any friction that results occurs in the oil itself—that is, it is **fluid friction**. Fluid friction generates considerably less heat than dry friction. The lubricating requirements of an engine oil can be classified as **thick film lubrication** and **boundary lubrication** (thin film). Thick film lubrication occurs where mating tolerances between components are wide. Boundary lubrication is required where mating tolerances are narrow, such as when pressure is applied to one of the components: A breakdown of boundary lubrication will result in metal-to-metal contact. Good quality engine oil should be capable of performing both thick film and boundary lubrication.

Because engine lube oil is usually petroleum based, it is flammable. The fact that engine oil is combustible must be taken into consideration when piston action sequentially applies and scrapes it from an engine's cylinder walls. The result is that inevitably some engine lube is burned during normal engine operation. Emission standards require that combusted engine oil be kept to a minimum.

PRINCIPLE OF HYDRODYNAMIC SUSPENSION

When a shaft is rotated within friction bearing shells such as those used to support an engine crankshaft, and that shaft is stationary, a crescent-shaped gap is formed on either side of the line of direct contact due to the clearance between the journal and the inside diameter of the friction bearing. A static film of oil (boundary) prevents shaft-to-bearing contact when stationary. When the shaft is rotated and the bearing is charged with engine oil under pressure, a crescent-shaped wedge of lubricant is formed between the journal and its bearing; oil is introduced to the bearing where the shaft clearance is greatest, usually at the top. This wedge of oil is driven ahead of the direction of rotation in a manner that permits the shaft to be "floated" on a bed of constantly changing, pressurized oil. This principle is used in most crankshaft and camshaft dynamics and is known as *hydrodynamic suspension*.

In hydrodynamic lubrication, maintaining a liquid film between moving surfaces is achieved by pumping lubricant through a circuit. In the case of a rotating shaft and a stationary friction bearing, the shaft acts as a pump to maintain the lubricant film. The result is that the shaft journal floats on a film of oil, the thickness of which depends on:

- Oil input: the rate at which oil is delivered to the bearing. This is why there is a problem if oil pressure is low.
- Oil leakage rate: the oil that spills from a bearing during operation. This is why the association between worn engine main bearings and low oil pressure is made.

The thickness of the hydrodynamic wedge therefore depends on the following four factors, any one of which will change that thickness:

1. Load increase: causes oil to be squeezed out of the bearing at a faster rate.

FIGURE 10-3 Concept of hydrodynamic viscosity.

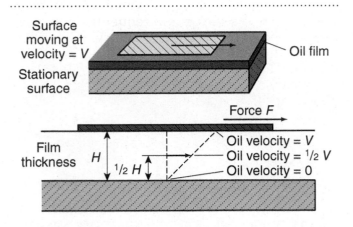

2. Temperature increase: causes oil leakage rate from bearing to increase.
3. Lower viscosity oil: flows with less resistance, causing more leakage.
4. Changing shaft speed: (remember, the shaft is the "pump") reduce speed and the film becomes thinner; increase speed and it thickens.

Figure 10-3 shows the principle of hydrodynamic lubrication.

ENGINE OIL CLASSIFICATION AND TERMINOLOGY

To fully understand the terms and codes used on the label of any engine oil probably requires the learning of a tribologist, that is, an expert in **tribology**, the study of friction, wear, and lubrication. However, every technician should have a rudimentary understanding of the codes and terms used to describe engine oils. The following section introduces some of the basic language of lubricants.

Viscosity

The **viscosity** rating of an oil usually describes its resistance to flow. High viscosity oils have molecules with greater cohesion ability. However, properly defined, viscosity denotes resistance to **shear**. When two moving components are separated by engine oil, the **lamina** (portion of the oil film closest to each metal surface) on each moving component should have the least fluid velocity while the fluid in the center has the greatest fluid velocity. Shear occurs when the lamina fluid velocity is such that it is no longer capable of adhering to the surface of the moving

components. When we use the term *friction bearings* to describe crankshaft main bearings, the friction being referred to is the fluid friction of the lube hydrodynamics in supporting the crankshaft.

Viscosity Index

The viscosity index (VI) is a measure of an oil's tendency to thin as temperature increases. Temperature affects viscosity. Viscosity may be considerably reduced with an increase in temperature and, to a smaller extent, as fluid pressure is increased. The greater the VI, the less of an effect temperature will have on the actual viscosity of an oil. In other words, oils that show relatively small viscosity changes with changes in temperature can be said to have high VI.

SAE Numbers and Viscosity

The viscosity of automotive engine oils is graded by the Society of Automotive Engineers (SAE). These gradings and the recommendations that accompany them are listed a little later in this chapter. SAE gradings specify the temperature window within which the engine oil can function to provide adequate shear resistance under boundary lubrication conditions.

Multiviscosity Oils

Multiviscosity engine oils are the lubricating oil of choice of commercial diesel engine OEMs. They have been around for many years but, initially, some manufacturers took a cautious approach before finally recommending them. The main advantage of multiviscosity oils over straight grade oils is that they provide proper lubrication to the engine over a much wider temperature range. In other words, they have a relatively flat viscosity-to-temperature curve.

Multiviscosity oils are produced by special refining processes and the addition of VI improvers. They possess good cold cranking characteristics and show comparatively small variations of viscosity over their nominal operating range. Synthetic oils, when marketed with an SAE grading, usually greatly exceed the nominal grading window.

Lubricity

Two oils with identical viscosity grades can possess different lubricity. The **lubricity** of an oil properly describes its flow characteristics. Lubricity is also affected by temperature: Hotter oils flow more readily, colder oils less readily. In comparing two engine oils, the one that has the lowest frictional resistance to flow can be said to possess the greater lubricity. In thick film fluid lubrication, flow friction is determined by the fluid's viscosity, that is, its resistance to shear. In thin film or boundary lubrication, flow friction is determined by the lubricity of the fluid. Sulfur compounds add to the lubricity of diesel engine oils. Synthetic oils tend to have high lubricity with low sulfur content.

Flash Point

Flash point is the temperature at which a flammable liquid gives off enough vapor to ignite momentarily. The **fire point** of the same flammable liquid, which is usually about 25°F (10°C) higher, is the temperature at which a flammable liquid gives off sufficient vapor for continuous combustion. The flash point specification has some significance when assessing a diesel engine lubricating oil because a large portion of the cylinder wall is swept by flame every other revolution in a four-stroke cycle engine. However, actual cylinder wall temperatures are significantly lower than the temperatures of the combustion gases, and the oil is only exposed to them for very short periods of time. Most diesel engine lubricating oils have flash points of 400°F (205°C) or higher.

Pour Point

The temperature at which a lubricant begins to gel or simply ceases to flow is known as the **pour point**. Engine lubricating oils formulated for extreme cold weather operation have pour point additives or depressants that act as "antifreeze" for lubrication oils. Pour point is an important engine oil specification, especially due to the tendency of many operators to use a multigrade engine oil viscosity nominally not suited for mid-winter conditions in the northern part of the continent. **Figure 10–4** demonstrates the cold weather flow ability of some common multigrade engine lubes.

Inhibitors

The term **inhibitors**, when applied to an engine lubricant, refers to the additives that protect the oil itself against corrosion, oxidation, and acidity. The objective of inhibitors is to make the oil less likely to participate in reactions with the contaminants that find their way into the crankcase, such as combustion by-products, moisture, and raw fuel. When lube oil inhibitors fail to work properly (usually due to extended service), the oil lacks protection and begins to degrade.

FIGURE 10–4 Demonstration of cold weather flow ability of different oil viscosity grades.

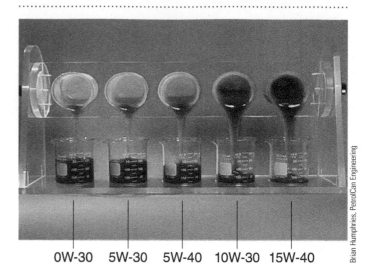

0W-30   5W-30   5W-40   10W-30   15W-40

Brian Humphries, PetrolCan Engineering

Ash

Ash in lubricant is mineral residue that results from oxide and sulfate incineration. Some ash content in diesel engine lube oils was desirable because it checked the formation of some acids. However, in the latest CJ-4, CK-4, and FA-4 diesel oils (described in detail later in this chapter), the objective is to keep ash levels at a minimum, because they can plug emissions control devices. When higher-than-spec ash levels are reported in oil analyses, this is usually caused by high-temperature operation.

Film Strength

Most engine oils possess adequate film strength to prevent seizure and galling of contacting metal surfaces, but those formulated for high-speed, high-output diesel engines usually contain additives to improve film strength and cohesiveness of the oil. *Cohesion* is the ability of molecules to stick together when pressure is applied. Most synthetic oils have superior cohesiveness to mineral oils. This can be tested by applying a couple of drops of each to a smooth surface: When cleaning them off the surface, you will find that the mineral oil is easily wiped away while the synthetic oil leaves a waxy film.

Detergents

Detergents are added to engine oils to prevent the formation of deposits on internal engine components. They also help keep soluble oxidation products from becoming insoluble when sludge could be formed. Polymeric detergents and amine compounds are used. Some engine oils require a high detergent load (especially those recommended for newer diesels), while others have almost no detergent.

Dispersants

Dispersants are added to engine oils to help keep insoluble oxidation products in suspension and prevent them from coagulating into sludge and deposits. When sludge and deposits do form in the crankcase, the capability of the dispersants in the engine oil has been exceeded. This is usually an indication that the oil change interval should be reduced, because the result is lube oil degradation.

OIL CONTAMINATION AND DEGRADATION

When oil becomes contaminated, it can result in complete engine failure. Contaminated engine oil has some characteristic tattletales. These can be quickly identified by visual and odor testing, and confirmed, if required, by oil analysis. The following are some common contaminants.

Fuel

When fuel contaminates engine oil, the oil loses its lubricity and appears thinner and blacker in color. The condition is usually easy to detect because small amounts of fuel in oil can be recognized by odor. When fuel is found in significant quantities in engine oil, the cylinder head, injectors, and certain types of fuel pumps are the likely sources.

Coolant

Coolant churned into engine lubricants gives the oil a milky, cloudy appearance. After settling, the coolant usually collects at the bottom of the oil sump. When the drain plug is removed, the heavier coolant exits first as long as sufficient time has passed for it to settle. When coolant is found in the engine oil, the cylinder head(s), cylinder head gasket, and liners are the probable sources. Within the cylinder head, the injector cup seals are usually the culprit.

Oil Aeration

Aeration of engine oil, also known as *foaming*, affects its ability to properly lubricate the engine. Aerated oil can be caused either by the chemical characteristics of the oil itself (such as detergent additives) or by contaminants such as water; surface tension is a factor. The conditions that aerate oil in the crankcase are the rotary action of the crankshaft, sucking of air into the oil pump inlet, and the free fall of oil into the crankcase from the oil pump **relief valve** and cylinder walls. Antifoaming additives inhibit oil aeration. Silicone polymers are used to prevent foaming in diesel engine lubricants.

Cold Sludge

Cold sludge is caused by oil degeneration that occurs during prolonged engine low-load operation at low temperatures. Routinely idling diesel engines for prolonged periods at truck stops creates cold sludge. The sludge settles in the engine crankcase and can accelerate engine wear rates. When a diesel engine is operated with its coolant thermostat(s) removed or stuck open, the result can also be the formation of cold sludge.

API CLASSIFICATIONS

The **American Petroleum Institute**, usually known as **API**, classifies all engine oil sold in North America. There are two main classifications, designated by the prefix letters G and C. The G classes of engine oil are those oils suitable for passenger cars and light trucks. The *G* represents GF or gasoline fueled. The C classes of engine oils are suitable for heavy-duty trucks, buses, off-road, and industrial and agricultural equipment. The *C* represents CI or compression-ignited engines, but note that from 2017 onward, the C category will be expanded by having an F category for fuel efficient engines. "Fuel efficient engines" will refer to diesel engines manufactured after EPA MY 2017.

The C category and the most recent G category oil classifications are listed and described here because many fleets use engine oils that claim to be suitable for both C and G classifications. Because of the changes to be introduced in 2017, the new F category will also be described.

In most cases, OEMs have specific requirements for engine lubricants; these should be observed because failure to do so could result in higher hydrocarbon (HC) emissions. It should also be noted that using inappropriate oil in current diesel engines can damage emission control hardware. Diesel engine API classifications for the past 20 years appear in the following list:

CF—May be used in diesel engines exposed to fuels that may have a sulfur content greater than 0.05%. Effective in controlling piston deposits, wear, and bearing corrosion.

May be used in place of earlier API Service Category recommendations.

CF-2—Service typical of two-stroke cycle engines that require effective control over cylinder and ring-face scuffing and deposits. May be used where API Service Category CE-II is recommended.

CF-4—Service typical of on-highway, heavy-duty truck applications. Designated for multigrade oils and introduced in 1991. Oils meeting this category will also meet API Service Category CE.

CG-4—For use in high-speed, four-stroke cycle diesel engines used on both heavy-duty on-highway and off-highway applications (with less than 0.05% sulfur fuel). CG-4 oils provide effective control over high-temperature piston deposits, wear, and soot accumulation. Effective in meeting 1994 exhaust emission standards and may also be used where API Service Categories CD, CE, and CF-4 are specified.

CH-4—For use in high-speed, four-stroke cycle diesel engines used in on- and off-highway applications that are fueled with fuels containing less than 0.05% sulfur. Supersedes all previous API category oils.

CI-4—Introduced in September 2002 for use in high-speed, highway diesel engines meeting 2004 exhaust emission standards, implemented in October 2002 by Environmental Protection Agency (EPA) agreement with engine OEMs. CI-4 oil is especially formulated for engines using fuels containing less than 0.05% sulfur and maximizes lube oil and engine longevity when exhaust gas recirculation (EGR) devices are used. CI-4 engine oil supersedes CD, CE, CF, CG, and CH category oils. It meets the requirements of heavy-duty engine oil (HDEO) standard PC-9, but should not be used in any post-2007 diesel engines. It was due to be phased out in 2010 but can still be obtained today. It has a lower cost than CJ-4, CK-4, and FA-4 oils, but because of a higher ash count may damage diesel particulate filters (DPFs) when used in post-2007 engines.

CJ-4—Formulated for use in 2007 and later diesel engines equipped with cooled-EGR and DPFs (see Chapter 48), but is also backward compatible. The main difference between CJ-4 and CI-4 is a change in the additive package designed to reduce ash generated when the oil is either combusted in the cylinder or routed through the closed crankcase ventilation system. Higher ash loads in the exhaust gas can plug the DPF or poison the catalyst.

CK-4 and **FA-4**—Formulated for use in MY 2017 engines. After 2017, two engine oil categories will be required for diesel engines, one for engines certified before 2017, and another for ultra-high efficiency engines for those certified after 2017. These new oils are explained in some detail in the following section.

The introduction of CJ-4, CK-4, and FA-4 changes the way we interpret diesel engine oil analysis reports (discussed later in this chapter), because sampled **total base number (TBN)** was increased. TBNs are a measure of used oil acidity. Ash increases the alkalinity of in-service engine oil and helps reduce acids generated by combustion. However, the post-combustion acids were mostly produced by combusting the sulfur component in diesel fuel, and the universal use of ultra-low sulfur (ULS) fuel combats this.

Although CJ-4 was designed with backward compatibility, it cost more. This meant that some operators continued to use CI-4 for pre-2007 engines and stockpiling means that some of this oil is still around today. Use of other than CJ-4 engine oil in post-2007 engines can result in voiding of engine and emission hardware warranty. CJ-4 engine oil will be around for a while. **Figure 10–5** shows the chemical limits required of CJ-4 diesel engine lube.

FIGURE 10–5 Chemical limits of API CJ-4 engine lube.

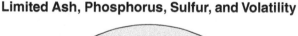

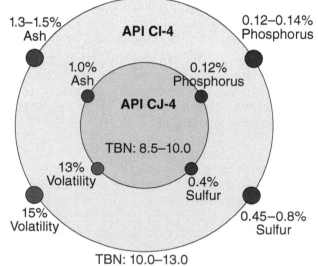

Limited Ash, Phosphorus, Sulfur, and Volatility

PC-11, CK-4, AND FA-4

To create a new engine oil category, the **Engine Manufacturers Association (EMA)** must formulate a request to the **American Society for Testing Materials (ASTM)**. From that point, it has typically taken around four years to formulate the chemistry for the new oil, which has to meet the EMA requirements plus have backward compatibility. This changed in 2009.

When a new engine oil is under consideration by the ASTM, the term **proposed category (PC)** is used. In 2009, the EMA recognized that a replacement would be required for CJ-4 in 2017, so the ASTM opened research into a replacement known as PC-11. The requirement for PC-11 was for a **high-temperature, low-shear (HTLS)** lubricant suited for a generation of more fuel-efficient engines being engineered for EPA model year (MY) 2017. Normally a new oil formulation would be delivered to refiners three to four years ahead of introduction, giving them ample time to prepare, but this did not happen with PC-11. The problem was with backward compatibility. The high shear (that is, ultra-low friction resistance) of these newer engine oil categories means that the oils may not be suited to many older engines.

The ASTM consensus decision process recently concluded. The result of this drawn-out process was two engine oils, one for "legacy" engines and the other for MY 2017 and later engines. Though the formulations for each oil have been determined, the actual names will not be finally approved until December of 2015. However, at the time of writing, it is likely that the two lubricants will be known as:

- CK-4. Under development, this oil was known as PC-11A and it has been formulated as a direct replacement for CJ-4. It will be offered in the same viscosity grades and types (mineral and synthetic) as CJ-4. It is expected to have full backward compatibility.
- FA-4. Under development, this oil was known as PC-11B and it was formulated to boost the fuel efficiency of next-generation diesel engines. The "F" signifies "fuel efficient." FA-4 will be available in XW-30 grades only, with the X representing 0, 5, or 10. One objective of this categorization is to wean the industry away from 15W-40 oil, something that OEM recommendations have failed to achieve. At the time of writing, FA-4 is necessarily a blend of petroleum-base and synthetic oils, so it will cost more than the current CJ-4 formulation.

Oils for SI Engines

Oils formulated for use in gasoline-fueled engines are categorized in much the same way, but they are no longer of much importance to diesel technicians because the days of dual fuel application engine lubes are past. The most recent engine oils formulated for service in gasoline engines areas are:

SH	1993
GF-2	1996
GF-3	2001
GF-4	2004
GF-5	2010

There are still some engine oils formulated that claim to meet the needs for both SI gasoline-fueled and diesel-fueled engines, a relic from the years when some fleets (such as school bus operators) had a mix of diesel- and gasoline-fueled vehicles. Most diesel engine OEMs recommend that multipurpose, multifuel specified oils be avoided. This is because such oils tend to be loaded with excessive additives in an effort to meet too wide a range of lube specs.

Oils for NG Engines

Engine lubes formulated for use in diesel and gasoline engines should not be used in natural gas (NG) fueled engines. Note that most NG-fueled engines require the use of a specialty lubrication oil; using general purpose diesel engine lubes can shorten engine life. The Cummins Westport recommended engine lube for all of its current NG-fueled engines lines is CES 20074. Oil to this specification is manufactured by all of the major oil suppliers. Most of the pre-2010 NG competitors of Cummins Westport also specified CES 20074, but check with the OEM before servicing.

SAE VISCOSITY GRADES

The following list includes the SAE engine oil grades and their recommended temperature operating ranges. Many multiviscosity oils that proclaim themselves to be "green" options use a 5W-X formulation. Lubricant marketing that claims the use of an engine oil can lower CO_2 emissions justifies such claims on the basis of lower internal friction between moving engine components, thus reducing fuel consumption. **Figure 10–6** shows the temperature range for some common SAE viscosity grades. The *W* denotes a winter grade lubricant.

FIGURE 10–6 SAE viscosity grades and temperature ranges for post-2010 engines.

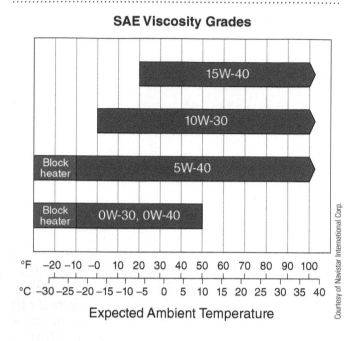

Courtesy of Navistar International Corp.

Multigrade engine oils:

0W-30—Recommended for use in arctic and subarctic winter conditions for engines requiring the use of CJ-4 engine lube. In 2017, 0W-30 multigrade oil will be one of three viscosities that FA-4 will be made available in: It will be recommended for year-round use in northern states, Canada, and subarctic climates.

5W-30—Recommended for winter use where temperatures frequently fall below 0°F (–18°C) and North American summer conditions. Most diesel engine OEMs recommend 5W-30 viscosity for year-round use in engines requiring CJ-4 engine lube. The popularity of the Castrol Elixion and Amsol Series 3000 synthetic oils that are sold at this viscosity indicate that a shift away from 15W-40 engine lubricants may have begun. Castrol marketing claims up to a 4% improvement in fuel economy when using Elixion versus a typical 15W-40 oil. When FA-4 is introduced for MY 2017, this is expected to become the most commonly used multigrade viscosity.

10W-30—Recommended for winter use where temperatures frequently fall below 0°F (–18°C) and North American summer conditions for engines that require a CJ-4 lubricant. One of three multigrade viscosities in which FA-4 will be made available.

5W-40—Recommended for severe-duty winter use where temperatures frequently fall below 0°F (–18°C). Citgo GreenWay-approved Syndurance is sold at this viscosity, along with Shell Rotella T6 synthetics; most tests indicate that these oils can produce at least a 2% improvement in fuel economy.

5W-50—Recommended for severe-duty winter use in arctic and subarctic conditions where temperatures frequently fall below 0°F (–18°C). A synthetic oil viscosity grade.

10W-30—Recommended for winter use where temperatures never fall below 0°F (–18°C). This is currently the most common OEM recommendation regarding viscosity range for commercial diesel engines.

10W-40—Recommended for severe-duty winter use where temperatures never fall below 0°F (–18°C).

15W-40—Recommended for use in climates where temperatures never fall below 15°F (–9°C). Despite this and diesel engine OEM recommendations that support the use of lighter multigrades in winter conditions, this is by far the most commonly used viscosity grade for truck and bus engines year round, often in climates that have severe winters. A true 15W-40 engine oil will freeze to a grease-like consistency in subzero conditions, making the engine almost impossible to crank; additionally, engine wear is accelerated during the warmup phase of operation. The most popular diesel engine oil in America is Shell Rotella 15W-40 (mineral base), despite OEM recommendations that it is not suited for winter operation. Figure 10–6 is a Navistar schematic showing its recommended viscosity grades by temperatures. Note that 15W-40 lube is not recommended by Navistar for engines operating in temperatures below 20°F (–6°C).

20W-40—Recommended for use in high-performance engines in climates where temperatures never fall below 20°F (–6°C).

20W-50—Recommended for use in high-performance engines in climates where temperatures never fall below 20°F (–6°C).

Straight grades:

Straight grade diesel engine oil is not suited for modern diesel engines that operate under variable speed and load conditions. The only justification for using these oils today is in engines that can be run within a protected climate with constant loads and rpms, such as some generator applications. However, they continue to sell, so here are the common grades:

10W—Recommended for winter use in climates where temperatures never fall below 0°F (−18°C) and never exceed 60°F (15°C).

20W-20—Recommended for use in climates where temperatures never fall below 20°F (−6°C).

30—Recommended for use in climates where temperatures never fall below 32°F (0°C). This grade of oil is the most widely used truck and bus diesel engine in operations that persist in using straight grade oils.

40—Recommended for severe-duty use in climates where temperatures never fall below 40°F (4°C).

50—Recommended for severe-duty use in climates where temperatures never fall below 60°F (15°C). Often used to disguise engine problems, especially oil burners and leakage.

SYNTHETIC OILS

Most diesel engine OEMs approve of the use of synthetic lubricants and often recommend them for severe-duty applications such as extreme cold weather operation, providing the oil used meets their specifications. Synthetic lubricants are largely petrochemically sourced, but some plant-based and coal-sourced additives are also used. *Synthesis* is the process of creating compounds in the laboratory, so while conventional lubricants are obtained from petroleum crude oils by distillation or other refining methods, synthetics are manufactured or "synthesized" in chemical plants by reacting components. Some examples are poly-alpha-olefins, diesters, polyesters, and silicone fluids.

Only the high cost of synthetic lubricants is limiting their use in diesel engines, because most trials have proven them to be superior. Amsol Series 3000 5W-30 oil retains fluidity at −50°F (−45°C), along with outperforming 15W-40 mineral oil in ambient temperatures exceeding 100°F (38°C). Synthetics have already become the oil of choice in transmissions and final drive carriers, but the frequency of service and volume required of diesel engine crankcase lubes has delayed their acceptance as an engine oil. This is gradually changing. Some OEMs now approve of extended service intervals for synthetic oils—but most do not. The stated reason is the effect of EGR fouling. In all cases, observe the OEM recommendations for

service intervals. The oils that constitute FA-4 (mentioned earlier) necessarily consist of both petroleum-base and synthetic blends.

WHAT OIL SHOULD BE USED?

Each engine OEM has specific requirements for the engine oils it wants used in its engines. These requirements are outlined in tests that engine oils are subjected to prior to an approval. Oil refiners attempt to meet as many standards as possible when marketing engine oils, for the obvious reason that they can service more potential buyers with a single product. The problem is that oil is like a brew: throwing more additives in does not necessarily improve it. For instance, if your preference is to drink orange juice, you probably would not consider it a better drink if some coffee and cola were added to it. For this reason, a general-purpose, heavy-duty engine oil is not necessarily better than the OEM-labeled oil, although of course it will be both cheaper and more advertised.

Developing a Formula

The best choice for any engine is to use the manufacturer-recommended engine oil. After all, the research and performance profiles have all been performed on the engine using this oil. This may not be the best choice for the pocketbook, and in fairness there are general-purpose diesel engine oils that have proven to perform well in engines over time. You should also know that engine OEMs usually do not "engineer" their own oils. This development is done by specialist oil research companies, such as Lubrizol (http://www.lubrizol.com), that have been contracted by the OEM. A company such as Lubrizol neither manufactures nor markets oil. The company is paid by an OEM to develop a formula (a "recipe," if you like). After the formula has been developed, the OEM presents the recipe to an oil refiner that then manufactures the product to specification. Developing the appropriate additive package for an engine oil is a science in itself and is usually the result of extensive testing by lubrication engineers known as tribologists.

LUBRICATION SYSTEM COMPONENTS

Engine lubricant must be retained in a reservoir, pumped through the lubrication circuit, filtered, cooled, and have its pressure and temperature monitored. The group of components that performs these tasks is known as the *lubricating circuit*. The components in a diesel engine lube circuit vary little from one engine to another, but OEM service literature should be consulted before servicing and reconditioning any components.

SUMP—OIL PAN

The *sump* or oil pan is a reservoir usually located at the base of the engine cylinder block enclosing the crankcase (**Figure 10–7**). Oil pans are manufactured from cast aluminum, stamped mild steel, and various plastics and fibers. The oil pan acts as the reservoir used to collect the lubrication oil, which gravity causes to drain to the crankcase, and from which the oil pump pickup can recycle it through the lubrication circuit. A more complete description of an oil pan is provided in Chapter 9.

> **TECH TIP:**
> Observe the torque sequence when fitting an oil pan, especially those designed to bolt both to the engine cylinder block and the flywheel housing. The consequences of not doing so can be leaks at the pan gasket or stress cracks to the oil pan.

DIPSTICKS

The *dipstick* is a rigid band of hardened steel that is inserted into a round tube to extend into the oil sump. Checking the engine oil level is performed daily by the vehicle operator, so the dipstick location is always accessible. In a cab-over-engine

FIGURE 10–7 A typical oil pan.

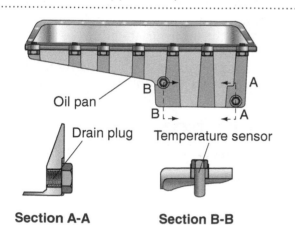

Oil pan

Drain plug   Temperature sensor

Section A-A   Section B-B

(COE) chassis, the dipstick must be accessible without raising the cab, so it may be of considerable length. It is crucial that the correct dipstick length be used for each specific engine.

Dipstick Replacement

When replacing a missing or defective dipstick, replace the engine oil and filters, installing the exact OEM-specified quantity. If it is an older engine equipped with an aftermarket bypass filter, you will have to plug the bypass circuit. Run the engine for a couple of minutes, then shut it down and leave it for 10 minutes. Dip the oil sump with the new dipstick and scribe the high-level graduation with an electric pencil. Measure the distance from the high-level to low-level graduations on the old dipstick and then duplicate them on the replacement. Remember, the consequences of low or high engine oil levels can be equally serious, so ensure that this operation is performed with precision.

Electronic Oil Level Indicators

Some electronically managed engines have an oil level sensor that signals oil level condition to the ECM, which can then initiate whatever failure strategy it is programmed for. Electronic oil level indicators use Hall-effect sensing to report real-time oil level values.

> **TECH TIP:**
> To obtain an accurate oil level reading, ensure that an engine has been shut down for at least 10 minutes before reading the dipstick indicated level.

OIL PUMP

Engine oil pumps are usually of the positive displacement type and have pumping capacities that greatly exceed the requirements of the engine. They are gear driven and usually located in the crankcase close to the oil they pump, though in some Cummins and Caterpillar applications they are external. Oil pumps are driven either directly or indirectly by the engine geartrain. In cases where the oil pump is located in the crankcase, the drive source is a vertical shaft and pinion engaged with a drive gear on the camshaft. A pickup assembly is located close to but not contacting the base of the oil pan, with enough clearance to ensure that minor impact damage does not inhibit oil

FIGURE 10–8 View of an oil pump and pickup on an inverted engine.

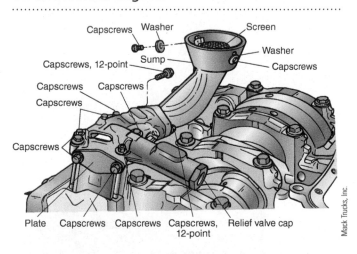

External Gear

External gear pumps consist of two meshed gears, one driving the other within a housing machined with an inlet (suction) port and outlet (charge) port. As the gears rotate, the teeth entrap inlet oil and force it outside between the gear teeth and the gear housing to the outlet port. Where the teeth mesh in the center, a seal is formed that prevents any backflow of oil to the inlet. This is by far the most common oil pump design on current engines. **Figure 10–10** demonstrates the operating principle of a typical external gear-type oil pump.

GEAR PUMP OVERHAUL Gear-type engine oil pumps seldom malfunction. When they show evidence of wear, the underlying reason is usually found in contaminated engine lube. To inspect a gear-type pump, remove the cover plate and, with the gears in the housing, use a thickness gauge to check the gear-to-housing radial clearance as shown in **Figure 10–11**. If this exceeds the OEM specification, the gears should be replaced.

Next, the gear-to-cover plate clearance (gear member axial clearance) should be measured using a straightedge and thickness gauges as shown in **Figure 10–12**. Replace the gears if the measurement exceeds specifications.

Before reassembling a gear-type pump, clean thoroughly using solvent and compressed air drying, ensuring that the pickup pipe and inlet screen are not overlooked. Reassemble using engine oil as assembly lubricant and check the drive gear teeth backlash as shown in **Figure 10–13**.

flow to the pump. **Figure 10–8** is an image of one type of oil pump and pickup tube, shown in an inverted engine; **Figure 10–9** shows an alternate design. Two basic types of oil pumps are used.

Gerotor

Gerotor-type oil pumps use an internal crescent gear pumping principle. An internal impeller

FIGURE 10–9 Oil pump and pickup assembly.

FIGURE 10–10 Operating principle of an external gear oil pump.

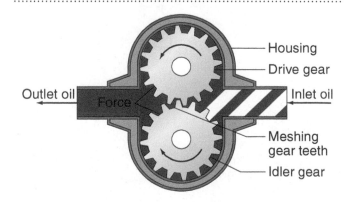

FIGURE 10–11 Checking gear side clearance.

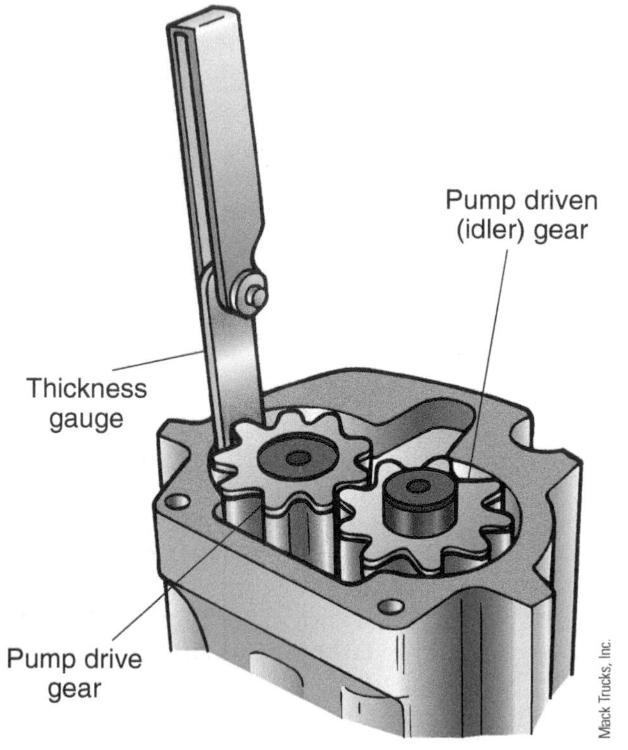

Thickness gauge

Pump driven (idler) gear

Pump drive gear

Mack Trucks, Inc.

FIGURE 10–13 Checking gear backlash.

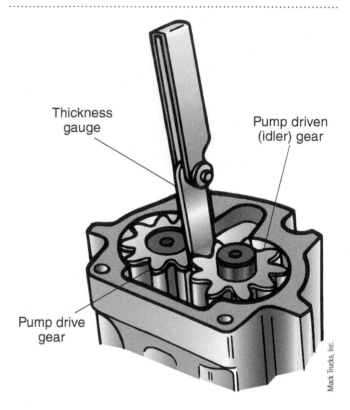

Thickness gauge

Pump driven (idler) gear

Pump drive gear

Mack Trucks, Inc.

with external crescent vanes is rotated within an internal crescent gear, also known as a *rotor ring*. The inner rotor or impeller has one less lobe than the rotor ring. The result is that

FIGURE 10–12 Checking gear end clearance.

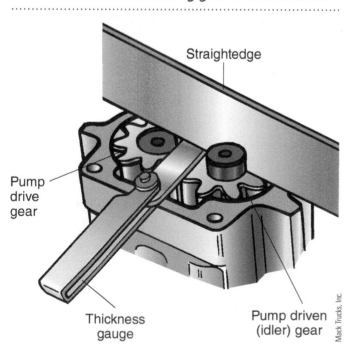

Straightedge

Pump drive gear

Thickness gauge

Pump driven (idler) gear

Mack Trucks, Inc.

as the inner rotor is driven within the outer rotor, only one lobe is engaged at any given moment of operation. In this way, oil from the inlet port is picked up in the crescent formed between two lobes on the impeller and, as the impeller rotates, forced out through the outlet port as the lead lobe once again engages. The assembly is rotated within the gerotor pump body.

Gerotor pumps tend to wear most between the lobes on the impeller and on the apex of the lobes on the rotor ring. These dimensions should be checked to OEM specifications using a micrometer. The rotor ring-to-body clearance should be checked with a thickness gauge sized to the OEM maximum clearance specification and the axial clearance of the rotor ring and impeller measured with a straightedge and thickness gauges. **Figure 10–14** shows a typical gerotor-type oil pump.

Scavenge Pumps/Scavenge Pickups

Scavenge pumps are used in the crankcase of some off-highway trucks (and other mobile heavy equipment) required to work on inclinations that could cause the oil pump to suck air. They are designed with a pickup located at either end of the oil pan.

FIGURE 10–14 A gerotor-type oil pump.

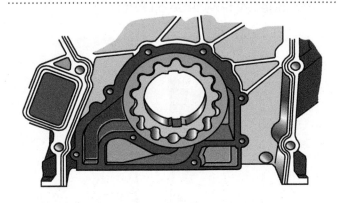

PRESSURE-REGULATING VALVES

Pressure-regulating valves are responsible for defining maximum system oil pressure. Most are adjustable. Typically, an oil pressure-regulating valve consists of a valve body with an inlet sealed with a spring-loaded, ball check valve. Other types of poppet valves are also used, but the principle is the same. The regulating valve body is plumbed in parallel to the main oil pump discharge line (**Figure 10–15**). When oil pressure is sufficient to unseat the spring-loaded check ball, it unseals, permitting oil to pass through the valve and spill to the oil sump; this action causes the pressure in the oil pump discharge line to drop. The regulating pressure value is adjusted by setting the spring tension of the spring, usually by shims

or adjusting screws. Some OEMs use color-coded springs to define the oil pressure values.

FILTERS

The role of oil filters in the diesel engine lubrication system is to remove and hold contaminants while providing the least amount of flow restriction in the lubrication circuit. Filters use different principles to accomplish this objective. Generally, oil filters can be classified as:

- Full flow: in series between the oil pump and lube circuit
- Bypass: ported off a lube gallery in parallel

Figure 10–16 shows the full flow lube oil filter used on a 2015 Cummins ISX. The term **positive filtration** is used to describe a filter that operates by forcing all the fluid to be filtered through the filtering medium. Most engine oil filters use a positive filtration principle. It should be noted that filters function at higher efficiencies when the engine oil is at operating temperature. Many full flow lube oil filters use a dual-stage process, as shown in the cutaway

FIGURE 10–15 Exploded view of an oil pump and integral pressure relief valve.

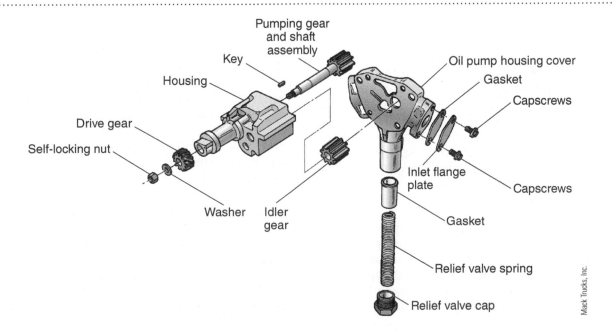

Mack Trucks, Inc.

FIGURE 10–16 Full flow lube filter on a 2015 Cummins ISX.

FIGURE 10–17 Cutaway view of two types of multi-stage full flow lube oil filters.

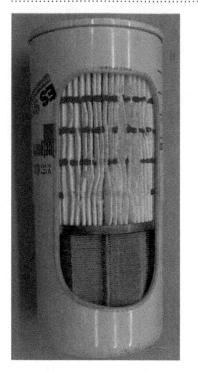

example in **Figure 10–17**. Filters work to clean the engine oil by using the following methods.

Mechanical Straining

Mechanical straining is accomplished by forcing the lubricant through a filtering medium, which if greatly enlarged would have the appearance of a grid. The sizing of the grid openings defines the size of the particle that may be entrapped by the filtering medium. Most current diesel engine oil filters make use of mechanical straining in conjunction with other principles. Straining media would include rosin-impregnated paper, often pleated to increase the effective surface area; and cotton fibers.

Absorbent Filtration

Absorbent filters work by absorbing or sucking up engine contaminants as a sponge would. Effective absorbent filtering media include cotton pulp, mineral wools, wool yarn, and felt. These filters not only absorb coarse particles but may also remove insoluble oxidized particulate, moisture, and acids.

Adsorbent Filtration

Filters adsorb by holding (by adhesion) the molecules of dissolved substances or liquids to the surface of the filtering medium. Adsorbent filtering media include charcoal, Fuller's earth, and chemically treated papers. Because adsorbent filters may act to remove oil additives, they are often used only where low-additive engine oils are specified.

Filter Types and Efficiencies

Most current filters are spin-on disposable cartridges. Older engines may have permanent canisters enclosing a replaceable element; the canister was mounted to the filter pad with a long threaded shaft that extended through the length of the canister. They are seldom seen today, as most OEMs made conversion adapters so that disposable spin-on cartridges could replace them. Filters are categorized by the manner in which they are plumbed into the lubrication circuit. **Figure 10–18** shows the right side of a post-2013 Mack MP-Series engine featuring the lubrication module and three filters.

Full Flow

The filter mounting pad is usually plumbed into the lubrication circuit close to the oil pump outlet, and all of the oil exiting the pump is forced through

FIGURE 10–18 Mack post-2013 MP-Series engine fuel module and filter pad assembly, featuring a pair of full flow filters, a bypass filter, and lube circuit valves. The centrifugal-type bypass filter is that located on the left of the filter pad.

the filter. The filtering medium is usually rosin or otherwise treated paper or cotton fiber. In most cases, these filters employ a mechanical straining principle, so the particles entrapped by the filtration media are those too large to pass through it. All **full flow filters** used on current truck and bus diesel engines use positive filtration and are rated to entrap particulates sized between 25 and 60 microns. **Bypass valves** located on full flow filter mounting pad(s) protect the engine should a filter become plugged. In this event, the oil exiting the oil pump would be routed around the plugged filter directly to the lubrication circuit.

Bypass

Bypass filters are used to complement the full flow filters on current highway diesel engines. These are plumbed in parallel in the lubrication circuit, usually by porting them into the main engine oil gallery. They filter more slowly, but are rated to entrap particles down to 10 microns in size. Two types are used.

CENTRIFUGAL FILTER Centrifugal filtration or centrifuging canisters have the highest filtering efficiencies. A **centrifugal filter** consists of a canister within which a cylindrical rotor is supported on bearings. Figure 10–18 shows a detailed view of a Mack Trucks oil module and filter pad assembly to which a pair of full flow filters and a bypass filter are mounted. The centrifugal bypass filter is mounted on the left side of the filter pad.

Study **Figure 10–19**, which shows how a Mack Trucks centrifugal filter is arranged in the lube circuit: It is identified as a CentriMax filter on the schematic. The filter is plumbed into the lubrication circuit so that the rotor is charged with engine oil at lube system pressure. It exits the rotor via two thrust jets, which are angled to rotate the assembly at high velocity. The centrifuge forces the engine oil through a stationary cylindrical filtering medium wrapped outside the rotor. The filtering medium is usually a rosin-coated paper element. The filtered oil drains back to the oil sump.

> ### TECH TIP:
> Bypass filters boast high filtering efficiencies, and failure to observe scheduled maintenance can result in plugged filters.

FIGURE 10–19 Schematic showing oil flow through a lubrication circuit equipped with a centrifugal filter. Note how the oil exits the centrifugal bypass filter to be returned to the sump.

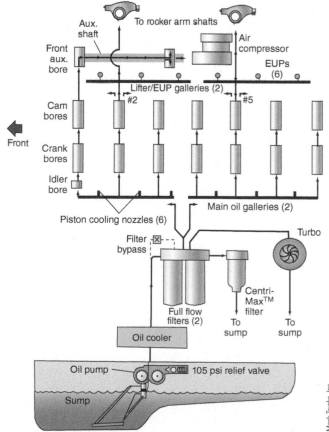

Mack Trucks, Inc.

Today, most centrifugal filters are OEM supplied as original equipment integrated into the lube circuit, such as the examples shown in Figure 10–18. However, there are many examples of aftermarket centrifugal filters on older engines, fitted to them because they did their job so well. Most of the aftermarket examples have to be serviced by:

- Draining the centrifuge canister
- Removing the filter element (usually a circular wrap)
- Cleaning the centrifuge jets with solvent
- Installing a new filter element
- Purging air from the canister after startup

LUBERFINER FILTER Older engines often used these large canister-type filters designed to entrap much smaller particles than full flow filters. Luberfiner filters could be supplied from any pressure port in the engine lubrication circuit. They returned filtered lubricant directly to the oil sump. Luberfiner filters served an additional role as an oil cooler, so they were often mounted in the airflow. Luberfiner filters are large volume filters that substantially increase the amount of engine oil required. This is important to remember when servicing the engine, because more oil will be required. A replaceable filter element is installed to a permanent canister. As with centrifugal filter canisters, they should be purged of air after engine startup.

TECH TIP:

Always crack the nut on the exit fitting of bypass filters after each oil change to purge the air. Failure to do this can result in an air-locked filter.

CAUTION:

The OEM-specified oil capacity of an engine may not include the volume of oil retained in the bypass filters. Purge bypass filters where required, and check the oil level after running the engine following the oil change.

Filter Bypass Valves

Filter mounting pad bypass valves operate in much the same way as the oil pressure-regulating valves, except that their objective is to route the lubricant around a restricted full flow filter to prevent engine damage by oil starvation. When a filter bypass valve is actuated and the check valve unseated, instead of spilling the oil to the crankcase it reroutes the oil directly to the lubrication circuit, effectively shorting out the filter assembly. So, when a bypass value trips, unfiltered oil is circulated through the lubrication circuit. Note the location of the filter bypass in the schematic in Figure 10–19.

Replacing Filters

Filters are removed using a band, strap, or socket wrench. In some cases where a plastic filter housing is used, a specific OEM socket may be required to avoid damaging the filter assembly. Ensure that the filter gasket and seal (if used) are removed with the filter. Precautions should be taken to capture oil that spills when the filter is removed: punching a hole in the filter canister and draining it directly into a catch sump may reduce the amount of spilled oil. Disposable filters and elements are loaded with toxins and must be disposed of in accordance with federal and local-jurisdiction legislation that applies to used engine oils and filters.

CAUTION:

When performing lube service on a truck that comes in off the road, expect the engine oil drained from the oil pan and filters to be *hot*. In fact, it is hot enough to cause serious burns, so take great care in dropping oil and filters from warm engines.

Most OEMs require that new oil filters be primed. If this is not done, in some cases, the lag required to charge the oil filters on startup is sufficient to generate a fault code and damage turbochargers, main bearings, and rod bearings. Priming an oil filter requires that it be filled with new engine oil on the inlet side of the filter until it is just short of the top of the filter; this will take a little while, as the oil must pass through the filtering medium to fill the outlet area inside the element. The sealing gasket should be lightly coated with engine oil. OEMs are usually fairly specific about how much the filter should be tightened and caution against overtightening. In most cases, the filter should be tightened by rotating it one-half to a full turn after the gasket and filter pad mounting face make contact.

OIL COOLERS

Oil coolers are heat exchangers consisting of a housing and cooling element or core through which coolant is pumped and around which oil is circulated. Oil temperatures in diesel engines run higher than coolant temperatures, typically around 110°C (230°F). However, the engine coolant reaches its operating temperature more rapidly than the oil and plays a role in heating the oil to operating temperature in cold weather startup/warmup conditions. Two types of oil coolers are in current use.

Bundle Type

The **bundle** type of oil cooler is the most common design. It consists of a usually cylindrical "bundle" of tubes with headers at either end that are enclosed in a housing. Engine coolant is flowed through the tubes and the oil is spiral-circulated around the tubes by helical baffles. The assembly is designed so that the oil inlet is at the opposite end to the coolant inlet. This arrangement means that the engine oil at its hottest is first exposed to the coolant at its coolest, slightly increasing cooling efficiency. **Figure 10–20** shows the routing flow through a typical bundle-type oil cooler.

The consequence of a failed cooler bundle or the header O-rings is oil charged to the cooling circuit. Most OEMs prefer that bundles be leak-tested by vacuum, because this tests the assembly in the direction of fluid flow in the event of a leak. One header should be capped with a dummy plate and the other fitted with the evacuation adaptor: Load to the OEM-recommended vacuum value and leave for the required amount of time to observe any drop-off.

Alternatively, the bundle can be pressure tested using regulated shop air pressure and a bucket of water. This is known as reverse-flow testing. Whenever oil has leaked into the coolant circuit, the engine cooling system must be flushed with an approved detergent and water, with the engine run at its operating temperature for at least 15 minutes. **Figure 10–21** is an exploded view of a bundle-type oil cooler and **Figure 10–22** is a photograph of a sectioned oil cooler bundle assembly.

FIGURE 10–20 A. Oil cooler location; B. Oil flow through a bundle-type oil cooler.

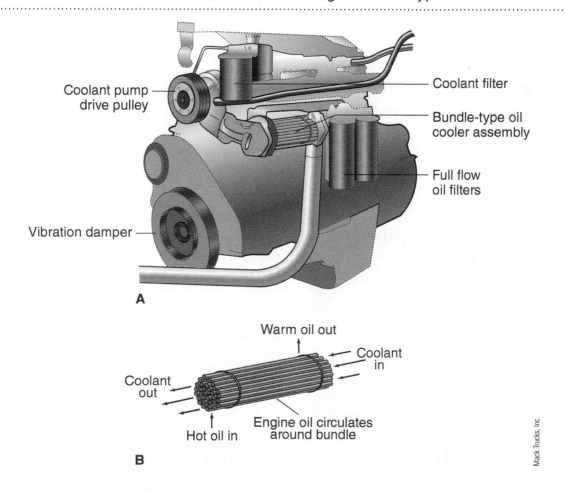

Mack Trucks, Inc.

FIGURE 10–21 Exploded view of a bundle-type oil cooler.

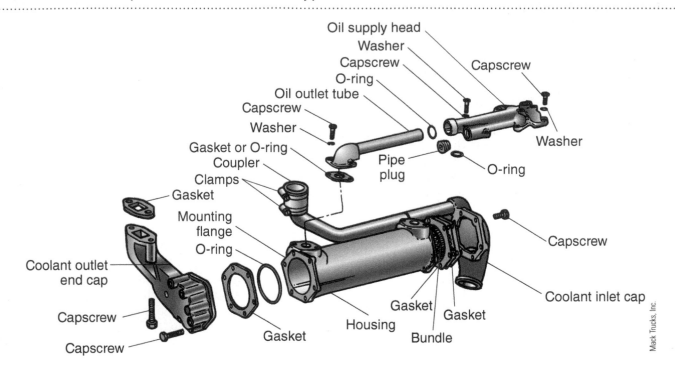

FIGURE 10–22 Sectioned bundle-type oil cooler assembly.

Plate Type

In the plate-type oil cooler, the oil circulates within a series of flat plates and the coolant flows around them within a housing assembly. They have lower cooling efficiencies than bundle element coolers, but they are easier to clean and repair. **Figure 10–23** shows a diagrammed image of a typical low-maintenance, plate-type oil cooler; **Figure 10–24** shows a photograph of the same cooler. Lower cost, lower maintenance, and more compact design mean that plate-type oil coolers are preferred by some engine OEMs.

Oil Cooling Jets

Piston oil cooling jets have always been a critical component of the engine lubrication circuit. They are plumbed into a cylinder block lubrication gallery and spray engine lube onto the underside of each piston. They have always played a critical role in managing piston temperatures, but it could be argued that they have become even more critical in today's engines, many of which have no other means of delivering oil to the pistons. Bushingless piston bosses such as those used in Monotherm pistons and conn rods with no delivery rifling have both added to the already important role played by piston cooling jets. **Figure 10–25** is a diagram of a typical piston cooling jet.

FIGURE 10–23 A diagram view of a typical plate-type oil cooler.

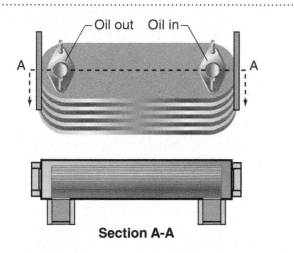

Section A-A

With cold SAE 5W-30 lubricant oil flow through the cooler is approximately 110 liter/min (29 U.S. gpm). Maximum coolant flow through the cooler assembly is 190 liter/min (50 U.S. gpm).

FIGURE 10–24 Plate-type oil cooler.

Targeting Piston Cooling Jets

Piston cooling jets usually have to be targeted to a specific area on the underside of the piston. As indicated in Chapter 7, what seems to be a slightly misdirected cooling jet can result in rapid torching of a piston due to overheating. By targeting the cooling jet, oil is delivered to a circulation gallery machined in the underside of the piston; this enables it to route engine lube to those areas of the piston that require lubrication and cooling. The procedure used to target piston cooling jets is covered in Chapter 7. The technician should ensure that the consequences of an improperly targeted cooling jet are understood. Just to make things more confusing, OEMs frequently alter the target window through different engine

FIGURE 10–25 A typical piston cooling jet.

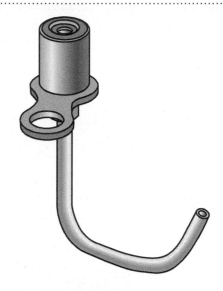

generations, so it is important to consult OEM service literature before undertaking the procedure. **Figure 10–26** shows a properly targeted piston cooling nozzle on a MaxxForce engine. The cooling jet directional target has a way of changing with each successive generation of an engine series, so ensure that the correct tooling is used. **Figure 10–27** shows a common means of targeting a piston cooling jet using a perspex template that fits to the engine cylinder bore.

FIGURE 10–26 Oil cooling nozzle on a Navistar MaxxForce engine.

FIGURE 10–27 Targeting an oil cooling nozzle using a perspex template that fits over the cylinder bore.

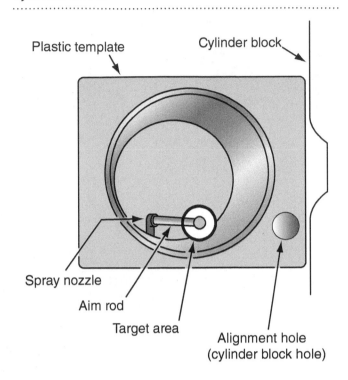

Plastic template

Cylinder block

Spray nozzle

Aim rod

Target area

Alignment hole
(cylinder block hole)

OIL PRESSURE MEASUREMENT

Of all the engine monitoring devices used on an engine, the oil pressure is one of the most critical. Loss of engine oil pressure will, in most cases, cause a nearly immediate engine failure. Back in the days when few of an engine's operating conditions were monitored and displayed to the operator, there was always a means of signaling a loss of oil pressure. Several types of oil pressure sensors have been used in diesel engines over the years, and they are identified here. However, for the past 20 years, only the first category remains relevant as a means of signaling oil pressure onboard the chassis.

Variable Capacitance (Pressure) Sensor

Almost all commercial diesel engines managed electronically use variable capacitance-type sensors. These are supplied with reference voltage output from the engine control module (ECM). Oil pressure acts on a ceramic disc and moves it either closer to or farther away from a stationary steel disc, varying the capacitance of the device and thus the voltage signal value returned to the ECM. The ECM is responsible for

broadcasting the signal that activates the dash display or gauge. It should be noted that engine oil pressure usually has to fall to dangerously low levels before programmed failure strategies are triggered. **Figure 10–28** is a Navistar schematic showing how a variable capacitance oil pressure sensor interacts with the engine ECM: The fault codes shown in the schematic are Navistar specific.

Bourdon Gauge

A flexible, coiled, bourdon tube is filled with oil under pressure. The bourdon tube will attempt to uncoil and straighten incrementally as it is subjected to pressure rise. This action of somewhat bending the bourdon tube rotates a gear by means of a sector and pinion. A pointer is attached at the gear across a calibrated scale and provides a means of reading it. A bourdon gauge is also known as a mechanical gauge.

Bourdon gauges are accurate when new, but as the bourdon tube ages, metal fatigue allows it to flex at lower pressures, producing higher than actual pressure readings as it does so. They are often used as "master" gauges in service facility diagnostics, but technicians would do well to remember that they do become inaccurate with age, so they should be subjected to routine calibration tests.

Electrical

Engine oil pressure acts on a sending unit diaphragm, which in turn moves a sliding wiper arm across a variable resistor that incrementally grounds out a feed from the electric gauge. The gauge is a simple armature and coil assembly that receives its feed from the vehicle ignition switch. They are not often used today on mobile diesel engines, due the low cost and accuracy of variable capacitance sensors.

> **TECH TIP:**
>
> Whichever means is used to display oil pressure, none should be used as the only means of diagnosing a low oil pressure complaint. Use a good quality master gauge, usually a bourdon gauge with a fluid-filled display dial, and ensure that the engine oil is at operating temperature.

Oil Temperature Management

As Environmental Protection Agency (EPA) noxious emissions standards become increasingly tougher,

FIGURE 10–28 A Navistar oil pressure sensing circuit.

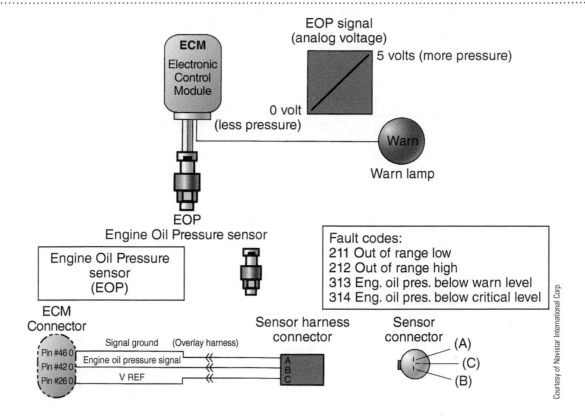

EOP signal
(analog voltage)

5 volts (more pressure)

0 volt
(less pressure)

ECM
Electronic
Control
Module

Warn

Warn lamp

EOP
Engine Oil Pressure sensor

Engine Oil Pressure
sensor
(EOP)

Fault codes:
211 Out of range low
212 Out of range high
313 Eng. oil pres. below warn level
314 Eng. oil pres. below critical level

ECM
Connector

Pin #46 0
Pin #42 0
Pin #26 0

Signal ground   (Overlay harness)
Engine oil pressure signal
V REF

A
B
C

Sensor harness
connector

Sensor
connector   (A)
(C)
(B)

Courtesy of Navistar International Corp.

there is an ever greater requirement to manage the combustion temperatures within a tight operating window. Engine oil temperatures are one of the most accurate indicators of actual engine temperature. It should also be remembered that engine oil plays a major role as a coolant in engines, especially in managing piston temperatures. In addition, when engine oil is used as a hydraulic medium, as it is in variable valve operation, engine brakes, and the hydraulically actuated electronic unit injector (HEUI) fuel system, its performance is to some extent dependent on its operating temperature. On the other end of the scale, the time required to heat engine oil to operating temperature is a factor in the higher emissions output during a warmup phase. **Figure 10–29** shows a Navistar temperature control circuit that enables the engine oil to bypass the oil cooler while the engine is warming up.

INTERPRETING OIL ANALYSES

Oil analysis has become a key component of good preventive maintenance (PM) practice, primarily because it has the potential to save operators money. Performing the analyses at each PM and responding appropriately to the lab

reports is key to making them cost-effective. An oil analysis is performed to determine:

- The viscosity
- The presence of coolant
- Dirt contamination
- Abnormal wear contamination

The engine oil temperature should be close to operating temperature when drawing a sample. Although the Technology and Maintenance Council (TMC) has guidelines on how to draw off oil samples (RP 318 2010C), they are not always easy to observe. There are three basic methods and all three require that the engine lube be at operating temperature:

1. Oil galley pressure valve. Described as the most accurate method, the sampling valve is located in a low-pressure oil line or galley. The valve should be petcock or automatic positive closed type. The sample should be drawn into the sample vial with the engine running.
2. Siphon method. The engine oil should be brought to operating temperature, then shut down. A siphoning syringe should be inserted into the dipstick tube and the sample drawn from the mid-sump level.

FIGURE 10–29 Navistar temperature control circuit shown in warmup and operating temperature modes.

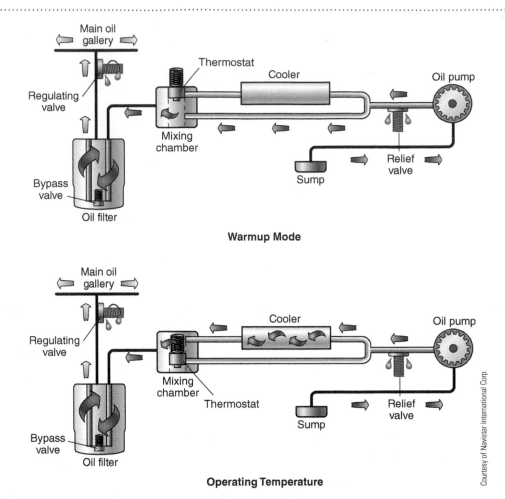

Warmup Mode

Operating Temperature

Courtesy of Navistar International Corp.

3. Oil plug drain method. The engine oil should be at operating temperature and the engine shut down. Remembering that the oil is hot, allow approximately 1 (4 liters) gallon of oil flow before filling the sample vial or bottle.

Practical reality suggests that most oil samples will be taken from diesel engines during routine PM oil change operations using method number 3.

The technician taking the sample should avoid taking the sample from either the beginning or the end of the drain-off. Precautions should be taken to avoid burns from the oil while obtaining the sample. Also avoid contaminating the sample after it has been taken. Label the container and complete the engine identification and data form that will accompany the sample to the laboratory. If the objective of the sample is diagnosis of a condition, the technician has no choice but to syringe the sample

either from the oil pan or a lubrication gallery: Again, the oil should be at running temperature when drawing the sample.

TYPES OF TESTING

When used engine oil is analyzed, the objective is to produce a report card on the rate of engine wear and the suitability of the oil change interval to the application, and perhaps to head off imminent engine problems before they become major problems. Oil-testing laboratories use primarily blotter and spectrographic testing to produce reports that reference the engine OEM limit specifications. A blotter test kit is available for nonlaboratory testing of engine oil. A **blotter test** is a relatively crude means of testing some of an oil's characteristics. A change in the oil's viscosity can be determined using a flow comparator. A significant increase in the engine oil's viscosity can be caused by prolonged high-temperature operation, aerated lubricant, or coolant contamination. A decrease in viscosity is normally attributable to fuel contamination. It should be noted that all truck diesel engine oil is affected to some extent by fuel contamination; however, this should not be sufficient to cause any significant alteration in viscosity.

Next, a measured drop of used oil is dropped on a test paper or blotter. The darkness of the sample relative to that on a code chart is used to indicate the amount of soot, dirt, and other suspended material in the sample. On some blotter test kits, the acidity can also be read on the test paper by a change of color. Laboratories perform more comprehensive testing usually involving the use of spectrochemical analyses.

Spectrographic testing produces more specific results and is used to identify metallic and organic contaminants in oil. A quantity of the sample is vaporized and subjected to ultraviolet radiation; the extent to which its constituent molecules react to the radiation is used to identify and quantify them.

Oil sample analyses must be interpreted comparatively not only with the OEM maximum specifications but also with the vehicle's service application. They are most meaningful when interpreted by a fleet equipped with identical engines in units engaged in similar operating modes. The following list includes some of the elements found on a typical oil analysis report:

Al—aluminum. A constituent of many friction bearings, pistons, turbo impeller housings, Roots blowers. Over-spec Al can indicate wear in any of these components.

B—boron. An engine coolant SCA (supplemental cooling additive) and an engine oil additive.

Cr—chromium. A common piston ring coating.

Cu—copper. A constituent of many oil cooler bundles, friction bearings, engine bushings, and thrust washers. Copper levels tend to be higher when an engine is new (100 ppm) and should drop down to lower levels (20 ppm) after 100,000 miles (160,000 km).

Fe—iron. Most of the engine components are iron-based alloys. High Fe readings could be an indication of rapid wear on almost any engine component exposed to the lube oil; engine cylinder and valvetrain components should be suspected first.

Pb—lead. A constituent of most friction bearings. High Pb suggests high load engine operation.

Si—silicon. Silicon dioxide from airborne fine sands and dusts ingested by the engine intake system often indicate malfunctioning air filter or intake ducting leaks. Silicon is a constituent of new engine oil in which it serves as an antifoam agent, so the silicon level reported by the laboratory is corrected to read only externally acquired silicon.

Na—sodium. Found in some lubricants as an additive, so the laboratory reading must be corrected to read acquired sodium. When the source is other than the engine oil, the culprit is usually coolant SCAs.

Sn—tin. A constituent of most friction bearings and occasionally used to coat pistons.

Soot—also known as total solids, soot is a form of fine carbon particle, a combustion by-product that is not readily identifiable in routine lab testing; in fact, some laboratories report total suspended particles as soot level. Fuel soot is present in all engine oil. It is nonabrasive but may increase the oil's viscosity.

TECH TIP:

Whenever a high reading in an oil analysis chart cannot be explained, contact the National Service Operations Department of the engine OEM before taking any other action. Their experience of failure feedback from across the continent may produce a simple explanation of the problem that could avoid an unnecessary engine teardown.

INTERNAL CIRCUIT VIDEO

Shell markets an internal lube circuit video monitoring system which it has demonstrated in highway diesel engines. While it is unlikely that this technology will find its way into everyday fleet trucks in the foreseeable future, it is used in research and creating the profiles used in condition-based diagnostics and prognostics. The system places minute video cameras at critical lubrication wear points on an engine for human eye observation and assessment. **Figure 10–30** shows the handheld imager used with the Shell system.

FIGURE 10–30 Handheld video imager used in the Shell internal lube circuit video monitoring system.

LUBRICATING CIRCUIT PROBLEMS

The following are some guidelines for troubleshooting lubrication circuit complaints. Be aware of the sequencing. You would be amazed at how many lubrication circuit problems are root sourced by insufficient oil in the sump.

- When investigating a low oil pressure complaint, first check the oil sump level. Next, check the appearance and odor of the oil.
- Low oil pressure complaints must be verified with a master gauge.
- High sump levels caused simply by excessive oil can aerate the lubricant, causing low pressure and fluctuations or surging.

- After an engine rebuild, it is good practice to pressure-prime the engine lubrication system with an external pump.
- Most OEMs recommend priming full flow filters on all turbocharged engines. Oil filters should be primed by filling with new engine oil poured into the inlet side of the oil filter, but consult the OEM service literature for the recommendations that apply to their engines. It is not necessary to prime bypass filters, although it may be necessary to purge air from them as the engine is started up after an oil change.
- When taking an oil sample, draw off midway through the sump runoff, never at the beginning or end. If an oil sample is required outside of the normal oil change interval, use a syringe. To obtain the most reliable results, oil samples should be taken shortly after an engine has been run.
- Oil change intervals are determined primarily by mileage in linehaul applications in conjunction with OEM recommendations. In fact, mileage rather than engine operating hours is used as the indicator of service intervals in most highway vehicles.
- Oil change intervals in off-highway vehicles are determined by engine hours or gallons of fuel consumed. In larger off-highway diesel engines with high-volume oil sump capacities, oil changes may be determined on the basis of oil analyses to reduce costs.

As with *all* troubleshooting on electronic engines, make sure to connect to the chassis data bus. Today, this is just part of routine shop practice.

Want to know more? Try these websites:

http://www.api.org: American Petroleum Institute

http://www.dieselnet.com: EPA diesel emissions news

http://www.lubrizol.com: Lubrizol home page

EXTENDED OIL CHANGES

Servicing trucks costs money. When oil change intervals can be extended, it saves money. Engine OEMs, in conjunction with those who research their oil requirements, are continually working on developing engine oils that will sustain longer service life before degradation, because their customers are asking for this feature. And until the almost universal adoption of EGR on diesel engines in 2004, they were doing a great job. Rerouting soot particles back into the engine with the intake charge in an EGR mixing chamber has a way of shortening the life of engine oils. The API CJ-4, CK-4, and FA-4 engine lube categories are formulated to buffer the effect of minute soot particles, but OEM-recommended oil service intervals have not been raised much in recent years, because EGR-introduced particles are contaminants that the lube circuit has to handle. Despite the vastly superior performance of synthetic diesel engine lubricants, they still have a threshold of dirt they can safely handle, and this is the major reason for the hesitancy on the part of OEMs to endorse longer engine service intervals.

It can be expected that diesel engine OEMs will work toward increasing oil change intervals over the next few years, but nothing dramatic is likely to happen in the near future. The clean gas induction (CGI) system used by Caterpillar ACERT for on-highway engines up to 2010, and off-highway engines to this day, produces cleaner combustion and lower levels of lube oil contamination, so the key may be in the broader use of this technology by OEMs intent on using EGR. That said, CGI is not used on the post-2013 Caterpillar CT15 (EGR only) and MaxxForce 13 (SCR) engines to meet NO_x emissions standards.

TECH TIP:

Petroleum-based engine lubes cease to provide adequate lubrication when oil operating temperatures exceed 265°F (130°C). Because this threshold is often equaled and sometimes exceeded by post-2010 engines used in extreme service environments, OEMs are becoming more inclined to recommend the use of synthetic lubes that will sustain considerably higher temperatures.

SUMMARY

- A diesel engine lubricant performs a number of roles, including those of minimizing friction, supporting hydrodynamic suspension, cooling, and cleaning.
- Viscosity describes a liquid fluid's resistance to shear.
- Lubricity describes the flow characteristics of a liquid fluid. Lubricity in engine oils is affected by temperature, with hot oils tending to flow more readily than cold oils.
- Diesel engine OEMs recommend the use of multigrade oils over straight grades and approve the use of synthetic engine oils, especially for operation in conditions of severe cold.
- The pour point of engine oil is the temperature at which the oil starts to gel. Oils formulated for winter use have pour point depressant additives.
- Sludged oil is usually a result of oil degradation caused by prolonged low-load, cold weather operation.
- Ash in used engine oils is mineral residue caused by oxide and sulfate incineration. High ash levels are indicative of high-temperature operation.
- Oil aeration can be caused by high oil sump levels.
- In API oil classifications, the GF prefix denotes oil formulated for gasoline-fueled engines and the C denotes oil formulated for compression-ignition engines.
- Post-2007 diesel engines with EGR and DPFs are required to use SAE CJ-4 rated engine lube.
- Post-2017 diesel engines are required to use SAE CK-4 or FA-4 rated engine lubes.
- CK-4 engine lube is formulated similar to CJ-4 lubricant and is backward compatible.
- FA-4 is formulated for new-generation fuel-efficient engines and has limited or no backward compatibility.
- Most field research indicates that synthetic oils substantially outperform traditional oils; however, only recently have OEMs begun to endorse extended oil change intervals that justify the additional cost.
- It is important to maintain the correct engine oil level, and the technician should be aware that the consequences of an excessively high oil level can be as severe as those of low sump levels.
- Positive displacement pumps of the external gear and gerotor types are used as oil pumps in diesel engines; most are of the external gear pump design.
- Oil pumps are designed to pump much greater volumes of oil than that required to lubricate the engine. An adjustable, pressure-regulating valve defines the peak system pressure.

- When an engine is overhauled, the oil pump should be disassembled and checked for wear.
- The filters used on a heavy-duty lubrication system may be classified as full flow and bypass depending on how they are plumbed into the circuit. Full flow filters are located in series between the oil pump and the lubrication circuit, whereas bypass filters are arranged in parallel, receiving oil from an oil gallery and returning it directly to the oil sump.
- Most OEMs prefer that filters be primed before installation; OEMs recommend that filters be primed by filling from the inlet side only.
- Filters are usually rated by their mechanical straining specification in microns, but they also filter by absorption and adsorption.
- Oil coolers are heat exchangers used on most heavy-duty, highway diesel engines; the cooling medium used is engine coolant.
- There are two types of oil cooler: the bundle type and the plate type.
- A bundle-type oil cooler consists of a housing within which coolant is pumped through a cylindrical "bundle" of copper tubes in one direction while engine oil is pumped around the tubes flowing in the opposite direction.
- Most OEMs prefer that bundle elements be vacuum-tested for leaks before assembly; pressure testing may also be used.
- Plate-type oil coolers have slightly lower cooling efficiencies but offer fewer in-service maintenance problems.

- Engine oil pressure measurement is, in most modern engines, performed by a variable capacitance type of sensor that signals the management computer. The dash gauge or display is therefore a computer output.
- Engine oil pressures usually have to fall to very low levels before programmed electronic failure strategies are triggered. Actual oil pressure correlates with rpm; for instance, a low oil pressure at idle speed represents a less serious condition than the same value oil pressure when the engine is run at rated rpm.
- Laboratory testing of used engine oil samples is a relatively inexpensive method of tracking engine wear rates and providing early warning alerts of engine malfunctions. It should be adopted as part of a regular PM schedule.
- Spectrographic testing performed by laboratories tends to produce more accurate and precise assessments of the engine oil than blotter tests.
- Routine engine oil samples should be taken when the engine oil is changed, preferably at the mid-flow point when draining the sump. When extracted for diagnostic purposes, the sample should be syringed either directly from a lube gallery or from the midpoint of the sump, with the engine oil at operating temperature.
- When interpreting oil sample analyses, it should be noted that a high silicon reading is often an indication of a leak in the air cleaner or suction side of the air intake system.

REVIEW QUESTIONS

1. Which of the following SAE multigrade oils would likely be recommended by most highway diesel engine OEMs for year-round use in North America?
   a. 5W-30
   b. 15W-40
   c. 20W-20
   d. 20W-50

2. Which of the following API classifications indicates that the oil is formulated for diesel engines meeting MY 2010 emissions standards up to 2017?
   a. GF
   b. CC
   c. CI-4
   d. CJ-4

3. Which of the following conditions could result from a high crankcase oil level?
   a. Lube oil aeration
   b. Oil pressure gauge fluctuations
   c. Friction bearing damage
   d. All of the above

4. When investigating a low oil pressure complaint, which of the following should be performed first?
   a. Perform a rod and main bearing rollover.
   b. Install a master gauge to verify the complaints.
   c. Test the oil for fuel contamination.
   d. Check the crankcase oil level.

5. A full flow oil filter has become completely plugged. What is the likely outcome if the engine is running?
   a. A bypass valve diverts the oil around the filter.
   b. Engine lubrication ceases.
   c. The oil pump hydraulically locks.
   d. The engine seizes.

6. Which of the following statements would usually correctly describe the relative temperatures of the coolant and lubricant when the engine is at operating temperature?
   a. Coolant temperatures are higher than engine oil temperatures.
   b. Engine oil temperatures are higher than coolant temperatures.
   c. Coolant and engine oil temperatures should be equal.

7. Which type of oil pump is most commonly used in current highway diesel engines?
   a. External gear
   b. Plunger
   c. Centrifugal
   d. Vane

8. Which of the following is usually the preferred OEM method of testing an oil cooler bundle?
   a. Pressure test using shop air and a bucket of water
   b. Vacuum test
   c. Die penetrant test

9. When interpreting a used engine oil analysis profile, which of the following conditions would be most likely to cause high silicon levels?
   a. Oil cooler bundle disintegration
   b. Plugged air cleaner
   c. Turbocharger bearing failure
   d. Air cleaner perforation

10. Which of the following correctly identifies the source of most diesel engine oils?
    a. Vegetable-based oil
    b. Crude petroleum
    c. Asphalt tars
    d. Glycol

11. Engine oil service classifications are standardized by which of the following organizations?
    a. SAE
    b. API
    c. ASTM
    d. EPA

12. Technician A states that the operating temperature of an engine oil should be within 5°F (2°C) of that of the engine coolant operating temperature. Technician B states that engine oil temperatures are probably a more accurate means of assessing actual engine operating temperature than the coolant temperature reading. Who is correct?
    a. Technician A only
    b. Technician B only
    c. Both A and B
    d. Neither A nor B

13. An auxiliary oil pump designed to feed oil to the lubrication circuit on a vehicle that operates at extreme working angles is known as a(n):
    a. gerotor pump.
    b. scavenging pump.
    c. vane pump.
    d. emergency pump.

14. Oil that has a milky, clouded appearance is probably contaminated with:
    a. fuel.
    b. engine coolant.
    c. dust.
    d. air.

15. Which of the following statements best describes *viscosity*?
    a. Resistance to temperature
    b. Lubricity
    c. Resistance to flow
    d. Breakdown resistance

16. Technician A states that an oil cooler operates by having coolant pumped through the bundle tubes and oil circulated around the tubes. Technician B states that a leaking oil cooler core must always be replaced. Who is correct?
    a. Technician A only
    b. Technician B only
    c. Both A and B
    d. Neither A nor B

17. Technician A states that 15W-40 is the most commonly used truck engine oil. Technician B states that 15W-40 oil is not an appropriate all-season oil, because winter temperatures are often much lower than the SAE recommended ambient temperature window for this oil. Who is correct?
    a. Technician A only
    b. Technician B only
    c. Both A and B
    d. Neither A nor B

18. Technician A states that the device used to signal oil pressure values to the ECM on most electronically managed engines uses a variable capacitance operating principle. Technician B states that an oil pressure sensor usually requires a V-Ref source from the engine ECM. Who is correct?
   a. Technician A only
   b. Technician B only
   c. Both A and B
   d. Neither A nor B

19. Technician A states that an engine equipped with EGR and DPF must use API CJ-4 or later engine oil. Technician B states that engines manufactured before 2017 may use API CK-4 engine oil. Who is correct?
   a. Technician A only
   b. Technician B only
   c. Both A and B
   d. Neither A nor B

20. A diesel engine dash oil pressure gauge displays low and fluctuating oil pressure values when the vehicle is operated. Technician A states that this could be caused by low engine oil level. Technician B states that this could be caused by high engine oil level. Who is correct?
   a. Technician A only
   b. Technician B only
   c. Both A and B
   d. Neither A nor B

11

Prerequisites: Chapters 4, 7, 8, and 9

ENGINE COOLING SYSTEMS

OBJECTIVES

After studying this chapter, you should be able to:

- Describe the cooling system components and their principle of operation.
- Define the terms *conduction, convection,* and *radiation.*
- Identify the four types of coolant used in current highway diesel engines and the relative merits and disadvantages of each.
- Outline the properties of a heavy-duty antifreeze and supplemental cooling additive package.
- Calculate the boil and freeze points of a coolant mixture.
- Mix coolant using the correct proportions of water, antifreeze, and SCAs.
- Perform standard SCA tests and measure antifreeze protection.
- Recognize the degree to which coolant system scaling can insulate and outline the steps required to eliminate it.
- List the performance and economic advantages claimed for extended life coolants.
- Outline the causes of wet liner cavitation and the steps required to minimize it.
- Describe the requirements of a heavy-duty radiator.
- Identify the types of heavy-duty radiators, including downflow, crossflow, and counterflow.
- Test a radiator for external leakage using a standard cooling system pressure tester.
- Describe the process required to repair radiators.
- Test the operation of a radiator cap.
- List the different types of thermostats in use and describe their principle of operation.
- Describe the role of the coolant pump.
- Describe the process required to recondition a coolant pump.
- Define the role of the coolant filters and their servicing requirements.
- List the types of temperature gauges used in highway diesel engines.
- Describe how a coolant level warning indicator operates.
- Define the roles played by the shutters and engine fan in managing engine temperatures.
- Outline the operation of an actively pressurized cooling system (APCS).
- Diagnose basic cooling system malfunctions.

KEY TERMS

actively pressurized cooling system (APCS)

antifreeze

cavitation

conduction

convection

counterflow radiator

crossflow radiator

diesel coolant additive (DCA)

double pass

downflow radiator

ethylene glycol (EG)

extended life coolant (ELC)

fanstat

headers

heat exchanger

hybrid organic acid technology (HOAT)

hydrometer

kinetic energy

Pencool

pH

pipette

propylene glycol (PG)

radiation

radiator

ram air

refraction

refractometer

rejected heat

reversible fan

shutters

shutterstat

single pass

supplemental coolant additives (SCAs)

thermostat

thermo-syphoning

total dissolved solids (TDSs)

universal coolant (UC)

waterless engine coolant (WEC)

weep hole

INTRODUCTION

Cooling systems are responsible for dissipating a percentage of engine **rejected heat**. Rejected heat (see Chapter 6) is that percentage of the potential heat energy of a fuel that the engine is unable to convert into useful **kinetic energy** (the energy of motion). Rejected heat has to be dissipated to atmosphere, either in the exhaust gas or indirectly using the engine cooling system. If an engine is operating at 40% thermal efficiency, 60% of the potential heat energy is *rejected*. Approximately half of the rejected heat is discharged in the exhaust gas, which leaves the engine cooling system responsible for dissipating the other half to atmosphere.

This task of dissipating rejected heat is complicated by the extremes of the North American climate, given that it is necessary to manage a consistent engine-operating temperature at all engine speeds and loads to ensure optimum performance and minimum emissions. Liquid cooling systems are universal in North American truck and bus applications, and only they are addressed in this section. The Deutz engine company of Germany manufactures air-cooled engines in the 200 to 500 BHP (150 to 373 kW) power range, but in North America their engines are generally found only in agricultural and mining applications.

FUNCTIONS OF THE COOLING SYSTEM

The functions of a diesel engine liquid cooling system are to:

- Absorb heat from engine components
- Absorb heat from engine support systems such as exhaust gas recirculation (EGR) and transmission coolers
- Transfer the absorbed heat by circulating the coolant
- Supply heat to cab and bunk heaters
- Dissipate the heat to atmosphere by means of heat exchangers
- Manage engine-operating temperatures
- Retain thermal energy to ensure an even temperature during cooldown
- Prevent oil sludging

The actual coolant temperature at any given moment of operation is one means the engine control module (ECM) uses to determine engine temperature. In fact, in older hydromechanical engines it was the only means used. In today's engines, ECMs use both coolant and oil temperature readings to make a determination of *engine* temperature. Note the following:

- Engine coolant warms to operating temperature faster than engine oil.
- Engine oil temperature is regarded as being a better indicator of actual engine temperature.
- When both coolant and lube oil are at operating temperature, engine coolant temperatures are always lower than oil temperatures by a good margin.

HEAT TRANSFER

The cooling system can dissipate combustion heat to atmosphere in three ways:

1. **Conduction**: the transfer of heat through solid matter, such as the transfer of heat through the cast-iron material of a cylinder block.

FIGURE 11-1 Coolant flow through a Navistar six-cylinder engine with no water manifold: Flow routing is from the front to the back.

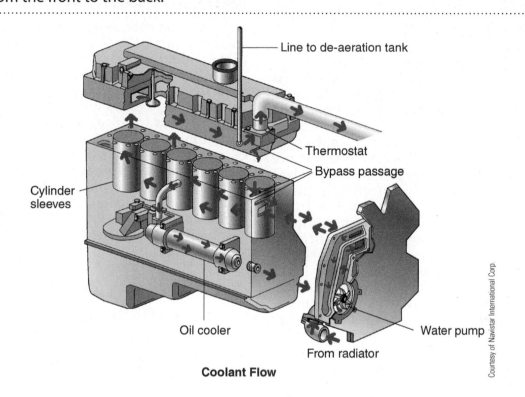

Line to de-aeration tank

Thermostat

Bypass passage

Cylinder sleeves

Oil cooler

Water pump

From radiator

Coolant Flow

Courtesy of Navistar International Corp.

2. **Convection**: the transfer of heat by currents of gas or liquids, such as in the movement of ambient air through an engine compartment.
3. **Radiation**: the transfer of heat by means of heat rays not requiring matter, such as a fluid or solid. The turbine housing of a turbocharger radiates a considerable amount of heat.

ANTIBOIL PROPERTIES

Cooling systems are sealed and maintained under pressure. By confining a liquid under pressure, its boil point is increased. Most cooling systems are designed to manage coolant temperatures at just below their boil points. The chemistry of the **antifreeze** and its concentration in the coolant will define the actual boil point of a coolant. Most antifreezes double as antiboil agents. When an engine is approaching an overheat condition, the coolant will first boil at the location within the system where the pressure is lowest. In most cases, boiling will occur first at the inlet (suction side) of the system water pump. **Figure 11-1** and **Figure 11-2** illustrate a couple of diesel engine cooling circuits, the first without and the second with a

FIGURE 11-2 Cooling system flow through an engine using a water manifold that ensures more even cylinder temperatures.

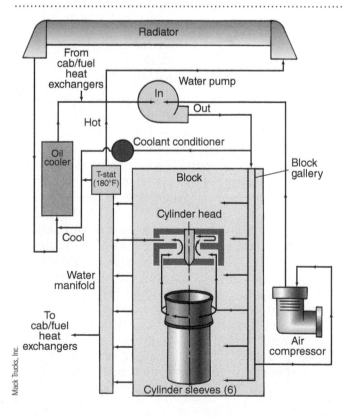

Radiator

From cab/fuel heat exchangers

Water pump

In

Out

Hot

Coolant conditioner

Oil cooler

T-stat (180°F)

Block

Cylinder head

Block gallery

Cool

Water manifold

To cab/fuel heat exchangers

Air compressor

Cylinder sleeves (6)

Mack Trucks, Inc.

water manifold. The role of water manifolds is discussed a little later in the chapter.

ENGINE COOLANT

Water-based coolant is the medium used to absorb engine rejected heat, transfer that heat to a **heat exchanger**, and then dissipate it to atmosphere. The coolant is circulated through the engine water jacket to absorb the heat of combustion in the manner shown in Figure 11–1. Engine coolant is usually a mixture of water, antifreeze, and supplemental coolant additives (SCAs). If the only objective of diesel engine coolant was to act as a medium to transfer heat, pure water would accomplish this more efficiently than any currently used antifreeze mixture. However, water possesses inconvenient boil and freeze points, has poor lubricating properties, and furthermore promotes oxidation and scaling activity. Recently introduced waterless engine coolant (WEC) is rapidly gaining popularity in fleets because it promises much lower maintenance costs over the life of a vehicle. This is described in detail later in this chapter.

TYPES OF ANTIFREEZE

Almost all current truck and bus engines use one of the four following types of antifreeze:

- **Ethylene glycol (EG)**
- **Propylene glycol (PG)**
- **Extended life coolant (ELC)**
- **Waterless engine coolant (WEC)**

EG, PG, and ELC are water-based solutions. EG and PG are usually sold as a concentrate and mixed with water just before introducing the mixture into the cooling system. ELCs are available as premix or concentrate. Alcohol-based solutions are no longer used because they evaporate at low temperatures. WECs are water-free and rapidly gaining in popularity due to the many advantages they offer to diesel engine operation.

Properly formulated diesel engine coolants require SCAs. When the antifreeze is an EG- or PG-based mixture with water, the SCAs require monitoring and routine replenishing. Premix ELC is low maintenance in that the coolant life can be up to 6 years, with only one SCA charge required in that period, and WECs may last the life of an engine providing they are never contaminated with water or any other type of antifreeze.

COOLANT EXPANSION AND CONTRACTION

Water expands about 9% in volume as it freezes, and it can distort or fracture a vessel it is housed in even when this container is a cast-iron engine block. Water occupies the least volume when it is in the liquid state and close to its freezing point of 32°F (0°C). As water is heated from a near freezing point to a near boiling point, it expands approximately 3%. A 50/50 mixture of water and EG will expand even more, approximately 4%, through the same temperature range. This means that cooling systems must be designed to accommodate the expansion and contraction of the engine coolant while it is in the liquid state. Just as important to its operation is that antifreeze is also antiboil.

CHARACTERISTICS OF GOOD ANTIFREEZE

The mixture of water, antifreeze, and SCAs that is referred to as *engine coolant* should perform the following:

1. Corrosion protection. Corrosion inhibitors in both the antifreeze and the SCA package protect the metals, plastics, and rubber compounds in the engine cooling system.
2. Freeze protection. The degree of freeze protection of the coolant depends on the type of antifreeze and the mixture proportions in EG- and PG-based coolants. WEC provides freeze protection to −40°F (−40°C).
3. Antiboil protection. The degree of antiboil protection provided by the coolant is again directly related to the proportion of antifreeze in EG and PG mixtures. WECs boil at 375°F (190°C).
4. Antiscale protection. The antifreeze should contain antiscale additives that prevent hard-water mineral deposits from adhering to the cooling system heat transfer surfaces.
5. Acidity protection. A pH buffer is used to inhibit the formation of acids in the coolant, which would result in corrosion.
6. Antifoam protection. This prevents aeration of the coolant that could be caused by the action of pumping and flowing it through the cooling circuit.
7. Antidispersant protection. This prevents insoluble matter from coagulating and plugging cooling system passages.

8. Low silicate. This, combined with a low total dissolved solids (TDSs) count, improves radiator and water pump life.

TOXICITY OF COOLANTS

Except for the antifreeze and antiboil characteristics of glycol-based coolant mixture, the remaining protection additives deplete with engine operation, especially at high temperatures. Because coolant degrades, the protection additives must be evaluated and restored at appropriate maintenance intervals. Both PG and EG are petrochemical products. EG has been used as the standard antifreeze for some time, but the Federal Clean Air Act and Occupational Safety and Health Administration (OSHA) have both come to regard EG as a toxic hazard. PG in its virgin state is said to be less toxic than EG, and for that reason it has gained some acceptance as an everyday antifreeze. However, leaks and spillage of both EG- and PG-based coolants should be regarded as dangerous to mammals (including humans) and plant life. The chemical characteristics of engine coolant are altered in use and the toxicity increased. Although premix ELC and WEC both use an EG base, they are regarded as safer because they require less handling (premixed and not required to be periodically tested) in service.

SOURCES OF GLYCOL

EG is derived from ethylene oxide, which in turn is produced from ethylene—a basic petroleum fraction. PG is derived from propylene oxide, which is produced from propylene—another basic petroleum fraction. When in a solution with water, both PG and EG are described as aqueous, meaning they mix pretty well with the water.

ANTIFREEZE PROTECTION

The temperature at which a glycol-based coolant solution ceases to protect against freezing depends on:

- Whether the antifreeze is EG or PG
- The percentage of antifreeze to water in the solution
- Whether water is in the solution (it is not in WECs)

Table 11–1 shows how temperature correlates with freeze point in both EG and PG antifreeze solutions. Note that when using EG,

TABLE 11–1 Antifreeze Protection by Percent Volume

Concentration of Antifreeze by Percent Volume	Freeze Point of Coolant			
	EG		PG	
0% (water only)	32°F	0°C	32°F	0°C
20%	16°F	−0°C	19°F	−7°C
30%	4°F	−16°C	10°F	−12°C
40%	−12°F	−24°C	−6°F	−21°C
50%	−34°F	−37°C	−27°F	−33°C
60%	−62°F	−52°C	−56°F	−49°C
80%	57°F	−49°C	−71°F	−57°C
100%	−5°F	−22°C	−76°F	−60°C

increasing the percentage of antifreeze ceases to reduce the freeze point of the coolant once it exceeds 60%. In contrast, the freeze point of PG is at its maximum at 100%, so it is often used as the coolant of choice in subarctic conditions.

COMPATIBILITY OF EG AND PG

PG- and EG-based coolants should *never* be mixed. The mixture in itself will not cause any immediate engine or cooling system problems, but it will be impossible to determine the antifreeze mixture strength with either a refractometer or a **hydrometer**. If a mixture of EG and PG is known to have taken place and the coolant, for whatever reasons, cannot be immediately replaced, use a refractometer with an EG and a PG scale and average the two readings. However, the cooling system should be drained and refilled with either aqueous PG or EG as soon as possible because slime formation may take place. In systems using premix, only ELC premix should be added to the cooling system, or in conditions of extreme cold, ELC concentrate. Premix ELC is incompatible with PG and EG.

WARNING:

The term *ELC* will be limited in this text to describe premixed solutions. In recent years, the term has been used by some suppliers to describe EG concentrate with unspecified extended-life properties. Mix so-called ELC concentrate with tap water and the resulting solution is anything but extended life.

ANTIFREEZE COLOR

Antifreeze is colored with dye. The color appearance of antifreeze is meaningless because the industry has never established any color identification standards. Antifreeze may be dyed green, yellow, blue, orange, red, and pink and any other color in the spectrum. Chemically identical antifreezes can be sold in a number of different colors according to which original equipment manufacturer (OEM) brand name is on the container. When green EG is mixed with orange EG, the result is a mud-colored solution that may or may not perform as specified. Because the solution looks pretty gruesome, you will probably be motivated to change it. If the appearance does not bother you, rely on the coolant tests outlined later in this chapter and base your decision to change or reuse on the tests.

MEASURING COOLANT MIXTURE STRENGTH

Standard antifreeze hydrometers are calibrated for measuring EG mixtures, and even when measuring these they tend to be inaccurate and require calculation to temperature-correct the reading. Changes in coolant chemistry in recent years have made testing with hydrometers obsolete. All of the major truck OEMs advise against using hydrometers. The Technology and Maintenance Council (TMC) and most OEMs recommend the use of a **refractometer** to test the antifreeze strength of a coolant.

A refractometer has an accuracy variable within 7°F (4°C) of the actual freeze point of the coolant. A refractometer designed for measuring diesel engine coolant will usually have a PG and EG calibration scale. Ensure that the correct scale is used for the antifreeze being tested. A refractometer measures **refraction** in a liquid: The refractive index of antifreeze increases with an increase in concentration. Refractometer readings are valid only in the context of a specific type of antifreeze.

TECH TIP:

Always use a refractometer to test the freeze protection of coolant solution and ensure that the correct scale is used for the type of antifreeze being tested.

SUPPLEMENTAL COOLANT ADDITIVES

Supplemental coolant additives (SCAs) are a critical ingredient of the coolant mixture. The actual SCA package recommended by an engine manufacturer will depend on whether wet or dry cylinder liners are used, the materials used in the cooling system components, and the fluid dynamics (high flow/low flow) within the cooling system. Operators may wish to adjust the SCA package to suit a specific operating environment or set of conditions. Abnormally hard water, for instance, requires a greater degree of antiscale protection.

Depending on the manufacturer, SCAs may be added to a cooling system in a number of ways. The practice of installing the SCAs in the system coolant filter is less commonly used today because it resulted in generally higher levels of additives than required, and an excess of additives can create problems. Most OEMs suggest testing the SCA levels in the coolant then adding an SCA such as **Pencool** or **diesel coolant additive (DCA)** to adjust to the required values. Never dump unmeasured quantities of SCAs into the cooling system at each preventive maintenance (PM) inspection, because the result can damage water pumps, plug thermostats, and create sludge deposits that destroy heat exchangers.

Cavitation

SCAs are especially important to controlling cavitation on engines that use wet liners. **Cavitation** is caused by vapor bubble collapse, which results in pitting of the exterior of the liner wall across the thrust faces of the piston. It may also occur at the inlet to the water pump. When a cylinder liner is subjected to the gas pressure of combustion, it rapidly expands then contracts, forming a low-pressure vapor bubble. The vapor bubble almost immediately collapses (implodes), resulting in high-velocity coolant impacting on the liner wall. This has been proven to produce surface pressures up to 60,000 psi (4,137 bar), which can cause pitting and erosion. If left unprotected, the liner wall can be perforated. The characteristic will normally appear on the exterior of the liner wall across the thrust faces of the piston.

Liner pitting can be controlled by adding molybdates and nitrite to coolant, which act to form an invisible, but very tough, protective oxide film on the liner wall. The vapor bubbles will still form, but the liner is shielded by the oxide film. The bad news is that this film breaks down as the coolant ages.

Scaling

A number of years ago, the Cummins Engine Company reported that a scale buildup of 1/16" (1.5 mm) had the equivalent insulating effect of 4" (100 mm) of cast iron. Scaling is caused by hard water mineral deposits (especially magnesium and calcium) adhering to the surfaces of the cooling system where temperatures are highest. Scale formation on wet liners is an especially serious condition because it seldom forms in an even layer and acts as an insulator. This limits the liner's ability to transfer heat. The resulting high temperatures may cause buckling and other distortions to the liner. Left unchecked, scale buildup insulates engine components designed to transfer heat, resulting in overheating and subsequent failure, as shown in **Figure 11–3**.

DESCALING ENGINES There are commercially available descalants that may work to remove minor scale buildup (followed by a cooling system flush), but most often by the time scale buildup has progressed to the point that it is causing an engine to overheat, the engine must be disassembled and the cylinder block and heads boiled in a soak tank.

TESTING SCA LEVELS

Generally, OEMs recommend that the coolant SCA level be tested at each oil change interval. Additionally, whenever there is a substantial loss of coolant and the system has to be replenished, the SCA level should be tested. The test kits usually consist of test strips that must be stored in airtight containers; the expiration dates on these strips should be observed. Standard coolant test kits permit the technician to test for the appropriate SCA concentration.

SCA Test Procedure

The coolant sample should be taken from the radiator, not from the recovery or overflow system. The coolant temperature should be between 50°F (10°C) and 130°F (54°C) during testing, and the test should be completed within 75 seconds.

FIGURE 11–3 How SCAs help prevent scaling and cavitation problems in wet liners.

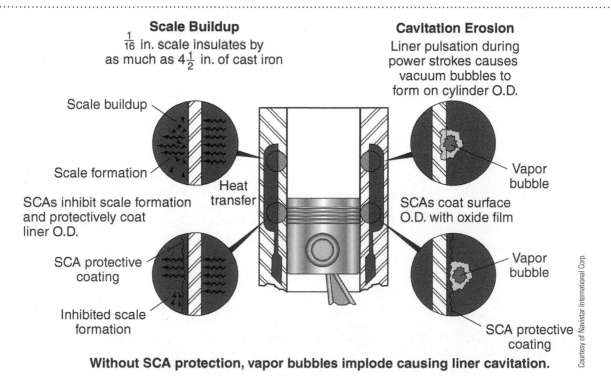

Scale Buildup
1/16 in. scale insulates by as much as 4 1/2 in. of cast iron

Scale buildup
Scale formation
SCAs inhibit scale formation and protectively coat liner O.D.
SCA protective coating
Inhibited scale formation
Heat transfer

Cavitation Erosion
Liner pulsation during power strokes causes vacuum bubbles to form on cylinder O.D.

Vapor bubble
SCAs coat surface O.D. with oxide film
Vapor bubble
SCA protective coating

Without SCA protection, vapor bubbles implode causing liner cavitation.

Courtesy of Navistar International Corp.

1. Remove a strip from the package or bottle without touching the pads. Discard if the nitrite test pad has turned brown.
2. Dip the strip into the coolant for 1 second; remove and shake to remove excess coolant.
3. Wait 45 seconds, then match the colors of the test pads to the colors on the chart.

End pad A	Tests freeze point. Low accuracy of about 10%.
Middle pad B	Tests molybdates. Buffers the formation of acids.
Top pad C	Tests nitrites. Help protect liner walls against cavitation.

Figure 11–4 shows an example of the test card used with a three-way Fleetguard coolant test strip.

FIGURE 11–4 Test card used with a three-way Fleetguard coolant test strip.

Fleetguard® 3-WAY™

Each strip tests:
• Freezepoint (EG & PG coolants)
• Molybdate
• Nitrite

Coolant test strips CC2602B
Contains: 1 test strip

Store at temperatures below 90°F (32°C)

% Glycol/freezepoint (°F) (end pad)

| 30% | | 40% | | 50% | | 60% |
| +4° | −3° | −10° | −20° | −30° | −45° | −60°F |

SCA units per gallon

Molybdate (MoO_4) middle pad

		A	B	C	D	E	F	G	H
Row 6	1200 PPM	0.0	1.7	2.8	3.1	3.7	4.1	4.9	5.7
Row 5		0.0	1.7	2.3	2.7	3.1	3.5	4.3	5.1
Row 4	600 PPM	0.0	1.4	1.8	2.0	2.4	2.8	3.6	4.4
Row 3		0.0	1.2	1.5	1.7	2.1	2.5	3.3	4.1
Row 2	300 PPM	0.0	1.0	1.2	1.4	1.8	2.2	3.0	3.8
Row 1	150 PPM	0.0	0.6	0.9	1.1	1.5	1.9	2.7	3.5
Row 0	0 PPM	0.0	0.3	0.6	0.8	1.2	1.6	2.4	3.2
		0 PPM	300 PPM		800 PPM		1600 PPM		3200 PPM

Test — Service — Pre charge

For best results read in incandescent, fluorescent, or natural sunlight.

Cummins Filtration

Nitrite (NO_2)

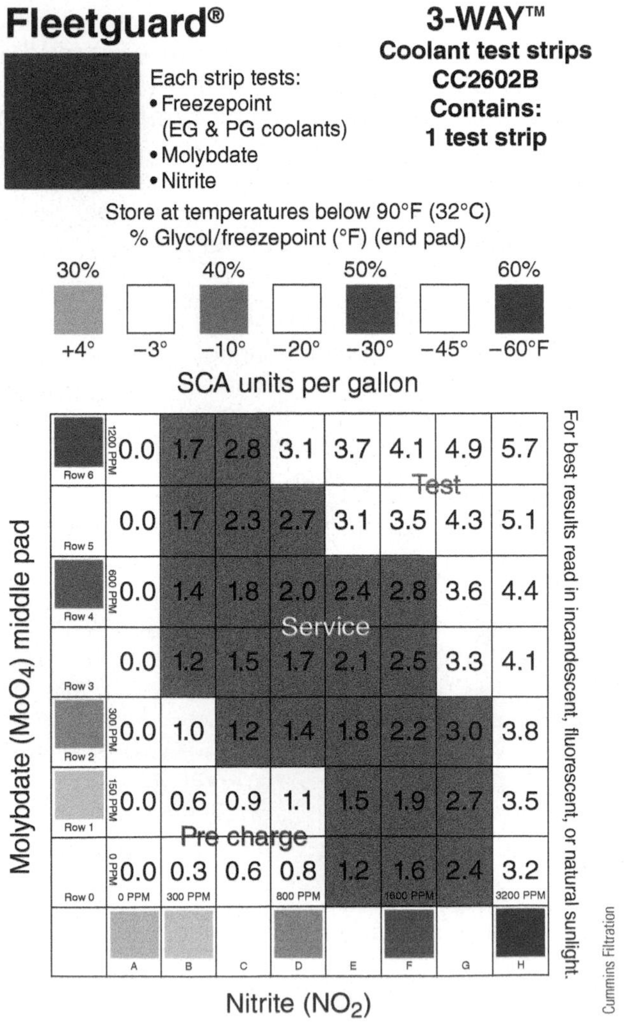

Pencool Test Procedure

Penray suggest that Pencool-protected diesel engine coolant should be changed based on a conductivity threshold of 3,000 micro-ohms or more, or when any of the following service limits are met:

• 200,000 linehaul miles
• 24 months operation
• 4,000 engine hours

Within these operational limits, the coolant should be tested at each engine oil change. Pencool-protected antifreeze can only be tested using Penray test strips. Using Fleetguard coolant test strips will produce false results.

Hot Climate Protection

In climates where the temperature never drops below 40 degrees Fahrenheit, use distilled water cut with 5% Pencool 3000. The mixture should be changed on the Pencool schedule outlined in the previous section. Note that running anything but pure water through diesel engine cooling systems can cause rapid damage whether or not they are "protected" by SCAs.

Testing Coolant pH

The **pH** level defines the relative acidity or alkalinity of the coolant. Acids may form in engine coolant exposed to combustion gases or, in some cases, when cooling system metals (ferrous- and copper-based) degrade. The pH test is a litmus test in which a test strip is first inserted into a sample of the coolant, then removed; the color of the test strip is indexed to a color chart provided with the kit. The optimum pH window is defined by each OEM, but normally falls within 7.5 and 11.0 on the pH scale. A pH of 9.5 is typical. Higher acidity readings (below 8.0 on the pH scale) in tested coolant are indications of corrosion of ferrous and copper metals, coolant exposure to combustion gases, and, in some cases, coolant degradation. Higher-than-normal alkalinity readings indicate aluminum corrosion and possibly that a low silicate antifreeze is being used where a high silicate antifreeze is required.

Testing TDS

Testing for **total dissolved solids (TDS)** requires using a TDS probe, which essentially measures the conductivity of the coolant by conducting a current between two electrodes. Distilled water does *not* conduct electricity. The ability of water to conduct electricity increases with its TDS content. The TDS test is performed by inserting the probe into the top radiator tank. A specified TDS, although expressed in parts per million (ppm), is measured by conductivity expressed in micro-ohms. The conductivity of different categories of water (not cut by antifreeze) is:

- Distilled water—0.5 micro-ohms or less
- City tap water—1,000 micro-ohms
- Brackish water—100,000 plus micro-ohms

When OEMs express maximum conductivity specifications, it is of the coolant mixture: antifreeze itself is conductive. A reading higher than the OEM-specified TDS count indicates that the coolant may be conducive to scale buildup.

BLENDING HEAVY-DUTY COOLANT

Ideally, coolant for use in heavy-duty diesel engines should not be blended in the engine cooling system, but in a container before being poured or pumped into the engine. Distilled or what is known to be good quality water (not excessively hard and with zero iron content; it should not appear reddish) should always be poured into the container first, followed by the correct proportions of antifreeze and, finally, the SCA package. Mix the solution before adding it to the engine cooling system.

Some OEMs manufacture premixed, heavy-duty coolant for use when adding coolant to compensate for a low coolant level. This shifts the responsibility for mixing coolant away from the technician because the water, antifreeze, and SCAs are premixed in the correct proportions; it also eliminates the problems associated with poor quality water.

Good Quality Water

One of the reasons premixed ELC significantly outlasts EG and PG solutions is that distilled water is used in the solution. There are so many variables associated with tap water that it does not make sense to use anything but distilled water when mixing antifreeze solution. Distilled water is not costly, just not as easily available on the shop floor as tap water. Fleetguard defines good quality water with the following specifications:

- Less than 40 ppm chloride
- Less than 100 ppm sulfate
- Less than 170 ppm calcium/magnesium (hardness)

High-Silicate Antifreeze

High silicate concentrations are used in less costly antifreezes to protect aluminum components exposed to the engine coolant. However, most diesel OEMs require that low- or no-silicate coolant be used in their engines. High-silicate and low-silicate antifreezes should not be mixed. Premixed ELCs do not use silicates, nitrates, borates, phosphates, or amines to inhibit scaling, but instead use a carboxylate additive.

EXTENDED LIFE COOLANTS

Premixed extended life coolants (ELCs) use an EG base and promise a service life of up to 600,000 miles (960,000 km) or 6 years with one additive recharge at 300,000 miles (480,000 km) or 3 years. This compares with a typical EG service life of 2 years, during which up to 20 recharges of SCAs would be required for conventional EGs and PGs.

Most true ELCs are organic acid compounds that should not be mixed with other antifreeze mixtures. For this reason, true ELCs are only available as premixed solutions, to ensure that the water quality (contaminant level) is at specification. The pricing of premixed ELCs by quantity is generally comparable with EGs and PGs, but because of reduced cooling system maintenance and extended service life it is fast becoming the coolant of choice of the engine OEMs. Some ELCs use **hybrid organic acid technology (HOAT)**, Dexcool (GM) being one example. HOAT antifreeze is almost always colored with an orange dye. No test kits are required to monitor the ELC SCA level. Notable among the advantages claimed for ELCs are:

- Greatly extended service life—6 years or 600,000 miles
- No inhibitor testing required
- Improved water pump life due to much lower TDS content (TDS are often abrasive)
- Reduced hard-water scaling
- Improved cavitation protection
- Improved corrosion protection
- Improved heat transfer ability
- No gelling problems: No silicates are used in premixed ELC, which eliminates the problem of silicate drop-out responsible for sludging EG and PG
- Improved aluminum corrosion inhibitors
- Better high-temperature performance than EGs and PGs

ELCs may be used in engine cooling systems that have previously used either EG or PG solutions. The EG and PG should be drained from the cooling system, which should then be flushed with clean water. The ELC can then be installed. If a coolant filter is used, replace the existing filter with an SCA-free filter. For mid-winter northern United States and Canada operation, the ELC premix should be strengthened with concentrate. Check with the ELC manufacturer. Most engine OEMs endorse the use of ELCs in their products. Examples of true ELCs include Texaco ELC, Caterpillar ELC, and Powercool Plus (DDC).

TECH TIP:

In an emergency, an ELC cooling system can be topped up using an EG mixture. However, the cooling system should be flushed and refilled with a fresh antifreeze mixture at the first opportunity.

WARNING:

When running a truck in severe winter conditions, the thermostats will exclusively circulate coolant through the engine to maintain operating temperature. This means the radiator, which is exposed to frigid ram air, is vulnerable to icing if there is not adequate freeze protection. Ensure that coolant freeze protection accounts for the lowest ambient temperature with a margin of at least −10°F (−6°C).

CAUTION:

After coming into contact with any antifreeze or coolant solution, wash the affected skin areas immediately and thoroughly.

TECH TIP:

Thirteen states currently require bitterants to be added to antifreeze to discourage consumption by animals and humans.

WATERLESS ENGINE COOLANTS

Waterless engine coolants (WECs) are a blend of nonaqueous propylene glycols (NPGs) and soluble additives—and almost zero water content. When formulated, WEC has a water content of less than 1% and the product can be considered to be degraded when contaminated by more than 2% water. Since being introduced, WECs have gained favor among fleets due to their promise of lower overall maintenance costs over the life of a vehicle. They have the following characteristics:

- Boil point 375°F (190°C)
- Pour point −40°F (−40°C)
- Low conductivity

For the purposes of describing WECs, the Evans waterless engine coolant will be referenced. This is stated to be a lifetime coolant so long as it never comes into contact with water.

Advantages of Waterless Engine Coolants

Among the advantages of Evans WECs are the following:

- Improved fuel economy. Testing has shown fuel economy improvements ranging from 3% to 8% because thermostat temperatures can be raised to 215°F (102°C) and fan-on temperatures raised to 230°F (110°C).
- Reduced maintenance costs. Internal cooling circuit corrosion is eliminated by not having water present, and no electrolytic activity takes place due to almost zero conductivity. In addition, there is significantly less thermal expansion of the coolant, along with much lower coolant operating pressure. With no water to attack hoses and gaskets, these components last much longer. Liner cavitation is also eliminated.

- No replacement costs. Use of WECs eliminates replacement costs of failed engine components such as gaskets, hoses, wet liners, and heat exchanger cores. Unlike EG and water mix coolants, waterless engine coolant will not evaporate.
- Environmental advantages. No periodic disposal costs; Evans states that its product has measurably lower toxicity despite the fact that it is glycol based.
- Extended life. Will not evaporate even when heated to operating temperature.

Other Factors

Water has marginally superior thermal conductivity than WECs so long as it remains in a liquid state; however, a 50/50 EG and water mix (standard coolant mixture) loses almost 85% of its ability to conduct heat when it vaporizes—which it will do at around 240°F (116°C), temperatures attainable during heavy haul operation in a diesel application. WEC has vastly superior characteristics when a hot shutdown occurs:

- Cooling system continues to function after hot shutdown and WEC will not boil.
- No increase in system pressure takes place under these circumstances.
- Engine can be restarted at any point after a hot shutdown.

WECs have been used in various heavy-duty truck applications and are also ideal in aircraft engines. They function much better at high altitudes and high temperatures than other equivalent coolants. At this time, they are not recommended for truck use in extreme cold, that is, when temperatures drop below −40°F (−40°C), what we would classify as subarctic temperatures.

Testing WEC

SCAs are not required in WECs and they will contaminate and degrade the coolant if added. WEC freeze protection should be tested with a refractometer to verify that it has not been contaminated. A disposable **pipette** (to ensure that the sample is moisture-free) should be used to draw a sample, which should then be deposited on the refractometer spectrum slide. WEC should also be tested for water contamination using test strips. Water is fully miscible in WEC, so this is the only way to test the solution. The test strips are designed to detect water contamination by color coding that begins with 1 represented by a solid green color that equals 0% H_2O and graduating to a solid yellow that equals 5% H_2O. It should

be noted that WEC is rendered completely ineffective with a water concentration exceeding 3%.

Replace and Flush WECs

A hygroscopic preparation fluid must be used to prep a cooling system that has previously been using EG or PG. This will purge any water from the system. EG can be used as a limp-home solution, but the preparation fluid must be run through the system before refilling with WEC. The filters used must not be charged with SCAs, and the system can be considered to be contaminated if SCAs are used.

UNIVERSAL COOLANTS

A recent addition to heavy-duty coolant options is **universal coolant (UC)**. A couple of brands are in the marketplace, one of which is EcoFreeze. UC is a premix that can be blended with any EG- or PG-based product without any negative impact on the coolant's performance properties. It is being used by some fleets as a cost-reduction measure because it minimizes the problems that result from cross-contamination of coolant mixtures. However, most OEMs do not recommend the use of universal antifreeze solutions.

> **TECH TIP:**
> Want to know what is really in an antifreeze? Ignore the manufacturer label and go straight to the mandatory MSDS. This will reveal exactly what chemicals are in the formulation and allow you to compare one coolant to another.

> **TECH TIP:**
> Antifreeze additive: An EG is composed of something around 94% ethylene glycol. In addition, it's cut with about 5% diethylene glycol to increase its boil point. Diethylene glycol is costly, but it has a boil point of 483°F (251°C), so it is used in small quantities to increase the antiboil capacity of coolants.

COOLING SYSTEM COMPONENTS

The components used to store, pump, condition, and manage engine coolant flow and temperature are known as the *cooling system components* (**Figure 11–5**). These components vary little from

FIGURE 11-5   Cooling system components.

Water pump

Cylinder block

Air compressor   Coolant conditioner   Cylinder head

Thermostat area   Water manifold

Bypass tubing   Radiator   Heater core hoses

Oil cooler

Water pump

Mack Trucks, Inc.

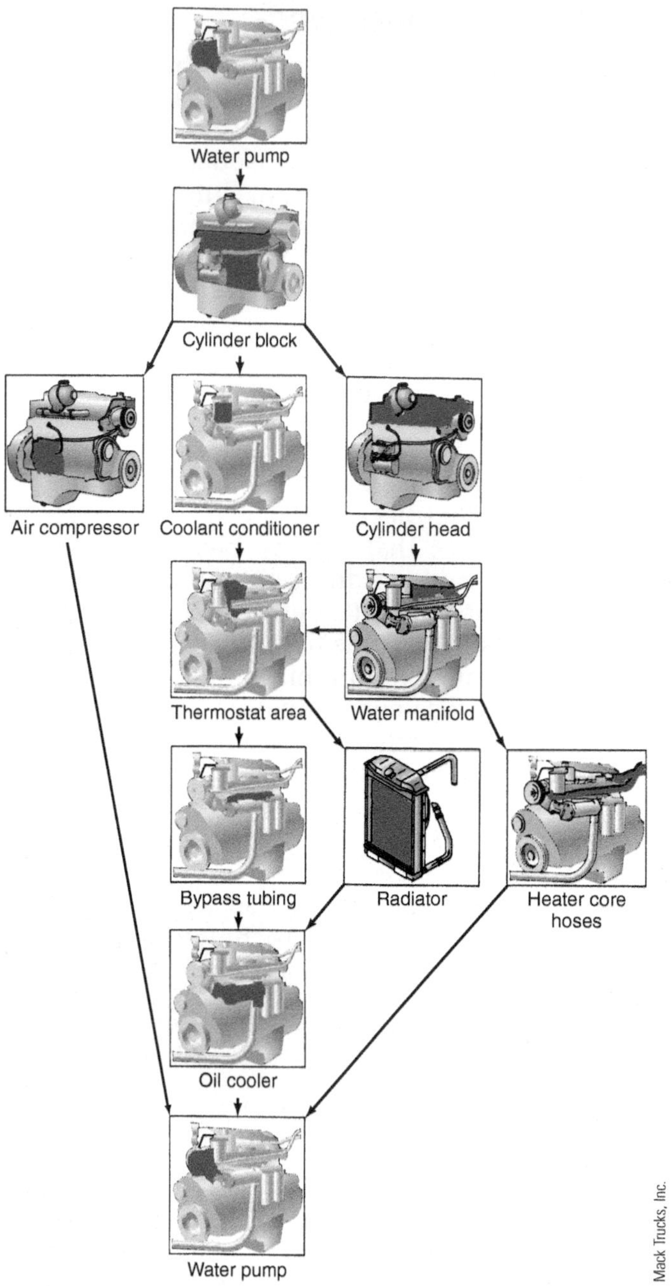

one diesel engine manufacturer to the next, but the way in which coolant is routed through these components tends to be specific to each OEM. Figure 11-1 and Figure 11-2 show two quite different diesel engine cooling circuits. For instance, note the location of the oil cooler in each figure. Oil coolers, although integrated into the cooling circuit, were studied in this book as part of the lubrication system in Chapter 10. When servicing and repairing cooling system components, always consult the appropriate service literature.

RADIATORS

Radiators are heat exchangers. The engine power rating usually dictates the frontal area of a radiator, typically 3 to 4 square inches per BHP unit. The cooling medium is **ram air**, ambient air forced through the radiator core as the truck is driven down the highway. Vehicle speed and ambient temperatures obviously determine the radiator's efficiency as a heat exchanger. Fan shrouds improve airflow through the radiator core and the efficiency of the fan.

Radiator Materials and Construction

Most truck diesel engine radiators are currently fabricated mainly from copper and brass components, but the use of aluminum and plastics is increasing. Radiators typically consist of bundled rows of round or elliptical tubes through which the coolant is flowed and to which are connected fins that increase the sectional area to which the ram air is exposed. The tubes are usually brass and the fins are copper in truck applications, but OEMs are experimenting with aluminum, which is widely used in automobile radiator construction, due to its lower cost and lighter weight. Copper, brass (an alloy of copper and zinc), and aluminum all have high coefficients of heat transfer and are ideal as base material for radiators. Aluminum is more susceptible to corrosion than copper and brass, both from within (coolant breakdown, poor water quality) and outside (salt, both ambient and road salt). Plastics are increasingly being used in the construction of radiator tanks, replacing metal tanks; plastic tanks are usually crimped onto the main radiator core, enclosing the **headers**.

All engine cooling systems are equipped with a drain valve located at a low point in the system, usually at the base of the radiator. In addition, the radiator is equipped with an inlet and outlet piping, and a filler opening sealed with a radiator cap. Most use a **single pass**, downflow principle, which requires that the cooling tubes run vertically from the top tank to the bottom tank. Radiators are classified by their flow characteristics. The following types may be found in current truck applications:

- **Downflow radiators**: Coolant enters the radiator through the top tank and flows, aided by gravity, to the bottom tank by means of vertical tubes that connect the upper and lower tanks. Downflow radiators are a single pass design, meaning that the coolant is routed

FIGURE 11–6 Cooling system flow with a downflow radiator.

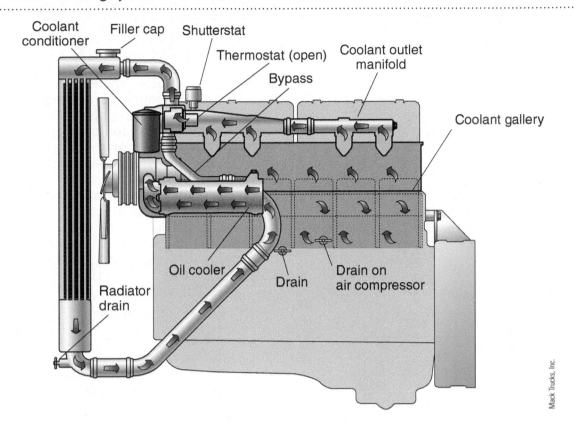

Mack Trucks, Inc.

from the top tank to the bottom and then exits. The location of a typical downflow radiator is shown in **Figure 11–6** and the coolant routing is illustrated in **Figure 11–7**.

- **Crossflow radiators**: The headers and tanks are positioned on either side of the radiator core. The coolant enters through one of the side tanks and then flows through horizontal tubes to the tank at its opposite side. This design affords a lower profile than the downflow design, and it is used by chassis OEMs using low-nose, aerodynamic truck designs. Flow is single pass.

- **Counterflow radiators**: The coolant usually enters through a bottom tank that is divided into inlet and outlet sections. The coolant flows vertically upward from the inlet section of the bottom tank to the top tank, then downward to the outlet section of the bottom tank before being returned to the engine cooling circuit. Essentially, the cooling efficiencies of this design are improved mainly because the coolant is retained in the radiator for a longer period. The flow of coolant through the radiator is **double pass**. The design was popular when

liquid-cooled, charge-air heat exchangers were common.

Aeration Avoidance

Air in a cooling system can cause many problems. It compromises the coolant's ability to transfer heat, it may promote corrosion, and in extreme instances it can cause a cooling system to become air bound. An air-bound system occurs when air becomes entrapped in the inlet to the coolant pump, and the pump effectively loses its prime. As a consequence, most cooling systems are designed to limit aeration problems. Some radiators have a divided top tank in which coolant enters the lower section from the cylinder head and the upper section from a standpipe; the two sections are separated by a baffle. This design tends to reduce cooling system aeration problems. Also, vent lines help to de-aerate the cooling system. The radiator top tank stores reserve coolant volume and accommodates the thermal expansion of coolant.

Servicing and Testing Radiators

Radiators in highway trucks tend to be left in the chassis with no maintenance until they fail,

FIGURE 11–7 Coolant flow shown on downflow, crossflow, and double pass radiators.

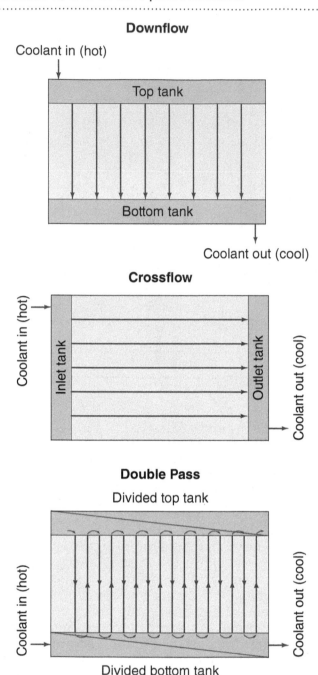

Downflow

Coolant in (hot)

Top tank

Bottom tank

Coolant out (cool)

Crossflow

Coolant in (hot)

Inlet tank

Outlet tank

Coolant out (cool)

Double Pass

Divided top tank

Coolant in (hot)

Coolant out (cool)

Divided bottom tank

either because they leak or fail to adequately cool. An often overlooked PM practice is the external cleanliness of the radiator; buildup of road dirt and summer bugs can severely compromise the radiator's ability to effectively cool. Radiators should be cleaned externally using a low-pressure steamer or regular hose, detergent, and a soft nylon bristle brush. Never use a high-pressure washer, because this will almost certainly result in damaging the cooling fins.

REPAIRING LEAKS

Leaks are more often the result of external damage than corrosion failure. They are indicated by white or reddish streaks at the location of the leak. Radiators are commonly pressure tested at around 10% above normal operating pressure, but be sure to consult the OEM test specifications, especially where plastic tanks are used. Pressure testing may help identify the locations of leaks. It is important that radiator leaks be promptly repaired. If the leak has been caused by external damage and the radiator is in otherwise good condition, the radiator may be repaired by shorting out the affected tubes. This usually involves removing the top and bottom tanks and plugging the damaged tube(s) at the headers. If a leaking tube is accessible, a soldering repair may be possible.

Soldering radiators is at best a risky business, so before beginning, assess how the heat will affect any nearby soldered joints. Low melt point solder has little structural strength, and although it may be used to seal a hairline crack or small impact leak, it should not be used otherwise. Silver solder is a preferred solder repair medium, but more heat is required to apply it than 50/50 lead-tin solder.

Radiator Flushing and Major Repairs

Most commercially available in-chassis radiator descaling solutions are a poor risk, as they are seldom 100% effective and may dislodge scale, which will subsequently plug up elsewhere in the cooling circuit. For the same reasons, reverse flow flushing of the cooling system makes little sense. When OEMs recommend radiator flushing, it is generally performed in the normal direction of flow and often aided by a cleaning solution.

Major radiator repairs should be referred to a radiator specialty shop. A scaled radiator falls into the classification of major repair. An ultrasonic bath will remove most scale rapidly and effectively. A properly equipped radiator repair shop will also be able to determine the extent of repairs required and whether recoring is necessary. One of the problems of performing radiator repairs without the proper test equipment is the inability to test the radiator until it is assembled and reinstalled in the chassis. Removing and installing radiators can be a labor-intensive operation in some chassis.

AUXILIARY HEAT EXCHANGERS

The engine cooling system may be required to provide the cooling media for other heat exchangers plumbed into the cooling system. Other heat exchangers that can be plumbed into the cooling circuit are:

- Aftercoolers and intercoolers
- Tip turbine heat exchangers
- Turbocharger cooling circuit
- EGR heat exchangers
- Oil coolers
- Clean gas induction (CGI) heat exchangers
- Cab and bunk heaters
- Transmission oil coolers
- DPF fuel injector circuit
- SCR DEF injector cooling circuit

We will discuss these heat exchangers in the chapters that deal with the specific systems they address; for instance, oil coolers were discussed in Chapter 10 dealing with engine lubrication systems.

RADIATOR CAP

Radiators are usually equipped with a pressure cap that functions to maintain a fixed operating pressure while the engine is running. This cap is additionally equipped with a vacuum valve to admit surge tank coolant (or air) into the cooling circuit (the upper radiator tank) when the engine is shut down, to accommodate coolant thermal contraction. Radiator caps permit pressurization of a sealed cooling system. For each 1 psi (7 kPa) above atmospheric pressure, coolant boil point is raised by 3°F (1.67°C) at sea level; for every 1,000 feet (300 meters) of elevation, the boil point decreases by 1.25°F (0.5°C). System pressures are seldom designed to exceed 25 psi (172 kPa); more typically, they range between 7 psi (50 kPa) and 15 psi (100 kPa).

Radiator caps are identified by the pressure required to overcome the cap spring pressure and unseat the seal: When this occurs, the coolant is routed to a surge tank. The surge tank coolant level is always at its highest when the engine is running hottest. As the engine cools, the pressure within the cooling system drops, and when it falls to a "vacuum" value of approximately ¼ psi, the radiator cap vacuum valve is unseated, which allows coolant from the surge tank (see **Figure 11–8**) to be pulled back into the radiator. **Table 11–2** shows how much coolant boil point is raised correlated with rad cap trip pressure.

FIGURE 11–8 A typical cooling system surge tank.

TABLE 11–2 System Pressure and Boil Point

Cooling System Max Pressure	Increase in Boil Point	Coolant Boils AT
7 psi (52 kPa)	21°F (12°C)	233°F (112°C)
10 psi (79 kPa)	30°F (17°C)	242°F (117°C)
15 psi (105 kPa)	40°F (22°C)	252°F (122°C)

TECH TIP:

When radiator hoses collapse as the engine cools, it indicates that the vacuum-relief valve in the radiator cap has failed. Collapsing hoses on diesel engines may destroy them internally, so they should be checked after this type of rad cap failure.

CAUTION:

Great care should be exercised when removing a radiator cap from the radiator: If the system is pressurized, hot coolant may escape from the filler neck with great force. Most filler necks are fitted with double cap lock stops to prevent the radiator cap from being removed in a single counterclockwise motion: If the radiator is still pressurized, the cap will jam on the intermediate stops. Never attempt to remove a radiator cap until the cooling system pressure is equalized.

Testing Radiator Caps

Radiator caps can be performance tested using a standard cooling system pressure testing kit. The radiator cap should first be installed to an appropriately sized adapter on the hand pump; then pump to the seal crack value (this should exceed the cap rated value by 1 psi [7 kPa]). Next, release the pressure and once again recharge to the exact rated pressure value of the cap and observe the pump gauge: Pressure drop-off should not exceed 2 psi (14 kPa) over 60 seconds.

WATER MANIFOLD

Most commercial diesel engines are equipped with a water manifold. OEMs opt to use a water manifold because it ensures an even distribution of coolant through the engine block, and therefore more consistent cylinder temperatures. For instance, if you study the coolant routing shown in Figure 11–1, you will note that coolant flows from the front to the rear of the engine. This results in higher temperatures at the rear of the engine. In the coolant system with a water manifold illustrated in Figure 11–2, note how coolant is routed through the cylinder block to cool the midstop cylinder liners: This ensures more even cylinder block temperatures.

WATER PUMPS/COOLANT PUMPS

Water pumps are usually nonpositive, centrifugal pumps driven directly by a gear or by belts. When the engine rotates the coolant pump, an impeller is driven within the housing, creating low pressure at its inlet, which is usually located at or close to the center of the impeller. The impeller vanes throw the coolant outward and centrifugal force accelerates it into the spiraled pump housing and out toward the pump outlet. Because the cooling system pressure at the inlet to the coolant pump is at its lowest (because of low pressure pull of the impeller at the inlet), system boiling always occurs at this location first. This will very rapidly accelerate an overheating condition, as the pump impeller will be acting on vapor. Coolant pumps are the main reason that engine coolants should have some lubricating properties, because they are vulnerable to abrasion damage when the coolant TDS levels are high. A sectional view of a Navistar water pump is shown in **Figure 11–9**.

Coolant pumps fail for the following reasons:

- Overloading of the bearings and seals caused by misalignment or tight drive belts
- High TDS levels in the coolant that erode the impeller

FIGURE 11–9 Sectional view of a water pump and housing.

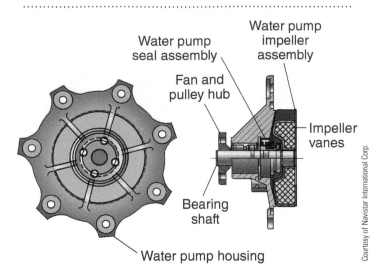

Courtesy of Navistar International Corp.

- Mineral scale buildup on the pump housing
- Overheating—boiling usually occurs first at the inlet to the water pump, so a system that is not properly sealed, or hot shutdowns, can cause vapor lock

Pump Impellers

Most diesel engine water pumps are designed to move something over 20% more fluid than the specification calls for: this means that the tolerance margin is small. Technicians should be wary of "upgraded" components such as water pump impellers that alter the fluid dynamics of the system. Recently, plastic impellers have become more popular. Like cast-iron impellers, these can be manufactured with higher precision than steel fabricated impellers, but when installed as an "upgrade," they must be properly tested after installation, preferably using a dynamometer.

Inspecting, Replacing, Rebuilding Coolant Pumps

A defective coolant pump should first be removed from the engine and analyzed for the cause of the failure, to avoid a repetition. Although they were commonly rebuilt by the technician a generation ago, this is seldom the case now. When defective, they are replaced as a unit with a rebuilt/exchange unit. Rebuilding of water pumps is usually performed at a rebuild center equipped with the proper equipment by persons who specialize in the process.

Although the technician who reconditions one or two coolant pumps a year may not be able to compete with the time of the specialist rebuilder, it is certainly possible to perform the work to the same standard. A slide hammer is usually required to remove the pulley from the impeller drive shaft, and an arbor press is generally preferred over power presses both for disassembly and reassembly. The pump is one of simpler subcomponents of the engine and essentially consists of a housing, an impeller, an impeller shaft, bearings, and seals.

When a pump is rebuilt, inspect the components thoroughly; in many cases, especially where plastic impellers are used, only the housing and shaft are reused. Examine the shaft seal contact surfaces for wear. When gear-driven coolant pumps are reconditioned, pay special attention to the drive gear teeth. The OEM instructions should be observed, and where ceramic seals are used, great care is required to avoid cracking them during installation. A critical specification is the impeller-to-housing clearance, and failure to meet this will reduce pumping efficiency. Other critical specifications are the impeller design and depth: any deviation from the original can result in major differences in the pumping capacity of the cooling system and result in overheating. **Figure 11–10** is a sectional view of a Caterpillar water pump with the rebuild specs and tolerances.

A **weep hole** is designed to transmit ("weep") very small quantities of coolant, and this can be considered normal operation of a water pump. However, when a weep hole discharges more than droplets of coolant, this can be considered a leak—and one that can take out water pump bearings.

TECH TIP:

Studies have shown that diesel engine overheat conditions are most likely to occur immediately after a water pump replacement. Pay special attention to part numbers: a minor difference in impeller geometry can significantly change the pumping capacity of a water pump.

Replacing Engine Coolant

Because of the quantity of coolant required in a truck cooling system, the coolant is seldom exchanged when scheduled. With EG- and PG-filled systems, the life of coolant is finite and it must be exchanged. In addition, engine coolant should be replaced whenever a water pump is replaced, although industry surveys indicate that this is seldom done.

Enter a truck service facility specializing in engine overhauls and make note of the fact that the used engine coolant is commonly stored in an open container for the duration of an in-chassis engine overhaul so it can be reinstalled in the reconditioned engine. This common practice simply does not make sense. Oxygen is the enemy of engine coolant. Not only does exposure to air oxidize and neutralize critical SCAs, but those additives that are not oxidized are boiled off into atmosphere.

FIGURE 11–10 Sectional view of a water pump and subcomponents.

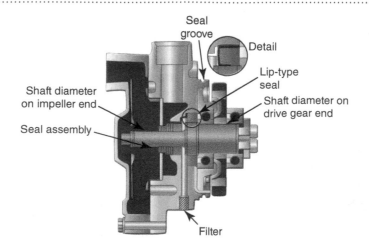

FIGURE 11–14 Exploded view of a thermostat housing.

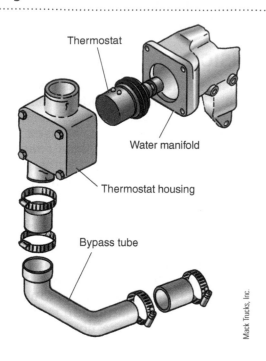

Mack Trucks, Inc.

- Permit zero coolant flow or a defined small volume of flow when in the fully closed position

The cooling system thermostat is normally located either in the coolant manifold or in a housing attached to the coolant manifold, such as that shown in **Figure 11–14**. It has three primary functions:

- It permits a rapid engine warmup by limiting flow to the in-engine cooling circuit.
- It maintains a consistent temperature once the engine has attained its normal operating temperature by optioning flow to the radiator.
- It helps manage engine temperatures by activating the bypass circuit.

The thermostat therefore functions by optioning flow to either the in-engine circuit or the radiator circuit. It opens and closes based on temperature. As it opens and closes, it defines a flow area; so, for instance, a partially open thermostat limits the flow area of coolant routed to the radiator.

OPERATING PRINCIPLE

Because a thermostat defines the flow area for circulating the coolant, there is often more than one. A heat-sensing wax-filled cylinder actuates a piston attached to the seal cylinder: this occurs when the wax expands and pushes on the piston. When the engine is cold, coolant is routed back to the coolant pump to be recirculated through the engine. When the engine heats to operating temperature, the seal cylinder gates off the passage to the coolant pump and routes the coolant to the radiator circuit.

The heat-sensing element consists of a hydrocarbon or wax pellet into which the actuating shaft of the thermostat is immersed. As the hydrocarbon or wax medium expands, the actuating shaft is forced outward in the pellet, opening the thermostat. When thermostats fail, it is usually due to age. Thermostats can be full blocking or partial blocking. **Figure 11–15** shows a typical engine thermostat in its engine warm and engine cold positions.

Top Bypass Thermostat

The top bypass thermostat simultaneously controls the flow of coolant to the radiator and the bypass circuit. During engine warmup, all of the engine coolant is directed to flow through the bypass circuit. As the temperature rises to operating temperature, the thermostat begins to open and coolant flow is routed to the radiator, increasing incrementally with temperature rise.

Poppet or Choke Thermostats

Poppet-type thermostats control the flow of coolant to the radiator only, with the result that the bypass circuit is open continuously. Flow to the radiator is discharged through the top of the thermostat valve.

Side Bypass or Partial Blocking Thermostat

The side bypass thermostat functions similarly to the poppet type. It has a circular sleeve below the valve that moves with the valve as it opens. This serves to partially block the bypass circuit, and in doing so direct most of the coolant flow to the radiator.

Vented and Unvented Thermostats

Vented thermostats have a small orifice in the valve itself or a notch in the seat; usually this must be placed in an upright position on installation. The function of the vent orifice is to help de-aerate the coolant by routing air bubbles out of the bypass circuit. Positive de-aeration type systems usually require nonvented thermostats.

Bypass Circuit

The term *bypass circuit* describes the routing of the coolant before the thermostat opens. When flow is confined to the bypass circuit, coolant flow is limited to the engine cylinder block and head.

FIGURE 11–15 Sectional view showing thermostat operation.

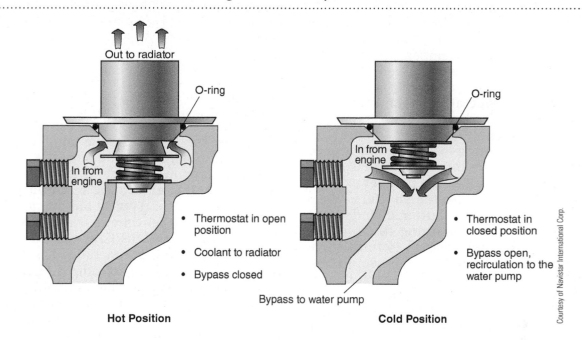

Hot Position   **Cold Position**

Courtesy of Navistar International Corp.

The flow of bypass coolant permits rapid engine warmup to the required operating temperature.

Running without a Thermostat

The practice of operating without a thermostat is not recommended, and engine OEMs may consider it to void the warranty. It also violates the Environmental Protection Agency (EPA) requirements regarding tampering with emissions control components. Removing the thermostat invariably results in the engine running too cool. This can cause vaporized moisture in the crankcase to condense and result in developing corrosive acids and sludge in the crankcase. Additionally, low engine running temperatures will increase the emission of hydrocarbons (HCs). Conversely, engines that should use top bypass or partial bypass-type thermostats may overheat when the thermostat is removed, as most of the coolant will be routed through the bypass circuit with little being routed into the radiator.

Thermostat Failures

When thermostats fail, it is usually due to age. This means that the wax or hydrocarbon-sensing agent has degraded. Thermostat problems can be classified as follows:

- Sticking: this can occur in either the open or closed position.
- Overheating: when a nonthermostat-related engine overheat condition occurs, the heat-sensing pellet can be degraded.

- Sludging: coolant sludge adheres and restricts coolant flow through the thermostat.
- Thermocycling: coolant leaks into the heat-sensing medium, creating rapid expansion-contraction cycles.

Testing Thermostats

Testing a thermostat can be performed using a specialized tool that essentially consists of a tank, a heating element, and an accurate thermometer. Such a test device can be manufactured from an open top electric kettle. Always consult the OEM specifications for testing a thermostat—and, remember, there is a difference between start-to-open and fully-open temperature values.

CAUTION:

Exercise extreme care when handling the water in a thermostat test tank, which is close to boiling; use eye protection, gloves, and tongs.

SHUTTERS

Shutters used to be common on highway trucks, but are not so often used today unless they are ECM-controlled because of their potential to *shock* the engine compartment with sudden temperature changes. Shutters were used to control the airflow through the radiator and into the engine compartment. A **shutterstat** was used to manage the system, and it was usually located in the coolant manifold.

Shutters are sets of louver-like slats that pivot on shafts and are interconnected to rotate in unison from a fully open to a closed position in much the same manner as a set of venetian blinds. The shutterstat is a temperature-actuated control mechanism. It receives a feed of system air pressure, which it will allow to pass through until the coolant temperature reaches a predetermined value specified on the shutterstat.

The shutter assembly is mounted on the radiator and is usually spring-loaded to the opened position. When air from the shutterstat is delivered to the shutter cylinder, the plunger extends to actuate a lever and close the shutters. When no air is available at the shutter cylinder, the shutters are held open by spring force, so we can say that the default position is fully open. During engine warmup, the shutters would normally be held closed once there was sufficient air pressure in the system.

While the use of shutters has become less common in heavy-duty trucks, they are more used today in light-duty vehicles where they are ECM-controlled. Shutters indicate the importance of managing ram air through the engine compartment, and because computers can manage them more effectively than the on-off devices of previous generation cooling systems, they are unlikely to disappear.

COOLING FANS

OEMs use two basic operating principles of engine compartment cooling, requiring the use of either suction or pusher fans. Suction fans pull outside air into the engine compartment, whereas pusher fans do the opposite and push heated air out. Highway vehicles that receive ram air assistance most commonly use suction fans. In fact, depending on the variables of engine size, radiator design, and vehicle application, ram air is often sufficient to perform cooling 95% of operating time, which is a good thing because driving a fan leaches engine power.

Due to new technology, most engine cooling fans today do not leach significant engine power, although much more cooling is required due to the increase in heat exchangers and emission control hardware. Lightweight, variable-pitch fan assemblies manufactured from carbon composites and plastics may draw as little as 6 BHP (4.5 kW) at engine rated speed and load depending on how the fan is driven. Older, heavy gauge steel fan assemblies with fixed pitch often drew as much 18 BHP (13.5 kW) at rated speeds and ran for longer periods. These heavy fan assemblies are still in use today, but not often in highway trucks. Their more likely application is where the cooling system is set up to run the fan constantly, such as in slow-moving quarry trucks.

FAN DESIGN

Because of the increased cooling requirements of each successive generation of diesel engines, fan design is important, because the objective is to draw the least possible amount of engine power. Although modern composite, fiberglass, or plastic fans are lighter in weight, to accommodate the greater cooling requirements, they have grown in size. Typical fan diameters today are 32 inches (80 centimeters) and most use flexible pitch. Because fans have tended to grow in size over the years, pulley ratios have increased from an average of 1:1 to today's 1.3:1.

Flexible-pitch blades have variable efficiency. They are aggressive (and efficient) at low rpm but as they are speeded up, the blade pitch flexes reducing both efficiency and the leaching of engine power. Fan assemblies must be precisely balanced. An out-of-balance fan (a small fragment missing from one blade is sufficient) may unbalance the engine driving it sufficiently to produce a torsional stress failure of the crankshaft. **Figure 11–16** shows some examples of fan blades used in some current trucks.

FAN CYCLES

Because driving a fan assembly draws engine power, most current truck engines use lightweight, temperature-controlled fans. Most post-2010 engines use variable speed controlled fans in preference to on-off types. Older on-off fan drives usually employ one of the following to manage fan cycles:

- **Fanstat** (measures coolant temperature somewhere in coolant manifold), in conjunction with an air/electric/oil pressure servo for fan clutch engagement.
- Thermomodulated (measures radiator flow-through temperature), with a viscous drive fan hub to engage the fan.

On-Off Fan Hubs

The disadvantages of any type of on-off fan hub are rapidly changing under-hood temperatures and excess fan noise. This can create havoc with ECM-managed emission controls which are highly sensitive to minor changes in engine temperature.

Most on-off fan hubs are spring-loaded to the engaged mode. This means that a pneumatic or electrical signal is required to disengage

FIGURE 11–16 Various diesel engine fan blades used in current trucks.

Windmaster plastic standard fans

Windmaster plastic ring fans

Windmaster composite standard fans

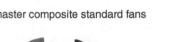

Windmaster metal standard fans

Horton Holding Inc.

the fan clutch to permit it to freewheel. The default mode is a fully engaged fan drive hub. When an air pressure–engaged, spring-released fan hub is used, the fan hub must be mechanically locked in the event of control circuit failure. On-off types of fan hubs leach the least amount of engine power when the coolant temperatures are below the trigger value, which is usually designed to be 90% to 95% of operating time. However, high ambient temperatures and the requirements of the vehicle air-conditioning system may change this ratio.

Thermomodulated Fan Hubs

Thermatic viscous drive fan hubs are integral units with no external controls. They use silicone fluid as a drive medium between the drive hub and the fan drive plate. The hub assembly consists of three main subcomponents:

- Drive hub (input section)
- Driven fan drive plate (output section)
- Control mechanism

They measure under-hood temperatures rather than engine coolant temperatures, but despite some ability to modulate drive efficiency they

are disadvantaged because they are basically on-off in operating principle. **Figure 11–17** shows a typical thermatic fan hub.

FIGURE 11–17 Thermatic fan hub.

ECM-CONTROLLED FAN HUBS

The objective is usually to have the fan running as little as possible and manage engine and under-hood temperatures as consistently as possible. In post-2010 engines, fan hub cycling efficiency is usually managed by the engine ECM. In this way, the ECM can use sensor input from a variety of sources to determine cycling efficiency and run the fan for much longer cycles at much lower speeds. This has the following advantages:

- Leaches less engine power
- Maintains consistent under-hood and cool-ant temperatures
- Yields considerably quieter operation

There are two categories of ECM-controlled fan hubs:

- Two- and three-speed drive hubs
- Variable speed (VS) clutches

Two- and Three-Speed Drive Hubs

Two-speed and three-speed drive hubs use eddy current to engage the hub, and control is by the engine ECM. One control circuit usually works on all OEM engines and the fan can be engaged by messaging off the data bus, that is, on A/C system request. Two- and three-speed fan drives reduce full engagement, thereby reducing par-asitic horsepower draw. This type of fan drive is generally serviceable and is regarded as an improvement on the on-off drive hub—but not by much. They still create inconsistent under-hood temperatures and are as noisy as their on-off predecessors.

VS Fan Hubs

ECM-controlled variable speed (VS) clutches can be either electromagnetically or pneumati-cally controlled and can be considered the more advanced of currently available fan drive technologies. The means of modulating the drive efficiency is by viscous oil, typically high-temperature automatic transmission fluid (ATF) in sealed circuit. **Figure 11–18** shows a typical ECM-controlled VS fan hub assembly and its belt drive mechanism.

The VS hub electromagnetic control valve is switched by a pulse width modulated (PWM) signal at a frequency of 2 Hz (explained in Chapter 32), which precisely manages the actual fan speed. The result is to enable the correct amount of under-hood airflow to man-age coolant temperatures within a tight win-dow (within 2°F to 3°F, or 1°C) using moderately

FIGURE 11–18 Electrically controlled fan hub and fan hub drive.

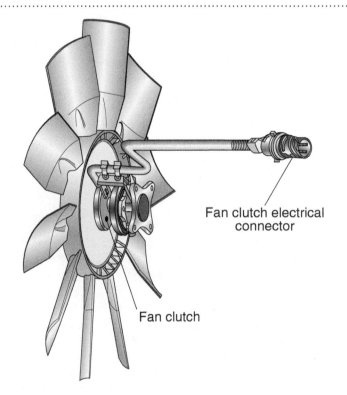

Fan clutch electrical connector

Fan clutch

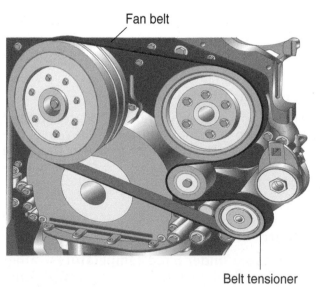

Fan belt

Belt tensioner

low and relatively constant fan speeds when coolant temperatures exceed the normal-high threshold. The normal threshold is typically the temperature rating of the fanstat used in older on-off applications. These temperatures can be compared with the much greater 5°F to 10°F (3°C to 5°C) cycling window of older on-off fan drive hubs. **Figure 11–19** shows the hub assembly of a VS fan drive and **Figure 11–20** shows a cutaway of the PWM-controlled hub actuator.

ADVANTAGES OF VS FAN DRIVES ECM control of fan speed provides a number of performance advantages, including:

- Reduced noise due to low driven speeds and elimination of kick-on, kick-off vibrations caused by on-off fan drives. Most drivers report they are unaware of the fan kicking on and off.
- Coolant and under-hood temperatures managed more precisely, within a 2°F to 3°F (1°C) window when coolant exceeds the normal-high threshold.
- Reduced thermal stress resulting from a narrow window of temperature swings.

FIGURE 11–20 Sectional view of the PWM-controlled actuator on an ECM-managed continuously variable speed fan hub.

FIGURE 11–19 Continuously variable speed fan drive hub used on a 2015 Paccar MX13.

- Reduced mechanical stresses resulting in increased drive belt and hub longevity.
- An ECM-controlled fan hub uses less than 0.3% of total engine energy compared with 0.8% of an on-off type. This is significant both in terms of fuel economy and performance because it reduces the frequency of downshifting on the part of the driver.
- During idle A/C operation, reduces fan cycling by over 70%.
- Reduced fan speeds mean that bugs and debris are less likely to become entrapped between the charge air cooler and the radiator.
- Proven track record of lower maintenance when compared directly with on-off fan drive hubs.
- Softer engagements and reduction in cycling intensity result in longer belt life.

The advantages of VS fan drives increase in vocational applications where fans typically cycle at increased frequency. Significantly lower fan speeds reduce clogging of engine compartment heat exchangers because bugs and debris are less likely to be drawn in.

Reversible Fans

A more advanced fan design is the **reversible fan**. Fan performance is determined by temperature sensing elements located in the hub that control the blade pitch angle during normal operating cycles, in the same way prop blades are rotated in propeller-driven aircraft. In addition, blade pitch can be set so that the fan blows outward to manage a cleaning mode. Air driven outward from the engine housing can loosen dirt and contaminants from the under-hood heat exchangers. At the time of writing, Cleanfix is the leading manufacturer. Most reversible fans use the thermatic principle described here, but ECM "smart" versions are beginning to gain some traction in the market. **Figure 11–21** demonstrates the operating principle of a reversible fan.

WARNING:

Winter fronts, which are installed on the hood grille to limit the amount of ram air driven through the engine compartment, can load a fan off its axis, creating an unbalancing effect whenever the fan is engaged. A winter front should not be necessary on most engines produced after 1990. When one is installed, ensure that it is approved by the truck chassis OEM. Never completely close a winter front.

Ram Air Management

The way wind devices are managed and maintained are critical in modern diesel engines.

Fan shrouds are usually molded fiber devices bolted to the radiator assembly and may partially enclose the fan, providing a small measure of safety if the fan is engaged when the engine is running and the hood is open and exposed to the technician. Shrouds play an important role in shaping the airflow through the engine compartment, and a missing or damaged shroud can result in temperature management problems. In hot weather conditions, fan efficiencies can be dramatically lowered by a defective or missing shroud, so they should be examined at each inspection. Attention to detail is important here: A small piece missing from a fan shroud can have a dramatic effect on how ram air is flowed through the engine compartment—enough to produce an engine overheat condition. **Figure 11–22** shows the fan shroud geometry of a typical diesel engine.

Air Dams

The aerodynamic design of a truck is a major consideration when analyzing cooling system complaints. Add-ons such as cattle guards can alter the ram airflow through the engine compartment and potentially create an engine overheat condition because the operating margins are so tightly engineered in modern trucks. Be especially aware of body shop repairs resulting from minor or major collision damage that could have altered the ram airflow dynamics.

FIGURE 11–21 Operating principle of a reversible fan.

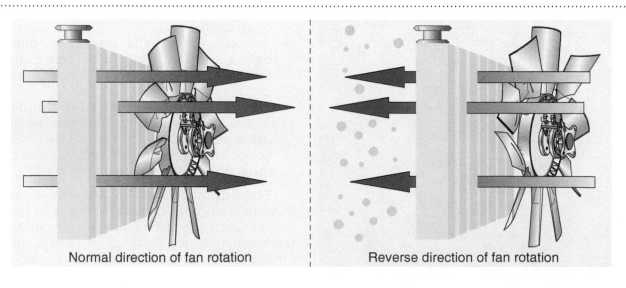

Normal direction of fan rotation　　Reverse direction of fan rotation

FIGURE 11–22 Fan shroud geometry on a typical diesel engine. Minor damage to the shroud can significantly alter airflow through the engine compartment. Replace damaged fan shrouds!

Fan Belts and Pulleys

Fan pulleys use external V or poly-V grooves and internal bearings of the roller, taper roller, and bushing types. Fan pulley ratios typically range from 1:1 (older engines) to 1.3:1 (newer engines), while it is common to use between 8- and 12-rib drive fan belts. The belt tension should be adjusted using a belt tensioner. The consequences of maladjusted belts are:

- Too tight: excessively loads the bearings and shortens bearing and belt life
- Too loose: causes slippage and destroys belts even more rapidly than a too tight adjustment

Belts should be inspected periodically as part of a PM routine. Replace belts when glazed, cracked, or nicked. Replacing belts with early indications of failure costs much less in the long run than the breakdowns that may be caused by belts that fail in service. **Figure 11–23** shows a poly-V fan hub drive favored by Caterpillar.

Water Manifolds

The water manifold acts as a sort of main artery for the cooling system. It is usually a cast-iron or aluminum assembly fitted to the cylinder heads and may house the thermostat(s). **Figure 11–24** shows a typical water manifold that is divided into two sections coupled by a rubber hose.

FIGURE 11–23 Sectional view of a poly-V fan drive.

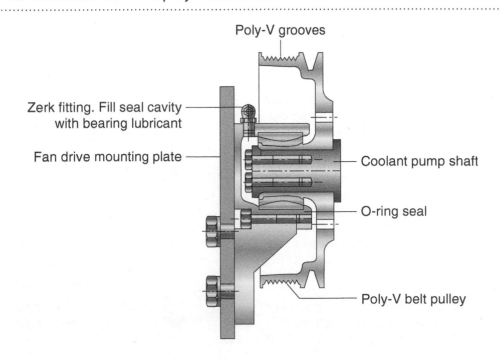

Poly-V grooves

Zerk fitting. Fill seal cavity with bearing lubricant

Fan drive mounting plate

Coolant pump shaft

O-ring seal

Poly-V belt pulley

FIGURE 11–24 Two-section coolant manifold on a six-cylinder engine with a two-cylinder head design: The intake manifold is located below.

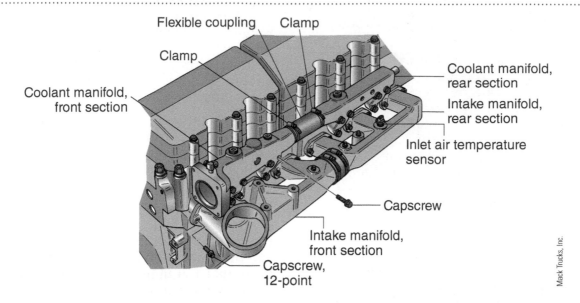

COOLING SYSTEM PROBLEMS

Troubleshooting cooling system problems is covered in more detail in Chapters 49 and 50. In this chapter, we take a brief look at some cooling system problems and their possible causes. Cooling system performance problems can be grouped into the following categories:

- Overheating
- Overcooling
- Loss of coolant
- Defective radiator cap
- Defective thermostat

LEAKS

Cooling system leakage is common, and the system should be inspected daily by the operator. Cold leaks may be caused by contraction of mated components at joints, especially hose clamps. Cold leaks often cease to leak at operating temperatures because everything expands. Many fleet operators replace all the coolant hoses after a prescribed in-service period, regardless of their external appearance, to avoid the costs incurred in a breakdown. Silicone hoses are more costly than the rubber compound type, but they usually have longer service life. Silicone hoses require the use of special clamps, and these are sensitive to overtightening. Take care to torque to the required specification. It is recommended that the technician use constant tension hose clamps such as that shown in **Figure 11–25**.

Internal Leaks

Pressure-testing a cooling system will locate most external cooling system leaks. A typical cooling system pressure-testing kit consists of a hand-actuated pump and gauge assembly calibrated from 0 to 25 psi (170 kPa) plus various adapters

FIGURE 11–25 Constant tension, stainless steel hose clamp required for silicone hoses and recommended for all others.

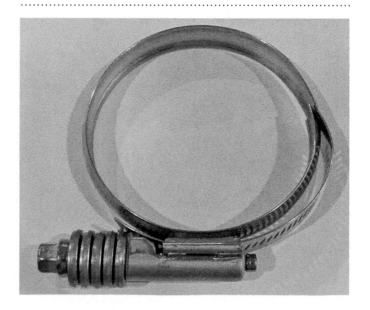

for the different types of fill neck and radiator cap. Some are capable of vacuum testing.

Internal leaks can be more difficult to locate. When coolant is present in the engine oil, it appears as a milky sludge before settling to the bottom of the oil pan. It is the first fluid to exit the oil pan when the drain plug is removed. When the leak is sourced to a failed wet liner seal, to locate the engine cylinder, remove the oil pan, allow the oil to drip for a period, then pressurize the cooling system using standard hand pump apparatus and place a sheet of cardboard under the engine. Wet liner O-ring seals may leak either cold or hot and even this detection method is not surefire.

Bubbles in Radiator

The appearance of bubbles in the radiator may indicate that combustion gases are leaking into the coolant or that the engine is being run without thermostat(s). There are a couple of ways of determining whether combustion gases are leaking into the cooling circuit, and the best method varies according to the engine being tested. Pressure-testing of the cooling system using the method outlined previously is the preferred method. On some engines, if you can disconnect the water pump drive, removing the piping to the upper radiator tank and the thermostat, filling the engine with coolant (water will do), and running the engine can identify cylinder pressure leakage to the cooling system.

WARNING:

The use of cooling system agents that claim to stop leaks should generally be avoided even in a situation that might be described as an emergency. They may work temporarily, but in doing so, they have been known to plug thermostats, radiator/heater cores, and oil cooler bundles. Generally, they cause more trouble than they cure.

STRAY VOLTAGE DAMAGE

Stray voltage grounding through engine coolant can result in electrolytic action that can cause considerable engine damage in unbelievably short periods of time. This electrolytic damage ranges from pinholes in heat exchangers to erosion pitting failures of cast-iron liners and cylinder blocks. The incidence of stray voltage damage has become more commonplace due to the increase in electrical and electronic components combined with the introduction

of nonconducting components such as plastic radiator tanks. Chassis static voltage buildup can also discharge through engine coolant.

One fleet hauling both tankers and flatbed trailers, using tractors with identical powertrains, reported that engine failures attributed to coolant electrolysis were only occurring in the tractors assigned to flatbeds. Trailer technicians will know that tankers have a dedicated ground circuit (known as *bonded ground*), whereas flatbeds do not. Use the following method to identify stray voltage and eliminate it.

Testing for Stray Voltage

Stray voltage can be alternating current (AC) (alternator diode bridge leakage) or direct current (DC), but is more likely to be the latter. Use a digital multimeter (DMM) on autorange to perform the following tests, checking for DC first.

1. Run the engine and turn on all the vehicle electrical loads.
2. Place the negative DMM probe directly on the battery negative terminal and the other into the coolant at the neck of the radiator without touching metal.
3. Record the voltage reading. 0.1 V-DC is okay; the maximum acceptable to most OEMs is 0.3 V-DC. If higher, locate the leakage source. 0.5 V-DC leakage is capable of eating out a cast-iron engine block.
4. Sequentially shut down each electrical component, checking the voltage reading. When the leaking component or circuit has been identified, repair its ground. Attempting to ground the coolant at the radiator will not repair the problem.

TECH TIP:

A 50/50 EG coolant mixture boils at 227°F (108°C), but that climbs to 263°F (128°C) when the system is under pressure of 14 psi (96 kPa). A minor cooling circuit leak can hugely affect the boil temperature of EG and PG coolants.

TECH TIP:

If the common practice of mixing antifreeze concentrate with tap water was eliminated today, within five years most specialty radiator shops would be out of business. The quality of engine coolant is critical to engine longevity: Ignore this and you'll pay the price!

COOLING SYSTEM MANAGEMENT

Most truck engine cooling systems are managed with the objective of opening the thermostat first, followed by the shutterstat (if equipped), and finally the fan will engage. Even though it is out of date, you should remember this sequence because this is usually what you are required to remember when tested on the subject. The thermatic fans discussed earlier in this chapter sense under-hood or engine compartment temperature. An under-hood temperature of 155°F (68°C) can be generally reckoned to an engine coolant equivalent of 190°F (88°C).

Because an engine fan leaches power, most OEMs go with the premise that it is desirable for it to be driven in such a way that it consumes as little of that power as possible. This is the reason that the most recent engine management systems use the ECM to manage fan cycles on a variable speed basis, rotating it at the lowest possible speed, producing just enough ram air circulation to maintain a consistent coolant temperature.

Thermo-syphoning

Thermo-syphoning is used to protect water-cooled turbocharger shaft and bearing housings against overheating when a hot shutdown occurs. The turbocharger cooling circuit uses convection and a loop to cycle coolant through the turbo bearing circuit until the temperature reaches parity with the mean coolant temperature. This can greatly extend turbocharger longevity in vehicles routinely subjected to poor driving practices, such as school buses and pickup and delivery vehicles.

ACTIVELY PRESSURIZED COOLING SYSTEMS

As diesel engines have evolved to adapt for reduced exhaust emissions, there has been a significant increase in the amount of heat the engine cooling system is required to dissipate. Cooled exhaust gas recirculation (C-EGR) heat exchangers in particular have increased the heat unloaded into the cooling system, and in early systems (2004) some engines experienced coolant boiling in the C-EGR heat exchanger. In the past, engine OEMs addressed increased heat dissipation requirements by increasing the core size of the radiator, increasing coolant capacity, and improving under-hood airflow. The limiting

factor of this approach was the physical space required by larger radiators and higher energy consumption required by increased coolant volumes. Recently, some engine OEMs have opted to increase diesel engine cooling capacity by using an external means of pressurizing the cooling system and thereby raise the boiling point of the antifreeze mixture. The system is known as an **actively pressurized cooling system (APCS)**.

An APCS is managed by the ECM and introduces air under pressure from an external pressurized source. This source is usually the intake manifold on turbo-boosted engines. This pressurized air from the engine intake manifold is plumbed into a cooling system expansion tank by means of a flow control check valve. The flow control valve is a spring-loaded nonreturn valve located in the connection plumbing for unidirectional flow between the intake manifold and the expansion tank.

Using higher system coolant temperatures requires proper pressurization under all operating conditions in order to control cooling characteristics, ensure adequate coolant flow, prevent cavitation, and especially to prevent coolant boiling and possible overflow. An independent module networked to the chassis data bus is used to manage the APCS system: It is assigned a source address (SA) 86/ message identifier address (MID 186) on the chassis data bus (SAs and MIDs are explained in Chapters 35 and 37). The functions of the APCS controller are to monitor:

- Coolant level
- Coolant pressure
- Coolant temperature
- System malfunctions

The APCS controller manages:

- Pressurization solenoid of the cooling system tank
- Broadcast of system status and faults to the chassis data bus

Because APCS is a networked, computer-controlled system, the specifics of control logic are not covered in this chapter, but appear later in Chapter 34.

COOLANT HEATERS

With many jurisdictions imposing anti-idling legislation and many more proposing to, there is suddenly some urgency about installing climate control devices on trucks. These function

FIGURE 11–26 Espar Hydronic coolant heater.

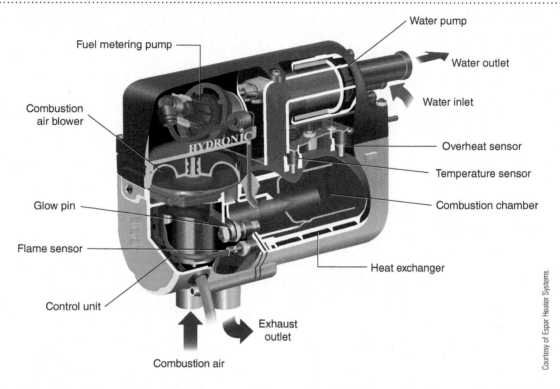

Fuel metering pump

Water pump

Water outlet

Water inlet

Combustion air blower

Overheat sensor

Temperature sensor

Combustion chamber

Glow pin

Flame sensor

Heat exchanger

Control unit

Exhaust outlet

Combustion air

Courtesy of Espar Heater Systems.

to either keep the cab warm enough or cool enough depending on the season. Some of these devices work independently from the diesel engine heating, ventilating, air-conditioning (HVAC) circuit, such as Webasto's Blue Cool system, which is air conditioning (A/C) based on the old icebox system. However, most are integrated in some way into the engine HVAC circuit. We are going to take a look at how a typical coolant heater functions. Before beginning, we should dispel a truck driver myth: namely, that a diesel engine cannot be started in temperatures below 0°F (−17°C). This might have been true with your dad's diesel engine, but it is not today. You can make it true today by ignoring the OEM recommendations for such critical items as the viscosity of the oil you are using.

DIESEL-FIRED COOLANT HEATER

A diesel-fired coolant heater sources the main fuel system for its supply of fuel. These units are intended to be operated only when the vehicle is parked with the engine off. A typical coolant heater consists of a burner nozzle, combustion chamber, heat exchanger, and coolant circulation pump. System control is electronic: key sensors in the system are a coolant temperature sensor, overheat sensor, and flame sensor. Some use spark ignition, but in the unit shown in **Figure 11–26** a glow pin is used. Heat regulation can usually be managed at several different levels. Most OEMs recommend the use of a coolant heater if the vehicle is regularly operated or parked in subzero (below −17°C) temperatures.

SUMMARY

- At its best, a diesel engine converts about 40% of the heat energy released by combusting fuel into useful mechanical energy delivered to the flywheel. The remaining 60% of the potential energy of the fuel is released as rejected heat.
- Approximately half of the rejected heat of combustion is transferred to the engine cooling

system, which is responsible for transferring it to atmosphere.
- The cooling system uses the principles of *conduction*, *convection*, and *radiation* to transfer heat from the coolant to atmosphere.
- A diesel engine cooling system has four main functions: to absorb combustion heat, to transfer the heat using coolant to heat

exchangers, to dissipate the heat from the heat exchangers to atmosphere, and to manage engine operating temperatures.

- The main components of a diesel engine cooling system are the water jacket, coolant, a coolant pump, a radiator, thermostat(s), filter(s), shutters, temperature sensing circuit, and a fan assembly.
- Water expands in volume both as it freezes and as it approaches its boil point. The engine cooling system must accommodate this change in volume.
- Engine coolant is a mixture of water, antifreeze, and supplemental coolant additives.
- Four types of diesel engine coolant are in current use: ethylene glycol (EG), propylene glycol (PG), premix extended life coolant (ELC), and waterless engine coolant (WEC).
- A properly formulated diesel engine coolant should protect against freezing, boiling, corrosion, scaling, and foaming and should inhibit acid buildup.
- The correct instrument for reading the degree of antifreeze protection of a coolant is a refractometer.
- Mixing of coolant solutions should be performed in a container outside the engine cooling system; the mixed solution is then added to the engine.
- Supplemental coolant additives (SCAs) are a vital component of EG and PG engine coolants. The SCA levels must be routinely tested in EG and PG coolants because they deplete in service.
- Premixed ELC is claimed to have a service life of 600,000 miles (966,000 km) or 6 years, during which a single SCA recharge is required.
- WECs can last the life of the engine providing they are never contaminated with other antifreeze mixtures, water, or other engine fluids.
- Where possible, the radiator is located in the airflow at the front of the chassis to optimize ram air cooling effect.
- Most radiators are of the single pass, downflow type, but crossflow and double pass routing are also used.
- Radiator caps are equipped with a pressure valve used to define the cooling system operating pressure and a vacuum valve to prevent hose collapse as the system cools and pressure drops.
- Coolant pumps are either belt- or gear-driven and are of the nonpositive, centrifugal type.
- Coolant pumps are lubricated by the coolant and tend to be vulnerable to high TDS levels, which are abrasive.
- Care should be taken when servicing coolant filters because some are precharged with SCAs and an excess of SCAs can cause coolant problems just like depleted SCAs.
- The commonly used coolant temperature sensor on today's electronically managed engines is the thermistor, which is a temperature sensitive, variable resistor.
- Coolant level sensors ground a reference signal into the coolant in the top radiator tank and trigger an alert when the ground circuit is broken for a programmed period.
- Thermostats are used to manage the engine temperature to ensure fast warmup and optimum performance, fuel economy, and minimum noxious emissions.
- Thermostats route the coolant through the bypass circuit to permit rapid engine warmup.
- Shutters control the airflow through the engine compartment by means of louver-like slats that open and close like venetian blinds.
- Shutters used on older truck chassis are controlled by a shutterstat, which is located in the water manifold and uses chassis system air pressure to open and close the shutters. They are designed to default to a fully open position in the event of a failure.
- When shutters are used on current trucks, they are usually seen on light-duty applications and are ECM-controlled.
- Most engine compartment fans are temperature controlled, either directly on the basis of coolant temperature measured by a thermistor or fanstat, or indirectly based on engine compartment temperature.
- Viscous-type, thermatic fans sense underhood temperatures and are driven by a fluid coupling designed to produce minimum slip at nominal operating temperature.
- The management of fan cycles in recent engines is electronically controlled by the ECM. The objective is to drive the fan at the slowest possible speed required to produce a consistent engine temperature; this ensures that the fan leaches the least amount of engine power.
- Flex-blade composite, plastic, or fiberglass fans are designed to alter their pitch based on their driven rotational speed, permitting higher fan efficiencies at low rpm.
- Fan assemblies are driven by V or poly-V belts whose tension should be adjusted using a belt tension gauge to avoid bearing and slippage problems.
- Testing a cooling system for external leaks is performed using a hand-actuated pressure testing kit consisting of a pump, a pressure

gauge, and a variety of fill neck and radiator cap adapters.
- Because of the increased heat load that diesel engine cooling systems have to sustain, some OEMs have opted to use APCS to raise the boil point of the engine coolant.

- Anti-idling legislation introduced by many jurisdictions has led to the increased use of engine coolant heaters. These are electronically controlled, diesel-fired heaters that keep coolant warm and circulating during engine-off in cool temperatures.

REVIEW QUESTIONS

1. Which type of diesel engine coolant is regarded as potentially the most harmful to humans?
   a. EG
   b. PG
   c. WEC
   d. ELC

2. Which of the following cooling media would transfer heat most efficiently?
   a. EG
   b. PG
   c. Pure water
   d. ELC

3. Wet liner cavitation is caused by:
   a. aerated coolant.
   b. combustion gas leakage.
   c. air in the radiator.
   d. vapor bubble collapse.

4. The cooling system hoses on an engine collapse when the unit is left parked overnight. Which of the following is the likely cause?
   a. This is normal.
   b. A defective thermostat.
   c. Improper coolant.
   d. A defective radiator cap.

5. If a radiator cap pressure valve fails to seal, which of the following would be the likely outcome?
   a. Coolant boil-off
   b. Cooler operating temperatures
   c. Higher HC emissions
   d. Cavitated cylinder liners

6. Which would be the warmest portion of a typical downflow-type radiator when the engine is at operating temperature?
   a. The top tank
   b. The surge tank
   c. The bottom tank
   d. The center of the core

7. The temperature rating of a thermatic viscous fan hub is a nominal 155°F (68°C). At approximately what equivalent coolant temperature will this produce minimum slip drive as temperatures rise?
   a. 155°F (68°C)
   b. 165°F (74°C)
   c. 190°F (88°C)
   d. 225°F (107°C)

8. In a typical diesel-powered highway truck at operating temperature, which of the following should be true?
   a. Coolant temperatures run cooler than lube oil temperatures.
   b. Coolant temperatures run warmer than lube oil temperatures.
   c. Coolant temperatures should be equal to lube oil temperatures.

9. Which of the following properly describes the operating principle of a typical coolant pump on a highway diesel engine?
   a. Positive displacement
   b. Centrifugal
   c. Constant volume
   d. Gear type

10. Which of the following controls the drive efficiency of a thermatic, viscous drive fan hub?
    a. Bimetal strip
    b. Viscosity of the silicone drive medium
    c. Fanstat
    d. Solenoid

11. When the thermostat routes the coolant through the bypass circuit, what is happening?
    a. The coolant is cycled primarily through the radiator.
    b. The coolant is cycled primarily through the engine.
    c. The coolant is cycled primarily through auxiliary heat exchangers.

12. Fiberglass fans with flexible-pitch blades are designed to drive air at greatest efficiency at:
    a. low speeds.
    b. all speeds.
    c. high speeds.

13. Coolant silicate drop-out usually causes:
    a. scaling.
    b. gooey sludge.
    c. high TDS readings.
    d. boiling coolant.

14. In the event of an engine overheating, where is the coolant likely to boil first?
    a. At the engine water jacket
    b. At the top of the radiator tank
    c. At the inlet to the coolant pump
    d. At the thermostat housing

15. What instrument do most OEMs recommend for checking the degree of antifreeze protection in heavy-duty diesel engine coolants?
    a. Hydrometer
    b. Refractometer
    c. Spectrographic analyzer
    d. Color-coded test coupon

16. Technician A states that premixed ELC has an approved service life of up to 6 years. Technician B states that water should never be added to premixed ELC even if the water is distilled. Who is correct?
    a. Technician A only
    b. Technician B only
    c. Both A and B
    d. Neither A nor B

17. Technician A states that when an ECM controls fan cycles, the fan is usually driven for longer periods than an equivalent on-off fan management system. Technician B states that when an ECM controls fan cycles, the fan can be driven at lower speeds than an equivalent on-off fan management system. Who is correct?
    a. Technician A only
    b. Technician B only
    c. Both A and B
    d. Neither A nor B

18. Technician A states that a double pass radiator offers higher cooling efficiencies than a similarly sized single pass radiator. Technician B states that crossflow radiators are often used in aerodynamic low hood and grille designs. Who is correct?
    a. Technician A only
    b. Technician B only
    c. Both A and B
    d. Neither A nor B

19. Which of the following is true of an APCS?
    a. Coolant boil temperature is raised.
    b. Cooling system pressure is raised by compressed air.
    c. The APCS helps the cooling system function with higher heat loads.
    d. All of the above.

20. Which of the following strategies is a recommendation when frequently starting diesel engines in subzero (below −17°C) temperatures?
    a. Use of an auxiliary diesel coolant heater
    b. Discharge a can of ether into the engine while cranking
    c. Avoid shutting the engine off
    d. All of the above

12

Prerequisites: Chapters 4, 7, 8, and 9

ENGINE BREATHING

OBJECTIVES

After studying this chapter, you should be able to:

- Identify the intake and exhaust system components.
- Describe how intake air is routed to the engine's cylinders and exhaust gases are routed out the tailpipe.
- Define the term *positive filtration*.
- Outline the operating principle of an air precleaner.
- Service a dry, positive air cleaner.
- Perform an inlet restriction test.
- Identify the subcomponents on a truck diesel engine turbocharger.
- Outline the operating principles of a constant geometry (CG) exhaust gas-driven, centrifugal turbocharger.
- Explain how wastegating and variable geometry (VG) are used to manage boost pressures.
- Describe the operation of series turbocharging.
- Explain how turbo-compounding functions.
- Troubleshoot common turbocharger problems and perform some basic failure analysis.
- Define the role of a charge air cooler and the relative efficiencies of each type.
- Test a charge air heat exchanger for leaks.
- Relate valve configurations and seat angles to breathing efficiency and cylinder gas dynamics.
- Describe how a pulse-type exhaust manifold can boost turbocharger efficiency.
- Outline the function of a pyrometer on a truck diesel engine.
- Describe the role of the exhaust silencer and its operating principles.
- Understand the basics of sound dynamics and how combustion noise is minimized in an engine.
- Understand some basic exhaust gas emissions chemistry and identify aftertreatment hardware.
- Describe the layout of diesel engine exhaust aftertreatment devices.

KEY TERMS

ACERT	exhaust gas recirculation (EGR)	parallel port valve configuration	selective catalytic reduction (SCR)
axial power turbine (APT)	exhaust throttle valve	platinum resistance thermometer (PRT)	sound absorption
catalytic converter	filter minder		thermo-syphoning
C-EGR	heat exchanger	positive filtration	tuned exhaust
charge air cooler (CAC)	I-EGR	pulse exhaust	turbine
clean gas induction (CGI)	impeller	pyrometer	turbocharger
compound turbocharging	induction circuit	quiescent	variable geometry (VG)
compressor housing	inlet restriction gauge	ram air	variable nozzle (VN)
constant geometry (CG)	intake circuit	rejected heat	variable valve actuator (VVA)
crossflow valve configuration	manometer	resistance temperature detector (RTD)	
diffuser	naturally aspirated	resonation	volute

INTRODUCTION

Over the years, the intake and exhaust systems on commercial diesel engines have become more interconnected because of the universal use of turbochargers and exhaust gas recirculation (EGR) systems, so it makes sense to group them together in one chapter and call it *Engine Breathing*. Turbochargers boost the intake manifold at pressures above atmospheric and they use rejected heat from the exhaust system to do it. EGR systems of one sort or another are also universal on current diesel engines and because these reroute exhaust gas back into the intake circuit, they play a role in both intake and exhaust systems. In addition, the exhaust system contains an ever more complex after-treatment canister to control emissions. The objective in this chapter is to identify emissions control hardware; the operating principles are discussed in Chapter 47.

The manifold-boosted compression ignition (CI) engine cylinder is *charged* with air rather than induced. In a naturally aspirated engine, air or an air-fuel mixture is drawn into the engine cylinder by the below-atmospheric pressure created in the engine cylinder on the downstroke of the piston on the first stroke of the four-stroke cycle. This air or air-fuel mixture is therefore *induced* into the cylinder. The correct term to collectively describe the components responsible for delivering breathing air in **naturally aspirated** engines is **induction circuit**. The preferred term for collectively describing the breathing air delivery components in an engine with turbo/manifold boost is air **intake circuit**. For that reason, we use this term exclusively in this chapter.

GAS FLOW IN BREATHING CIRCUIT

Figure 12–1 is an overview of the gas flow of a typical post-2010 engine breathing circuit equipped with exhaust gas recirculation (EGR), a diesel particulate filter (DPF), and selective catalytic reduction (SCR). We have used a series turbocharged (twin turbo) system because this is used in some post-2007 engines. The figure looks complicated, and it is. The reality is that this schematic simplifies the circuits shown, which are ECM controlled and monitored by numerous sensors. **Figure 12–2** shows a right-side view of a post-2010 Mack Trucks engine with cutaway views of the turbocharger and EGR circuits. This chapter focuses primarily on gas flow through the engine breathing circuit. We will take a closer look at sensors and details of emissions controls in later chapters.

ROLE OF INTAKE SYSTEM

The function of the air intake system in a diesel engine is to supply a charge of air or air/dead gas mixture to the engine cylinders for combustion, cooling, and scavenging. Diesel engines are designed for lean burn operation. This means that the air charged to the engine cylinder often

FIGURE 12–1 Schematic showing a typical post-2010 engine breathing circuit equipped with DPF and SCR.

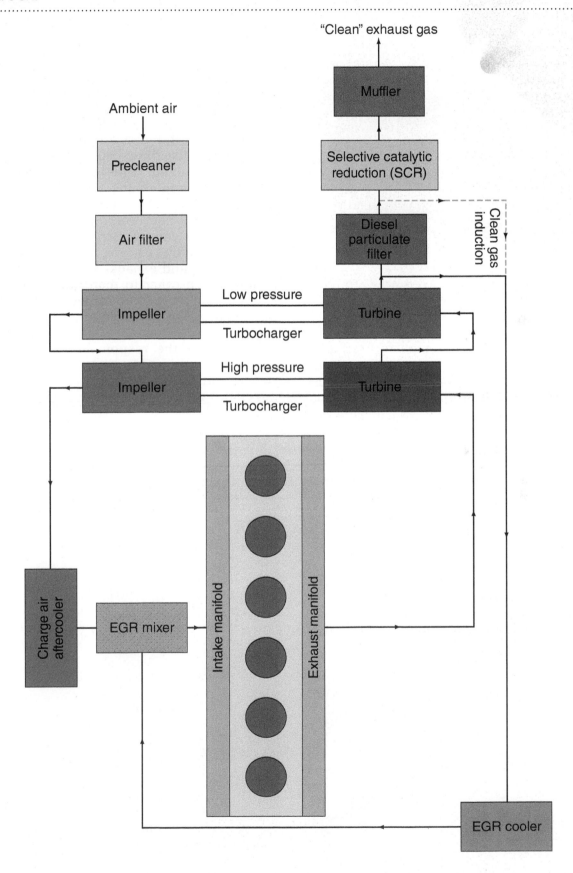

FIGURE 12–2 A right-side view of a post-2010 Mack Trucks engine with cutaways of the turbo and EGR circuits.

substantially exceeds that required to combust the fuel. In an earlier generation of diesel engines, the objective was to cram as much air (that is, oxygen) as possible into the engine cylinders. This was great for performance but bad news for emissions. Today, every engine outcome is managed with respect to the emissions it produces. In addition, engine life has increased significantly during the past 20 years, and this is in part due to improvements in air intake system components.

ROLE OF THE EXHAUST SYSTEM

The function of the exhaust system is to minimize both engine noise and noxious emissions while restricting the exhaust gas flow to a minimum degree. The turbocharger is a component common to both intake and exhaust systems. Its function is to use the exhaust system to recapture some of the engine **rejected heat** to pressurize the air delivered to the engine cylinders from the intake circuit. All current certified highway diesel engines have complex exhaust gas after-treatment systems to manage emissions. Diesel engine breathing requires that the gas dynamics of the intake and exhaust systems work to complement each other in managing engine output and minimizing emissions. Because this requires coordinating a wide range of intake and exhaust components, management of the engine breathing circuit is the responsibility of the engine control module (ECM). **Figure 12–3** shows the components of a pre-2004 diesel engine breathing circuit when things were simpler.

FIGURE 12–3 Typical pre-2004 diesel engine breathing circuit.

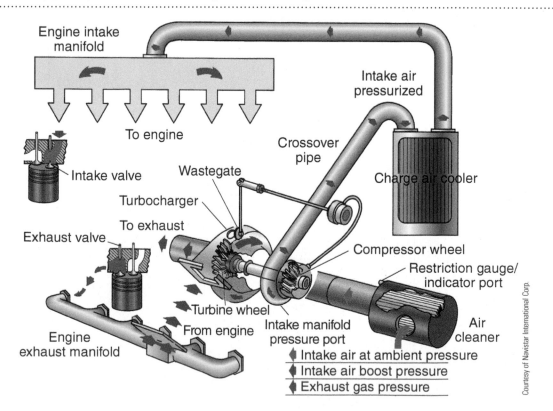

BREATHING COMPONENTS

We begin by identifying the breathing components used on a current four-stroke cycle, highway-certified diesel engine.

CURRENT FOUR-STROKE CYCLE

Bear in mind that older engines may not be equipped with all of the components listed here. EGR became commonplace in October of 2002 when Environmental Protection Agency (EPA) 2004 was implemented. Diesel particulate filters (DPFs) were universally introduced for EPA 2007, and selective catalytic reduction (SCR) was adopted by most engine original equipment manufacturers (OEMs) in 2010 to address NO_x emissions.

Intake system components:

1. Precleaner
2. Main filter
3. Intake ducting/piping
4. Turbocharger(s) and turbocharger controls
5. Charge air cooling circuit
6. Intake module for mixture management of EGR
7. Intake manifold
8. Valve porting and intake tract design

Exhaust system components:

1. Valve configuration and exhaust tract geometry
2. Exhaust manifold
3. Turbocharger(s) and turbocharger controls
4. EGR system
5. Exhaust piping
6. Catalytic converter(s)
7. DPF system
8. SCR system
9. Muffler

AIR INTAKE SYSTEM COMPONENTS

The air intake system components are those responsible for delivering ambient air and dead gas rerouted from the exhaust system to the engine's cylinders. The ambient air is filtered upstream from the turbocharger(s). Turbocharger(s) pressurize intake air well above atmospheric pressure values to increase the oxygen density of the intake charge. In pressurizing the air, the temperature increases and this has a reducing effect on its density. To counter this, most turbo-boosted engines use some form of heat exchanger to cool the boost air (while maintaining the pressure) before it is directed into the engine cylinders. The term used to describe this heat exchanger is **charge air cooler (CAC)**. When the air exits the CAC, it is routed to an ECM-controlled EGR mixer. Depending on how the engine is being operated, the boost air is mixed with dead gas routed from the exhaust system. We will follow the intake circuit component by component in this section.

AIR CLEANERS

The function of the air cleaner system on a highway diesel engine is to filter airborne particulates from the air that will be delivered to the engine cylinders. Airborne dirt can be highly abrasive, and when it finds its way past the air cleaner system, it can destroy an engine in a very short period of time.

Precleaners

Precleaners are required in trucks operating in dusty conditions or in North American winter conditions, especially where highways are salted. They can triple the service life of the main engine air cleaner. Located before the main air cleaner and sometimes designed to receive **ram air**, precleaners generate a cyclonic airflow with the objective of separating heavier particulates by centrifugal force. Depending on the design of the precleaner, the particulate removed from the airstream can either be discharged or collected in a dust bowl. Trucks operating in conditions in which they are subjected to high levels of larger airborne matter such as ash and grain chaff may use precleaner screens, but these are vulnerable to plugging, so they should only be used in conjunction with **inlet restriction gauges**. In agricultural and mining applications, a precleaner can be connected to the exhaust system so that exhaust backpressure pulls separated particulates into the exhaust gas exit stream. This is not permitted in on-highway applications.

Dry, Positive Filters

Dry, **positive filtration** air cleaners are used in all contemporary North American commercial vehicle diesel engines. Because they use a positive filtration principle, *all* of the air entering the intake system must pass through the filtering media, usually resin-impregnated, pleated paper elements. The filtering medium is surrounded by a perforated steel mesh, which provides the element with a limited amount of structural integrity. If a visible dent is evident in the surrounding mesh, the filter will probably not seal in the canister and should be replaced. Filtering efficiencies are high throughout the speed and load range of the engine, usually better than 99.5% and highest just before replacement is required. Some dry element filters are two stage and may eliminate the need for a precleaner; these induce a vortex flow and use centrifugal force to separate heavier particulates, which are then discharged by an ejector valve.

Servicing Air Filters

Dry paper element filters are designed to last for as long as 12 months in a linehaul application, and do not have to be serviced unless the inlet restriction specification exceeds the OEM maximum or a used oil analysis report indicates that dirt may be bypassing the air cleaner. Onboard inlet restriction gauges are not accurate instruments. When a filter-mounted inlet restriction gauge, often known as a **filter minder**, indicates that the filter element is plugging before the regular service interval is achieved, check the reading using a water-filled manometer or negative pressure gauge.

A **manometer** is a clear tubular column formed in a U shape around a calibration scale marked off in inches. The column is then filled with water (usually colored with dye for ease of reading) to a zero point on the calibration scale. When a manometer is connected to a fluid circuit, it produces a reading according to the pull (vacuum circuit) or push pressure acting on the fluid in the column. Never remove an air filter from its canister unnecessarily. Every time a filter is serviced, some dust will be admitted beyond the filter assembly, no matter how much care is taken. **Figure 12–4** shows a typical onboard inlet restriction gauge and **Figure 12–5** shows a manometer used to more accurately measure inlet restriction.

Checking filter restriction with a trouble light is a common practice that finds little favor with OEMs because whether the light is visible or not visible through the filtering medium depends more on the filtering medium materials than the extent to which the filter might be plugged up. The only valid reason for inspecting a dry filter with a trouble light is to locate a perforation. OEM specifications should always be consulted, but typical *maximum* inlet restriction specs are:

15" H_2O vacuum for naturally aspirated (NA) engines

25" H_2O vacuum for boosted engines

FIGURE 12–4 A typical onboard inlet restriction gauge, known as a *filter minder*. The calibration is in inches of H_2O vacuum; the band across the center shows green when inlet restriction is below 25 inches H_2O and red when it exceeds this value.

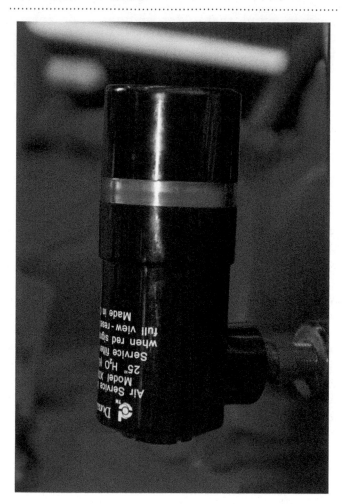

The practice of removing and attempting to clean a dirt-laden, dry filter on the shop floor should be avoided. A dirt-laden filter weighs many times the weight of a new filter, and dropping it onto a concrete floor to shake dust free is usually enough to damage the filter element (by crumpling the perforated mesh) sufficiently to prevent it from sealing in the housing. Another malpractice that invariably ends up costing more in the long term is blowing out of filters using reverse compressed air. Sharp particulates embedded in the filtering media can be dislodged, leaving an enlarged opening through which other larger particles may pass.

FIGURE 12–5 A manometer shown at atmospheric pressure when it is in a neutral state. When used to measure inlet restriction in an intake system, an H_2O-filled manometer must be used.

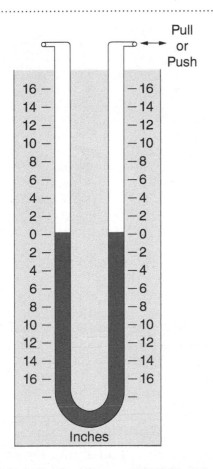

Pull
or
Push

Inches

Laundering Dry Element Filters

When a dry filter element has become plugged, the obviously ideal solution is to replace it. However, dry filter elements are expensive and in some operations, such as on construction sites, mining, and aggregate hauling, these filters may become restricted in a couple of working days even when precleaners are used. Professional laundering is perhaps a second best but necessary option to replacement. The laundering process usually requires that the filter element be soaked in a detergent solution for a period of time, followed by reverse flushing with low-pressure clean water. The element is next dried with warm air and inspected for perforations in the element and for seal/gasket integrity. OEM testing of professionally laundered filter elements indicates that filtering efficiencies are reduced with each successive laundering.

OIL BATH FILTERS—VISCOUS IMPINGEMENT OIL FILTERS

Low operating efficiencies have made oil bath (nonpositive) filters things of the past, so you are only going to see them on much older highway diesel engines and possibly some off-highway engines. They consist of a mesh-filled canister with a sump filled with engine oil. Airflow is cycloned through the canister and wets down a cylindrical mesh with engine oil to which dirt particles attach themselves. This principle works effectively to remove larger particles from the airstream and has higher efficiencies when induced airflow is highest, that is, at rated speed. They possess low filtering efficiencies at low-load, low-speed operation. Oil bath filters are serviced by replacing the sump oil and washing down the mesh with solvent.

TURBOCHARGERS

Turbochargers are used universally in North American medium- and large-bore highway diesel engines, and nearly universally in small-bore engines. By definition, a **turbocharger** is an exhaust gas-driven, centrifugal pump that "recycles" some of the rejected heat from the engine's cylinders. Turbochargers may be driven to speeds exceeding 200,000 rpm in certain race-car engine applications, but maximum speeds are about 30% lower in diesel engines. The turbocharger is used to deliver a pressurized charge of air to the engine's cylinders; in short, it increases the oxygen density in the intake charge. In addition, the exhaust gas-driven **turbine** may be used with a fluid coupling to drive reduction gearing connected to the engine crankshaft; in this instance, the turbocharger assists in driving the crankshaft. This is known as *turbo compounding*

FIGURE 12–6 A right-side view of a post-2010 Cummins ISX engine on which the turbocharger is located.

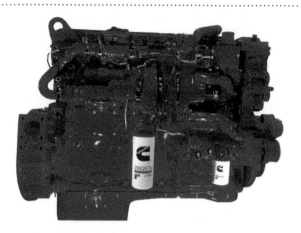

and it is used in the current generation of Detroit Diesel (DD) engines looked at a little later in this chapter. **Figure 12–6** shows a right-side view of a 2010 Cummins ISX on which the turbocharger is located.

PRINCIPLES OF OPERATION

A turbocharger is an exhaust gas-driven air pump consisting of a turbine and an **impeller** (see **Figure 12–7**) mounted on a common shaft. The shaft is floated (hydrodynamically suspended) on friction bearings supplied with pressurized lube oil. The turbine wheel is subject to engine

FIGURE 12–7 The impeller or compressor wheel from a turbocharger.

FIGURE 12–8 Sectional view of a turbocharger, the lubrication circuit, and gas flow.

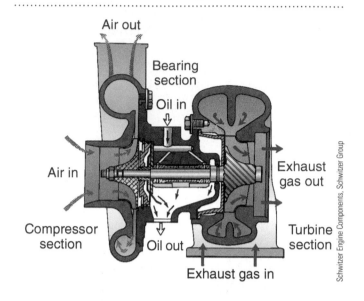

exhaust gas energy (heat) and is driven within a turbine housing through which the exhaust is routed. The impeller is enclosed in a separate **compressor housing** and acts on intake system air, pumping it through the charge side of the intake system. The exhaust gas that drives the turbine and the intake air the impeller acts on do not come into contact. **Figure 12–8** shows the gas and lubrication flow through a simple turbocharger.

Compressor Operation

Filtered intake air is pulled into the compressor housing the impeller on the compressor side of the turbine shaft. The turbine drives the impeller on the other side of the turbine shaft, so the actual speed of the impeller is determined by what is happening in the turbine housing. As the impeller rotates, the air from the intake system is accelerated to high velocities. High-velocity air flows radially outward to a diffuser. The **diffuser** is a restriction. It is designed to convert the kinetic energy (energy of motion) of the intake air into pressure as it attempts to drive it through the diffuser. The diffuser may be a voluted (snail-shaped) type or a blade type (see Figure 12–8). Blade-type diffusers have higher efficiencies.

Turbine Operation

Exhaust gas is routed to the turbine housing. The greater the engine rejected heat value (this increases somewhat proportionally with engine output), the greater the exhaust gas heat energy. The exhaust gas enters the turbine housing

FIGURE 12–9 Turbocharger gas flow schematic indicating the roles played by the volute and diffuser.

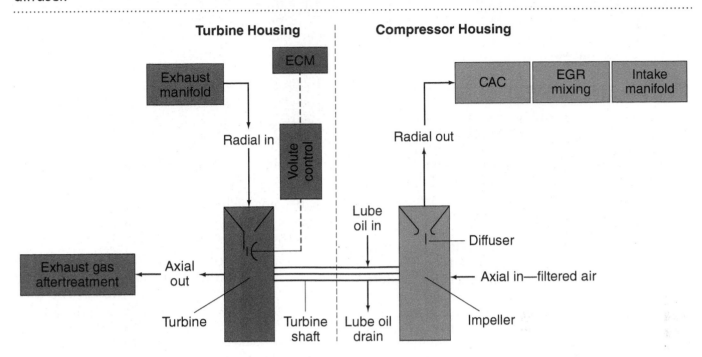

radially and is routed to flow into the **volute**, a snail-shaped, diminishing sectional area. The volute represents a restriction. However, when the exhaust gas exits the volute, it then expands, acting on the turbine vanes, after which it is routed axially to the exhaust circuit.

The extent of gas expansion in the turbine housing is determined by the amount of exhaust gas heat. Under high engine output, engine rejected heat increases, so exhaust gas expansion acting on the turbine vanes produces higher turbine speeds. It is important to underline the fact that turbocharger rotational speed is factored primarily by exhaust gas heat and not exhaust gas pressure. The importance of the volute should also be understood. The smaller its size, the greater restriction to flow it represents, but a smaller-size volute means that exhaust gas expands more when it exits. The best arrangement is to be able to control the volute flow area, which we will look at next. **Figure 12–9** is a turbocharger gas flow schematic indicating the key roles played by the volute and diffuser: Note the direction of gas flow into and out of the turbine and compressor housings.

Gas Flow Routing

Gas flow into the turbine housing is radial and has an axial outflow, as shown in Figure 12–9. Airflow through the impeller housing is axial

inflow and radial outflow. In the simplest type of turbocharger design, the turbine housing intake tract or throat is undivided, meaning that the exhaust ports of all of the cylinders feed gas into a single entry passage. However, variable-geometry turbochargers manipulate gas flows into and out of the turbine housing. This is discussed later in this section.

TYPES OF TURBOCHARGERS

First, it is important to make a distinction between constant geometry turbochargers and variable geometry turbochargers. The definitions used in this text are as follows:

- *Constant geometry (CG)*: a turbocharger in which all of the exhaust flow is routed through the turbine housing regardless of how the engine is being operated.
- *Variable geometry (VG)*: a turbocharger that uses either external or internal controls to either manipulate the flow areas through the turbine housing or allow some percentage of exhaust gas to bypass the turbine housing.

Until 2001, a majority of turbochargers used on highway commercial diesel engines were classified as constant geometry. This has changed. Today, when we see a constant geometry turbo on a truck diesel, it is usually one of a series-charge pair or in a compound turbocharger arrangement. Currently, almost all turbochargers use some means of varying (controlling) exhaust flow through the turbine housing, whether it be by the use of a wastegate or by using internal variable geometry.

CONSTANT GEOMETRY TURBOS

We begin by describing the operation of a **constant geometry (CG)** turbocharger. CG turbos were designed for optimum performance at a specific rpm and a specific rejected heat load. In other words, they were not versatile. This meant that engineers had to select when that moment of optimum turbine efficiency occurred. In most highway engines that used CG turbos, the turbos were usually spec'd to produce peak efficiencies under full load and at peak torque rpm— and when operated outside that spec point, there would be a performance deficiency. CG turbos are simple; that shown in Figure 12–8 is typical.

Spec'ing peak turbine efficiencies at peak torque rather than rated speed provided the CG turbo with a self-regulating characteristic, because as engine rpm winds up, the real time available for charging the cylinders with boost air and injecting fuel diminishes. Operate a CG turbo outside its specified rpm range and the engine torque curve rapidly drops off. This results in an engine that labors under lug and drops off rpm rapidly when load is applied at the top end of its rpm range. Fuel economy is also adversely affected.

WARNING:

Mismatching of CG turbochargers may result in high engine cylinder pressures that result in engine failure or, oppositely, may lead to low power, smoking, and high noxious emissions.

TECH TIP:

Although truck diesel engines using CG turbochargers are designed to produce peak gas efficiency at peak torque, most other diesel engines using CG turbos do this at *rated* speed (maximum horsepower). If you work on engines in off-road heavy equipment or gensets, you will find that CG turbochargers are common and, in most cases, are engineered for peak gas efficiency when wound out at full power.

VARIABLE-GEOMETRY TURBOS

A little earlier in this chapter, a **variable-geometry (VG)** turbocharger was defined as one that uses either external or internal controls to either manipulate the flow areas through the turbine housing or allow some percentage of exhaust gas to bypass the turbine housing. In looking at VG turbos, we will divide them as follow:

- Wastegate controlled
- Volute controlled

The objective of all VG turbos is to:

- Allow the turbo to act like a small turbocharger when engine loads are light.
- Allow the turbo to act like a large turbocharger when engine loading is high.

Today's ECM-controlled turbochargers will accomplish both the preceding objectives and every incremental stage in between. The payoff is a much faster response to requests for changes in engine output (reduced turbo lag) and, of course, reduced engine emissions. Some current turbochargers use a combination of an external wastegate and internal variable geometry to manage boost through the widest possible rpm and load range.

Wastegate Controlled

Wastegated turbochargers have been around for many years. In operation, they can either allow all of the exhaust gas to be routed through the turbine housing or option a percentage of it to bypass the turbine directly to the exhaust circuit. The *gate* in the wastegate functions as the exhaust gas control door. A current example of a wastegated turbocharger is found on Detroit Diesel's DD13 engine. Two methods are used to control the gate:

- Pneumatic: Wastegate movement depends on manifold pressure.
- Electronic: Wastegate is positioned by the ECM.

PNEUMATIC WASTEGATE A pneumatically controlled wastegate uses a wastegate actuator, which is usually a canister with an actuator rod to move the gate. The actuator rod connects the wastegate door and the other to a bellows inside the canister. An internal spring in the canister loads the actuator to a (default) closed position. In the closed position, all of the exhaust gas is routed through the turbine housing. On the other side of the bellows, manifold boost acts in opposition to the spring. When manifold boost reaches a prescribed value, it begins to overcome the spring pressure, moving the actuator rod to allow some of the exhaust gas to bypass the turbine housing.

ELECTRONIC WASTEGATE The engine ECM manages electronically controlled wastegates. For instance, some engines use wastegated turbos with dual entry ports. Using the example of an early version of the Cummins ISX engine, the exhaust manifold was designed so that end gas from the front three cylinders was constantly routed through the turbine housing, and the wastegate managed exhaust flow from the rear three cylinders. This meant that exhaust gas could either be full-flowed into, or incrementally bypass, the turbine housing. To achieve this, the engine ECM uses a combination of solenoids (inlet and vent) and manifold boost to precisely manage the pressure acting on the wastegate actuator bellows to provide four levels of boost. In other words, the mechanical movement of the wastegate is electronic-over-electric-over-pneumatic.

Volute-Controlled VG

Volute-controlled VG turbochargers have become commonplace on the diesel engine of today. Racecar engines have used variable aperture nozzles to control volute flow area for many years, and diesel engines have adapted this technology.

FIGURE 12–10 The VGT used on a 2015 Paccar MX 13.

The first volute-controlled diesel engine turbochargers appeared in the early 1990s and met with limited success, but today most diesel engine OEMs are using variable volute in preference to wastegated turbochargers, such as the example shown in **Figure 12–10** showing the VGT on a Paccar MX13. We are going to model our description of a volute-controlled VG turbocharger on the system used on a post-2007 Caterpillar ACERT C7 engine, shown in **Figure 12–11**.

FIGURE 12–11 Caterpillar C7 variable nozzle turbocharger cutaway.

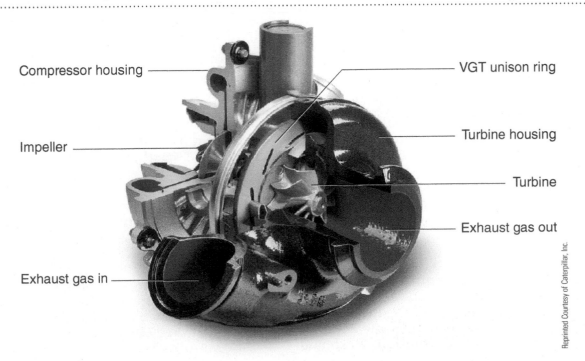

Compressor housing

Impeller

Exhaust gas in

VGT unison ring

Turbine housing

Turbine

Exhaust gas out

FIGURE 12–12 Component operation of a VN turbocharger.

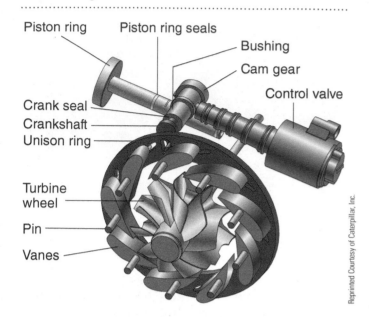

Reprinted Courtesy of Caterpillar, Inc.

FIGURE 12–13 VN turbocharger: Opening vane pitch to reduce turbine efficiency.

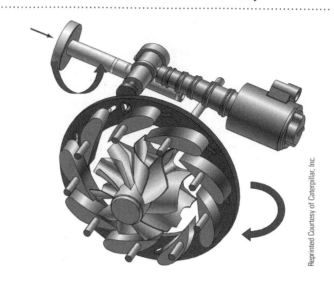

Reprinted Courtesy of Caterpillar, Inc.

Variable Nozzle Turbocharger

Figure 12–11 shows a sectioned view of the Caterpillar **variable nozzle (VN)** turbo. Identify the turbine, pin wheel, vanes, and unison ring, cross-referencing this figure with **Figure 12–12**.

The VN turbocharger manipulates the volute flow area by moving the vane pitch to produce the desired boost. This is accomplished when oil pressure acts on the piston, which is tooth-meshed to the cam gear and crankshaft: This "cranks" or turns the unison ring. The unison ring supports the vane assemblies. Each vane has a spiral slot: When the unison ring rotational position changes, vane pitch angle changes because each vane pivots on wheel pins. Whenever the crankshaft moves the unison ring, the vane pitch is altered simultaneously. In this way, the volute (inflow) flow area can be increased or decreased. Volute flow area onto the turbine determines gas efficiency in the turbine housing. In simple terms, this defines turbine rotational speed and therefore the boost pressure produced by the turbo compressor.

VN Control

The VN turbocharger is controlled by the VN control valve. The VN control valve is a proportioning actuator managed by the ECM: It converts the current delivered to the actuator into a specific piston ring position. Maximum

boost is produced when the vanes are held in the nearly closed position (they are never fully closed). Boost air is managed by vane position because vane pitch governs how gas acts on the turbine. **Figure 12–13** shows how oil pressure acting on the piston ring actuates the cam and crank assembly, turning the unison ring clockwise. Moving the unison ring clockwise opens the vanes, reducing turbine gas efficiency.

When oil pushes the piston to the left (**Figure 12–14**), the unison ring turns counterclockwise, moving the vane pitch to the nearly closed position, increasing turbine efficiency to

FIGURE 12–14 VN turbocharger: Closing down vane pitch to produce maximum boost.

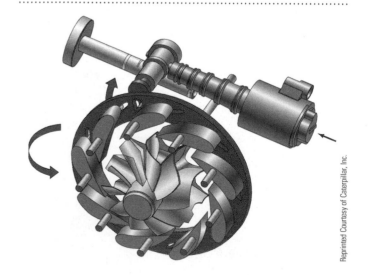

Reprinted Courtesy of Caterpillar, Inc.

FIGURE 12–15 Action of unison ring in controlling vane pitch.

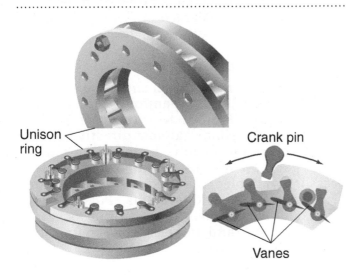

provide maximum boost. You can see this action in **Figure 12–15**.

The rotational speed of the VN turbocharger is signaled to the ECM by a shaft speed sensor that uses an inductive pulse generator principle (explained in Chapter 34). The trigger is flat on one section of the turbine shaft.

Sliding Ring Volute Turbos

Another way of varying the volute flow area is used by Cummins in some of its Holset turbochargers. The VG actuator moves a sliding ring that determines flow unload area. The objective is identical to that on the Caterpillar VN turbo; it is just achieved in a slightly different way. **Figure 12–16** shows the VG actuator module used on a typical post-2010 engine.

FIGURE 12–16 VG actuator module used on a typical post-2010 engine.

CONSTRUCTION

Turbochargers used in truck diesel engine applications can sometimes wind out at peak rpm of up to 150,000, perform continuously at shaft speeds of 75,000 rpm, and have to sustain temperatures that may exceed 1,400°F (760°C), so the materials used in turbo construction must be able to withstand high temperatures and centrifugal forces. The compressor components are often manufactured from aluminum alloys. Turbine housings must be able to sustain rotor burst. *Rotor burst* occurs when centrifugal force causes turbine or impeller disintegration. Turbine housings are manufactured from austenitic (a particular crystalline structure of iron and carbon) Ni-Resist™ cast iron, which has high hot strength and resistance to oxidation. The turbines are manufactured from nickel or cobalt steels and ceramics. The turbo shaft is usually an alloy steel to which the turbine is either welded or bolted and the impeller is bolted. Sometimes the turbo shaft, turbine, impeller, and bearing assembly are manufactured in a cartridge for ease of replacement. When a turbocharger is recored, this cartridge or core assembly is replaced as a unit and the hub, turbine, and compressor housings are reused.

Turbocharger Lubrication

All current turbochargers use floating friction bearings. Turbo bearings are designed to rotate in operation and do so at about one-third shaft speed floated with a film of oil on either side of the bearing. The operating principle is that of friction bearings, meaning that the turbine shaft is hydrodynamically suspended during operation. Accordingly, the radial play specification is a critical determination of bearing and/or shaft wear. **Figure 12–17** shows a method of measuring turbine shaft radial play using a dial indicator. A thrust bearing defines the axial play of the turbine shaft, and gas pressure on both the turbine and compressor housings is sealed by a pair of piston rings. The oil that pressure-feeds the bearings spills to an oil drain cavity and then drains to the crankcase by gravity by means of a return hose. The lubricating oil required for the bearings also plays a major role in cooling the turbocharger components. **Figure 12–18** shows the oil flow routing through a typical turbocharger.

Common Manifold Turbocharging

A single pipe manifold is flange mated to the exhaust tract of each engine cylinder, with the

FIGURE 12–17 Checking turbine shaft radial play.

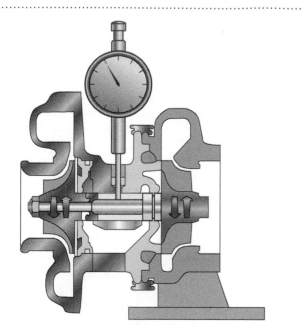

FIGURE 12–18 Oil flow through a turbocharger.

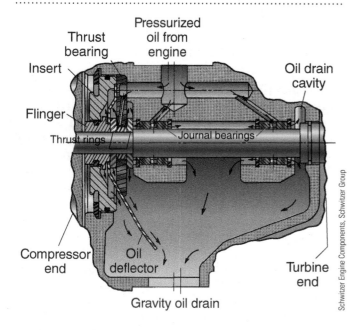

turbocharger turbine housing flange mounted to the center of the assembly in a manner that routes the exhaust gas through the turbine housing. This manifold design creates certain problems with the gas dynamics and produces inconsistencies in the effective heat per exhaust slug discharged into the manifold; simply, each exhaust slug volume discharge from cylinders 1 and 6 on an inline, six-configured engine must travel considerably farther before it enters the turbine housing tract than those discharged at cylinders 3 and 4 located at the center of the engine.

Pulse/Tuned Exhaust Manifold

OEMs of most current diesel engines often used **pulse/tuned exhaust** manifolds that use geometrically tuned pipes to direct the exhaust gas from each cylinder almost directly into the inlet tract of the turbine housing. This minimizes gas flow interference and exhaust slug pressure variables that reduce the efficiency of common manifold systems. Pulsed manifolds tend to diminish turbo lag (turbocharger response time) and increase low engine load performance.

TWIN AND DOUBLE FLOW TURBOS In a double flow design, the turbine throat is divided and each half feeds one-half of the turbine wheel circumference. Another variation is the twin flow, in which two passages are fed from a common throat for the full rotation of the turbine wheel. V-configured engines commonly use either the double or twin flow turbine housing design, as shown in **Figure 12–19**.

TWO-STAGE OR SERIES TURBOCHARGING Series turbocharging requires use of two turbochargers in series. The terms *primary* and *secondary turbochargers* (or *low-/high-pressure turbochargers*) designate the roles played by the two units used. This technology is used by Caterpillar in its electronic unit injector (EUI)-fueled ACERT engine family and by Navistar in MaxxForce 11 and 13 engines manufactured until 2013. Series turbocharging will likely become more common as OEMs strive for better management of the combustion process to maximize power and minimize emissions. **Figure 12–20** shows the series turbocharger arrangement used on a Caterpillar C13 engine.

PARALLELING Paralleling describes the use of multiple turbochargers, usually to charge each bank of a V-configuration engine. Parallel turbocharger configurations are not used on any current truck diesel engines, but they are used extensively in larger, off-highway applications. Paralleling is often used in railway locomotive applications.

FIGURE 12–19 Sectional view of a divided turbine housing. All housing types can have a water passage around the gas passage for cooling.

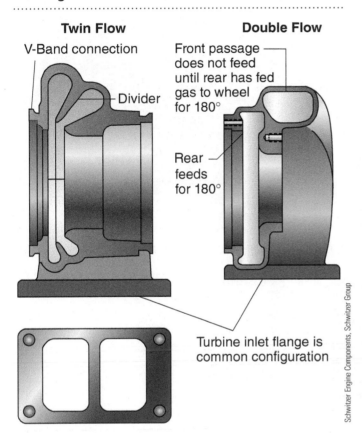

Compound Turbocharging

The term **compound turbocharging** is often incorrectly used to describe two-stage or series turbocharging. In a true compound turbocharger circuit, the turbine, rather than driving an impeller, is connected to a reduction gearing coupling with an output shaft indirectly connected to the engine crankshaft. Most turbo-compounded systems make use of a viscous drive. In other words, the turbocharger helps directly drive the crankshaft. Compound turbocharging has been used for many years in off-highway diesel engine applications, but has more recently been adopted for on-highway engines by DD in its DD15 and DD16 family of engines, some Scania and Volvo engines, Cummins industrial engines, and many off-road heavy equipment applications.

The examples shown here use a CG turbocharger. When a CG turbocharger is used in a modern compounded turbo arrangement, peak gas efficiency is set at the rated speed and load rpm of the engine: This allows the turbo compounding to provide maximum torque assist to the engine drivetrain when it is working hardest. **Figure 12–21** shows the critical components of a compound turbocharger circuit. We will base our description of compound turbocharging on the DD system described next.

AXIAL POWER TURBINE DD refers to its compound turbocharger system as an **axial power turbine (APT)** system. The APT used on DD engines is a Holset unit. APT makes use of a CG turbine housing to impart drive torque to the engine geartrain. This is achieved by connecting the exhaust gas-driven turbine to reduction gearing in the APT, as shown in **Figure 12–22**. DD states that turbo compounding on a DD15 engine can contribute an additional 50 horsepower (37 kW) at peak efficiency.

The APT reduction gearing connects to the engine geartrain by means of a viscous drive and pinion (see Figure 12–22). The APT pinion is in constant mesh with the APT-driven gear (see Figure 12–22). APT input can therefore be overridden during low boost, high rpm operation due to the viscous drive member. Turbo compounding allows a turbocharger to provide both manifold and direct-drive assist.

FIGURE 12–20 Series turbocharging used on a Caterpillar ACERT engine.

FIGURE 12–21 Principle of compound turbocharging.

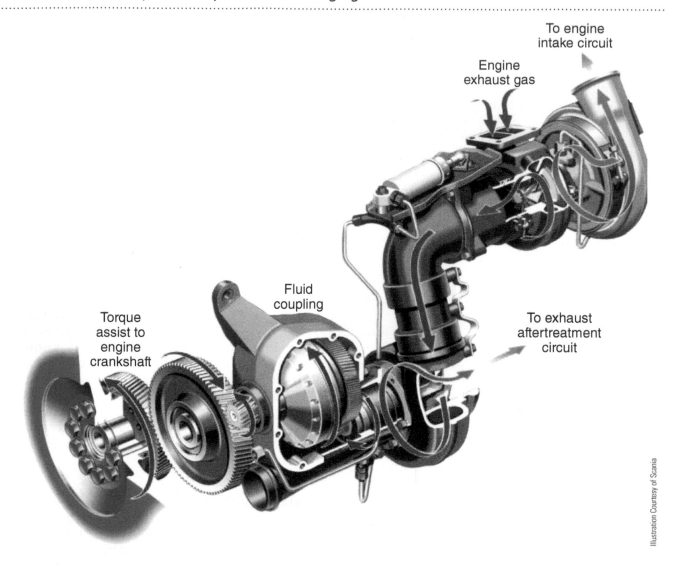

To engine
intake circuit

Engine
exhaust gas

Fluid
coupling

Torque
assist to
engine
crankshaft

To exhaust
aftertreatment
circuit

Illustration Courtesy of Scania

Turbocharger Precautions

1. Avoidance of hot shutdown: Allow at least 5 minutes of idling before shutting down the engine after prolonged loading on a dynamometer or road test.
2. Prelubing: Pour oil directly onto the turbine shaft through the oil supply flange when installing a turbocharger before connecting the lube supply line.

Some OEMs require that the oil filters be primed when replacing them at service intervals.

Thermo-syphoning

Thermo-syphoning protects water-cooled turbocharger shaft and bearing housings against overheating when a hot shutdown occurs. The turbocharger cooling circuit uses convection and a loop to cycle coolant through the turbo bearing circuit until the temperature reaches parity with the mean coolant temperature. This can greatly extend turbocharger longevity in applications such as school buses and pickup and delivery vehicles, which are routinely subjected to poor driving practices.

Turbocharger Failures

1. Hot shutdown. Extreme temperature failures producing warped shafts and bores.
2. Turbocharger overspeed. Caused by a number of conditions, including fuel rate tampering, high-altitude operation with a defective altitude compensation fuel control, and mismatching of complete turbocharger units.

FIGURE 12–22 Coupling arrangement of a compound turbocharger to a DD15 engine drivetrain located at the rear of the engine.

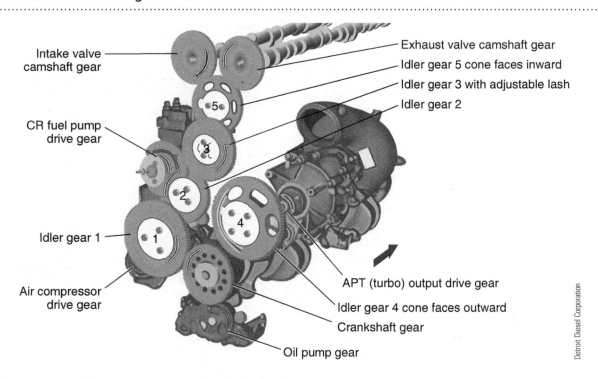

Intake valve camshaft gear

Exhaust valve camshaft gear

Idler gear 5 cone faces inward

Idler gear 3 with adjustable lash

Idler gear 2

CR fuel pump drive gear

Idler gear 1

Air compressor drive gear

APT (turbo) output drive gear

Idler gear 4 cone faces outward

Crankshaft gear

Oil pump gear

Detroit Diesel Corporation

3. Air intake system leaks. Allow dirt to enter the compressor housing, causing the impeller vanes to be eroded wafer thin.
4. Lubrication-related failure. Caused by abrasives in the engine oil, improper oil, broken-down oil, or restricted oil supply.

CHARGE AIR HEAT EXCHANGERS

The act of compressing the intake air charge by the turbocharger typically produces air temperatures of 300°F (150°C) at a 70°F (21°C) ambient temperature and proportionally more at higher ambient temperatures. The objective of charge air coolers (CACs), whatever their cooling medium, is to cool the air pressurized by the turbocharger. The objective is to cool the air as much as possible while maintaining the pressure. As intake air temperature increases, air density diminishes and the oxygen charge in the cylinder is reduced, resulting in lower power and higher cylinder temperatures. A CAC is a **heat exchanger** designed to cool hot, turbo-boosted intake air.

To minimize this loss of power potential, the boosted air charge is cooled using one of several types of heat exchanger. As a rule, a 1°C increase in intake air temperature will produce a 2°C increase in exhaust gas temperature. It should also be noted that because the performance of CACs greatly influences combustion temperatures and the density of the cylinder air charge, they are an integral component in the vehicle's noxious emissions control system. Most North American boosted diesel engines use some type of heat exchanger to cool intake air.

TYPES OF CHARGE AIR COOLER

For purposes of study, we will divide boost air coolers as follows:

- Air-to-air: Cooling medium is ram air.
- Aftercoolers and intercoolers: Cooling medium is a combination of engine coolant and ram air.
- Tip turbine: Cooling medium is turbine-fanned air to a heat exchanger, sometimes assisted by engine coolant.

The type of charge cooler used depends on the vehicle application. For instance, air-to-air coolers offer the highest efficiencies, but because these rely on a vehicle moving at some speed, they are not going to be effective in many vocational trucks or city buses. Tip turbines have been phased out in highway truck engines in recent years; they continue to be used in large off-highway mobile diesels and are described in previous editions of this book if you need to reference them.

AIR-TO-AIR HEAT EXCHANGERS

Air-to-air heat exchangers have the appearance of a coolant radiator and are often chassis mounted in front of the radiator (see **Figure 12–23** and **Figure 12–24**). As the vehicle moves down the highway, ambient air is forced through the fins and element tubing. Ram air is therefore the cooling medium. Cooling efficiencies are highest when the vehicle is moving at higher speeds. They are least efficient when the airflow through the cooler is minimal, and while the engine fan may assist, air-to-air cooling may not be suitable for construction applications. Under optimum conditions, air-to-air heat exchangers have better efficiency ratios than any liquid-cooled heat exchangers. Optimum conditions mean maximum airflow through the element, so the vehicle has to be traveling at full speed. Figure 12–23 shows the location and plumbing of a typical CAC.

TESTING AIR-TO-AIR COOLERS

When an engine is operating at close to rated speeds and loads, air enters a CAC at around

FIGURE 12–23 Charge air cooler plumbing.

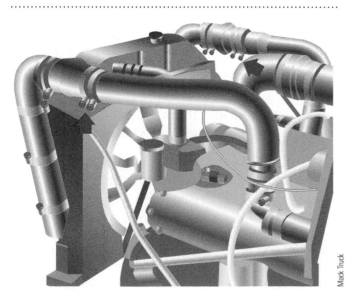

Mack Truck

FIGURE 12–24 Front-on view of a typical charge air cooler.

300°F (150°C). In cases where an air-to-air heat exchanger is used, the boost air should exit at around 110°F (44°C) when ambient temperature is 75°F (24°C), though there is some variability of this specification depending on the OEM. CACs are designed so that they can leak small amounts of air without any performance drop-off. When testing the air leak-off rate, plug the inlet and outlets of the CAC and pressurize to the OEM-recommended test value. Some examples of OEM-recommended test values are:

ENGINE OEM	PSI START TEST VALUE	PSI DROP-OFF OVER 15 SEC.
Caterpillar	30 psi	5 psi
Cummins	30 psi	7 psi
Detroit Diesel	25 psi	5 psi

If the pressure drop-off exceeds specifications, drop the pressure down to 5 psi and hold. Then attempt to locate the leak using a soap and water solution. **Figure 12–25** shows the equipment and method Caterpillar recommends to test its CACs.

Dyno Testing and CACs

When chassis dynamometer testing trucks with air-to-air CACs, it is essential to take into account that the absence of airflow through the engine housing drastically reduces cooling efficiency. Using a dyno airflow fan accomplishes little in comparison with the ram air effect that

FIGURE 12–25 CAC test kit: Charge CAC to 30 psi (200 kPa). Pressure drop-off should not exceed 5 psi (35 kPa) after 5 minutes.

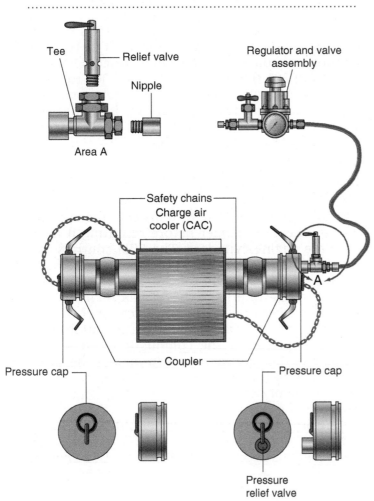

through which coolant from the engine cooling system is pumped. Cooling efficiencies tend to be lower than with air-to-air heat exchangers due to the heat of the cooling medium; they continue to be used in applications in which low airflow through the engine housing rules out the use of an air-to-air exchanger. Some use ram air assist in addition to engine coolant.

BOOST CIRCUIT TROUBLESHOOTING

When manifold boost is either too high or too low, engine performance complaints result. Common causes of lower-than-specified manifold boost are:

- Air system restriction upstream or downstream from the turbocharger impeller
- Air leakage downstream from the turbocharger impeller
- Low fuel delivery
- Mismatched turbocharger

Common causes of higher-than-specified manifold boost are as follows:

- Mismatched turbocharger
- Sticking unison rings on VG turbos
- Excessively high inlet air temperatures
- Deposits on the turbine volute or nozzle, discharge port, or turbine vanes
- Overfueling caused by the by ECM calibration programming, leaking injectors, intake system leaks, and sensor malfunctions
- Advanced fuel injection timing

CAUTION:

Never regulate the air pressure at a value above 30 psi (200 kPa) when testing for boost side leaks, because this may result in personal injury and damage to the components under pressure.

makes an air-to-air CAC so effective. Because of the inefficiency of the CAC under chassis dyno test conditions, reduced peak BHP readings and higher tailpipe NO_x result. During a dyno run cycle, you should test for peak BHP almost immediately after the coolant has reached operating temperature—then run any other tests after determining rated power.

AFTERCOOLERS AND INTERCOOLERS

The terms *aftercooler* and *intercooler* normally refer to heat exchangers that use liquid engine coolant as the cooling medium. The two terms are synonymous and the one used merely indicates the OEM's preference. Boosted air is forced through an element containing tubing

EXHAUST GAS RECIRCULATION

Until the introduction of the EPA 2004 emissions standards, truck diesel engine manufacturers had successfully avoided using **exhaust gas recirculation (EGR)** systems. From 2007 onward, all the diesel engine OEMs have been using some form of EGR, though they may not call it EGR. Because EGR is an emissions control strategy, in this chapter we will look at it primarily from the point of view of gas flow. The role of EGR in the emissions control system is discussed in more depth in Chapters 47 and 48.

EGR OPERATING PRINCIPLE

Oxides of nitrogen, or NO_x, are produced when engine combustion temperatures are high, which is a condition that occurs during lean burn combustion. Diesels run lean. Although EGR compromises performance output, after the issuance of EPA MY 2004 standards diesel engine OEMs had no option but to turn to EGR. An EGR system routes some of the exhaust gas back into the intake system. Exhaust gas is "dead" gas. That means it is unreactive. Dead gas is routed back into engine cylinders simply to occupy some space and reduce the extent of lean burn that makes NO_x formation more likely. A better way of saying this is that EGR *dilutes* the intake charge of oxygen. It is not popular for the following reasons:

- Putting end gas back into the engine cylinder in place of fresh filtered air adds wear-inducing contaminants and increases engine oil acidity, both of which reduce engine longevity.
- EGR reduces engine power. The net effect of this has been minimized by improved control of combustion.
- EGR reduces fuel economy. Again, the net effect of EGR on fuel economy has been minimized by engineering improvements in managing combustion.

It is not difficult to see why EGR has not been popular with the engine OEMs or their customers. The good news is that with the introduction of **selective catalytic reduction (SCR)** in 2010, EGR percentages have either been significantly reduced or eliminated in newer engines. Caterpillar adopted a variation on EGR for its post-2007 generation engines. The Caterpillar system is called **clean gas induction (CGI)** because it sources the exhaust gas after exits the exhaust gas aftertreatment process, justifying the term "clean."

EGR is an effective means of reducing NO_x emission because it inhibits its formation in the cylinder. Also, because dead or unreactive gas is required to make EGR work, there is no better source (it has no cost) of dead gas than the exhaust system. However, it fouls engine components and engine oil, especially in applications where it is used in high percentage concentrations. It can be argued that EGR defeats what took years of engineering to accomplish: the diesel engine with high engine breathing efficiency. With the introduction of SCR in 2010, many of the problems associated with high percentage EGR routing (sometimes more than 50% of total intake charge) were eliminated. Most persons in the trucking industry compare the post-2010 generations of commercial diesel engines (EPA MYs 2010 and 2013) favorably with the 2004 to 2010 engines. All engine OEMs continue to use EGR as a strategy for dealing with NO_x, but since the introduction of SCR, attempt to keep the cut percentage as low as possible.

COOLED EGR

Most diesel engine EGR systems cool the end gas using a heat exchanger before rerouting it back into the engine cylinders. The ECM controls the cycling of the EGR gas. Cooled EGR systems have produced the acronym **C-EGR**. Some OEMs have opted to use internal exhaust gas recirculation or **I-EGR** in engines powering vocational trucks. I-EGR functions by using the valve actuation train to permit some of the combustion end gas to remain in the cylinder. It accomplishes the same objective as C-EGR; that is, it dilutes the cylinder charge of oxygen by simply occupying space with *dead* gas. **Figure 12–26** is a schematic of a Detroit Diesel cooled EGR circuit on a Series 60 diesel engine, and **Figure 12–27** is the heat exchanger used on a post-2004 Volvo D12 engine.

FIGURE 12–26 C-EGR: Schematic of a DD Series 60 C-EGR system identifying flow routing and main components.

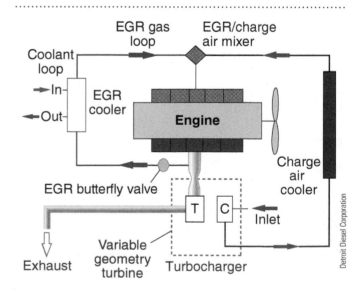

Detroit Diesel Corporation

FIGURE 12–27 C-EGR heat exchanger used on a 12-liter diesel engine.

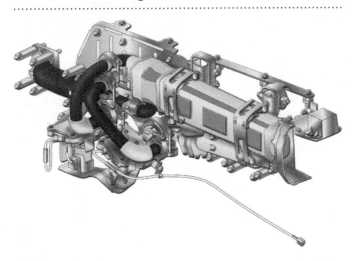

FIGURE 12–28 A 2011, Tier 4 John Deere engine showing the turbocharger: This engine features an exhaust throttle that chokes down on exhaust gas flow; the resulting back-pressure speeds engine warmup to lower emissions.

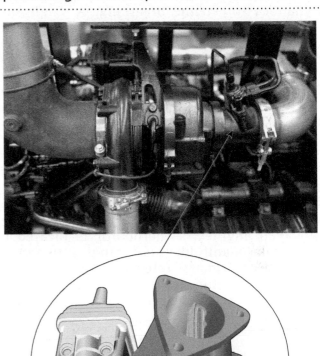

EGR COMPONENTS

A typical C-EGR system comprises the components identified in Figure 12–26, which should be referenced while reading through this description. In current commercial diesel engines, the control of EGR is by the engine ECM, and we will make that assumption as we go through the system.

- ECM. Receives inputs from system sensors, and output circuit drivers manage the operation of EGR flow gates and mixing.
- Sensors. Key sensors in the EGR circuit are ambient temperature, barometric pressure (altitude), boost pressure, mass airflow (MAF), coolant temperature, and oil temperature.
- Butterfly valve and flow doors. Manage flow rate from the exhaust circuit to the EGR circuit.
- C-EGR cooler. The C-EGR heat exchanger uses engine coolant to reduce the temperature of EGR gases to be recirculated back to the engine cylinders.
- EGR mixer. Combines exhaust gas with charge air from the intake system to be routed into engine cylinders. Controlled by the ECM. In systems using differential pressure-type MAF sensors, the venturi is usually integrated into the EGR mixer assembly.

The MAF sensors used in the diesel engine EGR breathing system can use either hot-wire or differential pressure operating principles. These are explained in Chapter 34. The way in which engine intake air and exhaust are routed in and out of the engine and the emissions hardware have given post-2010 diesel engines a cluttered appearance that complicates access for even the simplest procedures. **Figure 12–28** shows some of the congestion of routing pipes on a John Deere Tier 4 (post-2011) engine; this engine features an **exhaust throttle valve**. When actuated, the exhaust throttle valve chokes down on exhaust gas flow, creating high back pressure and thereby holding combustion heat within the engine. This enables the engine to warm up quickly, lowering its emissions.

INTAKE MANIFOLD DESIGN

Because of the almost universal use of turbochargers on diesels, intake manifold design is generally less complex than that for naturally aspirated spark-ignited (SI) engines. This usually means that the runners that extend from the plenum are of unequal lengths, and this does not notably compromise engine breathing. A *tuned* intake manifold is one in which the shape and length of each runner is similar and designed to establish optimum gas dynamics for engine breathing. A single box manifold supplied with boost air and EGR gas is usually all that is required on a turbocharged diesel to meet the engine's breathing requirements. Intake manifolds can either be wet (coolant ports) or dry, but dry tend to be used in truck and bus applications. Materials used are aluminum alloys, cast irons, poly-plastics, and carbon-based fibers.

When a tuned intake manifold is used in a boosted CI engine, it is designed to work with a tuned exhaust manifold and establish ideal gas dynamics for effective scavenging during valve overlap. In full authority, electronically managed engines, a thermistor is located in the intake manifold; this temperature sensor is often a primary reference for determining fuel-air ratio. Some OEMs use the term *tuned* to describe the mixing of boost air and EGR gas.

VALVE DESIGN AND BREATHING

Cylinder head valves were studied in some detail in Chapter 8, so our purpose here is to look at how they influence engine breathing. Most current diesel engines use multivalve configurations consisting of two inlet and two exhaust valves, but other arrangements, such as two inlet and one exhaust, are possible. Two basic breathing configurations are used for the more common four-valve cylinder heads, which are crossflow and parallel port.

CROSSFLOW CONFIGURATIONS

Up until the electronic era, most diesel engines used **crossflow valve configurations**. Crossflow breathing locates both sets of valves transversely, meaning that the flow of intake air to the inboard valve interferes with that from the outboard valve, creating turbulence. This is good if the objective is to maximize gas movement in the cylinder, which it was in older engines. Back in the days when diesel engines produced lower fuel injection pressures and were designed to maximize cylinder turbulence, crossflow four-valve configurations did the job. **Figure 12–29** compares crossflow with parallel port valve configurations.

PARALLEL PORT CONFIGURATIONS

Breathing efficiencies can be improved by using **parallel port valve configurations**, which permit each pair of cylinder valves to be responsible for an equal amount of gas flow without crossflow interference. Parallel port valve configuration improves both cylinder charging and scavenging, but requires a more complex camshaft assembly (or dual camshafts). It also reduces cylinder gas velocity and swirl effect. This is desirable in newer engines that use the **quiescent** combustion technology explained in Chapter 7.

FIGURE 12–29 Crossflow and parallel port valve configurations.

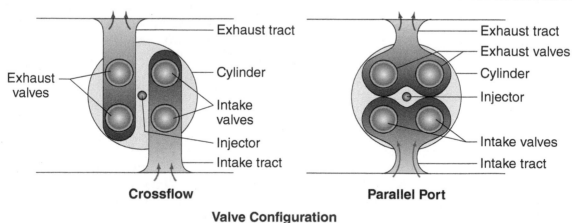

Valve Configuration

VALVE SEAT ANGLE

The valve seat angle also affects cylinder breathing. Valve seats in diesel engines are usually cut and machined at either 30 degrees or 45 degrees. Gas flow both into and out of the engine cylinder is generally around 20% greater using a 30-degree valve seat angle and the same lift as a 45-degree valve seat angle. However, 30-degree valves have less mass around the critical seat area, so they tend not to last as long. For this reason, 45-degree seats tend to be used more in diesel engines due to their higher seating force and distortion resistance. Sometimes both are used. If you have worked on a Volvo D13 engine, you might have observed that the intake valves are machined at a 30-degree seat angle while the (hotter running) exhaust valves are machined at a 45-degree angle.

VARIABLE VALVE TIMING

One of the strategies Caterpillar uses in its *advanced combustion and emissions reduction technology,* known as **ACERT**, is variable valve timing. In some Caterpillar engines using the ACERT system, intake valve closure can be delayed hydraulically (engine lube is the medium) by the ECM as an NO_x reduction strategy. This innovation allows the ECM to reduce the compression ratio and therefore the actual air quantity under certain operating conditions. The electronically controlled, hydraulically actuated **variable valve actuator (VVA)** assembly is mounted over the rocker assembly. Its operation can be directly compared with the actuation of engine brake cycles, which open the exhaust valves. **Figure 12–30** shows the VVA used on a Caterpillar ACERT C13 engine.

EXHAUST SYSTEM COMPONENTS

Because of the introduction of a complex array of exhaust aftertreatment devices in recent years, Chapters 47 and 48 in this textbook provide a more detailed study of emissions control equipment. This chapter limits itself to a brief look at emissions controls. Typically, an exhaust system is required to perform the following:

- Assist cylinder scavenging
- Minimize engine noise

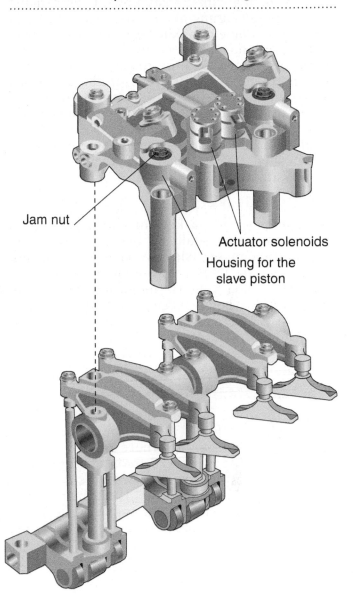

FIGURE 12–30 Variable valve actuator (VVA) used on a Caterpillar ACERT C13 engine.

Jam nut

Actuator solenoids

Housing for the slave piston

- Minimize engine noxious gas emission
- Exhaust heat, noise, and end gases safely to atmosphere

EXHAUST MANIFOLD

The exhaust manifold collects cylinder end gases from the cylinder head exhaust tracts and delivers them to the turbocharger. The exhaust manifold is usually manufactured in single or multiple sections of cast iron. Most diesel engine exhaust manifolds are "tuned" to deliver exhaust gas to the turbocharger with minimal and balanced flow resistance from each cylinder.

The term *tuned* is used to denote any exhaust system designed with at least a little consideration for the exhaust gas flow. If the exhaust manifold and piping are properly designed, as each slug of cylinder exhaust gas is discharged, it will not "collide" with that from another cylinder, but instead will be timed to unload into its tailstream. The pulsed manifolds discussed earlier in this section in the context of turbochargers are an example of a tuned exhaust system. Exhaust backpressure factors in a diesel engine are the turbocharger turbine assembly, the exhaust aftertreatment apparatus, and the engine silencer.

Manifold Gaskets

Exhaust manifold gaskets in truck/bus engine applications are usually of the embossed steel type, although occasionally fiber gaskets are used; they are usually installed dry. Note that embossed steel exhaust manifold gaskets are designed for one-off usage. When torqued into position, these gaskets are designed to yield (deform) to the two mating surfaces. Attempting to reuse them will almost certainly result in a leak sooner or later.

Tract and Manifold Insulation

One of the roles of the exhaust manifold is to route cylinder rejected heat to the turbine housing of the turbocharger, where it can be "recycled" by producing intake manifold boost. To achieve this at the highest efficiency, some OEMs have reduced heat losses by insulating both the exhaust tract and/or the exhaust manifold. The insulation usually consists of a stainless-steel liner.

Exhaust Heat Measurement

Although **pyrometers** are used in emissions control components, especially those built to meet 2007 emissions, they are not often used to signal exhaust gas temperature to the driver in any current highway diesel engines. In the older hydromechanical diesel engines of the 1980s and earlier, a pyrometer located 12 inches (30 cm) downstream from the turbine housing of the turbo was used as a means of alerting the driver to downshift when temperatures rose above a certain threshold. The practice of locating one pyrometer in the exhaust tract on each engine cylinder, to indicate cylinder balance, is used on larger diesels but seldom on highway commercial engines. A *pyrometer* is a thermocouple and its electrical principles are explained in Chapter 32.

DPFs require a method of accurately monitoring temperature. Pyrometers are one means of accomplishing this. DPFs may use several pyrometers—three is typical—to signal temperature conditions to either the ECM or the aftertreatment module. Another means of monitoring high temperatures is to use resistance thermometers. **Resistance temperature detectors (RTDs)** or *resistive thermal devices* measure the change in the electrical resistance of gases that occurs with temperature change. They are made of platinum, so these devices are commonly known as **platinum resistance thermometers (PRTs)**. RTDs can replace thermocouple-type pyrometers where temperatures do not exceed 1,100°F (600°C); this on the threshold of peak DPF temperatures, so some manufacturers have used these in place of pyrometers. There is some further explanation of RTDs in Chapter 34.

EXHAUST PIPING

Where mild steel piping, flex piping, and clamps are used, the steel is corrosion protected, usually by galvanizing (zinc coating). However, it is becoming more common to use stainless steels, which provide the exhaust system components with at least double the service life. Stainless-steel band clamps have been used for many years and are an effective means of sealing flex pipe to straight pipe, as they yield to shape at installation. Because they are stretched to yield (deform) at installation, they are not designed to be reused.

The function of exhaust piping is to collect the engine exhaust gases unloaded by the turbine housing and route them to the engine aftertreatment canister, from which they will discharge to atmosphere clear of the tractor cab structure and the trailer structure. If rain caps are used on vertical exit pipes, they should be mounted transversely, opening outward, away from the chassis. They should never be mounted longitudinally facing either forward or rearward, because this can adversely affect exhaust gas flow.

ENGINE EXHAUST AFTERTREATMENT

To meet EPA emissions standards, today's diesel engines have highly complex exhaust gas aftertreatment devices usually, but not always, housed within a single canister. Emissions control technology is the subject matter of Chapters 47 and 48, but at this point it is at least necessary to identify these components in the exhaust circuit. Typical exhaust gas treatment canisters may incorporate:

- A muffler or engine silencer
- A DPF
- An oxidation **catalytic converter**
- A reduction catalytic converter
- Clean air induction piping (routes "dead" gas back to intake)
- Selective catalytic reduction (aqueous urea injection)
- A diffuser (redirects DPF heat away from the trailer/ reefer, etc.)

The aftertreatment canister is equipped with many different sensors. Unlike an older exhaust system, the aftertreatment device is often manufactured by the engine OEM and *must* be replaced with an OEM-approved equivalent. Aftertreatment monitoring and management are performed electronically. In cases where a separate aftertreatment module is used, this is data bus networked to the ECM. Because aftertreatment systems are engine computer managed and part of the emissions control circuit, we will address them in some detail in Section 3 of this textbook. In this chapter, we address only the principles of a muffler or engine silencer on a diesel engine. The design of the aftertreatment canister attempts to minimize restriction in routing "clean" exhaust gas to atmosphere. A more complex, stanchion-mounted aftertreatment canister that uses its own module is shown in **Figure 12–31**. The operation and repair of these assemblies is explained in Chapters 47 and 48.

> ## CAUTION:
>
> It is illegal to tamper with emissions control hardware. Diesel exhaust aftertreatment canisters must be replaced with an OEM-approved equivalent that allows the engine to meet the emissions controls that prevailed in the year of the engine's manufacture.

SONIC EMISSIONS CONTROL

Sound is an energy form and it is produced in an engine by the firing pulses in engine cylinders. Sound energy from a running engine produces sonic nodes and antinodes at a frequency generally considered to be unpleasant to the human ear. The function of the silencer

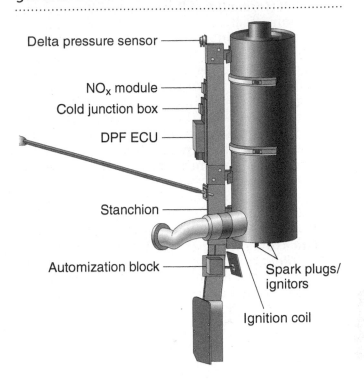

FIGURE 12–31 Stanchion-mounted, exhaust gas aftertreatment canister.

Delta pressure sensor

NO_x module

Cold junction box

DPF ECU

Stanchion

Automization block

Spark plugs/ ignitors

Ignition coil

or muffler is to modify the wavelength or frequency of engine noise to legally acceptable levels. Essentially, this process requires the scrambling of the frequency of the sonic nodes and antinodes produced by engine firing pulsations.

Before the tougher sonic emissions standards of the 1990s, a turbocharger in conjunction with piping design was in some cases able to meet the minimum sonic emissions standards, but this is no longer so. Pressure waves caused by the unloading of each slug of exhaust gas into the piping can have an amplifying effect on engine sound, and the turbocharger turbine housing is capable of smoothing these pressure waves and enabling a simpler muffler design.

Engine silencers use two basic principles to achieve their objective of dampening sound:

1. **Resonation**. Resonation requires reflecting sound waves back toward the source, thereby multiplying the number of sound emission points. Separate chambers connected by offset pipes as well as baffles are used to achieve the objective of scrambling the frequency of the engine's firing pulses. One of the reasons that the muffler section (usually the last section of the device) of

a post-2010 aftertreatment canister looks simpler is that the presence of DPF, catalytic converters, and SCR have a significant resonation effect.

2. **Sound absorption.** Exhaust gases pass through a perforated pipe enclosed in a canister filled with sound-absorbing material. Sound absorption involves converting sonic energy into heat by friction, and the efficiency of these devices depends on the packing density of the sound-absorbing media and the pipe perforation geometry. The media must be resistant to pressure pulsations and mechanical vibration; mineral and metal wools are used, most often basalt wool. Sound absorption mufflers generally have improved flow resistance characteristics over comparable resonator principle mufflers.

Muffler Volume

Muffler volume required in pre-2007 diesel engine systems was typically around five times the total cylinder exhaust slug discharge volume per cycle. Back then, the exhaust slug discharge volume was always somewhat greater than total swept volume in manifold-boosted diesel engines. This has changed due to the resonation effect of all that additional emission control hardware. The EPA MY 2007 is important because that was the year DPFs were mandated. Now there are no easy rules regarding muffler volume. In simple terms, mufflers used with post-2007 diesel engines are more compact and simpler in design than their predecessors because there is simply less noise to suppress after the exhaust has been routed through the aftertreatment circuit.

Diffusers

Because of the amount of heat generated by DPFs during regeneration cycles, it is necessary to fit a heat diffuser on stanchion-mounted, exhaust gas aftertreatment canisters. The heat diffuser simply redirects heat away from a trailing load that may be heat sensitive.

BREATHING CIRCUIT SENSORS

While we are not going to look at the operating principles of sensors until Chapter 34, we are going to identify those used in a typical

system. Both intake and exhaust circuits are comprehensively monitored in current diesel engines because of the need to manage emissions within statutory limits. The following is a list of sensors that may be found on a diesel engine and, in brackets, the electrical principles on which they operate. Many sensors on today's engines are multifunctional. That means they perform multiple tasks, so what appears to be one sensor may read both temperature and pressure.

- Ambient temperature (thermistor)
- Barometric pressure (variable capacitance)
- CAC in temperature
- CAC out temperature
- Boost circuit temperature (thermistor)
- Manifold boost pressure (variable capacitance or piezo-resistive)
- MAF (hot-wire or delta pressure differential)
- Turbocharger shaft speed (inductive pulse generator)
- Exhaust gas backpressure (variable capacitance)
- DPF in temperature (pyrometer or RTD)
- DPF combustion temperature (pyrometer or RTD)
- DPF out temperature (pyrometer or RTD)
- NO_x sensor (density)
- Aftertreatment canister mass flow (delta pressure sensor)

HOW DOES A VOLUTE WORK?

The word *volute* has been used a number of times in this chapter and students sometime struggle with understanding how it works. The following images should help. **Figure 12–32**

FIGURE 12–32 Operating principle of a variable volute turbocharger. The ability to vary the volute dimension is key to understanding how a VGT functions.

- VGT vanes work like the nozzle on a garden hose

- A narrower nozzle increases velocity so turbine speed and boost increase

- A wide open nozzle, velocity slows, so boost decreases along with exhaust backpressure

FIGURE 12–33 Vanes fully open: Volute flow area is largest, resulting in minimal restriction, highest flow, and lowest boost pressure.

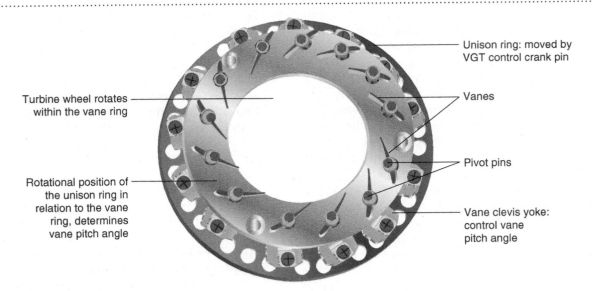

Turbine wheel rotates within the vane ring

Rotational position of the unison ring in relation to the vane ring, determines vane pitch angle

Unison ring: moved by VGT control crank pin

Vanes

Pivot pins

Vane clevis yoke: control vane pitch angle

shows how a variable volute operates and the resulting effect on manifold boost. The following is true of a variable volute:

- Nozzle fully open—produces the least restriction, the most flow, and the lowest pressure
- Nozzle nearly closed—produces the most restriction, the lowest flow, and the highest pressure

In a variable-geometry turbocharger, the vanes act similarly to the variable flow nozzle on the garden hose to manage boost pressures. In **Figure 12–33**, the vanes are fully open, so this produces the lowest manifold boost pressure. In **Figure 12–34**, the vanes are nearly closed (they are made so they are unable to completely close), so this produces the highest manifold boost pressure. Because the volute can be directly controlled by the ECM, boost can be precisely managed to suit every engine operating condition.

FIGURE 12–34 Vanes nearly closed (they never close completely: Volute flow area is smallest, resulting in higher restriction, lowest flow, and highest boost pressure.

SUMMARY

- Most current diesel engines use a dry, positive filter system.
- Trucks and equipment operated in environments with airborne particulates such as grain chaff dust, construction dust, and road dust should use a precleaner to extend air cleaner element service life.

- Dry, positive-type filters function at optimum efficiency just before their service life is completed.
- It is important not to overservice air filters, because every time the canister is opened, some dust will find its way downstream from the filter assembly and into the engine. Many

air filters will last for up to a year in a linehaul application.

- Air inlet restriction should be tested with a water manometer or negative pressure gauge. Onboard filter minders are a ballpark method of measuring inlet restriction and should not be relied on for accurate data.
- Charge air heat exchangers cool the turbo-boosted air charge, increasing its density. The result is more oxygen molecules packed into the intake charge delivered to the cylinder.
- Air-to-air charge air coolers boast higher cooling efficiencies than the liquid medium coolers, but must have adequate ram airflow. This makes them ideal for use in highway applications but not in high-load, low road speed vocational applications.
- Most current diesel engines use some type of EGR to dilute the intake charge with dead gas. Cooled-EGR (C-EGR) systems use engine coolant to reduce the temperature of exhaust gases before readmission to the engine.
- C-EGR and Caterpillar's clean gas induction (CGI) are ECM-managed with the objective of minimizing NO_x emissions. Both systems use mixing chambers to combine dead gas sourced from the exhaust system with boost air from the intake circuit.
- Valve configuration affects both the cylinder breathing efficiency and the cylinder gas dynamics.
- Parallel port valve configurations generally produce better and more balanced cylinder breathing efficiency, but result in lower cylinder turbulence. Lower cylinder turbulence may be desirable in some new engines.
- Valve seats cut at a 45-degree angle produce higher flow restriction and higher seating force than valves cut at a 30-degree angle, assuming identical lift.
- Turbochargers represent an exhaust backpressure factor, but their objective is to recapture some of the engine rejected heat by using it to pressurize the intake charge to the cylinders.

- Turbochargers are driven by the *heat* in the exhaust gas, so the more (rejected) heat, the faster the turbine speeds.
- Turbochargers in truck diesel engine applications may wind out at up to 150,000 rpm and have mean running speeds in the 70,000 to 80,000 rpm range.
- Truck diesel engine OEMs use wastegates and variable-geometry (VG) turbochargers to increase engine efficiency, minimize emissions, and reduce turbo lag.
- VG turbos may be managed internally by variable volute or externally by wastegates.
- Turbocharger radial and axial runouts should be routinely inspected at engine PM intervals.
- Some engines use series turbocharging, in which twin turbos are arranged in series with each other.
- Turbo compounding is another means of recapturing engine rejected heat. Exhaust gas heat drives a turbine, which connects to a viscous drive and reduction gearing so that drive torque can be imparted directly to the engine geartrain. Current compound turbochargers use constant geometry gas flow routing through the turbine housing.
- Hot shutdowns are a primary cause of turbocharger failures. After prolonged high-load operation, and especially after a dynamometer test, a cool-down period of at least 5 minutes is required.
- Sound is transmitted in sonic waves, producing nodes and antinodes. An exhaust silencer operates by scrambling (altering the frequency of) these nodes and antinodes, thereby altering the nature of the sound.
- Engine silencers use resonation and sound absorption principles to alter the frequency of the sound emitted from the engine; most use a combination of both principles.
- The exhaust aftertreatment canister on today's engines may contain a DPF, SCR system, oxidation and reduction catalytic converters, along with a muffler device.

REVIEW QUESTIONS

1. The tool of choice to accurately check the inlet restriction of a dry air filter would be a:
   a. mercury-filled manometer.
   b. trouble light.
   c. water-filled manometer.
   d. restriction gauge.

2. A typical maximum specified inlet restriction for an air filter on a turbocharged diesel would be:
   a. 25 inches H_2O restriction.
   b. 25 inches Hg (mercury) restriction.
   c. 25 psi.
   d. 25 kPa.

3. Which of the following types of air filters has the highest filtering efficiencies?
   a. Centrifugal precleaners
   b. Oil bath
   c. Dry, positive
   d. Dry, non-positive

4. Which of the following should be performed first when checking an engine that produces black smoke under load?
   a. Injection timing
   b. Plugged DPF
   c. Fuel quality by chemical lab analysis
   d. Air filter restriction test

5. Which of the following best describes the intended function of a C-EGR system on a diesel engine?
   a. It increases engine breathing efficiency.
   b. It dilutes the intake charge with cooled dead gas.
   c. It preheats the intake charge to the cylinder.
   d. It assists the turbocharger in boosting intake pressure.

6. Which of the following best describes the function of a wastegate in a current turbo-boosted diesel engine?
   a. Bleeds down intake boost air when excessively high
   b. Allows exhaust gas to bypass the turbine
   c. Adjusts the volute flow area
   d. Holds the exhaust valves open during low boost requirement

7. When series turbocharging is used on a current diesel engine, which of the following should be true?
   a. Intake air must pass through the turbine housing of both turbos.
   b. Exhaust gas must pass through the turbine housing of both turbos.
   c. The VG actuator is in series with the EGR mixer.
   d. Twin turbos are arranged in parallel.

8. What is the critical flow area managed by a VG turbo using a variable nozzle operating principle?
   a. Compressor diffuser
   b. Impeller inlet throat
   c. Turbine volute
   d. EGR gate

9. To produce peak manifold boost from a VN-type turbocharger, which of the following should be true?
   a. Vanes are in the nearly closed position.
   b. Vanes are in the fully open position.
   c. Wastegate is fully open.
   d. Wastegate is fully closed.

10. The constant geometry turbocharger used in a highway diesel engine with turbo compounding is usually designed to produce optimum efficiency at which rpm?
    a. Rated speed and load
    b. Top engine limit (TEL)
    c. Peak torque
    d. High idle

11. Technician A states that a dry air filter functions at optimum entrapment efficiency when it is new and that by the time it requires replacing, it has lower filtering efficiencies. Technician B states that oil bath filters are seldom used with today's highway diesel engines because they have low filtering efficiencies. Who is correct?
    a. Technician A only
    b. Technician B only
    c. Both A and B
    d. Neither A nor B

12. Technician A states that turbo-compounded diesel engines such as the Detroit Diesel DD15 use CG turbos to supply boost air to the intake manifold. Technician B states that turbo compounding allows the turbo to directly contribute drive torque to the engine drivetrain by means of reduction gearing. Who is correct?
    a. Technician A only
    b. Technician B only
    c. Both A and B
    d. Neither A nor B

13. Technician A states that the term *manifold boost* is used to describe breathing on a turbocharged engine. Technician B states that turbine speeds on truck diesel engines can exceed 100,000 rpm. Who is correct?
    a. Technician A only
    b. Technician B only
    c. Both A and B
    d. Neither A nor B

14. Technician A states that using a light bulb inside an air filter element is a reliable means of determining whether the filter is plugged. Technician B states that air filters are best left untouched between service intervals unless the filter restriction gauge indicates an out-of-specification reading. Who is correct?
    a. Technician A only
    b. Technician B only
    c. Both A and B
    d. Neither A nor B

15. Technician A states that the first item to be checked when an engine produces black smoke should be the air filter inlet restriction gauge. Technician B states that whenever an engine produces black smoke, the air filter should automatically be changed. Who is correct?
    a. Technician A only
    b. Technician B only
    c. Both A and B
    d. Neither A nor B

16. Which of the following methods would identify the location of a hole or tear in an air filter element?
    a. Lightbulb test
    b. Air inlet restriction gauge
    c. Manometer test
    d. Regulated air pressure test

17. When is a diesel engine turbocharger capable of highest rotational speeds?
    a. At peak engine rpm
    b. When rejected heat is greatest
    c. At peak torque
    d. When exhaust manifold pressure is greatest

18. Which of the following components would be located in a diesel exhaust gas after-treatment canister?
    a. DPF
    b. SCR
    c. Oxidation converter
    d. Any or all of the above

19. Which of the following best describes the function of a VG turbocharger?
    a. It behaves like a large turbocharger when engine load is high.
    b. It behaves like a small turbocharger when engine load is high.
    c. It reroutes NO_x back into the engine cylinders.
    d. It reroutes EGR gas into the DPF.

20. Technician A states that the function of a turbocharger wastegate is to divert exhaust gas around the turbine directly into the exhaust system. Technician B states that a wastegated turbocharger can improve turbine efficiencies at lower loads and rpms. Who is correct?
    a. Technician A only
    b. Technician B only
    c. Both A and B
    d. Neither A nor B

13

Prerequisites: Chapters 4 through 12. Some knowledge of the content of Sections 2 and 3 will also help.

ENGINE RETARDERS

OBJECTIVES

After studying this chapter, you should be able to:

- Identify some of the different types of engine brakes used on highway diesel engines.
- Describe the operating principles of each type of engine brake and the relative advantages and disadvantages of each.
- Outline the control mechanisms used to manage each type of retarder system.
- Interpret the electrical schematics used in the electronic and electric controls of engine brakes.
- Interpret a schematic representation of the hydraulic circuit of a typical internal engine compression brake.
- Describe how the hydraulic actuation of internal engine compression brakes is managed and timed.
- Outline the operating principles of some nonproprietary (Jacobs) and proprietary internal engine compression brakes.
- Explain how a progressive, multicylinder engine braking is managed.
- Describe the operation of a Mercedes-Benz constant throttle valve (CTV) brake.
- Describe how pneumatic controls can be used to manage external engine compression brakes.
- Explain how a Volvo EPG engine brake functions.

KEY TERMS

brake fade

coefficient of friction

CTV brake

exhaust brake

exhaust pressure governor (EPG)

external compression brake

Intebrake

internal compression brake

Jacobs brake

Jake brake

retarder

INTRODUCTION

Engine compression brakes are widely used on North American truck diesel engines. A large percentage of linehaul tractor trailer braking requires application pressures of 20 psi or less in a typical air brake system. This means that for the majority of vehicle braking requirements, less than a fifth of the air brake system's *peak* potential is being used. The objective of a supplementary brake system such as an engine compression brake is to relieve the vehicle braking system of some of the light-duty braking. This becomes especially important in instances that require prolonged light-duty braking, such as on an extensive downgrade.

The engine brakes examined in this chapter are those that are entirely dependent on the engine to achieve braking. The Caterpillar BrakeSaver was a flywheel-mounted hydraulic (engine oil) retarder used primarily in vocational trucks; it is no longer used in on-highway applications, but you can reference earlier editions of this book to study its operating principles. **Figure 13–1** shows an overhead view of a Jacobs engine brake on a Detroit Diesel Series 60 engine.

FIGURE 13–1 Overhead view of a typical Jacobs internal engine compression brake.

ENERGY CONVERSION IN AIR BRAKES

A typical truck braking system is air actuated and converts the kinetic energy (energy of motion) of the vehicle to heat energy. This takes place at the brake foundation assembly, and its mechanisms are drums (or rotors), brake shoes (or calipers), and an actuating apparatus that converts the potential energy of compressed air into mechanical force. When the brakes are applied, the friction facings on the brake shoes or calipers are loaded into a rotating drum or rotor and resultant resistance or friction retards the movement. The friction produces heat, so the brake system must be designed to sustain high temperatures and dissipate braking heat rapidly. The **coefficient of friction** describes the aggressiveness of friction materials. It is desirable to maintain a consistent coefficient of friction in foundation brake components, for obvious reasons.

However, coefficient of friction is altered by changes in temperature and the addition of a lubricant such as water. When foundation brake systems are subjected to the most amount of use, they are required to dissipate the most amount of heat to atmosphere. Failure to dissipate this heat can greatly increase foundation brake temperatures, causing both a reduction in the coefficient of friction of the critical friction surfaces at the shoe and drum and an expansion of the drum dimension. When a tractor-trailer combination has to run downhill for prolonged periods, even though brake application pressures are relatively light, excessively high foundation brake temperatures result, causing a reduction in braking efficiency at a time when it is most needed, a condition known as **brake fade**.

SUPPLEMENTARY BRAKE SYSTEMS

A supplementary braking system such as an engine compression brake or driveline retarder can support the main vehicle braking system, enhance peak braking performance, and automatically reduce some of the driver-actuated braking. The engine compression brake on which most current versions are modeled was invented by Clessie Cummins after he had officially retired from his position as chief executive officer (CEO) of the company that bears his name. The Jacobs Manufacturing Company, perhaps better known for its drill chucks in those days, has manufactured engine compression brakes since its introduction of Cummins's first engine brake in the late 1950s. Jacobs manufactures an engine brake for almost every highway diesel engine and, in doing so, has established universal brand identification. Today, the term "Jake brake" is used by many drivers to refer to any engine compression brake.

Trucks have also hydraulic retarders, which may be located anywhere in the driveline, but can be integral with the engine (the legacy Caterpillar BrakeSaver is an example) or transmission. Hydraulic driveline retarders use a torque absorption principle that can be compared to that used in a torque converter. Electric driveline retarders are also currently available, and one of them is marketed by Jacobs.

RETARDING PRINCIPLE

The term **retarder** can be applied to any component or system that affects braking action—that is, retards or slows motion. However, the primary vehicle braking system is seldom referred to as a vehicle retarder system, whereas engine compression brakes and driveline brakes are commonly described as retarders. Compression and driveline brakes do no more than supplement the primary braking system: The retarding powerflow is necessarily confined to those axles directly linked to the drivetrain, that is, through the wheels on the drive axles. The objective of the engine brake system is identical to that of the main vehicle braking system: namely, converting the energy of vehicle motion to heat energy. In the engine compression brake, kinetic energy (that of vehicle motion) is converted first to the potential energy of compressed air and then released into the exhaust system as heat.

BRAKE CYCLE CONTROLS

With the increased use of electronics in truck chassis systems, the way engine brake cycles are managed has changed considerably over the past few years. In older systems, control of the brake retarding cycle was left entirely to the driver, whereas in computer-controlled systems the chassis management electronics are playing an ever-larger role. An obvious use of a computer-controlled engine brake is by the cruise control system to help maintain a consistent road speed.

Multiplexing is now a factor for almost every truck on the road and this has opened the door for more widespread bus-message "requests" for engine braking from collision warning, lane tracking, and accident avoidance electronics. Engine braking makes sense both from safety and maintenance perspectives. It has become much more than a way of extending foundation brake, friction face service life.

PRINCIPLES OF OPERATION

The term *engine brake* can be used to describe retarder devices that use three distinct operating principles:

1. Internal engine compression brakes
2. External engine compression brakes
3. Hydraulic engine brakes

INTERNAL ENGINE COMPRESSION BRAKES

In the four-stroke cycle diesel engine, the piston is required to:

- Perform work (compression stroke)
- Receive work (power stroke)

On its upward travel during the compression stroke, the piston compresses the cylinder air charge. This is immediately followed by the power stroke, during which the piston is forced downward through its downstroke by expanding cylinder gases. For an engine to continue turning over, the work received by a piston during the power stroke must exceed the work it has to perform during the compression stroke. Back in Chapter 4 we learned that this net gain is what we describe as mean effective pressure, or MEP. Internal engine brakes use the MEP equation to change the role of the engine.

The **internal compression brake** operates by making the piston perform all of its usual work of compressing the air charge on the compression stroke. Then, just as the power stroke is about to take place, it releases cylinder pressure by opening the exhaust valves. This has the effect of negating (canceling) the power stroke by releasing the compressed cylinder gases to the exhaust system (gas blowdown) somewhere around top dead center (TDC). An internal engine compression brake reverses the normal engine function, converting it from an energy-producing pump to an energy-absorbing compressor.

All engine compression brakes use this principle of operation; the mechanisms used to actuate, time, and control the brakes vary. The braking powerflow of the vehicle begins at the drive axle wheels, extends through the transmissions and drive shafts, through the engine powertrain, and the kinetic energy is converted to pressure; the potential energy of the compressed air is then dumped into the exhaust system. Braking efficiencies are highest when engine rpm is highest.

EXTERNAL ENGINE COMPRESSION BRAKES

The operating principle of the **external compression brake** is not that different from the internal compression brake. External engine compression brakes are also known as **exhaust brakes**. They consist of a housing located downstream from the turbine housing discharge in the exhaust system, or they are integrated into the turbine housing of the turbocharger. The principle is simple. Inside the exhaust brake housing is a valve that, when actuated, chokes off the exhaust discharge. The result is that the piston, on its exhaust stroke, is being made to perform compressive work. Restricting exhaust gas flow in this way once again reverses the role of the engine, converting it into an energy-absorbing pump. However, in the internal engine compression brake, the effective pumping stroke is the compression stroke, whereas in the exhaust brake, the effective retarding stroke becomes the exhaust stroke. Therefore, as each succeeding exhaust slug is unloaded into the exhaust manifold, the pressure rises and braking efficiency increases.

Retarding efficiency is to some extent diminished by pressure loss to the intake during valve overlap. Operation of the exhaust brake is managed so that the engine is not fueled during braking; as with the internal engine compression brake, braking efficiencies are highest when the engine rpm is in its higher range. In many current diesel engines, retarding efficiencies are increased by combining internal and external engine compression brakes. This means that both upward strokes of the piston are "braking" strokes. In this way, many current engines are able to absorb (during retarding cycles) nearly as much power as they are capable of producing—at least when engine rpm are close to rated speed.

CONTROL CIRCUITS

Engine brakes typically use driver-actuated electrical control switches mounted on the dash. They may also be actuated by a message request from the chassis data bus. Depending on the chassis, the message request can come from anti-rollover electronics, smart cruise control, or potentially any other chassis electronic system that wants to brake the vehicle.

Whether actuated by an electromechanical switch or by controller logic, an electrical circuit is required to activate solenoids on the cylinder braking assembly. Solenoids then use engine lube as the hydraulic medium to control the actuators required by the brake circuit. Because electrical signals control engine brake operation, retarding cycles may occur in three different ways:

- Electromechanically switched by direct driver command
- Switched by the ECM using internal logic, such as in a smart cruise application
- Switched by request from other modules on the data bus, such as in an antirollover strategy

Electro-Hydromechanical

When engine brakes are used in hydromechanically managed engines, the switching of the engine brake is usually electrical, but the retarding effect must be actuated either hydraulically or pneumatically. In such engines, a control circuit requires that a series of switches be closed before engine braking can be effected. The first of this series of switches would be the driver control switch, which can be proportional depending on the system. In a proportional engine brake system, typical driver options are:

- Off
- Low: two-cylinder retarding
- Medium: four-cylinder retarding
- High: six-cylinder retarding

Once the dash switch has been closed, the next switch in the series is located at the clutch. The clutch must be fully engaged to operate engine braking, so the clutch switch closes when the clutch pedal is in the fully released position. The third essential switch in the series (though any number of others may be installed) ensures that the accelerator pedal is fully released: In other words, engine fueling is at zero (all engines since 1994) or at least at a minimum (i.e., idle fuel) in engines before 1994. The objective is to limit the quantity of raw fuel dumped into the exhaust system and into the atmosphere. Since 1994, federal regulations have prohibited the discharge of uncombusted fuel to atmosphere.

Electronic Management

Today's engines all use ECM control of engine brake cycles. The driver may still have the option of switching the engine brake on or off, but depending on the system the engine may manage braking cycles in ways that the driver may be entirely unaware of. Because many of today's engine brakes option many different levels of power absorption, they can be used to complement cruise control logic and be made to work in conjunction with data bus-driven strategies such as yaw (directional stability) and antirollover electronics. Although today's engine brakes are electronically managed, the outcomes may be electrically, pneumatically (chassis system air pressure), and hydraulically (engine lube) actuated.

EXHAUST BRAKES

As indicated earlier, most external engine compression brakes use the same general operating principles. What differentiates them is how they are switched. Switching may be classified as:

- Electromechanical initiated by the driver
- Electronic initiated by the ECM

In most modern vehicles, external engine brakes are used in addition to the engine internal compression brake; they are therefore switched "electronically."

Actuation Circuit

Control of the brake hardware is typically electric-over-pneumatic, as shown in **Figure 13–2**. If the switching circuit on the vehicle is electromechanical, the electrical circuit required to actuate the engine brake consists of three switches, all of which must be closed: a control switch (dash mounted), a clutch switch (clutch must be fully engaged), and an accelerator switch (accelerator must be at zero travel). If the switching is electronic, then the conditions that determine a braking cycle are based on ECM logic or by a request from the chassis data bus.

Operating Principle

The hardware that is used to brake the vehicle usually consists of a sliding gate that under normal engine operation remains retracted. However, when activated, the sliding gate chokes off exhaust gas flow, creating massive backpressure which the engine pistons on their exhaust stroke have to overcome.

The sliding gate exhaust brake uses a pneumatically activated gate. The brake solenoid is supplied by chassis system air pressure. The air supply to close the gate is controlled by an electrically switched pilot valve. An aperture in the sliding gate permits a minimal flow through the brake gate during engine braking. The butterfly valve version operates similarly (**Figure 13–3** and **Figure 13–4**).

Engine Warmup Mode

An external engine brake can also be used as a means of warming the engine more quickly.

FIGURE 13–2 Control and actuation circuits on mechanical and electronic exhaust brakes. When actuated, the retarding force is the exhaust stroke of the piston.

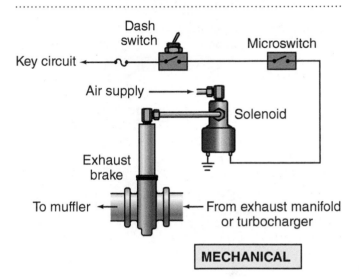

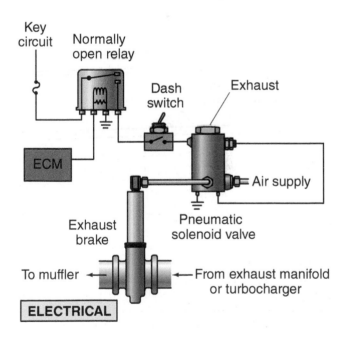

The backpressure created when it is activated retains heat in the engine rather than discharging it in the exhaust. This feature is only available on more recent electronically controlled external engine brakes.

EXHAUST PRESSURE GOVERNOR

Volvo Trucks have used what they call an **exhaust pressure governor (EPG)** on their engines. These use the principles of exhaust engine brakes as described earlier, specifically the choking down on exhaust flow downstream

FIGURE 13–3 Layout of an exhaust brake on a V-configured engine.

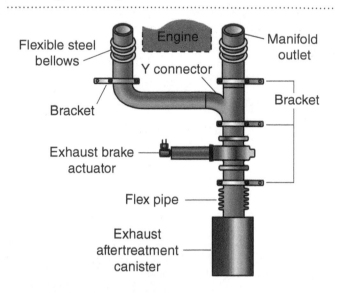

FIGURE 13–4 Exhaust brake components.

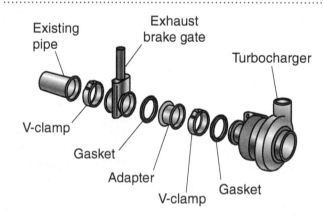

from the turbocharger. The EPG doubles as an engine warmup device because of the high back-pressure created by choking of the exhaust flow during actuation. The Volvo EPG is integrated downstream from the turbine housing of the turbocharger, as shown in **Figure 13–5**.

INTERNAL COMPRESSION BRAKES

In approaching the operation of internal engine compression brakes, we will take a look at an electrical-over-hydraulic engine brake, followed by a couple of more recent examples of electronically managed versions. The power absorption equation is the same in all internal engine

FIGURE 13–5 Volvo's exhaust pressure governor (EPG) variation of an exhaust brake; the EPG is mounted directly to the turbine housing of the turbocharger.

compression brakes regardless of how they are managed:

Drive axle tires to *chassis drivetrain* to *engine crankshaft* to *piston* (on compression stroke)

JACOBS BRAKES

People in the trucking industry use the term **Jake brake** to refer to any internal engine compression brake because, for a number of years, this manufacturer dominated the marketplace by designing its engine brakes for most of the major original equipment manufacturers (OEMs). There were other manufacturers of similar devices, but that did not stop all such devices from being referred to as Jake brakes. Today, Jacobs has partnerships with most of the engine manufacturers and engineers its product into OEM engines as standard equipment: Cummins Intebrake and the DTNA Detroit Diesel DD family of engines (Integrated Brake) use Jacobs engineered internal compression brakes.

Operating Principle

As an internal engine compression brake, a **Jacobs brake** operates by having the piston perform its usual work of compressing the cylinder air charge on the compression stroke and then negating the power stroke by opening the exhaust valves somewhere around TDC and releasing the cylinder compressed air to the exhaust. Jacobs engine brakes use electric switching of a hydraulic actuating circuit, so they adapt readily to electronic management, and have been used as an integral component in "smart" cruise control and external systems that make requests for engine braking over the chassis data.

Jacobs brakes hydraulically actuate the opening of the exhaust valve(s) in the engine cylinder performing the braking. The manner in which this hydraulic circuit is timed and actuated varies with the engine; however, the mechanical force required to actuate the hydraulic circuit

is typically provided by the engine camshaft. This means that the timing of the exhaust valve opening is also governed by cam profile: either the injector actuating cam profile or that on an adjacent exhaust valvetrain.

An example of an engine brake actuated by movement from an adjacent exhaust valve is shown in **Figure 13–6**. When you study this illustration, note that the image shows two different rocker arms. In this circuit, once oil is trapped in the engine brake hydraulic circuit, the master piston is forced inboard by exhaust

FIGURE 13–6 Jacobs compression brake schematic (on Caterpillar or Mack) and operating description.

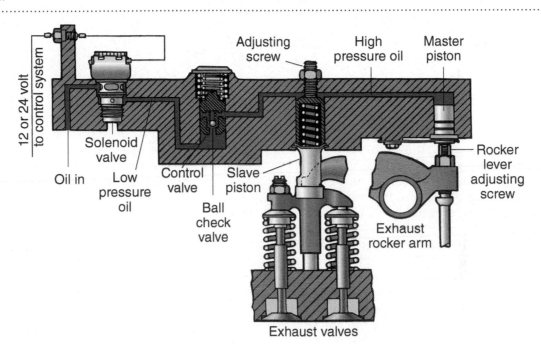

The blowdown of compressed air to atmospheric pressure prevents the return of energy to the engine piston on the expansion stroke, resulting in a net energy loss since the work done in compressing the cylinder charge is not returned during the expansion process.

Exhaust blowdown of the braking cylinder is accomplished by utilizing the pushrod motion of an exhaust valve of another cylinder during its normal exhaust cycle as follows:

1. Energizing the solenoid valve directs engine oil to flow under pressure through the control valve to both the master piston and the slave piston.

2. Oil pressure moves the master piston downward to bottom on the corresponding exhaust rocker arm adjusting screw.

3. The exhaust rocker pushrod begins upward travel (as in normal exhaust cycle), forcing the master piston upward and directing high pressure oil to the slave piston of the braking cylinder. The ball check in the control valve traps high pressure oil in the master/slave piston circuit.

4. The slave piston is forced downward by oil pressure, momentarily opening the exhaust valves while the engine piston is close to top dead center, releasing compressed cylinder air to the exhaust manifold.

5. Compressed air is discharged to atmosphere, completing a compression braking cycle.

The level of engine braking is controlled by using the solenoid to turn each housing ON or OFF. The above figure shows the relationships between master pistons, slave pistons, and control valves within the housing.

FIGURE 13-7 Jacobs brake on a Mack E-Tech engine.

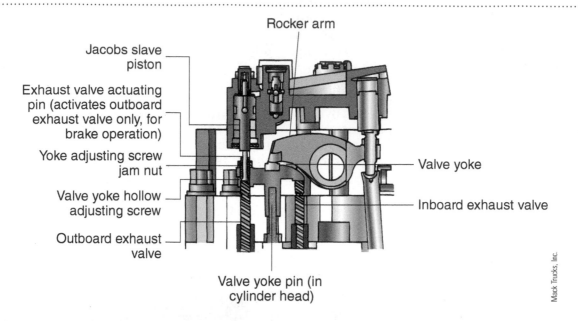

rocker upward (opening) movement that creates pressure rise. Pressure in the engine brake actuation circuit acts on the sectional area of the slave piston, which in turn acts on the exhaust valve bridge on the cylinder being braked. The slave piston thereby forces the valve bridge downward, opening both exhaust valves, dumping cylinder pressure created by the piston compression stroke.

Figure 13-7 and **Figure 13-8** show, respectively, sectional and exploded views of the hardware of a typical internal engine compression brake. Remember that all internal engine compression brakes use the same general principles despite minor differences in the hardware. **Figure 13-9** shows the setup of a Jacobs brake used on Mack Trucks E-Tech engines up to 2007. Since 2007, Volvo and Mack Trucks common platform engines use an in-house designed engine brake, but the operating principles have not changed. **Figure 13-10** and **Figure 13-11** show overhead and side views of typical Jacobs brake fixtures.

CATERPILLAR COMPRESSION BRAKE

Caterpillar has used an in-house design of engine compression brakes on its C11 and C13 family of electronic unit injector (EUI)-fueled engines. We will reference **Figure 13-12** in outlining the operating principles of this device. The Cat compression brake sources engine oil to use as the hydraulic actuation medium from around the studs of the rocker shaft pedestals. The actuator valve (see Figure 13-12 #5) controls oil flow in the compression brake housing. When the control valve is switched by the ECM, oil at lube system pressure passes from the actuator spool supply port (Figure 13-12 P) to the actuation port (Figure 13-12 A). The resulting oil flow opens the check valve (Figure 13-12 #1) and passes into the high-pressure oil passage (Figure 13-12 #2): This routes oil to both the slave (Figure 3-12 #7) and master pistons (Figure 13-12 #4).

As oil pressure overcomes the spring (Figure 13-12#8), the master piston moves toward the injector rocker arm, which is in its unactuated position (base circle): Oil charges the circuit between the master and slave pistons. When the injector rocker train ramps off base circle, the master piston is driven into the high-pressure oil circuit, closing the check valve (traps oil in the circuit) and actuating the slave piston. This results in the opening of the exhaust valves, dumping the compressed air from the compression stroke into the exhaust.

PROGRESSIVE STEP ENGINE BRAKING

Engine braking can be used most effectively when the greatest number of levels (steps) of braking is available. Over the years, engine OEMs realizing the potential of the engine brake

FIGURE 13–8 Exploded view of Jacobs compression brake components.

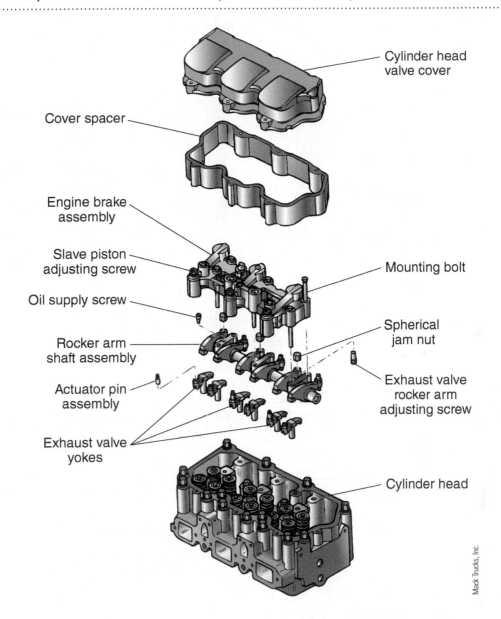

Cylinder head valve cover

Cover spacer

Engine brake assembly

Slave piston adjusting screw

Oil supply screw

Mounting bolt

Rocker arm shaft assembly

Spherical jam nut

Actuator pin assembly

Exhaust valve rocker arm adjusting screw

Exhaust valve yokes

Cylinder head

Mack Trucks, Inc.

have increased its versatility. Today, instead of on/off and/or two-stage retarding, up to six stages of progressive braking are available, sometimes using a combination of internal and external engine braking. We will take a look at two generations of the 15-liter Cummins ISX to examine how engine braking has adapted to significant changes in engine design to enable brake power absorption to equal the power rating of the engine at 600 BHP (447 kW).

ISX with HPI-TP

The pre-2010 Cummins ISX with the HPI fuel system had six-step engine braking. This meant that under a braking cycle, one cylinder progressing to all six can be used. Cummins called this **Intebrake** and it was achieved using engine oil as the hydraulic medium and three solenoids.

When one cylinder is selected for braking, only the solenoid between cylinders 1 and 2 (S1) is energized. The solenoid between 2 and 3 (S2) actuates, braking for cylinders 2 and 3. The solenoid between cylinders 4 and 5 actuates engine braking on cylinders 4, 5, and 6 (S3). **Table 13–1** shows how the Intebrake progressive braking is effected.

Cummins Intebrake departed from the slave and master pistons used by previous engine brakes. This provided both the driver and engine

FIGURE 13–9 Sectional view of Jacobs engine brake components.

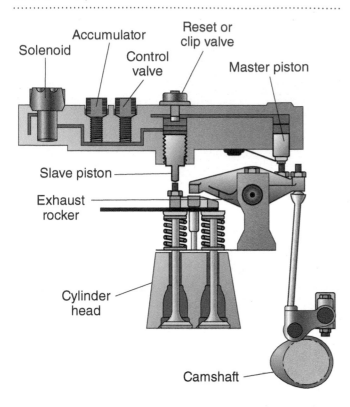

FIGURE 13–10 Overhead view of a Jacobs internal engine compression brake in which solenoids manage hydraulic force to actuate the retarding cycle.

electronics with an increased range of retarding options, reducing the occurrence of cam train–related engine-braking problems.

ISX with XPI

The post-2010 Cummins ISX was re-engineered for a common rail fuel system known as XPI.

FIGURE 13–11 Side view of a Jacobs engine compression brake cylinder head fixture.

This redesign eliminated one of the two overhead camshafts on the earlier ISX. Cummins moved to a two-solenoid system (permitting two-stage braking of the internal compression brake) and added an exhaust brake (external compression) and integrated it into the turbocharger. The redesign simplified engine brake cycles and permitted both upstrokes of the piston (compression and exhaust) to be retarding strokes.

CONSTANT THROTTLE VALVES

Mercedes-Benz (Daimler NA) used a variation on the internal engine compression brake called the continuously open throttle valve or **CTV brake** on its MB-900 and MB-4000 engines up until 2010. Small valves (the CTVs) are fitted into the engine cylinder head. These valves allow some cylinder leakage to the exhaust during both the compression and exhaust strokes. The result is that although some braking ability is lost, the engine brake is considerably quieter than comparable systems that use the exhaust valves to dump compression gas into the exhaust system. A CTV is fitted to each engine cylinder and the system is managed electrohydraulically, using engine oil as the medium. When activated, the CTVs remain open throughout the braking cycle. Actuation of the CTV brake requires that the accelerator pedal be at zero travel and the clutch be fully engaged. The system is designed to cease retarding when engine rpm drops below 1,100 rpm (factory preset), but this value can be reprogrammed up or down depending

FIGURE 13–12 Operation of a Caterpillar C13 internal engine compression brake.

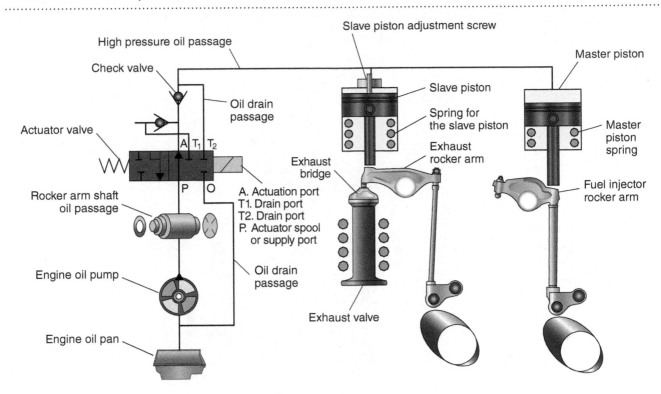

on application. **Figure 13–13** shows an MB-906 CTV.

When the CTV circuit is actuated on the compression stroke, the CTV permits cylinder compressed air to bleed through the valve into the exhaust circuit. By the time the piston moves away from TDC at the completion of the compression stroke, most of the compression charge has been dumped into the exhaust circuit. **Figure 13–14** will help guide you through the following explanation. After the electrical

TABLE 13–1 ISX Intebrake Stepped Braking Options

No. of Braked Cylinders	Solenoids Energized	Actual Braked Cylinder Number	Percentage of Total Braking
1	S1	1	17
2	S2	2 and 3	33
3	S3	4, 5, and 6	50
4	S1 and S3	1, 4, 5, and 6	67
5	S2 and S3	2, 3, 4, 5, and 6	83
6	S1, S2, and S3	1, 2, 3, 4, 5, and 6	100

FIGURE 13–13 Location of a CTV on the engine.

FIGURE 13–14 Components in a CTV engine brake on an EUP-fueled engine.

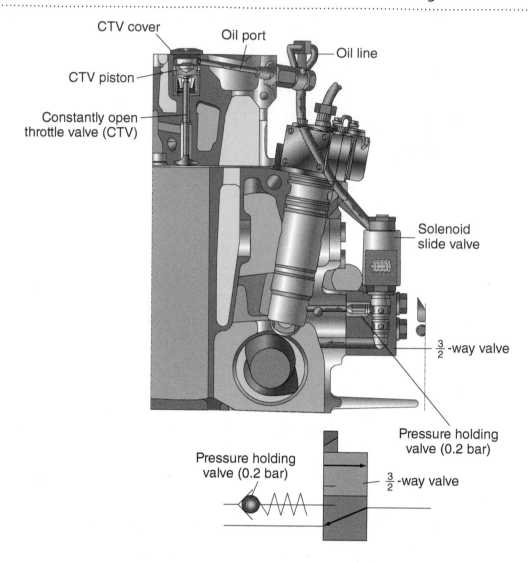

actuation of the solenoid slide valve by the control module, the 3/2-way valve spool opens, allowing engine oil to be directed into the cylinder head to each CTV, holding each open. Unintentional closure (fluttering) of the CTV by cylinder backpressure is prevented by a pressure-holding valve. To take the system out of the braking cycle, the solenoid slide valve is de-energized, closing the oil supply at the 3/2 valve spool and routing the oil back to the sump. This causes oil pressure in the pressure chambers above the CTV pistons to collapse, and the CTVs close to seal the cylinder by spring force. The normal engine cycle resumes at this point.

The constant throttle valve retarder is internal engine compression braking with a difference. By not using the engine camshaft to manage the engine braking, camshaft problems associated with engine braking are eliminated. The system is also notably quiet in operation.

OTHER INTERNAL RETARDERS

Although they may be referred to as Jake brakes, there are other internal engine compression brakes available on diesel engines marketed in North America, many of them manufactured offshore. More OEMs today are using two-stage engine brakes on their current engine families:

FIGURE 13–15 Schematic of how an engine brake communicates on the chassis data bus (J1939) and to the chassis controller (SAM) on a current Freightliner multiplexed chassis with DD power.

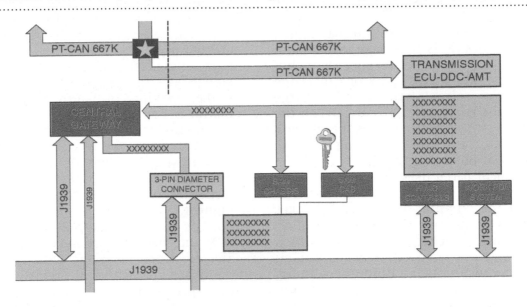

This combines an internal engine compression brake with an exhaust brake that can be classified as an internal/external engine retarder. Any engine brake described as an internal engine compression brake uses almost identical principles, so the only factor that changes is the means of managing the braking cycle. For instance, the engine electronics are increasingly used to control engine retarding.

> ## TECH TIP:
>
> Engine brake operation can be tough on camshafts on some engines, especially older ones. Where there are low power complaints and repeated top-end adjustments are required on an engine, suspect camshaft failure and check cam lift to specifications.

BUS REQUESTS TO ENGINE BRAKES

Electronic retarder cycles are managed by the ECM. Because the ECM has an address on the powertrain bus, any other controller with an address on the bus can request an engine braking cycle. A common example is the Wingman radar electronics, which can broadcast requests to use the engine brake for smart cruise control and accident avoidance strategy. **Figure 13–15** shows how the engine brake is networked into both the powertrain (J1939) and chassis controller (CAN) networks on a fully multiplexed Freightliner truck. This type of multiplexing transaction will be studied in more detail in Chapter 37.

SUMMARY

- Engine brakes are designed to complement the main vehicle brake system, not replace it.
- An engine compression brake's ability to absorb energy is low compared to the brake capacity of the vehicle; however, a large percentage of vehicle braking uses less than one-fifth of the total vehicle capacity, so engine brakes can greatly extend the life of the vehicle foundation brakes.
- Engine brake cycles can be managed either by electromechanical (dash) switches or electronically.
- Most engine brakes are controlled by an electric circuit which requires that a series of switches be closed. At minimum, the control switch, a clutch switch (driveline disengagement), and an accelerator (idle validation) or governor switch must be closed.

- Internal engine compression brakes use the electric control circuit to manage the brake's hydraulic circuit that uses engine oil as the actuation medium.
- The operating principle of an internal engine compression brake is to make the piston perform the work of compressing the cylinder air charge and then negate or cancel the power stroke by releasing the cylinder charge by opening the exhaust valves at TDC on the compression stroke. This changes the engine's role from that of a power-producing pump to that of a power-absorbing pump.
- The mechanical force used to time and actuate the hydraulic circuit of a Jacobs-type internal engine compression brake is rocker movement. This may be the movement of an injector actuation rocker, or in cases in which hydraulic injectors are used, movement of an exhaust valve rocker over a different cylinder.
- Engine external or exhaust compression brakes operate by choking down the exhaust flow: The retarding stroke of the piston is therefore the exhaust stroke.
- Exhaust brake cycles are managed electronically (ECM) or electrically (dash switches) and actuated pneumatically, hydraulically, or electrically.
- Some engines use an internal engine compression brake in conjunction with an exhaust brake, enabling both upward strokes of the piston to be retarding strokes. This increases engine braking capacity significantly.
- The Volvo EPG exhaust brake may also be used to speed the engine warmup cycle.
- All engine retarders operate at optimum efficiency when engine rotational speeds are highest.
- Today's engine brakes are managed by the ECM and therefore are in communication with any electronic systems with an address on the bus. This means that retarding cycles can be requested by other controllers on the bus, such as Wingman radar electronics.

REVIEW QUESTIONS

1. Which type of engine brake uses the compression stroke of the piston as its retarding stroke?
   a. Internal compression brake
   b. External compression brake
   c. Hydraulic retarder
   d. Volvo EPG

2. Which type of engine brake uses the exhaust stroke of the piston as its retarding stroke?
   a. Internal compression brake
   b. External compression brake
   c. Hydraulic retarder

3. Technician A states that the Cummins Intebrake on pre-2010 ISX is capable of optioning engine braking on just one engine cylinder. Technician B states that the Cummins Intebrake on post-2010 ISX functions as both an internal and external engine compression brake. Who is correct?
   a. Technician A only
   b. Technician B only
   c. Both A and B
   d. Neither A nor B

4. The effective braking cycle on most internal engine compression brakes fitted to hydromechanical engines is actuated by using which of the following sequences?
   a. Electric-over-hydraulic
   b. Electric-over-pneumatic
   c. Pneumatic-over-hydraulic
   d. Hydraulic-over-electric

5. When will any kind of engine brake usually operate at peak efficiency?
   a. At idle rpm
   b. At peak torque rpm
   c. At rated speed rpm
   d. At the highest rpm

6. Technician A states that on most internal engine compression brakes, the effective braking stroke of the piston is the compression stroke. Technician B states that on some engine brake systems, both the compression and exhaust strokes can deliver retarding force. Who is correct?
   a. Technician A only
   b. Technician B only
   c. Both A and B
   d. Neither A nor B

7. The operating principle of an internal engine compression brake is to convert the engine into an:
   a. energy-absorbing compressor
   b. energy-releasing machine
   c. inertia-absorbing device
   d. inertia-producing device

8. The energy of vehicle motion is ultimately converted to what energy form when an engine compression brake is used?
   a. Kinetic energy
   b. Heat energy
   c. Chemical energy
   d. Potential energy

9. Technician A states that the force used to actuate the hydraulic circuit in a typical Jacobs brake is delivered by an electrically actuated solenoid. Technician B states that Jacobs brake solenoids act as a pilot switch to control oil flow to the hydraulic actuation circuit. Who is correct?
   a. Technician A only
   b. Technician B only
   c. Both A and B
   d. Neither A nor B

10. When an internal engine compression brake is actuated, where does gas blowdown occur?
    a. At valve overlap
    b. Close to BDC following the power stroke
    c. At the beginning of the exhaust stroke
    d. Close to TDC at the completion of the compression stroke

11. Which of the following engine brakes offers progressive step braking using from one to all six cylinders?
    a. Cummins Intebrake on pre-2010 ISX
    b. Mercedes-Benz CTV
    c. Mack Trucks Jacobs on E-Tech
    d. Flywheel hydraulic retarders

12. What vehicle technology enables nonengine controllers to request engine braking cycles?
    a. Electromechanical switches
    b. Multiplexing
    c. Smart switches
    d. Electrohydraulics

14

Prerequisites: Chapters 10, 11, and 12

SERVICING AND MAINTENANCE

OBJECTIVES

After studying this chapter, you should be able to:

- Explain why it is sometimes important to connect to a chassis data bus even when performing routine service work.
- Outline the precautions to observe when breaking in a new or reconditioned diesel engine.
- Use the correct method to start up a diesel engine.
- Service a diesel engine air intake system.
- Identify the appropriate oil to use in a diesel engine.
- Identify the steps required to perform an engine service.
- Perform an engine oil and filter change.
- Mix and test coolant and service an engine cooling system.
- Identify the appropriate fuel and refuel/prime a diesel engine.
- Respond to a water-in-fuel alert and service a water separator.
- Service and replenish an SCR system with DEF.
- Identify when it is appropriate to service a DPF.

KEY TERMS

active code

biodiesel

dash display unit (DDU)

diesel exhaust fluid (DEF)

diesel particulate filter (DPF)

ethylene glycol (EG)

pre-delivery inspection (PDI)

propylene glycol (PG)

restriction gauge

selective catalytic reduction (SCR)

service information system (SIS)

service literature

ultra low sulfur diesel (ULSD)

water-in-fuel (WIF)

wet service

INTRODUCTION

Today, many OEMs prefer that a data bus connection be made with the chassis data bus as a first step to routine servicing. This connects the vehicle with the manufacturer data hub and a report card on the vehicle is established. This chapter will take a brief generic look at servicing and maintenance, but there is no substitute for using the vehicle manufacturer's service literature when undertaking maintenance procedures on the shop floor. When undertaking any kind of service work on today's vehicles, it makes sense to check if there are any **active codes** before servicing the vehicle. Some current vehicles also carry a data log with an address on the chassis data bus. The data log can be used to track maintenance, service, and warranty information, so it should be referenced each time service work is undertaken.

The objective of this chapter is to briefly outline some typical maintenance practices as they apply to diesel-powered trucks. One of the key elements of this chapter is familiarization with the procedure required to perform what is known as a **wet service** on a commercial vehicle. Wet service is a slang term for an oil and filter change.

SERVICE LITERATURE AND DIAGNOSTIC SOFTWARE

In this text, the term *electronic service tool* (EST) will be used to reference any data bus access tool, whether it is a scan tool or PC-based.

When PC-based diagnostic software is used in conjunction with an online link to the manufacturer's data hub, the technician always has access to the latest information pertinent to a service or repair procedure, along with a log specific to the vehicle being worked on providing alerts to recalls. Full coverage of diagnostic software and online **service information system (SIS)** is provided in Chapter 35. In this chapter, the term **service literature** will be used to represent service information, whether that information is available in electronic or hard-copy format. **Figures 14–1** through **14–4** show some different examples of launch and options fields for different types of service software.

FIGURE 14–1 Older soft-copy work order launch screen.

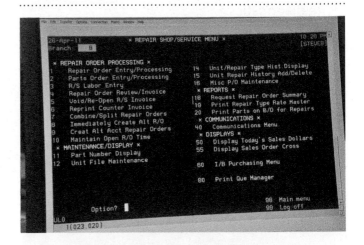

FIGURE 14–2 Tracking data entry fields used on an electronic copy work order launch screen.

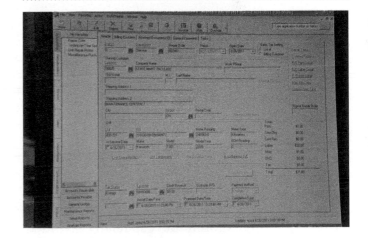

FIGURE 14–3 Windows environment soft-copy work order launch screen.

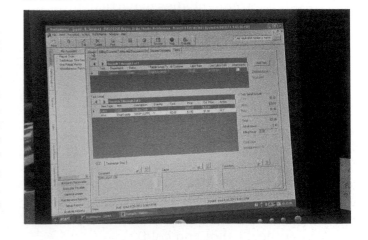

FIGURE 14-4 Cummins electronic service literature; this shows an options screen for InSite diagnostics.

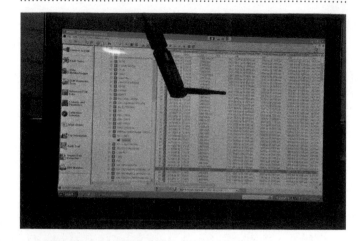

STARTUP AND ENGINE BREAK-IN

Unlike their automotive counterparts, most medium- and heavy-duty commercial diesel engines are factory dynamometer broken-in and require no additional break-in phase. Aftermarket break-in oils should never be added to diesel lube systems because they can actually interfere with the ability to seat new rings.

The main precaution for new or rebuilt diesel engines is to avoid idling. It should be emphasized that under no circumstances should a diesel engine be idled for prolonged periods; however, idling should be especially avoided with a new or newly reconditioned engine. The consequence of prolonged idling is to glaze the liners and create an oil-burning engine that can rapidly foul emission control catalytic elements and result in frequent diesel particulate filter (DPF) cycling and substrate failure.

However thoroughly a **pre-delivery inspection (PDI)** has been performed, there is always a chance something has been missed or components have shifted and changed during initial operation. For this reason, a post-break-in checkup is recommended after having put a thousand or so miles (1,600 km) on a new engine. The only instrument required to undertake this checkup is a set of eyeballs, but based on the inspection, some minor adjustments may have to be made on even the healthiest engine. Check for the following:

- Oil leaks
- Coolant leaks (hot and cold)
- Hose clamp integrity
- Belt tightness
- Air delivery pipes and hoses
- Radiator and heat exchanger leaks
- Wiring harness chaffing

STARTUP

Using the correct procedure to start a diesel engine is important, especially when temperatures drop below 32°F (0°C). The engine must have the correct grade of engine oil for the temperatures it must operate in. All computer-controlled engines use cold start strategy to limit smoke emission and engine loading when cold. Cold start strategy may disable the accelerator pedal, allowing the software startup map to be fully in command of the start strategy. Accelerator pedal input is usually disabled for a set period, such as 30 seconds or until a preset engine oil temperature has been achieved.

When starting the engine in temperatures below −15°F (−26°C), the engine should be run at around 1,100 rpm for at least 5 minutes before attempting to move the truck. Before cranking, the gearshift lever should be in park or neutral, the parking brake set, and the brake pedal depressed before pushing the start button or turning the key. It is never required that the accelerator pedal be depressed during startup in any chassis built since 1997.

Extreme Cold Weather Starting

Most manufacturers recommend that an engine block heater be used any time temperatures drop below −10°F (−23°C). Some manufacturers recommend the use of cetane improvers during extreme cold weather operation. These should be nonalcohol based. Generally, a medium- or heavy-duty engine should not be cranked for longer than 30 continuous seconds, because starter damage may occur. After a 30-second cranking cycle, wait a full 2 minutes before attempting another cranking cycle. If the engine has not fired up after three cranking cycles, it is likely that there is some other problem.

Avoid the use of starting fluids, such as ether, when cranking diesel engines, but realize that there are circumstances when these fluids must be used. Use with caution especially when dispensing from a spray can. Starting fluids are designed for carefully metered use on heavy-duty diesels, and may blow out the rings on light-duty diesels. Auxiliary power units (APUs) are becoming more common due to anti-idling legislation in many jurisdictions, and these can significantly reduce engine cranking duration and warmup time.

WARNING:

Never add gasoline, gasohol, kerosene, or alcohol to diesel fuel. This can cause fire hazards, engine performance problems, and costly fuel system damage.

Start Sequence

1. Turn the key to on, but do not crank the engine. If the engine is equipped with glow plugs, this activates the glow plug circuit. Wait until the glow plug preheat indicator turns off or until prompted by the **dash display unit (DDU)** before cranking.
2. On engines equipped with intake manifold preheaters or glow plugs, it is common for the circuits to remain energized for a short period of time after the engine starts. If the engine is not started before the preheater or glow plug activation time ends, the circuits will likely have to be reset by turning the key to off.
3. After the engine starts, allow it to idle for around 15 seconds and at least 1 minute in winter conditions. Then run at around 1,100 rpm to warm up the engine. Monitor the oil pressure during the warmup phase. With some types of automatic transmission in subzero conditions, shifting may be inhibited until the transmission fluid has been warmed to a threshold temperature.

Water-in-Fuel Alert

It is always possible for water-contaminated diesel fuel to be pumped into fuel tank(s) during refueling, especially when purchased from refuelers with lower fuel volume turnover. Most modern automotive diesels are equipped with **water-in-fuel (WIF)** sensors and a water separator to remove water from the fuel within the fuel subsystem. The WIF warning light will illuminate when the water separator has exceeded a threshold of water accumulation. Should the WIF light illuminate when the engine is running, the engine should be shut down and the water separator drained. Operating the vehicle with the WIF warning light illuminated can result in costly fuel injection system failures. Draining the water separator with the engine running will allow air to be pulled into the fuel system.

WARNING:

Do not attempt to drain a water separator while an engine is running, because air may be drawn into the fuel subsystem and shut the engine down.

DEF Alert

When the ignition circuit is switched into the key-on position, the **diesel exhaust fluid (DEF)** warning light will briefly illuminate and extinguish. When the aqueous urea fluid is either contaminated and/or low, the DEF light will remain illuminated and other intervention strategies will progressively kick in. If the vehicle runs out of DEF, it will enter a trimback mode that limits road speed and engine rpm. Depending on the manufacturer, engine output may be limited to idle only. The DEF must be replenished: It is a legal and operational requirement. Full coverage of DEF maintenance appears later in this chapter.

AIR INTAKE SYSTEM MAINTENANCE

For every gallon of diesel fuel by volume combusted by a diesel engine, between 10,000 and 15,000 volumetric gallons of air pass through the air intake system. The variance depends on how the engine is being operated. For this reason, a diesel engine air intake system must be closely scrutinized during operation. Forgetting about the air intake system between service intervals is an invitation to costly problems. **Figure 14–5**

FIGURE 14–5 A typical heavy-duty truck air filter housing mounted in the airflow outside the engine compartment.

shows a typical heavy-duty truck air filter housing mounted in the airflow outside the engine compartment. Trucks operated in agricultural or construction environments require special attention to be paid to air filter restriction gauges. Grain chaff is a special problem and can plug a brand-new filter in a single 8-hour work shift. Engines operated in these types of conditions should be fitted with an aftermarket precleaner.

AIR FILTER RESTRICTION GAUGE

The air filter **restriction gauge** is usually located on the air filter canister; the display readout may be located on the gauge itself or be set on the dash so the driver can immediately be alerted if there is a problem. A restriction gauge measures pressure values below atmospheric (vacuum) and therefore identifies the restriction that has to be exerted on air to pull it into the turbocharger compressor housing. The more the air filter is restricted (clogged), the higher the restriction value; the restriction value is displayed in inches of water (in./H_2O).

Most air filter restriction gauges are located either on the filter housing or somewhere on the dash display. Original equipment manufacturers (OEMs) recommend that an air filter restriction gauge be checked daily, that is, before each trip. The frequency should be increased when a vehicle is operated in hostile environments (to engines) such as agriculture or construction. The restriction gauge may be calibrated in in./H_2O or in dumbed-down gradients that culminate in "change filter."

> ## TECH TIP:
>
> An engine air filter functions at its *best* efficiency just before it fails. Avoid attributing a low power complaint to a filter with a gauge that indicates the unit is close to failure. It may be a good idea to change the filter at this point, but it is unlikely to be the root cause of the low power condition.

Engine performance and fuel economy are compromised when the maximum restriction is reached. Using compressed air to blow out air filter elements should be avoided. In most cases, the practice damages the filter element. You should also note that the physical appearance of a filter element is no guide as to whether it is functional. Learn to rely on the restriction gauge: If in doubt, you can double-check by fitting a reliable

FIGURE 14–6 A filter minder, an air filter inlet restriction gauge. This unit is shown reading 6 in./H_2O and is set to produce a restriction alert at 20 in./H_2O.

external gauge. **Figure 14–6** shows a typical air restriction gauge mounted on an under-hood air filter housing.

Resets

Most inlet restriction gauges are equipped with a reset button. When a gauge indicates that it is getting close to its maximum spec, depress the reset button. Check shortly afterward. However, note that a valid restriction reading will not occur until the engine is run at full load, because it has to be pulling the maximum amount of air through the filter. Note also that running a diesel engine at no-load high idle represents only a small percentage of peak loading. After installation of a new filter element, the restriction gauge should be reset.

Snow and Rain

Depending on the location of the air filter and whether a precleaner is fitted to the air intake system, vehicle operation in heavy snowfall or heavy rain can channel excessive quantities of snow/water into the filter element. This can temporarily plug and saturate the filter element; however, the condition is not terminal although engine performance may be severely compromised. Take the following action:

- Snow. At the earliest opportunity, open the hood and clear the snow and ice from the air filter housing inlet. Do *not* remove the filter element at this point, because you will likely damage it. Reset the restriction gauge and run the engine.

- Water saturation. After heavy rain, the filter element may saturate, resulting in reduced performance, but the air filter will usually dry within 15 to 30 minutes at highway speeds due to the high volume of air being pulled through it. While saturated, the restriction gauge will produce high readings, so reset the air filter restriction gauge at the earliest opportunity.

AIR FILTER REPLACEMENT

It should be noted that failure to use the specified air filter element may result in severe engine damage, as can attempting to run an engine without an air filter. To replace an air filter element, use the following general procedure—but note that it will vary from engine to engine:

1. Locate the mass air flow (MAF) sensor electrical connector on the air inlet pipe. If it can obstruct removal of the filter, unplug it.
2. Clean the exterior of the filter housing. Release the flange bolts or clamps that secure the sectors of the air filter housing. Separate the filter housing cover.
3. Carefully pull the air filter element from the air filter housing, making sure that as little dirt as possible falls into the intake ducting.
4. In cases where a foam pre-element is used, it may be possible to wash rather than replace, but go by the manufacturer's recommendation. If the foam filter is not to be replaced, ensure that it is clean and in place.
5. Vacuum out any loose dirt from inside the filter housing. Then wipe with a damp, lint-free rag. The object is minimize the amount of dirt that ends up in the engine intake ducting.
6. Install the new air filter element. Handle it with care and ensure that the seals on the element headers seat at both ends of the housing canister.
7. Replace the air filter housing cover and secure the clamps or torque the fasteners. In cases where plastic fasteners with brass threaded inserts are used, ensure that they are torqued to specification; overtorquing can compromise the seal.
8. If the mass air flow sensor was removed, reinstall it and ensure that its electrical connector functions.
9. Reset the air inlet restriction sensor (filter minder).

ENGINE LUBE SERVICE

The engine lubrication system must be routinely serviced. Using the specified engine lube oil is important, especially for diesel engines equipped with **diesel particulate filters (DPFs)**. All DPF-equipped engines must use American Petroleum Institute (API) service categories CJ-4, CK-4, or FA-4. Failure to use a CJ-4 or later category lube can plug or destroy a DPF. In addition to the API category, it is important to use oil of the correct viscosity for the temperature and conditions the engine will be subjected to. **Figure 14–7** shows a typical wet service display station in a truck shop that is designed to sell product.

PROPRIETARY LUBE SPECIFICATIONS

Manufacturers frequently specify an oil formulation that according to their research exceeds general industry standards. The current industry standard in North America is CJ-4 lube, but this will be upgraded to CK-4 and FA-4 in 2017. OEM-specific formulations meet the API standards, but are designed to better cater to a specific family of engines and can feature "enhancements" such as slightly lower ash, and contain brand-specific wear-enhancing additives. If a lubricant other than the OEM-specific lube is to be used, typically, the following are recommended options for post-2007 (DPF equipped) diesel engines:

- Severe duty, year-round usage: SAE 5W-40 API CJ-4 or CK-4
- Moderate duty, non-winter usage: SAE 15W-40 API CJ-4
- Post 2017 MY engines: SAE XW-30, API FA-4

FIGURE 14–7 An engine service marketing display in a dealership.

Most manufacturers recommend that an engine block heater be used when temperatures drop below –10°F (–23°C) when SAE 5W-40 is used. SAE 15W-40 begins to thicken at 30°F (–1°C) and turns to grease as temperatures descend. It is not recommended for use in typical North American winter conditions even when vehicles are garaged.

CHANGING THE ENGINE OIL AND OIL FILTER

Some modern vehicles are equipped with a smart oil condition monitor that prompts the operator when an oil change is required. When a dash display unit (DDU) message appears indicating OIL CHANGE REQUIRED, the engine oil, oil filter, and fuel filters should be changed.

Check Engine Oil Level

OEMs recommend that the engine lube level in commercial trucks be checked daily. Manufacturers will inform operators that it is normal to add some oil between oil changes. **Figure 14–8** shows the location of the oil fill neck and cap on a typical truck.

The procedure to accurately check the engine oil level is as follows:

1. The engine should be at normal operating temperature indicated by the engine coolant temperature gauge.
2. Park the vehicle on a level surface, then turn off the engine and open the hood.

3. Wait at least 10 minutes after engine shutdown to ensure that the oil contained in the upper sections of the engine has drained back to the oil pan.
4. Withdraw the dipstick, wipe it clean with a lint-free wiper, and reinsert it fully.
5. Withdraw the dipstick again and read the oil level on both sides of the dipstick to determine the actual engine oil level.
6. The oil level should be maintained within the crosshatch area of the dipstick by adding oil as required. The lower end of the crosshatch is usually the minimum oil level and the upper end of the crosshatch indicates the maximum oil level. Never overfill. The consequences of excessively high oil levels can be as severe as those of excessively low levels. On most heavy-duty commercial diesel engines, the distance from the top to the bottom of the crosshatch area on the dipstick represents 4 quarts (3.78 liters) of engine oil.

Procedure to Change Engine Oil

In describing this procedure, performing an engine lube job in a service pit is used for reference purposes, but the procedure would differ little if performed on a level surface, although it can be a little more awkward.

1. Place a catch sump under the engine large enough to contain the engine oil with a suitable margin of error. Place a catch sump under the filter and position a strap wrench (**Figure 14–9**) over the filter to loosen—then

FIGURE 14–8 A typical oil fill cap that seals the fill neck with a rubber locking boot when turned clockwise (CW).

Oil fill port

FIGURE 14–9 Loosening an oil filter(s) with an oil filter wrench.

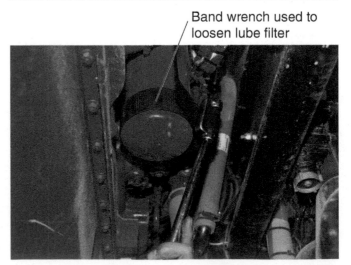

Band wrench used to loosen lube filter

FIGURE 14–10 After loosening, the filter can be spun off by hand—but take precautions if the oil is hot, because hot engine oil represents a burn hazard.

FIGURE 14–12 Remove the oil pan drain plug and allow sufficient time to fully drain the pan. If an oil sample is to be taken, do this midway through the runoff.

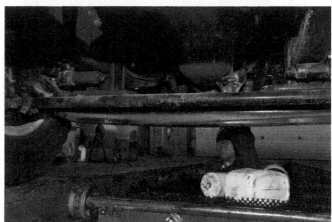

FIGURE 14–11 Fully drain the oil filter(s) in the catch sump before disposal.

unscrew the oil filter (**Figure 14–10**). After removing the filter, allow it to completely drain in the catch sump (**Figure 14–11**).

WARNING:

Take care not to sustain burns by handling hot oil or filters with bare hands.

2. Next, remove the oil pan drain plug and drop the oil (**Figure 14–12**). Wait for the oil to properly drain. Depending on the temperature of the oil, this can take up to 15 minutes.

3. Replace the filter. Most OEMs prefer that oil filters be primed with oil prior to startup because the oil filter(s) have to be filled before the lube circuit is supplied; some engines are equipped with an integral oil priming circuit. Alternatively, the oil filters can be filled with new engine oil prior to installation. If an oil filter is to be installed dry, smear oil over the filter sealing gasket and turret threads. Tighten exactly according to the instructions. Make sure it is not overtightened: this can damage the filter.

4. Reinstall the oil pan drain plug, replacing the sealing washer or O-ring if used. Note: Some newer oil pan drain plugs only require ¼ turn to either remove or install. Usually, just a ⅜-inch socket drive is required to remove or install the plug. Ensure that the plug is not overtightened during installation. Most OEMs publish a torque specification for oil pan plugs, so use it.

5. Locate the engine oil fill port (**Figure 14–13)** and identify the type of oil required to fill the crankcase. Refill the engine with new engine oil of the appropriate specification. For the specified quantity, consult the manufacturer's service literature, but remember that an aftermarket bypass filter can significantly add to the amount of oil required. **Figure 14–14** shows oil being pumped into an engine using a fill pump and flowmeter that displays the exact quantity of oil dispensed.

FIGURE 14–13 Locate the engine oil fill port and identify the type of oil and quantity required.

FIGURE 14–14 Refill the crankcase with the appropriate amount of new engine oil. This fill pump is equipped with a flowmeter that displays the exact amount of oil pumped.

Flowmeter oil fill pump

6. Reset the oil service life indicator in the vehicle maintenance log. This will alert the operator with remaining oil life data and when the next service is required.

> **WARNING:**
>
> Used engine oil is a known carcinogen. Protect your skin by wearing gloves and washing with soap and water after performing a wet service on an engine.

7. Make sure that oil samples taken for analysis are not contaminated by careless handling. **Figure 14–15** shows the sample container used by Caterpillar designed to be mailed in for analysis in their corporate laboratories.
8. Today, many service dealerships offer in-house oil analysis using equipment such as the On-Site Analyzer shown in **Figures 14–16**, **14–17**, and **14–18**. The Truck Check version of the On-Site Analyzer uses atomic emission spectrography, infrared spectrography, viscosity analysis, and particle counting to provide a faster report to the customer on the oil condition. It is easy to use and the test is driven by a touch screen in a step-by-step process.

FIGURE 14–15 Mail-in oil sample bottle favored by Caterpillar dealerships.

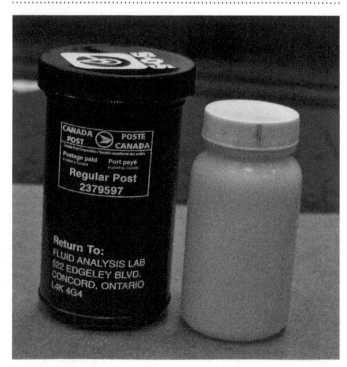

FIGURE 14–16 Shop floor sample and analysis equipment manufactured by On-Site.

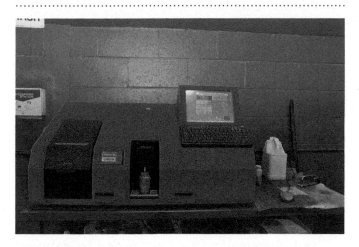

FIGURE 14–17 On-Site oil analysis display screen.

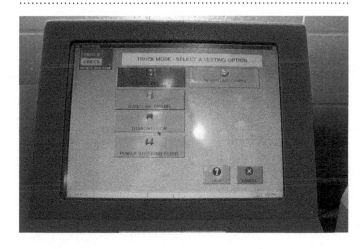

FIGURE 14–18 On-Site sample door.

Defining Severe Service Operation

When a diesel engine is subjected to severe service operation, the oil should be changed more frequently even when onboard lube oil monitoring is used. Some of the factors that determine severe service are:

- Frequent or extended idling (more than 10 minutes per hour of normal driving)
- Low-speed and low-load operation/stationary use
- Vehicle is operated in sustained ambient temperatures below –10°F (–23°C) or above 100°F (38°C)
- Frequent low-speed operation, consistent heavy traffic less than 25 mph (40 km/h)
- Operating in severe dust (aggregates, mining, construction) or agricultural chaff conditions
- Operating the vehicle off-road
- Hauling variable loads (e.g., load to maximum one way on a trip, returning empty)
- Frequent cold start, short distance, aggressive driving operation such as in fire truck, city bus, and garbage packer applications.

OIL CHANGE INTERVALS

It is not the function of any textbook to identify oil change intervals because there is so much variance between manufacturer recommendations and differences among the types of oil used. Always check OEM recommendations and specifications and attempt to define whether the engine can be categorized as *severe duty* in operation. In addition, many large fleets have produced their own service intervals which may be more rigorous than the OEM schedule.

With engines using the hydraulically actuated electronic unit (HEUI) fuel system, oil is used as hydraulic media (to actuate injector pumping). Because of this, the consequences of extending an oil change interval or using an inappropriate oil (high-detergent oils aerate more easily) can produce immediate drivability problems. Some oils are much cheaper than the manufacturer recommended oil (likely to break down earlier), whereas others are more costly, such as synthetics (suited for severe duty and high performance). The one thing that can be said is that extending oil change intervals can result in shortened engine longevity.

COOLING SYSTEM SERVICE

The cooling system in a modern vehicle can be the source of many problems if it is not properly maintained. The basics would be to ensure that the proper coolant was used and that its chemistry was routinely checked using the manufacturer's required procedure. Coolants break down. They break down faster in today's diesel engines than they might have a generation ago because of increased use of aluminum with the cooling system of the vehicle. During servicing, engine coolant should be checked for:

- Level
- Concentration (freeze point protection)
- Additive strength (corrosion inhibitor)
- Acidity

Make yourself familiar with the methods of testing diesel engine coolants described in Chapter 11.

COOLANT

As we said in Chapter 11, coolants may either be purchased as concentrate or premixed. That said, most antifreeze sold over the counter today continues to be as concentrate. Where **ethylene glycol (EG)** antifreeze is used, it should be maintained at a concentration of 50/50 antifreeze and water, which should provide freeze protection down to −34°F (−36°C). It also provides antiboil protection up to 265°F (130°C). A slightly higher degree of freeze protection can be obtained by using a 60/40 EG antifreeze and water mix; see Chapter 11 for a more detailed look at antifreeze/water cut ratios.

Temperatures below −34°F (−36°C) are classified as subarctic, and when operating in the central northern states, central northern Canada, and Alaska the use of **propylene glycol (PG)** should be considered. The antifreeze protection of PG increases with its percentage in a water solution, unlike EG; increasing the percentage of EG over water beyond 60% actually increases the freeze point temperature.

The type and condition of coolant run in an engine have a big say in how long that engine is going to last. With this in mind, it is important to say something about tap water. Tap water varies from town to town and district to district. In other words, it is a substance of variable and unknown chemistry. Avoid using it except in an emergency, and after the emergency, flush the engine cooling circuit. Common antifreeze options are:

- Premix extended life coolant (ELC). Best choice. Just make sure it is never contaminated with other antifreezes or water. Requires little testing during its service life. The problem is that anyone can use the term *ELC* to describe coolant, so it is a matter of buyer beware when shopping for this product. Some premix ELCs use hybrid organic acid technology (HOAT), Texaco being one example. HOAT antifreeze is almost always colored with an orange dye.
- Long-life EG concentrate mixed with distilled water. Distilled water costs little and pays for itself many times over by increasing the life of the engine. Must be routinely tested and chemically adjusted; prone to galvanic effect which can destroy an engine if left alone. Next best choice to ELC.
- Waterless engine coolant (WEC). When WECs are used, a sticker identifying the coolant should be placed on the radiator and fill cap. Providing that WEC is not contaminated with water or any other type of coolant, it is rated to last the life of the engine. That said, it should be visually inspected for obvious signs of degradation and contamination. WEC does not have to be tested for antifreeze protection.
- EG mixed with tap water. Must be routinely tested because it is subject to degradation, which can be rapid when the water used is of high mineral content. A poor choice and over the long term the most costly. The sad thing is that this malpractice is featured in many manufacturer dealerships.

As outlined in Chapter 11, a coolant mixture does much more than provide antifreeze and antiboil characteristics in a diesel engine. For this reason, ensure that only coolants approved by the manufacturer are used in the engine cooling system. In warm climates, where the temperature never drops below 40° Fahrenheit, distilled water cut with an additive package should be used. Additives designed for mixing with distilled water are sold by most antifreeze manufacturers. A distilled water coolant additive such as Pencool 3000 should be added at around a 5% concentration. It should be noted, though, that using water with a high total dissolved solid (TDS) count (tap or brackish water) renders a supplemental coolant additive (SCA) such as Pencool 3000 ineffective.

Coolant Color

The color of antifreeze means nothing. Despite attempts over the years to standardize antifreeze color, this has not been achieved. Antifreeze may be dyed yellow, blue, green, red, or any other color. The only color of significance in engine coolant is muddy brown: This usually indicates that the coolant has degraded and should be exchanged before it begins to damage internal engine components.

Coolant Concentration Testing

Coolant concentration can be tested with a hydrometer, specialized antifreeze tester (such as a Rotunda Antifreeze Tester), or refractometer. Refractometers (see Chapter 11) produce greater accuracy and do not require a temperature adjustment calculation, so most OEMs recommend that they be used.

COOLANT LEVEL TESTING

When the engine is cold, check the level of coolant in the reservoir(s). Some engines use a de-aeration tank equipped with a window, which makes checking coolant levels easy. Other vehicles use both a primary and a secondary cooling system, and it is important to regard each system separately. When cooling system maintenance has been overlooked, the main engine (primary) or secondary coolant reservoir may become low or empty. Should either reservoir become low or empty, add the specified coolant to the appropriate level.

Coolant Precautions

General guidelines:

- Never use alcohol, methanol, brine, or any engine coolants using an alcohol or methanol base.
- Avoid using recycled coolant unless it is from a known reliable source.
- Ensure that the engine has cooled (coolant temperature gauge reading below 100°F (38°C)) before attempting to unscrew the coolant pressure relief cap.
- When replenishing or replacing a coolant mixture, make sure the mixing of EG and distilled water takes place before the solution is poured into the cooling system.

ADDING COOLANT

Treat engine coolant with a high level of respect and it will pay dividends in increased engine

FIGURE 14–19 Coolant surge tank.

longevity. Depending on the design of the cooling system, the procedure used to check and add coolant depends on whether a surge tank (**Figure 14–19**) is integrated into the system. Always be careful when removing any cap from the cooling system even when a surge tank is used. The next section outlines the procedure that should be used to remove the pressure cap that defines the peak cooling system pressure.

Remove Pressure Cap

To remove a cooling system pressure cap, use the following procedure:

1. Before attempting to remove the pressure cap, make sure the ignition circuit is in the key-off position and the engine has cooled. The dash coolant temperature gauge should read below 100°F (38°C).
2. Having checked that the engine is cool, wrap a heavy cloth around the pressure cap. Slowly twist the pressure cap counterclockwise (CCW) until it contacts the first set of stops; this will allow any residual pressure to release.
3. Stand back with your face protected while the pressure releases.
4. When you are sure that the pressure has been relieved, use the cloth to twist the pressure cap CCW until the release cap tabs align with the neck release notches. This will permit the cap to be removed.

Replace Coolant Filter

Locate the coolant filter (see **Figure 14–20**) and identify what is required to remove it without losing coolant. Sometimes the coolant filter pad is equipped with a hand valve, but most more recent ones have an automatic lock-off ball that

FIGURE 14–20 Locate the engine coolant filter. Ensure that it has either a manual or automatic coolant stop valve before removing it.

Lube oil bypass (centrifugal) filter   Full flow lube oil filters   Coolant filter

engages as the used filter is removed, to prevent spillage. Check to see whether the coolant filter is DCA-loaded. In some cases, depending on OEM and the type of coolant mixture, an untreated replacement filter is required. Install the new filter hand tight and if the filter pad uses manual valves, ensure that they are opened.

Add Premix Coolant

The following procedure should be used when refilling the engine with premixed, long-life antifreeze solution. This is the simplest method of providing an engine with coolant system protection and does not require freeze point and maintenance monitoring so long as the engine is operated outside of arctic conditions.

1. Remove the pressure relief cap from the engine or secondary coolant reservoir using the procedure previously outlined.
2. Unseal a jug of long-life diesel engine coolant. Pour into coolant reservoir until the coolant level reads within the COLD FILL RANGE. Do not overfill.
3. Reinstall the pressure relief cap.
4. Start and run the engine at 2,000 rpm for a minimum of 2 minutes.
5. Shut the engine off and remove the pressure relief cap using the method previously outlined.
6. Check the level; add more premix to ensure that the coolant level is within the COLD FILL RANGE as identified on the reservoir. Do not overfill.

Mix/Add a 50/50 Coolant Solution

Use the following procedure to refill or add a 50/50 EG-to-distilled-water mixture to an engine or secondary cooling system after either has been drained or become low.

1. Remove the pressure relief cap from the engine or secondary coolant reservoir using the method previously outlined.
2. Using newly cleaned vessel with a capacity of at least 2 gallons (8 liters), add a full container of EG antifreeze and 1 gallon (4 liters) of distilled water. Using a clean utensil, stir the contents of the container until the color appears even. This will happen almost immediately at normal room temperatures but may take a little longer if the EG is cold.
3. Pour the 50/50 mixture of antifreeze and distilled water into the coolant reservoir, filling it until the coolant level reads within the COLD FILL RANGE on the reservoir. Re-install the pressure relief cap. If filling from empty, check with the manufacturer service literature for how coolant conditioner is added to the system; this may be in liquid form or contained within a coolant filter element. Use the manufacturer method of adding the protection package.
4. Shut the engine off, and remove the pressure relief cap using the method previously outlined.
5. Check the level. Add more of the 50/50 coolant solution to ensure that the coolant level is within the COLD FILL RANGE as identified on the reservoir. Do not overfill.

FUEL SYSTEM MAINTENANCE

Diesel fuel systems are damaged as often as they are helped by products known as diesel fuel conditioners. While these products are not exactly snake oil, they seldom do much good and often create performance problems. Diesel fuels meeting either the ASTM D 975 (diesel) or the ASTM D7467 (biodiesel) industry specifications should be used. Such fuels do not require additional additives unless they have been allowed to break down. Outside of North America, fuels meeting EN590 should be used. Most diesel engine manufacturers stipulate that they are not responsible for any repairs required to correct the effects of using diesel fuel conditioner. The only exception is much older hydromechanical systems, designed for an era of diesel fuels with higher lubricity than currently approved fuels. Alcohol-based conditioners especially should be avoided and used only in an absolute emergency to address water freeze-up problems in the tank.

CAUTION:

Never put known contaminated fuel into a vehicle fuel tank and expect additives to take care of the problems. Have degraded/contaminated fuel disposed of according to your state guidelines for waste disposal.

ULTRA LOW SULFUR DIESEL FUEL

The only fuel available at the pumps today for on-highway, and most off-highway, usage is **ultra low sulfur diesel (ULSD)**; sometimes the acronym ULS is used in place of ULSD. ULSD has a maximum sulfur content of 15 ppm. This can also be expressed as 0.0015% maximum sulfur.

Fueling the Vehicle

Diesel fuel should be purchased from a reputable refueling station that preferably sells large volumes of diesel fuel. Diesel fuel is seasonally adjusted by refiners and running summer fuel under winter conditions is inviting problems. Diesel fuel also has a shelf life of about 2 months before it begins to degrade; biodiesel fuels have a shelf life of around 1 month.

Most automotive highway vehicles powered by diesel engines are equipped with a fuel fill pipe that can receive fuel up to 20 gallons (75 liters) per minute from a 1⅛-inch (30 mm) nozzle. Attempting to pump fuel at higher flow rates may result in premature nozzle shutoff or spit-back.

CAUTION:

Diesel fuel should never be stored in a galvanized container. Diesel fuel reacts with the zinc, forming zinc compounds that can be pumped through the fuel system and destroy the injectors.

To fuel the vehicle:

1. Turn the engine off.
2. Turn the filler cap counterclockwise until it spins off.

WARNING:

Some more recent fuel systems may be under pressure, so take care when removing the fill cap. If the fuel filler cap is venting vapor or if you hear a hissing sound, wait until it ceases before completely removing the fuel filler cap. Failure to do this can result in pressurized fuel spraying out of the tank.

3. Rotate the cap CCW to remove it from the fill neck of the fuel tank.
4. To reinstall the cap after a fill-up, rotate it CW onto the fill neck of the fuel tank, making sure the threads are not cross-threaded. Do not overtighten.

Fuel Filler Caps

If a fuel filler cap has to be replaced, it must be replaced with one specified for the fuel system on the vehicle. The vehicle warranty may be voided if the correct fuel filler cap is not used, because excessive pressure or vacuum may build up in the fuel tank. This is important in fuel tanks that are not direct vented to atmosphere.

Priming the Fuel System

Depending on the type of fuel system, when air enters the fuel subsystem it may be necessary to prime the fuel system. When air enters the fuel subsystem, it is usually due to:

- Running out of fuel
- Failure to prime, or loss of prime of a fuel filter at servicing

It should be noted that some more recent, diesel engines are designed to be self-purging. Self-purge capable engines use an electric priming pump. Make sure you consult the OEM service literature before attempting to prime a fuel subsystem; you should also be able to identify the type of fuel system being worked on.

Typically, to run self-prime, turn the key on and do not crank. Repeat this several times in succession; typically OEMs suggest six cycles. Then crank the engine until it starts. When the engine fires, it may run rough and produce white smoke while air remains in the system; this condition should not last for more than a couple of minutes.

In engines without a self-prime feature, check the layout of the fuel subsystem. Chapter 19 introduces some typical diesel fuel subsystems, but assume *nothing*. Many current vehicles may locate filters in clusters, making it difficult to visually determine whether they are located in the primary or secondary section of the fuel subsystem. Consult the OEM service literature: Some OEMs have a guided prime sequence embedded in their diagnostic software.

For a typical diesel fuel subsystem divided by a primary and secondary circuit, use the following sequence, remembering that the OEM procedure should be consulted:

1. Remove the primary fuel filter. Replace/refill with clean, filtered diesel fuel. Install and torque the filter to specification.
2. Install a new secondary filter and install dry.
3. Identify the system priming pump. This may be a manually actuated plunger pump located downstream from the primary filter (often on the transfer pump assembly), or an electric pump activated at key-on. **Figure 14–21** shows a hand primer pump on a Paccar MX 13. On older engines, it may be necessary to fit a hand or electric priming pump into the circuit.

FIGURE 14–21 Paccar hand primer pump located in fuel subsystem.

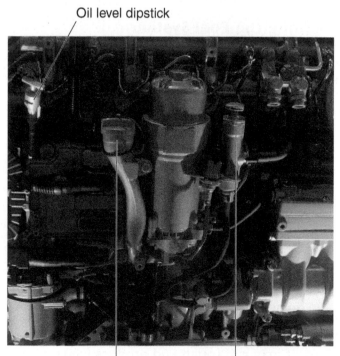

Oil level dipstick

Oil fill cap   Hand-actuated
                      primer pump

4. Locate a bleed valve downstream from the secondary filter. If there is no bleed valve, crack the exit fitting from the secondary filter mounting pad, placing a container under the opened line nut to capture spilled fuel.
5. Activate the priming pump until air-free fuel exits the fitting. Torque the line nut at the filter mounting pad to specification.
6. Run the priming pump for a short while. Where a hand priming is used, pump until resistance is felt.
7. Crank the engine in 30-second cycles, waiting for 2 minutes between each cycle. In most cases, the engine will fire within the three cranking cycles.

CAUTION:

Do not attempt to crack/open high-pressure pipes in any diesel engines manufactured after 1997. The injection pressure circuit in today's diesel engines is designed to be self-purging, so once you are sure the fuel subsystem is primed, failure to start is almost always caused by a condition not relating to loss of prime.

Fuel/DEF Refill Doors

While refueling diesel-powered vehicles with gasoline is primarily a problem in light-duty automotive diesels, this can occur in operations that run a mix of diesel and gasoline-powered vehicles, such as a school bus depot. Use of fuel doors to mark diesel fuel (**Figure 14–22**) and DEF fill points adds an extra reminder of which

FIGURE 14–22 Fuel door on a school bus clearly labeled to reduce the chance of an inattentive operator fueling the tank with gasoline.

fluid is required. When fuel becomes contaminated, reference the OEM-recommended procedure for rectifying the problem; this often means transporting the vehicle to a dealership.

BIODIESEL

Most commercial diesel engines manufactured after 2001 can be operated on **biodiesel** cuts ranging between 2% and 20%. Chapter 38 addresses biodiesel fuels in some detail. Petroleum-based diesel fuel cut with 20% is identified as B20. In addition to B20 fuel, B2 (2% biodiesel), B5 (5% biodiesel), and B10 (10% biodiesel) may also be available depending on geographic region, and all are approved for most post-2007 commercial engines. Because John Deere's market presence in agricultural regions is high, most of its post-2011 engines are approved for B20 fuel.

Biodiesel is more likely to be available in agricultural communities, and sometimes B100 (100%) is available. At this time, none of the major commercial diesel engine manufacturers approves B100, and using it can void warranty. Biodiesel, in any concentration, is less stable than petroleum-based diesel fuel, so there are some advisories that should be followed when using it:

- Never store biodiesel fuel in the vehicle fuel tank for longer than 1 month. Biodiesels are more susceptible to biological attack that can rapidly degrade the fuel quality and foul the fuel with metabolic waste. Note that use of biocides may kill the bacteria but will not remove the waste (observable as slime and a septic odor) they have already created.
- If cold temperature fuel gelling issues (usually first noticed by restricted fuel filters) are observed, change fuel to petroleum-based diesel.
- Never use unrefined oils, waste fat, or cooking greases as fuel. Only ASTM-approved biodiesels (see Chapter 38) should be used.
- If the engine/vehicle is to be parked or stored for longer than 1 month, drain the fuel tank(s), fill with a pure petroleum-based ULS diesel fuel, and then run it for at least 30 minutes.
- Never put home heating oil, agricultural fuel, kerosene, or jet fuel into a diesel fuel tank; you would not do this anyway, but note that this type of contamination produces more serious consequences when biodiesel cuts are used.

SEPARATOR SERVICE

A fuel filter and a water separator assembly are often combined into a single unit such as the diesel fuel conditioner modules shown in **Figure 14–23** and discussed in Chapter 19. This Fleetguard Diesel Pro unit is equipped with a WIF sensor and fuel heater. An earlier, simpler version of a fuel filter and water separator assembly is shown in **Figure 14–24**. Both units separate water from fuel using centrifugal action and are drained by opening a drain cock at the base of the sump.

Water should be drained from the module assembly whenever the driver alert warning light is illuminated by the WIF sensor; this is usually accompanied by a message displayed on the DDU. The water-in-fuel (WIF) alert is signaled when the separator drain bowl has accumulated a specific quantity of water in the module, usually around 0.5 pint (200 mL). If water is allowed to exceed this level, it may be pumped through the fuel system and result in serious damage to the fuel injection equipment. The typical

FIGURE 14–23 A Fleetguard Diesel Pro multifunction fuel filter/water separator assembly.

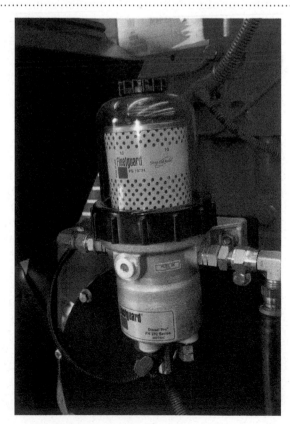

FIGURE 14–24 A FuelPro multifunction fuel filter/water separator assembly that uses an inverted filter cartridge. Before removal, clean the dirt off the housing with compressed air, then drain the assembly to avoid spilling fuel.

procedure required to drain a water separator is as follows:

1. Stop the vehicle and shut off the engine.

WARNING:

The vehicle must be stopped with the engine off when draining a water separator because fuel may ignite if the engine is running. In addition, air can be pulled into the fuel system if the water separator is drained while the engine is operating, resulting in shutdown.

2. Locate the water separator and place an appropriate container under the drain port.
3. Rotate the drain tap counterclockwise. Allow the separator to drain into an open container. If the objective is simply to remove accumulated water from the separator sump, drain until clean fuel is observed: rubbing a pair of fingers in the flow can help identify the point at which fuel begins to exit because it has higher lubricity. If you are draining the assembly to change the filter, run it dry. Rotate the drain clockwise to close off the flow.
4. Replace the filter if required. When the drain valve is fully tightened, remove the container from under the vehicle.
5. Restart the engine. In most cases, the WIF alert message and/or warning light should no longer be displayed on the DDU, but in some OEM management systems, you may be required to clear the alert using an EST.

FUEL FILTER SERVICE

Most current diesel engines are equipped with at least two fuel filters. They are usually but not always designated as primary and secondary filters. It is good practice to replace both filters at the same time, usually on a lube change schedule. Routine fuel filter changes are an important part of engine maintenance and failing to adhere to scheduled maintenance can produce engine performance issues and fuel injection system problems. In this section, the procedure required to change a typical set of filters is outlined first, followed by the specific procedure required to service a DDC Series 60. In all cases, the OEM service procedure should be consulted; for instance, to minimize contaminants in fuel, Caterpillar recommends that both the primary and secondary fuel filters be installed dry. After installation, the hand primer pump (see **Figure 14–25**) should be used to fill and purge air from both filters.

Servicing the Primary Fuel Filter

The primary fuel filter is usually located upstream from the transfer pump. In most systems, fuel is at lower than atmospheric pressure in the primary fuel filter when the engine is running. This means that if the filter cartridge is not properly sealed to its mounting pad, air can be pulled into the fuel subsystem.

FIGURE 14–25 Caterpillar hand-actuated primer pump located on the filter pad.

Hand primer pump   Filter pad assembly

Fuel filter

Removal

1. Drain the primary fuel filter. The filter may be equipped with a drain valve, in which case that valve should be opened. If there is no drain valve, loosen the filter canister by turning it CCW using a filter wrench. Drain the fuel into a container and dispose of in an environmentally approved waste oil container.
2. Remove and discard the used fuel filter element.

Installation

1. Fill the new primary fuel filter with clean fuel. Ensure that the mating surfaces of the filter mounting pad (gasket sealing surface and mounting threads) are clean and lubed with diesel fuel.
2. Rotate the new filter canister clockwise (CW) onto the threads of the filter mounting pad. Torque to the OEM-recommended specification.
3. In most cases, both primary and secondary filters are changed, but if only the primary fuel filter is serviced, remember that the system will have to be purged of air. Use the procedure outlined earlier in this chapter, titled "Priming the Fuel System."

Servicing the Secondary Fuel Filter

The secondary filter is almost always located downstream from the transfer pump. It is usually under what is described as *charging pressure* (see Chapter 19) when the engine is being operated. Charging pressures are typically around 70 psi (483 kPa), but may be as high as 250 psi (1786 kPa) depending on the engine. Residual pressures usually bleed down within a couple of minutes after shutdown. Today, it is common to use disposable cartridge-type filters.

Removal

1. Drain the secondary fuel filter. The filter cartridge may be equipped with a drain valve, in which case that valve should be opened. If there is no drain valve, loosen the filter canister by turning it CCW using a filter wrench. Drain the fuel into a container and dispose of in an environmentally approved waste oil container.
2. Remove and discard the used fuel filter element.
3. Clean the filter pad mating surface and mounting threads with a lint-free cloth.

Installation

1. Consult the OEM service literature. In most cases, you will find that the OEM prefers secondary filters to be installed dry, then primed using either a hand primer pump or an integral electric primer pump. Always use the OEM-recommended procedure. For purposes of this description, we will assume that the new filter is being installed dry, that is, not filled with fuel.
2. Lubricate the mounting surfaces and threads of the new filter with clean diesel fuel.
3. Rotate the new filter canister CW onto the threads of the filter mounting pad. Torque to the OEM-recommended specification.
4. The system will have to be purged of air after the replacement of the filter, so use the procedure outlined earlier in this chapter, titled "Priming the Fuel System."

Using a fuel that has higher than average impurities may require more frequent replacement of the fuel filters. After servicing the filters, a no-start or rough-running engine may indicate that air is entering the system through the filter bowl seal or drain. Ensure that the drain is tight.

CAUTION:

Most modern secondary fuel filters will plug on water. Relatively small quantities of water reaching the secondary fuel filter can result in an engine shutdown. Replacing a secondary fuel filter plugged on water is a temporary measure: the source of the water should be investigated and repaired to avoid a repeat failure.

Low Fuel Pressure

Most current engines using common rail (CR) fuel systems are equipped with a low fuel pressure detection system. If the DDU displays LOW FUEL PRESSURE, the following service routine should be run:

- Cold start or cold operation (below 32°F [0°C]): If this message appears during a cold start or during cold operation up to 10 minutes after the initial start, monitor the DDU. If it disappears and does not reappear after the engine has fully warmed up, the low fuel pressure message is most likely caused by waxed or gelled fuel. To repair a fuel gelling problem, consult the manufacturer's service literature; generally this will advise against using alcohol-based additives. Most manufacturers approve of at least one type of anti-gel additive providing it is not used as a general preventive.

- If a low fuel pressure message persistently appears after refueling during cold start and winter operation, then disappears when the engine has warmed up, the cause is probably summer fuel or a nonappropriate fuel (such as kerosene).

Low Fuel Level

If a low fuel level message appears on the DDU once the engine is warm, the tank level is at or very near empty, so refueling is required. Should the message return when the engine is at running temperature after refueling, the fuel subsystem is likely restricted and the filters should be replaced regardless of the maintenance schedule interval. If replacement of the fuel filter(s) does not correct the low fuel pressure alert, the problem is likely fuel subsystem restriction at the pickup tubes or transfer plumbing.

Combination Filter/Separators

Combination fuel filter and water separators are common in original equipment and, because of their effectiveness, as aftermarket add-ons. These units will in addition contain fuel heaters, water separators, and pressure sensors.

SERVICING DDC SERIES 60 FUEL FILTERS

1. Identify the fuel filters on the engine. Depending on the model, there are either two spin-on fuel filters (primary and secondary), or one spin-on (primary) and one cartridge containing a filter element (secondary).
2. Using a filter wrench, turn the primary fuel filter CCW until it can be spun off by hand. Remove the filter and drain into a bucket. Using the same procedure, remove the spin-on secondary fuel filter, and drain this into the bucket.
3. If a Davco-type filter is used in place of a spin-on secondary filter, place a bucket beneath the filter housing and open the drain valve. Drain all of the fuel from the filter. Using a Davco filter wrench, loosen the black ribbed collar that connects the plastic filter bowl and the main filter housing. Turn the Davco wrench CCW until the collar is loose

enough to remove by hand. After the collar has been removed, lift up and separate the plastic bowl. Remove the filter cartridge and drain in the bucket.
4. Apply lubricant (diesel fuel is good) to the rubber seal of the primary fuel filter. Spin the primary fuel filter onto the threads of the fuel filter housing in a CW direction until the filter is seated. Hand tighten using good pressure. Repeat these steps to install a spin-on secondary fuel filter.
5. If the secondary fuel filter is a Davco cartridge, insert the new element into the filter housing. Place the plastic bowl over the element followed by the collar. Hand tighten the collar. Remove the plastic fill plug in the top of the bowl and pour clean, filtered diesel fuel into the bowl until it exceeds the height of the element. Screw the plastic fill plug back into the top of the bowl.
6. Locate the primer pump located on the primary filter housing: it is a black rubber button about 1 inch (25 mm) in diameter. Continuously pump up until good resistance is felt. At this point the fuel subsystem is primed and the engine is ready to crank.

SELECTIVE CATALYTIC REDUCTION

Most post-2010 highway diesel engines over 70 BHP (52 kW) are equipped with a **selective catalytic reduction (SCR)** system to minimize NO_x emissions. The exceptions are Navistar and Caterpillar engines. SCR uses aqueous urea (see Chapter 47) as a reduction agent; aqueous urea is known as diesel exhaust fluid (DEF) in North America and as AdBlue in Europe. The SCR system automatically injects DEF into the exhaust system, but is essential to maintain the DEF level.

DEF LEVEL

For the SCR system to operate properly, the DEF level must be maintained. Generally, the DEF tank should be checked each time the vehicle is refueled. It should be noted that when engines show higher than specified DEF ratios to fuel consumed, it can be indicative of aggressive driving.

The ECM monitors the fluid level in the DEF tank. Running a system check in the driver digital display electronics will indicate to the

FIGURE 14–26 A typical DEF tank used on a post-2010 highway truck.

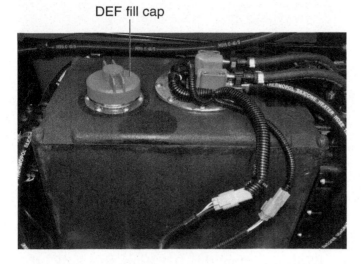

DEF fill cap

operator whether the DEF level is okay or if it is less than half full. A message will automatically come on in the display window when the DEF level is low and needs to be refilled. When this message appears, the DEF tank must be refilled. **Figure 14–26** shows a typical DEF tank and the monitoring head. Note that the DEF fill cap is always colored blue. In operations such as school buses where the drivers may be less savvy, the DEF reservoir is often safeguarded with a fill door such as the one shown in **Figure 14–27**. This helps to avoid accidental filling of the DEF tank with fuel.

When the vehicle is operated while the DEF level is either low or contaminated, it defaults

FIGURE 14–27 The clearly identified DEF door used on a school bus.

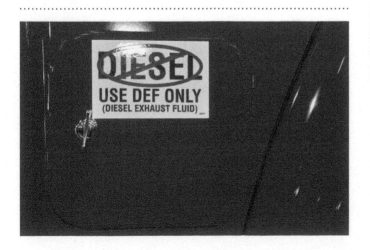

DIESEL
USE DEF ONLY
(DIESEL EXHAUST FLUID)

to a trimback or ramp-down mode in which road speed is limited. At the first ramp-down, the vehicle speed may be limited, progressing to more aggressive ramp-down limits if the warnings are ignored. Under ramp-down conditions, the truck should be driven with caution and the DEF replenished immediately. Should the DEF tank become completely empty (or contaminated), the vehicle speed will be limited to idle speed once stopped.

The driver display unit is designed to display a sequence of messages regarding the amount of DEF available in the tank. A systems check displays messages indicating the DEF available in the following sequence:

- OK.
- Under half full.
- Warning message displaying the mileage (kilometers) remaining as the fluid in the DEF tank nears empty. Vehicle drives normally.
- Warning message and audio alert as DEF projected driving distance drops below 300 miles (483 km), along with road speed trimback accompanied by a message posted to the DDU.
- Continued operation without refilling the DEF tank will result in the engine being limited to idle-only operation after refueling. At this point, it is required that a minimum of 0.5 gallon (1.9 liters) of DEF be added to the tank to exit the idle-only mode, but the vehicle will still be in speed-limiting mode until the tank is refilled.
- To exit the vehicle speed-limiting or idle-only condition, refill the DEF tank; normal vehicle operation will resume only after the DEF tank is refilled.

TECH TIP:

When refilling the DEF tank from empty, there may be a short delay before the ECM detects the increased level of DEF. This has to occur before the ramp-down mode is exited and normal operation is resumed.

Filling the DEF Tank from a Container

The vehicle is equipped with a DEF tank with a blue-capped filler port (see Figure 14–22), usually located next or close to the diesel fuel fill inlet. The tank can be filled using a nozzle at a DEF filling station (similar to fuel fill) or using a portable DEF container with a spout.

WARNING:

Do not put DEF in the fuel tank. This can result in damage and void the warranty.

TECH TIP:

Immediately wipe away any DEF that has spilled on painted surfaces with water and a damp cloth, to prevent damage to the paint.

DEF can be purchased at most manufacturer dealerships and all highway truck stops. Only DEF certified by the API meeting ISO 22241 should be used in the DEF tank, so look for the API certification trademark on dispensers and containers.

WARNING:

Refill DEF in a well-ventilated area. When the cap on the DEF container is opened, ammonia vapors may escape. Ammonia can irritate skin, eyes, and mucous membranes. Inhaling ammonia vapors can cause burning to the eyes, throat, and nose and cause coughing and watery eyes.

Use the following step-by-step procedure to refill the DEF tank:

1. Remove the cap from the DEF container. Remove the spout from the bottle and insert the straw end into the bottle. Ensure that the arrow above the nut is aligned with the bottle handle and that the small tube end extends into the far corner of the bottle. Twist the spout nut on the container until it is tight.
2. Open the DEF filler port on the vehicle by twisting open the blue cap counterclockwise. **Figure 14–28** shows the DEF fill cap on a school bus located behind a door with a posted warning to fill only with DEF.
3. Lift and hold the DEF container (see **Figure 14–29**), without tipping, and insert the spout into the DEF filler port until the small black seal on the spout is fully seated into the DEF filler port.

FIGURE 14–28 The blue DEF fill cap located behind the DEF door on a school bus.

4. While pouring the DEF into the tank, the fluid level on the container will be seen to drop.
5. When the vehicle DEF tank is full, the fluid level in the bottle will cease to drop. This indicates that the fluid is no longer flowing.
6. When the level in the DEF container has ceased to drop, return the container to a vertical position slightly below the DEF filler port and allow any DEF to drain from the spout. Do not attempt to continue to add DEF to the tank by shaking or repositioning the container to induce flow, because this can result in spillage and overfilling.
7. Once the spout has drained, remove it from the DEF filler port and reinstall the blue cap

FIGURE 14–29 A standard 1 gallon jug of DEF sold at most service facilities.

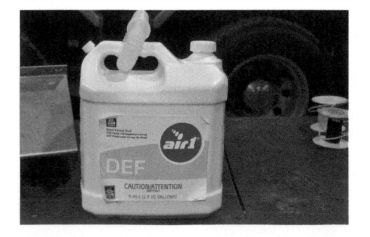

on the DEF filler port. Remove the spout from the DEF container and install the cap back on the bottle.

8. If the container has been emptied, recycle it and the spout. If some DEF remains in the container, retain it and the spout for later use. Ensure that the spout stays clean.

9. Use water and a damp cloth to wipe away any DEF that has spilled on painted surfaces.

DEF Refill from a Fuel Station Nozzle

Filling the DEF tank using a nozzle is similar to a normal fuel fill. The nozzle is designed to shut off automatically when the tank is full. Do not continue to fill the tank, as this may cause spilling and overfill the tank, which can cause damage.

TECH TIP:

Some filling station nozzles may hinder the filling of a DEF tank due to a magnetic mechanism in the nozzle. This is not a problem with most North American-built post-2010 vehicles. Where this is a problem, another refueling station or portable container will have to be used to fill the tank.

Filling DEF in Winter Conditions

DEF freezes at 12°F (–11°C) but that said, most vehicles designed for operation in North America are equipped with an automatic preheating system. This allows the DEF system to function below 12°F (–11°C). When a DEF-equipped vehicle is not in operation for an extended period of time with temperatures at or below 12°F (–11°C), the DEF tank may freeze. If the tank is overfilled and it freezes, it could be damaged. DO NOT OVERFILL.

DEF Storage

DEF should be stored away from direct sunlight and in temperatures between 23°F (–5°C) and 68°F (20°C). Always make sure the DEF is protected from being exposed to temperatures below 12°F (–11°C). DEF containers should not be stored in vehicles because, in the event of a leak, it can damage interior components and release an ammonia odor inside the vehicle. DEF should never be diluted with water or any other liquid. It is normal to smell an ammonia odor when removing the container or tank caps.

TECH TIP:

DEF is a nonflammable, nontoxic, colorless, and water-soluble liquid. However, refilling with DEF should always be undertaken in a well-ventilated area.

DIESEL PARTICULATE FILTER SERVICE

All highway diesels (and many off-highway diesels) manufactured since 2007 are equipped with diesel particulate filters (DPFs). As described in Chapters 47 and 48, DPFs entrap combustion soot and then burn it off in regeneration cycles. What remains of the burn-off are residual ashes that collect over time. Each manufacturer has slightly different guidelines for DPF service, so the following is general. A DPF may have to be removed for ash cleaning at approximately 120,000 miles (192,000 km) depending on how the vehicle is operated and how ash levels are monitored. In addition, the DPF may have to be replaced at approximately 250,000 miles (400,000 km), and again this depends on engine/vehicle operating conditions. In most cases, the engine management system will set an alert to advise the operator that the DPF requires service attention.

DPF REGENERATION

The frequency with which a DPF requires regeneration depends on the manufacturer and whether it is original equipment or aftermarket. In most cases (but not all), DPF regeneration cycles are driven by the engine software. In some cases, the regeneration is designed to occur while the vehicle is on the highway operating under conditions of normal speed and load; in others, the regeneration cycle must be initiated and managed by the technician using an EST. When a DPF alert is displayed on the DDU or by dash warning lights, the manufacturer service literature must be referenced and the procedures outlined therein followed precisely.

OTHER ENGINE SERVICE FACTORS

When an engine service is performed, the technician is almost always required to perform nonengine-related service procedures as well. While it is not the business of this textbook to outline these nonengine service procedures, they must not be overlooked. These service procedures can include inspecting and correcting any fluid reservoirs on the chassis, the integrity of lines and hoses, and fan belt appearance and tension. Truck technicians often overlook the fact that a very small percentage of trucks today use hydraulic brakes (see **Figure 14–30**) and that it is critically important to check the brake fluid level when performing an engine service.

> ## WARNING:
> When checking coolant hose clamps, be careful to avoid overtorquing silicone hoses. The clamping pressure required of silicone hoses is surprisingly low, and when they are overtorqued, they tend to develop leaks. Check the OEM torque specs.

FIGURE 14–30 It is important to remember that when performing a wet service on an engine, all under-hood fluids should be checked; that includes fluids that may not be typical on most heavy-duty trucks.

SUMMARY

- Some OEMs prefer that the first step in any routine service procedure be to connect an EST to the chassis data bus and establish a communication link between the vehicle and the manufacturer's online data hub.
- Most medium- and heavy-duty truck diesel engines do not require a break-in period. However, it is important to observe the OEM recommendations for new engines. Light-duty commercial diesel engines may require a break-in phase that requires the engine to be operated under lighter than rated loads for a set number of linehaul miles or engine hours.
- Servicing of air filters in commercial diesel engines should be determined by the status of an inlet restriction gauge that monitors vacuum pull.
- Selecting the appropriate oil for use in today's diesel engines is critical; DPF-equipped engines require the use of an API CJ-4, CK-4, or FA-4 engine lubricant. OEM oils are tailored for their engines and while they tend to be more costly, they may maximize engine life.
- A diesel engine service, at minimum, requires testing air filter restriction, changing the fuel filters, and checking the coolant, along with performing an engine oil and filter change.
- Where engines use a coolant mixture of EG and distilled water, the mixing should be performed before pouring into the cooling system.
- The only fuel available for on-highway use today is that classified as ultra low sulfur (ULS), with a maximum sulfur content of 15 ppm. Most manufacturers approve of the use of ASTM-rated biodiesel cuts up to B20 in post-2010 diesel engines.
- Technicians should be familiar with the procedure required to prime a fuel subsystem, as this may be required after performing a service.
- When a WIF alert is broadcast to the DDU, the water separator sump should be drained to avoid the costly damage that may occur if water is pumped through the fuel system.
- The SCR system is managed by the engine controller and when the DEF levels run low, a series of alerts are broadcast on the DDU. If the alerts are ignored and the DEF is not replenished, the engine may be first derated, then inhibited to idle-only operation.
- A DPF requires servicing when it becomes loaded with the ash that results from regeneration cycles that burn off soot; always use the OEM required procedure to service the DPF. This may require replacement of the DPF.

REVIEW QUESTIONS

1. Which of the following engine lubricants is suitable for use in an engine equipped with a DPF?
   a. Any synthetic lubricant
   b. Any biodiesel lubricant
   c. API CI-4
   d. API CJ-4

2. Which of the following would best describe the color of DEF?
   a. Blue
   b. Clear
   c. Amber
   d. Red

3. What quantity of oil does the distance from the top to the bottom of the crosshatch area on a typical heavy-duty diesel engine represent?
   a. 1.0 quart (0.95 L)
   b. 2.0 quarts (1.9 L)
   c. 4.0 quarts (3.8 L)
   d. 8.0 quarts (7.5 L)

4. Technician A says that the fastest way to break in a diesel engine is to add a charge of aftermarket break-in solution to the engine oil. Technician B says that most truck engine OEMs recommend adding fuel conditioners to diesel fuel tanks to improve the winter drivability of diesel engines. Who is correct?
   a. Technician A only
   b. Technician B only
   c. Both A and B
   d. Neither A nor B

5. What color is used to denote a DEF fill cap?
   a. White
   b. Green
   c. Red
   d. Blue

6. Which of the following solutions would provide the highest level of antifreeze protection?
   a. Pure distilled water
   b. A 50/50 solution of EG and distilled water
   c. A 100% solution of PG
   d. A 100% solution of EG

7. Technician A says that EG is always colored green. Technician B says that PG is always colored red. Who is correct?
   a. Technician A only
   b. Technician B only
   c. Both A and B
   d. Neither A nor B

8. Technician A says that DEF is available at most diesel refueling stations. Technician B says that DEF can be obtained from most manufacturer dealerships. Who is correct?
   a. Technician A only
   b. Technician B only
   c. Both A and B
   d. Neither A nor B

9. Which of the following is the correct course of action when a WIF alert is posted to the DDU?
   a. Drain the water separator sump.
   b. Replace the fuel filters.
   c. Replace the water separator.
   d. All of the above.

10. Which of the following is the best indicator of when a diesel engine air filter be changed?
    a. At every engine wet service
    b. Every time the oil filter is changed
    c. Every 6 months
    d. When the restriction gauge indicates it is beginning to plug

15

ENGINE REMOVAL, DISASSEMBLY, CLEANING, INSPECTION, AND REASSEMBLY GUIDELINES

OBJECTIVES

After studying this chapter, you should be able to:

- Describe the procedure required to remove an engine from a typical truck chassis.
- Disassemble an engine for reconditioning.
- Outline the process of cleaning and inspecting engine components.
- Understand the importance of systematically tagging components and connectors.
- Describe some of the key reconditioning procedures.
- Develop good inspection and failure analysis habits.
- Evaluate components for repair or replacement.
- Describe the procedure required to reassemble a diesel engine.
- Outline some of the reassembly steps that require special attention or precautions.

KEY TERMS

air conditioning (A/C)
anaerobic sealant
buttress
cab-over-engine (COE)

diamond dowels
flywheel housing concentricity
high-pressure washer

magnetic flux test
master bar
service literature
soak tank

spreader bar
Tempilstick

INTRODUCTION

Most of the procedures and terms used in this chapter have been used elsewhere in this textbook. The objective of this chapter is to put some of the content together in sequences typical of disassembly, cleaning, inspection, and reassembly of a truck diesel engine. It should never be used as a replacement for original equipment manufacturer (OEM) literature. Remember that every engine—and, for that matter, every truck chassis—presents its own small and larger distinct problems that can only be addressed using product-specific guidelines. In describing the disassembly and reassembly procedure of a typical commercial diesel engine, several different medium- and heavy-duty engines are referenced in text and images.

SERVICE LITERATURE

In this textbook we have used the term **service literature** to refer to what used to be known as a *service manual*. Service literature today is seldom available in hard-copy format. Most manufacturers provide service literature using their online service information systems (SIS) (covered in Chapter 35) because information can easily be corrected, updated, and enhanced by tagging it with the latest technical service bulletins (TSBs). In this chapter the term *service literature* is used to include the following:

- Hard-copy (paper) service manuals
- Data-disk (CD, DVD) service literature
- Online service information systems
- Technical service bulletins

REMOVAL OF AN ENGINE FROM A VEHICLE

Details of this procedure obviously vary from one vehicle to another and depend to a large extent on the specific engine and whether it is hydromechanically or electronically managed. The following is intended to act as a rough set of guidelines and show the sequencing of the steps required to remove an engine from a highway tractor chassis.

GETTING READY

1. It is good practice, before beginning, to pressure-wash or steam-clean the engine and engine compartment to remove road grime, grease, and oil. This will provide a clean work area that will enable more precise inspection and promote a more professional work environment.

2. Park the vehicle on a clean, level surface and ensure that the engine compartment can be accessed by the hoist required to lift the engine. Engage the vehicle parking brakes, block wheels, and ensure that there is sufficient bench space or a mobile steel cart on which removed components can be placed. Ensure that some adhesive labels and masking tape are at hand so that electrical wiring and fluid hoses can be identified. Failure to do this can considerably lengthen the reinstallation time. If the truck is of the **cab-over-engine (COE)** design, ensure that the cab lift hydraulics operate properly and that the positional locks are in place. With the COE chassis, the cab must usually be elevated to its extreme travel position, so check that the mechanical stops are in place and that the extended lift rams are not supporting the weight of the cab for the duration of the engine job.

3. If the engine is electronically managed, download the engine/chassis identification data and the customer data programmable options using a personal computer (PC) (and OEM software) or a handheld electronic service tool (HH-EST) and retain on a disk or printout. Disconnect the main battery leads at the battery terminals.

WARNING:

On electronic engines with a nonvolatile random access memory (NV-RAM) component, all NV-RAM data is lost the instant the batteries are disconnected. Check the OEM instructions before disconnecting the batteries.

4. Remove the radiator cap. To avoid injury when removing a radiator cap, rotate it counterclockwise (CCW) to the first stop, but do not depress. This will allow any residual pressure to bleed from the cooling system. After the pressure has equalized, press the cap downward and continue turning to remove. Open the cooling system drain cocks (usually located on the lower radiator tank and somewhere on the engine block) to drain the coolant. If the coolant is to be reused, store it in a sealed container: Do not leave coolant

in drainage tubs exposed to the shop atmosphere. If the coolant is to be replaced (and it really should be at an engine overhaul), ensure that the used coolant is disposed of in an environmentally safe manner consistent with federal and local jurisdiction regulations.

5. Shut off the air supply to any engine pneumatic controls such as shutterstats, fan controls, puff limiters, air-controlled exhaust brakes, and any other pneumatic apparatus in the engine compartment that may have to be removed or disconnected.

6. Remove the oil pan plug and drain the engine oil. Remove the oil, fuel, and coolant filters and dispose of them and the engine oil in an environmentally safe manner consistent with federal and local jurisdiction regulations.

TECH TIP:

When the reason for the engine failure is not known, cutting filters open and internally inspecting them may provide some clues as to root cause.

REMOVING THE ENGINE FROM THE CHASSIS

1. Disconnect the piping/ducting to charge air heat exchangers such as aftercoolers, air-to-air coolers, and tip turbine assemblies, labeling any plumbing that could be a problem during reassembly. Remove the intake ducting, capping the turbocharger intake and exhaust porting. Ensure that all intake ducts, air hoses, and the air filter assembly are capped to prevent contaminants from entering the intake system.

2. On vehicles with **air conditioning (A/C)**, it is often possible to remove the engine without losing the refrigerant charge. Remove the condenser from the heat exchanger cluster at the front of the engine housing and fully support it so that it is not hanging by its hoses. Remove the A/C compressor, again without disconnecting its plumbing, and fully support it somewhere where it is not going to hinder further work in the engine compartment. If the refrigerant must be discharged, connect the appropriate recovery station and evacuate the system, plugging any open hoses.

3. Usually the radiator should be removed. In most cases the radiator tie rods obstruct access to the engine, so at minimum these should be removed. To remove the radiator, when possible, leave the air-to-air-type charge air coolers attached to the rad assembly and attach chains to the radiator tie-rod upper brackets. Support the assembly using a shop crane (chain hoist or cherry picker). Next, disconnect the upper and lower radiator hoses. Inspect the hoses for cracks and general overall condition to note whether replacement is required. This should be done on removal of the engine from the chassis so that quotes to customers are reliable and parts can be ordered when necessary. Remove the radiator lower mounting support bolts and rubber insulators. Lift the radiator/air-to-air charge air cooler assembly from the chassis using the shop crane. Lift slowly and carefully to avoid damaging any components.

4. When the assembly is out of the chassis, separate the two heat exchangers. Carefully place the radiator upright on a flat surface. Use extreme care when handling heat exchanger cores—they are easily damaged. Remove the fan shroud, brackets, and other hardware if the radiator is to be recored.

5. Remove the fan and fan hub assembly.

6. Clearly label all the electrical leads before disconnection. Do the same with fuel lines, all linkages, oil lines, and water hoses. Cap all disconnected fuel lines to keep out dust.

7. Locate the rear engine mounts. These are either on the engine flywheel housing or on the transmission bell housing. When the rear engine mounts are located on the flywheel housing, the transmission must be fully supported. Position a mechanical transmission jack or blocks under the transmission. In some vehicles it may be necessary to completely separate the transmission from the engine *before* attempting to remove the engine.

8. Loosen and remove the capscrews that hold the transmission bell housing to the engine flywheel housing.

9. Obtain or fabricate a suitable **spreader bar** and lifting chain so that the engine can be lifted without lift chain contact to critical engine components. Fit engine lifting eyes to the OEM-recommended location on the engine. Move into position the hoist to be used to lift the engine from the chassis: a portable adjustable boom hoist (often known as a cherry picker) such as that shown in **Figure 15–1** is recommended. Attach lift chain hooks to the engine lifting eyes.

FIGURE 15–1 Mobile boom hoist (cherry picker) ready for use (see Figure 2–31 showing the same hoist lifting an engine).

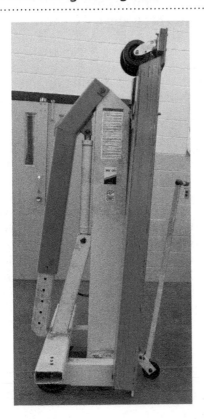

FIGURE 15–2 Diesel engine mounted in heavy-duty engine fixture.

CAUTION:

Never attempt to lift an engine using only rope slings or cable slings. Never support the engine on its oil pan and never place any kind of sling around the oil pan.

10. After the hoist is chained to the engine lift eyes, apply a slight load to the lifting chain.
11. Remove the engine mounting bolts. Perform a thorough visual inspection to ensure that everything that has to be uncoupled is and that nothing is obstructing the planned removal path of the engine.
12. Separate the engine from the transmission, taking care not to force anything or overload the transmission input shaft. Use the hoist to remove the engine from the chassis. This may be a two-person operation, depending on the chassis. If unfamiliar with the chassis, ensure that someone is around to assist, even if it means just having an extra pair of eyes.
13. Remove external accessories as required: alternator, starter, power steering pump, oil, coolant and fuel filter mounting pads, and anything else on the block that might obstruct the engine overhaul mount stand. Bolt the engine into the overhaul stand, such as that shown in **Figure 15–2**, and do not release the weight from the hoist until the engine stand mounting plate bolts are tight.
14. Remove the hoist chain hooks and then the lifting eyes from the engine unless they were originally on the engine.
15. Remove the turbocharger oil supply and return lines. Remove the turbocharger and assess its condition.
16. Remove the crankcase breather assembly if fitted.

TECH TIP:

Always work on an engine with the assumption that it may have to be reinstalled by someone else. Tag every electrical wire and hose coupling. Failure to do this can result in greatly increased reassembly times.

TECH TIP:

Work cleanly and methodically. Use several containers to put fasteners in and label each container by component and location. Inspect every disassembled component for reusability: By doing this, you make it possible to issue an accurate repair quote to the customer.

ENGINE DISASSEMBLY

In most cases the engine will be removed from the location of the chassis before it is disassembled. If an engine is to be rebuilt in a general area of the shop floor, it is essential to ensure that no work, such as welding, be undertaken in close proximity to the engine work.

1. For electronic engines using injectors or pump units with programmable fuel flow codes, it is critical that you tag each unit by cylinder number if you intend to reuse them. On engines that use integral or unit high-pressure injection pumps, remove the injection lines and any electrical wiring by separating the connectors. On engines using integral hydraulic injectors accessible without removing the valve covers, remove the injectors, capping the leak-off and feed ports. On some engines the high-pressure pipe is connected to a cylindrical injector through a port in the rocker housing. The two nuts that locate and seal this connector pipe must be backed off and the pipe removed before any attempt is made to remove the injector.

2. Remove the exhaust and intake manifolds plus the exhaust gas recirculation (EGR) assembly. Carefully observe the location of sensors and actuators, tagging each for location. Be especially cautious when disassembling EGR components: The sensors and actuators located in the EGR heat exchanger(s), venturi, and mixing chamber(s) are sensitive and easily damaged.

3. Remove the water manifold assembly, complete with the thermostat housing when possible. Sometimes the EGR heat exchanger is integrated into the water manifold and it may be easier to remove both as a unit.

4. Separate the vibration damper using great care, especially with viscous-type units. Thoroughly inspect the vibration damper to assess its serviceability. Next, remove the crank pulley and crankshaft hub assembly. Usually this requires removal of the hub retaining capscrew(s) and then use of a universal T-puller (**Figure 15–3**).

CAUTION:

You must refer to the OEM service literature before removing the injectors and pumps from engines, especially those controlled by computer. The consequences of not doing this can be costly fuel system damage and extended reassembly times.

TECH TIP:

As you disassemble any engine, make a habit of inspecting every component you remove to evaluate whether it should be reused or replaced. This is essential if an accurate quote is required once the engine is completely disassembled and takes three steps:

1. Thoroughly clean the component using solvent, detergents, and/or compressed air as appropriate.
2. Assess serviceability: If replacement is required, immediately note this on the work order.
3. Seal the component: If the component is to be reused, protect it by sealing it, using clear plastic wrap. This will help ensure that the product does not get damaged during the time required to recondition the engine.

FIGURE 15–3 Removing a pulley using a T-puller.

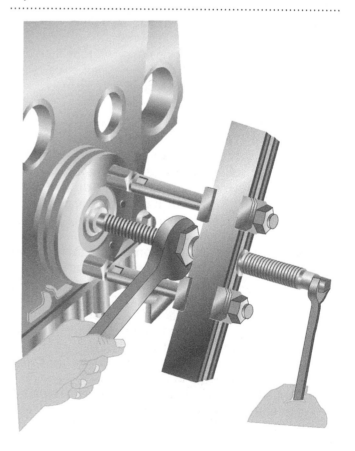

WARNING:

Exercise extreme caution when pulling the hub and damper from a crankshaft—damaging either a crankshaft or vibration damper is likely to more than erase any profit that might be earned on the engine overhaul. Always consult the engine OEM service literature.

5. Remove the engine timing gear cover. If the timing gear cover has thrust buttons fitted, back these off before removing. On engines where the timing indicator is fastened by the timing gear cover screws, remove them first and ensure that they are not damaged.

6. Remove the oil cooler assembly. With bundle-type oil coolers, test the core using either the pressure or vacuum methods outlined in Chapter 10 and then seal using plastic wrap.

7. Disconnect any plumbing to the water pump that has not already been removed, then remove the water pump itself. It has become almost standard practice to replace water pumps with a rebuilt exchange unit when reconditioning engines today. But if you are reusing the pump, visually check it for evidence of weeping at the ceramic seal, and the seal itself for cracks.

8. Remove the clutch pack assembly from the flywheel and assess its serviceability.

9. Remove the flywheel assembly using a suitable hoist.

10. Remove the flywheel housing and any attached components, checking for sensors and connecting wires. Check for eccentricity at the locating dowel holes.

11. Remove all accessory drive components not already removed, such as power steering pumps, air compressors, and so forth. Remove accessory drive pulleys using a suitable puller (see Figure 15–1).

12. Remove the oil filler and dipstick tubes.

13. Remove the mechanical tachometer drive, if fitted.

14. If the engine is fitted with electronic unit pumps (EUPs), remove them and store them per OEM recommendations. If the engine has an inline injection pump, remove any electrical wiring from the rack actuator housing (electronically managed, port-helix metering), transducer module, or governor housing. Disconnect the throttle arm and fuel stop arm from hydromechanical pumps. Check that all the plumbing is disconnected from both sides of the pump and remove any support brackets: Loosen the pump mounting capscrews, and, using a smooth motion, pull the injection pump away from its mounting flange. Pressure-time (PT), common rail (CR), and Cummins Accumulator Pump System (CAPS) pumps can be removed in a similar fashion. The various types of transfer pumps used with the electronic unit injector (EUI) systems are relatively straightforward to remove, but the OEM service literature should be consulted whenever hydromechanical or electronic fuel pumping apparatus is removed from the engine. When performing a complete engine overhaul, it may be part of the procedure to recondition or replace with rebuilt/exchange fuel injection components, so check with the OEM and shop work order instructions.

15. Remove the rocker housing covers.

16. Remove the rocker shaft assemblies, including valve bridges where used. On overhead camshaft engines, remove the camshaft assembly.

TECH TIP:

Most OEMs recommend that rocker arm shaft assemblies and valve bridges/yokes be tagged for position to help maintain the same wear surfaces if they are to be reused.

17. Remove the injectors, using the appropriate puller. When cylindrical hydraulic injectors are used, make sure that all the plumbing is clear of the injector seat before attempting to remove them. Where EUIs, electrohydraulic injectors (EHIs), EUPs, and hydraulically actuated electronic unit injectors (HEUIs) are used, ensure that all electrical and hydraulic connections are removed. This is especially important where transverse cylinder head, high-pressure pipes are used.

18. Check the injector nozzle gasket. Most current nozzle seals/spacers are manufactured from soft steel, so if they are not adhered to a removed injector, you can remove them from the injector bore with a magnet or small tapered rod. In cases where copper injector seals are used, an O-ring pick or brass bore cleaning brush can be used. Do not leave nozzle gasket/spacers in the cylinder head, because this could cause problems on reassembly.

19. Remove the push tubes or rods where fitted. It is good practice to inspect each for serviceability on disassembly. Some OEMs recommend that the push tubes be tagged for position in the engine.

20. Remove fuel manifolds (internal charge and return lines) where fitted, jumper pipes, and crossover pipes.

21. Remove all the cylinder head capscrews and washers. Remove the cylinder head(s).
22. Remove the cylinder head gasket and the sealing grommets and fire rings if not integral with the cylinder head gasket. Inspect the cylinder head gasket for signs of failure, paying special attention to the fire rings. **Figure 15–4** shows a partially disassembled engine in a portable engine overhaul fixture.
23. Invert the engine. Remove the oil pan capscrews and the oil pan. **Figure 15–5** shows an inverted engine in an overhaul stand.
24. Remove the oil pump, which may be located in the crankcase or outside, fastened to the engine cylinder block.
25. Before removing each piston and connecting rod assemblies, scrape carbon deposits (ring ridge) from the upper inside wall of each cylinder liner using a flexible knife.
26. Plan to remove the pistons on an inline six-cylinder engine in companion pairs; that is, 1 and 6, 2 and 5, 3 and 4.
27. First, remove the connecting rod bearing capscrews and separate the cap from the rod by tapping with a light-duty nylon hammer.
28. If possible, remove the piston cooling nozzles/jets to avoid damaging them when the rods are removed. Remove each connecting rod and piston assembly carefully, guiding the rod bottom end clear of the cylinder liner wall. If the piston cooling oil nozzle/jet was not removed, take special care to avoid contact between it and the rod bottom end: this could misdirect the nozzle. In some engines, the piston, conn rod, and liner have to be removed as an assembly because the big end will not pass through the liner bore: observe the OEM instructions when pulling

FIGURE 15–4 Partially disassembled Mack E-Tech engine mounted in an engine stand.

FIGURE 15–5 Invert the engine by rotating it in the stand.

piston packs. Arrange the piston assemblies sequentially on a bench or place them in a rack as shown in **Figure 15–6**, making note of any unusual characteristics.
29. Remove the cylinder block located piston cooling nozzles. Oil will be trapped in the gallery that supplies the piston cooling jets, so be prepared to capture it. If the engine is rotated to an angle on the stand, remove either 1 or 6 first and allow the oil in the gallery to drain.
30. Disassemble the engine timing geartrain. Remove accessory drive gears, idler gears, and an in-block camshaft gear and camshaft

FIGURE 15–6 Place the piston assemblies in sequential order in an organizer rack.

as an assembly. Rotating the engine upside down will ease the removal of an in-block camshaft because this will drop the cam follower/lifter assemblies out of the way so they do not interfere with the cam lobes and journals as the shaft is withdrawn.

31. Remove the cam follower/tappets/valve lifter assemblies. If the camshaft is to be reused, inspect and tag individual lifters for reassembly to position. Where cam follower housings are used, tag for position. In engines where the cam follower housing shimming defines engine timing, it is advisable to measure and record the shim (gasket thickness) with a micrometer even when the engine is to be retimed on reassembly.

32. Disassemble any remaining gears in the engine geartrain and remove any auxiliary or balance shafts remaining in the engine cylinder block.

33. Remove the crankshaft rear seal housing assembly.

34. Remove all the camshaft bushings using the correct sized driver and slide hammer.

35. With the engine still inverted, remove the main bearing cap capscrews, the cap brackets, and the main bearing caps by gently tapping with a nylon hammer. Tag the bearings by location for inspection and failure analysis purposes.

CAUTION:

Some lightweight cylinder blocks use transverse buttress screws in the main caps. You will not be able to remove main caps with these in place, and attempting to do so can damage both the cap and the cylinder block. Remove them from the side of the block.

36. Fit a crank-lifting yoke to the crank throws on a pair of companion cylinders (preferably 2 and 5 on an inline six). The yoke should have rubber conduit installed over the throw hooks to prevent damage to the throw journals. Lift the crankshaft free from the cylinder block using a hoist.

TECH TIP:

Due to the weight of the crankshaft, extreme care must be observed during removal. Lift the crankshaft straight up to avoid damage. No scratches, nicks, burrs, or any other kinds of distress are permitted on the main or throw journals and their fillets.

FIGURE 15–7 Removing a cylinder sleeve.

Courtesy of Navistar International Corp.

EG-5341

37. Remove the cylinder liners using a suitable puller, as shown in **Figure 15–7**. Wet liners are retained by O-rings and it does not usually require a great amount of force to separate them from the block. Dry liners and combination wet/dry liners may require considerable force, and hydraulic and air-over-hydraulic pullers with the appropriate adapter plates are usually required. In cases where even hydraulic pullers fail to move the liner, a single vertical-down welding bead using a $\frac{1}{8}$" (3.2-mm) deep penetration electrode (such as E6010 or E6011) followed by the immediate application of cold water will often work. Whenever such a practice has to be resorted to, it should be recognized that a mistake may destroy the cylinder block. Always ensure that the welding is performed well away from any engine components. Also, always use a fast-drag, vertical-down technique to avoid overheating the liner.

38. Remove all expansion (frost) press-fit plugs and threaded oil passage plugs from the cylinder block before cleaning.

TECH TIP:

Although cleaning and inspection are covered in the following section, it is important that an engine not be simply ripped apart. Technicians should get in the habit of inspecting every component as it is removed and tagging it when it is important for it to be reinstalled in the same location. Once again, the practice of cleaning, inspecting, and verifying serviceability of each component as it is disassembled can help produce accurate quotes: Nothing is worse to a customer than costly surprises that inflate a bill way beyond the quoted dollar value.

CLEANING AND INSPECTING COMPONENTS

The cleaning and inspection of an engine is a critical stage in the engine reconditioning procedure. If the reason for the engine rebuild is a failure, ensure that the cause is identified before any attempt at reassembly is made.

1. Use a gasket scraper to remove all the gasket material and heavy dirt from the cylinder block. Install the cylinder block into a (preferably heated) **soak tank** using a heavy-duty alkaline soak cleaner for a period of 1 to 2 hours. One OEM reports that $\frac{1}{16}$" (1.5 mm) of coolant scale has the insulating properties of 4" (100 mm) of cast iron. It is therefore important not to skip this procedure.

> ## CAUTION:
> Use extreme care and wear protective clothing when working with alkaline solutions, which may be caustic.

2. Remove the cylinder block from the cleaning or soak tank. Thoroughly flush the cylinder block using a shop **high-pressure washer**, ensuring that all particles and sludge produced by the block boiling are removed.
3. Visually inspect the cylinder block, checking all the coolant passages and ensuring that they are clean and unobstructed. Ream or drill out if necessary to dislodge any deposits.
4. Check to see that there are no casting fins or residues that might obstruct coolant flow by removing any casting irregularities with a pry bar.
5. Run a cylindrical wire brush in all the oil passages to ensure that they are unobstructed.
6. Flush the oil passages with air and solvent.

MAGNETIC FLUX TEST

It makes sense to **magnetic flux test** engine cylinder blocks, crankshafts, and all connecting rods at every major engine overhaul. These processes are neither expensive nor time-consuming, and as the consequences of a single warranted engine failure out of 20 overhauls will demolish the profits of the other 19, it is shortsighted to overlook it. Remember, this expense is passed on to the customer, and if it is to be passed over, it is the customer who should make the decision: Get a refusal in writing. The usual drawback is not having the equipment on site, but in most cases, the equipment is accessible and machine shops usually pick up and deliver.

ENGINE REASSEMBLY GUIDELINES

Although engines may be disassembled with little or no reference to service literature (not recommended practice), they must be assembled precisely according to the sequencing in the OEM workshop manual. Maybe the only excuse for not observing this practice could be made by the technician who continually overhauls the same engine series and who makes a point of studying every OEM technical service bulletin (TSB). Even for the experienced engine overhaul technician, using service literature as a guide is simply good practice. For the novice engine overhauler, the service literature should guide every move: It is important that shortcuts are never experimented with. As every experienced diesel technician will acknowledge, there are a few shortcuts to some procedures, but these must involve a zero risk factor, and that requires an intimate knowledge of the engine that comes only with experience.

Providing a general guide for an engine (re)assembly procedure would simply reverse the general guidelines for disassembly, and the point is that engines cannot be successfully rebuilt according to general guidelines; rather, they should be assembled in the precise sequence outlined by the OEM. However, the following lists some general precautions that the engine rebuilder may encounter when assembling engines.

O-RINGS ON WET LINERS

Use the lubricant recommended by the manufacturer when installing full wet and midstop, wet/dry liners. The lubricant recommended may be antifreeze, engine oil, silastic, or nothing at all. An inappropriate lubricant may chemically interact with the O-ring material and cause it to swell, contract, or disintegrate, generating a premature failure.

USE OF ANAEROBIC SEALANTS

The use of **anaerobic sealants** (silicone, silastic/RTV, and others) has become popular in recent years. Only use these where specified, and do not overuse, as they may plug up apertures.

NOTE:

Many sealants do not cure when in contact with any type of oil or grease.

CYLINDER BLOCK INSPECTION

The flowchart illustrated in **Figure 15–8** is an excellent guideline for evaluating the serviceability of an engine cylinder. Although it relates specifically to a recent model Detroit Diesel Corporation (DDC) Series 60, most of the steps apply to any diesel engine. Make sure you understand exactly what is required in each step.

Test the Cylinder Block Line Bore

This check is performed most easily using a **master bar**, which is clamped into the block line

FIGURE 15–8 Flowchart for repair or replacement of a cylinder block.

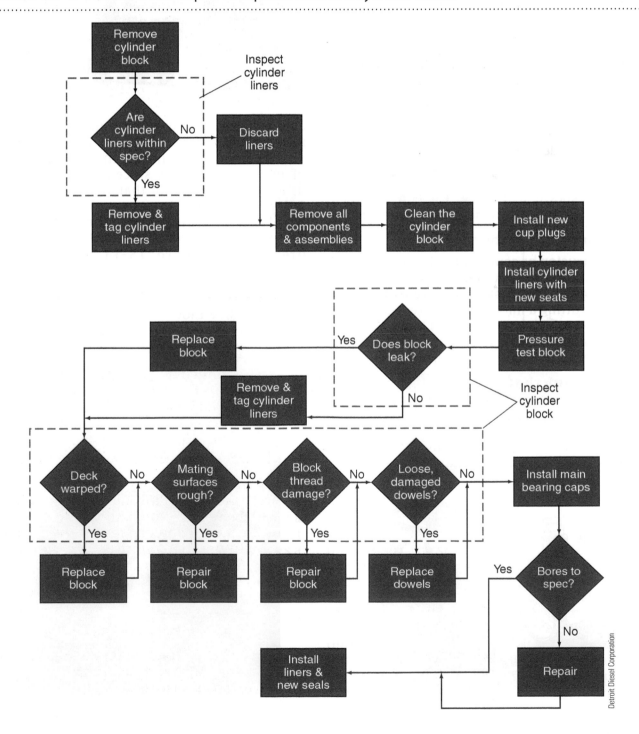

Detroit Diesel Corporation

Piston Cooling Jets

Always check the directional aim using the appropriate tooling, usually a perspex template and rod. Some cooling jets may be bent to correct aim, some may not: Check OEM literature. The general procedure for targeting spray jets is illustrated in Chapter 7, Figure 7–10.

PISTON ASSEMBLY

It is essential to inspect a piston assembly prior to installation. When the piston is to be reused, it should be carefully checked. We will take a look at some of the critical steps in checking out piston and connecting rod assemblies. The components of a piston assembly are shown in **Figure 15–13**. Note that what is often referred to as a *piston kit* includes the liner in some OEMs' terminology. **Figure 15–14** shows the procedure used to measure the big end of a connecting rod: Note that the rod cap is assembled and torqued into position.

Measuring Connecting Rods

The procedure for verifying the serviceability of conn rods is addressed in Chapter 7, and you should be aware of the importance some OEMs place on magnetic flux testing of conn rods at each major overhaul. The flowchart shown in **Figure 15–15** is a guide to assessing conn rod serviceability.

Connecting Rod Weight Classifications

Connecting rod weights are coded by manufacturers. When replacing connecting rods, it may be possible to either increase or decrease the weight class by one increment, but not more.

FIGURE 15–13 Connecting rods, pistons, rings, and sleeves.

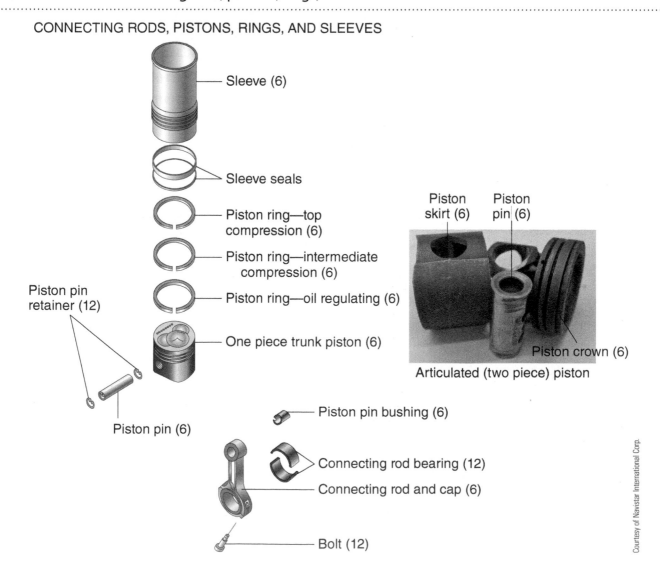

CONNECTING RODS, PISTONS, RINGS, AND SLEEVES

Sleeve (6)

Sleeve seals

Piston ring—top compression (6)

Piston ring—intermediate compression (6)

Piston ring—oil regulating (6)

Piston pin retainer (12)

One piece trunk piston (6)

Piston skirt (6)   Piston pin (6)

Piston crown (6)

Articulated (two piece) piston

Piston pin (6)

Piston pin bushing (6)

Connecting rod bearing (12)

Connecting rod and cap (6)

Bolt (12)

Courtesy of Navistar International Corp.

FIGURE 15–14 Using a telescoping gauge to check the out-of-round specification of a connecting rod big end.

The consequence of an overweight or underweight rod is to unbalance the engine and generate a premature failure. Always check OEM service literature.

Assessing Pistons and Rings

Pistons and rings should be assessed for serviceability using a flowchart such as the one illustrated in **Figure 15–16**. More recent piston assemblies such as Ferrotherm (articulating) and Monotherm (steel trunk) can often be safely reused providing they are properly inspected.

Rod Assembly

Great care should be taken to ensure that rod caps are not mismatched. Each OEM does this in different ways, so observe the instructions in service literature. Ensure that connecting rods are matched with the rod caps because they are classified by weight; mismatching can result in premature failure. It is more difficult to

FIGURE 15–15 Flowchart for repair or replacement of a connecting rod.

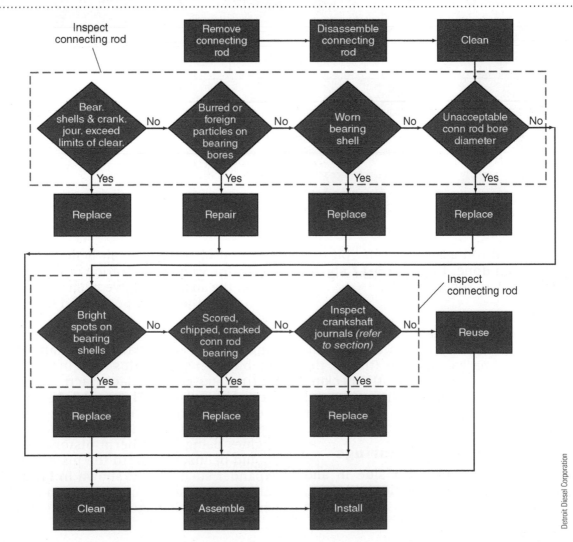

FIGURE 15–16 Flowchart for repair or replacement of piston and piston rings.

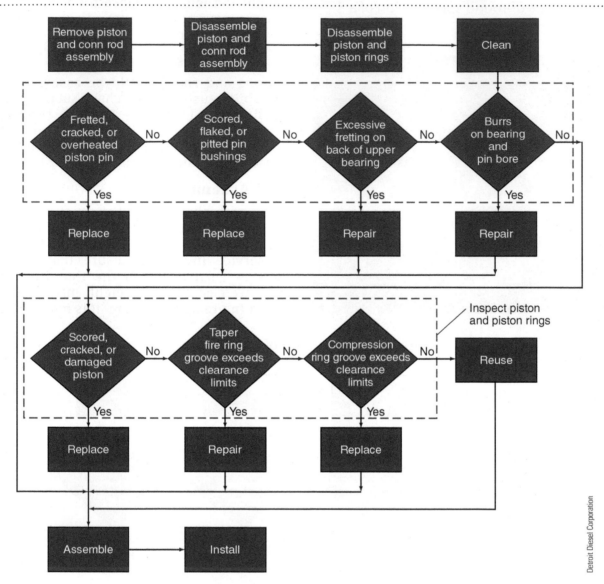

Detroit Diesel Corporation

mismatch a cracked rod assembly, but you can bet that it has been done. **Figure 15–17** shows a mismatched cracked rod assembly.

Ring End Gap

A procedure often overlooked by experienced diesel technicians, probably due to the reliability of machining and packaging today (that is, the nominal dimension is usually correct), checking the ring end gap specification takes little time and should be done. Insert the ring into the cylinder bore and measure the gap with thickness gauges.

Piston Wrist Pin Retainer Snaprings

Snaprings should be installed flat side in and with the gap either up or down (varies with OEM, but usually down) and never crossways to the direction of piston travel. Believe it or not, the inertia forces on acceleration or deceleration acting on the snaprings have been known to unseat them when the gap is positioned horizontally.

Ring Stagger

Ring stagger is crucially important when reassembling engines. Most engine OEMs prefer that no end gap be placed across either thrust face of the piston. **Figure 15–18** shows DDC's preferred method for installing and staggering ring end gap on its recent model Series 60 engines using Monotherm pistons. Piston rings should be installed onto the piston using a ring expander such as that shown in **Figure 15–19**. Failure to use a ring expander can result in broken rings and damage ring surface cladding.

FIGURE 15–17 Incorrect rod cap assembly on a cracked/fractured connecting rod.

FIGURE 15–18 Detroit Diesel (DD) Monotherm piston ring stagger.

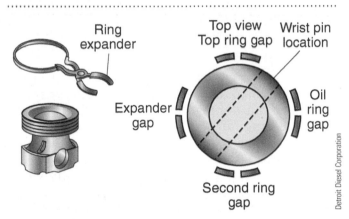

Detroit Diesel Corporation

FIGURE 15–19 Ring expander used to both remove and install rings onto a piston.

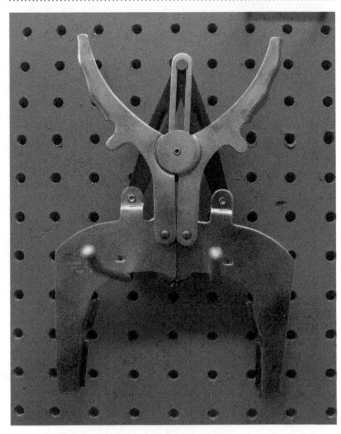

FIGURE 15–20 Clamp-type ring compressor.

Courtesy of Navistar International Corp.

Installing the Piston Assembly

Ensure that both the piston and connecting rod are properly oriented, remembering that OEMs usually do this by stamping the components with an arrow pointing toward the front. Use of multipurpose band-type ring compressors should be avoided when installing piston assemblies into the cylinder block, because more often than not they damage rings. **Figure 15–20** and **Figure 15–21** show two common types of ring compressors. One uses a clamp, the other a taper principle. The taper-type ring compressor can actually be machined using a discarded liner from the same engine series. Ensure that the piston assembly and ring compressor are well oiled (with engine lube) before installing the unit. **Figure 15–22** shows a piston pack being pushed into place using a taper cylinder ring compressor.

Install Rod Cap

In the case of cracked or fractured rods, eyeball the orientation prior to installing the rod cap: Although cracked rod caps will only fit when correctly oriented, it is easy enough to damage

FIGURE 15-21 Tapered sleeve ring compressor.

FIGURE 15-22 Taper-type ring compressor used to install piston pack into a diesel engine cylinder liner.

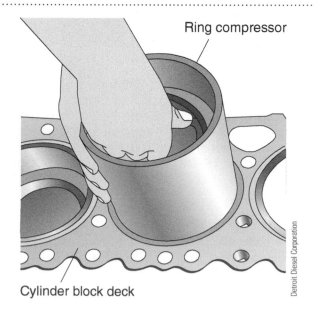

Ring compressor

Cylinder block deck

Detroit Diesel Corporation

FIGURE 15-23 Correct orientation of a connecting rod assembly, noting that the arrow points to the front of the engine.

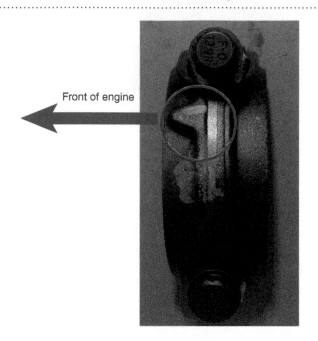

Front of engine

the mating faces by attempting to fit them improperly. In the case of stepped or clean face machined rod caps, make sure to fit the clamp as indicated by the directional arrow or number on the cap. **Figure 15-23** shows the directional arrow on a typical rod cap.

Rod Side Play

Side play is a critical specification on any rods with machined big end faces. Slightly cocked rod caps can damage crankshafts and promote rapid bearing failure. The use of a pair of equal-sized thickness gauges close to the side play specification value inserted on one side of the cap may assist with alignment problems while torquing the rod cap. Cracked rods used on some engines make this check unnecessary. All correctly assembled rods must have side play.

Buttress Screws on Main Bearing Caps

Some engines use **buttress** screws on some of the main bearing caps to add rigidity to the block assembly. These are usually installed after the main bolts have been torqued: Do not omit them. Cylinder blocks for the high-horsepower engines of today are made from castings of higher strength and lower weights, enabling them to flex more than those of a generation ago, which is the reason the buttress screws are now engineered into some engines.

TIMING GEARTRAIN ASSEMBLY

The procedure for setting up and timing the engine geartrain varies considerably from engine to engine. It may be a simple procedure, but in the example of some overhead camshaft (OHC) engines such as the pre-2010 Cummins ISX with its double OHCs, some specialized tooling (and training) is required. Some of the procedures you may encounter are listed next.

Camshaft Inspection

There is a detailed account of camshaft inspection in Chapter 8. The camshaft should first be visually inspected, and if this appears okay, it should be mounted in V-blocks as shown in Figure 8–11. The journals should be miked and the profiles indicated as shown in Figure 8–12. Pay special attention to areas of the cam profile that sustain the most abuse. This would include peak cam lift on symmetrical cam profiles. For camshafts that actuate open nozzle injectors, pay special attention to the end of the inner base circle (IBC) to outer base circle (OBC) ramp. This bottoms the plunger train components into the injector cup to establish mechanical crush and can be especially tough on the cam profile.

Heat Shrinking Gears to Shafts

A bearing hot plate may be used to heat interference-fit gears to the OEM-specified temperature. A kitchen toaster oven (dedicated to the purpose of heating engine components) has an accurate thermostat and works better, because the gear is more evenly heated. **Tempilstick** crayon may be used to check the temperature of a heated component and is required if you are using the hot-plate method. Do not use an oxyacetylene torch to heat components, because the steel may carburize. Gears should not be heated for periods exceeding 45 minutes.

Timing the Geartrain

The OEM procedure must be adhered to. Some guidelines are provided in Chapter 8 of this book, but it should be emphasized that this is no substitute for OEM service literature. **Figure 15–24** shows the location of the timing gear marks on a Caterpillar C15 engine. This is an overhead

FIGURE 15–24 Timing a Caterpillar C15 geartrain.

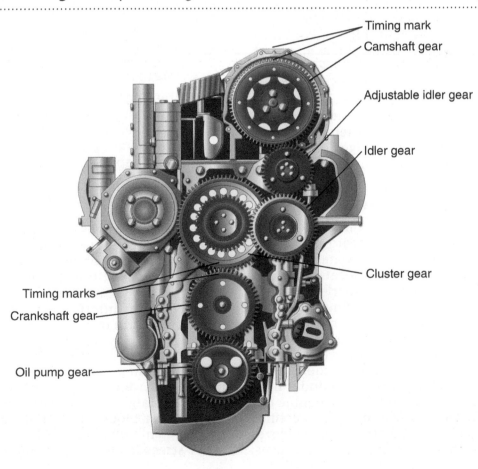

Timing mark

Camshaft gear

Adjustable idler gear

Idler gear

Cluster gear

Timing marks

Crankshaft gear

Oil pump gear

camshaft engine with a front timing geartrain. The timing indices used on this engine are Vs and circles.

Rear Cam Bushings

When performing an in-chassis engine overhaul, when the cam bushings are removed, it should be noted that the rear cam bushing in some engines may not be removed without unseating the rear cam plug. Because replacement of the rear cam plug involves the removal of the transmission/clutch assembly and flywheel housing— procedures that are unlikely to have been factored into the estimate—it is advisable to leave the rear cam bushing in place. Record the fact that it was not replaced on the hard copy of the work order.

CYLINDER HEAD SERVICING

Because OEMs have adopted single slab cylinder heads manufactured from lighter (and stronger) base metal, a cylinder head must be measured and pressure tested before being returned to service. Some of the required checks are outlined here.

Cylinder Head Warpage

Check the cylinder for head warpage with a straightedge and thickness gauges. This test is critical in today's low-weight, high-brake power engines, especially those using single slab castings on six-cylinder engines. Check the OEM maximum warpage spec. Select a feeler gauge equivalent to the maximum spec, and while positioning the straightedge corner to corner on the inverted cylinder head, attempt to insert the gauge under the straightedge. If it can be inserted, this fails the cylinder head and it should be reconditioned.

Pressure Testing Cylinder Heads

It is preferable to run hot water through cylinder heads for about 10 minutes to heat them before hydrostatically testing them. Hot water and shop air regulated at 100 psi should locate any leakage problems. Consult with an experienced technician to check whether that engine series has a track record of cylinder head problems and where leakage problems occur. With most engine series, the number one source of cylinder head leaks is the injector sleeve: Because the injector sleeve is in direct contact with the cylinder head water jacket, coolant leakage into the engine cylinder can occur. The problem has been rectified to some extent as copper base injector sleeves have been replaced by stainless steel (SS) sleeves.

CAUTION:

Some injector sleeves are swaged into position and can be tough to remove. Sometimes these are threaded to enable them to be pulled out with a screw plug and a slide hammer. Do not attempt to cut them out. This may have worked with copper injector sleeves, but the SS is harder than the cylinder head material and damage will result.

Measure and Recut the Cylinder Head Fire Ring Groove

Measure to specification and recut when necessary. This is not a complex procedure, but it does require the correct tooling. In engines that use a cylinder head fire ring groove, the fire ring is designed to deform into the recess when the cylinder head is torqued to spec. This fire ring yield deformation is a key to creating a good seal.

CYLINDER HEAD VALVES

You should be familiar with the procedure required to inspect and service valves as outlined in Chapter 8. The flowchart illustrated in **Figure 15–25** sets some guidelines for assessing cylinder valve serviceability.

Valve Margin

When dressing valves, remember that the valve margin specification is critical, and if it cannot be met, the valve should be replaced. Refer to Chapter 8 if you are uncertain what the valve margin spec represents.

VALVE INTERFERENCE ANGLE

Most cylinder valves in today's diesel engines are not designed with an interference angle, because this reduces the valve's seating contact surface area. Additionally, most current diesel engines use valve rotators, and it is not common to machine an interference angle into a valve using a valve rotator.

Cylinder Head Alignment

When installing multiple heads on an engine block deck, align the heads before torquing, using a straightedge. Perform this even when the cylinder block has cylinder head alignment dowels. This enables improved sealing and lower stress loads on the manifolds.

FIGURE 15–25 Flowchart for repair or replacement of cylinder head valves.

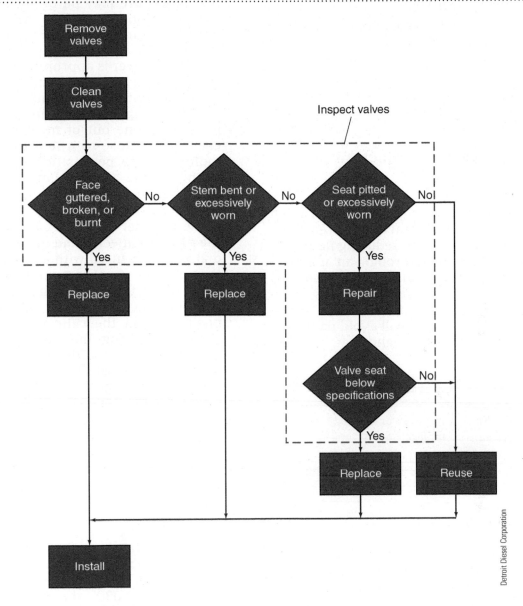

Most current cylinder head gaskets are of the integral design; that is, the fire rings and sealing grommets are incorporated in the head gasket template. However, in nonintegral gasket designs, especially those installed on a cylinder block deck that is angled (such as on a V engine), always use alignment dowels and eyeball the gasket components before finally decking the cylinder head.

SETTING VALVES AND INJECTORS

When setting cylinder valves and cam-actuated injectors, always use the correct engine locations to perform the adjustment. The general procedure for setting valves is outlined in Chapter 8,

but the OEM recommended procedure should always be observed.

Injector Installation

When installing EHIs, MUIs, EUPs, EUIs, and HEUIs, always use the OEM-recommended procedure. Lubricating the O-rings with the correct medium is critical. Generally, the use of anti-seize compound on cylindrical injectors with O-ring seals is never approved, and though the technician may believe he is making the next removal of that set of injectors easier, their removal may come a lot sooner than anticipated. Use the correct lubricant medium for the O-rings and accept that occasionally injectors do seize in their bores. Note that when injectors are removed and replaced, either or both of the following may be required:

- Mechanically actuated injectors may have to be timed (height adjusted).
- Calibration codes may have to be reprogrammed to ECM.

These procedures are covered in later sections of this textbook in chapters addressing each specific OEM system.

Torque High-Pressure Injection Pipe Nuts

Overtorquing high-pressure injection pipe nuts at the rail, at the injector, or at the injection pump can ridge the nipple seat and, more significantly, collapse the aperture, reducing flow area. A reduction in flow area through an injection high-pressure pipe may result in low power and engine fueling balance problems. Torquing injector lines using a line wrench socket and torque wrench is good practice and will avoid damaging the high-pressure pipe nipple and seat.

CAUTION:

Some OEMs require that the high-pressure pipes used with CR fuel systems be replaced every time they are removed. They are one-use components because they yield to deform and seat the first time they are torqued.

VERIFYING TRUE TDC

On engines that use an external timing index, it may be necessary to precisely position the timing indicator before undertaking any timing procedure. When a piston reaches the top of its travel on its upstroke, it remains stationary while the crank throw turns through its apex before beginning the downstroke. True top dead center (TDC) is the exact midpoint between the moment the piston stops moving upward and the moment it begins its downstroke. A timing indicator must be set at true TDC, and not simply at any point where the piston is at the top of its travel, to ensure that components such as injection pumps are accurately timed to the engine. The following steps give the procedure for determining true TDC for a typical four-stroke cycle, inline, six-cylinder engine.

1. Locate the fixed engine timing marker and rotating calibration scale; this may be on the vibration damper pulley, any other pulley driven at engine speed, or on the flywheel. The procedure may be performed on either the #1- or #6-engine cylinder on inline six-cylinder engines. Ensure that the fuel system is no-fueled either mechanically or electrically, whichever is appropriate. Manually bar the engine in its normal direction or rotation to locate cylinders #1 and #6 at indicated TDC by using the fixed timing indicator or by making one out of mechanic's wire and clamping it close to where the fixed timing indicator is to be positioned. The flywheel (using a gear and ratchet barring tool) or crank hub (using a barring fixture) should be used to rotate the engine.

2. If the cylinder heads are installed, remove the #1 or #6 injector and install in its place a dial indicator fitted with an extension probe long enough to contact the piston crown. In cases where the cylinder heads are removed from the engine, the dial indicator may be positioned on the cylinder block with the probe contacting the piston crown. Next, zero the indicator at the highest point of piston travel by barring the engine slightly both sides of TDC.

3. Cut a 4" strip of masking tape and place it on the flywheel or pulley calibration scale.

4. If the dial indicator was properly zeroed, barring the engine in either direction (before top dead center [BTDC] and after top dead center [ATDC]) will produce a negative scale reading on the indicator. Pick an arbitrary value such as that represented by a complete rotation of the dial indicator (0.050" or 0.100"; for the purposes of this explanation of the procedure, 0.050" is used), then bar the engine BTDC until the chosen value is exceeded by 0.030", that is, until the indicator reads 0.080". Next, bar the engine back in the normal direction of rotation until 0.050" is read at the dial indicator. With a pencil, draw a line under the fixed or temporary timing indicator. Then reverse bar the engine until 0.050" is read at the dial indicator. Draw a second line under the fixed or temporary timing marker. The reason for turning the engine 0.030" beyond the selected value is to eliminate backlash factors while performing this procedure.

5. Next, place a third mark exactly between the first two. One way of accurately performing this is with a knife. Neatly cut the masking tape at both of the two lines drawn and fold back one end of the masking tape so that the two cut ends align. Rotate the engine

until the fold crease is positioned under the fixed or temporary timing marker. When the engine is rotated back to the exact midpoint between the two lines, it will be positioned at true TDC.

6. With the engine located at true TDC, the tape can be removed and the fixed timing marker adjusted to the TDC point on the engine calibration scale.

FLYWHEEL HOUSING CONCENTRICITY

Never take any risks with a flywheel housing. They are regarded as indestructible by many technicians but can cause more problems than you may think. Flywheel housings are subjected to high torque shock loads and minor misalignment problems can cause a range of problems. Always observe the OEM measurements when reinstalling flywheels *any* time they are removed.

Diamond Dowels

Diamond dowels work to retain the alignment of mated components much better than cylindrical dowels. However, all the critical alignment checks should still be performed. For instance, if a flywheel housing has been removed, the housing should be radially indicated (dial indicator) for its concentricity to the crankshaft even when diamond dowels are used. If they are used, there is much less chance of an eccentric measurement (**Figure 15–26**).

Indicating a Flywheel Housing

Any time a flywheel is removed from the cylinder block, the housing inner flange face concentricity with the crankshaft should be checked using a dial indicator. The maximum tolerance for the crankshaft-to-flywheel housing eccentricity is low, typically around 0.012" (0.3 mm) or less total indicated runout (TIR); the consequences of installing a flywheel housing that exceeds the allowable specification are severe. When this occurs, the drive axis is broken, which can result in clutch, engine mount, transmission, and engine failures. The flywheel housing to crankshaft concentricity is preserved by interference-fit cylindrical or diamond dowels. These may be relied on to properly realign the flywheel housing on the cylinder block at each reinstallation, but the specification is so critical that it should always be checked. The following procedure outlines a method of checking **flywheel housing concentricity**, and a couple of typical strategies for correcting an out-of-specification condition.

1. Ensure that the engine is properly supported. Indicating a flywheel housing may be performed with the engine in-chassis or out; obviously a procedure such as this is made easier if the engine is out of chassis. Locate the flywheel inner flange face-to-crankshaft concentricity TIR tolerance in the OEM technical literature. Either mechanically or electrically ensure that the engine fuel system is no-fueled.

2. Mount the flywheel housing to the engine cylinder block using the dowels to align the assembly and snug the flywheel fasteners at about half of the OEM-specified torque value.

3. Using fabricators' chalk, mark the flywheel flange face with indices in the following rotational positions: NE, NW, SW, SE, or N W S E (shown in **Figure 15–27**).

FIGURE 15–26 Diamond dowel installation.

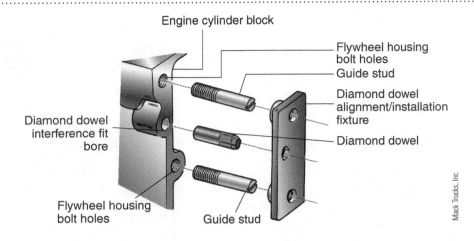

FIGURE 15-27 Recommended method for checking flywheel housing radial concentricity.

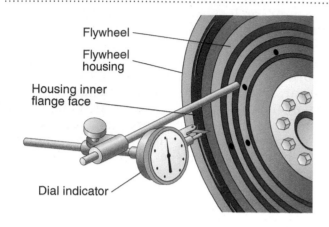

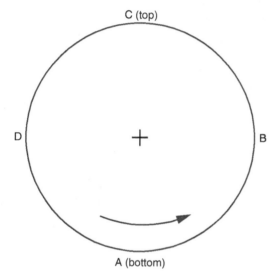

C (top)

D

B

A (bottom)

4. Next, thoroughly clean the inside face of the flywheel housing with emery cloth and fix a magnetic base dial indicator to any position on the crankshaft, setting the probe to contact the flywheel housing inside face as demonstrated in Figure 15–27. Using an engine barring tool, rotate the engine in its normal direction of rotation until the indicator probe is positioned at any one of the chalk indexes. Now set the indicator at zero.

5. Bar the engine through a full rotation, recording the indicator reading at each of the indexes. The indicator should once again read zero when the revolution is complete. If the readings were as follows: NE:0, NW: minus 0.003", SW: minus 0.005", SE: plus 0.004", the TIR would be the highest negative value (0.005") added to the highest positive value (0.004"), giving a reading of 0.009". If

the OEM TIR maximum specification were 0.012", this reading would be within it.

Correcting Flywheel Housing Radial Runout

If the flywheel housing to crankshaft concentricity is outside of the specification, it must be reset. The following outlines this procedure for an engine that aligns the flywheel housing using cylindrical locating dowels. Begin by removing the dowels. Check the availability of oversize locating dowels with the parts department. Loosen the flywheel mounting capscrews until they are barely snug, permitting the flywheel housing to be moved fractionally when struck with a rubber mallet. Perform the flywheel housing concentricity sequence as in the foregoing steps. Adjust the position of the flywheel housing by tapping with the rubber mallet on the basis of the readings of the dial indicator. Repeat the procedure until the readings meet the required specification. When they do, fully torque the flywheel housing capscrews to specification. Next, the locating dowel holes in the cylinder block and flywheel housing will have to be reamed to an oversize specification, factoring in the interference fit requirement. Drive the oversize dowels into the reamed holes.

Checking Flywheel Housing Axial Runout

Flywheel housing axial runout failures are rare, but you should still perform the check. Check the flywheel housing mating face runout as shown in **Figure 15–28**. When a failure to meet specification occurs, it is most likely caused by coincidental damage from some other problem such as missing fasteners. If measured out of specification, machining or replacement is required.

FIGURE 15-28 Checking flywheel housing axial concentricity.

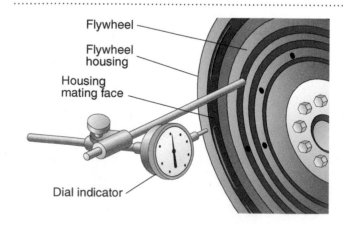

Reinstall Engine to Chassis

If an adequate amount of care was taken in removing the engine from the chassis, the reinstallation should be straightforward. Usually, this takes less time than the removal because the components are clean and the hoses and connectors are tagged. Never hesitate to obtain assistance, especially in snub-nose conventional chassis with an engine compartment that extends into the cab. The overhaul procedure should be completed by running the break-in test profiles covered in Chapter 16.

REPROGRAMMING THE ECM

Depending on the engine OEM and exactly what has been done during the overhaul procedure, it will probably be necessary to reprogram some of the data fields to the ECM. Reprogramming may involve little more than flashing calibration codes for any injectors that have been replaced (see later chapters in this textbook), or it may mean downloading a new set of engine files. Make sure you consult the OEM service literature for the engine being worked on prior to making any attempt to start a reconditioned engine.

SUMMARY

- Most of the procedures outlined in this chapter are covered in greater detail elsewhere in the book. The content in this chapter is intended to be used as a general guideline for the novice technician, remembering that some steps are not covered by this book until later chapters.
- Ensure the work area around the chassis and the engine during rebuild is clean, organized, and uncluttered.
- The importance of tagging components, lines, linkages, and connectors cannot be overemphasized.
- When working on an engine always follow the OEM recommended sequence so that if another technician were to take over the rebuild at any point in the procedure, he or she would have no problem in determining what the next step is. This also makes it easier for you to pick up where you left off.
- Remember to note the condition of every engine component as it is removed for failure analysis, especially until the root cause of the failure has been diagnosed.
- When the reason for the engine rebuild is a failure, never begin the engine reassembly before defining the root cause of the failure.
- Always use the OEM technical service literature when undertaking engine overhaul.

REVIEW EXERCISES

The contents of this chapter are entirely practical. Simply, it is the application of some of the theory dealt with in previous chapters. At this point, it is probably essential to take down and reassemble a diesel engine and put into practice some of the theory covered thus far.

The following are some tasks to prepare you for the experience.

1. Identify the engine to be worked on and obtain the required OEM service literature.

2. Review the disassembly procedure of any diesel engine according to the OEM service literature. Ensure that something to write on and a pencil are available so that you can record any observations, especially those procedures that are not common to all engines.

3. Review the OEM-recommended cleaning and testing procedures for all the engine components, including the cylinder heads, cylinder block, connecting rods, and crankshaft. List all those procedures requiring the use of specialized equipment.

4. Review the OEM-recommended reassembly procedure for the same engine, once again noting any procedures that are distinct to that particular engine.

5. Review the OEM requirements for initial startup of the engine following an engine overhaul. Make a list of each step in the procedure. Take special notice of the recommended break-in procedure.

16

Prerequisites: Chapters 4, 6, 7, 8, 9, 10, 11, 12, and 14. Some reference to Sections 2 and 3 of this textbook is desirable.

DIESEL ENGINE RUN-IN AND PERFORMANCE TESTING

OBJECTIVES

After studying this chapter, you should be able to:

- Understand the basics of power analysis and dynamometer testing.
- Outline the OEM requirements of engine run-in after rebuild.
- Describe the process required to check out both the engine and vehicle before a chassis dynamometer test.
- Outline personal and equipment safety while operating an engine or chassis dynamometer.
- Describe the objectives of run-in and performance testing on a dynamometer.
- Interpret the data on a dynamometer test profile.
- Describe how a heavy-duty truck is installed onto a chassis dynamometer test bed.
- Outline the objectives of a chassis dynamometer performance and engine run-in tests.
- Describe how to road-test a truck with a newly rebuilt diesel engine.

KEY TERMS

brake horsepower (BHP)

chassis dynamometer

droop curve

dynamometer

dyno

eddy-current dynamometer

engine dynamometer

engine longevity

linehaul

machine under test (MUT)

peak torque

prelubricator

preventive maintenance (PM)

rated speed

run-in

torque

torque rise profile

INTRODUCTION

Running-in and testing a rebuilt diesel engine is key to ensuring that it performs properly. The procedures outlined here are designed to complement those produced by the manufacturers of engine test apparatus and the engine original equipment manufacturers (OEMs) and not to replace them.

In the larger truck facility, the chassis **dynamometer (dyno)** is commonly used as a tool for loading an engine with the objective of diagnosing malfunctions, and it may not always be necessary to connect all of the instrumentation with which the dyno is equipped. Also, most electronically managed engines are capable of replicating the dynamometer data. It is strongly recommended, however, that all the available dynamometer instrumentation be used for every dyno test, regardless of what data is generated by the vehicle management system. This will verify the engine control module (ECM) calibration data and help develop a dynamometer performance database, which can be referenced in future testing of similar engine/chassis configurations. In addition, a dynamometer test can assist in determining whether the emission controls are functioning properly, especially when exhaust opacity and gas analysis equipment is used.

When using the road test for engine break-in and testing, the technician should be always aware that the primary responsibility is to safely operate the vehicle on the road. The road test is definitely the least preferred method of engine testing, but nevertheless one that many repair and service operations must use if they cannot access a dynamometer. It makes sense to develop a set of guidelines to be observed by technicians when road-testing at a service operation, to ensure some consistency of test conditions; this can be useful as a comparative performance reference. If the data generated by dynamometer and road testing is recorded to a database, it will not be long before sufficient data is retained to provide an invaluable reference for diagnosing engine conditions.

Most of the terms used in this chapter concerning power terminology are covered in an earlier chapter of this textbook. However, dynamometer manufacturers commonly use the term **machine under test (MUT)** to refer the unit being tested. In this chapter, the MUT will always be an engine.

The terms and principles concerning engine governing, electronic management systems, and diagnostic instruments are covered in the later sections. In other words, to fully understand all of the concepts introduced in this chapter, you will have to reference other sections of the textbook.

REBUILT ENGINE RUN-IN PROCEDURE

When OEMs talk about **engine longevity**, they are referring to the projected operational service life of the engine from manufacture to first overhaul and thereafter, between engine overhauls. Actual engine longevity is determined by a large number of factors, including the type of chassis it powers, the physical conditions under which it is operated, preventive maintenance practices of the operator, and the skills of the driver. There is no doubt that in recent years, expected engine life of electronically managed, highway diesels has more than doubled, sometimes tripled.

ENGINE LONGEVITY

Engine longevity can be measured either in engine hours or by highway miles completed. In most truck operations, highway miles are used to evaluate engine life. This can be misleading, as it would not take into account factors such as prolonged idling, power takeoff (PTO) operation, and the conditions of the operating environment. For instance, a truck engine used for short pickup and delivery runs in a large city will have a much tougher life than one used in a long-distance, linehaul application. The same would apply in the comparison between the city bus and the intercity highway coach. The type of service a vehicle is subjected to is always a factor.

LINEHAUL MILES

Today, it is not unreasonable to expect a service life of 3 million *linehaul* miles or around 5 million km from a current truck engine when supported with sound maintenance practices ... and a good driver. Within this life span, one major out-of-chassis and two in-chassis overhauls would be expected at appropriate intervals. **Linehaul** refers to terminal-to-terminal, long-distance highway travel, which is usually regarded as the least punishing operating condition for every chassis system. The same engine in a truck hauling aggregates out of a quarry and running them short distances might be lucky to achieve a sixth of that mileage, and that would require conscientious **preventive maintenance (PM)** and a knowledgeable operator. Diesel engines are not designed to be idled. The toughest job a linehaul diesel has to routinely perform is to idle while its driver eats lunch or sleeps. With many states and provinces adopting tough new anti-idling legislation for reasons of emissions and fuel economy, a major beneficiary will be engine longevity.

RUN-IN

A critical factor in the expected operational life of a rebuilt engine is the initial **run-in** following the overhaul. After a complete overhaul or major repair job involving the installation of piston rings, pistons, cylinder liners/sleeves, or bearings, the engine must be "run-in" before release for service. The procedure for run-in varies depending on the method used, and that largely depends on the equipment available. Engine dynamometer, chassis dynamometer, or highway run-in methods may be used. There is no doubt that the preferred diesel engine run-in method is the engine dynamometer, but time constraints make this method impractical in many operations.

The chassis dynamometer is probably the most commonly used method of engine break-in, but dynamometer equipment is costly and only larger truck service facilities can justify the expense. The least preferred method is the highway run-in. Many rebuilders have no choice but to use this method of engine break-in, but even when the operator is knowledgeable it is difficult to fulfill the proper requirements of the break-in procedure on a highway road test with little control over load and limited monitoring instrumentation. The main reasons for medium- and heavy-duty diesel engine run-in are as follows:

- Seat the piston rings
- Test for fluid leaks
- Check engine power ratings
- Check ECM calibrations

After performing the OEM run-in procedure, the engine should be capable of being safely operated at full load.

PREPARING AN ENGINE FOR THE FIRST START-UP

Regardless of the method to be used for engine run-in, the engine must be properly prepared before starting for the first time. The following list may be used as a general guide:

1. Lubrication system: The lubricating oil film on the rotating parts and bearings of an overhauled engine is usually insufficient for proper lubrication when the engine is started up for the first time after an overhaul. Install new oil filters. Fill a pressure **prelubricator** (usually an electrically or pneumatically actuated external oil pump) with the OEM-recommended oil and connect the supply line to the main oil gallery. Prime the engine lubrication system with sufficient oil. There are various points on the engine into which the pressure line may be tapped, but if no other is apparent, the oil gauge line may be disconnected and the pressure tank applied at that point. Remove the oil level dipstick, and check crankcase level. Add oil, if necessary, to bring it to the full mark on the dipstick. *Do not overfill!* When using a prelubricator it is unnecessary to prime the oil filters. Some OEMs prefer that the oil filters never be primed prior to installation, due to the risk of contaminating the oil during the procedure. The preferred method of priming the lube oil circuit is by using a prelubricator (**Figure 16–1**).

2. Turbocharger: Disconnect the turbocharger oil inlet line and pour approximately 1 pint (half a liter) of clean engine oil into the turbo, ensuring that the bearings are lubricated for the startup. Reconnect the oil line.

3. Air intake system: Check the integrity of the air intake system, checking all the hose clamps, support clamps, piping, charge air cleaner, and the air cleaner element(s). Always replace the air cleaner element after an engine overhaul.

4. Cooling system: Fit a new coolant filter and, if required, separate conditioning additives. Fill the cooling system with the recommended coolant mixture. Ensure that all or at least most air is purged from the cooling system; remove a plug from the water manifold during filling to allow air to escape.

5. Fuel system: Install new fuel filters, priming them as required, with the correct grade of filtered fuel. Next, prime the fuel system by actuating a hand pump or external priming pump. Avoid priming a fuel system by charging the fuel tanks with compressed air; the practice can be particularly dangerous when ambient temperatures are high.

6. Electrical system: Ensure that the batteries hold a proper level of charge. This is especially critical with some electronically managed engines in which the ECM requires a specific minimum operating voltage.

7. Initial startup: Crank the engine with no fuel for 15 seconds; check for leaks. Next, start

FIGURE 16–1 Prelubricator setup to prime a diesel engine.

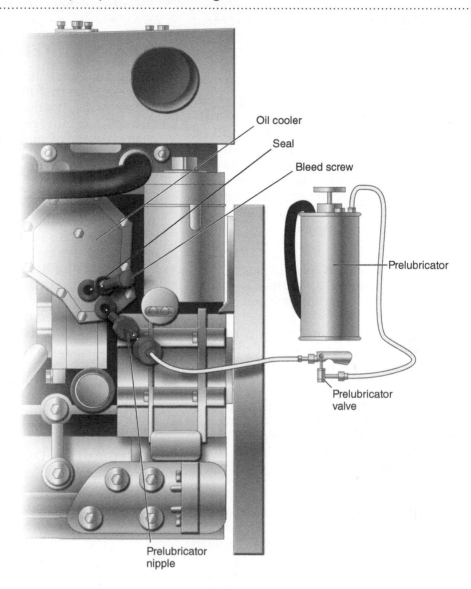

the engine, run for 2 minutes, and then shut down. Check for leaks. Do not run for a period longer than 2 minutes.

TECH TIP:

Do not allow the engine to run for more than 2 minutes during the initial startup test. The run-in objective after an engine rebuild is to apply a moderate load to the engine until it achieves its normal operating temperature and then to run the engine somewhere close to full load for at least 15 minutes to seat the rings. Idling an engine for any length of time after an overhaul can glaze the liner walls and make it impossible for the piston rings to seat.

CAUTION:

Avoid priming a dry fuel system by pressurizing fuel tanks with shop air, whether regulated or unregulated. In hot weather conditions, potentially explosive mixtures of air and diesel fuel are formed, especially when the tank fuel levels are low.

LOADED ENGINE RUN-IN

Regardless of the run-in method, the technician performing the procedure must be observant throughout to detect and act on any problems that may develop. Instrumentation displaying engine and chassis functions must be monitored constantly and all readings recorded. Even if a computerized dynamometer with a printout capability is used, also record the cab instrument display and data from the chassis bus. Compare the downloaded data where possible. During dynamometer or road testing on electronically managed systems, use an electronic service tool (EST) to take data "snapshots" as required.

If an engine develops any abnormal running characteristics during run-in, it should be immediately shut down and the problem investigated and corrected before continuing the run-in procedure. The technician should use all his or her senses during the entire startup/break-in process. The following should act as a guideline for conditions that may develop and require immediate investigation:

- Any unusual noises, such as knocking, scraping, squealing, or combustion knock.
- Any vibration in the engine or elsewhere in the drivetrain.
- Any significant drop in engine oil pressure. Check the OEM parameters for oil pressure values—they vary widely.

NOTE:

The low oil pressure value that triggers an electronic alert is often much lower than the minimum acceptable normal oil pressure value.

- A rise in coolant temperature that exceeds the maximum specified by the OEM, typically between 200°F (95°C) and 220°F (104°C) (maximum values vary—check OEM specifications).
- A rise in engine oil temperature that exceeds the maximum specified by the OEM, typically 240°F (115°C) (maximum values vary—check OEM specifications).
- An exhaust temperature that exceeds maximum limit for the specific engine being tested, as measured by a chassis pyrometer or a dynamometer pyrometer. If the latter is used, ensure that it is positioned in the correct location for the specification reading (12" [25 cm] downstream from the turbine exhaust outlet is typical), and that the probe is not contacting any metal components.
- Any oil, coolant, fuel, manifold boost, or air intake system leaks.
- Any nonengine chassis system malfunction. When using a chassis dynamometer or road test to make engine break-in easier, never forget that while the engine may be the focus of the testing, every chassis system is getting a thorough workout.

DYNAMOMETER TEST OBJECTIVES

The dynamometer is primarily designed to measure *power*, a term fully defined in an earlier chapter. Essentially, the dynamometer is an instrument that applies turning resistance to the torque output (twisting effort) of another machine and accurately measures the applied resistance. Power is the *rate* of accomplishing work. When power is tested on a dynamometer, its factors are torque and time. The **torque** output of an engine is accurately measured by the dynamometer and factored with time (rpm) to calculate its power. Most dynamometers take care of the math and usually display power in units of **brake horsepower (BHP)** or kilowatts (kW). For a full explanation of power characteristics and terminology, refer to Chapter 6.

When you use a dynamometer to break in an engine, the test is used to fully load the engine rather than simply measure its power output. There are two general categories of dynamometers used in the diesel service facilities, and they are defined by the method used to apply a resistance to the turning effort of the engine or chassis being tested.

Electromotive Dyno

An electromotive or **eddy-current dynamometer** is basically an electric motor turned in reverse. The engine is coupled to the dynamometer armature by means of a driveshaft assembly and rotates it: As current is switched to flow through the induction coils of the electromotive dynamometer, resistance to the turning effort of the engine increases, producing the eddy current. The more current flowed through the dynamometer coils, the stronger the electromagnetic field produced and the greater the amount of torque required by the engine.

Hydraulic Dyno

The second category of dynamometer is hydraulic. The hydraulic medium used is usually water, but other types of hydraulic media can be used. The critical component in the hydraulic dynamometer is a load cell or multiple load cells. These use a principle similar to that used by a hydraulic driveline retarder such as the Caterpillar brake saver: Water is flowed through the cell and acts on an impeller. Inlet and outlet valves are used to control the flow of the hydraulic medium into and out of the load cell and define the torque required to rotate the impeller.

Dyno Data

All dynamometers measure torque. Most also measure rotational speed. When both torque and rpm are known, BPH can be calculated using the equations introduced in Chapter 6:

$$BHP = \frac{T \times rpm}{5252} \qquad T = \text{Torque expressed in lb-ft.}$$

or

$$kW = \frac{T \times rpm}{9429} \qquad T = \text{Torque expressed in N·m.}$$

$$Torque = \frac{BHP \times 5252}{rpm}$$

or

$$Torque = \frac{kW \times 9429}{rpm}$$

When performing chassis dynamometer testing of diesel engines, whether for purposes of diagnosis or to perform an engine run-in routine, all of the gauges and instrumentation should be connected to the engine being tested. Loading an engine down on a dynamometer is the ultimate performance test for an engine, and it should be monitored as thoroughly as possible. It takes a little extra time to connect all the required gauges and instruments, but they will assist to ensure accurate diagnoses and complete reports. Electronic printouts do not look professional when half the data categories are left blank.

CHASSIS DYNAMOMETER TESTING

Because of the time required to mount and dismount an engine to an engine dynamometer test bed, the chassis dynamometer is used for most truck engine diagnosis and testing. **Chassis dynamometers** use a roller or rollers to receive input. The truck chassis therefore must be located so that its drive axles are properly aligned and contacting the rollers, and then be chained into position. Determine that the dynamometer is in calibration before starting the test. When double roller chassis dynamometers are used, periodic testing by running a single drive axle chassis on each roller separately will provide an indication of the condition of each absorption unit and the display instrumentation. The following outlines the procedure to be followed when running a truck chassis on a dynamometer.

NOTE:

When preparing to chassis dyno test, for most trucks today, you must first consult the OEM service literature. At minimum you will be required to disable the automatic traction control (ATC) and directional stability electronics using the appropriate EST. The disablement of ATC and yaw stability is usually performed by accessing the controller source addresses (SAs)/message identifiers (MIDs) on the data bus, and not via the engine electronics. Many OEMs today option either by accessing the chassis or engine electronics. Failure to do this will result in the engine/chassis default mode response (limp home) or possible drivetrain component damage.

1. Check all the chassis fluid levels, including engine oil, fuel, coolant, transmission, and drive axle carrier. Check the tire pressure and the wheel lug integrity. Inspect suspension components, driveline, and brake adjustment, ensuring that the chassis rolls freely with brakes released.
2. If the dynamometer is not self-centering, measure the truck chassis drive axle spread and set the rollers on the dynamometer to the required spread. Some double roller dynamometers have a self-centering feature (see **Figure 16–2**), and will automatically center when the wheels are spun up by a tandem drive truck; after centering, the bogies should be locked before applying any load. When a tandem chassis dynamometer is not self-centering (see **Figure 16–3**), the axle spread should be measured before moving the truck onto the test bed.

FIGURE 16–2 Double roller chassis dynamometer: this style of tandem double roller dyno is normally self-centering.

FIGURE 16–3 Single roller dynamometer test bed. This style of tandem is not self-centering.

3. The roller brake should be engaged to lock the roller(s), to enable the truck to be driven onto the dynamometer test bed. Back the truck onto the dynamometer roller(s), release the brake, and align by running up the "road speed" to around 10 mph (16 km/h) in one of the low-range gears for 15 seconds or so, then shut down the engine. Chock the front wheels using 4 wheel wedges and install the safety chains; when performing the latter, be sure to securely fasten the safety chains. Generally, single roller dynamometers require the truck to be fastened down with more chain slack than double roller versions. Check on the procedure outlined by the dynamometer manufacturer.

CAUTION:

Do not crank down the chassis security chains, especially when the truck is equipped with an air suspension. Suspensions must be allowed to oscillate normally during the test.

4. All chassis operating on a dynamometer must be provided with adequate cooling air. This is almost impossible to achieve in the modern, sound-insulated dynamometer room. A large fan can assist, but it does not come close to inducing the airflow transfer rate of a tractor driving down the highway at 60 mph (100 km/h). To make matters worse, air-to-air charge air coolers have generally replaced coolant medium heat exchangers, and while these boast higher efficiencies in highway operation, they have lower operating efficiencies when ambient air transfer rates are low, such as operation in a mining pit or an enclosed chassis dynamometer. Fit the exhaust gas extractor pipes to the truck exhaust pipes.

5. Connect all the dynamometer gauges (these are usually of superior quality and accuracy) to the vehicle dash instruments, and, when possible, additionally monitor the engine running data using an EST and the appropriate software. Do not omit connecting monitoring gauges with the belief that it will save time. In the event of a malfunction, critical diagnostic data may be unavailable. Typical dynamometer gauges include: crankcase pressure, air inlet pressure, manifold boost pressure, fuel subsystem charging pressure, coolant temperature, coolant pressure, oil temperature, oil pressure, ambient air temperature (engine compartment), exhaust temperature (pyrometer), and exhaust back pressure. A chassis dynamometer control and monitoring console is shown in **Figure 16–4**, and **Figure 16–5** is a screen capture from the display monitor.

FIGURE 16–4 Chassis dynamometer control and monitoring station.

FIGURE 16–5 Data display screen view.

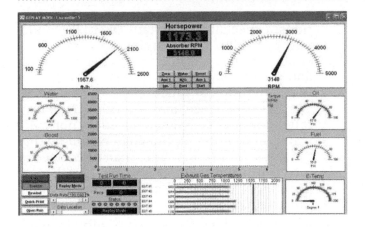

6. If the engine is hydromechanically managed, ensure that the accelerator linkage is properly set. This should be tested by having someone fully depress the accelerator pedal with the engine stopped while observing the throttle arm/fuel control lever. Normally, a visible travel breakover is required, which is typically ±0.125" (3 mm). With electronically managed engines, ensure that the throttle position sensor (TPS) calibration programming is correct. **Figure 16–6** shows the monitoring and display circuits used in a typical chassis dynamometer.

7. On certain vehicles with front axle/rear axle drives, the transfer case to the front axle drive will have to be disabled. In some cases, this might involve removal of the propeller shaft. Check with the OEM technical service literature on the appropriate test method.

8. Remove any stones lodged in the tire grooves. Switch on the exhaust extraction system and the ambient air transfer system. The fumes produced by burning tire rubber while dyno testing are harmful and should not be inhaled. Wear hearing protection.

9. Obtain the OEM test data for dynamometer testing; take particular note of the engine **torque rise profile** (often identified by the recommended gear shift points), rated speed rpm low, high idle speeds, and **droop curve**. Either obtain or make up a dynamometer test profile and record the running data while testing. It is good practice to do this even when a dynamometer printout is available. Familiarization with

FIGURE 16–6 Chassis dynamometer monitoring and display circuits.

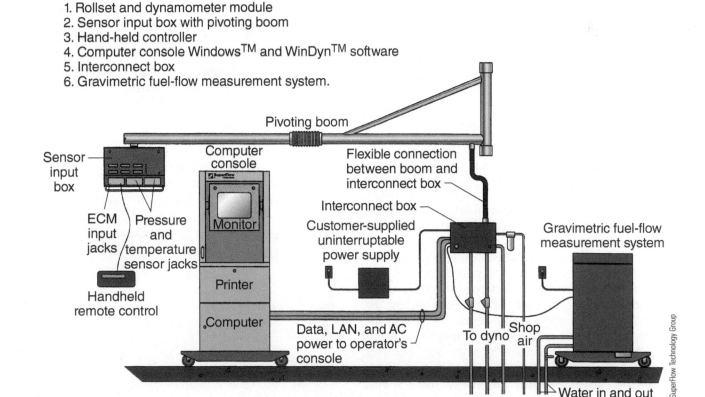

SuperFlow Dynamometer typically includes:
1. Rollset and dynamometer module
2. Sensor input box with pivoting boom
3. Hand-held controller
4. Computer console Windows™ and WinDyn™ software
5. Interconnect box
6. Gravimetric fuel-flow measurement system.

all critical maximum and minimum running parameters for the engine being tested will help in conducting a thorough engine test.

10. Start the engine and, while stationary, test idle and high idle engine speed. On a hydromechanically governed engine, if there is any irregularity with either parameter, cease the test and adjust the governor/set engine overhead as necessary before resuming. On a tandem drive axle unit, be sure to engage the interaxle differential lockout, especially when testing on a double roller dyno test bed. Smoothly shift through the gear ratios (skip shifting is acceptable) with no applied dynamometer load until the chassis is being run in the OEM-recommended ratio for testing, which is usually 1:1. Generally, overdrive ratios are not used. Record the road speed at both the base **(peak torque)** and peak **(rated speed)** rpm of the torque rise profile.

11. Run at the rated speed and load down the engine to approximately 50% of the engine rated power value until the engine coolant and/or oil are at operating temperature. Monitor all the engine data parameters, but pay particular attention to the coolant and exhaust pyrometer temperatures.

WARNING:

In testing using the double roller type of chassis dynamometer, the two bogie axles must never exceed 5 miles per hour (8 km) difference in road speed. With the engine run at a given test speed, the two dynamometer <Load> application buttons (one for each set of axle rollers) must be applied evenly while carefully monitoring the <MPH> display for each axle, ensuring that they are within 5 mph and are preferably identical. Application of the <Load> and <Unload> control buttons should always be balanced. Remember, whenever vehicles are equipped with a power divider lockout control, the lockout should be engaged during testing.

12. Never exceed a maximum limit—but remember that "maximum" means you are within a specification: Dynamometers are designed to explore the maximum an engine is capable of. However, when excessively high temperatures are observed and the dynamometer ambient temperature is not suspected to be the cause, check the boost air temperature. Install a calibrated temperature gauge downstream from the charge air cooling core, preferably at the intake manifold. Temperatures should generally not exceed

150°F (65°C), but check OEM specifications because exhaust gas recirculation (EGR) mixing variables can result in unusual conditions, especially on certain OEM EPA model year (MY) 2007–2010 engines.

13. When the engine is at operating temperature and the displayed data indicate that its systems are properly functional, the dynamometer test sequence may proceed. Full load rated power or "governed speed" is normally tested first. Running the engine rpm held at the rated speed (not higher than rated speed), load down the roller(s) until the accelerator pedal is at full travel; at the point at which the engine is unable to sustain the rated speed rpm, record the brake power value. Ensure that the air compressor is unloaded, the air conditioning (A/C) system is switched off, and the engine fan is disabled so that the results of the test are as accurate as possible. Check twice. Allow power readings to stabilize before recording. Next, perform the same test at 100 rpm below rated speed. Use the dyno loading to drop the engine rpm in 100 rpm increments, recording the engine power descending through the torque rise profile to its base rpm. This may be (but does not have to be) the "peak torque" rpm.

14. If the objective of the dynamometer test is to run-in a rebuilt engine rather than to diagnose engine performance, the engine should be run at full power at rated speed, then reduced through 100 rpm increments through the torque rise profile for a period not less than 20 minutes. This should be sufficient to properly seat the rings.

15. The technician undertaking the dynamometer test should constantly monitor the engine data displays for abnormal readings, especially those indicating temperature values. It is not unusual for engines using air-to-air charge air coolers to approach overheat values when performing full load chassis dynamometer testing, due to low airflow factors.

WARNING:

After running a full load dynamometer test on an engine, allow the engine to run at no-load idle speed for a period of at least 5 minutes following the test. This provides the turbocharger with adequate oil for lubrication and cooling during the shutdown period and permits engine cooling system flow to assist with cooling the engine down when it is at its hottest.

TEST CONDITION VARIABILITY

Chassis dynamometer test results vary from dynamometer to dynamometer. It is up to each service facility to establish acceptable at-the-wheel horsepower ranges on the dynamometer it uses for testing. Generally, BHP output at the wheels should approximate 80% to 85% of the OEM engine brake power specification for tandem drive axle chassis and 85% to 90% of the OEM brake power specification for single drive axle chassis. The variables in the vehicle drivetrain are always a factor. Variations from one dynamometer to another can be due to variables such as the altitude of the location, wheel roller diameter, ambient temperature, and humidity. The type and condition of the tires on a vehicle will cause traction variations, and small-roller dynamometers generally produce more tire slippage than dynamometers equipped with larger-diameter rollers. Single, large-diameter roller dynamometers used on tandem drive trucks produce less slippage and generally more accurate results than multiple-roller types. The specific values obtained from chassis dyno tests are most useful for comparisons to data obtained from testing similarly configured chassis on the same dynamometer. See **Photo Sequence 1**.

WARNING:

Never perform a dynamometer test with mismatched duals, recapped, or snow tread tires mounted on the vehicle drive axles. Tread separation may occur when using recapped tires; snow tread tires can produce erratic dynamometer test readings. Using a set of "slave" tires (used solely for dyno testing) when testing a chassis equipped with inappropriate tires is an option, especially as dyno testing is hard on tires.

CAUTION:

When a truck is run on a chassis dynamometer, ensure that no person is outside the cab in the test cell. Stones and rocks lodged in the tire treads can free up and be propelled behind the truck at high velocity. It is also important to ensure that no equipment is located behind the truck chassis. Vaporized tire rubber can also represent a respiratory health hazard.

ENGINE DYNAMOMETER TESTING

The **engine dynamometer** method of checking engine power is more accurate than the chassis dyno method because it removes all the variables involved when transmitting power through a transmission, drive shafts, drive axle carriers, and wheel assemblies. This method is ideal for engine run-in because it affords the test technician perfect observation of the engine throughout the test sequence—something not possible when the engine is in-chassis.

Two types of engine dynamometer are used: the test bed type, which is a permanent fixture usually isolated in an insulated, soundproof room often with a separate observation room; or the portable unit, which is coupled directly to the engine to be tested. The disadvantage of engine dynamometer testing is that it adds considerable time to an engine overhaul to fit and subsequently remove the engine from the dynamometer test bed, and test conditions are far removed from the more realistic chassis dyno test.

In this respect, the portable unit usually requires less time to fit to the engine, but these can seldom be safely used in a large truck garage due to the noise levels emitted and the potential for danger when operating an engine under high loads in a room not dedicated to the purpose. **Figure 16–7** shows a DD15 coupled to a portable-style dynamometer.

FIGURE 16–7 A DD15 coupled to a portable-style dyno ready for testing.

Photo Sequence 1

CHASSIS DYNO TEST PREPARATION

PS1–1 On the control console, lock the dyno rollers. Back the truck onto the rollers. Release the roller lock and in a low gear, spin the wheels up to center the rollers.

PSI–2 Visually check the truck from the front to ensure that it is properly aligned. Chock both steer tires on the dyno.

PS1–3 Install the anchor chains to the rear of the chassis, ensuring they do not interfere with any moving suspension components.

PS1–4 The hold-down chains should have the amount of slack shown in this image. When testing a truck with a steel spring suspension, the chains can be slightly more taut but not enough to exert downward force.

PS1–5 With the roller lock released, run the truck through the gears to a highway speed with no load on the rollers.

PS1–6 Connect the chassis data bus (J1939) to an EST (see Chapter 35). Connect master gauges to monitor the engine and fuel system; never rely solely on the vehicle dash gauges.

PS1–8 Insert the gas sample nozzle(s) into the vehicle exhaust pipe(s). Activate the exhaust extraction and make-up air circuits.

PS1–7 Activate the exhaust gas analyzer. This should be done even when running a simple power performance test, but especially after an engine rebuild.

PS1–9 Set the desired test profile on the dynamometer console. Now the test can be run. Remember to wear PPE with sufficient hearing protection.

Before using an engine dynamometer for run-in or testing, the technician should become familiar with the procedure outlined previously for checking power using a chassis dynamometer. The first step is to obtain the OEM dynamometer test data, connect and properly phase and align the drive shaft, connect the appropriate gauges, plumb in a cooling tower, and check all the engine fluid levels.

1. With the engine no-fueled, crank until an oil pressure value is observed on the oil gauge. Program the engine electronics to run in <dyno test> mode. Then start the engine.

2. Check the engine idle and high idle rpm, and on hydromechanical engines ensure that the dyno fuel control linkages produce full travel plus the required breakover factor. On electronic engines, ensure that the TPS is properly calibrated and programmed to the engine ECM.

3. Start the engine, and run at around 1,000 rpm with no load for 5 minutes to check for oil pressure, noises, vibration, leaks, and drive shaft runout. Shut down the engine, and check and correct oil and coolant levels.

4. Run the engine at a midpoint rpm within the torque rise profile, and load the engine at around 50% of its rated power value. Operate the engine under this half-load condition until the coolant and oil temperatures are each in the operating temperature window.

5. Set the accelerator/throttle to produce the rated speed rpm and smoothly load the engine until it is unable to sustain the rated speed. Determine the peak power setting and then test at descending increments of 100 rpm engine power through the torque rise profile.

6. Monitor and record all the engine running data during the test sequence, including: crankcase pressure, air inlet pressure, manifold boost pressure, fuel subsystem charging pressure, coolant temperature, coolant pressure, oil temperature, oil pressure, exhaust temperature (pyrometer), and exhaust backpressure. **Figure 16–8** shows an engine test report format favored by Detroit Diesel (DD) when undertaking dyno testing.

7. Run under conditions of peak loading for a minimum period of 20 minutes when the dyno test is being performed to run-in the engine.

Photo Sequence 2 demonstrates the procedure of how to run a diesel engine on an engine test bed.

WARNING:

After running a full load dynamometer test on an engine, allow the engine to run at no-load idle speed for a period of at least 5 minutes after the test to provide the turbocharger with adequate oil for lubrication and cooling during the shutdown period and permit the engine cooling system to assist with cooling the engine down when it is at its hottest.

ROAD TESTING

Before performing a road test, the technician should ensure that the state or provincial jurisdiction qualifications for operating a heavy-duty truck or bus on the highway are met. It should be emphasized that although the engine may be the chassis system being tested, all the vehicle systems are subjected to a performance workout, and it is any vehicle operator's responsibility to ensure that they are both safe and functional. When diagnosing an engine malfunction, the road test usually takes second place to a chassis dynamometer test. When the objective is the run-in of a rebuilt engine, the road test is the least preferred method after engine and chassis dyno loading, simply because there are too many variables and unknown factors that may arise during a road test.

When an engine is being run-in, it should be loaded close to its maximum for at least some of the procedure and, therefore, the truck should be coupled to a (preferably loaded) trailer. Using the vehicle braking system to achieve this can seriously overheat the foundation brakes.

When road-testing an electronically managed engine, the operator should be thoroughly familiar with the characteristics of the management system and its programming. Before the road test, scan the ECM for active and historic codes, download any tattletales, and also download the customer and proprietary data programming that might affect the diagnosis. During the road test, connect an EST loaded with the appropriate software to the J1708/J1939 data link connector (DLC) to scan and snapshot, when required, vehicle running data.

FIGURE 16–8 Typical dynamometer test profile recommended by Detroit Diesel (DD) for engine testing.

ENGINE TEST REPORT

Date: _____
Repair Order Number: _____
PROM I.D.: _____
Rated F/L RPM: _____
Idle RPM: _____

Unit Number: _____
Model Number: _____
Max. N/L RPM: _____

A. PRESTART

1. PRIME LUBE OIL SYSTEM	2. PRIME FUEL OIL SYSTEM	3. FILL COOLING SYSTEM

B. START-UP AND IDLE FOR 30 SECONDS

START_____ STOP_____ OIL PRESSURE_____ WATER TEMPERATURE_____

C. WARM-UP — 5 MINUTES   START _____   STOP _____

RPM MAX. SPEED	LOAD 50%	OIL PRESSURE	COOLANT TEMPERATURE
1. LUBE OIL LEAKS	2. FUEL OIL LEAKS	3. COOLANT LEAKS	4. LOOSE BOLTS

D. RUN-IN — 5 MINUTES   START _____   STOP _____

RPM MAX. SPEED	LOAD 75%	OIL PRESSURE	COOLANT TEMPERATURE

E. FINAL RUN-IN — 20 MINUTES   START _____   STOP _____

RPM MAX. SPEED	LOAD 100%	CRANKCASE PRESSURE AT F/L	EXHAUST BACK PRESSURE AT F/L
LUBE OIL PRESS. AT F/L	LUBE OIL TEMP. AT F/L	FUEL OIL TEMP. AT F/L	FUEL OIL PRESSURE AT F/L
COOLANT TEMP. AT F/L	TURBO BOOST PRESS. AT F/L	LUBE OIL PRESSURE AT IDLE	IDLE RPM

REMARKS: _____

OK_____ Reject_____ Dynamometer Operator_____ Date_____

Detroit Diesel Corporation

If a digital dash display is installed in the truck, determine what data may be displayed during the test that would be most useful in assessing the engine condition.

While road-testing, the technician should never forget that the primary responsibility is to operate the vehicle safely; the distractions of the dash and electronic displays used to diagnose must not interfere with that responsibility. The following is intended to act as a guide to road test performance whether the objective is engine run-in or malfunction diagnosis:

1. Perform a pretrip inspection or circle test. Most state and provincial jurisdictions require this test to be performed by the driver of any heavy-duty highway vehicle before operating it on a road. At minimum, this test would require that the following be checked and corrected before running the vehicle on a highway: vehicle lighting, tire inflation, tire condition, brake adjustment, air system pressure buildup time and values, audible air leaks, mudflap condition, suspension condition, fifth wheel or pintle hook integrity, and load securement.

2. If the objective of the road test is to run-in a newly rebuilt engine, perform the sequence outlined earlier in this chapter entitled "Preparing an Engine for the First Start-Up." If the objective is to diagnose a malfunction, the engine fluid levels should be checked.

Photo Sequence 2

ENGINE DYNO TEST PREPARATION

PS2–1 After mounting and securing the engine on the test bed, pay special attention to the driveshaft alignment: It must be properly phased and the U-joint working angles within specification. The driveshaft connects the flywheel to …

PS2–3 Secure the driveshaft protective cowl, then start the engine and run at no load to check driveshaft integrity. When inside a test cell with an engine running, wear PPE and sufficient hearing protection.

PS2–2 … the dynamometer module. Install and adjust the shaft speed sensor as shown here.

PS2–4 Install the exhaust extraction ducting and heat shields.

PS2–5 If the engine is to be run for the first time after reconditioning, run at rated speed at around half load for three minutes. Then visually inspect for leaks.

PS2–8 Activate the dynamometer module. Set to monitor and control the test run outside of the test cell, if possible.

PS2–6 Connect the engine electronics (in this DD15 the CPC and MCM) to an EST to monitor the test.

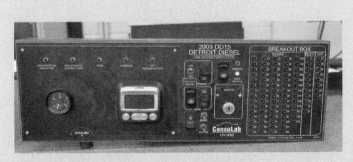

PS2–7 If performing troubleshooting, connect in a breakout box to enable circuit testing.

PS2–9 With engine idling, perform a final visual inspection before exiting the test cell and running the test profile.

3. Next, the technician should become familiar with the setup of the primary drivetrain components, making a mental note of the engine rated speed, torque rise profile, and any customer-programmed data such as progressive shifting, road speed limit, and governor type that could be a factor while performing the road test. Note the recommended gear shift points (often identified on the visor or elsewhere in the cab) when mechanical engine/ transmissions are to be tested.

4. Start the engine and check the idle and no-load high-idle speeds, correcting the values as required. Warm the engine up with the vehicle stationary, but avoid idling for longer than 5 minutes, especially where the engine has been newly rebuilt. The test procedure outlined for chassis dyno testing should be reviewed because a road test attempts to replicate some of this. Road traffic largely dictates how thoroughly a road test can be performed, so try to select a highway where traffic is known to be light. When undertaking a road test (**Figure 16–9**), ensure that you are properly qualified to drive the vehicle and that it is properly licensed and insured.

5. Once on the highway, bring the vehicle up to speed and test the performance through the torque rise profile. It really helps if the operator is not forced to maintain a consistent road speed, but this factor will be determined by the amount of road traffic. A road test of 30 minutes after the specified engine-operating temperature has been reached is usually sufficient to break in a rebuilt engine (seat the rings). When diagnosing engine malfunctions, the road test duration will depend on the data revealed during the procedure.

FIGURE 16–9 Before undertaking a road test, the driver must be qualified and the vehicle properly insured and licensed. When using a road test as the means of breaking in an engine rebuild, the operator must prioritize safe operation of the vehicle over any test results.

WARNING:

After running a road test on an engine, allow the engine to run at no-load idle speed for a period of at least 5 minutes after the test to provide the turbocharger with adequate oil for lubrication and cooling during the shutdown period and permit the engine cooling system to assist with cooling the engine down when it is at its hottest.

SUMMARY

- The entire content of this chapter involves practical test procedures and to properly understand it, some exposure to the technology is required, even if it is just observation.
- Before operating a truck chassis on a dynamometer, it is advisable to acquire some driving skills. Consult a fleet driver-trainer or experienced technician for some advice.
- Engine dynamometers present a certain potential for danger that can be minimized by

properly aligning the engine on the test bed and always using safety guards and shrouds around rotating components such as fans and driveshafts.

- Chassis dynamometers must be properly harnessed to the test bed. Consult the dynamometer operating manual and an experienced operator before running the engine.
- Before road-testing vehicles, ensure that you hold a valid license to operate the vehicle on

a highway and that you fully understand how to operate the vehicle.

- Whether dynamometer- or road-testing, ensure that all the appropriate observation instrumentation is connected; in the case of most current electronic engines, this means that data is duplicated, but this duplication also corroborates the data. Apart from reducing the scope of data on which an analysis must be made, it looks unprofessional to display dynamometer printouts with half of the critical data fields displayed as NA (not available).

REVIEW EXERCISES

1. Obtain an OEM engine power and torque performance chart. Using calculation, confirm that the nominal BHP value is correct at three points in the torque rise profile.

2. Use a college dynamometer or visit a local service facility with the objective of observing the procedure for mounting an engine to a dynamometer test bed.

3. Visit a facility with a chassis dynamometer and observe the procedure for harnessing a truck to the test bed.

4. Access the data bus of a current truck using the appropriate EST and find out what is required to electronically prep the vehicle for a chassis dyno test.

5. Using an OEM dynamometer performance test profile for either a chassis or an engine dynamometer, record the preparation and test sequence.

REVIEW QUESTIONS

1. Technician A states that a truck rebuilt diesel engine run-in procedure usually requires that the engine be operated at medium to low loads for the first 1,000 miles (1,600 km) of operation. Technician B argues that it is usually essential to run a rebuilt diesel engine at full load for a short period after a rebuild to seat the piston rings. Who is correct?
   a. Technician A only
   b. Technician B only
   c. Both A and B
   d. Neither A nor B

2. Technician A states that an engine dynamometer is likely to produce a brake power rating closer to the OEM-specified power than a chassis dynamometer test. Technician B states that the chassis dynamometer produces brake power readings at the wheels that are always lower than OEM-rated power. Who is correct?
   a. Technician A only
   b. Technician B only
   c. Both A and B
   d. Neither A nor B

3. If all three options were available and time is not a consideration, which of the following options would be the preferred method of running-in a rebuilt engine?
   a. Engine dynamometer
   b. Chassis dynamometer
   c. Road test

4. Technician A states that when performing dynamometer testing of an engine, the altitude of the test location must be considered when analyzing the power. Technician B states that ambient temperature variations have a greater effect on brake power produced than altitude. Who is correct?
   a. Technician A only
   b. Technician B only
   c. Both A and B
   d. Neither A nor B

5. Which of the following electronic controllers would have to be disabled before performing a chassis dynamometer test?
   a. Engine ECM
   b. Transmission ECU
   c. Automatic traction control (ATC)
   d. Collision warning system (CWS)

SECTION

2

DIESEL FUEL SYSTEMS

Section 2 addresses the fuel systems used on diesel engines. It begins with a look at some basic chemistry and the composition of current diesel fuel, before taking on an examination of contemporary diesel fuel subsystems—one of the most important chapters in the book. There follows a detailed study of the many distinct types of diesel fuel systems, with a primary focus on the electronically controlled fueling used over the past two decades. The approach is generic and there is special emphasis on those fuel systems used to manage post-2010 commercial diesel. Chapters on both types of diesel common rail system complete this section.

CHAPTERS

17

CHEMISTRY AND COMBUSTION

OBJECTIVES

After studying this chapter, you should be able to:

- Understand basic chemistry and its application to fuel systems.
- Define *elements*, *mixtures*, and *compounds*.
- Describe a simple chemical reaction and chemical bonding.
- Outline the structure of an atom.
- Define the states of matter and the conditions that predetermine them.
- Describe the properties of common elements, mixtures, and compounds.
- Outline the dynamics of combustion in an engine cylinder.
- Define the conditions required for a stoichiometric reaction.
- Calculate air-fuel ratio.
- Describe the stages of combustion in a diesel engine cylinder.
- Explain how burning 1 gallon of diesel fuel produces more than 20 pounds of CO_2.
- Describe the dynamics of detonation.

KEY TERMS

afterburn	detonation	hypothesis	neutron
air-fuel ratio (AFR)	diatomic	ion	particulate matter (PM)
atom	diesel knock	kinetic	propagate
balanced atom	direct injection (DI)	kinetic molecular theory	proton
chemical bonding	dosing	lambda	stoichiometric
compound	electron	mass	sublimation
condensation	element	matter	triatomic
covalent bonding	fluidity	mixture	vaporization
cylinder gas dynamics	fuel-air ratio	monatomic	

INTRODUCTION

It is important for any mechanical technician to have a fundamental understanding of chemistry for purposes of explaining fuel composition and combustion dynamics in engines, and for developing an ability to work with electricity and electronics. Some knowledge of basic chemistry can be an especially useful diagnostic tool for the technician specializing in engines, fuel systems, and emission controls. In addition, this is a NATEF requirement (narrative for *Science and Related Skills*) because it is recognized that if a technician aspires to attaining the highest level of competency, then it is important to understand the foundations on which the technology is based.

This chapter briefly addresses basic chemistry, atomic structure, combustion dynamics, and the language of fuel technology—all topics that have individually been the subject of many textbooks. Our approach will be to look at the basics. Technicians are encouraged to explore this subject matter to a greater depth using other specialized texts.

Chemistry is the science that seeks to understand the composition of **matter** (physical substance in general), the **elements** (any substance that cannot be resolved into simpler substances), the **compounds** (substances containing two or more elements combined in definite proportions and held together by chemical force) they form, and the reactions they undergo. It is one of the oldest sciences, and it evolved from the observations of thinkers in times well before the modern age. The chemist would observe a natural phenomenon, hypothesize (attempt to reason) its causes, then confirm the **hypothesis** (supposition) by experiment. When it seemed that a hypothesis could be conclusively proven by documented observation of cause and effect, a law was established.

Of course, the history of science is generally littered with hypotheses that became irrelevant or disproven as knowledge progressed, so a theory of physics or chemistry today may not necessarily be valid tomorrow. The opposite can also occur: Something that seemed insignificant in the past can become the foundation of a core technology, as in the case of Hero's development of the reaction turbine aeolipile (see Chapter 5) 2,000 years ago. Not only was the reaction turbine the first heat engine, it was the basis for both steam and jet turbine engines, which are technologies that had to wait 1,600 and 2,000 years, respectively, after the initial invention.

BASIC CHEMISTRY

The building blocks of all matter are **atoms**. All atoms are electrical. Electrical charge is a component of all atomic matter. This section examines some key definitions required to develop an understanding of atomic theory. Some of this information is revisited in Chapter 32 on electrical fundamentals.

ELEMENTS

An *element* is any one of more than 100 substances, most naturally occurring, that cannot be chemically resolved into simpler substances. Elements consist of minute particles known as *atoms,* which, for purposes of study, are considered to be indivisible. An atom is the smallest particle of an element that can take part in a chemical reaction. The atoms of any one element are exactly alike and possess identical **mass** (quantity of matter a substance contains: weight). The name of an element is always a single word, such as hydrogen or oxygen (**Figure 17–1** and **Figure 17–2**).

All elements have a short-form symbol usually derived from the Latin name for the substance. Sometimes the symbol is obvious because the Latin word for an element is similar to the English word (much of the English language is derived from Latin), such as that for the element oxygen, which is O. However, the symbol for the element iron is Fe, derived from the Latin word for iron, which is *ferrum*. Atomic number

FIGURE 17–1 Hydrogen atom.

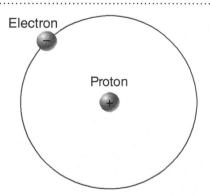

FIGURE 17–2 Oxygen atom.

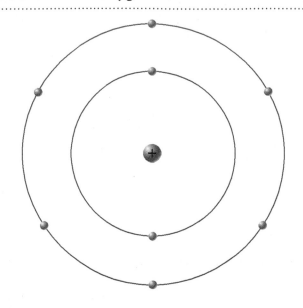

identifies the number of **protons** in an atom of the element. **Table 17–1** shows the symbols and atomic numbers of some common elements that you are likely to come across if you work with vehicle technology.

MIXTURES

A **mixture** is composed of two or more elements and/or compounds, all of which retain their own characteristics and identity. Air is an example of a mixture; it is composed of 23% oxygen and 76% nitrogen by mass (plus about 1% of inert gases). These percentages change to 78% nitrogen and 21% oxygen by volume, so we can immediately determine that oxygen is slightly heavier than nitrogen. This fact explains why there is less oxygen on top of Mount Denali than at sea level.

Both oxygen and nitrogen retain their own identity and can take part in reactions independently of each other when they are in this mixture we call air. The oxygen in air, for instance, is commonly involved in reactions that do not involve nitrogen. The properties of a mixture depend on the substances in it; the compound water (H_2O) is a pure substance with identifiable characteristics that are dissimilar from any other pure substance. However, salt water is a *mixture* of salt and H_2O; it boils at a higher temperature and freezes at a lower temperature than pure H_2O.

CHEMICAL BONDING

Chemical bondings are interactions that account for the association of atoms into molecules, ions, and crystals. When atoms approach one another, their nuclei and **electrons** interact and distribute themselves in such a way that their combined energy is lower than it would be in an alternative arrangement. Whenever the total energy of a group of atoms is lower than the sum of energies of its component atoms, they are chemically bonded; bonding energy accounts for the overall lowering of energy.

Valency

The number of bonds an atom can form is called its *valency* (or valence number). The valency

TABLE 17–1 Symbols and Atomic Number of Common Elements

Some Common Metallic Elements	Atomic Number	Some Common Nonmetallic Elements	Atomic Number
Iron—Fe	26	Hydrogen—H	1
Sodium—Na	11	Carbon—C	6
Magnesium—Mg	13	Helium—He	2
Aluminum—Al	13	Sulfur—S	16
Nickel—Ni	28	Silicon—Si	14
Rhodium—Rh	35	Selenium—Se	34
Silver—Ag	47	Oxygen—O	8
Zinc—Zn	30	Nitrogen—N	7
Gold—Au	79	Argon—Ar	18
Platinum—Pt	78	Radon—Rn	86

of an atom is simply the number of unpaired electrons in its valence shell. The valence shell is the outermost shell of electrons. An H_2O molecule consists of an oxygen atom with a valency of two combined with two hydrogen atoms, which each have a valency of one. An electrovalent or ionic (**ion**: an atom with either an excess or deficiency of electrons) bond occurs when an electron is transferred from one neutral atom to another; the resultant charge results in the atoms being held together by electrostatic attraction.

COMPOUNDS

A *compound* is a substance composed of two or more elements combined in definite proportions and held together with chemical force. A compound is composed of identical molecules made up of atoms of two or more elements. Most commonly occurring materials are mixtures of different chemical compounds. Pure compounds can usually be obtained by physical separation processes such as filtration and distillation. Compounds themselves can be broken down into their constituent elements by chemical reactions.

Carbon atoms are unique among the chemical elements in their ability to form covalent bonds with each other and with other elements. **Covalent bonding** occurs when two electrons are shared by two atoms. Because of its atomic structure, carbon is more likely to share electrons than to gain or lose them. There are 10 times as many carbon compounds as compounds of all other elements combined; common carbon compounds are formed with hydrogen, oxygen, and nitrogen. Petroleum-based fuels such as diesel fuel are hydrocarbon compounds. In fact, petroleum fuels are usually carefully balanced mixtures of a large number of hydrocarbon compounds.

MOLECULES

A *molecule* is the smallest particle of a compound that can exist in a free state and take part in a chemical reaction. When an H_2O molecule (**Figure 17–3**) is chemically reduced, it ceases to have the properties of H_2O and instead possesses those of elemental oxygen and hydrogen.

The oxygen found at sea level in the earth's atmosphere combines to form **diatomic** molecules, that is, two oxygen atoms to a

FIGURE 17–3 Water molecule: Observe the shared electrons.

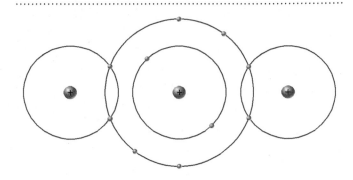

FIGURE 17–4 Oxygen (O_2) molecule: Oxygen in the lower atmosphere is mostly diatomic.

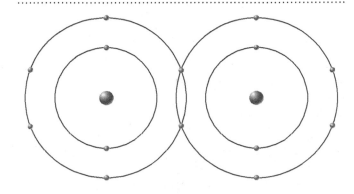

molecule (**Figure 17–4**). Diatomic oxygen is expressed as O_2.

ATOMIC STRUCTURE

Atomic theory seeks to explain both the composition of matter and the laws that apply to chemical combination. It was conceived in 1801 by a chemist, John Dalton, who confirmed theorizing by some great thinkers in the era around 400 BC, suggesting that matter could not be subdivided indefinitely without altering the properties of that substance. Dalton's atomic theory suggested:

1. Each element is made up of minute, indivisible particles called atoms.
2. Atoms cannot be created or destroyed.
3. Every atom that a specific element is composed of is identical.
4. Atoms of different elements are different.
5. Atoms of one element may combine with other elements to form compounds.

Dalton's atomic theory was developed into our current notions of the structure of an atom by the scientists Thomson, Rutherford, and Chadwick in the early part of the twentieth century. These scientists identified the following subatomic particles:

1. The electron—symbol e–. Discovered by J. J. Thompson in 1897. Electrons carry a negative charge and orbit in the shells around the atom's nucleus. An electron has 1/1,837 of the mass of a proton.
2. The proton—symbol p⁺. Discovered by Ernest Rutherford in 1911. Protons carry a positive charge and are located in the atom's nucleus. A proton has 1,837 times the mass of an electron.
3. The **neutron**—symbol n°. Discovered by James Chadwick in 1932. Neutrons are electrically neutral and are located in the atom's nucleus. A neutron has slightly more mass than a proton.

In 1911, Ernest Rutherford described the nuclear model of the atom and asserted:

1. An atom consists mostly of empty space.
2. Each atom has a minute, extremely dense nucleus.
3. The nucleus is surrounded by a large volume of nearly empty space.
4. Most of the mass and *all* of the positive charge is located in the nucleus.
5. The nearly empty space surrounding the nucleus is sparsely occupied by electrons that possess a fraction of the mass but a negative charge that balances the positive charge of the protons.

Balanced Atoms

A hydrogen atom (see Figure 17–1) consists of a single proton in the nucleus and one electron in its orbital shell; the electron orbits the nucleus in much the same manner Earth orbits our sun. The electrical force attracting the electron toward the positive charge of the nucleus is balanced by the mechanical force acting outward on the rotating electron; this ensures that the electron remains in its orbital shell and is not drawn into the nucleus. All atoms are electrical. An electrically **balanced atom** is one in which there is an equal number of electrons and protons (**Figure 17–5** and **Figure 17–6**). While electrons can move from atom to atom in many substances, protons do not, and they are held in the nucleus of the atom. An atom with either an

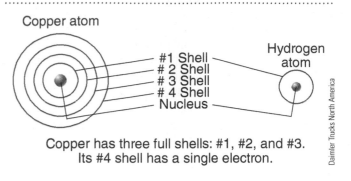

FIGURE 17–5 Copper atom: A copper atom has four shells, three of which are full.

Copper has three full shells: #1, #2, and #3. Its #4 shell has a single electron.

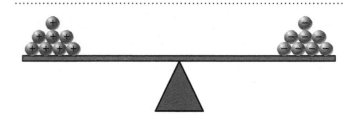

FIGURE 17–6 Atomic charge balance: If an atom has eight protons, it will want to have eight electrons.

excess or a deficit of electrons is known as an *ion*. An ion is an atom in an electrically unbalanced state.

Current atomic theory suggests that, in much the same way protons and neutrons make up atomic nuclei, these particles are themselves made up of quarks. Quarks are therefore subatomic particles that are theorized to be the fundamental constituents of all matter. However, the study of quarks probably goes beyond what today's technician needs to know of atomic structure.

STATES OF MATTER

In physics, *matter* is defined as anything that has mass and occupies space. Matter can be generally classified into one of three states or phases within the earth's atmosphere: solid, liquid, or gas. Water is the only substance that is familiar in all three states, which we describe as ice, water, and steam (**Figure 17–7**). A solid does not readily change in size or shape when subjected to physical forces. Like a solid, a liquid has a definable volume, but it has **fluidity** and will change its shape if poured from one

FIGURE 17–7 States of matter: H_2O is the only substance readily observed in all three states.

Ice

Water   Steam

container to another. A gas generally expands to fill the volume of the vessel in which it is contained.

Determining State

On Earth's surface, under a given set of temperature and pressure conditions, a substance will be in one of these states; most substances can exist in any of the three states. The differences between solids, liquids, and gases can be explained in terms of **kinetic molecular theory**; **kinetic** refers to motion. Kinetic molecular theory states that all matter consists of molecules that are constantly in motion and their extent of motion in a substance will be greater at high temperatures and less at cooler temperatures. A certain amount of attraction exists between all molecules in a substance, and whenever repulsive forces are weaker than the intermolecular attractive forces, the molecules stick together. However, as temperature increases, so does the molecular motion.

In a solid, intermolecular attractive forces overcome the disruptive thermal (heat) energy of the molecules and they are bound together in an orderly arrangement called a *crystal*. The molecules in a crystal vibrate due to their thermal energy and, again, the amount they vibrate is determined by temperature or the amount of retained heat energy.

As a solid is subjected to heat, its molecules vibrate with increasing energy until they are capable of overcoming the intermolecular attractive forces. At this point, the substance melts or changes to the liquid state and acquires

fluidity. A change of state works in reverse; the freeze point of a substance is the same as its melt point.

Changes of State

Kinetic molecular theory also explains the change of state from that of a liquid to a gas, known as **vaporization**. As heat is applied to a liquid, some molecules acquire sufficient thermal energy to overcome the intermolecular attraction and break free from the surface of the liquid; these molecules are converted to a gaseous state. If heat continues to be applied to the liquid, more molecules will move away from the liquid until the substances' boil point is achieved and all the molecules escape the liquid state. When vaporization is reversed, it is known as **condensation**. The distance between molecules of a gas is large in comparison with that of a liquid because the intermolecular forces are weak. A gas molecule will move until it either strikes another gas molecule or the walls of the vessel that contains it. The effect of many gas molecules striking a container wall is known as *pressure*.

It is possible for a substance to pass directly from the solid to the gaseous state in a process known as **sublimation**. Dry ice (CO_2) sublimates at atmospheric pressure and temperature. Snow can also be sublimated.

PLASMA AND OTHER STATES OF MATTER

At very high temperatures, atoms may collide with each other with a force that results in some electrons being jolted free of the nuclei. A mixture containing these positive and negative ions (an ion is an atom that has lost or gained one or more electrons) is defined not as a gas but as *plasma*. Scientists commonly refer to a plasma state as being the fourth state of matter; in fact, most of the known universe is in this state. In the universe, matter may be found in forms that cannot be grouped into these previously described states of matter. Dying stars are theorized to collapse into forms in which matter is so dense that their gravitational force pulls in all matter and radiation. Because no light can escape from a black hole, little is known of them.

STATES OF MATTER—CONCLUSION

As far as the technician is concerned, a basic understanding of what we know as the three states of matter should suffice. A practical example of some of the preceding information can be observed in what happens in a typical injection pulse. Fuel directly injected to a diesel engine cylinder is atomized. Atomized fuel is in the liquid state. This fuel, when exposed to the heat of compression in the engine cylinder, vaporizes; it must change state before it can be combusted. If liquid fuel contacts the piston crown, it remains condensed longer and can result in a failure because more heat energy is required to vaporize it, retarding its ignition. Gases condensing (raw fuel or coolant) in the exhaust gas stream will be observed as white smoke. Partially combusted fuel exiting in solid state in the exhaust gas stream will be observed as black smoke. In diagnosing these and many other conditions, the technician will benefit from a basic understanding of chemistry.

CHEMICAL REACTIONS

There are many classes of chemical reactions, most of which are not of significant interest to the student of diesel technology. However, combustion is an oxidation reaction. The reactant in the engine cylinder is whatever oxygen is present at the time of ignition. In a chemical reaction, the ingredients present undergo significant chemical alteration. In the engine cylinder, the ingredients of the chemical reaction are the fuel (hydrocarbon molecules) and the reactant (oxygen in the cylinder). What results from the oxidation reaction in the engine cylinder are compounds with fundamentally altered states. In other words, what goes into an engine cylinder is quite different from what comes out. We will attempt to explain some of the reasons for this in the following section, beginning with learning a little more about elements and compounds.

PROPERTIES OF SOME COMMON ELEMENTS

Each element has a special identity and set of characteristics that make it unique in terms of both its behavior and appearance. Some of the characteristics of common elements are outlined below.

HYDROGEN (H)

Hydrogen is a colorless, odorless, tasteless, flammable gas—the simplest member of the family of chemical elements with a nucleus consisting of one proton that is orbited by one electron. Hydrogen atoms are reactive and combine in pairs, forming diatomic (combinations of two atoms to a molecule) molecules: H_2. Hydrogen is the most abundant element in the known universe, accounting for about 75% of matter, although only around 1% of all matter on Earth. It is present in all animal and vegetable substances in the form of compounds, most often carbon. It also constitutes 11% of the mass of water. Combustion of hydrogen with oxygen produces temperatures in the region of 4,700°F (2,600°C).

Atomic No.: 1
Melting point: –435°F (–259.2°C)
Boiling point: –423°F (–252.8°C)

CARBON (C)

Carbon is a nonmetallic element that exists in a number of forms and combines to form compounds more readily than any other element. About 0.2% of the earth's crust is composed of carbon. Elemental carbon exists in three forms: diamonds, graphite, and carbon black, which includes charcoal and coal. Pure diamond is the hardest substance known. It is a poor conductor of both electricity and heat, and it is used in industrial applications as a cutting and drilling medium. Graphite has many opposite characteristics: Notably, it is a conductor of heat and electricity and is commonly used as a lubricant. When iron is alloyed with small quantities of carbon, *steel* is formed.

Atomic No.: 6
Melting point: 6,420°F (3,550°C)
Boiling point: 8,721°F (4,827°C)

OXYGEN (O)

A colorless, odorless, tasteless gas, oxygen is the most plentiful element in the earth's crust. Oxygen is present in air (23% by mass), water (86%), and in the earth's crust (47%). Almost all atmospheric oxygen is the result of photosynthesis. During respiration, animals and some plants process atmospheric oxygen to form carbon dioxide; by photosynthesis, green plants assimilate carbon dioxide in the presence of sunlight to produce oxygen. Most of the gaseous oxygen found in the atmosphere consists of molecules of two atoms known as diatomic oxygen (O_2).

Monatomic (O) and **triatomic** (O_3) oxygen (ozone) are more predominant in the upper strata of the atmosphere where ozone filters the sun's ultraviolet radiation. Commercial oxygen is produced by fractional distillation of liquid air. Oxygen has a valence of 2 and forms a large range of covalently bonded compounds. Molten oxygen forms a blue liquid, and solid oxygen is attracted by a magnet.

Atomic No.: 8

Melting point: −361°F (−218°C)

Boiling point: −297°F (−183°C)

NITROGEN (N)

A colorless, odorless, tasteless gas, nitrogen is the most plentiful element in the earth's atmosphere; the mixture *air* contains approximately 76% nitrogen by mass. Nitrogen is a constituent of all living matter. Chemically, nitrogen is fairly inert at ambient temperatures, but during combustion it will combine to form various oxides, especially in high-temperature, lean burn conditions. The automotive industry identifies those various oxides collectively as NO_x and they are subject to Environmental Protection Agency (EPA) standards and regulation as noxious emission.

Atomic No.: 7

Melting point: −346°F (−210°C)

Boiling point: −320°F (−196°C)

SULFUR (S)

A nonmetallic element, sulfur is also one of the more reactive elements. Pure sulfur is a tasteless, odorless, brittle solid that is a pale yellow in color and a poor conductor of electricity. Sulfur is perhaps important to the diesel technician mostly because it is a constituent of petroleum. Sulfur appears prominently in the residual oil fractions (those left over after distillation and other refining practices) of a diesel fuel that provide the fuel with its lubricating properties.

Atomic No.: 16

Melting point: 235°F (113°C)

Boiling point: 832°F (445°C)

SULFUR IN DIESEL FUEL

Current United States and Canadian statutory requirements of on-highway and off-highway diesel fuels permit no more than 0.0015% sulfur content. This fuel is known as *ultra-low sulfur (ULS)* fuel. The implementation dates for ULS diesel fuel were October 2006 for on-highway and January 2012 for off-highway. This means that sulfurous emissions from diesel engines have been all but eliminated. Sulfur is oxidized to sulfur dioxide (SO_2) in the combustion process. SO_2 is a colorless and poisonous gas regarded by the EPA as a noxious emission; it readily forms acidic compounds such as H_2SO_4 (sulfuric acid). Sulfur is also a constituent of lubricating oils.

IRON (FE)

A metallic element that makes up about 5% of the earth's crust, iron is the second most common metal after aluminum. It combines with many other elements to form hundreds of minerals. Iron almost always contains small amounts of carbon, which modifies its properties. When alloyed with small amounts of carbon, steel is produced—the most widely used of all metals. Elements other than carbon can also be added to iron in the alloying process to modify the characteristics of steel. Common alloying metals are nickel, chromium, molybdenum, tungsten, vanadium, titanium, and manganese. Iron is extensively used in vehicle technology, mostly as steel.

Atomic No.: 26

Melting point: 2,795°F (1,535°C)

Boiling point: 5,432°F (3,000°C)

ALUMINUM (AL)

A lightweight, silver-white colored metal that makes up about 8% of the earth's crust, aluminum is therefore the most common metal. Aluminum never occurs in the metallic form naturally, but its compounds are present in most rocks, vegetation, and animals. Modern commercially produced aluminum is obtained from bauxite and isolated by electrolysis. Pure aluminum tends to be soft and weak, but when alloyed with small amounts of silicon and iron, it becomes harder and tougher. It is an excellent conductor of heat and electricity. Like iron, it is extensively used in vehicle technology.

Atomic No.: 13

Melting point: 1,220°F (660°C)

Boiling point: 4,473°F (2,467°C)

PROPERTIES OF SOME MIXTURES AND COMPOUNDS

The way in which mixtures and compounds behave when they undergo chemical reactions can be explained by the constituent elements of which they are composed. The following section describes some of the mixtures and compounds that occur in or result from combustion reactions in an internal combustion engine. Many of the by-products of combustion described here are referred to in more detail in Chapter 47.

AIR

Air is a mixture of oxygen and nitrogen. This mixture contains a group of gases with nearly constant concentrations and another group of gases that are variable. Atmospheric gases of more or less consistent concentration by volume are:

Nitrogen (N_2)	78.084%
Oxygen (O_2)	20.946%
Argon (Ar)	0.934%
Neon (Ne)	0.0018%
Helium (He)	0.000524%
Methane (CH_4)	0.0002%
Krypton (Kr)	0.000114%
Hydrogen (H_2)	0.00005%
Nitrous oxide (N_2O)	0.00005%
Xenon (Xe)	0.0000087%

Of gases present in variable concentrations, H_2O vapor, ozone, and carbon dioxide are of principal importance and are critical to the maintenance of life on the planet. H_2O vapor is the source for all forms of precipitation and is also both an absorber and an emitter of infrared radiation. Carbon dioxide is also an absorber and an emitter of infrared radiation and is critical to the process of photosynthesis. Ozone (triatomic oxygen, O_3) is found principally in the upper strata of the atmosphere 6 to 30 miles (10 to 50 kilometers) above the earth's surface. It shields Earth from most cosmic radiation waveforms. Photochemical reactions between nitrogen oxides (NO_x) and hydrocarbons (HC) can produce ozone in quantities large enough to cause respiratory problems in animals, including humans. Concentrations of these gases in air are:

Water vapor (H_2O): 0–7%
Carbon dioxide (CO_2): 0.01–0.1%
Ozone (O_3): 0.01%

CARBON DIOXIDE (CO_2)

CO_2 is a compound. It is a colorless gas with a sharp odor and a sour taste. It is an oxidized form of carbon produced in a number of ways, most notably in respiration (exhalation) by animals; as a by-product of the combustion of carbon-containing substances (such as a HC fuel); in the fermentation of vegetable matter; and by plants in the photosynthesis process. The presence of CO_2 in the atmosphere permits the retention of radiant energy (primarily from our sun) received by the Earth. CO_2 is commonly used as a refrigerant and in fire extinguishers. It is also, by mass, the primary product of the combustion of hydrocarbon (HC) fuels. However, CO_2 is not classified or regulated as a noxious emission, although the excess of it in our atmosphere contributes to global warming. In its solid form it is known as dry ice.

WATER

Water is a compound. It can be readily observed in its three physical states: ice, water, and steam. It is vital to sustenance of all life forms. In its liquid state it is colorless, tasteless, and odorless. An oxygen atom has six electrons in its valence shell; when bonded to two hydrogen atoms, it shares an electron from each hydrogen atom and fills its valence shell. Like CO_2, it is a by-product of the combustion of a HC fuel (the result of oxidizing hydrogen), so it is emitted from any internal combustion engine in the form of steam.

Melting point: 32°F (0°C)
Boiling point: 212°F (100°C)

CARBON MONOXIDE (CO)

Carbon monoxide is a compound of carbon and oxygen. It is a highly toxic, colorless, odorless, and flammable gas. Concentrations of 0.3% can be lethal within 30 minutes.

CO is produced in the stoichiometric or slightly fuel rich combustion zone. It is associated with incomplete combustion in spark-ignited (SI) engines, but tends not to be an important factor in compression ignition (CI) engines due to the considerable excess air factors in diesel engines. CO's toxicity results from its absorption by red blood cells in preference to oxygen. CO poisoning initially produces headaches, dizziness, and nausea, and culminates in respiratory failure.

Melting point: −314°F (−192°C)
Boiling point: −326°F (−199°C)

SULFUR OXIDES (SO$_x$)

SO_2 emission is the primary product of oxidizing sulfur impurities in HC fuels. Sulfur tends to be present in the residual oil fractions constituent in diesel fuel, and legislation limiting the sulfur content in on-highway diesel fuel to 0.0015% (from 0.335% in 1994) has diminished the diesel engine's responsibility for producing this emission. SO_2 is a *compound* of sulfur, is odorless and nonflammable, and is a potential source of H_2SO_4. SO_2 smog tends to be more of a problem in geographic areas where burning of solid fuels and heavy oils is not regulated. This type of smog is especially worsened by dampness and high concentrations of suspended particulate.

OXIDES OF NITROGEN (NO$_x$)

By mass, nitrogen represents the largest ingredient in the engine cylinder during the combustion process in any engine aspirated with air. At ambient temperatures and pressures, nitrogen is relatively *inert*, that is, unlikely to become involved in chemical reactions. However, subjected to engine cylinder heat and pressure, nitrogen may become involved in the oxidation process, producing compounds of nitrogen known collectively as NO_x:

1. Nitric oxide (NO)—a colorless, odorless gas that in the presence of oxygen will convert to NO_2
2. Nitrogen dioxide (NO_2)—a reddish-orange gas that has corrosive and toxic properties
3. Nitrous oxide (N_2O)—a colorless, odorless gas better known as laughing gas

NO_x emission is generally the result of a number of fuel/engine parameters, the most important of which are actual reaction temperatures and the excess air factor. Generally but not consistently, high combustion temperatures tend to produce higher NO_x emission. NO_x is a major contributor to photochemical smog because it reacts with HC to form O_3 molecules, or ozone.

UNBURNED HYDROCARBONS

Unburned hydrocarbons (UHCs) consist of any emitted unburned fuel fractions and represent the range of fractions in the fuel. They include paraffins, olefins, and aromatics (see Chapter 18). The least volatile elements of a fuel are more likely to result in UHC emissions. UHCs are classified as potentially harmful emissions, so the exhaust gas aftertreatment systems we have seen introduced on more recent diesel engines have focused on combusting in the exhaust system what was not properly burned in the engine cylinder.

PARTIALLY BURNED HYDROCARBONS

A result of low-temperature combustion, partially burned hydrocarbons (PHCs) are substances (aldehydes, ketones, and carboxylic acids) resulting from quenching (extinguishing the flame front) before a molecule is completely combusted. One way in which this can happen is when an engine is overspeeded by overfueling, resulting in insufficient time for the combustion reaction to be taken to completion.

PARTICULATE MATTER

Any liquid or solid matter emitted from an exhaust stack that can be detected in light extinction test apparatus, such as a smoke opacimeter, is classified as **particulate matter (PM)** for purposes of emissions certification and enforcement. However, the term is more appropriately applied to emitted ash and carbon soots that are in the solid state. Diesel engines, even when operating under conditions of optimum efficiency, can emit carbon soot particulates sized 1 micron (μ) or less in small quantities. Microscopic particulates are considered to be as harmful to human respiratory systems as larger particulates. This is a contributing reason for the adoption of diesel particulate filters (DPFs) in all post-2007 highway diesel engines.

COMBUSTION

Despite the fact that human society has used fire in one form or another since prehistoric times, no person was able to explain it in appropriate chemical terms until Antoine Lavoisier in 1783. Lavoisier proved that combustion, the rusting of metals, and the breathing of animals all involved the combining of oxygen with other chemicals. It is from him that we began to use the term *oxidation*.

When a fuel is heated to its ignition temperature in the presence of oxygen, a chemical reaction takes place in which the heat energy contained in the fuel is liberated, resulting in a large volume of hot gases. In the oxidation reaction that results from igniting a fuel charge in an engine cylinder, oxygen molecules attack HC molecules, and if they succeed in penetrating their central nuclei (that is, completely combust/oxidize the fuel), they produce the compounds H_2O (in the form of steam) and CO_2 (carbon dioxide). Despite much research concerning the chemical processes that take place during combustion in an engine cylinder, knowledge of the thermodynamic process is largely limited to initial and end states and the intermediate pressure rise profile, because it occurs within a minute time frame and at high temperatures.

COMBUSTION WITH AMBIENT AIR

Combustion calculations are simplified when the reaction ingredients are limited to an HC fuel and pure oxygen. But combustion in an engine cylinder uses the oxygen available in the ambient air mixture, so proportionally the largest ingredient of the reaction is always the element nitrogen. Ideally, the elemental nitrogen aspirated by the engine should remain inert and be exhausted, unaffected by the oxidation of the fuel. However, under some circumstances the nitrogen too is oxidized, producing a number of oxides (known collectively as NO_x) that are identified as a noxious emission. The tendency to involve nitrogen in the oxidation reaction taking place in the cylinder generally increases as combustion temperatures increase and the fuel concentration in the mixture decreases—that is, under lean burn conditions.

COMBUSTION IN AN ENGINE CYLINDER

Compression pressures in diesel engines range generally from 27 bar/400 psi (2,750 kPa) to 48 bar/700 psi (4,862 kPa), but in most current **direct injection (DI)** engines, actual pressures typically would be close to the middle to high end of that range. This produces cylinder temperatures at the end of the compression stroke approximating 930°F (500°C), which is around twice the minimum required to ignite the fuel. Peak combustion pressures of between two and five times the compression pressure values result, depending on the actual engine and how it is being fueled. Peak cylinder pressures are managed (by the fuel system) to occur somewhere between 10 to 20 degrees after top dead center (ATDC) (**Figure 17–8**) so as to optimize

FIGURE 17–8 Pressure volume curve in a diesel engine.

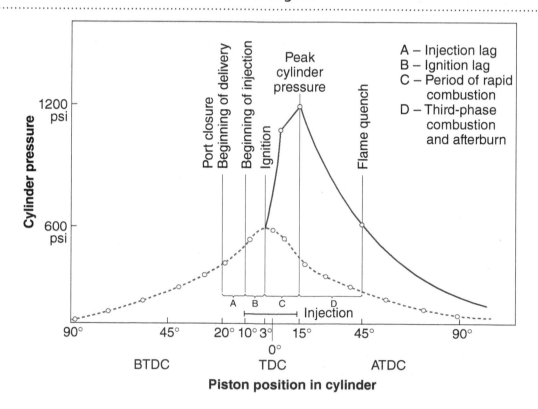

the relationship between cylinder pressure and the mechanical advantage of the crank throw vector angle (see Chapter 6). Most current diesel engines are capable of introducing fuel into the engine cylinder in multiple short shots of fuel. Because the quantity and duration of each shot of fuel into the engine cylinder is managed by computer, the resulting cylinder pressures closely complement the crank throw angle and leverage this produces. The result is a much smoother application of torque to the engine drivetrain components and an engine with greater longevity.

CYLINDER GAS DYNAMICS

Piston crown design, valve configuration, manifold boost, and the engine breathing manifolds all play a role in determining the **cylinder gas dynamics**, that is, how injected fuel is dispersed, mixed, and subsequently combusted in the cylinder. The intent is to create cyclonic turbulence (*swirl*) in the cylinder as the piston is driven upward through its compression stroke (*squish*), and current piston design theory for diesel engines suggests that the Mexican hat crown design best enables this. The way in which cylinder gas behaves under compression and through the expansion or power stroke governs both the engine's performance efficiency and noxious emissions. The way in which cylinder gas behaves during breathing (intake and exhaust strokes) determines how effectively combustion end gases are expelled and a new air charge is induced.

Because commercial diesel engines are almost always turbo-boosted, volumetric efficiencies exceed 100% by a wide margin in most performance operating phases. In fact, it would be true to say that all diesel engines are designed to operate with an excess air factor. The actual excess air percentage is usually highest when the injected fuel quantity is lowest (engine loads are lightest). The excess air factor may exceed 600% at low idle and drop to values that only slightly exceed the stoichiometric requirement when operating in the upper portion of the torque rise profile at full power loads. The use of exhaust gas recirculation (EGR) in engines reduces excess air factors when they are more likely to contribute to NO_x formation. Selective catalytic reduction (SCR) permits NO_x to be created in-cylinder, but reduces it back to N_2 and O_2 in the exhaust aftertreatment phase.

STOICHIOMETRY

The term **stoichiometric** is derived from the Greek school of philosophy called the Stoics, which, among other things, preached the avoidance of excess. In chemistry this has come to mean the relationship between the relative quantities of substances involved in a reaction. In engine technology, managing a stoichiometric burn ratio means controlling fueling so that the air in the engine cylinder is precisely that required to completely oxidize the fuel. No more, no less. A more comprehensive definition of stoichiometric is: the actual ratio of the reactants in any reaction (not necessarily just a combustion reaction) to the exact ratios required to complete the reaction.

The stoichiometric ratio or **lambda** (λ) factor is therefore dependent on the actual chemical composition of the fuel to be burned: When this is known, the stoichiometric air-to-fuel ratio may be calculated. Many SI automobile engines are electronically managed to run at stoichiometric air-fuel ratios. This is not a requirement of the diesel engine, although it should be noted that the ignition location in a diesel engine cylinder will occur where the mixture proportions are close to stoichiometric.

$>$ = greater than

$<$ = smaller than

$$\lambda = \frac{\text{Actual air supplied}}{\text{Stoichiometric requirement}}$$

$\lambda > 1$ lean burn

$\lambda < 1$ rich burn

$\lambda = 1$ stoichiometric AFR

CALCULATING AIR-FUEL RATIO

Gasolines and diesel fuels are refined from crude oil petroleum. Petroleum on a mass (weight) basis consists of the following elements:

Carbon: 84–87%

Hydrogen: 11–15%

Sulfur: 0–2%

So, on a mass basis, petroleum products, whether they are gasoline, diesel fuel, or engine lubricating oil, are not going to possess widely differing stoichiometric requirements in combustion reactions. That is, the theoretical **air-fuel ratio (AFR)** will not change that much when different petroleum products are combusted. This means that diesel fuel, gasoline, or, for that matter, engine oil all have roughly equivalent stoichiometric ratios. As soon as the exact chemical composition of the fuel is known, the stoichiometric air requirement to combust it can be calculated using the following data. To oxidize:

1 kg carbon (C) requires 2.66 kg of oxygen (O)

1 kg hydrogen (H) requires 8.0 kg of oxygen (O)

1 kg sulfur (S) requires 1.0 kg of oxygen (O)

Air is a mixture composed of 23% oxygen and 76% nitrogen by mass. Therefore, 1 kg of air would contain 0.23 kg of oxygen. So:

$$\frac{1}{0.23} = 4.35$$

Therefore, 1 kg of O would be contained in 4.35 kg of air.

Example:

1. A hypothetical diesel fuel contains by mass 86% carbon, 13% hydrogen, and 1% sulfur. What *mass* of air would be required to completely oxidize 1 kg of this fuel?

O required = (2.66 × .86) + (8.00 × .13) + (1.00 × .01)
               carbon   hydrogen   sulfur

Air required = 4.35 {(2.66 × .86) + (8.00 × .13) + (1.00 × .01)}

Air required = 4.35 (2.29 + 1.04 + .01)

Air required = 4.35 × 3.34

Air required = 14.5 kg

Therefore, AFR = 14.5:1

2. A hypothetical gasoline contains by mass 86% carbon and 14% hydrogen. Calculate the stoichiometric ratio for this fuel.

Air required = 4.35 {(2.66 × .86) + (8.0 × .14)}

Air required = 4.35 (2.29 + 1.12)

Air required = 4.35 × 3.41

Air required = 14.8 kg

Therefore, AFR = 14.8:1

SOME FACTS

In combustion:

1 lb carbon combines with oxygen and releases 14,540 Btu.

1 lb hydrogen combines with oxygen and releases 62,000 Btu.

AFR is normally expressed as a ratio of masses. AFR by mass of diesel fuels and gasolines falls within a fairly narrow window, ranging from 14.5:1 up to about 15.2:1, depending on the exact chemical constituents of the fuel. AFR by volume ranges from around 10,000:1 up to around 14,000:1.

HOW CAN 1 GALLON OF FUEL PRODUCE MORE THAN 20 POUNDS OF CARBON DIOXIDE?

This is a question you will never have to answer in an ASE test, but students and technicians ask it all the time, so here goes. As diesel fuel ignites, the carbon and hydrogen separate. During combustion, oxygen reacts with hydrogen to form H_2O and with carbon to form CO_2. The atomic weights of the reactants in combustion are:

- Hydrogen 1
- Carbon 12
- Oxygen 16

However, we are not interested in what happens to the hydrogen to answer this question, so we can ignore it. A single molecule of CO_2 has an atomic weight of 44 (12 from the C atom and 32 from the two O atoms). One U.S. gallon of diesel fuel weighs approximately 7.2 pounds. If we divide 44 (CO_2 molecule weight) by 12 (C atomic weight) we get 3.7; remember this figure, you will need it to finish the calculation. By mass, carbon represents about 85% of gasoline, so:

7.2 × 0.85 = 6.12 (weight of carbon)

Now we multiply 6.12 by 3.7 and the answer is: 22.6 pounds.

Easy? No, not really, but simple questions do not always have simple answers.

THE ACTUAL COMBUSTION CYCLE IN A DIESEL ENGINE

Harry Ricardo was the first diesel engine designer to focus on emissions. During World War II, a column of diesel-powered tanks could be seen by the enemy 50 miles away by the cloud of smoke produced. His research helped reduce visible smoke from diesel engines, but he also produced detailed analyses of diesel combustion that we still reference today. The following briefly outlines Ricardo's description of the diesel engine combustion cycle, which we have updated a little where necessary.

IGNITION DELAY OR IGNITION LAG

Ignition delay or ignition lag occurs between the *events* of the start of injection (injector nozzle opening) and the moment ignition occurs. Although some chemical reaction begins the moment the first liquid fuel droplet enters the cylinder, the moment of ignition is normally considered to occur either when a visible flame or measurable pressure rise occurs.

In an SI, gasoline-fueled engine, the moment of ignition is controlled by a spark to the engine cylinder in which the fuel is already vaporized and mixed. Things are not so precise in a diesel engine. Injecting fuel merely begins a sequence of events we know as *ignition delay*. The duration of the ignition delay is defined by the evaporation rate of the fuel, itself factored by the ignition quality of the fuel and the actual temperature in the cylinder, which rises during injection and combustion.

In a DI diesel engine, the term *AFR* cannot be used to compare the conditions in the cylinder with those evident in the premixed charge present in an SI engine, because as long as the fuel is not completely evaporated, the complete range of **fuel-air ratios** must be present from zero (no fuel) to infinity (no air within the fuel droplets). Ignition will occur where local AFR is most favorable. That is going to be where the mixture conditions are somewhere close to the stoichiometric requirement. In modern diesel engines, this location is engineered by the design of the combustion chamber. For obvious reasons, the landscape of the piston crown toward which the injection pulse is directed is the major influencing factor. However, the variability of the fuel chemistry and actual cylinder temperature influence the rate at which fuel evaporates and therefore the specific location of ignition in the cylinder.

PERIOD OF RAPID COMBUSTION

In this phase, the fuel that evaporated and mixed during the ignition delay period is burned, so the rate and duration of *rapid combustion* are closely associated with the length of the delay period. Generally, as ignition delay is prolonged (for whatever reasons), the rate and resultant pressure rise increase in the second phase. In modern diesel engines with electronically managed variable timing, ignition timing can be controlled so that the period of rapid burning produces peak cylinder pressure at an ideal crank angle under all operating conditions from idle speed/load up to rated speed/load. This may be assisted by using the multipulse injection potential of more recent diesel fuel systems. However, in many older engines with static injection timing (fuel delivery timing could neither be advanced or retarded), this period of high cylinder pressure could occur out of phase with the mechanical dynamics of the crank throw angle.

THIRD PHASE OF COMBUSTION

The third phase of the combustion cycle begins at the moment of peak cylinder pressure (wherever that happens to occur) and ends when combustion is measurably complete; that is, the available fuel has been oxidized. Under conditions of an extended fuel delivery pulse (high engine loads), some portion of the fuel will be injected into the cylinder during this third phase, so the burn rate will be influenced by the rate of injection as well as the mixing rate. Generally, engines are designed with cylinder gas dynamics to enable rapid mixing of fuel and air during the third phase so that the combustion process is completed as early as possible.

AFTERBURN PHASE

Afterburn in the diesel combustion cycle is a period in which any unburned fuel in the cylinder may find oxygen and burn. Most modern engines incorporate this phase in the third phase of combustion because, with improvements in cylinder gas dynamics and computer-controlled injection timing, it should not be a significant factor in the present-day diesel engine.

DOSING INJECTION

In some of the latest multipulse diesel injection systems capable of up to seven injection events per cycle, the final shot of fuel into the engine cylinder is often not intended to be combusted in the cylinder. The **dosing** shot of fuel is injected with the intention that it be discharged into the exhaust system as raw fuel to be combusted in exhaust gas aftertreatment systems. Original equipment manufacturers (OEMs) are calling this final shot of fuel *dosing* or *afterburn injection*.

DETONATION

Detonation describes the phenomenon that the diesel technician describes as **diesel knock** and a driver of any car knows as "ping." In the diesel engine, it is identified by sound caused by intense pressure rise that vibrates the cylinder walls.

Following the ignition of the fuel charge, as the flame **propagates** (spreads) through the combustion chamber, the portion of the charge farthest from the primary flame front is subject to both radiated heat and compression caused by the gas expansion of the primary flame front. The heat and compression may cause unburned portions of the charge to ignite before the arrival of the primary flame front. This multiple flame front condition causes an abnormally high rate of combustion and the resultant pressure rise in the cylinder known as diesel knock.

When the terms *combustion* and *explosion* are used to describe oxidation reactions in an engine cylinder, the physical results of the reaction are the same; however, the term *explosion* is used to describe an oxidation reaction that takes place at higher speeds. *Detonation* is therefore correctly described as combustion occurring at explosive rates. Its causes relate generally to the fuel chemistry, prolonged ignition lag, and advanced injection timing but, generally, detonation is seldom a significant problem in contemporary electronically managed diesel engines using North American fuels. It was, and still is, a problem in diesel engines fueled by hydromechanical injection, and the condition can be observed when starting a cold engine during winter conditions.

SUMMARY

- An element is any one of more than a hundred substances that cannot be chemically resolved into simpler substances.
- Elements consist of minute particles known as atoms.
- A mixture is composed of two or more elements and/or compounds, all of which retain their own characteristics and identity.
- A compound is composed of two or more elements combined in definite proportions and held together by chemical force.
- A molecule is the smallest particle of a compound that can exist in a free state and take part in a chemical reaction.
- Electrons carry a negative charge and orbit in shells around the atom's nucleus.
- Protons carry a positive charge and are located in the atom's nucleus.
- Neutrons are electrically neutral and are located in the atom's nucleus.
- Matter can be classified into three states: solid, liquid, or gas.

- Water is the only substance that is familiar in all three states: ice, water, and steam.
- Hydrogen is the simplest of the chemical elements and one of the most reactive.
- Carbon exists in a number of forms and combines to form compounds more readily than any other element.
- Most fuels are elementally composed of carbon and hydrogen.
- The products of combustion of an HC fuel are water and carbon dioxide.
- When nitrogen is oxidized in the combustion process, it forms several compounds known collectively as NO_x.
- A stoichiometric combustion reaction occurs when the exact proportions of the reactants (fuel and air) are present.
- Stoichiometric ratios for typical diesel fuels and gasoline range between 14.5:1 and 15:1.
- The moment of ignition in an engine cylinder occurs when there is visible flame or measurable pressure rise.
- Diesel knock is a detonation condition.

REVIEW QUESTIONS

1. Which of the following statements correctly describes air?
   a. A mixture of nitrogen, oxygen, and inert gases
   b. A compound of nitrogen, oxygen, and inert gases
   c. A molecule of nitrogen, oxygen, and inert gases
   d. An element of nitrogen, oxygen, and inert gases

2. A cubic centimeter of a typical diesel fuel would require approximately what volume of air at sea level to completely oxidize it?
   a. 12 cc
   b. 15 cc
   c. 1,000 cc
   d. 12,000 cc

3. The smallest particle of a compound that can exist in the free state and retain the chemical identity of the compound is known as a(n):
   a. quark.
   b. nucleus.
   c. atom.
   d. molecule.

4. The theory that explains the atomic differences in the three states of matter is known as:
   a. covalent bonding.
   b. kinetic molecular theory.
   c. atomic theory.
   d. plasma theory.

5. The most abundant element found in the known universe is:
   a. oxygen.
   b. carbon.
   c. hydrogen.
   d. nitrogen.

6. The most abundant element found in the earth's crust is:
   a. oxygen.
   b. carbon.
   c. hydrogen.
   d. nitrogen.

7. Oxygen has a valence of:
   a. 0.
   b. 2.
   c. 4.
   d. 8.

8. Proportionately, the largest ingredient in an in-engine cylinder, combustion reaction is:
   a. HC fuel.
   b. oxygen.
   c. water.
   d. nitrogen.

9. The term used to describe a combustion reaction in which the exact proportions of fuel and air are present is:
   a. stoichiometric.
   b. perfect burn.
   c. afterburn.
   d. gas blowdown.

10. Combustion in an engine cylinder that takes place with more than one flame front is correctly known as:
    a. stoichiometric.
    b. normal.
    c. detonation.
    d. afterburn.

11. Calculate the stoichiometric requirement of a fuel composed of 84% carbon, 15% hydrogen, and 1% sulfur when combusted in pure oxygen.

12. Calculate the stoichiometric requirement of a fuel composed of 84% carbon, 15% hydrogen, and 1% sulfur when combusted in ambient air.

13. How many protons would a balanced atom of oxygen contain?
    a. 1
    b. 2
    c. 8
    d. 16

14. How many electrons would a balanced atom of carbon contain?
    a. 2
    b. 6
    c. 12
    d. 24

15. The atomic number of an element indicates the number of ___ in an atom of the element.
    a. electrons
    b. neutrons
    c. protons
    d. quarks

16. Technician A states that the stoichiometric requirement of a gasoline combusted in air at sea level must be precisely 14.7:1. Technician B states that the stoichiometric requirement of a diesel fuel ranges between 14.5:1 and 15.1:1. Who is correct?
    a. Technician A only
    b. Technician B only
    c. Both A and B
    d. Neither A nor B

17. Technician A states that when diesel fuel is combusted, one of the products of combustion is water. Technician B states that carbon dioxide results from burning diesel fuel. Who is correct?
    a. Technician A only
    b. Technician B only
    c. Both A and B
    d. Neither A nor B

18. Technician A states that most electronically managed diesel engines are run at precise stoichiometric ratios of air and fuel after the engine is at operating temperature. Technician B states that most diesel engines are managed to run at rich fuel-to-air ratios. Who is correct?
    a. Technician A only
    b. Technician B only
    c. Both A and B
    d. Neither A nor B

19. Technician A states that hydrogen is an inert element. Technician B states that carbon can be classified as a reactive element. Who is correct?
    a. Technician A only
    b. Technician B only
    c. Both A and B
    d. Neither A nor B

20. Technician A states that the end products of both an explosion and a combustion reaction are similar. Technician B states that an explosion is an oxidation reaction that occurs in much less time than what would be described as combustion in an engine cylinder. Who is correct?
    a. Technician A only
    b. Technician B only
    c. Both A and B
    d. Neither A nor B

18

Prerequisite: Chapter 17

DIESEL FUEL CHARACTERISTICS

OBJECTIVES

After studying this chapter, you should be able to:

- Define the terms used to describe diesel fuel.
- Describe how the cetane number of a diesel fuel is determined.
- Outline the minimum requirements of a highway diesel fuel.
- State what constitutes low- and ultra-low sulfur (ULS) diesel fuel.
- Identify the consequences of running DPF-equipped engines with anything but ULS.
- Calculate how much ignition accelerator is required to restore original CN value.
- Determine the calorific or heating value of a fuel.
- Understand some of the problems associated with storing fuel.
- Identify degraded diesel fuel.
- Explain the effects of contaminated or degraded fuel on a typical fuel subsystem.
- Explain how cloud point and pour point specs affect cold weather engine performance.
- Outline the constituents of a typical aftermarket diesel fuel conditioner.

KEY TERMS

AFR
API gravity
ash
ASTM
ASTM #1D fuel
ASTM #2D fuel
boil point
bomb calorimeter test
calorific value
catalyst
cetane number (CN)
cloud point

compressed natural gas (CNG)
crude oil
diesel fuel
diesel particulate filter (DPF)
distillate
fire point
flame front
flame propagation
flash point
fossil fuel
fraction

fuel-air ratio
gasoline
heat energy
ignition accelerators
kerosene
liquefied petroleum gas (LPG)
load specific fuel consumption (LSFC)
low sulfur (LS)
microorganism growth
natural gas (NG)
octane rating

oil window
oxidation stability
photochemical smog
pour point
Saybolt universal seconds (SUS)
specific gravity
stoichiometric ratio
ultra-low sulfur (ULS)
viscosity
volatility

INTRODUCTION

In a couple of earlier chapters we have suggested that diesel engines will happily burn just about any fuel introduced into the engine cylinders, and this is true. For sure, an engine oil can fuel an engine to a runaway destruction in just seconds. The key to modern highway diesel fuels is to optimize performance over an ever-increasing engine life, which is generally measured in highway miles. Only fuels meeting the highest standards are able to achieve this. In this chapter we examine current petroleum-based diesel fuels.

Almost all current diesel engines are engineered to run on petroleum-based diesel fuel; although we are seeing some increase in the use of biodiesel, this is mainly confined to low-percentage cuts into petroleum diesel. What is described as diesel fuel today is likely to change a decade from now. Mercedes-Benz has recently introduced a direct-injected, gasoline-fueled engine that options a combination of spark and compression ignition depending on how the engine is run at any given moment. Its advantage is the production of better thermal efficiency, and that means less carbon dioxide (CO_2) out the tailpipe.

Although considerable attention has been devoted to hybrid technology in North America, at the time of writing this has not resulted in significant sales, outside of large inner-city bus transportation. This will change, but how much it changes is going to depend on how aggressive legislation is on greenhouse gases (GHGs). It is important to note that almost all hybrid buses rely on diesel power.

In North America we see diesel power as being primarily confined to commercial vehicles, but in Europe the diesel engine has captured around 50% of the automobile market. A betting person would probably be smart to back the advance of diesel over hybrid technology, at least in the near future, as far as private vehicles are concerned.

FUEL TERMINOLOGY

Before studying some basic fuel chemistry and what happens in the cylinder combustion process, it helps to understand some key terms. This chapter uses the building blocks of the combustion chemistry introduced in the previous chapter and uses some of those terms that apply to the characteristics of diesel fuel. It is probably important, if not essential, that the diesel technician have a fundamental understanding of fuel chemistry and combustion when it comes to troubleshooting engine malfunctions at a higher level. You do not have to memorize most of the terms defined here, but it is important to be familiar enough with them so you can reference them in the future. In addition, this is a NATEF requirement (narrative for *Science and Related Skills*) because it is recognized that if a technician aspires to attain the highest level of competency, then it is important to understand foundations on which the technology is based.

AFR—air-to-fuel ratio. The *actual* ratio of air to fuel in a combustion reaction. Distinct from stoichiometric AFR, which describes the proportions of the reactants in a combustion reaction required to complete the reaction. Normally expressed by mass (weight).

Ash—diesel fuels normally contain a certain quantity of suspended solids or soluble metallic compounds such as sodium and vanadium. The fuel's ash content can affect the injector, fuel pump, and any engine components subjected to high temperatures, such as piston rings, exhaust valves, and turbochargers.

ASTM—American Society for Testing and Materials. Organization that classifies diesel fuel (and other fuels) to a standard.

ASTM #1D Fuel—fuel recommended for use in high-speed, on-highway diesel engines required to operate under variable load and variable speeds. Minimum cetane number (CN) must be above 40 and is typically close to 50. In theory, the ideal fuel for highway truck and bus diesel engines; in practice, it is not as often used as #2D fuel, because it has less heat energy by weight, making it less economical.

ASTM #2D Fuel—fuel recommended for use in high-speed, on-highway diesel engines required to operate under constant loads and speeds. Like #1D fuel, the minimum CN is required to be above 40 and is typically around 45 during summer operation. Widely used in highway truck operations because it produces better fuel economy than #1D fuel, due to its higher calorific value, albeit at the expense of slightly inferior performance.

Boil point—the temperature at which a liquid vaporizes. When applied to liquid hydrocarbon (HC) fuels, it becomes a measure of volatility.

Calorific value—heat energy. The potential heat energy of a fuel is measured in British thermal units (Btus), joules, or calories.

Catalyst—a substance that enables a chemical reaction without itself undergoing any change.

Cetane number (CN)—a measure of the ignition quality of a diesel fuel, defined in some detail later in this section.

Cloud point—the temperature at which the normal paraffins in a fuel become less soluble and begin to precipitate as wax crystals. When these become large enough to make the fuel appear cloudy, this is termed the "cloud point." Cloud point exceeds the pour point by 5°F (3°C) to 25°F (15°C) in HC fuels.

Compressed natural gas (CNG)—see *Natural gas*.

Crude oil—raw petroleum. It consists of a mixture of many kinds of HC compounds of differing molecular weights and small quantities of organic compounds such as sulfur. Crude oil is distilled and cracked in the refining process to produce residual oils, distillates, and fractions, which are blended to manufacture fuels, oils, and tars.

Diesel fuel—term used to describe distillate petroleum compounds and fractions formulated for use in on-highway compression ignition (CI) engines. They are generally composed of fractions from the paraffin (the most volatile range used in a diesel fuel), naphthalene, and aromatic (the least volatile range found in a diesel fuel) series of crude oil fractions and are graded by the ASTM. Highway-use diesel fuel has a distillation range between 300°F (150°C) and 550°F (290°C) and specific gravity values ranging from 0.78 to 0.86. (See further references to diesel fuel in this text.)

Distillate—term sometimes used to describe diesel fuel formulated for on-highway use. The term *diesel fuel* is preferred.

Fire point—the temperature at which a liquid HC fuel evaporates sufficient flammable vapor to burn continuously in air. Fire point generally exceeds flash point by about 20°F (10°C) in HC fuels.

Flame front—the forward boundary of the reacting zone in cylinder combustion. Usually luminous depending on the fuel used.

Flame propagation—the way in which a fuel combusts inside the engine cylinder as determined by the manner the flame front spreads; dependent on cylinder gas dynamics, the actual AFR, temperature, and fuel chemistry.

Flash point—the temperature at which a liquid HC fuel evaporates sufficient flammable vapor to momentarily ignite when a flame is brought near its surface.

Fraction—a portion of a mixture separated by distillation or a cracking procedure such as hydrocracking or catalytic cracking. Most fuels are carefully balanced brews of combustible petroleum fractions with a range of volatility. Each fraction possesses distinct characteristics.

Fuel-air ratio—commonly used to describe the ratio of fuel to air in diesel combustion: "fuel" appears before "air" in the ratio because it is the *control* variable.

Gasoline—the group of liquid petroleum fuels blended for use in spark-ignited (SI) engines. The actual composition of gasolines varies according to the crude oil source, refining processes, and blend requirements. Typically, they have a volatility range that extends from 90°F (35°C) to 400°F (210°C) and a specific gravity that ranges from 0.70 to 0.78.

Kerosene—made up of heavier fractions than gasoline, kerosene is widely used in heating oil and jet fuel. Kerosene typically has a distillation range between 300°F (150°C) and 510°F (270°C) and specific gravity values ranging from 0.78 to 0.85.

Liquefied natural gas (LNG)—see *Natural gas*.

Microorganism growth—airborne bacteria and fungi commonly enter vehicle and storage tanks through their venting systems. When water is present in the bottom of the tank, bacteria may reside in it and feed off the fuel HCs. The metabolic waste from such microorganisms is acidic and may corrode fuel injection components. Fungal growth can plug fuel filters when pumped through the fuel subsystem. It is good practice to fill truck onboard tanks before parking the vehicle to minimize water condensation problems; water draining tanks daily (at the sump tap) also helps. However, when the problem is sourced at the storage tank, chemical treatment of the fuel with biocides is required.

Natural gas (NG)—the gaseous product of petroleum either suspended above liquid crude oil or dissolved in it, in which case it becomes the first product to be separated in the distillation process. Natural gas is composed primarily of methane (CH_4) with a lesser amount of ethane (C_2H_6), propane (C_3H_8), and butane (C_4H_{10}). Propane and butane are extracted from natural gas and stored as liquids under pressure. Both are used as an automotive fuel and are usually known as **liquefied petroleum gas (LPG)**.

Octane rating—a measure of the antiknock quality of a fuel, usually a gasoline. *Knock* in an actual engine depends on complex combustion reaction phenomena and on the engine design. However, as a method of classifying gasoline, the ASTM has standardized two methods: the Motor method (MON) and the Research method (RON). Both relate the antiknock performance of a test gasoline to that of an actual fuel. Two primary reference fuels are used: iso-octane, with "ideal" antiknock characteristics and assigned an octane number of 100; and heptane, with poor antiknock characteristics and assigned an octane number of 0. A mixture of these two primary reference HC fuels is then used as the means for grading the actual performance of a gasoline. Therefore, a mixture of 90% iso-octane and 10% heptane would theoretically have equivalent antiknock characteristics as a gasoline sold at the pumps as "90 octane."

The actual test conditions used in the Motor and Research methods differ. The Motor method testing operates at higher speed and inlet mixture temperatures than the Research method. The Research method is generally the better indicator of fuel antiknock quality for engines operating at full throttle and low speeds, whereas the Motor method is the better indicator at full throttle and high speeds. Federal regulations in the United States and Canada require the posting of the *average* of Research Octane Number (RON) and Motor Octane Number (MON) at dispensing pumps. This is expressed (R + M)/2.

A gasoline's tendency to knock can be decreased by the addition of antiknock additives, which are metalo-organic compounds that precipitate in the burn and slow the combustion rate. Tetraethyl lead (TEL) and tetramethyl lead (TML) were used until legislated out of use. Currently potassium and oxygenated compounds are used as octane boosters. Manganese compounds are still used in some Canadian gasolines to increase octane number, but these are not permitted in the United States.

Finally, when the octane rating of a gasoline is greater than 100, it is based on the milliliters of TEL required to be added to the reference fuel iso-octane to produce the improved rating. Although the sale of poisonous tetraethyl lead is generally prohibited in Western countries, it is still used in research and development. Unleaded fuels are available at the pumps with (R + M)/2 of between 85 and 95, generally depending on geographic region. Higher ratings are used for performance and specialty applications.

Oxidation stability—the products of oxidizing stored diesel fuel can result in deposits, filter plugging, and lacquering of fuel injection equipment. Antioxidants in the fuel inhibit the condition.

Photochemical smog—results from the photochemical reaction of HCs and oxides of nitrogen (NO_x) with sunlight in the lower atmosphere. It manifests itself as a brownish haze and the ozone that results may cause reduced visibility, plant damage, eye irritation, and respiratory distress. A photochemical reaction occurs when a physical substance absorbs visible, infrared, or ultraviolet radiation.

In the case of photochemical smog, the radiation source is the sun; its ingredients are HC and NO_x from combustion processes and subjecting these substances to still air and sunlight will cause the required molecular decomposition, producing ozone. Photochemical smog is primarily a problem in the urban metropolis with ample sunshine and low air movement. Of these, the metropolis of greater Los Angeles, California, is most notable—having an urban population of 17.7 million inhabitants (www.wikipedia.com) effectively walled-in on its east side by the San Gabriel mountains, limiting air movement that is generally inclined to move from west to east. Chapter 47 gives a full account of photochemical smog.

Pour point—as fuel temperature drops below the cloud point, paraffin wax crystals increase in size and the pour point generally denotes the lowest temperature at which the fuel can be pumped. Pour point is generally 5°F (3°C) to 25°F (15°C) below cloud point. Pour point depressant additives are required for extreme cold weather operation in #1D and #2D on-highway fuels. Pour point depressants have no effect on cloud point.

Specific gravity—the specific gravity of a liquid is the weight of a volume of the liquid compared to the weight of the same volume of water. The specific gravity of a petroleum-based fuel is a direct measure of its heating value (calorific value).

At 60°F (15°C), a diesel fuel measured to a specific gravity of 0.85 releases 139.50 Btu per gallon when combusted.

Stoichiometric ratio—an expression of the exact ratio of the reactants required for a chemical reaction to take place. In the internal combustion engine, the specific stoichiometric ratio of a fuel at sea level depends on the chemistry of the fuel and not on the conditions of combustion. It is a ratio of masses.

Sulfur content—on recommendation of the American Petroleum Institute (API), the Environmental Protection Agency (EPA) decreed a maximum sulfur content of 0.0015% by weight in fuel effective in October 2006 in the United States and Canada. This fuel is known as *ultra-low sulfur (ULS) fuel*. ULS replaced low-sulfur (LS) fuel, which was specified with a maximum sulfur load of 0.05%. European standards have permitted higher sulfur content until recently: the EURO V standard (graduated implementation from 2009 to 2014) requires a maximum of 0.0010% S, slightly bettering the North American standard.

Viscosity—a measure of a liquid's resistance to shear, a value that generally decreases as temperature increases. It also influences the liquid's resistance to flow and therefore its fluidity. The fluidity of a liquid is graded by **Saybolt universal seconds (SUS)**—a measure of its ability to flow through a defined flow area against time at 100°F (39°C). The SUS rating is used for comparing the viscosity of diesel fuels; #1D is typically 34.4 SUS, #2D is typically 40 SUS, and #4D is typically 125 SUS (preheating required). Viscosity and volatility in diesel fuels are closely associated. Fuel viscosity directly affects fuel injection pump service life.

Volatility—the tendency of a liquid to vaporize. The volatility rating of a fuel is more important in SI engines, as it determines the vapor-to-air ratio at the time of ignition. The volatility rating of diesel fuel is critical in summer operation when its higher fractions tend to boil off, reducing CN.

PETROLEUM

The word *petroleum* is derived from the Latin words "petra," meaning rock, and "oleum," meaning oil. Petroleum is broadly used to describe HC fossil fuels found in the upper strata of the earth's crust, ranging from solid tars through crude oil to natural gas. Somewhere around 70% of the energy consumed in North America and 40% worldwide is derived from petroleum products.

Most of this fuel is extracted from crude oil and the natural gases that are often contained in the proximity of petroleum deposits or boils off from them at surface pressures and temperatures. Crude oils are usually black, but many reflect a yellow or greenish tint. They range in density from light, very fluid liquids of high volatility to viscous tars of lower volatility.

FORMATION OF PETROLEUM

The origin of the carbon and hydrogen that are the elemental components of petroleum is in the organic materials that made up the primordial (existing at the beginning) Earth. These elemental components passed through an organic phase, usually as single-celled plants and algae and mostly located in aquatic environments. Many such simple organisms were known to have been abundant 570 million years ago; rapid burial of these organisms preserved them in sedimentary rock and enabled a series of biological, physical, and chemical changes that permitted them to evolve to what we know as petroleum. Put simply, this evolution requires heat, pressure, and eons of time. Petroleum is therefore a **fossil fuel**, an unrenewable energy source with limited reserves. It has never been duplicated in a commercial laboratory.

Crude Oil

Crude oils are loosely classified by their content, which indicates exactly what can be extracted from them in refining processes. There are three types:

1. Asphalt-based crudes: These are usually black. Generally, the higher the fluidity of a crude oil, the better its quality, meaning that

FIGURE 18–3 Diesel fuel blending.

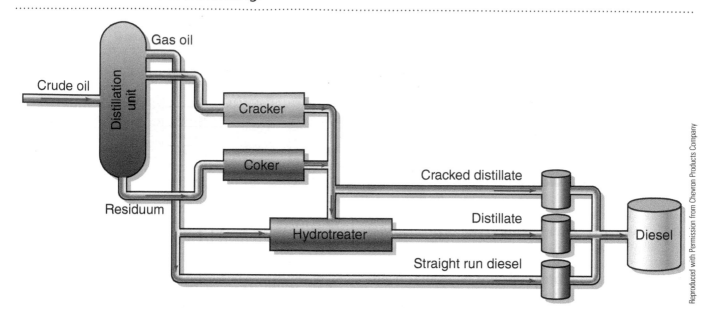

DIESEL FUEL CHARACTERISTICS

Because we have become accustomed to readily available, good quality, uncontaminated highway fuels in North America, we are often slow to attribute a fuel system or engine problem to the actual fuel being used. There is a much higher tendency for fuel-related problems in off-highway equipment, due to the more intermittent use of that equipment (including seasonal use) and poor fuel storage practices. Filling a set of vehicle tanks with contaminated or degraded fuel can create performance conditions that remain in the vehicle fuel system well beyond the fuel that caused them. When this happens, the cause is usually the purchase of fuel from a source in which the fuel is retained for prolonged periods in storage tanks (most fuel degrades in contact with air). For this reason, many original equipment manufacturers (OEMs) recommend bulk fuel filtration procedures prior to refueling.

Fuel filtration is especially important before testing an engine on a dynamometer or running fuel economy profiles. **Figure 18–4** shows a bulk fuel filtration station. As North American trucking activity extends into Mexico, Central America, and South America and fuel is purchased in those countries, fuel contamination-related problems are increasing. You should also be aware of some of the potential problems

of using biodiesel cuts. There are a number of advantages to using biodiesel and biodiesel cuts, but they have a short shelf life compared with diesel fuel. When biodiesel degrades, it can create difficult-to-diagnose fuel problems. We will take a closer look at biodiesel in Chapter 38.

CETANE NUMBER

Cetane number (CN) is a measure of the ignition quality of a diesel fuel. CN by ASTM definition is the percentage by volume of a test fuel consisting of *cetane* (ideal ignition quality, CN 100) mixed with heptamethylnonane (poor ignition quality, CN 0) required to match the fuel to be classified. A mixture of 45% cetane with 55% heptamethylnonane would have a CN of 45. In North America ASTM #1D and #2D diesel fuels for on-highway use must have a minimum CN of 40. The CN directly determines the ignition delay phase of the diesel combustion cycle, and it is not uncommon for diesel fuel refiners to adjust CN seasonally. However, increasing CN generally reduces fuel density and, therefore, the fuel mileage. As the CN of a diesel fuel increases, its ignition temperature decreases (**Figure 18–5**).

Actual CN values in diesel fuel vary regionally and seasonally. Summer diesel CN in #2D fuel is typically between 44 and 48, while winter diesel CN ranges from 46 to 52. Using a diesel fuel with a CN exceeding 55 can result

FIGURE 18–4 Bulk fuel filtration.

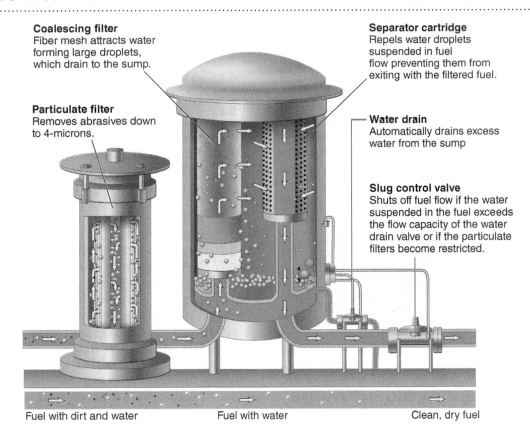

Coalescing filter
Fiber mesh attracts water
forming large droplets,
which drain to the sump.

Separator cartridge
Repels water droplets
suspended in fuel
flow preventing them from
exiting with the filtered fuel.

Particulate filter
Removes abrasives down
to 4-microns.

Water drain
Automatically drains excess
water from the sump

Slug control valve
Shuts off fuel flow if the water
suspended in the fuel exceeds
the flow capacity of the water
drain valve or if the particulate
filters become restricted.

Fuel with dirt and water   Fuel with water   Clean, dry fuel

FIGURE 18–5 Cetane number versus ignition delay.

Pressure (and Temperature) Cycle in a Diesel Engine

Long ignition
delay —
low cetane fuel

Fast pressure rise —
higher pressure

Short ignition
delay —
high cetane fuel

Proper pressure rise —
more gentle slope

Start of
injection

Normal compression —
no-fuel ignition

Bottom
dead center

Top
dead center

Bottom
dead center

Crank Position

Reproduced with Permission from Chevron Products Company

in engine smoking under torque. Using diesel fuel with a CN lower than 40 can result in hard starting, lower power, smoking, and increasing frequency of **diesel particulate filter (DPF)** regeneration cycles. DPFs are fully covered in Chapters 47 and 48.

IGNITION ACCELERATORS

Ignition accelerators (a.k.a. cetane improvers) are fuel additives that increase the CN value of a fuel. They are used as a scientifically preferable option to adding alcohol-based fuel conditioner to tanks. An ignition accelerator should only be added to fuel after testing and on the recommendation of the fuel supplier.

Cyclohexanol nitrate when added to fuel at a 0.2% concentration will raise CN by 7 points. It should always be added to a known quantity of fuel, and that usually means full tanks on either onboard or ground storage tanks. Other alkyl nitrates are also used as ignition accelerators.

numeral. For instance, the EURO IV standard, which runs from 2003 to 2013, calls for a maximum sulfur content of 0.0020% S (20 ppm), slightly higher than U.S. ULS, and the EURO V standard of 0.0010% S (10 ppm) has a graduated implementation schedule beginning in 2009 to be completed in 2014. However, European standards are subject to greater loopholes than permitted in the United States, meaning that a pedestrian stroll down a Manhattan street is likely to compare favorably with one in London or Paris, both similar sized cities. Take a walk down any street in a large city outside of North America or Europe and you will experience plenty of evidence that our emission controls and fuel quality standards are working.

ULS Introduction Schedule

It is a federal requirement that from December 2010, ULS standard fuel is universal for all on-highway diesel-powered vehicles. The following is also true:

- ULS became mandatory in all off-highway fuel retail outlets from December 2010.
- Marine and locomotive industries began transitioning to ULS fuel in 2009. The transition schedule was completed in 2014.
- Initiatives to reduce sulfur content in bunker grade oils used in large marine and generating stations are being currently worked on and are set for phased implementation beginning in 2015.
- Since 2014, ULS is the only fuel that refiners are allowed to dispense to retail outlets.

CAUTION:

ULS *must* be used in all diesel engines equipped with a diesel particulate filter (DPF). Running the pre-2007 spec LS fuel in a post-2007 engine can destroy a DPF in as little as 1 hour of operation. Running ULS in legacy engines (pre-2007) neither increases nor decreases engine performance.

Off-Highway Fuels

We have said a number of times that diesel engines are capable of burning just about anything combustible, and noted that some of the earliest diesels ran on coal dust. Because the main focus of this textbook are those engines that power highway vehicles, we have not looked at specialty and off-highway diesel fuels

categorized as ASTM #4D, #5D (bunker B), and #6D (bunker C): Bunker fuels require preheating prior to injection. These heavy fuels can only be used to fuel large, low rpm engines because they require longer to vaporize (even when preheated) and more time to properly combust. Fuels used in subarctic regions (Alaska and Northern Canada) are chemically similar to ASTM #1D diesel except that they are cut with glycol and other antigel compounds, similar to jet fuel. Like the glycol added to jet fuel, the glycols added to diesel fuel are fully combustible.

FUEL STORAGE, DETERIORATION, AND PERFORMANCE

The fuel chemistry of both gasolines and diesel fuels is adjusted seasonally by the refiner/supplier, largely because what is required of a fuel varies with temperature. To further complicate matters, a truck hauling a cargo of fruit from Miami, Florida, to Edmonton, Alberta, can be subject to temperature extremes in excess of 85°F (30°C) to 0°F (−17°C) within the span of a single trip. Generally, fuel purchased directly from the refiner/supplier presents fewer problems than fuel that is bulk-stored in reservoirs by operators.

Whenever fuel is drawn out of a tank, it is replaced by air. Replacement air always contains some percentage of moisture; in areas of high humidity, such as the Great Lakes region, this can be extreme. When temperatures cool, vaporized moisture in the tank condenses to water, which because of its greater weight settles at the bottom of the fuel tank. Most vehicle and storage tanks contain some water, and draining the tanks periodically (just the water trap sump of the tank: ensure that fuel is settled before attempting to do this) helps to prevent excessive water buildup. Both storage reservoirs and vehicle fuel tanks locate the pickup tube in a position so that trace quantities of water present in the bottom of the tank are not usually drawn out.

WATER IN FUEL

Water presents two main problems while it is actually in a fuel tank. However, it presents a host of others should it actually be drawn out and pumped through a fuel system. Some older trucks carry fuel in a pair of cylindrical tanks mounted at either side of the chassis that have a single pickup tube located in one of the tanks; the tanks are connected by a crossover pipe at the lowest point. If an appreciable quantity of water were present in such an arrangement, the heavier water would tend to collect in the crossover pipe, which becomes vulnerable to freeze-up given its location in the airflow. The common preventive and antidote for this condition is to add methyl hydrate (alcohol) to the tank. While this will prevent water freeze-up, the water and alcohol form a solution that can be absorbed by the fuel and then be pumped through the fuel system. It should be noted that water in solution with alcohol can bypass fuel-water separators and is the primary cause of injector nozzle water-based failures.

MICROORGANISM GROWTH

Another problem associated with water in tanks is microorganism growth. Airborne-source bacteria reside in the tank sump water and feed off the HCs in the fuel, causing a certain amount of degradation of the fuel. More serious, their metabolic waste is acidic and has a corrosive effect on fuel system components; it is also capable of plugging up water separators and filters. This type of problem would be more likely in an emergency power genset engine and its fuel system that only runs a couple of times a year than in mobile diesel engine applications that are likely to run at least daily. Fungi may also develop in fuel tanks and can plug fuel filters and damage in-tank transfer pumps.

TECH TIP:

It is good practice to keep fuel tanks full. This keeps moisture-laden air out of the tanks and reduces water-in-fuel problems. Fill truck fuel tanks before parking overnight.

INFLUENCE OF CLIMATE

Hot weather presents other problems. The year-round average CN value of #1D and #2D ASTM fuels sold in North America is around 47. The legal minimum for both fuels is 40. It makes sense that fuel supplied in the northern states and Canada in winter has higher mean CN values than that sold in the same geographic areas in the summer. However, when fuel is stored and exposed to high temperatures, its more volatile fractions are boiled off, effectively lowering the CN value at a time of year when the supplier has already lowered the CN because the seasonal requirement has dropped.

Cloud Point and Pour Point

Cloud point and pour point are important diesel fuel characteristics in frigid temperature conditions. The cloud point value indicates the temperature at which filters can become plugged, especially the secondary filters in some current applications designed to entrap particulates sized between 2μ and 4μ. At the fuel's pour point temperature, it is on the verge of gelling. *Pour point* is the lowest temperature at which a fuel can be pumped through the fuel system. The viscosity of the fuel is temperature related. High-viscosity fuel can result in excessive pump resistance and filter damage. Low-viscosity fuel may result in excessive wear in fuel injection apparatus and account for leaks. As temperature-conditioned ASTM #2D fuel is, in practice, the fuel used by a majority of operators year-round, fuel heaters are sometimes used to help compensate for deficiencies in cloud point, pour point, and viscosity ratings.

Generally, onboard fuel tanks and stationary reservoirs should be maintained as full as possible to minimize the quantity of moisture-laden air the fuel is exposed to. It is good practice for fleets to require refilling of vehicle tanks at the point of returning from a journey and before overnight parking.

FUEL CONDITIONERS

There are no Society of Automotive Engineers (SAE)/ASTM standards that apply to diesel fuel conditioners. Although most engine OEMs disapprove of their use, they are commonly sold in their dealerships—a measure of the profitability of the product rather than worth. Diesel fuel conditioners are a vague mixture of cetane improvers, cleansing additives, and pour point depressants in an alcohol base, usually priced well beyond the cost of their ingredients. In a freeze-up, reality dictates that the addition of methyl hydrate is the fastest way out of the problem, and in those circumstances the negatives of putting water in solution with the alcohol are understandably overlooked. However, the addition of methyl hydrate to the tank under these circumstances is arguably preferable to pouring in the contents of a "fuel conditioner" container, in that it specifically addresses the problem.

Similarly, when the objective is to improve the CN value of the fuel, then adding a cetane

TABLE 18–3 Recommended Cutting Fluid Processes

Classification	Type	Function
Contaminant Control		
Biocides	Boron compounds, ethers of ethylene glycol, quaternary amine compounds	Inhibit bacterial and fungal growth; prevent filter clogging
Demulsifiers and Dehazers	Surface-active materials that increase water/oil separation	Improve separation of water and prevent hazing
Rust and Corrosion Inhibitors	Organic acids, amines, and amine phosphates	Prevent rust and corrosion in fuel systems, pipeline, and storage facilities
Fuel Stability		
Metal Detectors	Chelating agents	Inhibit gum formation
Oxidation Inhibitors	Alkyl amines	Minimize oxidation, gum, and precipitate formation
Dispersants	Polymeric amine surfactants	Prevent agglomeration and disperse residue
Engine Performance		
Detergents	Polyglycols, polyether amines	Prevent injector deposits Extend injector life
Dispersants	Basic nitrogen polymeric amine surfactants	Peptize injector deposits Increase filter life
Cetane Improvers	Alkyl nitrates	Increase cetane number
Smoke Suppressants	Overbased barium compounds	Minimize exhaust smoke
Fuel Handling		
Pour Point Depressants	Polymeric compounds	Reduce pour point and improve low temperature fluidity properties
Cold Point Depressants	Polymeric compounds	Reduce cloud point and improve low temperature filterability
De-icers	Low molecular weight alcohols	Reduce freezing point of small amounts of water to prevent fuel line plugging
Antifoam	Silicone and nonsilicone surfactants	Minimizes the formation of fuel foam

improver in a precisely measured quantity is a more scientific and less costly strategy. Most diesel fuels are carefully balanced by the refiner, so the use of additives should be avoided whenever possible. Under circumstances such as the effect of reduced lubricity of modern 0.0015% ULS fuel (compared with pre-LS fuel) on some fuel systems, the OEM will recommend an additive on certain older engines to specifically address the lubricity problem. Aftermarket fuel conditioners generally create more problems than they solve, but the reality is that there are occasions when they have to be used. The technician should recognize the problems that can be caused by fuel conditioners and use them only when there is no other option. Diesel fuel conditioner should always be used according to the engine manufacturer's recommendations (**Table 18–3**) rather than those of the additive manufacturer.

COSTS OF OPERATING A TRUCK

The major expense in truck operation is fuel. Nothing else comes close to it in cost. A minor upsurge in the price of diesel fuel reverberates through the trucking industry and significantly impacts the operating profitability. Operators on tight margins go out of business. The increase in fuel prices since 2002 has shifted business away from brokers and small operations into the major fleets. The major fleets can manage the logistics required to make money on low margins, so they have been the big winners—and will continue to be as fuel prices continue fluctuate. Sadly, this is resulting in the gradual disappearance of independent truckers, who have been a part of our culture for more than 60 years. **Figure 18–7** shows a pie chart that represents the operating costs of a truck in 2005, with fuel costs representing 75%.

FIGURE 18–7 Costs of operating a truck.

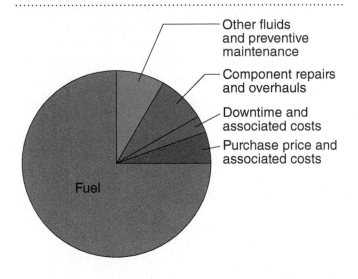

The emerging use of biodiesel is examined later in this book, but we can summarize this chapter with a reminder that a diesel engine can run on nonpetroleum-based fuels, including one that flows as sap in trees.

FUEL EFFICIENCY VERSUS FUEL ECONOMY

Using the term *fuel economy* in commercial trucking is so misleading that it should be avoided. Fuel economy relates to miles per gallon and says nothing about what is being done with the truck to produce the data. We should be referring to *fuel efficiency*, meaning that **load specific fuel consumption (LSFC)** is factored. LSFC has vastly improved in trucking operations since 1940 when data was first recorded nationally. In 1970, the cost in 2010 dollars of hauling 1 ton per mile was 40 cents. By 2010, this cost had dropped to 15 cents per mile. More remarkable is the fact that the most notable improvement during this period occurred between the years 2000 and 2010. This is an indicator that trucking should consider higher-productivity vehicles when tackling the challenges of fuel efficiency and carbon dioxide emissions over the coming years. LSFC goals for commercial vehicles were announced by the Obama administration in 2011 and will be put into effect beginning in 2017.

SUMMARY

- Crude petroleum is the basis of diesel fuel and many other HC fuels.
- Petroleum is a nonrenewable fossil fuel with limited reserves.
- Crude petroleum must be refined to separate the fractions used to formulate the fuels identified as diesel fuel, gasoline, kerosene, and heavy furnace oil.
- Several different cracking processes may be used to obtain the lighter fraction constituents of diesel fuels and gasolines.
- Diesel fuels and gasolines are a brew of many different petroleum fractions.
- Gasolines are usually more chemically complex brews than are diesel fuels.
- The ignition quality of a diesel fuel is rated by its CN. A CN number can be correlated to an actual ignition temperature.
- Minimum CN values for on-highway #1D and #2D diesel fuels are legislated in North America at 40.
- There is a correlation between a fuel's density and its heating value.

- Temperature-conditioned (by the refiner) #2D fuel is the common, on-highway fuel.
- Fuel deteriorates chemically and can be subject to microorganic contamination when stored for prolonged periods.
- Addition of methyl hydrate and other alcohols to fuel tanks should be corrective and not precautionary, because it may cause other problems.
- ULS diesel fuel with 0.0015% sulfur or less is the current fuel standard mandated by the EPA for both on-highway and most off-highway usage.
- Use of anything but ULS in a diesel engine equipped with a DPF can destroy the DPF in as little as 1 hour of operation.
- The cost of fuel is by far the greatest factor in the expense of operating commercial trucks.
- Fuel efficiency relates to the cost per ton, per mile hauled and is measured as LSFC. This indicates that trucking should pursue high-productivity vehicles rather look to *fuel economy* for answers.

REVIEW QUESTIONS

1. As the octane rating value of a gasoline increases, what can be said of its burn rate?
   a. It is not affected.
   b. It decreases.
   c. It increases.

2. As the CN value of a diesel fuel increases, what happens to its ignition temperature?
   a. It is not affected.
   b. It decreases.
   c. It increases.

3. The temperature at which a fuel evaporates sufficient flammable vapor to momentarily ignite when a flame is brought close to its surface is known as:
   a. flash point.
   b. fire point.
   c. boil point.

4. What is the minimum CN requirement of #1D or #2D on-highway diesel fuel?
   a. 30
   b. 40
   c. 45
   d. 50

5. Which of the following specific gravity values would correspond to that of a typical #2D diesel fuel?
   a. 0.710
   b. 0.840
   c. 0.970
   d. 1.170

6. Which of the following diesel fuel additives is a commonly used cetane improver?
   a. Isopropyl alcohol
   b. Kerogen
   c. Kerosene
   d. Cyclohexanol nitrate

7. The temperature at which a diesel fuel begins to form paraffin wax crystals is known as:
   a. cloud point.
   b. pour point.
   c. flash point.

8. The lowest temperature at which a diesel fuel can be pumped through a fuel system is known as:
   a. cloud point.
   b. pour point.
   c. gel point.

9. If an additive were required to prevent freeze-up of a fuel crossover pipe, which of the following would be the preferred option?
   a. Add 8 oz. (250 cc) of fuel conditioner to the tanks.
   b. Add 8 oz. (250 cc) of methyl hydrate to the tanks.
   c. Add 8 oz. (250 cc) of gasoline to the tanks.
   d. Add 8 oz. (250 cc) of cetane improver to the tanks.

10. Current diesel fuel formulated for on-highway use and classified as ULS is required to have what maximum sulfur content?
    a. 0.0015%
    b. 0.005%
    c. 0.300%
    d. 0.500%

11. Technician A states that #2D diesel fuel will, in most cases, produce slightly better fuel mileage from a highway truck engine than a #1D fuel. Technician B states that #2D usually has more heat energy than a #1D fuel. Who is correct?
    a. Technician A only
    b. Technician B only
    c. Both A and B
    d. Neither A nor B

12. Technician A states that all #1D and #2D fuels must be sold with a CN number of exactly 40. Technician B states that refiners and fuel suppliers seasonally adjust the ignition quality of fuels. Who is correct?
    a. Technician A only
    b. Technician B only
    c. Both A and B
    d. Neither A nor B

13. Which of the following best describes the term *octane rating* when applied to a fuel?
    a. Volatility
    b. Burn rate
    c. Antiknock resistance
    d. Ignition temperature

14. Which of the following components would be more likely to fail if LS fuel were used instead of ULS in a highway diesel engine manufactured after 2007?
    a. Exhaust gas recirculation (EGR) circuit
    b. NO_x reduction catalyst
    c. Diesel particulate filter (DPF)
    d. Selective catalytic reduction (SCR) system

15. Technician A states that a catalyst is a substance that enhances or enables a chemical reaction without itself undergoing any change. Technician B states that the laws of thermodynamics dictate that a catalytic reaction must involve a change in the state of the catalyst. Who is correct?
    a. Technician A only
    b. Technician B only
    c. Both A and B
    d. Neither A nor B

16. Technician A states that denser fractions of crude petroleums tend to command higher prices than lighter fractions. Technician B states that diesel fuel tends to be more volatile than gasoline. Who is correct?
    a. Technician A only
    b. Technician B only
    c. Both A and B
    d. Neither A nor B

Prerequisite: Chapter 17

FUEL SUBSYSTEMS

OBJECTIVES

After studying this chapter, you should be able to:

- Identify fuel subsystem components on a truck or bus chassis.
- Describe the components used in a diesel engine fuel subsystem.
- Define the functions of internal and external fuel tank components.
- Troubleshoot a fuel sending unit.
- Define the role of primary and secondary fuel filters.
- Service primary and secondary fuel filters.
- Describe the three ways water can be suspended in fuel.
- Explain how a water separator functions.
- Service a water separator.
- Define the principles of operation of a transfer or charge pump.
- Prime a fuel subsystem.
- Test the low-pressure side of the fuel subsystem for inlet restriction.
- Test the charge side of the fuel subsystem for charging pressure.
- Identify some typical sensors used in diesel fuel subsystems.

KEY TERMS

canister	crossover	inlet restriction	section modulus
cartridge	emulsify	micron (μ)	sending unit
centrifuge	fuel filter	pickup tube	suction circuit
charging circuit	fuel heater	plunger pump	transfer pump
charging pressure	fuel subsystem	positive displacement	venting
charging pump	fuel tank	primary filter	water detection paste
clockwise (CW)	gear pump	prime mover	water-in-fuel (WIF) sensor
coalesce	Hg manometer	secondary filter	water separator

INTRODUCTION

The diesel **fuel subsystem** on a commercial vehicle is best defined as the group of components responsible for storing fuel and transferring it to the injection pumping apparatus. Although injection pumping mechanisms can differ greatly from manufacturer to manufacturer, the fuel subsystems that supply them tend to have much in common. Many of the problems that challenge the diesel technician at the novice level focus on the fuel subsystem. The principal components described in this chapter are often dismissed as being straightforward and exempted from study.

However, a thorough knowledge of how these components interact and how they affect the performance of the fuel injection apparatus is essential. Although the basic components used in a fuel subsystem have not altered much as we have progressed through different generations of emissions controls, the way in which the fuel subsystem is monitored has changed. A generation ago, the fuel subsystem had one monitoring sensor called a *sending unit*. Today, depending on the original equipment manufacturer (OEM), system pressure and temperature are monitored at different locations in the circuit. **Fuel tanks, fuel filters, water separators, transfer pumps, fuel heaters**, and their interconnecting plumbing are examined in this chapter. **Figure 19–1** shows the main fuel system components used on a typical common rail (CR)–fueled engine; **Figure 19–2** shows a Navistar fuel subsystem schematic. Study the fuel routing in both systems.

FUEL SUBSYSTEM OBJECTIVES

If you take a look at the fuel systems shown in Figure 19–1 and Figure 19–2, you will observe a clear divide between the low-pressure side and the charge side of the fuel subsystem. The fuel transfer pump divides the two sections. Most fuel subsystems are of this type and the terms **suction circuit** (low-pressure side) and **charging circuit** (high-pressure side—do not confuse with injection pressures, which are much higher) are commonly used to describe each. A full explanation of

FIGURE 19–1 Fuel system components and routing used on a typical CR-fueled engine.

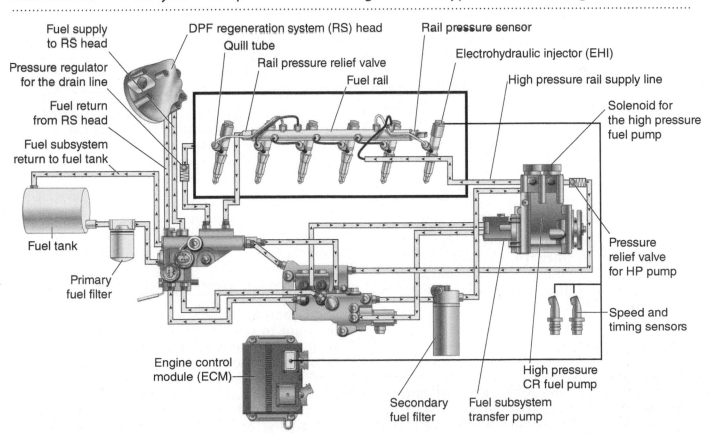

FIGURE 19–2 Fuel subsystem schematic.

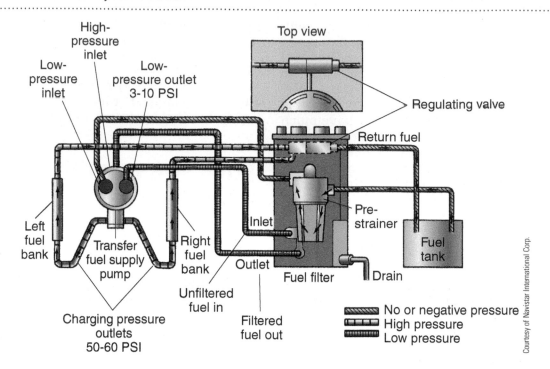

Courtesy of Navistar International Corp.

the hydraulics of how fuel is moved through the fuel subsystem appears later in this chapter under the heading "Fuel Charging/Transfer Pumps."

A **primary filter** is most often located on the suction side of the transfer pump, while the **secondary filter** is located on its charge side. However, there are some fuel systems, notably some manufactured by Cummins, in which all movement of fuel through the fuel subsystem is under suction. When such a fuel system uses multiple filters, the terms *primary* and *secondary* tend not to be used. This section attempts to generally describe fuel subsystems and troubleshooting methods. The characteristics of particular fuel subsystems are described in sections dealing with proprietary systems. We can summarize the objectives of the fuel subsystem as follows:

- Stores fuel in tanks until required
- Removes moisture from the fuel
- Filters fuel to remove abrasive particulates
- Delivers fuel to the injection components at the proper temperature

FUEL TANKS

On commercial vehicles, fuel is stored in fuel tanks. In most highway trucks, fuel tanks are mounted to the frame. It is common to use a pair of fuel tanks. This balances the considerable

weight of onboard fuel as it is consumed. A typical fuel tank arrangement is shown in **Figure 19–3**. Many diesel fuel management systems are designed to pump much greater quantities of fuel through the system than are required for actually fueling the engine. This excess fuel factor varies from a minimal amount to values exceeding 60% of pumped fuel. The excess fuel is used to:

- Lubricate high-pressure injection components
- Cool high-pressure injection components (especially those exposed to extreme temperatures)
- Cool electronic components such as engine control modules (ECMs) and injector drivers

As a cooling medium, the fuel transfers heat from engine components to the fuel tank. This provides the fuel tank(s) with a role as heat exchanger.

FUEL TANK RECOMMENDATIONS

Engine and fuel injection system manufacturers tend not to manufacture most of the fuel subsystem components, but often make specific recommendations to the chassis OEM, which may or may not be observed. The fuel tank is always a chassis OEM-supplied component. Figure 19–3 shows a typical truck fuel tank. Essentially, a vehicle fuel tank will function

FIGURE 19–3 Dual fuel tank arrangement that eliminates the fuel crossover pipe.

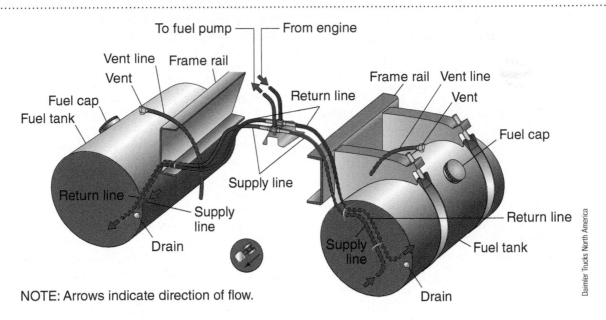

NOTE: Arrows indicate direction of flow.

most effectively as a heat exchanger if the following is true:

1. Located in the airflow. Truck fuel tanks tend to be mounted in cradle brackets bolted to the outboard side of laddered frame rails such as those shown in Figure 19–3. This ensures fairly good airflow around the tank into which heat removed from the cylinder head by the fuel can be dissipated.
2. Cylindrically shaped. A cylindrically shaped vessel (see Figure 19–3) helps maximize the surface area of the tank exposed to the airflow. This shape additionally has higher **section modulus** (relates the shape of a vessel or beam to rigidity) than a rectangular-shaped vessel, permitting thinner wall thickness. That means an overall lighter fuel tank.
3. Aluminum construction. The coefficient of heat transfer of aluminum is high, enabling heat to be transferred efficiently from the fuel to atmosphere.
4. Aluminum is less susceptible than steel to water corrosion at the base of the tank and is much lighter.
5. Maintained 25% full or better. In a fuel system that circulates fuel through the system at a high rate, such as most more recent systems, the fuel can heat up to temperatures where its lubricity is compromised when the tanks are near empty. It is good practice in such systems to maintain the tank level at better than 25% full.

DUAL TANKS

Most heavy highway trucks use multiple fuel tanks (usually two) to increase onboard fuel capacity and also to evenly distribute fuel weight. It should be noted that 100 U.S. gallons of a typical diesel fuel weigh between 700 and 730 pounds. To maintain even weight distribution as fuel is consumed, a Y-type **pickup tube** pulls fuel from both tanks simultaneously; assuming that the tanks are of equal volume, fuel level is automatically equalized. Most of today's trucks use a Y (sometimes known as a T-type) fuel pickup, but you still see some older-style fuel tank arrangements with single pickup and crossover pipes.

Each tank requires a fuel cap (**Figure 19–4**) and must be filled separately when no crossover pipe is used. Older-style crossover pipes can be a source of problems that the diesel technician should be aware of. The location of the pipe—slung at the lowest point between the two fuel tanks—makes it vulnerable to damage from road debris and animals; the angle iron bracket that supports the crossover line provides little more than minimal protection. The crossover is also exposed to the airflow under the truck and in the middle of winter, water present in the line will freeze. When crossover lines freeze up, alcohol (methyl hydrate) has to be added to the fuel tanks. Most current trucks use dual fuel tank designs that eliminate the crossover pipe, such as that shown in Figure 19–3; in this configuration, the pickup lines draw in a parallel

FIGURE 19–4 Fuel tank cap.
....

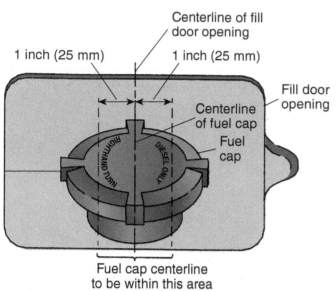

Daimler Trucks North America

arrangement from each tank. This arrangement is known as a Y- or T-type pickup depending on who manufactures the device.

PICKUP TUBES

Fuel pickup tubes are positioned so that they draw on fuel slightly above the base of the tank and thereby avoid picking up water and sediment. Pickup tubes are quite often welded into the tank; in this case, if they fail the tank may have to be replaced. Fuel pickup tubes seldom fail, but when they do it is usually by metal fatigue crack at the neck; this results in no fuel being drawn out of the tank by the transfer pump whenever the fuel level is below the location of the crack.

FUEL TANK SENDING UNITS

Most medium- and heavy-duty commercial truck fuel subsystems use remote (from the tank) fuel transfer pumps rather than assemblies that incorporate the **sending unit** and a transfer pump. Therefore, the fuel sending unit is an integral assembly flange fitted to the tank. It consists of a float and arm connected to a variable resistor whose function it is to control current flow to a cab gauge proportionally with fuel tank level.

Most older dual fuel tank truck chassis in which the tanks were connected underneath by a **crossover** pipe (a crossover pipe connects a pair of cylindrical fuel tanks, mounted on the

outside of opposing frame rails) often used a single sending unit located in one of the tanks. The tank with the sending unit was that opposite the tank with the pickup tube. It is generally preferable to locate a sending unit in each tank and provide a dash gauge for each, providing the operator with some advance warning of a crossover pipe restriction.

Testing Sending Units

Variable resistance-type fuel sending unit problems can be diagnosed by disconnecting the terminals and using a digital multimeter (DMM) in resistance mode. When the float arm is moved through its arc, the readings observed should change as the arm angle changes.

Diagnostic Procedure for a 240-Ohm Fuel Sending Unit

1. Remove the wire lead from the sensor terminal.
2. Connect the ohmmeter across the sensor terminal and mounting flange (ground).
3. Visually estimate the amount of fuel in the tank.
4. Correlate the visual fuel level estimate with the following values:

   Full tank   About 20 to 50 ohms
   Half tank   About 80 to 120 ohms
   Empty tank   About 220 to 260 ohms

5. Values that differ widely from those listed here indicate a defective sending unit.

Diagnostic Procedure for a 90-Ohm Fuel Sending Unit

1. Remove the wire lead from the sensor terminal.
2. Connect the ohmmeter across the sensor terminal and mounting flange (ground).
3. Visually estimate the amount of fuel in the tank.
4. Correlate the visual fuel level estimate with the following values:

   Full tank   About 86 to 94 ohms
   Half tank   About 40 to 50 ohms
   Empty tank   About 0 to 4 ohms

5. Values that differ widely from those listed here indicate a defective sending unit.

Venting

Currently, most jurisdictions in North America permit **venting** of diesel fuel tanks to atmosphere, but some OEMs prefer that ingested air be filtered to prevent the admission of road dirt and excessive moisture into the fuel. Venting permits gas movement both in and out of a fuel tank. As fuel is pumped out of onboard tanks to fuel the engine, it is replaced by ambient air drawn in through a breather. Gas movement is reversed on refueling or if the fuel becomes heated. In hot weather conditions, some of the lighter fuel fractions boil off coincidentally, causing a slight reduction in the fuel cetane number (CN) value. However, this boil-off seldom occurs at a rate sufficient to significantly compromise the fuel except in instances in which a tank of fuel is retained for a prolonged period in extreme heat.

Boiled-off fuel fractions from diesel fuel have so far not been considered a noxious hydrocarbon (HC) emission worthy of legislated controls. Fuel tank vents or breathers should be routinely inspected for restrictions and should be protected from ice buildup. A plugged fuel tank vent or breather will rapidly shut down an engine, creating a suction side **inlet restriction** value that the transfer pump will not be capable of overcoming.

Breather Filters

As fuel is drawn out of a fuel tank, ambient air is drawn in. This ambient air contains whatever dust and dirt contaminants happen to be suspended in the air. One OEM has determined that more than 60% of the dirt trapped by a 4-micron secondary filter has passed through unfiltered fuel cap vents or breathers. As a consequence, the OEM recommends the use of a high-efficiency fuel tank breather similar to that shown in **Figure 19–5**. The practice of using breather filters in diesel vent circuits is expected to expand.

WIF Checking

Diesel fuel tanks should be periodically checked for water in fuel (WIF). To check for the presence of water in fuel tanks, first allow the fuel tanks to settle, then insert a probe (a clean aluminum welding rod) lightly coated with **water detection paste** through the fill neck until it bottoms in the base of the tank; withdraw the rod and examine the water detection paste for a change in color. This test will give some idea of the quantity of water in the tank by indicating the height on the probe where the color has changed. Trace quantities (just the tip of the probe changes color) in fuel tanks are not unusual and will not necessarily present any problems. Some examples of water detection paste are:

- Gasoila WF25
- Kolor-Kut M1
- Shell water detector

Typically, a water detection paste is originally colored mustard yellow or brown, but turns a brilliant red when in contact with trace quantities of water. Ensure that the water detection indicator is intended for use in diesel fuel: Some gasoline contaminant detection agents change color when exposed to any substance that is not gasoline, including diesel fuel.

> **TECH TIP:**
>
> The appropriate way to check for water in diesel fuel tanks is to use water detection paste. Lightly paste a small quantity onto a bare wire aluminum welding rod. The original mustard yellow or brown color changes to red when in contact with water. Allow a mobile fuel tank to settle for at least an hour before testing: this will allow you to determine how much water is in the tank. Always expect a trace quantity at the base of the tank.

FUEL TANK REPAIR

Generally, OEMs recommend that a defective fuel tank be replaced rather than repaired. However, corroded and punctured fuel tanks are going to be repaired regardless of OEM recommendation, so the following suggestions are offered—not to endorse fuel tank repair practice, but to promote some safety awareness. It is essential to recognize the explosion hazard represented by diesel fuel vapors.

If a metal fuel tank must be welded, all fittings and plugs should be removed and the tank high pressure steamed until the temperature exceeds 200°F (95°C) throughout or for a minimum of 1 hour; it should also be remembered

FIGURE 19–5 Fuel tank breather filter recommended by Caterpillar.

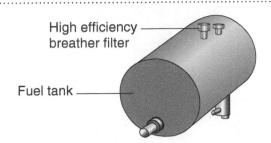

High efficiency breather filter

Fuel tank

that in some jurisdictions, the practice of steaming fuel storage vessels to atmosphere is prohibited. Fuel tanks sectioned with internal baffles must be directly subjected to the steam within each section. After steaming, the tank should be filled with nitrogen gas before repair welding and/or weld patching. When a gasoline tank is to be repair-welded, it should be steamed and then evacuated with a vacuum pump to a moderate vacuum before filling with nitrogen gas.

TECH TIP:

When evacuating fuel tanks, check with the tank OEM for the safe vacuum test value. A high vacuum value may collapse a fuel tank; as a rule, cylindrical tanks will withstand higher vacuum test values than square section tanks.

The practice of welding full fuel tanks in position, though arguably safer than welding on an empty tank filled with fuel vapors, should never be undertaken. A single mistake or metallurgical defect in the tank wall would result in the death of the welder and any other person in the vicinity.

FUEL FILTERS

Diesel fuel injection equipment is manufactured with minute clearances, so impurities in fuel, if not removed by the fuel subsystem, can cause premature failures. Most dirt found in fuel is a result of conditions in stationary fuel storage tanks, refueling practices, and improper fuel filter priming techniques by service technicians. The function of a fuel filter is to entrap particulate (fine sediment) in the diesel fuel; although some current secondary filters filter to the extent that water in its free state will not pass through the filtering media, a water separator is often used to remove water (H_2O). All diesel fuel systems require clean fuel, and the function of the filters in a fuel system is to ensure that the fuel is as clean as possible before it is delivered to the injection pumping components.

A typical fuel subsystem with a primary circuit and a secondary circuit in most cases uses a two-filter arrangement, one in each circuit. Two basic types of filter are used: the currently more common spin-on, disposable **cartridge** type and the **canister** and disposable element type. Spin-on filters are obviously easier to service and are

the filter design of choice by most manufacturers. **Figure 19-6** shows some filter options and flow routing.

FIGURE 19-6 Types of fuel filters.

Fuel Filter
Two-stage multifunction filter housing

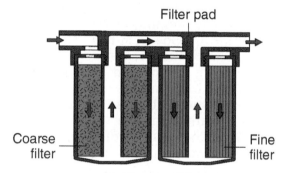

Multistage Filter
With spiral V-form filter element

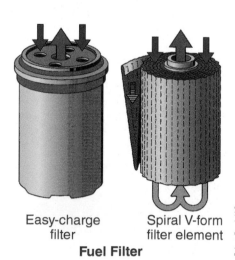

Easy-charge filter   Spiral V-form filter element

Fuel Filter

DEFINING CLEAN FUEL

Fuel filters are rated by their ability to entrap particulates. They function on a sort of fishnet principle whereby particles smaller than a certain size pass through the mesh—and those too large get entrapped. The unit by which we measure particle size is the **micron**. One micron (1μ—the Greek letter mu) is equal to one millionth of a meter. So, a typical secondary fuel filter rated at 5μ is designed to entrap most solids of that size that attempt to pass through it. You should note that the human eye is unable to see a particle smaller than 40μ in size. There is an International Standards Organization (ISO) standard used to identify the particles. **Figure 19-7** shows the sectional size of a human hair in relation to some of the dimensions we reference when talking about clean fuel.

The ISO fuel standard relates to the number of fuel particles suspended in fuel in three critical sizes: those of 4μ, 6μ, and 14μ, respectively. Caterpillar's definition of clean fuel is ISO standard 18/16/13; this refers to the counts of particles of those sizes and in that sequence as shown in Figure 19-7. Caterpillar also states that the maximum H_2O content in its fuel should not exceed 1,000 parts per million or 0.01%. So, what this OEM is saying is that provided fuel cleanliness is 18/16/13 or better, then the engine filtration system can perform the job it needs to do in cleaning the fuel. If fuel contaminants are worse than specified, then the filters are likely to plug. All fuel filters are rated by their ability to trap particles of a specified size. A filter with a specified rating of 2 microns at 99% efficiency means that it will entrap particles that are 2 microns and larger 99% of the time.

PRIMARY FILTERS

Primary filters represent the first filtration stage in a typical two-stage filtering fuel subsystem. Primary filters are therefore usually under lower than atmospheric pressure in operation, plumbed in series between the fuel tank and the fuel transfer pump. They are designed to entrap particles larger than $10-30\mu$ depending on the fuel system. They achieve this using media ranging from cotton-threaded fibers, synthetic fiber threads, and resin-impregnated paper. **Figure 19-8** shows a typical spin-on type primary filter with a water separator feature.

FIGURE 19-8 Spin-on primary filter and water separator.

FIGURE 19-7 ISO fuel code interpretation and definition of a micron.

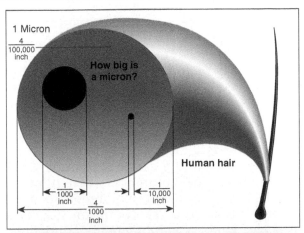

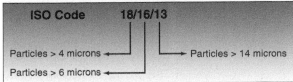

Range numb.	Micron	Actual particle count range (per ml)
18	4+	1,300 - 2,500
16	6+	320 - 640
13	14+	40 - 80

SECONDARY FILTERS

Secondary filters represent the second filtration stage in two-stage filtering. In a typical fuel subsystem, the secondary filter is charged by the transfer pump, and this enables use of more restrictive filtering media. The secondary filter would therefore normally be located in series between the transfer or **charging pump** (the pump responsible for pulling fuel from the fuel tank and charging the fuel injection components) and the fuel injection apparatus. In some diesel fuel subsystems using two-stage filtering, the primary and secondary filters may both be located on the same circuit, usually the charge circuit. In such cases, both filters are mounted on the same base pad with the primary filter feeding the secondary filter in series. Such an arrangement is more likely to be found in off-highway applications of diesel engines.

Current secondary filters may be specified to entrap particulates sized as small as 1μ, but filtering efficiencies of $2-5\mu$ are more common. Secondary filters use a variety of media, including chemically treated pleated papers and cotton fibers. **Figure 19–9** shows the secondary

FIGURE 19–9 Volvo secondary filter pad assembly.

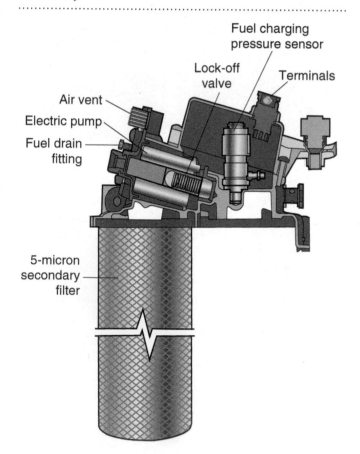

filter pad assembly used on newer Volvo engines equipped with a fuel pressure sensor.

Water and Secondary Filters

H_2O in its free or emulsified state (terms defined just a little later) cannot be pumped through most current secondary fuel filters with nominal ratings of 5μ or less. This results in the filter plugging on H_2O and shutting down the engine by starving it for fuel. Water-plugged filters should be replaced. As an emergency measure, you can clean the filters using methyl hydrate or other pure alcohol, then reprime with fuel.

Single Circuit Subsystems

In a fuel subsystem that is entirely under suction, such as some Cummins systems, the terms *primary* and *secondary* are not used to describe multiple filters when fitted to the circuit. Because every filtering device used in the fuel subsystem is held at a lower-than-atmospheric pressure (i.e., under "suction"), the inlet restriction specification is critical and, if exceeded, would result in a loss of power caused by fuel starvation.

SERVICING FILTERS

Most fuel filters are routinely changed according to preventive maintenance schedules that are governed by highway miles, engine hours, or calendar months. They are seldom *tested* to determine serviceability. When filters are tested, it is usually to determine if they are restricted (plugged) to the extent that they are reducing engine power by causing fuel starvation.

Testing and Servicing a Primary Filter

Primary filters or a filter under suction should be tested for inlet restriction with a negative pressure gauge calibrated in inches of mercury (Hg) restriction. The negative pressure specifications are based on using an **Hg manometer**. A manometer is a clear tubular column formed in a U shape around a calibration scale marked off in inches. The column is then filled with either Hg or H_2O (usually colored with dye for ease of reading) to a zero point on the calibration scale. When a manometer is connected to a fluid circuit, it produces a reading according to the pull (vacuum circuit) or push pressure acting on the fluid in the column. The negative pressure gauge produces the same readings without the danger potential associated with Hg. Actual inlet restriction values vary considerably with the fuel system, and specifications should always be referenced.

The Hg-calibrated, negative pressure gauge should be connected into the circuit between the filter mounting pad and the transfer pump. Transfer pumps are usually **positive displacement** (unload a constant slug volume of fluid per cycle), so they pump more fuel proportionally with rpm increase; this means that valid test results can be obtained without loading the engine. When testing circuit restriction on a fuel subsystem that is entirely under suction, the specifications are likely to be fairly exacting. Circuit restriction specification readings on some Cummins systems that pull large volumes of fuel should be 4–6" Hg with a new filter, but 7" Hg is the maximum specification; if this value is exceeded, it will result in fuel starvation. Typical primary circuit inlet restrictions could be specified at lower or higher values than this, so always check OEM specifications.

TECH TIP:

The technician should note that most filters function with optimum efficiency just before they completely plug—In other words, at the end of their service lives. Accordingly, a filter testing at the maximum restriction specification is still functioning properly, and though it may not have much service life remaining, it should not produce performance problems.

Testing and Servicing a Secondary Filter

Secondary filters are usually charged by the transfer pump. Testing **charging pressure** (the pressure downstream from the charging/transfer pump) is normally performed with an accurate, fluid-filled pressure gauge (**Figure 19–10**) plumbed in series between the transfer pump and injection pump apparatus; it is not generally used as a method of determining the serviceability of a secondary filter. Secondary filters tend to be changed by preventive maintenance schedule rather than by testing, or when they plug on H_2O or midwinter fuel waxing and shut down an engine. In summary:

- Primary filters are tested for inlet restriction measured in inches of Hg.
- Secondary filters are restriction-tested using a pressure gauge in psi.
- The pressure downstream from the transfer pump is known as *charging pressure*.

FIGURE 19–10 Fluid-filled pressure gauge used to measure charging pressure.

CAUTION:

In many EPA post-2007 and 2010 certified diesel engines, charging pressures may be much higher than their predecessors. This is because the charge side of the fuel subsystem may be used to supply diesel particulate filter (DPF) dosing injectors, which often require higher pressures. Check specs and exercise caution.

Procedure for Servicing Spin-on Filter Cartridges

Much dirt is placed in diesel fuel systems by technicians using improper service techniques. Most diesel service technicians realize that sets of replacement filters should be primed, that is, filled with fuel before installation, but few concern themselves about the source of the fuel used. Filters should be primed with filtered fuel. Shops performing regular engine service should have a reservoir of clean fuel; any process that requires the technician to remove fuel from vehicle tanks will probably result in it becoming contaminated at least to some extent, however much care is exercised. The container used to transport the fuel from the tank to the filter should be cleaned immediately before it is filled with fuel. Paint filters (the paper cone-shaped type) can be used to filter fuel. The inlet and outlet sections of the filter cartridge should be identified.

The filter being primed should be filled only through the inlet ports, usually located in the outer annulus (ring) of the cartridge, and never directly into the outlet port, which is usually located at the center. Most manufacturers prefer that only the primary filters be primed before installation during servicing, but check the OEM service literature: One OEM specifies that both the primary and secondary fuel filters should be installed dry, then primed using the integral hand primer pump. After the primary filter(s) has been primed and installed, the secondary filter should be installed dry and primed with a hand primer pump or inline electric primer pump if equipped. A number of post-2007 model year diesel fuel systems are equipped with electric priming pumps, primarily to prevent priming shortcuts on secondary filters.

Replacement Procedure

1. Remove the old filter cartridge from the filter base pad using an appropriately sized filter wrench.
2. Drain the fuel to an oil disposal container.
3. Ensure that the old filter cartridge gasket(s) has been removed. Wipe the filter pad gasket face clean with a lint-free wiper.
4. Remove the new filter cartridge from the shipping wrapping. Fill the filter cartridge with clean, filtered fuel poured carefully into the inlet section. The inlet ports are usually located in the outer annulus of the cartridge. Fuel poured into the filter inlet ports passes through the filtering media and fills the center or outlet section of the filter; this method will take a little longer because it requires some time for the fuel to seep through the filtration medium.
5. The fuel oil itself should provide the gasket and/or O-ring and mounting threads with adequate lubricant; it is not necessary or good practice to use grease or white lube on filter gaskets.
6. Screw the filter cartridge **clockwise (CW)**: (right-hand threads are used) onto the mounting pad; after the gasket contacts the pad face, a further rotation of the cartridge is usually required. In most cases, hand tightening is sufficient, but each filter manufacturer has its own specific recommendations on the tightening procedure and these should be referenced.

TECH TIP:

When a hand primer pump is fitted to a fuel subsystem, externally prime only the primary filter, ensuring that all the fuel is poured through the inlet side only. Install the secondary filter dry and prime using the hand primer pump. When an electric primer pump is fitted to the circuit, use it.

WARNING:

When removing filter cartridges, ensure that the gasket is removed with the old filter. A common source of air induction in the fuel subsystem is double gasketing of the primary filter. Double gasketing will usually produce a leak at the secondary filter.

WATER SEPARATORS

Most current diesel engine-powered highway vehicles have fuel subsystems with fairly sophisticated H_2O removal devices. Water appears in diesel fuel in three forms:

- Free state
- Emulsified
- Semi-absorbed

H_2O in its free state appears in large globules and, because of its greater weight than diesel fuel, readily collects in puddles at the bottom of fuel tanks or storage containers.

H_2O emulsified in fuel appears in small droplets; because these droplets are minutely sized, they may be suspended for some time in the fuel before gravity takes them to the bottom of the fuel tank. When free-state H_2O collects in the base of fuel tank, 3 miles (5 km) of driving on a rough class B road is enough to **emulsify** it (finely dispersing it into the fuel), making it more of a problem.

Semi-absorbed H_2O is usually water in solution with alcohol, which is a direct result of the methyl hydrate (type of alcohol added to fuel tanks as deicer or in fuel conditioner) added to fuel tanks to prevent winter freeze-up. H_2O that is semi-absorbed in diesel fuel is in its most dangerous form, because it may emulsify in the fuel injection system where it can seriously damage components.

Why Water Damages Fuel Systems

Generally, H_2O damages fuel systems for three reasons. H_2O possesses lower lubricity than diesel fuel, has a tendency to promote corrosion, and its different physical properties affect the pumping dynamics. Diesel fuels are compressible at approximately 0.5% per 1,000 psi; H_2O is less compressible, at approximately 0.35 per 1,000 psi. Modern fuel injection pumping apparatus is engineered to pump diesel fuel at very high pressures, and if H_2O with its lower lubricity and compressibility is pumped through the system, the resultant pressure rise can cause structural failures, especially at the sac/nozzle area of the fuel injectors. When you see a modern fuel injector with its tip blown off, the cause can often be traced to a water-in-fuel condition.

H_2O Separator Operating Principle

H_2O separators have been used in diesel fuel systems for many years. Often these were crude devices that used gravity to separate the heavier H_2O from the fuel. However, over the past two decades, as injection pumping pressures have steadily risen and the consumer's expectation of engine longevity has greatly increased, H_2O separators have developed accordingly. Often an H_2O separator will combine a primary filter and H_2O separating mechanism into a single canister. Many of these combination primary filter/H_2O separators are manufactured by aftermarket suppliers such as Racor, CR, Davco, Dahl, and others. These use a variety of means to separate and remove H_2O in free and emulsified states; they will not remove H_2O from fuel in its semi-absorbed state.

H_2O separators use combinations of several principles to separate and remove H_2O from fuel. The first is gravity. H_2O in its free state or emulsified H_2O that has **coalesced** (where small droplets come together to combine into larger droplets) into large droplets will, because of its heavier weight, be pulled by gravity to the bottom of a reservoir or sump. Some H_2O separators use a **centrifuge** to help separate both larger globules of H_2O and emulsified H_2O from fuel; the centrifuge subjects fuel passing through it to centrifugal force, throwing the heavier H_2O to the sump walls where gravity can pull it into the sump drain. A centrifuge acts to separate particulate from the fuel in the same manner. Fuel directed through a fine resin-coated, pleated paper medium passes through the medium with greater ease than H_2O. Water entrapped by the filtering medium can collect and coalesce in large enough droplets to permit gravity to pull it down into the sump drain. In many cases, aftermarket fuel filter/H_2O separators are designed to replace the fuel system OEM's primary filter; in others

FIGURE 19–11 The combination fuel filter and water separator used on a 2013 Cummins ISX.

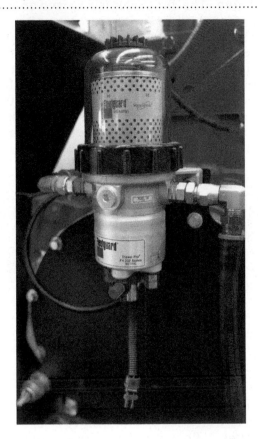

this unit may work in conjunction with the primary filter. **Figure 19–11** shows a fuel water separator used on a Cummins ISX 15-liter engine.

When installing an aftermarket filter/H_2O separator unit on the suction side of a fuel subsystem, it is good practice to locate the manufacturer's maximum restriction specification and test that it is not being exceeded. An Hg manometer or negative pressure gauge is the appropriate test tool. In cases in which the entire fuel subsystem is under suction, the consequences of exceeding the restriction specification are generally more severe, the result being fuel starvation to the engine. Servicing H_2O separator units is a simple process, but one that should be undertaken with a certain amount of care because it is easy to contaminate the fuel in the separator canister, either by priming it with unfiltered fuel or by permitting dirt to enter when the canister lid is removed. Most aftermarket H_2O separators have a clear sump through which it is easy to observe the presence of H_2O.

All H_2O separators are equipped with a drain valve. The drain valve may be operated manually or electrically. The purpose of this valve is to siphon H_2O from the sump. Water should be routinely removed from the sump using the drain valve. The filter elements used in combination primary filter/H_2O separator units should be replaced, in most instances, along with the other engine and fuel filters at each full service. However, some manufacturers claim that their filter elements have an in-service life that may exceed the oil change interval by two or more times. Whenever an H_2O separator is fully drained, it should be primed before attempting to start the engine.

TECH TIP:

To troubleshoot the source of air admission to the fuel subsystem, a diagnostic sight glass can be used; it consists of a clear section of tubing with hydraulic hose couplers at either end, and it is fitted in series with the fuel flow. However, the process of uncoupling the fuel hoses will always admit some air into the fuel subsystem, so the engine should be run for a while before reading the sight glass.

FUEL HEATERS

In recent years it is more common to find trucks equipped with fuel heaters. In fuel systems in which fuel is flowed through the injection system circuitry at a rate much higher than that required for fueling the engine, constant filtering of fuel removes some of the wax and therefore some of its lubricity even when the appropriate seasonal pour point depressants are present.

Pour point depressants tend not to have too much effect on the cloud point of a fuel, which is its first stage of waxing. This is a condition to which ASTM #2D fuels are more prone than #1D. However, there is some debate about the use of fuel heaters, and the fuel system/engine manufacturer should always be consulted when fitting such a device. One engine OEM warns that its warranty is voided if electric element type fuel heaters are used in its system.

There are two types of fuel preheaters in current use:

1. Electric element type. An electric heating element uses battery current to heat fuel in the subsystem. This type offers a number of advantages, most notable of which is that the heater can be energized before startup so that cranking fuel is warmed up. Electric element fuel heaters may be thermostatically managed so that fuel is only heated as much

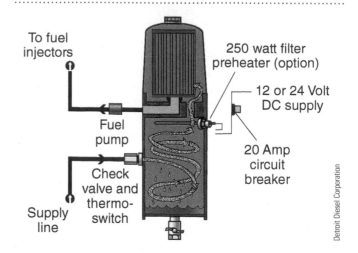

Detroit Diesel Corporation

FIGURE 19–12 Detroit Diesel Fuel Pro assembly that combines a filter, water separator, and thermostatically controlled heating element.

To fuel injectors

250 watt filter preheater (option)

12 or 24 Volt DC supply

Fuel pump

20 Amp circuit breaker

Check valve and thermo-switch

Supply line

as required and not to a point that compromises some of its lubricating properties.
2. Engine coolant heat exchanger type. This type of fuel heater consists of a housing within which coolant is circulated in a bundle (heat exchanger core) and over which the fuel is passed. A disadvantage of this type is that the engine cooling system must be at operating temperature before the fuel can be heated.

Fuel heaters exist that use both electric heating elements and coolant medium heat exchangers and, furthermore, manage the fuel temperature. Optimally, fuel temperature should be managed not to exceed 90°F (32°C). Once fuel exceeds this temperature, its lubricating properties start to diminish, and the result is reduced service life of fuel injection components. **Figure 19–12** shows a Detroit Diesel Fuel Pro assembly: This combines a filter, H_2O separator, and thermostatically controlled heating element.

WATER-IN-FUEL SENSORS

Most current systems use a **water-in-fuel (WIF) sensor** to alert the data bus of H_2O contamination of fuel. A WIF sensor can be built into a replaceable filter cartridge or be integrated into a combination filter/H_2O separator assembly. The sensor uses a couple of probes and a 12-volt supply. Because H_2O has electrical resistivity (known as *dielectric properties*) different from that of fuel, a return signal is output from the sensor when the electrical path across the probes acts through H_2O rather than fuel. At this point, the WIF broadcasts a service alert. Note

FIGURE 19–13 WIF sensor and its circuit.

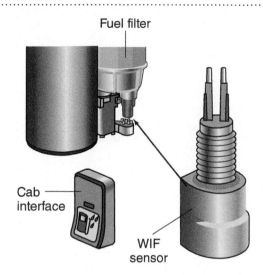

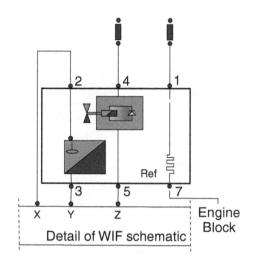

Detail of WIF schematic

that sometimes a WIF can produce a service alert immediately after draining the H_2O sump: The reason is that water-resident bacteria can coat the probes after draining and trigger a false signal. **Figure 19–13** shows a typical WIF sensor and its circuit used in a Volvo fuel subsystem.

COMBINATION FILTER/ SEPARATORS

Combination fuel filter and water separators are common in original equipment and, because of their effectiveness, as aftermarket add-ons. These units often function as both primary and secondary filters and water separators, and may in addition contain fuel heaters, water separators, and pressure sensors. They may be integrated into a fuel subsystem module assembly, depending on the engine. A detailed account of how to service typical multifunction fuel filter assemblies appears in Chapter 14 and is demonstrated in a video segment in the e-resource that accompanies this textbook.

FUEL CHARGING/TRANSFER PUMPS

Fuel charging or transfer pumps are positive displacement pumps driven directly or indirectly by the engine. A positive displacement pump displaces the same volume of fluid per cycle; therefore, fuel quantity pumped increases proportionately with rotational speed. Because of this, if a positive displacement pump unloads to a defined flow area, pressure rise is proportional with rpm increase. On most current diesel fuel systems, two types of transfer pump are used:

- Plunger-type pumps
- Gear-type pumps

Plunger-type pumps are less commonly used today. **Figure 19–14** shows a typical plunger-type pump used by Caterpillar on its hydraulically actuated electronic unit injector (HEUI) fueled engines: The reciprocating pumping action is created by a cam and the assembly is mounted behind the HEUI swash plate (oil) pump. **Figure 19–15** and **Figure 19–16** show two views of a Volvo external gear-type pump and its mounting location behind the power steering pump. Gear pumps are the commonly used fuel transfer pump today, and they share common operating principles with other external gear pumps such as oil pumps.

Pumping Principle

In describing pump operation in the fuel subsystem, in common with most truck OEMs we use the terms *suction circuit* and *charge circuit*. Fuel movement through a fuel subsystem is created by a positive displacement pump, sometimes known as a **prime mover**, though some would prefer that this term be used only for the engine that drives the pump. The way a transfer pump works is by creating flow that forces fuel out its discharge circuit: In doing this, lower-than-atmospheric pressure is created upstream from the pump inlet. This allows atmospheric pressure acting on the fuel in the tank to exert "push" on the fuel, forcing it toward the pump inlet. In this way, fuel is moved through the fuel subsystem.

FIGURE 19–14 Caterpillar plunger-type transfer pump.

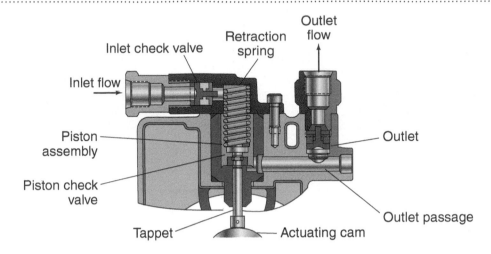

FIGURE 19–15 External view of a Volvo external gear, fuel transfer pump driven off the power steering pump, itself driven by an accessory drive.

PLUNGER-TYPE PUMPS

Plunger-type pumps are often used with port helix metering injection pumps (such as that shown in **Figure 19–17**) and some HEUI fuel systems (see Figure 19–14). They are usually flange mounted to the injection pump cam-box (port helix) or swash plate pump housing (HEUI), and driven by a dedicated cam or eccentric on the pump camshaft. Single-acting and double-acting plungers may be used, with the latter type specified in higher output engines requiring more fuel.

FIGURE 19–16 Volvo external gear-type transfer pump.

Fuel Pump and Mounting

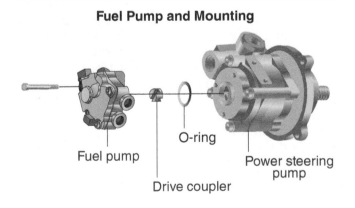

FIGURE 19–17 Bosch charging pump with integral hand primer and primary filter.

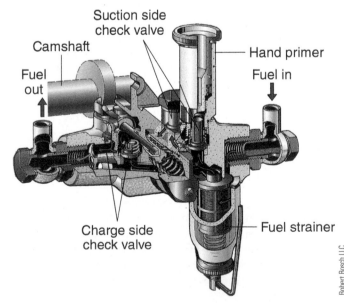

FIGURE 19–18 Action of single- and double-acting plunger pumps.

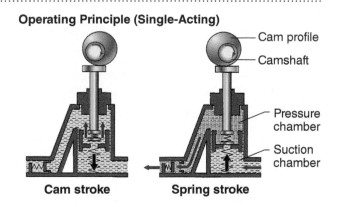

Operating Principle (Single-Acting)

Cam profile
Camshaft
Pressure chamber
Suction chamber

Cam stroke   Spring stroke

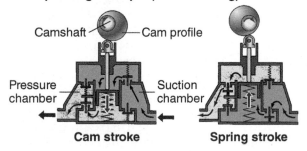

Operating Principle (Double Acting)

Camshaft — Cam profile
Pressure chamber   Suction chamber

Cam stroke   Spring stroke

Robert Bosch LLC

SINGLE- AND DOUBLE-ACTING

A single-acting **plunger pump** (one with a single reciprocating element capable of a unidirectional effective stroke such as a bicycle pump) has a single pump chamber and an inlet and outlet valve. Fuel is drawn into the pump chamber on the inboard stroke and pressurized on the outboard or cam stroke. Another way of saying this is that we aspirate the pump chamber on the pull stroke, and pump on the discharge stroke. The principle of a single-acting plunger pump is shown in **Figure 19–18**.

A double-acting pump has twin chambers, each equipped with its own inlet and outlet valve. This permits the plunger to pump on both strokes. On the cam stroke, a two-way plunger pulls fuel in behind the plunger while discharging fuel in front of the plunger. The reverse occurs as the plunger is pulled back on its retraction stroke. The principle of a double-acting plunger pump is shown in Figure 19–18.

GEAR-TYPE PUMPS

Gear pumps are also commonly used as transfer pumps, especially on most electronically managed engines. These are normally driven from an engine accessory drive and are located

wherever convenient. Gear pumps usually have an integral relief valve that defines the system charging pressure. In addition, fuel systems may use a restriction fitting or relief valve at the exit of the cylinder head charging circuit to define the charge pressure value. Fuel injection systems designed to be charged at pressure values higher than typical tend to use gear-type transfer pumps instead of cam-actuated plunger pumps. In instances in which a gear pump feeds an injection system with no main filter in series, a filter mesh is sometimes incorporated to protect injection pumping apparatus; when gear pumps are used, there is a small chance that gear teeth cuttings can be discharged into the system. A majority of the full authority electronic management fuel systems use gear-type transfer pumps. They can also produce the much higher flow and pressures required by DPF dosing systems used on post-2007 diesel engines.

HAND PRIMER PUMPS

A hand primer pump may be a permanent fixture of a fuel subsystem, located on the fuel transfer pump body or a filter mounting pad (see **Figure 19–19**). A hand primer pump can be a useful addition to the technician's tool kit, and it can be fitted to a fuel subsystem when priming is required. The function of a hand primer pump is to prime the fuel system whenever prime is lost. Typically, it consists of a hand-actuated plunger and uses a single-acting pumping principle. On the outward stroke, the plunger exerts suction on the inlet side, drawing in a charge of fuel to the pump chamber; on the downward stroke, the inlet valve closes and fuel is discharged to the outlet. When using a

FIGURE 19–19 Hand primer located on a Caterpillar filter pad.

FIGURE 19–20 Hand primer pump used on a 2013 Paccar MX13.

hand primer pump, it is important to purge air downstream from the pump on its charge side. Some fuel subsystems mount a hand primer to the transfer pump housing. **Figure 19–20** is an image of the hand primer pump used on a 2013 Paccar MX13 diesel engine.

ELECTRIC PRIMER PUMPS

More and more truck diesel engines today are equipped with self-contained, electric priming pumps whose primary function is to prime the fuel subsystem after servicing. In addition, they may be used to pressurize the primary circuit prior to cranking. Because of the emphasis on speed, shortcutting the priming of last-in-line or secondary fuel filters by dumping unfiltered fuel directly into the discharge port is a common abuse. Electric primer pumps are a means of quickly and safely priming secondary fuel filters. Some more recent filters are designed to discourage any external priming methods, making it more likely that an electric prime feature will be used.

PRIMING A FUEL SYSTEM

Although priming a fuel system is a relatively simple procedure, it is usually advisable to consult the appropriate service literature. Most OEMs prefer that the technician avoid pressurizing air tanks with regulated air pressure to prime a diesel fuel system. It should be remembered that diesel fuel contains volatile fractions and that the act of pressurizing a fuel tank with air pressure will vaporize some fuel. Air exiting an air nozzle creates friction and the potential for ignition. Avoid this practice in extreme hot weather conditions.

Recommended Procedure

When a vehicle runs out of fuel and it is determined that the fuel subsystem requires priming, remove the filters and fill with filtered fuel.

1. Locate a bleed point in the system—on an inline injection pump system, this will often be at the exit of the charging gallery—and crack open the coupling. A fuel manifold outlet coupling in the cylinder head should be opened in most other systems.
2. Next, if the system is equipped with a hand primer pump, actuate it until air bubbles cease to exit from the cracked-open coupling. If the system is not equipped with a hand primer pump, fit one upstream from the transfer pump and actuate until air bubbles cease to exit from the cracked-open coupling.
3. Retorque the coupling. Crank the engine for 30-second segments with at least 2-minute intervals between cranking cycles until it starts; this will allow for starter motor cool-down. In most diesel engine systems, the high-pressure injection circuit will self-prime once the subsystem is primed.

There is additional information on fuel filter servicing and priming procedures that you may want to reference in Chapter 14.

Refueling

It is good practice to refuel tanks on returning from a trip; filling the tanks with fuel displaces the air present in the tank that replaced the fuel as it was consumed. When tanks are left in a near-empty condition for any length of time (overnight is long enough), the moisture in the air condenses and contaminates the fuel.

CAUTION:

When refueling tanks, many drivers and technicians overlook the fact that diesel fuel vaporizes and combines with air to form combustible mixtures that only require an ignition source to cause an explosion. Diesel fuel is less volatile than gasoline, but it should always be handled with care, especially in the heat of summer.

COMPLETE FUEL CIRCUIT

Now that we have taken a look at all of the individual components that make up a fuel subsystem, we should take a brief look at how they interact as a system. Figure 19–19 shows how a current fuel subsystem supplies fuel to an electronic unit injector (EUI) fuel circuit. See if you can identify the sensors used in the circuit: The electrical principles of these sensors are not covered until Chapter 34, but you can see how they are used to signal status conditions of the

fuel subsystem. Some examples of sensors used in diesel fuel subsystems are:

- Sending unit
- Fuel temperature
- WIF
- Fuel pressure

Management Module

Fuel subsystems today often use a low-pressure fuel module such as that shown in schematic form in **Figure 19–21** and in photographic form

FIGURE 19–21 Fuel subsystem supplying EUIs.

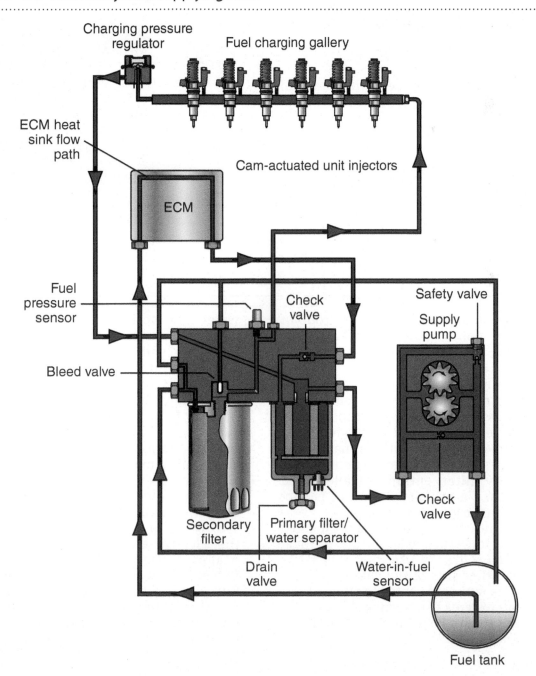

FIGURE 19–22 The fuel subsystem module used on a post-2010 Volvo engine.

FIGURE 19–23 The multifunction Diesel Pro filter system used on many current Cummins engines.

in **Figure 19–22**. The objective is to collect all the key components and sensors within a compact device and reduce the quantity of external plumbing and wires. Another approach is to combine multiple filtering functions into a stand-alone assembly, such as the Cummins Diesel Pro filter assembly shown in **Figure 19–23**. Both approaches are designed to reduce the amount of external plumbing and facilitate servicing.

SUMMARY

- The fuel subsystem is defined as the group of components responsible for storing fuel transferring it to the injection pumping apparatus.
- The typical fuel transfer system can be divided into a primary (a.k.a. *suction*) circuit and a secondary (a.k.a. *charge*) circuit, separated by a transfer or charge pump.
- Some fuel systems may locate a transfer pump in the tank itself, whereas others may retain the entire fuel subsystem under suction.
- The secondary filter entraps smaller-sized particulates than a primary filter and is subject to system charging pressure.
- Aluminum-alloy, cylindrical fuel tanks located in the airflow on truck chassis act as heat exchangers. Most trucks use dual fuel tanks mounted on either side of the chassis.
- Most diesel fuel tanks are vented to atmosphere. Some current systems use breather filters.
- Many current secondary filters will plug on water and shut down the engine.

- Water may be found in fuel in three forms: free state, emulsified, and semi-absorbed.
- Many fuel subsystems are equipped with a water separator designed to remove free-state and emulsified water from fuel. WIF sensors signal water buildup in a water separator or primary filter.
- Fuel system inlet restriction values are tested on the suction side of the fuel subsystem using an Hg manometer.
- A common source of air ingestion into the fuel subsystem is double-gasketing of a filter under suction.
- Two types of fuel heater are in current use: the electric element and coolant medium, heat exchanger types.
- Diesel fuel systems commonly use one of two different fuel transfer or charge pumps: reciprocating plunger pumps and gear pumps. Both use a positive displacement pumping principle.

- Some fuel subsystems are equipped with a hand primer pump; the function of a hand primer pump is to purge air from the fuel subsystem.
- Technicians should prime secondary filters after installation using a hand or electric priming pump.

- Many current fuel subsystems use a low-pressure fuel management module to reduce the amount of external plumbing and sensor wiring. An alternative is to make use of a multifunction fuel canister such as the Diesel Pro.

REVIEW QUESTIONS

1. On the typical truck diesel fuel subsystem, which of the following is usually subject to the lowest pressure in the circuit?
   a. Fuel heater
   b. Primary filter
   c. Secondary filter
   d. Charging gallery

2. A secondary filter is located:
   a. upstream from the transfer pump.
   b. on the charge side of the transfer pump.
   c. in the fuel rail.
   d. in the return gallery.

3. The main reason for filling vehicle fuel tanks before overnight parking is:
   a. to minimize moisture condensation within the tank.
   b. to minimize fuel evaporation.
   c. to help cool down onboard fuel.
   d. drivers may forget the next morning.

4. Besides fuel storage, the fuel tank may play an important role in a high-flow fuel system as a(n):
   a. heat exchanger.
   b. fuel heating device.
   c. ballast equalizer.
   d. aerodynamic aid.

5. Approximately how much does 100 U.S. gallons of #2D diesel fuel weigh?
   a. 500 lb
   b. 730 lb
   c. 1,000 lb
   d. 2,000 lb

6. The correct instrument for testing the low-pressure side of most fuel subsystems for inlet restriction is a(n):
   a. diagnostic sight glass.
   b. H_2O manometer.
   c. Hg manometer.
   d. accurate pressure gauge.

7. The correct instrument for testing fuel subsystem charging pressure is a(n):
   a. diagnostic sight glass.
   b. H_2O manometer.
   c. Hg manometer.
   d. accurate pressure gauge.

8. The correct instrument to use for checking for the admission of air to a fuel subsystem is a(n):
   a. diagnostic sight glass.
   b. H_2O manometer.
   c. Hg manometer.
   d. accurate pressure gauge.

9. Which type of fuel charging/transfer pump is more commonly used by today's electronically managed engine/fuel systems?
   a. Plunger pumps
   b. Centrifugal pumps
   c. Diaphragm pumps
   d. Gear pumps

10. What type of pumping principle is used by a typical hand primer pump?
    a. Single-acting plunger
    b. Double-acting plunger
    c. Rotary gear
    d. Cam-actuated diaphragm

11. Technician A states that when servicing fuel filters on a fuel subsystem with a primary and a secondary filter, a transfer-pump-located, hand primer pump can be used to prime both filters. Technician B states that if a transfer-pump-located, hand primer pump is used to prime the secondary filter after installation, it reduces the chances of dirt contamination downstream from the filter. Who is correct?
    a. Technician A only
    b. Technician B only
    c. Both A and B
    d. Neither A nor B

12. Charging pressure rise is usually directly related to which of the following?
    a. Throttle position
    b. Engine load
    c. Peak power
    d. Increased rpm

13. Technician A states that in current truck dual fuel tanks, fuel pickup tubes are located in each tank. Technician B states that some older dual fuel tanks used a single pickup tube located in one of the tanks that were connected by a crossover pipe. Who is correct?
    a. Technician A only
    b. Technician B only
    c. Both A and B
    d. Neither A nor B

14. Technician A states that the water in fuel tanks can be detected using a probe and water detection paste. Technician B states that the presence of water in the fuel subsystem can usually be detected by a WIF sensor. Who is correct?
    a. Technician A only
    b. Technician B only
    c. Both A and B
    d. Neither A nor B

15. Technician A states that some water-separator units use a centrifuge to separate water from fuel. Technician B states that because fuel is heavier than water, fuel can easily be separated from the water because it always settles under the water. Who is correct?
    a. Technician A only
    b. Technician B only
    c. Both A and B
    d. Neither A nor B

16. Technician A states that gear pumps are of the positive displacement type. Technician B states that plunger pumps are positive displacement. Who is correct?
    a. Technician A only
    b. Technician B only
    c. Both A and B
    d. Neither A nor B

17. If the fuel tank vent valve on a diesel-powered vehicle is plugged, which of the following would be the likely outcome when running the engine?
    a. The tank would explode.
    b. The engine would run away due to excess fuel.
    c. The tank would implode.
    d. The engine would shut down due to fuel starvation.

18. Technician A states that diesel engine fuel tank caps are fitted with a two-way valve that permits both fuel vapor seepage and air admission to the tank. Technician B states that most commercial truck diesel engines use a vane-type transfer pump located in the fuel tank to pump fuel to the transfer pump. Who is correct?
    a. Technician A only
    b. Technician B only
    c. Both A and B
    d. Neither A nor B

19. Technician A states that diesel fuel can combine with air to form potentially explosive mixtures. Technician B states that diesel fuel CN is likely to degrade more quickly during the winter than in the heat of summer. Who is correct?
    a. Technician A only
    b. Technician B only
    c. Both A and B
    d. Neither A nor B

20. At refueling on the completion of a journey, fuel is steaming in the tanks. Technician A states that this condition is a result of normal operation in some fuel systems. Technician B states that such a condition can be a result of running the tanks low on fuel in a high-flow fuel system. Who is correct?
    a. Technician A only
    b. Technician B only
    c. Both A and B
    d. Neither A nor B

FUEL INJECTION BASICS AND GOVERNOR PRINCIPLES

OBJECTIVES

After studying this chapter, you should be able to:

- Understand the objectives of a fuel management system.
- Interpret the contents of later chapters dealing with hydromechanical and electronic engine management.
- Define *timing* and explain the need to vary it for optimum performance and emissions.
- Define *metering* and its application in a fuel system.
- Explain atomization and the droplet sizings required for a direct-injected diesel engine.
- Describe the factors that determine emitted droplet sizing.
- Explain the overall objectives of an engine fuel system.
- Describe the relationship between cylinder pressure and crank throw to crank axis angle.
- Relate how the fuel system manages engine cylinder pressures.
- Describe the relationship between pumping, injection, and combustion in hydromechanical and electronic engines.
- Understand why "smart" injector nozzles are required on most post-2007 diesel engines.
- Outline the reasons why diesel engines have to be governed.
- Classify governors by management mode.
- Interpret electronic governor performance terminology.
- Interpret a flat profile diesel engine fuel map.

KEY TERMS

after top dead center (ATDC)	compression ignition (CI)	droop	engine control module (ECM)
algorithm	crank angle	droop curve	governor map
atomization	crank axis	duty cycle	high-idle speed
automotive governor	crank throw	electronic governor	hunting
common rail (CR)	diesel knock	electronic management	

hydromechanical engine management	limiting speed governor (LSG)	orifice	road speed governing (RSG)
idle speed	lugging	orifii	timing
ignition lag	mechanical advantage	overspeed	top dead center (TDC)
injection lag	mechanical governor	peak torque	top engine limit (TEL)
injection rate	metering	power takeoff (PTO)	torque rise
isochronous governor	min-max governor	pulse width (PW)	torque rise profile
lever	motoring	rated power	variable speed governor (VSG)
	multipulse injection	rated speed	

OVERVIEW OF DIESEL FUEL INJECTION PRINCIPLES

The fuel system *manages* the engine. Because the diesel engine is operated with excess air—that is, much more air than that required to combust the fuel—the timing and quantity of fuel introduced into the engine cylinders determine:

- Engine power
- Engine emissions

Diesel engines can be managed in two ways:

1. **Hydromechanical engine management** (engines managed without a computer). Until 1991, most truck diesel engines were managed by mechanical governors. A governor was required to accurately sense engine speed and convert operator requests into outcomes. If you see a mechanical governor on a truck diesel engine today, it will be a much older engine. Mechanical governors were used on off-road vehicles of more than 70 horsepower until 2011; they continue to be used on small-bore diesel engines, including those fueling many trailer reefer engines.
2. **Electronic management** (engines managed by computer). Computer controls on most diesel engines on our roads today have passed through several generations, but they all accomplish exactly what the hydro-mechanical governor did in older engines. They just do this with more precision.

Because of the excess air factor in diesel engines, if something should go wrong and they are provided with unlimited fuel, they will accelerate at up to 1,000 rpm per second until they self-destruct. This means that the fuel systems in all diesel engines have to be precisely managed. The term used to describe this management is *governing*.

Today, a governor is no longer a piece of hardware attached to the fuel system; rather, it is software programmed to the **engine control module (ECM)** memory. Throughout this book we will continually reference the ECM because so much of what goes on in a modern diesel directly depends on the way it is programmed. This is not to say that the operator or driver no longer plays a role in running the engine. Just as the governor on the diesel engine in 1990 acted as a link between the driver and the fuel system, so does the ECM play the same role on a current engine.

As you read through this chapter, you will note that almost all of the terms used to describe hydromechanical governors have been recycled when it comes to electronically managed engines. However, through this chapter we will mostly reference only electronic management and governing. If you are interested in learning more about hydromechanical governors, you may wish to reference earlier versions of this textbook.

MANAGING FUELING OUTCOMES

In any **compression ignition (CI)** engine, a power stroke will take place only if the fuel system is accurately phased to the engine and performs the following four objectives:

1. Timing
2. Pressurizing and atomization
3. Metering
4. Distribution

1. Timing

Fuel delivery **timing** is critical during all engine operating phases. Typically, fuel injection begins just slightly before the piston completes its compression stroke. Current engines are required to provide the ECM with a variable timing window: this means that fuel injection may be advanced or retarded according to software instructions written to the ECM management files. Computer-controlled, variable timing is required in today's engines to produce optimum performance and minimal noxious emissions. In addition, almost all current diesel engines use **multipulse injection** timing. This means the injection pulse is broken up into two or more separate injection events during one fueling cycle.

PILOT INJECTION The simplest form of multipulse injection consists of two pulses that we describe as:

- Pilot pulse
- Main injection

Pilot injection has been used since the mid-1990s. The objective of pilot injection is to initiate a flame field ahead of the main delivery using a small amount of fuel. After the pilot shot of fuel into the engine cylinder, injection ceases and the ECM calculates how much time is required (based on input sensor-signaled conditions) to ignite it. At the point of igniting the pilot pulse of fuel in the engine cylinder, fuel injection resumes with the delivery of a main pulse—or pulses, as will be discussed next.

MULTIPULSE INJECTION The use of multipulse injection is almost universal in any on-highway commercial diesel engine manufactured after 2007. Multipulse injection can mean breaking an injection pulse into up to seven events per injection cycle. The timing of each successive injection pulse is precisely managed by the engine ECM. It enables the ECM to make the best use of the heat energy released by the fuel, along with minimizing emissions and smoothing the application of force to the piston. Sometimes, a substantially late shot of fuel in a multipulse fueling sequence is not intended to be combusted in the engine cylinder: instead, it is exhausted as uncombusted fuel to dose exhaust aftertreatment devices.

TIMING AND EMISSIONS In a general sense, the timing of fuel injection also influences tailpipe emissions. A fueling strategy that minimizes one controlled emission may have a counterproductive effect on another. In terms of injection timing and emissions, it can be said that the following is true:

- Advanced injection timing means more time to completely burn the fuel introduced to the engine cylinder, so it has the effect of reducing hydrocarbon (HC) emissions.

- Advanced timing produces higher cylinder temperatures and tends to increase the chances of oxidizing nitrogen, thus producing harmful oxides of nitrogen (NO_x) compounds.
- Retarded timing results in lower cylinder temperatures and therefore reduces the tendency to produce NO_x.
- Retarded timing reduces the time available to completely burn injected fuel and can result in higher HC and soot at the tailpipe.

We will take a much more detailed approach to emissions management in Chapters 47 and 48 of this book and examine how different engines manage timing strategy in the chapters dealing with specific fuel systems. In short, though, what this means is that often an engine has to be managed outside its window of peak efficiency in order to meet emissions standards.

2. Pressurizing and Atomization

The fuel system must be capable of pressurizing the fuel sufficiently to prepare the fuel charge for combustion. Fuel exiting diesel fuel injectors is atomized. When high-pressure fuel is forced through a restricted flow area, it breaks up into minute droplets: This is known as **atomization**. The restricted flow area is located in injectors. Fuel exits from injectors by means of an **orifice** (single hole) or **orifii** (multiple holes). Atomized fuel is in *liquid* state. The degree of atomization is defined by the size of the atomized fuel droplets. The size of fuel droplets emitted from an injector is determined by:

- The pressure of the fuel supplied to the nozzle orifii
- The flow area or sizing of the nozzle orifii

The means used to pressurize the fuel to the required injection pressures vary with the type of fuel system. Depending on the fuel system, injection pumping apparatus is actuated by some type of mechanical pumping element. The source of the pump drive may be the engine timing geartrain or main engine camshaft. Pumping fuel to injection pressures may take place at the injector (EUI systems) or remotely. The most recent fuel systems are capable of producing up to 35,000 psi (2,450 bar) peak pressures, and can do this independently from engine rpm. Regardless of fuel system, pressure is always the control variable when it comes to determining droplet size.

DROPLET SIZE In order to meet stringent emissions controls and optimize fuel economy in current engines, the ECM is required to control the droplet size emitted from injectors. It does this by managing injection pressures. Fuel droplets burn from the outside in (**Figure 20–1**), meaning that:

- Larger fuel droplets require more time to ignite and more time to burn completely. This means that larger fuel droplets have to be injected earlier in the cycle if they are going to burn properly during the power stroke.
- Smaller fuel droplets respond more rapidly to whatever heat is in the engine cylinder, so they ignite more quickly and take less time to burn completely.

Older diesel engines, whether hydromechanically or electronically managed, had injector nozzles with hard opening and closing values. This meant that if the nozzle opening pressure (NOP) of an injector was specified at 5,000 psi (350 bar), at the beginning of the injection pulse fuel droplets were always the same size regardless of how the engine was being run. These older diesel fuel systems had fuel systems designed to increase pressure during the injection pulse: This was generally desirable because as fuel injection extended into the cycle, the amount of real time available to complete the burn was reduced.

In commercial diesel engines of the past couple of decades, with wind-out speeds not exceeding 2,000 rpm, the extent of fuel atomization requires emitted droplet sizing to be within a range of between 10 and 100 microns (μ); the reasons for this are dealt with in Chapter 17, which covered combustion. However, it should be stressed here that current high-pressure fuel systems maintain droplet sizing close to the 10μ minimum and, more importantly, have to achieve something close to this at cold cranking and warmup in order to meet emissions standards. Smaller-bore diesel engines equipped with glow plugs are not required to reduce droplet sizing to this extent during cranking and startup.

3. Metering

Metering is the precise control of fuel quantity. As we said earlier, the only factor that controls the output of a diesel engine is the amount of fuel put into it. Whereas gasoline-fueled, spark-ignited engines define peak output by the amount of air that can be induced into the engine cylinders through a throttle bore, diesels do this by metering. The excess air factor of a diesel engine means that under any load or operating condition, there is always significantly more air present than the minimum required to completely combust the fuel.

All diesel engines precisely meter fuel into the engine's cylinders. Metering in the engines of today is achieved by several distinct means, the subject matter of many of the chapters that follow this. When technicians refer to the metering of fuel into diesel engine cylinders, they may use one of two different terms:

- **Injection rate** is the fuel quantity injected per **crank angle** degree. In today's multipulse injection systems, injection rate can be very precisely managed by the ECM so it can match cylinder pressure to crank mechanical position, something we will discuss a little later in this chapter.
- **Duty cycle** is a term more commonly used today to describe metering in electronically controlled diesels. It is displayed as **pulse width (PW)** on electronic service tools (ESTs). PW is usually measured in milliseconds.

FIGURE 20–1 Fuel droplets burn from the outside in: Large droplets take longer to burn completely, so droplet size influences combustion rate.

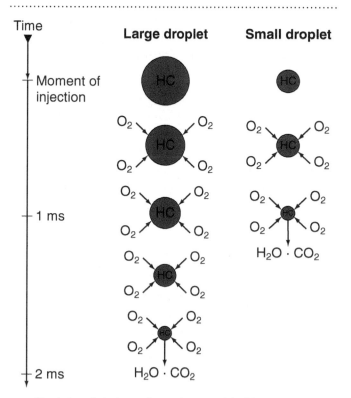

Fuel droplets burn from the outside in: large droplets take longer to completely burn.

4. Distribution

In multicylinder engines:

1. The fuel system must be phased (sequenced) to deliver the fuel to each engine cylinder at the correct time and in the correct firing order. Correct fuel system phasing is required to balance the engine output. If in a given engine-operating range the ECM computes that ignition should occur at 3 degrees before top dead center (BTDC), then injected fuel must be delivered sufficiently in advance of that in each engine cylinder so that ignition really does occur at exactly 3 degrees BTDC.

2. The fuel must be dispensed to the correct area of the combustion chamber so that the fuel droplets combust at the appropriate time (spray dispersion). The position of the fuel injector is critical in ensuring that the injected fuel droplets are directed to the correct area of the combustion chamber in DI engines. For instance, if an injector is seated on double sealing washers (a not uncommon occurrence), the nozzle would be effectively too high in the cylinder; the result would be to inject fuel above the combustion bowl on a Mexican hat piston crown, often causing it to condense on the piston headland and cylinder walls. Fuel exiting each nozzle orifice should be propelled toward the bowl or recess around the peak of the Mexican hat in the piston and vaporized before it actually comes into contact with any hardware. Fuel that contacts the relatively cooler hardware in the cylinder before reaching its ignition point may condense. Fuel that condenses on the piston boils off during combustion, increases emissions (because it is not properly burned), and results in erosion (pitting).

ENGINE MANAGEMENT OBJECTIVES

The fuel system manages *engine* output. The overall objective of any engine—whether it powers a lawnmower, a ship, or a highway truck—is to transmit the force developed in its cylinders as smoothly and evenly as possible to the power takeoff device, which is usually a flywheel. To achieve this objective, the fuel system must manage fueling to complement the geometry of the engine powertrain components or, most specifically, that of the crankshaft.

THROW LEVERAGE

First, it is important to understand the mechanical relationship of the **crank throw** (the crankshaft connecting rod journal) with the crankshaft axis (centerline); it is a **lever**. The greater the offset of a crank throw, the greater leverage it can exert. High-compression diesel engines use crank throws with greater offset than their gasoline-fueled counterparts so they can achieve higher compression ratios and apply greater leverage through the power stroke.

When a piston is at **top dead center (TDC)**, the crank-throw-to-**crank-axis** (center point of crank main journal) angle is zero, so there is zero leverage. In this position, no matter how much force is applied to the piston by cylinder pressure, none can be transmitted to the engine powertrain because of the zero leverage. However, the piston only has to move slightly beyond TDC to achieve some throw leverage. As the piston continues to be driven downward through its stroke, the crank-throw-to-connecting-rod angle increases; this means that the leverage also increases. Given an exactly even amount of pressure applied to the piston on its downward travel, this would mean that the torque applied to the crankshaft would progressively increase consistent with increase in leverage.

CYLINDER PRESSURE

Remembering that the objective is to *smoothly* and *evenly* transmit force developed in the engine cylinders to the engine flywheel, ideally the fuel system should be managed so that cylinder pressures peak when the crank throw angle offers low **mechanical advantage** (but not zero, which would be true when the throw and piston are at TDC) and progressively diminish as the crank throw is driven to a 90-degree angle with the connecting rod, in which position mechanical advantage (leverage) peaks. With this in mind, most spark-ignited and diesel cycle engines are engineered to attempt to produce a peak cylinder pressure in the range of 10 to 20 degrees **after top dead center (ATDC)** at any phase of load or speed operation. Managing cylinder pressure to synchronize with crank throw leverage can achieve even and smooth application of torque to the engine powertrain.

SYNCHRONIZING PRESSURE WITH LEVERAGE

To get this relationship between cylinder pressure (controlled by the engine fuel system) and crank throw leverage (a hard value dependent on specific engine rotational position) right, today's engines use computerized management. The ability of older hydromechanical fuel systems to achieve this was limited at best. It was based on strategies such as advancing either the ignition timing (SI engines) or the injection timing (CI engines) as engine speed increased and the real time available for combustion diminished. In fact, if the only objective was to get the absolute best fuel economy without worrying about tailpipe emissions, today's ECM-managed diesels could produce far better combustion efficiency than they are actually capable of. **Figure 20–2** demonstrates the relationship between crank throw angle and cylinder pressure.

Real Time and Metering

A modern engine management system has to manage engine fueling and the resulting cylinder pressures within time dimensions so small that they are difficult to envisage. Think of this. A complete engine effective cycle is 720 degrees or 2 engine revolutions. At its maximum, a diesel fueling pulse cycle (multipulse injection) is spread over less than 70 crank angle degrees of the 720 degrees. A four-stroke cycle diesel engine rotating at 2,000 rpm produces approximately 17 power strokes in each of its cylinders every second. It should come as no surprise that the pumping, metering, and injection activity required to manage the engine has to be measured in milli- and microseconds.

DELIVERY, INJECTION, AND COMBUSTION

The function of any diesel fuel injection system is to manage the fueling of an engine so that it produces the desired performance outcomes. Regardless of the actual fuel system, the timing and volume of fuel injected to the engine cylinders determine:

- When combustion takes place
- The intensity of combustion and resulting cylinder pressures
- The duration of combustion

Until the introduction of **common rail (CR)** fueling, whether an engine is managed hydromechanically or electronically, the events of injection and combustion are managed by what is happening in the high-pressure pump. Although we have not addressed specific fuel systems at

FIGURE 20–2 Relationship between cylinder pressure and crank leverage.

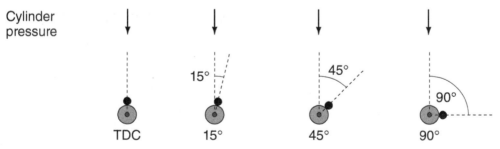

The diagram above depicts the angle between the crank throw and piston travel plane: this should not be confused with crank angle degrees ATDC.

Throw vector angle	0°	15°	45°	90°
Leverage	Zero	Minimal	Increasing	Maximum
Ideal cylinder pressure	Zero	Maximum	Decreasing	Decreasing

⊙ Crankshaft axis

● Crank throw

FIGURE 20–3 The phasing of the events of delivery, injection, and combustion in a fuel system in which the ECM does not directly control the injector nozzle.

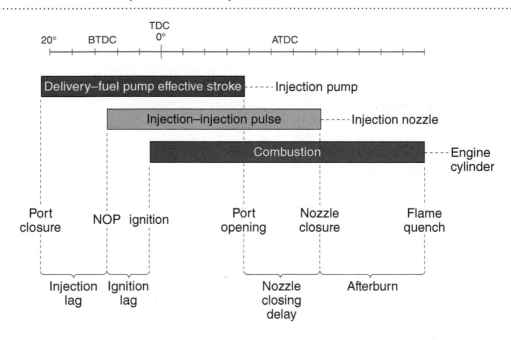

this point, **Figure 20–3** demonstrates the relationship between what is occurring in the high-pressure fuel injection pump (an EUI, EUP, HEUI, or older PLN system), a hydraulically actuated injector nozzle, and the engine cylinder in real time. This graphic has been simplified because many current fuel systems are capable of pilot and multipulse injection events. In a computer-controlled multipulse system, the events shown in Figure 20–3 can actually repeat several times over within a real time period of less than 3 milliseconds: Follow the sequencing through each phase in the figure with the text that describes the phase in detail. Note that during pilot and multipulse injection sequencing, ignition lag only applies to the first delivered pulse.

INJECTION LAG

Injection lag is the time measured in crank angle degrees between an effective stroke in the injection pump (such as PLN, EUI, HEUI, or EUP) and the moment the injector nozzle opens to begin injection. It is accounted for primarily by the time required to raise pump chamber pressure (charging pressure) to the NOP value.

In the case of a CR fuel system, the fuel within the electrohydraulic injector (EHI) is already at injection pressures. Consequently, injection lag is almost nonexistent.

IGNITION LAG

Ignition lag is the time period between the events of NOP and the point at which the fuel charge is ignited. It can be measured in crank angle degrees or fractions of a second. Ignition lag real time depends on:

- The size of the atomized droplets
- The quality of the fuel
- The actual temperature in the cylinder

Liquid droplets exiting the injector have to be vaporized and ignited. This takes time, and the time period is variable. It depends on the ignition quality of the fuel (cetane number [CN] value) and the actual compression temperature.

Because the ignition lag phase is variable (in real time), in older fuel injection systems the actual amount of fuel in the cylinder at ignition was also variable. This variability meant that in cold weather startup conditions, excessive fuel could be present in the cylinder at ignition. Once ignited, the larger than intended amount of fuel in the engine cylinder burned at explosive rates, resulting in a detonation condition known as **diesel knock**.

In ECM-controlled injection systems, fueling can be precisely controlled during the ignition lag phase. The usual strategy is for the ECM to inject a pilot shot of fuel into the engine cylinder, cease injection, calculate the moment of ignition, then resume the injection pulse or pulses. This has all but eliminated diesel knock in modern engines.

COMBUSTION

The duration of combustion depends on:

- The length of the injection pulse, which determines fuel quantity per cycle (hydromechanical and first-generation electronic engines)
- The duration, pressure, and number of injection pulses in a fueling cycle (current electronic engines)

Managing combustion in modern engines is not just about optimizing cylinder pressure and crank angle leverage synchronization. Meeting Environmental Protection Agency (EPA) emissions standards means that producing maximum power and fuel economy has to take second place to managing exactly what comes out of the tailpipe.

NOZZLE CLOSURE LAG

Nozzle closure lag is the time period between the end of injection pump delivery and actual nozzle closure. Almost all electronic management systems used hydraulic injector nozzles up until 2004. This meant that regardless of what the pressure peaked out at during the injection pulse, it had to collapse to a value below NOP before the nozzle would close and cease injection: In fact, the higher the peak injection, the longer the nozzle closure lag. This tail end of the injection phase is known as the *collapse phase.*

Throughout the nozzle closure lag, combustion in the engine cylinder continues. In older fuel injection systems, the collapse phase produced larger injected droplets of fuel. There was insufficient real time to properly combust these larger droplets, so they increased hydrocarbon emissions.

"SMART" NOZZLES

Few on-highway EPA-certified commercial diesels after 2007 use hydraulic nozzles; the exceptions are the few hydraulically actuated, electronic unit injector (HEUI) and single-actuator EUI fueled engines that remain in production. The electro-hydraulic injectors (EHIs) used in common rail (CR) and electronic unit pump (EUP) systems, and ECM-switched nozzles used with twin-actuator EUIs, allow the ECM to command the beginning and ending of fuel injection regardless of pressure at the nozzle valve. Any time an ECM can directly control nozzle opening and closing, we use the term *smart* to describe the nozzle. Smart nozzles eliminate both injection lag and nozzle closure lag. Eliminating nozzle closure lag eliminates the collapse phase and the emissions it produced. It became all but a requirement of meeting 2007 emissions standards for higher-horsepower engines. **Figure 20–4** shows what the engine event map looks like when the ECM has control over every critical event that

FIGURE 20–4 The phasing of the events of injection and combustion in a common rail (CR) fuel system using EHI "smart" injectors: Here the ECM manages the rail (injection) pressure and has direct control over the injector nozzle.

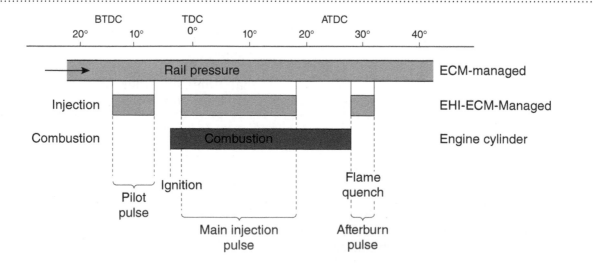

relates to combustion. The ECM directly manages rail pressure (this equals injection pressure) and switches EHIs so that many of the lag phases observed in Figure 20–3 are either eliminated or minimized. Figure 20–4 shows a multiple-pulse injection event, something that will be studied in more detail in Chapter 21 and later chapters in this book.

AFTERBURN

Afterburn is the normal combustion of fuel in the engine cylinder after injection nozzle closure. Its duration depends on the length of the injection pulse, the actual quantity of fuel in the cylinder, and many other factors, including droplet sizing just before nozzle closure. Afterburn duration is managed to be as short as possible in later versions of hydromechanical fuel systems. It is not desirable because it creates fluctuations in cylinder pressure toward the end of the power stroke. In current electronic management systems with smart nozzles, undesirable afterburn is eliminated by keeping the droplet sizing small at the end of the injection event. Small droplets are more susceptible to being ignited by whatever heat is in the engine cylinder, and there is time to properly combust them.

GOVERNING OBJECTIVES

At the beginning of this chapter we said that the output of any diesel engine is limited only by the quantity of fuel injected into its cylinders. This is because diesel engines are aspirated with excess air. This excess air is usually considerably above the stoichiometric requirement, especially under conditions of high turboboost. This makes managing the amount of fuel injected into the cylinders of a diesel engine critical. Although we do use stand-alone governors on the engines of today, the ECM must be programmed with governing software. It is common to refer to this as *electronic governing*.

ELECTRONIC GOVERNING

The primary function of a diesel engine governor is to sense engine speed and limit fueling when the engine is run at its specified maximum speed. Today, **electronic governors** are used on all highway, and most off-highway, diesel engines. Electronic governors do all that their hydromechanical predecessors were designed

to do, only they achieve those functions with more precision.

An electronic governor manages engine output based on command inputs from the vehicle operator and the range of sensor signaling information sent to the ECM. The governor software (in the engine ECM) then maps a fueling profile. The fueling profile is the set of output commands that control such things as:

- Fuel quantity
- Injection timing
- Pilot and multipulse injection events

Governor Programming

The ECM in a truck diesel engine is responsible for both the "thinking" (computations) and the switching (actuation) required of a computer. We spend some time explaining vehicle computers later, in Chapter 34, and we should make it clear here that to properly understand today's highway diesel engine governors, you have to understand the basics of vehicle computer controls. When we talk about an ECM's role in governing engine output, we should identify two distinct phases:

- The "processing" (thinking) phase. Engine OEMs call this the governing **algorithm**. Another way of saying this is the **governor map**. Based on its software instructions, the ECM analyzes all of the inputs such as engine speed and throttle position and computes a fueling "plan." This fueling plan then has to be communicated to the part of the ECM responsible for switching.
- The switching phase. After the ECM has processed the governing algorithm, this has to be converted into action by the ECM switching apparatus. In an ECM, the components responsible for converting "thinking" into outputs are known as *drivers*. The drivers responsible for controlling the fuel injectors are known as *injector drivers*. Injector drivers control the duty cycle of fuel injectors.

Today's ECMs may be programmed with comprehensive fuel maps, engine malfunction strategy, and a wide variety of customer data options, but most of the language used to describe engine governing conditions originated from James Watt's 1786 centrifugal governor. James Watt (see Chapter 5) invented the **mechanical governor** because he wanted to regulate the speed of his steam engines. To regulate the speed of an engine, you have to have a way of knowing its exact speed. We call this *speed sensing*.

James Watt accomplished speed sensing by driving a set of flyweights in a carrier at a speed proportional to engine speed; the flyweights pivoted in the carrier and were loaded into their most retracted position by a spring. As the carrier was rotated, the centrifugal force produced by the flyweights would act against the applied spring force; the spring tension could then be set so that at a specified maximum speed, centrifugal force would overcome the spring force to act directly on a fuel control mechanism to limit fueling. Most truck and bus governors classified as "hydromechanical" use variations of Watt's governor.

WHAT GOVERNORS DO

A governor determines how an engine is fueled. At a minimum, it limits fueling at the highest intended engine rpm to prevent overspeed. In addition, it is also required to define the lowest no-load rpm of the engine, to enable the engine to idle without any input from the driver's accelerator pedal. A governor must also provide a means of no-fueling the engine to shut it down. Most modern governors also have many other features, such as the ability to provide extra fuel over the intended operating rpm window: We call this *normal engine operating rpm*.

TORQUE RISE

The normal engine operating rpm is the range of the rpm spectrum where the engine OEM calculates that the engine should be operated to produce the best combination of power and fuel economy. As truck technicians, we call this **torque rise** rpm. In the days before the engine and transmission electronics were networked, the torque rise profile was identified to the truck driver by a sticker on the visor identifying the upper and lower shift rpm. This information indicated to the drivers the engine rpm at which they should be making upshifts and downshifts.

In more recent engines, the ideal shift point rpms are broadcast to the chassis data bus, so when an automatic or automated transmission is used, shifting is phased to the appropriate engine rpm. In other words, the responsibility has been shifted away from the vehicle operator and passed on to the chassis electronics. Removing the human element has greatly increased drivetrain longevity.

Fuel Maps

Figure 20–5 shows the fuel map used on a typical highway diesel engine. This engine has its fuel system set up to produce peak torque at 1,400 rpm

FIGURE 20–5 Simplified fuel map showing key governor points and how they correlate with rpm and fuel quantity.

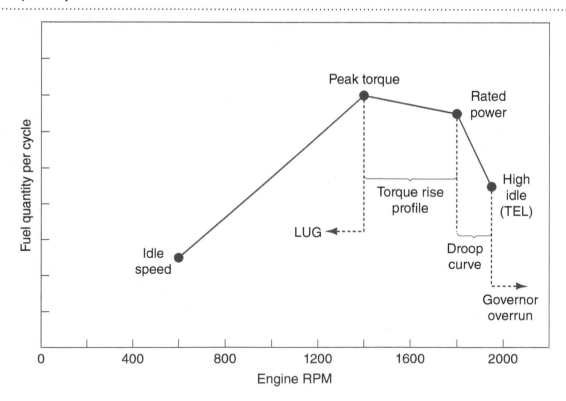

and rated power at 1,800 rpm. The torque rise profile on this engine is therefore between 1,400 and 1,800 rpm. This can be expressed as percentage torque rise. Because the torque rise duration is 400 rpm, when we divide 400 by 1,800 the result can be rounded to 22%. Back in the days when we did not care too much about fuel consumption, it was not unusual to find *high torque rise* engines with 50% torque rise. One way of producing this would be to trim the fuel system so that rated speed and power were achieved at 2,000 rpm and peak torque at 1,000 rpm.

Back then, drivers liked high torque rise engines because when one was coupled with a manually shifted transmission, it would require a lot less shifting. The driver of today, with the luxury of an automated or automatic transmission, is unlikely to know what a shift point is … and as we indicated earlier, this is a good thing. Even the best drivers have bad days and miss shifts, so why not *shift* the responsibility to a computer?

RATED SPEED AND LOAD

One important role of the governor is to define the specific engine rpm at which peak power is achieved. This is usually expressed as horsepower in North America, but with the growing influence of European and Asian technology on our trucking industry, we hear kilowatts used to express power more and more frequently. When an OEM specifies diesel engine power (see Chapter 6), it is always done so that it is correlated with the rpm at which that power is achieved. Thus, in highway truck applications, peak horsepower is expressed as **rated power**, but more often engine OEMs use the term **rated speed**. If the peak power in an engine is 600 horsepower at 1,800 rpm, this could also be referred to as the rated speed. The way power ratings are expressed in off-highway diesel engines varies. Because they do not have to be spec'd with actual (hydromechanical governor) or virtual (electronic governing) droop curves, peak horsepower does not have to be produced on or close to the upper rpm.

PEAK TORQUE

If you read Chapter 6, you will know that **peak torque** in a diesel engine is produced whenever cylinder pressures peak. Peak torque rpm is important in understanding governor operation because in most cases it represents the lowest rpm within the "normal engine-operating range." This means that it represents the lowest speed at which the driver wants to run an engine before he makes a downshift. In the simplified fuel map in Figure 20–5, peak torque represents the base (lowest rpm) of the torque rise profile. Assuming that the driver has her foot to the floor, as engine rpm is driven down by load, if a downshift fails to occur at the peak torque rpm, the engine drops into the lug rpm.

Lugging a diesel engine can result in a number of problems that may include high cylinder pressures, dangerously high driveline torsionals, fuel wastage, and exhaust smoking. However, the engine and chassis electronics of today's engines will not permit an engine to get into a lug condition. In instances where the engine and transmission electronics are networked, the transmission is simply downshifted.

IDLE AND HIGH IDLE

Governors also have to define idle speeds. Whenever we use the term *idle* in reference to a diesel engine, it means there is no load on the engine. There are a couple of key idle rpm. The first is usually just called **idle speed**. In Figure 20–5, the idle speed is 600 rpm. On a highway truck, this is the speed that a diesel engine runs without any input from the accelerator pedal. You can also refer to it as *low idle*. Low idle is usually a reprogrammable governor option on current engines.

Next, the term **high-idle speed** is important. High idle is the fastest speed that the engine should run under no load: Caterpillar refers to this speed as **top engine limit (TEL)**. In Figure 20–5, high idle is 1,950 rpm. On hydromechanical engines governed for mobile applications, high-idle speeds exceed rated speeds by something between 5% and 20%. On older engines, a crude method of increasing engine power was to increase the high-idle speed, often with just a trim screw adjustment. On most electronic engines, the high-idle and rated speeds may not differ, though they are usually reprogrammable options.

DROOP CURVE

Rated speed is the highest rpm that a diesel engine should be operated under load, and most ECM-managed engines will only allow engine rpm to run above rated under exceptional circumstances. However, all diesel engines powering mobile equipment are top-end governed with **droop curve**. Droop curve rpm runs between rated speed and high idle rpm. Its objective is to prevent

TECH TIP:

Accelerator pedal angle in a VS-managed truck diesel engine requests a specific engine rpm. Within the limitations of the fuel system, the governor attempts to maintain that rpm as engine load conditions change. Driving a VS-managed engine requires a smoother foot on the accelerator pedal.

CAUTION:

Try to identify the governor type or programming before driving any truck. If you attempt to drive a VS-governed truck engine by handling the accelerator pedal in the same way as that in your car, the result will be a truck that bucks and lurches, sometimes leaving the driver bouncing uncontrollably on an air-suspended seat. This is because each time the accelerator pedal angle changes, you are signaling a request for a different engine rpm. Do this fast enough and you will confuse even the fastest-responding engine ECM.

ISOCHRONOUS

An **isochronous governor** is only required when driving a generator. In this application the engine must respond instantly to load changes with zero droop (*no* rpm fluctuation when engine load changes) or the (electrical) frequency will alter. However, the term is being used to describe an option in diesel engine electronic management systems. In this instance, isochronous governing mode would be used to manage PTO fueling while stationary, and one OEM uses the term to describe engine fueling at an electronically managed, default (when critical input signals are lost) rpm.

GOVERNOR PROGRAMMING OPTIONS

In the days when a governor was a piece of hardware, adjustments were required from time to time. In those days, we referred to the adjustments as *trim* options. Now that governing has evolved into a set of software instructions, many continue to use the word *trim* to describe what is really reprogramming. The way in which a diesel engine governor manages the engine can be changed in two ways:

- Customer data programming: customer "owned" data that includes fields such as governor type

(LS or VS), PTO operating modes, idle rpms, and so forth. This data is owned by the vehicle owner and can be altered by that owner.
- Proprietary data programming: the OEM "owned" data that includes such fields as the horsepower setting and fuel maps. These can be reprogrammed, but only by downloading new files from the OEM data hub. There is usually some cost associated with the download data.

As far as the technician is concerned, governor reprogramming options refer to primarily to customer-adjustable values. If you reprogram the high-idle trim, you are adjusting the high-idle rpm. When performing any governor trim adjustments, consult the OEM service literature and make sure you understand the exact consequences of the adjustment—one of which could be that you are doing something illegal. In addition, most of the customer reprogrammable options are password protected.

Altitude Compensation

All current engines have altitude compensation maps programmed into the governing software. As altitude increases, oxygen density begins to decrease. Electronically managed engines use ambient pressure sensors that measure even minute changes in altitude, allowing the governor maps to immediately adjust fueling. The objective is to derate fueling as altitude increases. Deration is required because as altitude increases, there is a lower charge of oxygen molecules in the engine cylinder: Were the deration not to occur, the result would be "overfueling" and smoke discharge into the exhaust.

Altitude compensation means reducing engine power at altitude. For this reason, the high-torque, 600-horsepower engine tends to be popular with operators who have to run at higher altitudes. Engine power is progressively reduced as altitude increases.

In early-generation electronic and hydromechanical engines, altitude compensation was achieved using a barometric capsule (similar to that used in a household barometer). The barometric capsule signaled the governor to limit engine fueling as the oxygen density in air decreased with an increase in altitude. They were not as sensitive as the electronic pressure sensors used today and did not begin to become a factor until an altitude of 1,000 ft. (300 m) had been exceeded. Again, the objective was to derate fueling at altitude.

ROAD SPEED GOVERNING

All of today's drive-by-wire commercial vehicles offer a range of road speed governing options. This section briefly describes some of them, but for a more detailed understanding you should read ahead to those chapters that deal with the specific OEM engine management systems.

ROAD SPEED

Road speed governing (RSG) is usually, but not always, the maximum programmed road speed permitted by the vehicle electronics. Some vehicle electronic management systems will permit the programming of maximum cruise speed at a higher value than "maximum" road speed, to encourage drivers to use cruise control. The reason for this is that most truck cruise control systems have been proven to produce significantly better fuel economy than an "average" driver is capable of achieving.

DROOP

The term *droop* means a drift outside a programmed value. It can be applied to an engine rpm or to a road speed value. Try not to confuse this term with droop curve, which was discussed a little earlier in this chapter. Typically, droop occurs as the governor or governing electronics attempt to respond to a change in conditions. For instance, road speed droop would occur when a truck running on level pavement encountered a hill. Typically, droop should be transient (short term) unless intentionally programmed otherwise.

SOFT CRUISE

Soft or smart cruise can only be achieved on electronically managed engines. Because this involves understanding some basics of vehicle computer-controlled chassis, this term is explained more fully later on in Chapter 34. Simply put, smart or soft cruise is a way that road speed droop can be programmed to benefit fuel economy. Instead of attempting to maintain road speed at a programmed "hard" value, the electronics permit some drift, both higher and lower, than the set mph. Soft cruise may also use other vehicle systems such as the engine brake to manage the up-and-down droop of programmed cruise speed.

DEFAULT GOVERNING

The term *default mode* is used to describe how the engine manages itself in the event of the loss of a key input sensor. The best example would be loss of throttle position sensor (TPS) input signal. Rather than shutting down the engine completely, the engine runs at a default speed (say, 1,000 rpm) so that the vehicle can be safely maneuvered to a safe location on or off the highway. The engine runs isochronously at the default rpm so it can be loaded during this emergency mode of operation—that is, it is designed to not stall when a load is applied.

OTHER GOVERNOR TERMS

We have already introduced most of the key terms required to understand governor operation, but because of the ever-increasing programmability of governing fields in ECMs, some OEMs use other governor terms. Some of the more popular are:

Deadband: Term used to describe the sensitivity of a governor. It is the speed window around set speed in which fueling correction is made by the governor.

Governor cutoff: Speed at which the governor cuts off fueling.

Hunting: Rhythmic change in engine speed often caused by unbalanced fuel delivery in multicylinder engines.

Motoring: Running an engine at zero throttle, with chassis momentum driving the engine.

Overrun: The inability of a governor to keep the engine speed below the high-idle speed when it is rapidly accelerated.

Overspeed: Any speed above high idle.

Road speed governing (RSG): Any governor system in which engine fueling is moderated by a predetermined road speed value.

Sensitivity: Ability to respond to maintain a set rpm without rpm fluctuation as load changes.

Speed drift: In which engine speed rises above or below the set speed, often in surges; differentiated from hunting by the fact that it is not rhythmic.

Stability: Ability to maintain a set rpm.

Underrun: A governor's inability to maintain the engine low-idle speed when rpm is quickly dropped.

WOT: Wide-open throttle. A term used mainly on SI automotive engines and less often on diesels; it means *full-fuel request*.

SUMMARY

- In any CI engine, a power stroke takes place only if the fuel system is accurately phased to the engine.
- Timing of fuel injection is ECM controlled in current diesel engines. This provides for continuously variable timing so that changes in engine-operating conditions can produce the best performance outcomes.
- Current diesel fuel systems can produce injection pressures exceeding 35,000 psi, and this is expected to increase.
- Today's engines provide the ECM with the ability to precisely control the atomized fuel droplet size.
- When a hydraulic injector nozzle is used, the size of the emitted droplets depends on fuel pressure and the nozzle orifice size. Because the nozzle orifice size does not change, the pump element pressure determines the actual size of fuel droplets injected into an engine cylinder.
- In more recent electronically managed engines, the ECM has the ability to control pump pressure. In most post-2007 EPA-compliant diesel engines, the ECM controls droplet sizing either by managing pump pressure (EUI and EUP systems) or by managing rail pressure (CR systems).
- Fuel droplets burn from the outside in. This means a larger atomized fuel droplet requires more real time to completely combust than a smaller droplet.
- Fuel delivered to the engine cylinders must be precisely metered. The terms *duty cycle* and *injection rate* are key to understanding metering.
- *Duty cycle* is the term used to describe metering duration in real time in most electronically managed engines. It is usually measured in ms or crank angle degrees. Duty cycle is often displayed as pulse width (PW).
- Injection rate refers to fuel injected per crank angle degree and is usually governed by the injection pump actuating mechanism geometry or by the ECM in cases where smart injectors are used. This term is more commonly used in relation to hydromechanical engines.
- A modern diesel engine fuel system must be capable of atomizing fuel to precise dimensions. Failure to achieve this will result in combustion problems.
- Atomized fuel is in the liquid state. After injection, atomized droplets are exposed to cylinder heat. They are first vaporized, then ignited by the heat in the cylinder.
- The fuel system must deliver the fuel to the correct cylinder at the correct time to ensure balanced power output.
- The relationship between the crank throw and the crankshaft centerline is that of a lever.
- The ECM uses the fuel system to manage engine cylinder combustion pressures.
- The combination of cylinder pressure and crank throw leverage produces torque. In a properly managed fuel system, torque applied to the flywheel should be smooth and even.
- To optimize the relationship between cylinder pressure and mechanical advantage to provide smooth torque application, cylinder pressure should ideally peak between 10 and 20 degrees ATDC regardless of speed or load conditions.
- A four-stroke cycle engine run at 2,000 rpm will produce approximately 17 power strokes per second in each of its cylinders.
- Understanding how pumping, injection, and combustion relate to each other is a key to properly understanding engine management.
- Diesel engine governors, whether electronic or hydromechanical, must be able to sense engine speed and be capable of modulating engine fueling in the event of an overspeed condition.
- Because the output of any diesel engine is determined by the fuel quantity metered into its cylinders, a fuel map graph can be helpful when it comes to understanding governor operation.
- An LS governor can also be referred to as an *automotive* or *min-max governor*.
- Accelerator pedal angle in an LS-managed truck diesel engine defines a fuel quantity. If the driver wants either more or less fuel, the pedal angle must be either increased or decreased.
- A VS governor can also be referred to as an *all speed* or *full range* governor.
- On a VS governor, accelerator position requests a specific engine speed. As engine load increases and decreases, the governor adjusts engine fueling to attempt to maintain that set engine speed. VS governors are a programmable option of the ECM.

- Accelerator pedal angle in a VS-managed truck diesel engine requests a specific engine rpm. Within the limitations of the fuel system, the governor attempts to maintain that rpm as engine load conditions change.
- Road speed governing is commonly specified in current truck engine applications.

- Electronic governors are altered by reprogramming, either with OEM or customer data programming. Older hydromechanical governors are altered by trim adjustments, sometimes requiring hardware changes.

REVIEW QUESTIONS

1. The precise control of injected fuel quantity is known as:
   a. timing.
   b. metering.
   c. atomization.
   d. spray dispersion.

2. Which two factors define the emitted droplet sizings from a nozzle assembly?
   a. Injection pressure and orifice size
   b. Load and rpm
   c. Accelerator position and governor
   d. Cylinder pressure and crank angle

3. Given unlimited fuel, a diesel engine may accelerate at a rate up to:
   a. 60 rpm per second.
   b. 120 rpm per second.
   c. 120 rpm per minute.
   d. 1,000 rpm per second.

4. If a four-stroke cycle engine is run at 1,000 rpm, approximately how many power strokes per second will occur in any one of its cylinders?
   a. 1,000
   b. 8
   c. 17
   d. 32

5. In what position through the power stroke is crank throw leverage at its maximum?
   a. TDC
   b. 10 degrees BTDC rod-to-throw angle
   c. 10 to 20 degrees ATDC rod-to-throw angle
   d. 90 degree rod-to-throw angle

6. An ideal fuel system manages fueling to produce peak cylinder pressure at which location on the power stroke to produce optimum performance on any given engine cycle?
   a. TDC
   b. 15 degrees ATDC
   c. 90 degrees ATDC
   d. BDC

7. When the term *pilot injection* is used to describe the initial shot of fuel in a multipulse injection system, which of the following best describes its function?
   a. It lubricates the cylinder walls.
   b. It doses the diesel particulate filter.
   c. It initiates the flame front for the main pulse.
   d. It cools the piston crown.

8. In which engine position does the crank throw provide the least amount of leverage?
   a. TDC
   b. 15 degrees ATDC
   c. 90 degrees ATDC
   d. 120 degrees BTDC

9. Technician A states that the degree of atomization is controlled by managing injection pressure. Technician B states that atomized droplets are in a gaseous state. Who is correct?
   a. Technician A only
   b. Technician B only
   c. Both A and B
   d. Neither A nor B

10. What units are typically used to express *duty cycle* in electronically managed diesel engines?
    a. Crank angle degrees
    b. Microns
    c. Milliseconds
    d. Microseconds

11. What acronym is commonly used to display *duty cycle* on electronic service tools (ESTs)?
    a. PW
    b. PWM
    c. DC
    d. IRT

12. Technician A states that some multipulse diesel fuel injection systems can break up an injection pulse into seven separate injection events in one cycle. Technician B states that multipulse diesel fuel injection can be hard on powertrain components because it produces spiked cylinder pressures. Who is correct?
   a. Technician A only
   b. Technician B only
   c. Both A and B
   d. Neither A nor B

13. When attempting to cold-start an electronically controlled diesel engine in subzero (lower than −17°C) conditions, which of the following would provide the most help?
   a. Larger than normal fuel droplet sizing
   b. Smaller than normal fuel droplet sizing
   c. Substantial advance to injection timing
   d. Pushing the accelerator to the floor

14. Rhythmic fluctuation in engine rpm is known as:
   a. governor overrun.
   b. governor underrun.
   c. dieseling.
   d. hunting.

15. An engine run at a speed exceeding rated, but less than high-idle, speed would be operating:
   a. in the torque rise profile.
   b. at peak torque.
   c. in the droop curve.
   d. in an overrun condition.

16. When an engine is rapidly accelerated and momentarily exceeds the nominal high-idle speed, the condition is known as:
   a. runout.
   b. governor cutoff.
   c. speed drift.
   d. overrun.

17. Technician A states that an LS governor is designed to produce accelerator response close to that of an automobile throttle. Technician B states that a VS governor is capable of increasing and decreasing fuel quantity per cycle without moving the accelerator pedal. Who is correct?
   a. Technician A only
   b. Technician B only
   c. Both A and B
   d. Neither A nor B

18. Technician A states that an isochronous governor could be used on a vehicle engine providing it had a fluid clutch. Technician B states that an isochronous governor is normally used to manage a genset. Who is correct?
   a. Technician A only
   b. Technician B only
   c. Both A and B
   d. Neither A nor B

19. Technician A states that a high-speed diesel engine given unlimited fuel will accelerate to self-destruction. Technician B states that a governor is designed to derate engine fueling as altitude increases. Who is correct?
   a. Technician A only
   b. Technician B only
   c. Both A and B
   d. Neither A nor B

20. Technician A states that when governed high-idle speed is increased in an on-highway engine, an increase in brake horsepower is a more likely result than a decrease. Technician B states that drivers are more likely to complain about a lack of power on an engine with a short torque rise profile than one with high torque rise. Who is correct?
   a. Technician A only
   b. Technician B only
   c. Both A and B
   d. Neither A nor B

21

Prerequisite: Chapter 20

INJECTOR NOZZLES

OBJECTIVES

After studying this chapter, you should be able to:

- Identify the subcomponents of a nozzle assembly.
- Describe the role of the injector nozzle in system pressure management.
- Identify four types of injector nozzles.
- Describe the hydraulic principles of operation of poppet, pintle, multi-orifii, electrohydraulic, and piezoelectric nozzles.
- Outline the operating principles of electrohydraulic injectors (EHIs).
- Describe the differences between solenoid and piezo actuators.
- Reprogram fuel flow codes to an ECM.
- Define *nozzle differential ratio*.
- Describe a valve closes orifice (VCO) nozzle.
- Explain the difference between a low and high spring injector.
- Bench (pop) test a hydraulic injector nozzle.
- Disassemble, ultrasonically bathe, and reassemble an injector.
- Test a nozzle for forward and back leakage.
- Set injector nozzle opening pressure (NOP).
- Evaluate the serviceability of a hydraulic injector nozzle.
- Evaluate the serviceability and test the performance of an EHI.

KEY TERMS

atomization	electrohydraulic	mechanical injector	nozzle valve motion sensor (NVMS)
back leakage	pintle nozzle (EPN)	micron (μ)	orifice nozzle
calibration code	forward leakage	multi-orifii nozzle	peak pressure
cavitation	high spring injector	nozzle differential ratio	pencil injector nozzle
chatter	hydraulic injector	nozzle opening pressure (NOP)	piezo actuator
direct injection (DI)	indirect injection (IDI)	nozzle seat	piezoelectricity
electrohydraulic injector (EHI)	leak-off lines/pipes		piezo injector
	low spring injector		

pintle nozzle	pop test	residual line pressure	trim code
poppet nozzle	quick response (QR) code	sac	valve closes orifice (VCO) nozzle
popping pressure		spindle	

INTRODUCTION

Diesel fuel is injected into an engine cylinder using an injector. When the diesel technician refers to an *injector*, the nozzle holder assembly is generally being described. A nozzle holder assembly may be a single-function device we know as an integral injector assembly, or a subcomponent of a multifunction assembly such as mechanical unit injectors (MUIs), electronic unit injectors (EUIs), and hydraulically actuated electronic unit injectors (HEUIs). In a modern high-pressure fuel injection system, the velocity of fuel exiting a fuel injector can exceed the speed of sound. In describing nozzle assemblies and their operating principles in this chapter, we will reference:

- Integral injector assemblies: single-function devices used to atomize fuel and may define the hydraulic opening pressure. They are usually connected to the metering and high-pressure pump by a line.
- Subcomponent nozzles: a subassembly incorporated into MUIs, EUIs, and HEUIs that is responsible for performing the metering, timing, and pumping functions of diesel fuel injection.

In general terms, we can describe injector nozzles as devices with the following functions:

- Valves that open and close to begin or end fuel injection
- Define **nozzle opening pressure (NOP)** (hydraulic nozzles only)
- Atomize fuel to the correct size for combustion

In this chapter we reference both **hydraulic injectors** (one original equipment manufacturer [OEM] refers to these as **mechanical injectors**) and **electrohydraulic injectors (EHIs)**. Until the 2007 model year, almost all the nozzles used in commercial vehicle highway diesel engines were hydraulic nozzles. However, the reverse is true with the post-2007 model year, following which all but a couple diesel fuel systems use variations of EHI nozzles. Most off-highway diesel engines followed suit in 2008. Almost all on-highway commercial diesel engines that are EPA 2010 compliant use either EHIs or electrohydraulic nozzles. Notable exceptions are those engines, such as the MaxxForce DT, that continue to use the HEUI fuel system.

FUNCTIONS

Injectors are classified by nozzle design. Nozzles are simple hydraulic or electrically switched valves whose functions are to open and close at the correct moment to atomize fuel as it exits the nozzle assembly, thereby injecting fuel into the engine cylinders. There are four basic types of injector nozzles, two of which are effectively obsolete in medium- and heavy-duty truck and bus engine applications. However, both the obsolete types are briefly described in this chapter for two reasons:

- Some older equipment with these nozzle types is still in service.
- They are still included in college curriculum and certification testing.

Older poppet and pintle nozzles are best suited to indirect-injected engine applications and therefore are not used in any current North American medium- and heavy-duty engines. Our main focus will be on:

- **Multi-orifii nozzles** used in most **direct-injection (DI)** diesel engines using inline, port-helix metering injection pumps, and as an integral subcomponent of mechanically and electronically controlled unit injection systems.
- Electrohydraulic injector (EHI) nozzles used in common rail (CR), EUP, and EUI fuel systems.

All of the injector nozzles covered in this chapter are closed-nozzle systems. Open-nozzle injectors exist, but they have very different operating principles. The open-nozzle Cummins injectors used in on-highway diesels until 2010, and beyond in off-highway applications, are covered in later sections of this textbook.

NOP IN HYDRAULIC INJECTORS

An injector nozzle is a hydraulically or electrically actuated *switch*. Switch status is changed either by hydraulic pressure rise or fall, or by an electrical signal. All older hydraulic injector nozzles were specified with a hard value opening pressure. This opening pressure was defined by the hydraulic pressure required to *switch* the device and open it: It could be adjusted by a technician, but only when out of the engine. This trigger pressure required to open a nozzle valve was known either as nozzle opening pressure (NOP) or by the term **popping pressure**. In all hydraulic injector nozzles, the NOP value was defined by the mechanical spring tension of an internal nozzle spring. This spring tension loaded the nozzle valve onto its seat: It therefore defined specifically how much hydraulic pressure was required to unseat (and open) the valve to begin injection.

Most hydraulic injectors incorporated a means of adjusting the injector spring tension so that the NOP value could be set to a precise specification. The means of adjusting the spring tension that defined NOP was either internal shims or an adjusting screw and jam nut. The NOP value is always one of the first performance specifications to be evaluated when performing a **pop test**. Pop testing of injector nozzles is performed on a bench test fixture also known as a pop tester, and we will look at this in more detail later in the chapter.

EHI OPENING AND CLOSING

In more recently introduced EHIs, NOP is a *soft* value. We use the term *soft value* because both opening and closing of the injector valve are controlled by the engine control module (ECM) managing the engine. This gives EHI injectors the advantage of opening at whatever pressure the ECM calculates is appropriate for combustion. Almost all post-2007 engines are using some form of EHI nozzles or injectors, so in this chapter we will take a close look at the advantages they provide. One term we will *not* use when describing EHI operation is NOP, because it is not a fixed value.

SINGLE ORIFICE NOZZLES

Poppet and pintle nozzles should be of little significance to diesel technicians who work with current trucks and heavy equipment. However, they are addressed briefly here because they are integrated into some syllabi and certification testing. The NATEF and ASE no longer include either nozzle category in their current task lists, so most students should be able to skip this section. However, **electrohydraulic pintle nozzles** are used by some OEMs to dose diesel particulate filter (DPF) systems (with fuel) and selective catalytic reduction (SCR) systems (with aqueous urea), so technicians should have a basic understanding of how they function. These nozzles may also be used in some of the small-bore engines used as auxiliary power unit (APU) and reefer powerplant engines.

POPPET NOZZLES

Poppet nozzles were used by Caterpillar in the past on **indirect injection (IDI)** engines using a precombustion chamber, as shown in **Figure 21-1**. If you see one of these today, it is likely going to be in an ancient bulldozer or grader: the reason these legacy vehicles exist in service is that they have high replacement values that make repairs worthwhile.

Poppet nozzles are the simplest of the hydraulic injector nozzles and thus were the least costly to manufacture. Poppet nozzles are not easily reconditioned; the technician is normally required to bench-test the nozzle for the correct NOP value and observation of spray pattern and either reject or accept it for continued service.

Poppet nozzles use an outward or forward opening valve principle. This means that all the fuel pumped to the injector ultimately ends up in the engine cylinder, eliminating the necessity for the leak-off lines (return circuit) used with most other nozzle types. NOP values were low (compared to today's values), generally ranging between 500 and 1,800 psi (35 and 125 bar). For example, the Caterpillar poppet nozzles referenced in this section had NOPs of around 800 psi (55 bar).

Poppet nozzles operate as hydraulic switches to define the NOP and atomize the fuel. The nozzle spring loads the poppet valve onto its seat. Hydraulic line pressure (from the injection pump) acts on the sectional area of the seated upper portion of the poppet valve, and when the injection pump delivers pressure rise sufficient to unseat the poppet valve, fuel passes around the poppet to exit from the nozzle's single orifice.

When a precombustion chamber design is used, the engine cylinder clearance volume is generally too large to generate compression temperatures in cold weather sufficiently high

FIGURE 21–1 Poppet injector and prechamber assembly.

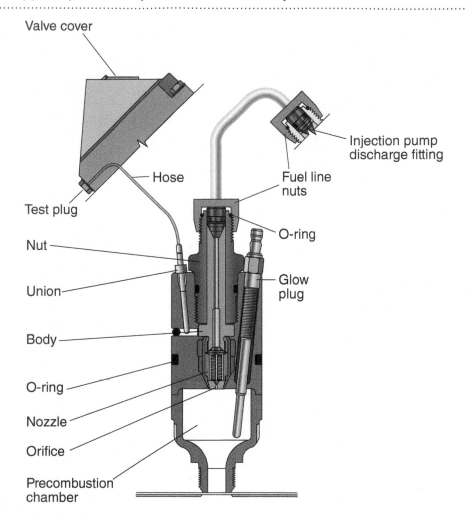

to ignite the fuel charge (Figure 21–1). Glow plugs were often designed into IDI engine systems as a cold weather starting aid. It should be remembered by technicians who come across older precombustion chamber engines that the use of ether should be avoided whenever a glow plug circuit is energized. The result of ether usage in IDI engines is possible explosion damage to the prechamber.

PINTLE NOZZLES

Like poppet nozzles, **pintle nozzles** are used mainly in IDI engine applications and seldom in truck/bus-sized compression ignition (CI) engines of the recent past. You can find them in older automobile diesel engines manufactured by GM, Ford, and VW. Like the poppet nozzle, the pintle nozzle body is designed with a single exit orifice. The valve pintle protrudes through this single orifice even when in the fully open

position. This means that the fuel exiting the nozzle is forced around the pintle, producing a conical (cone-shaped) spray pattern. The valve body and pintle valve were lapped together in manufacture, often to a tolerance of around 2μ (μ: **micron** or one-millionth of a meter), which means that the components cannot be interchanged.

Pintle nozzles achieve better **atomization** (reduction of a liquid to minute droplets) than poppet nozzles and generally much greater service life because they are easily reconditioned. NOP parameters range between 1,470 and 2,200 psi (100 and 150 bar), with peak system pressures seldom exceeding 7,350 psi (500 bar).

ACTION

Fuel is delivered to the pintle injector from the fuel injection pump by means of a high-pressure pipe. The nozzle valve is held in the closed

FIGURE 21–2 Pintle nozzle operation: Terminology. **A.** Nozzle seated; **B.** Opening; **C.** Open.

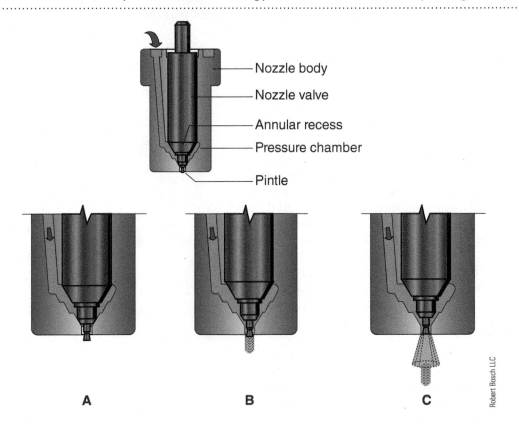

— Nozzle body
— Nozzle valve
— Annular recess
— Pressure chamber
— Pintle

A   B   C

Robert Bosch LLC

position mechanically by spring pressure either acting directly on the pintle valve or transmitted by means of a **spindle** (shaft that transmits spring force to the nozzle valve). Fuel is ducted through the injector assembly to the pressure chamber within the nozzle; this permits the line pressure to act on the sectional area of the pintle valve exposed to the pressure chamber. Whenever the hydraulic pressure generated by the injection pump acting on the sectional area of the pintle valve exposed to the pressure chamber is sufficient to overcome the spring pressure loading the valve on its seat, the valve retracts, permitting fuel to flow past the seat and exit through the nozzle orifice. Fuel will continue to flow through the nozzle orifice for as long as hydraulic pressure exceeds the mechanical force represented by the injector spring. The length of a fueling pulse is determined by the fuel injection pump; when line pressure collapses, the spring reseats the nozzle valve, ending injection.

The pintle nozzle uses an inward opening valve principle, thus requiring the use of **leak-off lines/pipes** to return fuel to the tank. The leakage takes place at the pintle valve-to-nozzle body clearance and tends to increase as these matched components age. The shaping of

the spray pattern emitted from a pintle nozzle depends on the pintle design. Throttling nozzles are designed to emit less fuel at the beginning of the injection pulse and may be identified by their conically shaped pintle valves. **Figure 21–2** shows the operation of a typical pintle nozzle closed, at NOP, and fully open. **Figure 21–3** compares the external appearance of a pintle nozzle with the multi-orifii nozzles we will study next.

FIGURE 21–3 A. Multi-orifii nozzle; **B.** Pintle nozzle.

A   B

Nozzle Valve Motion Sensor

During the early years of the electronic age, some Bosch hydraulic injectors with pintle nozzles were equipped with **nozzle valve motion sensors (NVMSs)**. The NVMS is integrated into the injector body and consists of a coil and pressure pin. Pressure pin movement through the coil winding changes the coil reluctance, inducing a signal voltage proportional to the valve's speed of movement. The NVMS enables the ECM to determine the precise moment of start of injection, which helps build the algorithms required for injection timing and exhaust gas recirculation (EGR) management. It is designed to detect and signal nozzle valve movement (at NOP) because the pressure pin moves with the nozzle valve. An example of a pintle injector equipped with NVMS is shown in Chapter 24 (see Figure 24–13) dealing with electronically controlled Bosch VE injection pumps.

Electromechanical Pintle

The gasoline fuel injectors (GFIs) used in automobile engines use an electromechanical principle. So do some of the dosing injectors we use in diesel engines equipped with DPF and SCR systems. The function of a DPF dosing injector is to deliver fuel upstream from the DPF housing to enable a regeneration combustion event. The function of an SCR dosing injector is to deliver aqueous urea known as diesel exhaust fluid (DEF) upstream from the SCR aftertreatment catalyst to assist in reducing NO_x emission. Both systems are studied in detail in Chapters 47 and 48.

The pintle-style nozzle valve in a typical dosing injector is integral with an armature: When the solenoid is energized, the dosing injector opens in exactly the same way a GFI injector opens. When opened electrically, the fuel is forced around the pintle to exit through a single orifice: This produces a conical spray pulse. Dosing pressures vary, but are usually considerably lower than diesel fuel injection pressures.

MULTIPLE ORIFICE NOZZLES

As mentioned in the introduction to this chapter, until recently most current truck and bus diesel engines use closed hydraulic injector nozzles. Until 2007, an overwhelming majority of injector nozzles could be classified as multi-orifii. Multi-orifii nozzles appear in truck engines in traditional, pump-line-nozzle configurations, but

FIGURE 21–4 Sectional view of a multi-orifii injector nozzle.

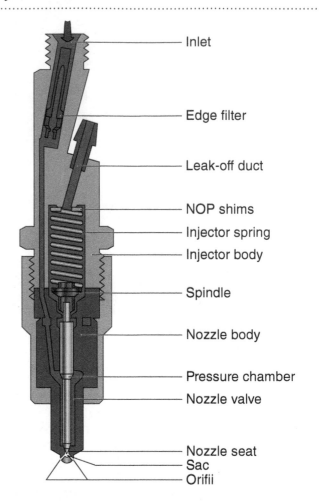

in addition they were an integral subcomponent in EUI, EUP, and HEUI injection circuits. **Orifice nozzles** and the closely related EHI nozzles are required in most high-speed DI diesel engines because only these produce the necessary degree of atomization: droplets sized between 10μ and 100μ. **Figure 21–4** shows a sectional view of a typical multi-orifii injector. It should be stressed that when EUIs or HEUIs use hydraulic nozzles as a subassembly, the operating principles are identical to those of the injector shown in Figure 21–4.

DROPLET SIZING

The emitted droplet sizing from a hydraulic injector nozzle depends on two factors:

- Flow area (size of nozzle orifii)
- Pressure (managed by injection pumping apparatus)

Flow area is defined by the sizing of the nozzle orifii and therefore remains constant. However, the pressure values are designed to vary through a wide range. This range extends from values lower than NOP up to the **peak pressure** (the highest pressure attainable in a fuel injection system) value. Because the flow area remains constant, as pressure increases, the droplet sizing decreases. The more prolonged the injection pulse (that is, the longer the duration of the effective pump stroke), the higher the circuit pressure at the injection pump port opening (end of delivery) and, therefore, the smaller the atomized droplet sizing.

The reduction in droplet sizing that occurs as the fueling pulse is extended is generally favorable for the complete combustion of the fuel. Fuel droplets burn from the outside inward. Larger droplets require more burn time; smaller droplets, shorter burn times. This means that as a fuel pulse is extended, the emitted droplet size reduces, as does the time available to completely combust them. This is true except for the short period of fueling that takes place while the system pressure is collapsing to *end* injection. This collapse phase that occurs at the end of injection depends on the peak pressure attained in that cycle: the higher the peak pressure, the longer the collapse phase. And right up to the point that the nozzle valve closes, fuel is injected into the engine cylinder. Because emitted droplet sizing increases during the collapse phase and fuel continues to be injected until the moment the nozzle valve actually closes, it is desirable for the pressure collapse to occur as rapidly as possible.

You might recall from Chapter 20 that atomized droplet sizings of 10μ or less can result in erratic ignition or no ignition at all. Atomized droplet sizings of 100μ or more will produce extended ignition lag and are too large to be completely combusted (oxidized) in the available time window of diesel engines with rated speeds of 1,600 to 2,600 rpm. The real time window within which combustion of the fuel must take place is defined by engine rpm. If an engine is run at 2,000 rpm, it takes exactly 0.030 second or 30 milliseconds for a single revolution of the engine; this means that a piston travels from top dead center (TDC) to 90 degrees after top dead center (ATDC), more or less the period available for combustion, in 7.5 milliseconds. Top end engine speeds dictate the combustion or burn duration window and, therefore, the maximum atomized droplet sizing.

BACK LEAKAGE

Orifice nozzles use an inward opening valve principle, and that requires leak-off lines. The leakage, known as **back leakage**, is that occurring at the nozzle-valve-to-nozzle-body clearance and measured on the injector test bench. Where orifice nozzles are used in diesel engines, the following range of values is typical:

- NOPs (opening pressures) range from 1,800 to 5,500 psi (120 to 400 bar).
- Peak system injection pressures range from 2 to 10 times the NOP value.

Multi-orifii nozzles used in older hydro-mechanical engines typically have NOPs in the region of 3,000 psi (200 bar). The multi-orifii nozzles used in EUIs, EUPs, and HEUIs generally have NOP values close to 5,000 psi (350 bar).

ACTION

The multi-orifii nozzle is usually dowel-positioned in the injector assembly to ensure that the spray pattern is directed to a specific location of the engine cylinder. In most DI engines, the correct area is the toroidal recess (crater) around the Mexican hat peak in the piston (see Figure 7–1 in Chapter 7). Fuel from the injection pump mechanism is delivered to the nozzle holder and then ducted to an annular recess in the upper nozzle valve body. Either single or multiple fuel ducts extend from the annular recess to the pressure chamber, meaning that the pressure here will be the same as that in the high-pressure pipe.

The nozzle valve is loaded to a closed position on its seat, either directly by the injector spring or indirectly by spring pressure relayed to the nozzle valve by means of a spindle. This spring tension is adjustable by either a screw or by shims and will set the NOP value. When line pressure is driven upward by the injection pump, pressure increases in the nozzle pressure chamber. When this pressure is sufficient to overcome the mechanical force of the injector spring, the nozzle valve retracts, permitting the fuel to flow past the seat into the **sac** and exit the nozzle orifii. At the center of the nozzle valve seat, a single duct connects to the nozzle sac, which is a spherical chamber into which the nozzle orifii are machined. The sac hydraulically balances the fuel exiting the orifii, so that droplets start to exit from each orifice at approximately the same moment at the beginning of the fuel pulse.

The injection pulse continues for as long as the nozzle valve remains open. Depending on the specific means used to generate injection pressures, *maximum* fueling pulses can extend from 25 to 50 engine crank angle degrees. Minimum fueling pulses in hydromechanical engines may be as short as 5 engine crank angle degrees. A fueling or injection pulse ends when the pressure is collapsed by the metering/pumping element and the pressure in the nozzle assembly drops to a value below NOP. Control of the injection pressure always occurs outside the nozzle assembly.

NOZZLE DIFFERENTIAL RATIO

Nozzle differential ratio describes the geometric relationship between the sectional area of the **nozzle seat** and that of the pressure chamber or valve shank. Nozzle valves are opened by hydraulic pressure acting on the sectional area of the valve subject to the pressure chamber; when this overcomes the spring pressure that loads them on their seats, they retract. However, the instant the nozzle valve unseats, hydraulic pressure is permitted to act over the whole sectional area of the nozzle valve. The whole sectional area of the nozzle valve is the sectional area of both the seat and that of the pressure chamber combined (**Figure 21–5**).

When pressure rise begins in the injection line circuit before the opening of the nozzle valve, the hydraulic circuit being acted on is closed (it is sealed at the nozzle seat). The instant the NOP value is achieved, the nozzle valve unseats and opens the circuit. This must result in a drop in line pressure. However, because at the moment the nozzle valve opens the sectional area over which the hydraulic pressure acts is increased by that of the seat sectional area, less pressure is now required to hold the nozzle open. Nozzle differential ratio must be sufficient to prevent nozzle closure when this pressure drop occurs. After NOP, fuel passing around the seat fills the sac and pressure rise resumes because of the restriction represented by the minute sizing of the nozzle orifii. Nozzle differential ratio means that nozzle closure at the end of injection occurs at a value somewhat below the NOP value. It also helps define the specific **residual line pressure** (pressure that dead volume fuel is retained at in the high-pressure pipe) value.

The bottom line is that more pressure is required to unseat a nozzle valve than is required to hold it off its seat, due to nozzle differential ratio. This means that any hydraulic injector (including those used in conjunction with EUIs, EUPs, and HEUIs) will have a nozzle closing pressure somewhere around 20% lower than its specified NOP.

NOZZLE HOLDERS/INJECTORS

Injectors are simply mounting devices for hydraulic nozzles. They come in many different shapes and sizes for a variety of reasons; for instance, long stem nozzles are easier to cool. Older hydraulic injectors tended to be of the high spring design. **High spring injectors** located the spring in the upper portion of the holder and relayed the spring tension to the nozzle value by means of a spindle. Spring tension was altered directly by an adjusting screw, and setting the NOP value on the pop tester was a quick and easy procedure. A disadvantage of the high spring design was that at NOP, the nozzle valve slammed open until it was mechanically prevented from further inboard travel. Because of its high opening velocity, the spindle was driven into the spring, which rebounded sufficiently to hammer the nozzle valve from its open position back into the seat, interrupting the injection pulse.

More recent hydraulic injector nozzles have tended to use a low spring design that eliminates the spindle and thus reduces the mass of moving parts; this has minimized rebound interference of the injection pulse. However, **low spring injectors** generally use shims acting on the spring to define the NOP value, which extends the time required to set the NOP value on the test bench.

PENCIL-TYPE INJECTOR NOZZLES

Pencil injector nozzles are a type of multiorifii injector nozzle and, in fact, share common operating principles with a couple of small exceptions. They are seldom found in any current truck engine applications. Caterpillar used

FIGURE 21–5 Nozzle differential ratio: sectional areas of a nozzle valve.

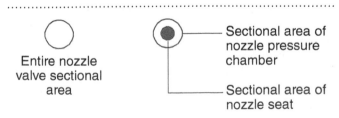

Entire nozzle valve sectional area

Sectional area of nozzle pressure chamber

Sectional area of nozzle seat

them in some of its older hydromechanical engines. The pencil nozzle assembly is cylindrical and has the approximate appearance of a pencil. Within the nozzle body, the nozzle valve extends through nearly the full height of the injector assembly, and the injector spring acts directly on top of the nozzle valve shaft. Adjustment is by means of an adjusting screw and locknut located at the top of the assembly. Some pencil nozzles have no leak-off lines; fuel that bleeds by the nozzle valve during injection is accumulated in a chamber above the valve, and pressure equalization with line pressure occurs after nozzle closure. Pencil nozzles are most often damaged in the process of removal and service. When making any adjustments, use the recommended mounting fixture and observe the specified torque procedure.

VCO NOZZLES

Valve closes orifice (VCO) nozzles have eliminated the sac (see Figure 21–4). The function of the sac in the nozzle is to provide balanced fuel dispersal, which is especially important in keeping the ignition lag time consistent. However, at the completion of the injection pulse, the volume of fuel in the sac was essentially wasted fuel that added to hydrocarbon (HC) emission. It was a small volume of fuel, for sure, but in today's technology, any fuel waste or contributor to emissions counts. At the instant of nozzle closure, the sac and the nozzle orifii would contain fuel that would be vaporized due to the heat of combustion but at best, only partially combusted. Current injector nozzle designs have either substantially reduced the sac volume or eliminated it entirely. A true VCO nozzle has orifii that extend directly from the seat. VCO nozzles are most often used on electronically managed injection systems that use high NOP values, which can to some extent compensate for the compromising of the balanced fuel dispersal offered by nozzle sacs. **Figure 21–6** shows a VCO nozzle design.

FIGURE 21–6 Valve closes orifice (VCO) nozzle.

Robert Bosch LLC

ELECTROHYDRAULIC INJECTORS

Electrohydraulic injectors (EHIs) were introduced in the late 1990s and used on the first generation of CR, diesel fuel injection systems such as those used in Mack Trucks light-duty engines, Cummins ISB, and the GM/Isuzu family of engines. The first generation of EHIs were similar to multiorifii hydraulic injectors in most ways, but were controlled electrically by solenoids rather than hydraulically. More recently, **piezo actuators** have been introduced, as the need for more precise management of combustion within the engine cylinder has increased. The operating principles of solenoid-actuated and piezo-actuated injectors are almost identical. The **piezo injectors** (most OEMs use this term) respond faster to control inputs and require less current than solenoid-actuated versions. We will take a look at the general operating principles of EHIs first, then examine piezoelectric actuators afterward.

The principles of solenoids and piezoelectricity are covered later in this textbook in Chapter 32: You may want to reference that chapter while studying this. In both solenoid-actuated and piezoelectric-actuated EHIs, hydraulic pressure in the rail is used to effect the opening of the nozzle when the unit is switched. The EHI (**Figure 21–7**) can be subdivided as follows:

- Nozzle assembly
- Hydraulic servo system
- Actuator valve (either a solenoid or piezoelectric actuator)

EHI OPERATION

Referencing **Figure 21–7**, fuel at rail pressure is supplied to the high-pressure connection, to the nozzle through the fuel duct, and to the control chamber through the feed orifice. The control chamber is connected to the fuel return via a bleed orifice that is opened by the actuator valve. With the bleed orifice closed, hydraulic force acts on the valve control plunger, exceeding that at the nozzle-needle pressure chamber (located between the shank and the needle of the nozzle valve). Although the hydraulic pressure values acting on the top of the nozzle valve and that in the lower pressure chamber are identical, the sectional area at the top of the nozzle valve is greater. As a result, the nozzle needle is loaded into its seated position, meaning that the injector is closed.

FIGURE 21-7 Electrohydraulic injector.

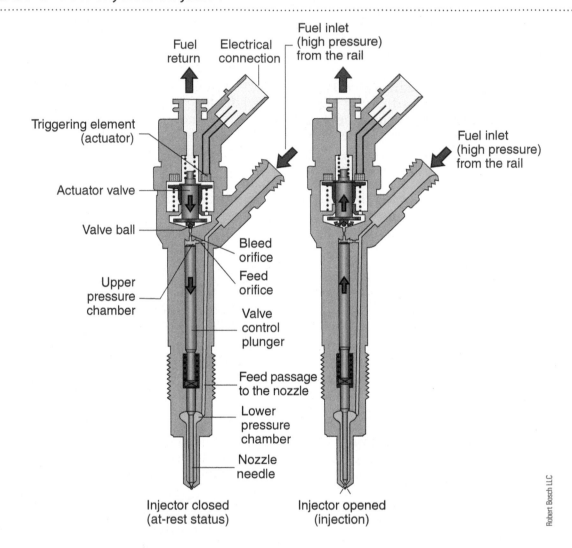

Injector closed
(at-rest status)

Injector opened
(injection)

Robert Bosch LLC

When an ECM signal triggers the actuator valve, the bleed orifice opens. This immediately drops the control chamber pressure and, as a result, the hydraulic pressure acting on the top of the nozzle valve also drops. When hydraulic force acting on top of the nozzle valve drops below the force on the nozzle-needle pressure shoulder, the nozzle valve retracts and allows fuel to pass around the seat to be injected through orifii into the combustion chamber. The hydraulic assist and amplification factors are required in this system because the forces necessary for rapid nozzle valve opening cannot be directly generated by the actuator valve alone. Fuel used as hydraulic media to open the nozzle valve is in addition to the injected fuel quantity, so this excess fuel is routed back to the tank. In addition to this fuel, some leak-by fuel losses occur at the nozzle valve-to-body clearance and the valve-plunger guide clearance.

EHI Operating Phases

When the engine is shut down, all injector nozzles are closed, meaning that their nozzle valves are loaded onto their seats by spring pressure. In a running engine, injector operation takes place in three phases.

INJECTOR CLOSED In the at-rest state, the actuator valve is not energized, and therefore the nozzle valve is loaded onto its seat by the injector spring combined with hydraulic pressure (from the rail) acting on the sectional area of the valve control plunger. With the bleed orifice closed, the solenoid valve spring forces the armature ball check onto the bleed-orifice seat. Rail pressure builds in the injector control chamber, but identical pressure will be present in the nozzle pressure chamber. Given equal pressure acting on the larger sectional area of the nozzle control plunger (which is mechanically connected to the nozzle valve) and in the nozzle pressure chamber, this pressure and the force of the nozzle spring combine to load the nozzle valve on its seat, holding the injector closed.

NOZZLE OPENING When the actuator valve is energized by the ECM injector driver, it is actuated at a spiked voltage value typically around 100 V-DC with either solenoid or piezo actuators, although one small-bore OEM using piezoelectric actuators drives them on a 48 V-DC pulse. Current draw also varies depending on whether a solenoid or piezoelectric actuator is used, with the latter requiring lower amperage. Force exerted by the actuator valve overcomes that of the valve spring, and the bleed orifice opens. As the bleed orifice opens, fuel flows from the valve-control chamber into the cavity above it and out to the return circuit. This collapses the hydraulic pressure acting on the valve control plunger that was helping to hold the nozzle valve closed. Now pressure in the valve-control chamber (upper pressure field) is much lower than that in the nozzle pressure chamber (lower pressure field) below it, which is maintained at the rail pressure. The result is that the force that was holding the nozzle valve closed collapses and the nozzle valve opens, beginning the injection pulse.

The nozzle-needle opening velocity is determined by the difference in the flow rate through the bleed and feed orifices. When the actuator control plunger contacts its upper stop, it is cushioned by fuel generated by flow between the bleed and feed orifices. When the injector nozzle valve has fully opened, fuel is injected into the combustion chamber at a pressure very close to that in the fuel rail.

NOZZLE CLOSING When the actuator valve is de-energized by the ECM injector driver, its spring forces the valve downward and the check ball closes the bleed orifice. The closing of the bleed orifice creates pressure buildup in the upper control chamber via the input from the feed orifice. This pressure should be the same as that in the rail, and now it exerts an increased force on the nozzle valve control plunger through its end face. This force, combined with that of the nozzle spring, exceeds the hydraulic force acting on the nozzle valve sectional area and the nozzle valve closes, ending injection. Nozzle valve closing velocity is determined by the flow through the feed orifice. The injection pulse ceases the instant the nozzle valve seats.

PIEZOELECTRIC INJECTORS

Piezoelectric actuators are based on reversibility of piezoelectric effect. For a full explanation of piezoelectricity, refer to Chapter 32; we only briefly describe the principles here. When certain crystals are subjected to pressure, a voltage is produced in a process known as **piezoelectricity**. These same crystals are capable of reversing the process, so when we subject them to a voltage, the crystal bonds change almost instantly, resulting in either expansion or contraction. This change of shape produces a powerful force that makes it possible for them to be used as actuators. Wafered layers of piezo crystals are stacked within the actuator body. As such, they function much like solenoids in producing a mechanical response to an electrical signal. They can therefore be used for actuating injector valves, but are capable of much higher speeds while using less electrical energy. Solenoids use electromagnetism and respond more slowly due to the time required to build and collapse electromagnetic fields. **Figure 21–8** is a cutaway shot of a Bosch piezo-actuated EHI.

FIGURE 21–8 Cutaway of a Bosch piezo-actuated EHI.

Features of Piezoelectric Actuators

Piezoelectric actuators can theoretically be used to replace any solenoid. They have the following characteristics when compared with equivalent solenoids:

- They respond more quickly when a control voltage is applied.
- They require much less electrical energy to operate.
- They are usually a little larger than an equivalent solenoid.

Piezoelectric actuators for diesel injectors were first developed by Siemens in Germany for CR injectors. The fact that piezoelectric injectors can be switched at much higher speeds (compared with solenoid valves) has enabled multipulse injectors to break up a fueling pulse into up to seven separate injections per cycle. Multipulse injection events are a key to quieter diesel engines that emit fewer pollutants.

Diesel engine fuel systems are now developing smaller-sized piezoelectric actuators that are integrated directly into the injector valve shaft. This is allowing current CR systems to produce EHI pressures up to 35,000 psi, and still higher pressures are predicted to become the norm.

Piezoelectric Injector Operation

A piezo actuator is constructed of several hundred piezo crystals in stacked wafers. These piezo crystal wafer stacks have the ability not only to operate nozzle needles against the extremely high diesel fuel injection pressures, but they do so quickly and repetitively. The high frequency at which the injectors can be switched makes it possible to reduce the intervals between each injection pulse during a single power stroke. This capability can divide the total fuel injected in one cycle into up to seven separate injection events. Piezoelectric actuator technology has been a key to improving fuel economy, emissions, and noise levels in the latest generation of diesel engines. It allows the ECM precise control over combustion and cylinder pressure.

EHI Pulse Frequency

Since the introduction of the first solenoid actuator EHIs in the late 1990s, the pulse frequency has increased by nearly 10 times, thanks to piezoelectric actuators. This explains why the technology has become attractive to OEMs who increasingly rely on the precise management of in-cylinder combustion to minimize emissions. Some examples of fastest real-time interval dimensions between fuel pulses used in Bosch EHIs are:

First-generation EHI with solenoid	0.7 ms pulse interval capability
2004 to current EHIs with solenoid	0.4 ms pulse interval capability
Post-2010 EHI with piezo actuator	0.1 ms pulse interval capability

NOZZLE HOLE GEOMETRY

EHIs use both sac-chamber nozzles and what are generally referred to as VCO nozzles. Both sac and VCO nozzles were covered a little earlier in this chapter, but VCO nozzles tend to be required in most current engine families. Current EHI injectors use a 4-mm to 6-mm nozzle valve diameter.

Both sac-hole and seat-hole nozzles have input edges of each orifice rounded (radiused) by hydroerosive (HE) machining. HE machining helps prevent edge wear caused by the abrasive particles in the fuel and carbon coking that can reduce flow and disrupt the spray geometry. For reasons of structural strength, the nozzle tip is conically shaped.

Calibration Codes

Although EHIs are electronically switched, they are hydromechanical devices. As such, the rate at which they flow fuel has some variability that can be measured on a flow bench. Injectors are rated with a flow code for balancing: this can be known by terms such as **calibration code**, *flow code*, or **trim code**. Depending on the OEM, this code may have to be programmed to the ECM to enable it to balance fueling. Flow codes will be examined in more detail in later chapters of this book. The codes are usually inscribed on the injector and may be alphanumeric or optical. **Figure 21–9** shows the optical **quick response (QR) code** used on some EHIs.

FIGURE 21–9 One method of defining the calibration code on an injector: On this Bosch EHI, it is an optical QR code.

SUMMARY OF EHIs

Because of their soft opening and closing pressures and their capability of providing high injection pressures at low engine rpm, the use of CR fuel systems and EHIs, especially those with piezoelectric actuators, has become commonplace. The advantages of EHIs include:

- They can be integrated as a subcomponent of an EUI to provide it with soft (computer-controlled) opening and closing values.
- They are designed to open and close precisely when the ECM electrically switches them, so they are not limited by factors such as cam profile.
- They produce injection pressure values that remain relatively consistent through a fueling pulse.
- They close almost instantly, eliminating the collapse phase that disadvantages comparable hydraulic injectors.
- They may use either solenoid or piezoelectric actuators. Piezoelectric actuators respond much more rapidly to control signals and are used in more recent fuel systems requiring multipulse injection.

NOZZLE TESTING AND RECONDITIONING

Injector nozzles are probably subjected to more abuse than any other engine component. They are exposed to temperature peaks of 2,550°F (1,400°C) outside and to pressures exceeding 35,000 psi (2400 bar) internally. Manufacturers' service intervals are seldom respected, and maintenance often is overlooked until a problem occurs. In today's world, the diesel technician is seldom required to fully recondition nozzle assemblies, due to the high cost of labor and service tooling versus the relatively low cost of nozzle replacement. However, because most manufacturers can determine injector efficiency by electronically running multicylinder cutout tests (these can accurately measure cylinder balance), it is usually possible to identify problems before they can create serious engine damage.

Consult OEM service literature before attempting to service injectors. In cases where hydraulic injector nozzles are a subcomponent of EUIs and HEUIs, OEMs require that a problem injector be identified and replaced rather than reconditioned. However, where integral injectors are used in pump-line-nozzle (PLN) and in EUP fuel systems, most manufacturers include the injectors in preventive maintenance schedules. Servicing this type of nozzle requires a simple bench-test fixture (or pop tester) and ultrasonic bath. Servicing a set of injectors is a safe and easy procedure, but some precautions are required.

CAUTION:

- Eye protection should be worn when working with or near high-pressure fluids.
- High-pressure atomized fuel is extremely dangerous and no part of the body should be in danger of contacting it.
- Never touch the nozzle assembly on the pop tester when it is at any pressure above atmospheric—and remember that the entire injector assembly is under pressure.
- Diesel fuel oil is a known carcinogen, that is, a cancer-causing agent. Always wash hands after contact with it.

REMOVAL OF INJECTORS FROM THE CYLINDER HEAD

The OEM-recommended method of removing an injector from a cylinder head must be adhered to; failure to do so can result in failed injectors. Before attempting to remove injectors, thoroughly clean the surrounding area, remembering that any dirt around the injector bore can end up in the engine cylinder below it. It is also good practice to drain high-pressure lines when removing the pipe fittings. Thin-bodied, pencil-type nozzles are vulnerable to any side load force, and the correct pullers should always be used. Additionally, whenever pencil-type nozzles are removed from a cylinder head, they must be tested in a test fixture before reinstallation, because they are so easily damaged during the removal process.

Many injector assemblies are flanged, in which case the hold-down fasteners and clamps (crabs) should first be removed and the injector levered out using an injector heel bar. The injector heel bar is 8" to 12" (20 to 30 cm) in length to prevent the application of excessive force to the injector flange. Where cylindrical injectors are used, a slide hammer and puller nut that fits to the high-pressure inlet of the injector should be used to pull the injector. With certain cylindrical injectors, the high-pressure delivery pipe fits to a recess in the injector through the cylinder head; the high-pressure pipe must be backed away from the cylinder head before attempting to remove the injector, or both the injector and the seating nipple on the high-pressure pipe will be damaged.

When removing injectors from cylinder heads, make a practice of removing the injector nozzle washer at the same time; these have an inside diameter (id) less than the cylinder injector aperture id, so providing the piston is not at TDC, they can usually be removed either by inserting an O-ring pick, copper injector bore brush, or (in cases of difficult-to-remove washers) the tapered end of the injector heel bar and jamming it into the washer. It is not good practice to reuse injector washers. Both steel and copper washers harden in service. The copper washers can be annealed by heating to the point at which they shimmer green, then quenching with water. Steel washers are a poor reuse risk and no attempt should be made to anneal them.

After removing the injector, clean the bore and blow out any fuel that may have drained into the cylinder using compressed air. In fuel systems that feed fuel to cylindrical injectors through the cylinder head, the feed and return galleries should be siphoned before removing injectors to prevent fuel from entering the engine cylinders.

When the injector has been removed, use plastic caps to seal the cylinder head injector bores, the injector inlet, and high-pressure pipe nipples. Ensure that a set of injectors is marked by cylinder number and properly protected in an injector tray; wrapping the injectors in shop rags will do if no injector tray is available.

Seized Injectors

Occasionally, an injector may seize in a cylinder head and defy any normal means used to remove it. Once the injector becomes damaged (for instance, the line threads that fit the injector to the puller are destroyed), the technician has no option but to remove the cylinder head. Never risk damaging a cylinder head attempting to remove an injector. With the cylinder head removed, a seized injector can usually be removed from below with a punch and hammer.

TESTING

OEM specifications and procedures should be consulted before placing the nozzle to be tested in the nozzle test fixture. A typical procedure for testing nozzle assemblies is as follows.

Assessment Procedure

Perform the following tests in sequence. At the first failure, cease following the sequence and proceed to the next section.

1. Clean the injector externally with a brass wire brush.
2. Locate the manufacturer's test specifications.
3. Mount the injector in the bench-test fixture. Build pressure slowly using the pump arm, watching for external leakage.
4. Bench-test the NOP value and record. Use three discharge pulses and record the average value. Sticking or a variation in NOP value that exceeds 150 psi (10 bar) fails the nozzle.
5. Test **forward leakage** by charging to 150 psi (10 bar) below the NOP value and holding the gauge pressure at that value while observing the nozzle. Any leakage evident at the tip orifii fails the nozzle.
6. Check back leakage by observing pressure drop from a value 150 psi (10 bar) below NOP. Pressure drop values should typically be in the range of 700 to 1,000 psi (50 to 70 bar) over a 10-second test period. Pressure drop that is less than OEM specification indicates too little valve-to-body clearance (possibly caused by valve-to-body mismatch). A rapid pressure drop exceeding the OEM specification indicates excessive nozzle valve-to-body clearance, which is a condition usually caused by wear.
7. Once again, actuate the bench fixture pump arm and observe the nozzle spray pattern, checking for orifii irregularity. Ignore nozzle **chatter** (rapid pulsing of the nozzle valve); this can be regarded as a test bench phenomenon due to *slow* rate of pressure rise and

inability to drive pressure much above NOP. In some modern injectors, the intensity of chatter noise is reduced due to the use of double seats.

Reconditioning

The function of the assessment procedure is to determine whether the nozzle should be reconditioned or placed back in service. Reconditioning in the service shop of today seldom means regrinding the valve nozzle seat or reaming nozzle orifii (**Figure 21–10**), due to high labor and tooling costs in comparison with the cost of nozzle replacement. However, the practice is common in specialty fuel injection shops. The following simple procedure probably summarizes what most operations interpret as reconditioning in a typical truck service facility:

1. A nozzle that fails the inspection procedure should first be removed from the injector. Disassemble the injector and remove the nozzle, separating the nozzle valve from the nozzle body. Ensure that nozzle valves remain matched with the nozzle bodies they are removed from, because they are not interchangeable.

FIGURE 21–10 Top: Cleaning nozzle orifii. Bottom: Performing valve-to-nozzle slide test.

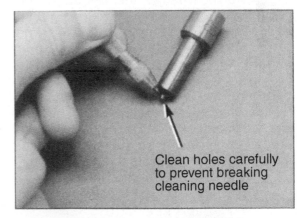

Clean holes carefully to prevent breaking cleaning needle

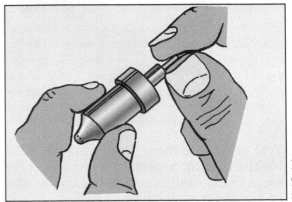

Mack Trucks Inc.

FIGURE 21–11 Typical ultrasonic bath.

2. Prepare the nozzle valve and body for ultrasonic cleaning in an ultrasonic bath (**Figure 21–11**). An ultrasonic bath filled with clean soapy water should be used. In other words, change the cleaning solution regularly. Alternatively, diesel test oil can be used, but it is not as effective. A 5-minute ultrasonic bath is generally sufficient. This should be followed by dehumidification either in a dehumidifier or an oven. If a dehumidifier is not available, fuel test oil rather than soapy water should be used as the ultrasonic soaking medium. Remember, lapped components are not interchangeable, so if cleaning multiple nozzle assemblies, do not mismatch components.

CAUTION:

Ultrasonic baths emit sound waves that are outside the frequencies detected by the human ear and have been known to trigger seizures in those susceptible to epilepsy. It is good practice to vacate a room in which ultrasonic cleaning is being performed even though it represents to most people nothing more than an irritating buzzing.

3. Test or replace the injector spring. Reassemble the injector assembly using diesel fuel as an assembly lubricant. Never use engine oil or any grease-based lubricant.

4. As a general rule, set the NOP value at 150 psi (10 bar) above the recommended specification if no parts have been replaced. Add another 75 psi (5 bar) if using a new spring, and a further 75 psi (5 bar) if using a new nozzle assembly. After 100 engine hours, the nozzle will function at the specified NOP value. In other words, when reassembling an injector with a new nozzle assembly and a new spring, the NOP would be set 300 psi (20 bar) above the recommended specification. Always consult the appropriate service literature for the NOP setting procedure.
   - Screw type: Back off the locknut, then turn the adjusting screw clockwise (CW) to increase or counterclockwise (CCW) to decrease NOP.
   - Shim type: Add or subtract shims acting on the injector spring.
5. Check forward leakage.
6. Check back leakage.
7. Check back leakage pipe restriction.
8. Observe spray pattern and check for nozzle orifii irregularity, preferably using a template.

A critical function of the nozzle washer (spacer) is to ensure optimum droplet penetration into the engine cylinder. It is not a mere joint gasket. Spacer thickness is critical and determines the nozzle protrusion dimension. Use of an incorrectly sized washer, two washers, or no washer can result in rapid engine failures. Most current nozzle washers are manufactured from soft steel, but there are still some copper washers: Always use the OEM-specified nozzle washer.

Reinstallation of Injectors

The injector bore should be cleaned before installation, using a bore reamer or copper bore brush to remove carbon deposits. Blow out the injector bore using an air nozzle. Where injector sleeves are used, service/replace per OEM instructions. Most diesel engine OEMs prefer that injectors be installed dry; lubricants such as Never-Seize™ can hinder the ability of the injector to transfer heat to the cylinder head. It is good practice to turn the engine over and pump fuel through the high-pressure pipe before connecting it to the injector; this will purge the pipe of air and possible debris that may have intruded into the line while it was disassembled.

Always torque the nut on the high-pressure pipe with a line socket; failure to do this can result in damage to both the line nut and the nipple and seat.

WARNING:

Whenever fuel has spilled over an engine, ensure that the engine is pressure-washed afterward.

A Reason Not to Recondition Nozzles

Earlier we said that it is not good practice to recondition hydraulic injector nozzles because, even with the best shop practice procedures and equipment, reconditioned nozzles tend to have much shorter service life than new nozzles—and may also produce poor performance. Here is one reason why. When carbon residues collect on nozzle orifii, they initially have a soot-like appearance. However, once subjected to the inevitable high-temperature/cool-off cycles of an engine cylinder, the carbon begins to crystallize, and in the process of doing so, leaches iron from the nozzle orifice. This process is known as *coking*. When a nozzle with established carbon deposits is ultrasonically cleaned, crystallized carbon is vibrated free, taking with it some of the base material at the nozzle orifice. This alters the orifice geometry and therefore the injection spray pattern. The inevitable result is poor performance.

NOZZLE TROUBLESHOOTING

While there are some general guidelines to injector nozzle troubleshooting, the nature of problems observed depends on which of the four general types of nozzle is used with a system. **Table 21–1** outlines some typical engine

TABLE 21–1 Nozzle-Related Engine Performance Problems

Engine Symptom	Nozzle Malfunction	Possible Nozzle-Related Causes
• Smoking • Higher fuel consumption • White smoke at start-up • Slightly higher power output	• NOP is slightly below specification: usually within 70% of OEM spec • Enlarged nozzle orifii	• Fatigued nozzle valve spring • Erosion of nozzle orifices caused by wear or ultrasonic reconditioning
• Misfire • Smoking • Overfueling	• NOP more than 70% below OEM-specified value • Severely eroded nozzle orifii	• Fatigued injector spring • Severely enlarged nozzle orifii caused by erosion, carbon leeching, or physical damage
• Misfire • Light smoking • Erosion of center piston crown	• Nozzle valve not seating • Injector dribble	• Cylinder gas leaking into the nozzle • Carbon nozzle seat and tip
• Severe smoking • Misfire at all loads and speeds • Fuel in the crankcase • Combustion gases in the fuel system • Overfueling	• Nozzle stuck open	• Broken injector spring • Coked (carboned) nozzle valve • Seized nozzle valve • Short-circuited nozzle armature (electrohydraulic nozzles)
• Slightly low power • Intermittent engine miss	• High nozzle back leakage caused by excessive clearance of nozzle valve shank to nozzle body	• Abrasive wear of nozzle valve shank caused by fuel contamination • Mismatched nozzle valve to nozzle body after reassembly
• Erratic engine surge below requested rpm • Misfire	• Nozzle seizure, higher NOPs, nonpositive nozzle closure	• Almost always caused by mismatch of nozzle valve to nozzle body during reassembly
• Low power • High fuel consumption • Rough operation • White smoke at start-up	• Plugged nozzle orifice/orifii	• High sulfur fuel • Contaminants in fuel such as ATF or other oils • Prolonged cold operation
• Low power • Black smoke emission • Poor pickup	• In EUI, EUP, and HEUI systems, internal leakage in the control cartridge	• Nozzle functions OK: Replace the control cartridge or the EUI, EUP, or HEUI as per OEM
• Engine misfire • Piston damage • White smoke at start-up • Black smoke under load	• Nozzle tip blown away	• Usually caused by water ingression into high-pressure injection circuit

symptoms that result from certain types of nozzle malfunctions.

HIGH-PRESSURE PIPES

In most hydromechanical fuel injection systems and some electronically managed systems, fuel is delivered from the pumping elements in the fuel injection pump to the nozzle holders by high-pressure pipes. These are subject to very high pressure values and are manufactured from alloyed steels with substantial wall thickness. Pressure wave reflection caused by pressure fluctuations and high-speed switching must also be accommodated. Failures are caused by pipe erosion, **cavitation** (vapor bubble collapse), and technician abuse-related problems such as overtorquing and bending.

High-pressure pipes should never be repair-welded or brazed when worn through, due to the extreme pressures they are required to contain. Weld or brazing repairs can penetrate into the worn-away area and reduce the flow area within the high-pressure pipe. They may also completely plug the pipe, and when a pump is capable of generating pressures exceeding 35,000 psi (2400 bar), something has to let go. Perhaps the most important reason that high-pressure pipes should never be repair-welded is that if the weld is unseated by the pipe pressure in operation, it can be propelled with substantial force and have the potential to injure anyone in the vicinity.

In multicylinder engines, it is critical that the high-pressure pipes be of equal length and identical bores. Small variations in length or bore size can substantially alter injection timing and unbalance engine performance. High-pressure pipe nuts at both the injector and injection pump ends should always be torqued to specification. When attempting to locate a cylinder misfire, technicians sequentially crack the high-pressure pipe nuts in a procedure known as "shorting out injectors." In practice, where no torque wrench is used, the result is usually overtorquing—this has the effect of crushing the sealing nipple of the high-pressure pipe and reducing flow through the line. The nipple sealing seats on high-pressure pipes should be inspected for ridging and aperture (bore) size at each removal. It should also be noted that this condition can result in low power and/or unbalanced fuel delivery.

> **TECH TIP:**
> Always use the engine OEM's specification, a line socket, and torque wrench to torque line nuts. A common cause of low-power complaints is collapsed nipple seats due to overtorquing, which reduces the line flow area.

EHI TESTING AND RECONDITIONING

Until 2007, troubleshooting EHIs was usually a matter of using OEM software to identify a malfunctioning injector, then replacing the defective unit. However, the proliferation of CR fuel systems in the industry, along with their susceptibility to problems related to fuel impurities, have resulted in an extensive repair infrastructure. In many cases, this has revived diesel fuel injection specialty shops that were in danger of extinction.

Most truck service facilities have focused on the accurate diagnosis of EHI failures rather than the repair of the injectors, leaving that to the specialty shops. The approach in this chapter will be to take a look at some of the methods used to diagnose malfunctions rather than to outline repair procedures. In doing this, we will look at some of the latest diagnostic equipment preferred by truck shops.

REASONS EHIs FAIL

A high percentage of EHI failures are related to fuel quality, especially contaminants that find their way into fuel. Accordingly, the incidence of failures tends to be much higher in geographical areas where fuel quality is suspect. Caught early, bad fuel may require only disassembly, cleaning, and reassembly of the EHI. However, fuel-related problems are seldom caught early. Once the EHI has been diagnosed as defective, the internal subcomponents are subject to damage. Some recent Bosch research classifying EHI failures produced the following data:

Valve seat failure	35%
Nozzle assembly failure	30%
High-pressure sealing failure	25%
Actuator assembly failure	5%
Armature set failure	3%
Body failure	2%

PROPRIETARY TESTING OF EHIs

The procedure for testing EHIs in-engine requires using manufacturer electronic service tools (ESTs) and software-driven diagnostic routines. The initial objective is to identify a defective EHI so it can be removed for further diagnosis, followed by replacement or repair. Each OEM outlines a number of in-engine diagnostic tests, such as measuring leak-off volumes and capping individual lines; however, exercise caution when undertaking these tests, because they tend to be OEM-specific. Consult the OEM online service literature for the specific engine you are working on before assuming that a test that you undertake on a MaxxForce engine will be OK on a Cummins—even though the injectors may be identical.

After an EHI has been condemned in-engine, there are a number of OEM and generic test benches that may be used to identify the specific problem. Although most OEMs state that their proprietary service equipment is required to repair their EHIs, this is not really the case, because there are good generically manufactured alternatives. Bosch recommends the following test benches to test its CR pumps and EHIs:

- Test Bench EPS 200—tests EHIs only
- Test Bench EPS 708—tests Bosch CR pumps (CP1, CP3, CP4) and EHIs, including those with piezo actuators
- EPS 815—tests all Bosch, Siemens (including HEUI), and Denso/Continental CR pumps and EHIs

EPS is a German language acronym. **Figure 21–12** shows a simple Bosch EPS 200 bench-test fixture; this will test the basic functionality of

EHIs. To do more than this, a Bosch EPS 708 is required. This can test CR EHIs at up to 2,500 bar, including EHIs with piezo actuators. The bench is simple to use. The EHI is placed in bench fixture and run through a test sequence. The EPS 708 software environment is Windows managed and the bench is equipped with a 19-inch light-emitting diode (LED) display. The software is known as EPS and the versions are numerically categorized and Web downloadable.

GENERIC TESTING OF EHIs

There are a number of aftermarket test fixtures designed exclusively for testing EHIs, varying from the simple DieseLogic test bench fixture shown in **Figure 21–13** to the more comprehensive test benches shown in the photo sequence that follows. In all cases, the procedure is software-driven, so testing involves little more than simply following instructions. At the conclusion of the test sequence, the results leave no doubt to how they should be interpreted. The outcome can be one of:

- OK
- Not OK

FIGURE 21–12 Bosch EPS 200 EHI test unit.

FIGURE 21–13 DieseLogic computerized EHI test bench fixture.

Photo Sequence 3

BENCH TESTING A COMMON RAIL (CR) ELECTROHYDRAULIC INJECTOR (EHI)

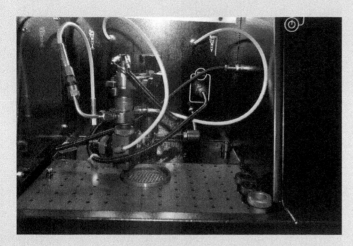

PS3–1 Mount the injector into the test fixture. Plumb in the fuel lines. Connect the electrical terminals.

PS3–3 Test step one. This is the warmup phase and may take a little time. The test fuel temperature is warmed to specification and the EHI is fired to ensure that the actuator responds appropriately to trigger voltages.

PS3–2 Run the pretest. This verifies that the EHI is properly plumbed into the test fixture and responds electronically to ECM-driven triggers. Any anomaly will trigger a repair/remediation instruction.

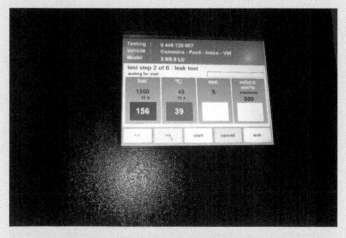

PS3–4 Test step two. Leak test. The EHI is charged with typical rail pressures. It is then checked for both internal and external leakage.

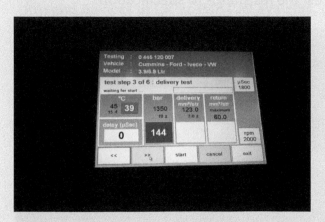

PS3-5 Test step three. The first of two delivery tests. This verifies fuel flow at a specific test rail fuel pressure on the high side.

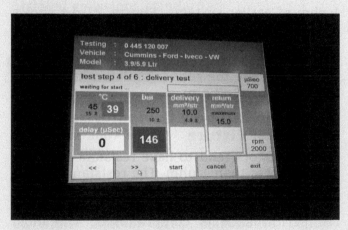

PS3-6 Test step four. The second delivery test. This verifies fuel flow at a specific test rail fuel pressure on the low side.

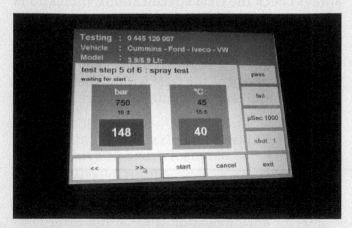

PS3-7 Test step five. Spray test. Verifies that there are no abnormalities in the spray geometry. An abnormality could be caused by a restricted or coked injector orifice.

PS3-8 Test step six. Option to report. In this step, technicians will address a field in which they can choose to report the data gleaned from the test. This may be display only, printable, or networkable.

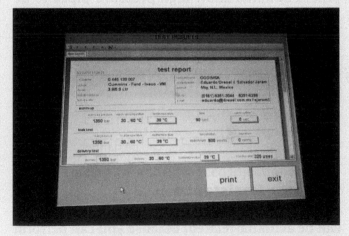

PS3-9 View report fields. This will display the test data and provide an option to print it. The result is always binary: OK or Not OK.

8. What is the distinguishing feature of a VCO nozzle?
   a. The sac is eliminated
   b. High spring location
   c. Low spring location
   d. Used only in IDI engines

9. What type of fuel injector nozzles are required on almost all on-highway diesel engines that are certified for EPA 2010?
   a. Poppet
   b. Hydraulic multiple orifice
   c. Electrohydraulic
   d. Pintle

10. Which of the following resistance values indicates a typical within-specification value for a current EHI solenoid actuator?
    a. 1 ohm
    b. 5 ohms
    c. 10 ohms
    d. 1,000 ohms

11. Technician A states that hydraulic injector nozzles are designed so that the pressure required to open the nozzle valve is greater than the pressure required to hold it open. Technician B states that after NOP, the nozzle line pressure steadily decreases until the nozzle closes at the end of the injection pulse. Who is correct?
    a. Technician A only
    b. Technician B only
    c. Both A and B
    d. Neither A nor B

12. Nozzle differential ratio is a ratio of:
    a. nozzle seat sectional area and total nozzle sectional area.
    b. the high-pressure pipe sectional area and the orifii flow area.
    c. the nozzle pressure chamber sectional area and the high-pressure pipe sectional area.
    d. the mechanical spring force and hydraulic pressure.

13. Which of the following factors does most to prevent secondary injections?
    a. Pressure wave reflection
    b. Nozzle differential ratio
    c. The nozzle sac
    d. The pressure chamber sectional area

14. Which of the following is another way of stating the NOP specification?
    a. Not operating properly
    b. Residual line pressure
    c. Peak pressure
    d. Popping pressure

15. Most diesel engine OEMs recommend that injectors be installed into the cylinder head injector bore:
    a. dry.
    b. coated with engine oil.
    c. coated with Never-Seize.
    d. coated with lubriplate.

16. Technician A states that when a hydraulic multi-orifii injector is used in an electronically managed fuel system, nozzle opening and closing are switched hydraulically. Technician B says that the opening and closing of an EHI are controlled by the ECM. Who is correct?
    a. Technician A only
    b. Technician B only
    c. Both A and B
    d. Neither A nor B

17. Excessive fuel returned into the leak-off lines from a set of hydraulic injector nozzles is an indication of:
    a. nozzle seat leakage.
    b. wear in the nozzle-body-to-nozzle-valve fit.
    c. wear in the nozzle seat.
    d. a weak injector spring.

18. Technician A states that EHI injector nozzles using solenoid actuators should test at resistance values of 1 ohm or less. Technician B states that EHIs using the most common type of piezoelectric actuators should test at resistance values of 0.6 ohms or less. Who is correct?
    a. Technician A only
    b. Technician B only
    c. Both A and B
    d. Neither A nor B

19. Technician A states that the injector nozzles used on pre-2007 EUIs and HEUIs use the same operating principles as those on any hydraulic pump-line-nozzle system. Technician B states that hydraulic injector nozzles use a soft value NOP. Who is correct?
    a. Technician A only
    b. Technician B only
    c. Both A and B
    d. Neither A nor B

20. Which of the following types of injectors would be best suited to multipulse injection?
    a. Hydraulic poppet
    b. Hydraulic multi-orifii
    c. EHI with solenoid actuator
    d. EHI with piezoelectric actuator

22

Prerequisites: Chapters 19, 20, and 21

PORT-HELIX METERING INJECTION PUMPS

OBJECTIVES

After studying this chapter, you should be able to:

- Identify the major components in a typical port-helix metering injection pump.
- Explain the principles of operation of an inline, port-helix metering injection pump.
- Define the terms *effective stroke, port closure, port opening, NOP, residual line pressure,* and *peak pressure.*
- Explain how the pump element components create injection pressures.
- Define *metering* and the factors that control it.
- Identify the differences between hydromechanical and electronically controlled versions of port-helix metering injection pumps.
- Explain the operation of aneroid devices, altitude compensators, and variable timing/ timing advance mechanisms.
- Time an injection pump to an engine using spill timing, pin timing, or electronic timing devices.
- Outline the operating principles of electronically controlled versions of inline port-helix metering injection pumps.
- Describe the functions of a Bosch rack actuator housing in electronically controlled versions of port-helix metering injection pumps.
- Time a Bosch electronic PE pump to an engine using the appropriate timing tool.

KEY TERMS

altitude compensator	calibration	control sleeve	effective stroke
aneroid	cambox	dead volume fuel	ELAB
bar	camshaft	delivery valve	electronic control unit (ECU)
barometric capsule	charging pressure	double helix	
barrel	charging pump	dual helices	flutes
boosted engines	control rack	Econovance	fuel control actuator

fuel injection control (FIC)	plunger geometry	rack actuator housing	static timing
helix/helices	plunger leading edge	rack position sensor	tappets
high-pressure pipe	port closure	reference coil	timing actuator
linear magnet	port opening	register	timing event marker (TEM)
lower helix	proportional solenoid	residual line pressure	
metering recesses	pump drive gear	retraction collar/piston	transfer pump
phasing	pump-line-nozzle (PLN)	retraction spring	upper helix
plunger	rack actuator	spill timing	vials

INTRODUCTION

The first high-pressure liquid fuel injection to a high-speed diesel combustion chamber was developed in 1927 by Robert Bosch. This evolved into the **pump-line-nozzle (PLN)** fuel pumps used by Caterpillar, Mack, Navistar, Deere, Volvo, and other diesel engine manufacturers into the 1990s in on-highway and well into this century in off-highway applications. In fact, inline port-helix metering pumps continue to be used to fuel engines under 70 horsepower (52 kW) and in applications where there are fewer regulations, such as marine propulsion and generating engines.

The principles of pumping and metering a fuel charge have changed little since Bosch's first 1927 high-pressure injection pump. However, the last generation of port-helix (*helix*: scroll shaped) metering injection pumps—those certified for Environmental Protection Agency (EPA) on-highway emissions up until 1997—was managed electronically. Port-helix metering fuel pumps lived on after 1997 in off-highway equipment, but in recent years off-road and highway emissions standards have come close to converging. If you see a port-helix metering pump on any engine manufactured after 2011, it will usually be on an off- highway application of 70 horsepower or less, or in a marine or stationary application.

The last generation of port-helix metering injection pumps used on North American highways was managed electronically. This did not change the basic operating principles, but the hydromechanical controls were upgraded for computerized management. Electronic controls enabled PLN pump technology to have a short afterlife into the electronic age. The challenge to PLN diesel fueling was more complex than merely being able to comply with emissions standards. Newer engines designed in the electronic age were not only meeting emissions standards but also achieving much better fuel economy.

This chapter describes the port-helix metering pumps engineered and manufactured by Bosch, Delphi-Lucas, and Caterpillar and used on Caterpillar, Mack, Cummins, Navistar, John Deere, Volvo, and other older highway and off-highway diesel engine applications. **Figure 22-1** shows a Bosch port-helix metering injection pump with sectional views of the front two pump elements. **Figure 22-2** is a schematic showing how to interpret a Bosch injection pump serial number.

In this chapter we will study both the hydromechanical and electronically controlled versions of port-helix metering pumps, beginning with those that use no computer controls. Although a much less common sight today, these PLN systems will live on for a while longer, especially in off-highway applications, because of the large volumes of heritage equipment in existence.

TECHNICAL DESCRIPTION

The typical port-helix metering pump used to fuel a diesel engine is inline configured and flange mounted to an engine accessory drive. The pump is driven through one complete rotation (360 degrees) per complete engine cycle (720 degrees). The internal pump components are housed in a frame constructed of cast aluminum, cast iron, or forged steel. The engine crankshaft drives the injection pump by means of timed reduction gearing. The gear-driven pump drive plate is connected to the injection pump **camshaft** (the fuel pump shaft fitted with eccentrics designed to actuate the pump elements), so rotating the pump

FIGURE 22–1 Inline, port-helix metering injection pump components.

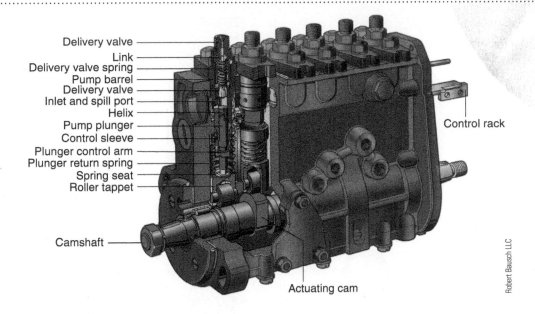

Delivery valve
Link
Delivery valve spring
Pump barrel
Delivery valve
Inlet and spill port
Helix
Pump plunger
Control sleeve
Plunger control arm
Plunger return spring
Spring seat
Roller tappet

Control rack

Camshaft

Actuating cam

Robert Bausch LLC

FIGURE 22–2 Interpreting a Bosch injection pump serial number.

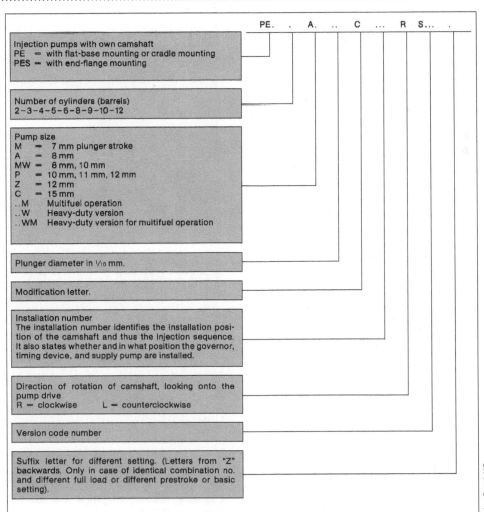

PE. . A. . . C . . . R S . . . .

Injection pumps with own camshaft
PE = with flat-base mounting or cradle mounting
PES = with end-flange mounting

Number of cylinders (barrels)
2–3–4–5–6–8–9–10–12

Pump size
M = 7 mm plunger stroke
A = 8 mm
MW = 8 mm, 10 mm
P = 10 mm, 11 mm, 12 mm
Z = 12 mm
C = 15 mm
..M Multifuel operation
..W Heavy-duty version
..WM Heavy-duty version for multifuel operation

Plunger diameter in 1/10 mm.

Modification letter.

Installation number
The installation number identifies the installation position of the camshaft and thus the injection sequence.
It also states whether and in what position the governor,
timing device, and supply pump are installed.

Direction of rotation of camshaft, looking onto the
pump drive
R = clockwise   L = counterclockwise

Version code number

Suffix letter for different setting. (Letters from "Z"
backwards. Only in case of identical combination no.
and different full load or different prestroke or basic
setting).

Robert Bausch LLC

FIGURE 22–3 Actuating a port-helix type pump element.

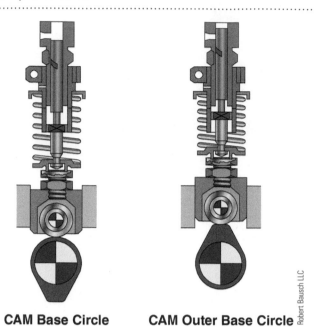

CAM Base Circle   CAM Outer Base Circle

Robert Bausch LLC

FIGURE 22–4 Actuating cam geometry.

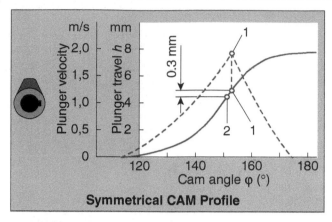

Symmetrical CAM Profile

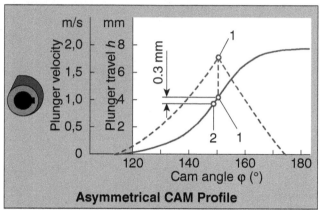

Asymmetrical CAM Profile

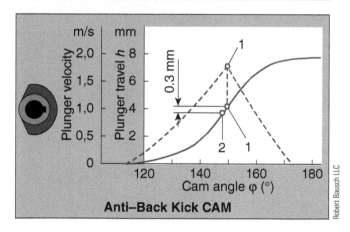

Anti–Back Kick CAM

Robert Bausch LLC

drive plate rotates the pump camshaft. The camshaft is supported by main bearings and rotates within the injection pump **cambox**. The cambox is the lower portion of the injection pump that houses the camshaft, **tappets**, and an integral oil sump. A sectional view of a port-helix pump element and its actuating cam is shown in **Figure 22–3**. The actuating cam geometry (see **Figure 22–4**) comes in three basic designs:

- Symmetrical (mostly inner base circle [IBC] design)
- Asymmetrical (around 50% inner, 50% outer base circle [OBC])
- Anti–back kick (mostly OBC)

Each pumping element is actuated by a dedicated cam profile on the pump camshaft. Riding each cam profile is a tappet assembly driving a pump element consisting of a **plunger** and a **barrel**. The barrel is stationary and drilled with two ports in its upper portion, which are exposed to the fuel charging gallery.

FUEL ROUTING

The fuel gallery is charged with low-pressure fuel, typically between 15 and 75 psi (1 and 5 **bar**). This charging pressure fuel flows into and through the barrel ports when they are not obstructed by the plunger. The plunger

reciprocates within the barrel; it is loaded by spring pressure to ride its actuating cam profile. Therefore, actual plunger stroke is constant. Plunger-to-barrel tolerances are close, the components being lapped in manufacture to a tolerance of 2 μ to 4 μ, or laser micromachined for even greater precision. Fuel quantity to be delivered in each stroke is controlled by managing plunger **effective stroke** (see **Figure 22–5**, **Figure 22–6**, **Figure 22–7**, and **Figure 22–8**).

FIGURE 22–5 Port closure.

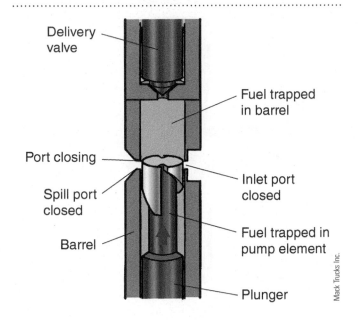

Delivery valve

Fuel trapped in barrel

Port closing

Inlet port closed

Spill port closed

Fuel trapped in pump element

Barrel

Plunger

Mack Trucks Inc.

FIGURE 22–7 Port opening.

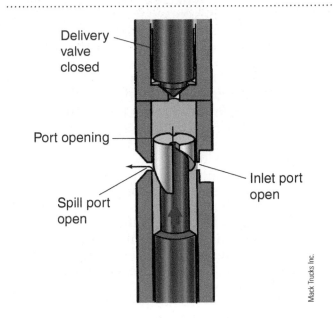

Delivery valve closed

Port opening

Inlet port open

Spill port open

Mack Trucks Inc.

FIGURE 22–6 Effective stroke.

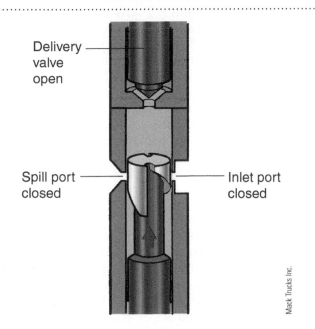

Delivery valve open

Spill port closed

Inlet port closed

Mack Trucks Inc.

FIGURE 22–8 Plunger travel through the effective stroke.

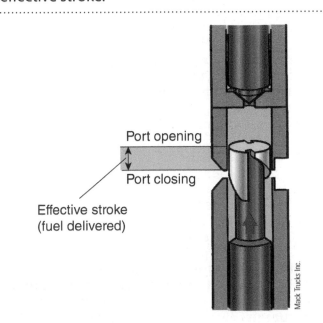

Port opening

Port closing

Effective stroke (fuel delivered)

Mack Trucks Inc.

Pump Element Design

Each plunger is milled with a vertical slot or cross and center drillings and helical recesses. The function of the vertical slot or cross and center drillings is to maintain a constant conduit between the pumping chamber above the plunger and the helical recesses. In other words, whatever pressures exist in the pumping chamber must also exist in the helical recess. Initially, only plunger designs with a **lower helix** or **helices**

are discussed. The plungers are actuated by cam profiles. Therefore, the amount and how they move depends on the shape of the cam profile.

The barrel is the stationary member of the pump element. Each is positioned in the charging gallery of the fuel pump and drilled with fill and spill ports. This allows the pump chamber inside the barrel to be filled with fuel at the charging pressure at any time the top of the plunger is below the spill ports.

EFFECTIVE STROKE

Effective stroke describes the delivery stroke. The delivery stroke begins when the plunger is forced upward by cam profile and the **plunger leading edge** (uppermost part of the plunger) traps off the spill port(s). As the plunger rises through its stroke in the barrel after trapping off the spill port, rapid pressure rise occurs, creating the required injection pressures. The precise moment that begins effective stroke is known as **port closure** (Figure 22–5). It is of critical importance to the diesel technician because its precise setting is used to control ignition timing. As pressure rises (Figure 22–6) in the pump chamber, it acts first on a **delivery valve**; next on the fuel confined in the high-pressure pipe, transmitting fuel to the injector nozzle; and, finally, delivering a fuel pulse to the engine cylinder. Effective stroke ends at **port opening** (Figure 22–7). This is the precise moment that the upward travel of the plunger exposes the helical recess(es) to the spill port. High-pressure fuel is spilled back to the charging gallery, causing a rapid collapse of pressure in the pump chamber, line, and nozzle.

Collapse Phase

The injection pulse ceases when there is no longer sufficient pressure to hold the delivery and nozzle valves open. Port opening always occurs while the plunger is moving in an upward direction, that is, not at plunger top dead center (TDC) or beyond. This is required because the pressure in a port-helix pump element is designed to rise through the delivery stroke, thereby producing smaller atomized droplets from the injector toward the end of the effective stroke; however, at the point of port opening, regardless of the length of the effective stroke, pump pressure should collapse as rapidly as possible and minimize the larger droplets emitted from the injector as pump pressure falls to a value below nozzle opening pressure (NOP).

Control of Effective Stroke

The length of plunger effective stroke (Figure 22–8) depends on where the plunger helix **registers** (vertically aligns) with the spill port. **Control sleeves** lugged to the plunger permit the plunger to be rotated while reciprocating. Rotating the plunger in the bore of the barrel changes the location of register of the spill port with the helix. Therefore, plunger effective stroke depends entirely on the rotational position of the

FIGURE 22–9 Control rack and sleeve gear.

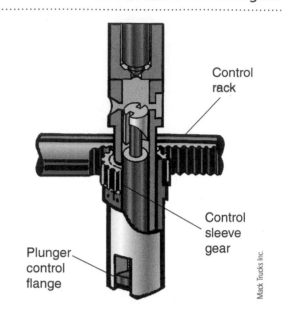

plunger. In multiple cylinder engines, the plungers must be synchronized to move in unison to ensure balanced fueling at any given engine load.

The control sleeves are tooth meshed to a governor **control rack**, which when moved linearly, rotates the plungers in unison (**Figure 22–9**). This is important. It means that in any linear position of the rack, all of the plungers will have identical points of register with their spill points, resulting in identical pump effective strokes. The consequence of not doing this would be to unbalance the fueling of the engine, that is, to deliver different quantities of fuel to each cylinder.

No-Fuel

Engine shutdown is achieved by moving the control rack to the no-fuel position. The rotational position of the plungers is now such that the vertical slot will be in register with the spill port for the entirety of plunger travel; the plunger will merely displace fuel as it travels upward, with no pumping action possible. In other words, as the plunger is driven into the pump chamber, the fuel in the chamber will be squeezed back down the vertical slot to exit through the spill port and return to the charging gallery (**Figure 22–10**). **Figure 22–11** shows the relationship between control rack linear position and plunger effective stroke.

Most port-helix metering injection pumps use delivery valves to reduce the amount of work required of each pump element per cycle. Delivery valves function to isolate the high-pressure

FIGURE 22–10 Rack position and relationship to fuel delivery quantity.

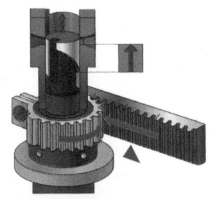

**Full Fuel
Maximum Effective Stroke**

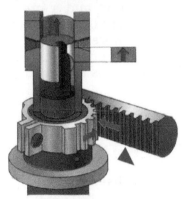

**Medium Fuel
Partial Effective Stroke**

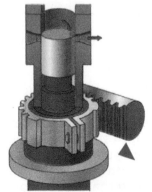

**No Fuel Rotational Position
No Effective Stroke**

Robert Bausch LLC

FIGURE 22–11 Typical delivery valve assemblies in closed and open positions.

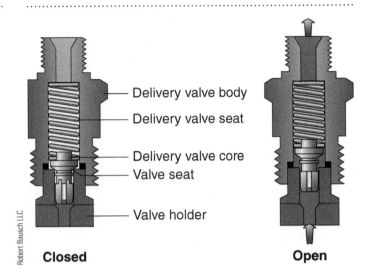

Robert Bausch LLC

— Delivery valve body
— Delivery valve seat
— Delivery valve core
— Valve seat
— Valve holder

Closed　　　　　　　　　**Open**

Residual Line Pressure

Dead volume fuel is retained at a pressure necessarily somewhat below the NOP value; the high-speed hydraulic switching that occurs in the high-pressure circuit creates pressure wave reflections, which may have the effect of spiking (causing surges in) line pressures. To ensure that these pressure spikes do not exceed the NOP value and cause secondary injections, the dead volume fuel is retained at about two-thirds of the NOP value; this is known as **residual line pressure**.

Role of Delivery Valve

The delivery valve is loaded into its closed position on its seat by a spring and by the residual line pressure. If, for whatever reason, the residual line pressure value were zero, hydraulic pressure of around 300 psi (20 bar) would have to be developed in the pump element to overcome the mechanical force of the spring. This mechanical force is therefore compounded when the residual line pressure acts on the sectional area represented by the delivery valve and establishes the pressure value that must be developed in the pump chamber before it is unseated.

The delivery valve **flutes** provide a means of guiding the valve in its bore while permitting hydraulic access between the **retraction collar** or **retraction piston** (both terms are used) and the pump chamber (plunger and barrel assembly). The retraction collar (see **Figure 22–12**) seals the pump chamber from the dead volume

circuit that extends from the injection pump chamber to the seat of the nozzle valve. Fuel retained in the **high-pressure pipes** (pipes or lines that connect the injection pump elements with hydraulic injectors) between pumping pulses is known as **dead volume fuel**.

FIGURE 22–12 Delivery valve core terminology.

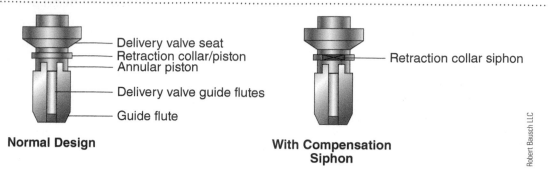

Robert Bausch LLC

fuel, which is retained at a higher pressure value. Consequently, when the delivery valve is first unseated, it is driven upward in its bore by rising pressure in the pump chamber and acts as a plunger driving inward onto the fuel retained in the high-pressure pipe.

The moment the retraction collar clears the delivery valve seat, fuel in the injection pump chamber and that in the high-pressure pipe unite and the injection pump plunger is driven into a volume of fuel that extends from the plunger to the nozzle valve seat. Rising pressure subsequently unseats the injector nozzle valve (NOP) and forces atomized fuel into the engine cylinder.

At port opening, the effective pump stroke ends, beginning a rapid pressure collapse as fuel spills from the barrel spill port. When there is insufficient pressure in the pump chamber to hold the nozzle valve in its open position, spring pressure overcomes hydraulic pressure and the nozzle valve seats, sealing the nozzle end of the high-pressure pipe. Almost simultaneously, the delivery valve begins to retract. The instant the retraction collar passes the delivery valve seat, it hydraulically seals the pump end of the high-pressure circuit. However, after sealing the pump end of the high-pressure circuit, the delivery valve must travel farther before it seats, increasing the volume available for dead volume fuel storage. This causes a drop in line pressure and defines the residual line pressure value.

In short, the volume available for fuel storage in the high-pressure pipe is increased by the swept volume of the retraction collar. This volume of fuel is known as *dead volume fuel* and is retained at residual line pressure. Retraction collar swept volume is matched to the length of the high-pressure pipe to achieve a precise residual line pressure value, so that pipe length should not be altered.

Most delivery valves are of the constant volume type described here. However, some fuel systems have a constant pressure delivery valve that consists of a forward delivery valve in the forward flow direction and a pressure holding valve (spring and ball) in the reverse flow direction. This rather more complex valve design helps minimize the effects of pressure wave reflection, which causes wear and cavitation.

INJECTION PUMP COMPONENTS

The following is a list of subcomponents that, assembled, will form a typical port-helix metering injection pump.

PUMP HOUSING

The *pump housing* is the frame that encases all the injection pump components and is a cast-aluminum, cast-iron, or forged-steel enclosure. The pump housing is usually flange mounted by bolts to the engine cylinder block to be driven by an accessory drive on the engine geartrain. In some offshore applications of inline, port-helix metering injection pumps, the pump assembly is cradle mounted on its base, in which case it is driven by an external shaft from the timing geartrain.

CAM BOX

The cam box is the lower portion of the pump housing incorporating the lubricating oil sump and main mounting bores for the pump camshaft. Camshaft main bearings are usually pressure-lubed by engine oil supplied from the engine crankcase, and the cam box sump level is determined by the positioning of a return port. In older injection pumps, the pump oil was isolated from the main engine lubricant, and the oil was subject to periodic checks and servicing.

Camshaft

The camshaft is designed with a cam profile for each engine cylinder and supported by main bearings at the base of the pump housing. It is driven at one-half engine rotational speed in a four-stroke cycle engine by the pump drive plate, which is itself either coupled directly to the **pump drive gear** or to a variable timing device. Camshaft actuating profiles are usually symmetrical (that is, geometrically similar on both sides of the toe) and mostly inner base circle (IBC: the smallest radial dimension of an eccentric) in profile, though asymmetrical (the geometry of each cam ramp or flank differs) and mostly outer base circle (OBC: the largest radial dimension of an eccentric) designs are used. For a full explanation of cam geometry, refer to Chapter 8.

TAPPETS

The tappets are arranged to ride the cam profile and convert the rotary motion of the camshaft to the reciprocating action required of the plunger. A **retraction spring** is integral with the tappet assembly. This is required to load the tappet and plunger assembly to ride the cam profile, and it is necessarily large enough to overcome the low pressure (vacuum) established in the pump chamber on the plunger return stroke. This low pressure can be considerable when plunger effective strokes are long, but it enables a rapid recharge of the pump chamber with fuel from the charging gallery. The time dimension within which the pump element must be recharged decreases proportionately with pump rpm increase.

BARREL

The *barrel* is the stationary member of the pump element, located in the pump housing so its upper portion is exposed to the charging gallery. This upper portion of the barrel is drilled with diametrically opposed ports known as *inlet* and *spill ports* that permit through flow of fuel to the barrel chamber to be charged. Because it contains the spill ports, both its height and rotational position in relation to the plunger are critical. Barrels are often manufactured with upper

flanges so that their relative heights can be adjusted by means of shims, and fastener slots permit axial movement for purposes of **calibration** and **phasing** (the procedures of calibration and phasing are covered in more detail later in this chapter).

Plunger

Plungers are the reciprocating (something that reciprocates, moves backward and forward such as in the action of a piston in an engine cylinder) members of the pump elements, and they are spring-loaded to ride their actuating cam's profile. Plungers are lapped to the barrel in manufacture to a clearance close to 2 μ, ensuring controlled back leakage directed toward a viscous seal consisting of an annular groove and return duct in the barrel. Each plunger is milled with a vertical slot, helical recess(es), and annular groove. In truck engine applications, a lower helix design was generally used, but both **upper helix** and **dual helices** designs are sometimes used.

Plunger Geometry

The positioning and shape of the **helices** (plural of **helix**) on a plunger are often described as the **plunger geometry**. Plunger geometry describes the physical shape of the **metering recesses** machined into the plunger, and this defines the injection timing characteristics. The function of the vertical slot is to ensure a constant hydraulic connection between the pump chamber above the plunger and the plunger helical recess(es).

Timing and Plunger Geometry

A plunger with a lower helix will have a constant beginning, variable ending of delivery timing characteristic, whereas an upper helix design will be of the variable beginning, constant ending type. When port-helix metering injection pumps were used in truck applications, lower helix plunger geometry was used: An external means of varying port closure timing was used in these pumps. **Double helix** designs have both an upper and a lower helix and a variable beginning and variable ending of delivery; this geometric design tends not to be used often in highway diesel engines. Another, perhaps more common, plunger design is the dual helices design—identically shaped helices are machined into the plunger, diametrically opposite each other. Plungers with diametrically opposed helices were used in more recent high-pressure injection pumps to provide hydraulic balance to the pump element; specifically, this design prevents the side loading of the plunger into the barrel wall that may occur at high-pressure spill-off.

A further feature of some plungers is a start retard notch. Start retard notches are milled recesses in the leading edge of plungers with lower helix geometry. The start retard notch is usually on the opposite side of the vertical slot from the helix and in a position that would correlate close to a full-fuel effective stroke; the governor or **rack actuator** of the injection pump is designed to permit the start retard notch to register with the spill port only at cranking speeds (under 300 rpm) and with the accelerator fully depressed.

The objective of the start retard notch on a lower helix design plunger is to retard the injection pulse until there is a maximum amount of heat in the engine cylinder, usually when the piston is close to top dead center (TDC). The instant the engine exceeds 300 rpm, it becomes impossible for the start retard notch to register with the spill port. Figure 22–10 illustrates the delay produced when the start retard notch is positioned in register with spill port(s).

RACK AND CONTROL SLEEVES

The rack and control sleeves permit the plungers in a multicylinder engine to be rotated in unison to ensure balanced fuel delivery to each cylinder. Plungers must therefore be timed either directly or indirectly to the control rack. The rack is a toothed rod that extends into the governor or **rack actuator housing**. The rack teeth mesh with teeth on plunger control sleeves, which are either lugged or clamped to the plunger. It must be possible to rotate the plungers while they reciprocate, to permit changes in fuel requirements while the engine is running. Linear movement of the rack will rotate the plungers in unison, alter the point of register of the helices with their respective spill ports, and thereby control engine fueling. Timing of the plungers to the control rack is the means used to adjust the effective stroke in individual pump elements, in a procedure known as *calibration*.

This timing procedure is effected either directly, by adjusting the relationship of the plunger with the rack; or indirectly, by adjusting the rotational position of the barrel and therefore its relationship with the plunger geometry. The means of calibrating an injection pump depends on the make and model.

DELIVERY VALVES

Delivery valves isolate the high-pressure circuit that extends from the injection pump chamber to the seat of the injector nozzle valve. They act somewhat like check valves. Because they seal before they seat, they permit line pressure to drop to a residual value well below the NOP value, and this helps prevent secondary injections. The delivery valve is machined with a seat, retraction collar, and flutes to guide it in the bore of the delivery valve body (see Figure 22–12).

CHARGING PUMPS

The terms **charging pump** and **transfer pump** are used interchangeably, depending on the original equipment manufacturer (OEM). The charging pump is responsible for all fuel movement in the fuel subsystem. In truck applications using port-helix metering injection, the charging pump is normally a plunger pump flange mounted to the fuel injection pump and actuated by a dedicated eccentric on the injection pump camshaft. The charging or transfer pump is responsible for producing **charging pressure**.

Charging pressures range from 15 to 75 psi (1 to 5 bar) depending on the system. The role of charging/transfer pumps is dealt with in greater detail in the context of the fuel subsystem, the subject of Chapter 18.

GOVERNOR OR RACK ACTUATOR HOUSING

Either a governor or a rack actuator housing must be incorporated with a port-helix metering injection pump. This acts as the control mechanism for managing fueling.

The only factor that determines the output of a diesel engine is the amount of fuel metered into its cylinders. Given unlimited fuel, a diesel engine is capable of accelerating at a rate of 1,000 rpm per second until self-destruction occurs. To prevent such an "engine runaway" and to provide the engine with a measure of protection from abuse to ensure that it meets the manufacturer's expectations of longevity, fuel quantity delivered to the engine cylinders must be precisely managed under all operating conditions. The fuel control mechanism on a port-helix metering injection pump is the rack. Therefore, the governor or rack actuator controls engine fueling by precise positioning of the rack.

Hydromechanical governors are not used to manage medium- and heavy-duty, on-highway diesel engines sold after 1998. On older engines, they consist of a self-contained housing mounted to the rear of the injection pump. In a simple mechanical governor, the vehicle accelerator linkage connects to a throttle arm or governor input lever located on the side of the governor housing. Enclosed within the governor housing, a weight carrier is mounted to the rear of the camshaft. Flyweights are mounted in the weight carrier, which is loaded inboard by spring force.

Governor Operation

As the camshaft rotates, centrifugal force acting on the flyweights thrusts them outward. The faster the rotational speed, the more centrifugal force is generated. Countering the centrifugal force generated by the flyweights is an accumulation of spring forces. The amount of spring force is usually variable and is increased as the accelerator arm is moved. A thrust collar acts as an intermediary (that is, something in between two other components) between the mechanical force of the spring(s) and the centrifugal force generated by the flyweights. The fuel control mechanism or rack is connected to the thrust collar. Spring force acting on the thrust collar attempts to increase engine fueling. Centrifugal force acts in opposition to the spring force and attempts to diminish engine fueling.

Maximum engine speed is defined by ensuring that at a set speed, the centrifugal force generated by the flyweights will overcome any amount of spring force the governor can counter it with. Even the simplest mechanical governor suitable for managing a highway truck engine will define idle speed, rated speed, and the droop curve (graduated engine defueling as engine speed rises from rated speed to the high-idle speed), leaving intermediate speed selection to the operator. A simple governor may also provide torque rise fuel enhancement and an **aneroid** (light pressure sensing device) to sense manifold boost and limit fueling until manifold pressure achieves a predetermined value.

Two main categories of hydromechanical governor exist. The first is the LS or limiting speed governor, which defines idle and high-idle engine speeds, leaving the intermediate speed ranges to the operator. The second category is the variable speed governor, in which throttle arm position (angle) defines an engine rpm value; the governor then attempts to maintain this speed while engine loading varies.

Hydromechanical governors are not capable of managing today's high-power engines that must achieve statutory and customer requirements of low-emissions operation and high fuel economy. They have seldom been used since 1997 in on-highway diesel engines; however, they can occasionally be seen in off-highway diesel engines up to EPA year 2011, and may still be found in sectors of low regulation. However, they continue to be widely used on diesel engines rated at 70 horsepower (52 kW) or less, so they are commonly used on reefer engines. Governor operating principles are looked at in some detail in Chapter 20.

Rack Actuator Operation

When the port-helix metering injection pump is managed by a computer, engine governing depends on how the electronic control module (ECM) is programmed. The governor housing attached to the rear of the injection pump is replaced by a rack actuator housing consisting of switched ECM output devices and sensors. The housing contains a rack actuator, either a linear magnet (proportional solenoid) controlled directly by the ECM or an electric-over-hydraulic device (engine oil acts as the hydraulic medium) that is also ECM controlled. The rack actuator sets rack position on ECM command and nothing more.

A **rack position sensor** reports the exact rack position to the ECM. Additionally, the rack actuator housing may house other sensors to report rotational speed (pulse wheel fitted to the rear of the camshaft), engine position, and timing data to the ECM. Rack actuator housings are not governors. Where a rack actuator housing is fitted to an inline, port-helix metering injection pump, the engine governing functions are undertaken by the software programmed into the fuel management ECM.

Electronic governing offers infinitely improved control over engine fueling, and it allows OEMs to meet a higher level of statutory noxious emissions requirements and achieve better fuel economy. Additionally, it can easily be programmed/reprogrammed with customer data to tailor the engine for varying engine and chassis applications.

LUBRICATION

The lower portion of the port-helix metering injection pump is lubricated by engine oil. In older versions, the injection pump lubricating circuit was often isolated from that of the engine, and the lube level would be checked and replenished through a dipstick located in the cambox. Contemporary injection pumps tend to be plumbed into the main engine lubricating circuit. The camshaft main bearings are often pressure-lubed directly from an engine oil gallery, and the remainder of the cambox components are splash-lubricated from the oil held in the sump.

The upper portion of the injection pump is lubricated by the diesel fuel being pumped through the charging gallery, so the lubricity of the diesel fuel is critical. Compromising the lubricating qualities of the fuel may cause premature failure and/or leakage, and some manufacturers have reported such problems following the introduction of low-sulfur, low-lubricity fuels mandated by EPA standards. It is critical for the operation of both the fuel injection pump and the engine it manages that the fuel used to lubricate the upper portion of the pump never come into contact with the engine oil in the cambox. Plunger-to-barrel clearance is lapped in manufacture to a minute tolerance, and fuel that leaks by the recessed metering areas bleeds to an annular belt in the barrel.

A duct connects the annular belt in the barrel to the charging gallery, permitting bleed-by fuel to be routed there. This is known as a *viscous seal.* Trace leakage of a viscous seal can rapidly cause engine oil contamination and lead to lubricant breakdown. Viscous seals fail due to plunger-side loading (single helix design), prolonged usage wear, and fuel contaminants—especially water. Fuel that bleeds by the metering recesses flowing to the annular belt guides the plunger true in the barrel bore, minimizing metal-to-metal contact. When studying the results of engine oil analysis, it should be remembered that failure of the injection pump's viscous sealing ability is probably the least likely source of a fuel-in-engine oil condition.

TIMING ADVANCE AND VARIABLE TIMING MECHANISMS

Older port-helix metering injection pumps were usually directly driven by reduction gearing from the engine camshaft gear. Such a system would dictate that the **static timing** value (port closure) occur at the same number of crank angle degrees before top dead center (BTDC), regardless of engine load or speed, when lower helix geometry is used. Fuel economy and noxious emission considerations led to the development of first mechanical advance mechanisms and, in the last generation of PLN pumps, electronically managed variable timing.

Mechanical Variable Timing

Mechanical timing advance mechanisms (**Figure 22–13**) are actuated using a set of flyweights and eccentrics to advance the drive angle of the pump camshaft in relation to the pump drive gear, using a spiral gear on a shaft. In other words, the position of the fuel injection pump relative to that of the engine is advanced in direct proportion to the centrifugal

FIGURE 22–13 Mechanical timing advance mechanism.

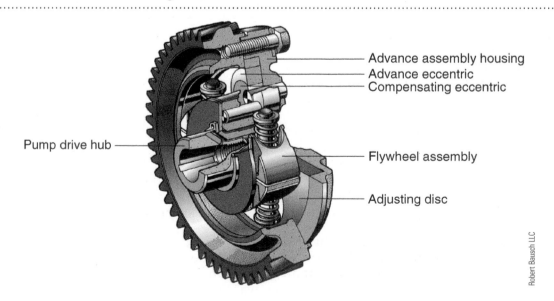

Pump drive hub

Advance assembly housing
Advance eccentric
Compensating eccentric

Flywheel assembly

Adjusting disc

Robert Bausch LLC

force generated by the weight carrier. Port closure was therefore advanced as engine rpm increased. The extent of the advance offered by mechanical advance mechanisms can be as little as 3 degrees crank angle and seldom more than 10 degrees crank angle.

Electronic Variable Timing

Electronically managed variable timing devices, such as those used by Mack and Caterpillar partial authority PLN management, employ a variable timing coupling mechanism between the pump drive gear and the pump camshaft. This intermediary was designed to establish a variable timing window of up to 20 degrees crank angle, which is managed by the engine electronics.

The static timing value (that is, port closure) specified is usually the most retarded parameter in the variable timing window. For example, an injection pump timed at 7 degrees BTDC with a 20-degree variable timing mechanism would permit the ECM to select any port closure value between 7 degrees BTDC and 27 degrees BTDC. Injection pump static timing (port closure) specs of as little as 4 degrees BTDC are used to limit combustion heat and, therefore, oxides of nitrogen (NO_x) emission; substantially retarded injection timing does not generally enhance either performance or fuel economy. In fact, the trade-off of retarded injection timing is an increase of hydrocarbon (HC) emission—but all emissions legislation is about keeping the exhaust noxious emissions within a window of acceptability. Both Mack and Caterpillar manage their variable timing devices in different ways. The Mack system is discussed later in this chapter.

GOVERNOR TRIM DEVICES

Governor trim devices were used primarily on hydromechanical PLN pumps. Their objective was to modulate fueling as either ambient pressure (altitude) or manifold boost pressure changed. Their objective was essentially to prevent over-fueling the engine when running or ambient conditions resulted in lower oxygen content in the cylinder. Two basic types are described here.

ANEROIDS

By definition, an *aneroid* is a low-pressure sensing device. In application, it is used on a turbocharged diesel engine to measure manifold boost and limit fueling until the boost pressure achieves a predetermined value. Such devices are known variously as puff limiters, turbo-boost sensors, air-fuel control (AFC) valves, and smoke limiters, and all seek to accomplish the same objective. They typically consist of a manifold containing a diaphragm; boost air is piped from the intake manifold to act on the diaphragm. Such devices were used on most PLN **boosted engines** (turbocharged engines).

When an aneroid was used on an inline, port-helix metering pump, it was usually a mechanism consisting of a manifold, spring, and control rod. The manifold is fitted with a port, and a steel line connects it directly to the engine intake manifold. In this way, boost pressure is delivered to the aneroid manifold where it will act directly on the diaphragm within. Attached to the diaphragm is a linkage connected either directly or indirectly to the fuel control mechanism (rack); a spring loads the diaphragm to a closed position, which limits fueling by preventing the rack from moving into the full-fuel position.

When manifold boost acting on the diaphragm is sufficient to overcome the spring pressure, it acts on the linkage, permitting the rack full travel and thus maximum fueling. Such systems were easily and commonly shorted out by operators in the mistaken belief that aneroids reduce engine power. The emission of a "puff" of smoke from the exhaust stack at each gear shift point is an indication that the aneroid-/boost-sensing mechanism has been tampered with. As aneroids evolved, they were designed to be more tamper-proof. However, when older diesel engines with PLN fueling fail roadside emissions tests, it is a safe bet that the engine aneroid system has been tampered with. **Figure 22–14** and **Figure 22–15** illustrate the operation of a typical aneroid under conditions of low and high manifold boost.

ALTITUDE COMPENSATOR

An **altitude compensator** device contains a **barometric capsule** that measures barometric pressure and on this basis downrates engine power at higher altitudes to prevent overfueling. They are required when running hydromechanical PLN-fueled engines at higher altitudes because the oxygen density in the air charge decreases with an increase in altitude and, unless the fuel system responds to this, it effectively overfuels the engine. The critical altitude at which some measure of injected fuel

FIGURE 22–14 Aneroid operation at low boost.

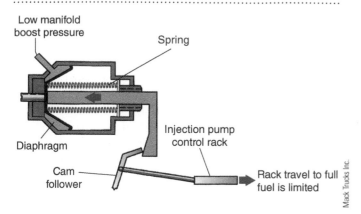

FIGURE 22–15 Aneroid operation at high boost.

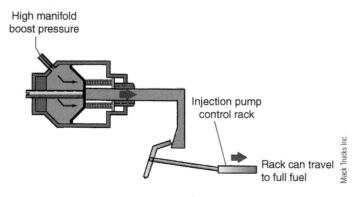

quantity deration is required is 1,000 ft., but in older engines this may not actually occur until 3,000 ft. in altitude. The result of an altitude compensator malfunction is engine smoking under load at altitude.

TIMING INJECTION PUMPS TO AN ENGINE

Port-helix metering injection pumps are timed to the engine they manage by phasing port closure on the #1 cylinder (usually in North American–engineered engines; check the specification—for a variety of reasons, the pump may be required to be timed to the #6 cylinder) to a specific engine position. All injection pumps must be accurately timed to the engine they will fuel.

This usually means the phasing of pump port closure to a specific number of degrees

BTDC on the cylinder to be timed to a specification that seldom can be outside of 1 degree crank angle and may have to be within ¼ degree crank angle. Methods used to time the injection pump to the engine vary by OEM. Actual spill timing of the pump to the engine is a procedure that has become obsolete on highway diesel engines; when you are required to spill time an engine, it is most likely to be an off-highway, usually small-bore engine. However, most would argue that it continues to be a procedure that diesel technicians should understand, because it can be used in the absence of OEM tooling.

> **TECH TIP:**
>
> Most injection pumps on North American engines are timed to the #1 engine cylinder but not all, so watch for those that are not. The #6 cylinder (on an inline 6) is the next most common, but *assume nothing.* Always check the specifications in the service literature.

SPILL TIMING PROCEDURE

Before beginning the **spill timing** procedure, check the engine (and OEM chassis) manual for positioning of the fuel control lever, stop fuel lever, brake valve, and gear shift lever position. See Photo Sequence 4.

1. Check the injection pump data plate for port closure value. Manually bar the engine in the direction of rotation to position the piston within the #1 cylinder on its compression stroke. Locate the engine calibration scale, usually to be found on the front pulley, vibration damper, or flywheel. Position the engine roughly 20 degrees before the port closure specification.

2. Remove the high-pressure pipe from the delivery valve on the injection pump #1 cylinder. Unscrew the delivery valve body and remove the delivery valve core and spring. Replace the delivery valve body and install a spill tube. (A discarded high-pressure pipe neatly cut and shaped to a goose neck will suffice.) When the hand primer pump is actuated, the charging gallery will be pressurized. The amount of pressure created by the hand primer pump will be insufficient to open the delivery valves, so the fuel will exit through the spill tube fitted to the #1 cylinder. The fuel should exit

in a steady stream, and it should be captured in a container held under the spill tube. Next, slowly and smoothly bar the engine in its direction of rotation, observing the stream of fuel exiting the spill tube.

When the plunger leading edge rises to trap off the spill port, the steady stream of fuel exiting the spill tube will first break up into droplets and then cease as the plunger passes the spill port.

The objective of this step is to locate the pump precisely at port closure. This means that the flow area at the spill port should exist but be minimal; 2 to 6 drops per 10 seconds should be within the specification window. Ensure that the pump has not been barred past port closure cutting the fuel off altogether, as it is impossible to determine how much beyond port closure the plunger has traveled.

3. Next, check the engine calibration scale. The specification is typically required to be within 1 degree crank angle of the port closure (PC) specification. If this is so, the pump can be assumed to be correctly timed to the engine. If it is not, proceed as follows.

4. Remove the accessory drive cover plate. Loosen the fasteners that couple the pump drive gear to the pump drive plate. Bar the engine to the correct PC specification position. By uncoupling the pump drive plate from the pump drive gear, it is hoped that the pump will remain stationary at PC on the #1 cylinder while the engine is barred independently. When the engine is in the correct position, torque the fasteners that couple the pump drive gear to the pump drive plate. Back the engine up roughly 20 degrees before the PC specification and then repeat steps 1 through 3.

Every diesel technician should be acquainted with the foregoing procedure even though he or she may seldom practice it. Spill timing can also be performed using compressed air as the test medium; the setup procedure is the same as just listed, but regulated compressed air is ported into the charging gallery. Instead of a spill tube, a flexible hose is connected to the pump element used for the spill timing procedure and immersed in a water-filled glass jar; when air is supplied to the charging gallery, it will pass through the barrel spill ports and exit through the flexible hose, producing bubbles in the glass jar. As the pump is rotated toward the PC location and the plunger leading edge starts to trap off the spill port, the stream of bubbles will turn into smaller bubbles produced less frequently. Using air to spill time injection pumps is probably the least recommended method. The air supply should always be equipped with an air dryer/filter assembly; and even when it is so fitted, the danger of moisture and other air-suspended contamination does not warrant the risk of using this method. OEMs prefer alternative methods of static timing of port-helix metering injection to be used that do not require the removal and disassembly of the delivery valve. Following are some of the alternatives.

1. Timing pin. This is probably the simplest method and the least likely to present problems. It is also the least accurate. The engine is located to a specific position by inserting a timing pinion or bolt usually in the cam gear, but sometimes in the flywheel. Similarly, the injection pump is pinned by a timing tool to a specific location. The injection pump is always removed and installed with the timing tools in position. It goes without saying that the timing tools must be removed before attempting to rotate or start the engine.

2. High-pressure pump. This involves connecting a high-pressure timing pump into the circuit. This portable electric pump charges the charging gallery at a pressure in excess of the 20 bar required to crack the delivery valves, which causes them all to open; consequently, the injector leak-off circuit and pump gallery return must be plugged off. Next, the high-pressure pipe on the #1 cylinder is removed at the pump, and a spill pipe discharging into the portable pump sump is fitted. The procedure then replicates that used to spill time the injection pump: the engine must be correctly located well before the PC specification (to eliminate engine gear backlash variables) and then barred to spill cutoff.

If the settings are out of specification, they are rectified by altering the coupling location of the pump drive gear to the pump drive plate.

3. Electronic. This method tends to be used with later-generation hydromechanical and electronically managed port-helix metering injection pumps. The static timing value is checked with an electronic timing tool that senses the positioning of a raised notch located on the pump camshaft.

Photo Sequence 4

SPILL TIMING FOR AN INLINE, PORT-HELIX METERING INJECTION PUMP

PS4–1 Check the pump port closure specification on the injection pump ID plate, noting which engine cylinder the pump is timed to. Locate the engine in the correct position for the spill timing procedure by observing the valve rocking action on the companion cylinder to the one being timed. Position the engine to ±20 before the port closure specification value.

PS4–2 The injection pump in the photograph is timed on its #1 cylinder. Remove the hydraulic nut on the #1 high-pressure pipe and move the line out of the way; it will probably be necessary to remove some line clamps to enable this.

PS4–3 Remove the delivery valve body and the delivery valve core and spring. Ensure that no dirt gets into the exposed injection pump chamber.

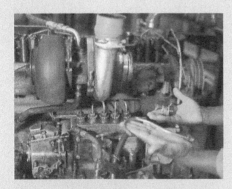

PS4–4 Insert a spill tube (an old injection high-pressure pipe, cut and shaped to a gooseneck) into the delivery valve body in place of the delivery valve. Actuate the hand primer pump to ensure that fuel exits from the spill tube. Capture the fuel exiting the spill tube in a container.

PS4–5 Next, manually bar the engine slowly in the correct direction of rotation …

PS4–6 … while actuating the hand primer pump. The exact point of injection pump spill cutoff is achieved when the stream of fuel exiting the spill tube breaks up into droplets. This occurs when the leading edge of the plunger rises in the barrel bore to begin to cut off the spill port.

PS4–7 Spill cutoff. Be sure that when the hand primer pump is actuated, droplets of fuel still exit the spill tube. If no fuel exits the spill tube, the engine has been barred past the point of injection pump port closure. If this is so, back the engine up at least 20 degrees before the port closure specification and repeat the previous steps.

PS4–8 After locating the port closure on the pump, check the engine calibration plate. On this engine, the calibration plate and pointer are located on the vibration damper; in some other engines the calibration plate is on the flywheel. If the engine location reading is within 1 crank degree of the port closure specification, assume the engine to be properly timed. If not …

PS4–9 … remove the pump drive gear cover plate located directly in front of the injection pump.

PS4–10 Loosen the pump drive gear to pump drive plate fasteners; this should be loose enough to permit the engine to be rotated independently of the gear pump.

PS4–11 Carefully bar the engine to the correct port closure location on the engine calibration plate. The objective is to rotate the engine while the injection pump remains stationary in its location port closure at the #1 pump element.

PS4–12 With the engine in the correct location, torque the pump drive gear to pump drive plate fasteners. Then repeat the sequence outlined in steps 4 through 8 to confirm that the injection pump is properly timed to the engine.

PS4–13 When the port closure specification has been confirmed, remove the spill tube and carefully reassemble the injection pump delivery valve, reconnecting the high-pressure pipe.

Injection pump-to-engine timing is critical. It should be checked each time a pump is reinstalled to the engine and as a step in performance complaint troubleshooting. Pump timing may be checked using a diesel engine timing light. This consists of a transducer that clamps to the high-pressure pipe and signals a strobe light when it senses the line pressure surge that occurs when the delivery valve opens. The test is not an accurate one, and the values read on the timing light should not be confused with the pump manufacturer's PC specification, because the pressure rise pulse used to trigger the light occurs after PC. The test has some validity as a comparative test (using data obtained from other engines in the same series, which are timed at the same PC value) and is a good means of verifying the operation of timing advance mechanisms.

TECH TIP:

Although approved by manufacturers of older automotive diesel engines, using a timing light is not considered to be a sufficiently accurate method of testing commercial diesel engine timing. Limit the use of a timing light to verify the operation of timing advance mechanisms.

Removing a Port-Helix Metering Injection Pump from an Engine

Probably close to half the port-helix metering injection pumps that are removed from engines have nothing wrong with them. This is due to poor field diagnostics caused by a low level of understanding of the operating principles of injection pumps, combined with inaccurate interpretation of service literature. Another factor is a tendency of field technicians to black-box fuel pump technology as the responsibility of the pump room technician and, as a result, package up problems for someone else to repair.

The correct location to diagnose most fuel injection pump problems is with the pump on the vehicle engine. If the OEM-recommended onboard tests are performed before removing the fuel injection pump, the job of the pump room technician has been made easier if the pump then has to be removed from the engine. When it has been determined that the injection pump is responsible for a fuel problem and it must be removed, the procedure should be as follows:

1. Power-wash the injection pump and surrounding area of the engine.

2. If the fuel pump and engine are equipped with locking/timing pins, position the engine to install them.
3. Remove the fuel supply and return lines. Remove the lubricating oil supply and return lines.
4. Remove the accelerator and fuel shutoff linkages (if equipped) or the electronic connector terminals.
5. Disconnect the high-pressure pipes from the delivery valves. Ensure that the high-pressure pipes can be moved away from the delivery valves without forcing or bending them; this usually means releasing insulating and support clamps. Cap both the high-pressure pipe nipples and the delivery valves.
6. Unbolt the fasteners at the pump mounting flange. Depending on the pump, the pump may have to be removed separately from the variable timing/advance timing mechanism. Some pumps may require that the pump drive gear be separated from the pump drive plate or the variable timing device from the front of the pump drive gear, requiring the removal of the timing gear cover plate. Most pumps should slide back easily after this, but care should be taken not to support the weight of the injection pump on its drive gear.

Reinstallation

Essentially, the foregoing procedure is reversed for reinstallation, but the PC timing should be confirmed using the OEM-recommended method (outlined earlier in this section). When installing the pump, ensure that it is installed with the pump drive gear/plate correctly registered with the engine timing gear. Resistance can be an indication that the pump is being installed a tooth out of register and contacting a dowel or key; never force an injection pump into position. When resistance is encountered, remove the pump and check both the pump position and its drive mechanism for problems.

CAUTION:

If resistance is encountered while installing a fuel injection pump, remove and check for the cause. Forcing a pump home on its mounting flange using the fasteners can damage the pump drive and will almost certainly result in an out-of-time pump.

PHASING AND CALIBRATION

Calibration and phasing of port-helix metering injection pumps is the responsibility of the manufacturer-trained pump technician; these operations require the use of specialized tooling, a comparator bench, and the manufacturer's technical data. However, the diesel technician should be capable of defining the procedures.

PHASING

Phasing the injection pump sets the phase angle between the individual pump elements, essentially to ensure that PC on each occurs at a precise spacing. On a six-cylinder engine this would be exactly 60 degrees. Phasing the injection pump ensures balanced, multicylinder engine timing. It is checked on the comparator bench using a degree wheel (protractor located on the comparator drive turret) and adjusted either by varying the barrel height or shimming the plunger tappets. The critical specification is the *lift to PC*, which is a measure of the positioning of the plunger in relation to cam lift. Depending on the type of pump used, either the tappet height or the barrel height is adjusted to ensure that PC in each pump element is phased to occur at a precise interval.

A typical method of phasing a port-helix pump is outlined in the following procedure. A dial indicator assembly fitted with a spill tube is mounted in place of the delivery valve on the cylinder to be phased; when a hand primer pump is actuated and the pump is rotated, fuel will be cut off by the leading edge of the plunger at PC. The dial indicator probe rides on top of the pump plunger and thus its position relative to the moment of PC can be determined. An adjustment would require the raising or lowering of either the barrel height (by means of split shims) or the raising or lowering of the tappet height (by means of phase angle shims or an adjusting screw).

For a pump required to fuel a six-cylinder engine, PC in each of the six cylinders should be phased to be exactly 60 degrees apart. Using the degree wheel as a reference, PC in each cylinder would be set in engine firing sequence at the required interval. Phasing can be also checked/adjusted using the spill method in conjunction with the degree wheel on the comparator bench turret. It should be noted that primary phasing is the responsibility of the camshaft geometry, and a failing cam profile will result in a phasing problem.

CALIBRATION

Calibrating the injection pump dynamically balances fuel delivery quantity output from the individual pumping elements. The injection pump is mounted to a comparator bench with sufficient power to handle the torque required to drive the pump when it is delivering full-fuel loads. The output from each pump element is measured in calibrated **vials** (graduates/burets) and often displayed on an LCD monitor. In a typical test profile, fuel output is recorded through a sequence of specified rotational speeds and simulated fuel demands.

Fuel quantity output in a pump element is adjusted by one of two methods. In certain fuel pumps, the barrels are manufactured with upper flanges that are located by means of eccentric stud holes; these permit some rotation of the barrels in their mounting bores. This rotation turns the spill ports relative to the plunger geometry and therefore alters plunger effective stroke. Another method used to balance fueling in port-helix pump elements is the use of control sleeve lock collars to clamp the plungers. When the lock collar is loosened, the plunger can be rotated within and retorqued to adjust the delivered fuel quantity.

BENCH TESTING

Comparator bench testing is a specialty. It requires manufacturer training and a properly equipped fuel injection pump repair facility to develop the techniques required to test fuel injection pumps. It also requires the manufacturer's service literature and specifications. The term *comparator* is used to describe the test bench because the performance output values of the pump being tested are *compared* directly with the manufacturer's specifications. A typical comparator bench procedure requires a test sequence that includes:

1. Phasing
2. Full-fuel quantity calibration
3. Peak torque rpm fuel quantity calibration
4. Droop calibration
5. High-idle rpm calibration
6. Idle speed calibration
7. Cranking fuel calibration
8. Start retard fueling
9. Aneroid operation and adjustment
10. Supply pump charging pressure

CRITICAL SYSTEM PRESSURE VALUES

The following is a review of some of the system values in a typical port-helix metering injection pump system. Much of the language of fuel injection systems stems from this original high-pressure injection pump system, and is still used in many of the systems that have evolved from it.

CHARGING PRESSURE

Charging pressure is generated by the transfer pump. It is the pressure in the injection pump charging gallery—usually between 15 and 75 psi (1 and 5 bar)—and it varies according to the system.

DELIVERY VALVE CRACK PRESSURE

When there is no residual line pressure in the high-pressure pipe, pressure equivalent to about 300 psi (20 bar) is required to crack the delivery valve that is held closed only by the delivery valve spring. This plus the residual line pressure is required to crack the valve when the engine is running.

RESIDUAL LINE PRESSURE

Residual line pressure is the pressure at which the dead volume fuel is retained in the high-pressure pipe. It is usually about two-thirds of the NOP value. Most fuel pumps attempt to hold this value static during operation, but in some injection pumps, the delivery valve seat has a compensation siphon (see Figure 22–13). The siphon port permits priming through the high-pressure pipe to the injector (unlike other systems), and also limits the time high pressure can be retained in the injection pipe.

NOZZLE OPENING PRESSURE

Also known as *popping pressure*, NOP is the pressure at which the nozzle valve unseats in a hydraulic injector. NOP parameters range between 2,200 and 5,100 psi (150 and 375 bar) in PLN multi-orifii nozzles. NOP represents the beginning of injection.

PEAK PRESSURE

Peak pressure is the highest pressure a system can generate. In most systems, the pressure increases as the injection pulse is prolonged, so peak pressure will be attained only at full fuel. Peak pressure parameters range between 2 and 10 times NOP values.

ELECTRONIC PORT-HELIX METERING

Electronically controlled versions of port-helix metering injection pumps were used for a short time by Caterpillar and for a longer time by Mack Trucks. Although Caterpillar manufactured what it called its PEEC (programmed electronic engine control) up until 1997, those systems were significantly outsold by Caterpillar's own EUI fuel systems available on an otherwise nearly identical engine. In contrast, the Bosch electronically controlled port-helix metering injection pumps were the only available system on the first two generations of computer-controlled Mack engines. For this reason, the focus on electronic port-helix metering injection pumps that follows will be on the Bosch versions used on Mack engines, but note that nearly identical Bosch pumps have been used by off-road vehicle OEMs. Both the Bosch and Caterpillar pumps share much in common, but if you want to research more detail on the Caterpillar PEEC system, reference earlier editions of this textbook. **Figure 22–16** shows an early ECM controlled Mack PLN pump schematic.

BOSCH ELECTRONIC PORT-HELIX METERING PUMPS

The electronic fuel injection pumps used on Mack engines were manufactured by Bosch. Two generations of pumps were used:

- P7100
- P8500

FIGURE 22–16 V-MAC I system overview.

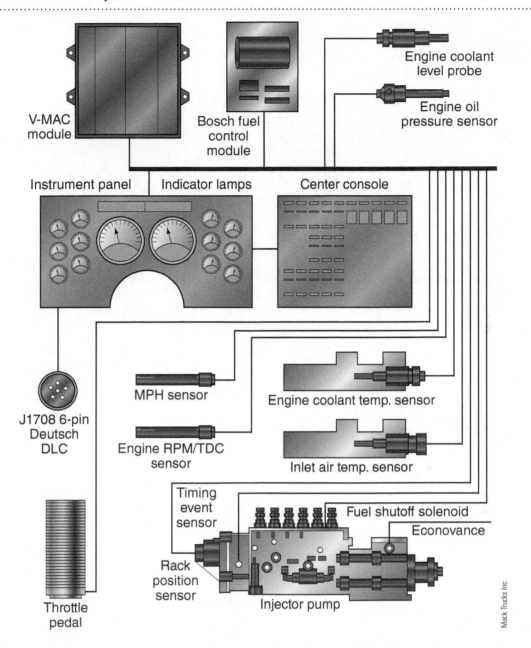

The two generations were nearly identical in terms of appearance and operating principles. They were essentially beefed-up versions of the Bosch PE3000 series injection pump: "beefed up" because they were capable of higher peak injection pressures. The PE7100 was used with the first V-MAC I system whose system layout is shown in Figure 22–16: This used a two-module control system consisting of a V-MAC engine/ chassis control module connected by means of a proprietary bus to a Bosch **fuel injection control (FIC)** module. The injection pump (see **Figure 22–17**) was designed to produce peak injection pressures of 15,500 psi (1,050 bar or 106.4 MPa) using 10-mm plungers with lower helix geometry and a cam lift of 12 mm. The pumping elements were fitted with funnel spill deflectors and a reinforced housing. The later version, PE8500, is closely related to the PE7100 in most of its critical specifications but is capable of peak injection pressures of 16,900 psi (1,150 bar or 116.5 MPa). The PE 8500 was managed by V-MAC II, a single-module management system, which eliminated the Bosch FIC module, incorporating its functions within the V-MAC II housing. Both pumps are driven off the engine

FIGURE 22-17 Bosch PE7100 injection pump with RE30 rack actuator.

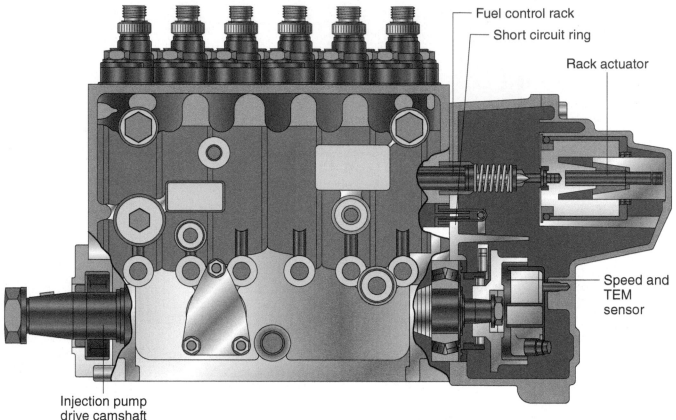

- Fuel control rack
- Short circuit ring
- Rack actuator
- Speed and TEM sensor
- Injection pump drive camshaft

timing geartrain at camshaft speed and use an electronically controlled, electric-over-hydraulic variable timing device, **Econovance**, which is located between the pump and the engine accessory drive gear.

VARIABLE TIMING

As we stated earlier in this chapter, an injection pump with plungers of the lower helix design will have a constant beginning and variable ending of the fuel pulse, the length of which would be measured in crank angle degrees. By using a variable timing device, beginning of injection timing can be "soft"—that is, the ECM can be given some control over injection timing. In this way, the hard timing parameters represented by plunger and helix geometry can be modulated by the ECM, providing it with a window within which it can select effective stroke. The constant beginning, variable ending timing characteristic of the typical lower helix geometry is adapted into a variable beginning, variable ending of the delivery pulse. Both generations of Mack V-MAC system Bosch injection pumps use Econovance

variable timing. The extent to which the port closure value can be managed depends on the application and generation of the pump.

ELECTRONIC GOVERNING

The function of the hydromechanical governor was to manage fueling on the basis of inputted fuel request (accelerator/speed control lever), manifold boost (puff limiter), and engine rotational speed (sensed centrifugally). The V-MAC-controlled Bosch pump entirely eliminated the hydromechanical governor, replacing it with a rack actuator housing (see Figure 22-17). In addition to an electromagnetic rack actuator, the rack actuator housing incorporates sensors that input data to the ECM (V-MAC module).

RE24/30 RACK ACTUATOR HOUSINGS

The rack actuator housing is a unit that contains sensors for reporting status data to the system module(s) and one actuator for effecting the fueling commands that result from ECM

FIGURE 22-18 Sectional view of Bosch RE30 rack actuator housing.

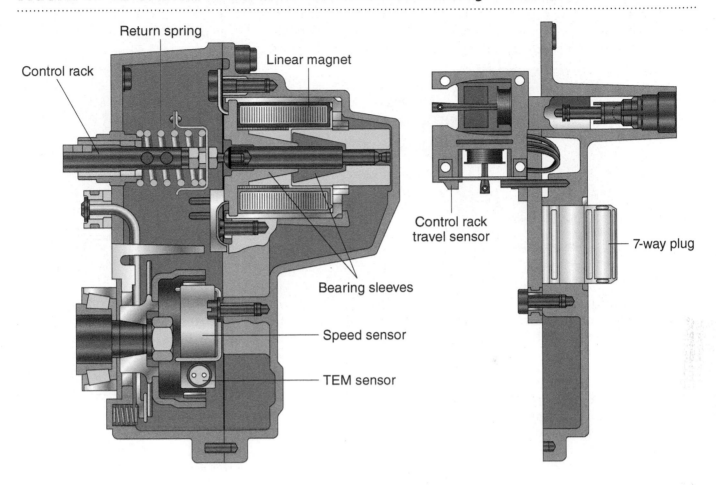

processing logic. The fueling parameters can be described as "soft" or nonrigid. The **ECU** (Mack Trucks uses ECU or **electronic control unit**, rather than the acronym ECM) software provides the governing capability in a V-MAC management system.

A sectional view of a RE30 rack actuator housing is shown in **Figure 22-18**.

Rack Actuator

The function of the "rack" in an inline, port-helix metering injection pump is to rotate the plungers in unison within their barrels when it is moved linearly. When plungers with lower helices are used, port closure ("static" timing) determines the beginning of the fueling pulse at a constant timing location of the engine, while port opening sets the end of the pulse, which will vary according to the amount of fuel to be pumped.

The fueling window is therefore defined precisely by where the plunger helices register with the barrel spill ports. Plunger rotation is effected by linearly moving the rack, which is tooth meshed to plunger control sleeves. In Bosch rack actuator housings, the control rack extends into the rack actuator housing and is attached to the rack actuator mechanism (**Figure 22-19**); the rack actuator can be electrically defined as a **linear magnet** or **proportional solenoid**. The rack actuator is also known as the **fuel control actuator**. The rack assembly is spring-loaded to the rack "no-fuel" position. This no-fuel rack position rotationally positions all the pump plungers so their vertical slots register with the barrel spill ports throughout their cam-actuated stroke. This plunger position permits them to do no more than displace fuel as the plungers are actuated, so in the absence of electrical supply, the default position of the rack is no-fuel.

When the rack actuator is energized by V-MAC module switching, the rack moves linearly in opposition to this spring pressure, thereby altering the rotational position of the plungers to increase plunger effective stroke.

FIGURE 22–19 Rack actuator assembly components.

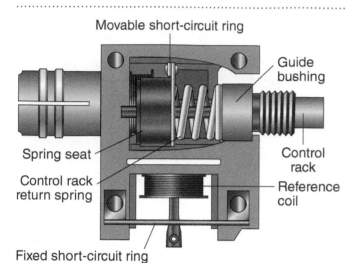

Fixed short-circuit ring

FIGURE 22–20 Rack travel sensor components.

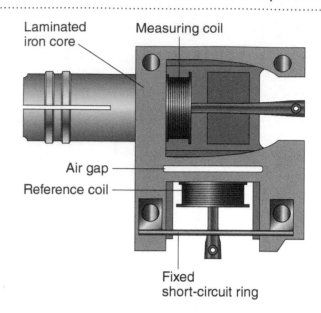

As the amount of current flowed through the rack actuator coil increases, the further inboard the rack is forced. As the rack is forced inboard against this spring pressure, the length of the plunger effective stroke increases, thereby increasing the quantity of fuel pumped per cycle. The rack retraction spring would therefore be fully compressed in the full-fuel position when the rack is forced to its fully inboard position by the rack actuator proportional solenoid. The rack actuator is an ECU module-switched output and therefore returns no data back to the module itself. It simply responds to command signals.

Rack Travel Sensor

The function of the rack travel sensor is to report exact rack position to the ECM. It does so 60 times per second. The assembly is mounted in a laminated iron core and consists of a measuring coil that is energized with reference voltage (5 V-DC). Attached to the rack is a short-circuit ring, and protruding from the fixed measuring coil is an iron bar (**Figure 22–20**).

Short-Circuit Ring

The short-circuit ring attached to the rack is designed to slide over the iron bar without physically contacting it. As the fuel control rack is moved linearly by the rack actuator, the short-circuit ring will either move closer to or further away from the measuring coil, thereby varying the electromagnetic field spread by the coil and, therefore, the induced voltage signal returned to the V-MAC module. This component is extremely sensitive and signals precise rack

position data to the ECM. **Figure 22–21** and **Figure 22–22** show the rack travel sensor components at low-idle and full-fuel positions: Note how the voltage signal is induced by the measuring coil.

Reference Coil

All electromagnet fields are temperature sensitive, so in order to accurately interpret the voltage signal returned to the V-MAC module by the rack travel sensor, a precise "thermometer" is required to verify the signal. The **reference coil** is located close to the rack travel sensor coil; its location is shown in Figure 22–20. It is wound identically to the rack travel sensor coil.

FIGURE 22–21 Rack travel sensor at low-idle fuel rack position.

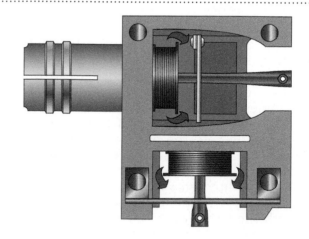

FIGURE 22–22 Rack travel sensor at maximum rack (peak fuel per cycle) position.

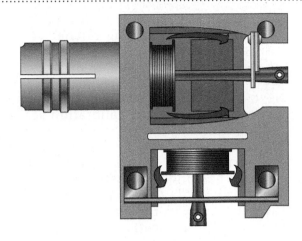

When it is energized, this coil provides a fixed magnetic field. The signal sent to the ECM by the rack position sensor will be modulated by the actual temperature conditions in the rack actuator housing; thus, when the rack is in a certain linear position, the signal outputted by the rack position sensor will be different when the engine is cold compared to that when the engine is at running temperatures.

To enable the ECM to accurately interpret the signal from the rack actuator, the reference coil is used. For instance, as temperature in the rack actuator housing rises, so does the temperature in both electromagnets used in the rack position sensor and the reference coil. The result of the temperature rise is that resistance increases in each coil winding and the signal returned to the ECM varies. The opposite occurs when the temperature decreases. The signal returned by the reference coil is varied only by temperature change. By comparing the signals from both electromagnets, the ECM is able to accurately evaluate the voltage signal returned from the measuring coil on the rack position sensor and thereby determine exact rack position.

Pulse Wheel

The pulse wheel is the only rotating component in the rack actuator housing. The pulse wheel is a toothed impeller located at the rear of the injection pump camshaft and driven within the rack actuator housing. It is a sintered steel component whose total indicated runout (TIR) deviation must not exceed 0.001^2 (0.03 mm). The impeller or pulse wheel (tone wheel) is responsible for two inputs to the V-MAC module.

The first is engine speed (it is the primary reference for engine rpm) and the next is engine location reported by the **timing event marker (TEM)**. There are 16 protruding teeth on the pulse wheel impeller that cut through the rpm sensor's magnetic field to produce an alternating current (AC) voltage signal to the ECM, whose frequency increases proportionally with an increase in rotational speed. The TEM sensor consists of a single notch that cuts the magnetic field of the TEM sensor, producing a signal that works on the same principle as the rpm sensor, but whose input is used by the ECM as an engine position reference. The TEM notch is also used for the electronic static timing of the pump to the engine (this procedure is covered later in this chapter). Both these sensors can be electrically classified as induction pulse generators that feed a small AC analog signal to the ECM.

ECONOVANCE

The PE7100 or PE8500 injection pump is driven off the engine crankshaft gearing at camshaft speed on Mack engines. The Econovance unit serves as an intermediary between the engine-driven pump drive gear and the injection pump drive; it provided P7100 and P8500 pumps with their variable timing feature. Econovance provides an advance on the static timing, port closure location of 8-degree, 10-degree, or 20-degree crank angle depending on the engine model. The last-generation versions of V-MAC tended to use a 20-degree Econovance. For example, if static timing was set at 7 degrees BTDC on a V-MAC engine with 20-degree Econovance, V-MAC could select port closure occurrence at any value between 7 degrees BTDC and 27 degrees BTDC.

Econovance works by altering the position of the injection pump camshaft relative to that of the engine. The device is controlled electronically by the V-MAC module. The engine's injection pump drive gear rotates a hub within which is a sliding sleeve machined with a helical spline; this is spring-loaded to a nonadvanced position, meaning that the default is to have no advance over base timing. For Econovance to advance timing, engine oil used as a hydraulic medium acts to move the sliding sleeve along the axis of rotation of the helical splines. The following components are critical in actuating Econovance:

- Proportional solenoid. The proportional solenoid used is known as the **timing actuator**. It is a linear magnet that can be smoothly moved to any position within its range of travel by varying current flow through the coil. The proportional solenoid is switched by the V-MAC module, and its function is to control the Econovance hydraulic spool valve.

- Hydraulic spool valve. This controls oil flow (engine lube) to the Econovance sliding sleeve. The hydraulic spool valve is directly controlled by the proportional solenoid, and it establishes the extent of advance by managing oil flow. Actual engine oil pressure values will not affect its operation (so long as the oil pressure is above the V-MAC "failure" value), because the operation of Econovance is flow dependent. The ECM monitors the advance location of the injection pump by reading the TEM signal.

ELECTRONIC PUMP-TO-ENGINE TIMING

This procedure can be performed electronically with Mack V-MAC. First-generation Bosch PE7100 RE30 injection pumps were fitted with **ELAB**, a German acronym for *fuel shutoff solenoid*. This apparatus was located near the front of the pump, requiring that it be timed on the #6 cylinder. ELAB actually provided a secondary no-fuel method of shutting the engine down by gating off the supply fuel when the ignition was turned off. On the later PE7100 and its successor PE8500, fuel shutdown is achieved by simply moving the rack to the no-fuel position. However, all V-MAC PE7100 injection pumps are timed to the engine referencing #6 cylinder. All V-MAC PE 8500 pumps are timed on the #1 cylinder.

Electronic timing is performed by electromechanically positioning the protruding TEM notch using a Mack timing device. Essentially, this consists of positioning the pump so that a pair of lights on an electronic service tool (EST) illuminate simultaneously, ensuring a timing accuracy within ½ degree crank angle if the gear installation procedure has been performed accurately.

STATIC TIMING AN E-7 ENGINE

The following procedure is outlined according to Mack Trucks recommended procedure; the assumption made here is that the engine is timed to the #1 engine cylinder as on a P8500 managed by V-MAC II. The static timing procedure requires the use of Mack Trucks' fixed timing tool; this consists of a display box with a pair of lights marked

A and B, a ground wire and clamp, and a sensor. Attempting to static time a V-MAC engine without this tool will result in out-of-specification timing.

1. Using an engine barring device, preferably the toothed Mack barring ratchet adapter, turn the engine CCW as viewed from the front to a location around 45 degrees BTDC of the #1 engine cylinder.
2. Next, rotate the engine CW until the timing pointer aligns with the calibration scale on the flywheel or vibration damper.
3. Remove the TEM sensor from the fixed timing port located on the side of the rack actuator housing, and install the fixed timing sensor tool. Take care to ensure that the sensor (fixed timing tool) is properly aligned with the locating groove in the TEM aperture.
4. Attach the ground clamp from the fixed timing tool sensor to the engine; ensure that there is continuity between the two points. A poor ground will render the timing tool inoperative.
5. Using the hub rotation tool, rotate the engine timing gear hub CW until both lights on the fixed timing tool illuminate. It is important that the inner shaft nut not be used to rotate the hub, or incorrect static timing will result.
6. Install the injection pump–driven gear on the Econovance outer shaft hub so that the screw holes in the hub are properly centered in the gear slots.
7. Install the timing gear hub screws and install finger tight. This should permit the hub gear to be held in place while allowing relative movement between the Econovance hub and the pump-driven gear.
8. Using the hub rotation tool, rotate the timing gear hub CCW until the screws contact the stops at the end of the slots in the injection pump drive gear. At this point, both lights on the static timing tool should not be lit.
9. Rotate the timing gear hub CW until both lights on the fixed timing tool illuminate. If the hub is rotated too far CW so that the A light extinguishes, back up and repeat step 8.

WARNING:

Both lights illuminate for a narrow band of rotation (the equivalent of ½ degree crank angle), so the foregoing step must be undertaken carefully.

10. Torque the fasteners that clamp the injection pump–driven gear to the Econovance hub to the specified value. During the torquing procedure, it is normal for one of the two lights to extinguish, and this can be expected.

11. Next, bar the engine CCW to a minimum of 45 degrees BTDC; this will cause both the A and B lights to extinguish.

12. Validate the timing by rotating the engine CW until both the A and B lights illuminate. Ensure that the engine is only rotated CW during this procedure; once again, if the engine is barred past the point where both lights are lit, back up and repeat from step 11. When both lights are illuminated, check the engine calibration scale and pointer. The specification should be within ½ degree of the specified static timing (port closure) value; if out of specification, the timing procedure will have to be repeated.

FUTURE OF PORT-HELIX METERING PUMPS

Although the port-helix metering injection pump has not been used in any on-highway North American trucks since 1997, vast numbers of these injection pumps are still manufactured, and can be both EPA Tier 4 and CARB compliant. If you work on reefers, these pumps can be seen daily in the most recently manufactured refrigeration diesel engines.

Figure 22–23 shows the diesel engine used to power the compressor in a Carrier refrigeration unit. This is a 2015 EPA Tier IV engine featuring a hydromechanical port-helix fuel system: the identical engine can also be made CARB compliant by adding a DPF into the exhaust. Despite a highly sophisticated

FIGURE 22–23 Diesel engine used in a 2015 Carrier reefer unit. The port-helix metering injection pump has no electronic controls and is 49-states EPA compliant. The same engine is 2015 CARB compliant when fitted with a DPF.

electronic system for managing the refrigeration controls, none are used on the engine. For diesel technicians who work on reefers, knowledge of how to service, troubleshoot, time, and prime these fuel systems continues to be required.

SUMMARY

• The hydromechanical pumping apparatus using inline port-helix metering injection pumps changed little from the time of their introduction in 1927 until emissions standards legislated them off-highway except in applications under 70 horsepower (52 kW), such as reefer engines.

• Management of the port-helix metering injection pump evolved from hydromechanical governing to electronic governing introduced in the late 1980s.

• Most inline port-helix metering injection pumps are flange mounted to the engine cylinder block or timing cover and gear-driven at camshaft speed.

- The port-helix metering pump is driven through one full rotation (360 degrees) per full effective cycle of the engine (720 degrees in a four-stroke cycle).
- The pump camshaft is supported by main bearings and driven in the cambox, which also acts as a lubrication sump.
- Pump element actuating tappets are spring-loaded to ride the cam profiles.
- Cam geometry dictates the pump element activity.
- There is a pump element dedicated to each engine cylinder.
- A pump element consists of a stationary barrel and a reciprocating plunger.
- The plunger is milled in manufacture with a metering recess known as a helix or scroll.
- Plunger rotational position determines the point of register of the barrel spill port and the helix.
- The plungers are rotated in unison by a toothed rack meshed to slotted control sleeves, themselves lugged to the plungers.
- Plunger effective stroke begins at port closure and ends at port opening.
- Delivery valves separate the pump elements from each high-pressure pipe and act to retain dead volume fuel at pressure values approximating two-thirds NOP.
- Delivery valves are designed to seal before they seat.
- Delivery valves increase the volume available for dead volume fuel storage in the high-pressure pipe by the swept volume of the retraction collar.
- Most later-generation port-helix metering injection pumps have a variable timing mechanism that acts as an intermediary between the pump drive gear (on the engine) and the pump camshaft coupling.
- Hydromechanically managed injection pumps often incorporate an aneroid device and an altitude compensator to prevent more fuel being injected to an engine cylinder than there is oxygen to burn it.
- Inline port-helix metering injection pumps must be accurately timed to the engine.
- Caterpillar and Bosch electronically controlled port-helix metering fuel injection pumps used similar operating principles.
- Bosch P7100 and P8500 injection pumps were port-helix metering injection pumps adapted for electronic control.
- The primary ECM outputs used to manage Bosch P7100 and P8500 injection pumps are the rack actuator and Econovance.
- Timing of Bosch P7100 and P8500 injection pumps to the engine requires the use of a Mack electronic timing device.

REVIEW QUESTIONS

1. The beginning of the injection pump effective stroke is known as:
   a. port closure.
   b. port opening.
   c. injection lag.
   d. afterburn.

2. The ending of injection pump effective stroke is known as:
   a. port closure.
   b. port opening.
   c. NOP.
   d. flame quench.

3. The device used to rotate the injection pump plungers in unison is known as a:
   a. barrel.
   b. tappet.
   c. rack.
   d. control sleeve.

4. Charging pressures in a port-helix metering injection pump are created by a(n):
   a. supply pump.
   b. accumulator.
   c. vane pump.
   d. centrifugal pump.

5. What component replaces the governor housing at the rear of a port-helix metering injection pump if it is managed by a computer?
   a. Electronic governor
   b. Rack actuator housing
   c. ECM
   d. Module

6. Static timing can also be referred to as:
   a. port closure timing.
   b. NOP timing.
   c. point of ignition.
   d. completion of injection.

7. Which of the following components would limit engine fueling at high altitudes?
   a. Barometric capsule
   b. Aneroid
   c. Governor
   d. Variable timing

8. A port-helix metering injection pump managing a direct-injected diesel engine would typically be port closure timed to what position on the engine?
   a. 50 degrees BTDC
   b. 50 degrees ATDC
   c. 20 degrees BTDC
   d. 20 degrees ATDC
   e. Pre-ignition

9. 360 degrees of pump rotation is equal to how many degrees of engine rotation?
   a. 120 degrees
   b. 180 degrees
   c. 360 degrees
   d. 720 degrees

10. Which type of cam geometry is used to actuate the high-pressure pump elements in most inline port-helix metering injection pumps?
    a. Symmetrical of mostly inner base circle design
    b. Asymmetrical of mostly outer base circle design
    c. Anti–back kick
    d. Double lobe

11. What is the function of the flutes machined into a typical delivery valve core?
    a. Guide the valve in the body
    b. Permit the valve to seal before it seats
    c. Define the residual line pressure
    d. Define valve core travel in the valve body

12. What is the function of the retraction collar/piston on the delivery valve core?
    a. Guide the valve in the body
    b. Permit the valve to seal before it seats
    c. Limit pressure wave reflection
    d. Limit back leakage to the pump chamber

13. An electronically managed port-helix metering injection pump has ECM-managed variable timing with a 20-degree window statically timed at 8 degrees BTDC. What is the timing window within which the ECM can select the port closure event?
    a. 28 degrees BTDC to 8 degrees BTDC
    b. 8 degrees BTDC to 12 degrees ATDC
    c. 8 degrees BTDC to 28 degrees ATDC
    d. 12 degrees ATDC to 8 degrees BTDC

14. Which of the following components inputs data to the ECM that defines metered fuel quantity in any given moment of operation?
    a. Rack actuator
    b. Rack position sensor
    c. Reference coil
    d. Timing event marker

15. Which of the following components could be described as a linear magnet?
    a. Rack actuator
    b. Rack position sensor
    c. Reference coil
    d. Pulse wheel

16. How many fuel pump elements are required on a Bosch 8500 injection pump fueling an inline six-cylinder engine?
    a. One
    b. One per cylinder head
    c. Three
    d. Six

17. Technician A states that a Bosch rack actuator can be described as a linear proportioning solenoid. Technician B states that the rack position sensor is a piezoelectric device. Who is correct?
    a. Technician A only
    b. Technician B only
    c. Both A and B
    d. Neither A nor B

18. Technician A says that the reference coil in a Bosch RE30 rack actuator housing moves when the rack moves. Technician B says that the only rotating component within an RE30 rack actuator housing is the Econovance. Who is correct?
    a. Technician A only
    b. Technician B only
    c. Both A and B
    d. Neither A nor B

19. When both lights illuminate on a PE pump electronic timing tool fitted to a PE 8500 pump, which of the following should be true?
    a. #1 engine cylinder is at TDC
    b. #1 pump element is at PC
    c. #6 engine cylinder is at TDC
    d. #6 pump element is at PC

20. What type of voltage signal is triggered by the TEM notch on the pulse wheel within a RE30 rack actuator?
    a. V-Ref
    b. AC
    c. DC
    d. PWM

23

Prerequisites: Familiarity with Section 1 and Chapters 19, 20, and 21.

INLET-METERING ROTARY DISTRIBUTOR PUMPS

OBJECTIVES

After studying this chapter, you should be able to:

- Identify the main components of an inlet-metering, distributor injection pump.
- Describe the operating principles of an opposed-plunger, inlet-metering rotary injection pump.
- Explain how fuel is routed, pumped, and metered from the fuel pump to the injector during an inlet-metering, opposed-plunger injection pump cycle.
- Outline the circuits in an inlet-metering, opposed-plunger rotary distributor pump.
- Describe the operating principles of Stanadyne Roosa and Delphi Lucas CAV rotary injection pumps.
- Describe how an inlet-metering, opposed-plunger, rotary injection pump can be adapted for partial authority electronic control.

KEY TERMS

distributor head	hydraulic head	internal cam ring	partial authority
distributor rotor	inlet metering	opposed plungers	

INTRODUCTION

In the days before electronic engine management systems, a significant disadvantage of port-helix metering injection pumps was up-front cost due to its requirement for close-tolerance manufacture and a pump/ metering element for each cylinder on the engine. In the quest for lower-cost alternatives, manufacturers looked at rotary distributor pumps that used a single pump element in combination with a **distributor head** to fuel all the engine cylinders. Among the advantages offered by rotary distributor injection pumps are:

- Lower up-front cost
- Simple disassembly and reassembly (for purposes of cleaning) not requiring costly calibration equipment
- Hard value phasing of injection pulse not influenced by wear
- Balanced cylinder fueling

Rotary distributor injection pumps have a significant initial cost savings advantage over equivalent port-helix metering pumps, but they also have the disadvantage of overall reduced longevity. Over the years, rotary distributor pumps have used a number of different operating principles, but only a couple of designs have survived. Today, rotary distributor pumps are mostly associated with small-bore diesel engines of the 1990s and earlier.

In theory, larger-bore engines could be fueled by rotary distributor pumps, but this was seldom the case in North America where the market requires good longevity and minimal downtime, both of which are disadvantages of rotary distributor pumps. Because rotary distributor pumps are simple in construction, they have been popular in geographic regions where fuel quality is less reliable and necessitates frequent pump disassembly and cleanup. Many distributor pumps can be disassembled for cleaning without requiring complex comparator bench adjustments following reassembly.

ROOSA MASTER

The first practical design for a rotary distributor pump was engineered by Vernon Roosa, a diesel mechanic employed by the city of New York, where he maintained and repaired diesel-driven generators. Roosa patented his design in 1941, but it was not until the 1950s that the first prototypes of his invention were manufactured by the Hartridge Machine and Screw Company. Also in the 1950s, CAV (later absorbed by Lucas, then Delphi) in the United Kingdom started to work with the Vernon Roosa blueprints, resulting in the simultaneous introduction of the Roosa pump (manufactured by Hartford Machine and Screw Company, later absorbed by Stanadyne) and a CAV version known as the DPA. The CAV DPA version pump became the biggest selling fuel injection pump ever manufactured worldwide, and it is still used today in areas of the world in which noxious emissions and fuel economy are subject to less regulation than in North America.

Although the Roosa design for a rotary distributor injection pump was not the first, it was easily the most successful and, accordingly, it generated a succession of copycat designs. The Hartford Machine and Screw Company was absorbed by the Stanadyne Corporation, but the Roosa injection pump continued to be known as a Roosa Master. The two versions of the Roosa pump (Stanadyne and Delphi/Lucas/CAV) lend themselves to a small amount of adaptation to partial authority management electronics, discussed at the end of this chapter.

Truck technicians should be aware that, while they are unlikely to come across too many rotary injection pumps in commercial highway trucks, in rural areas where the truck shop does all the diesel repair work in the vicinity (including all the agricultural equipment), having some knowledge of these pumps can be invaluable. In addition, they were used in U.S.-built automotive diesels (found mostly in pickup trucks) in the era when most consumers shied away from light-duty diesel power.

OPPOSED-PLUNGER, INLET-METERING INJECTION PUMPS

In terms of operating principles, the Roosa injection pump and its close relative, the CAV DPA, are nearly identical. Although the DPA significantly outsold Stanadyne/ Roosa pumps worldwide, this was not true in North America, where both GM and Ford used the Stanadyne pump. For purposes of describing the operation of the pump, the DB2 version of the Roosa pump is primarily referenced, but it should be remembered that there are a number of slightly different versions within the Stanadyne Roosa and Delphi/Lucas/CAV families of opposed-plunger pump.

ROOSA DB2

The Roosa Master DB2 injection pump is an opposed-plunger, inlet-metering, distributor-type, diesel injection pump. It was designed for low-cost production and simplicity. A typical DB2 pump has a total of around 100 component parts and only 4 main rotating members. There are no spring-loaded components, none are lap-finished in manufacture, and there are no ball bearings or gears. The pump has a single pumping chamber in which two **opposed plungers** are actuated by an **internal cam ring**.

The geometry of the **hydraulic head** determines the distribution of fuel between cylinders, and because fuel flow can be preset, lengthy periods on the fuel pump test bench are avoided. DB2 pumps are self-lubricated (by fuel) and contain roughly the same number of component parts regardless of the number of cylinders served. They may be mounted in any position on the engine. Both the DB and DPA pumps are vulnerable to the lower lubricity of ULS fuel, so this is a unique case where OEMs recommend the use of fuel additives, but buyer beware: Stanadyne Performance Formula is recommended.

MAIN PUMP COMPONENTS

The operation of an inlet-metering, opposed-plunger distributor pump is not complicated. First, it is necessary to be able to identify the major components and circuits of the pump. A cutaway version of the DB2 version of the Roosa pump, which we use as our primary reference for study, is shown in **Figure 23–1**.

Referencing Figure 23–1, note that the drive shaft directly engages with the **distributor rotor** in the hydraulic head. In other words, the distributor rotor rotates within the stationary hydraulic head. It is difficult to see in Figure 23–1, but the drive end of the DB2 rotor incorporates two pumping plungers that oppose each other in a single chamber. These plungers are actuated by the inlet-metering circuit internal cam ring.

OVERVIEW OF OPERATING PRINCIPLES

The DB2 injection pump is driven through one complete rotation per complete engine cycle. This means that it is rotated at camshaft

FIGURE 23–1 Cutaway of a Stanadyne DB2 injection pump.

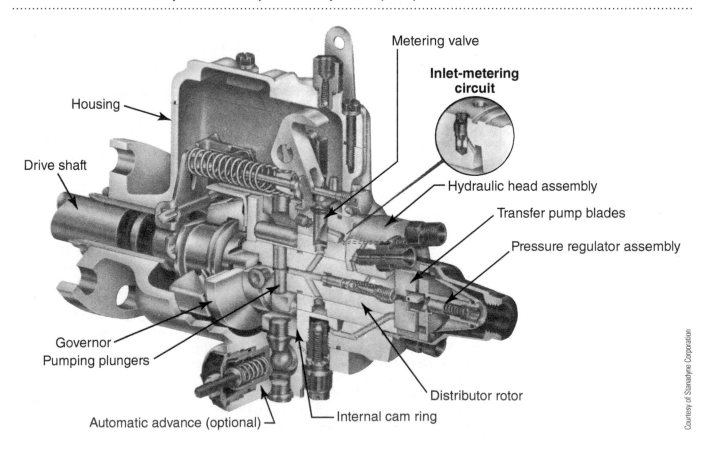

Courtesy of Stanadyne Corporation

speed—that is, to turn the pump through one full 360-degree rotation, the engine has to be turned through two complete rotations, or 720 degrees. The pump chamber is formed between the pump plungers, and they are actuated toward each other simultaneously by an internal cam ring. The plungers ride on rollers and shoes that are carried in slots at the drive end of the rotor. The number of cam lobes normally equals the number of engine cylinders and in turn determines how many effective strokes will occur during each pump cycle.

Pump Components

A fuel transfer pump is located at the rear of the rotor. The pump is a positive displacement vane type, so it will displace fuel in proportion to rotational speed. The assembly is enclosed in the end cap, which also houses the fuel inlet strainer and the transfer pump pressure regulator. The face of the regulator assembly is compressed against the liner and distributor rotor and forms an end seal for the transfer pump. The injection pump is designed so that end thrust acts against the face of the transfer pump pressure regulator. The distributor rotor incorporates two charging ports and a single axial bore with one discharge port. This discharge port aligns with stationary distribution ports in the hydraulic head dedicated to each engine cylinder. As the distributor rotor rotates, it is brought in and out of register with each discharge port once per pump cycle. The hydraulic head contains the bore within which the distributor rotor rotates, the metering valve bore, charging ports, and the hydraulic head discharge fittings. High-pressure injection pipes connect these discharge fittings to hydraulic fuel injectors. In most cases, the hydraulic fuel injectors use pintle-type nozzles.

Governing and Metering

The DB2 pump uses a mechanical governor. Other versions of inlet-metering, opposed-plunger injection pumps use hydraulic governors. When a mechanical governor is used, speed regulation is achieved by using centrifugal weights to measure the driven speed of the pump (to sense engine speed). This is opposed by variable spring force, which is regulated by the driver's accelerator position (this inputs a fuel demand request). In the governor weight carrier, centrifugal force is transmitted through a sleeve to the governor arm and from there uses a linkage to the metering valve.

All fuel that is allowed to enter the pump chamber formed by the two opposed plungers must pass through the metering valve. The metering valve rotates in its bore and defines a flow area to the duct that feeds the pump chamber. Depending on its rotational register with this duct, fuel flow to the pump chamber can be managed from no fuel graduating up to full fuel. The no-fuel rotational position of the metering valve is achieved by moving a dedicated shut-off solid linkage by an independently operated shutoff lever (outside of the governor housing) or by an electrical solenoid.

Hydraulic Governing

Many versions of the Delphi Lucas CAV pumps use hydraulic governing. Hydraulic governing simplifies the injection pump and reduces its size. In hydraulically governed versions of this pump, the metering valve moves longitudinally in its bore instead of rotationally.

Because the fuel transfer pump is a positive displacement vane type of pump, it displaces fuel proportionately to engine rpm. If this fuel is unloaded into a defined (and unchanging) flow area, it makes sense that fuel pressure correlates with engine rpm.

METERING VALVE OPERATION The metering valve is cross and center drilled and milled with a graduated metering recess. This graduated metering recess can be brought into and out of register with the metering duct that directs fuel to the pump chamber: Its longitudinal position is determined by the forces that act above and below it. Below the metering valve, fuel pressure acts against the sectional area of the valve, attempting to force it upward, tending to reduce fuel delivery. Fully upward, no fuel is metered to the pump chamber and shutdown occurs.

Opposing the hydraulic force acting below the metering valve is spring force. This force is variable and determined primarily by the accelerator pedal position.

As the operator pushes harder on the accelerator pedal, increasing the pedal angle, the spring force acting against the hydraulic pressure is increased, resulting in more fuel delivery. So, in any running condition, the inlet-metering valve establishes equilibrium between the spring and the hydraulic forces that position it to define a fuel quantity.

Advance Mechanism

Most inlet-metering, opposed-plunger pumps are equipped with an automatic advance device that can advance fuel injection timing. This can be either a hydraulically or electrically actuated mechanism that advances or retards the pumping cycle. The internal cam ring is responsible for actuating the pumping plungers. When the rollers contact the internal cam ramps, the plungers are forced inboard against each other, pressurizing the fuel in the pump chambers in between them. If the cam ring is rotated toward the direction of rotor rotation, an advance is achieved. An external lug protrudes from the cam ring into the advance chamber below it, permitting a window of advance.

In the case of hydraulic advance, spring force acts on one side of the cam ring lug, positioning it in the most retarded location. An advance piston is located on the other side of the lug, and fuel pump pressure from the vane pump is allowed to act on this piston. Because a vane pump is positive displacement, when it unloads to a defined flow area, pressure rise will be proportional to pump rotational speed. When this fuel pressure acts on the advance piston, it overcomes the spring pressure, opposing it to move the cam ring to advance fuel delivery timing. The result is that any advance achieved will be entirely speed sensitive. The same thing can be accomplished electrically in later versions of the pump by using a linear proportioning solenoid controlled by the engine electronic control module (ECM).

FUEL FLOW

Now that you have some understanding of the pump operation, we can take a look at exactly how the fuel is routed through the pump during its cycle. It makes sense to use both the text and the figures to understand how this is achieved. Refer to **Figure 23–2**, which is a fuel flow schematic of the DB2 pump.

Movement of fuel through the fuel subsystem is the responsibility of the transfer pump, which is the vane pump integral with the injection pump. Fuel is pulled from the main fuel tank through a

FIGURE 23–2 Fuel flow schematic of a Stanadyne DB2 pump.

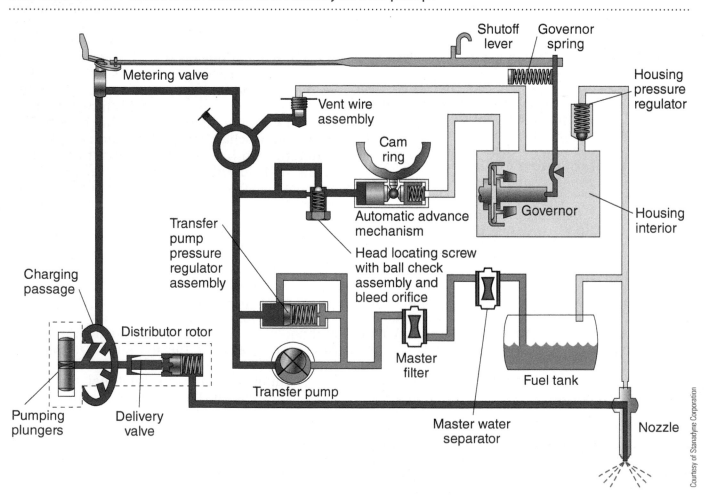

filter or filters into the pump inlet. At the pump inlet, fuel is pulled through the inlet filter screen by the transfer pump. Some fuel is bypassed through the pressure regulator: this fuel is routed back to the suction side of the pump.

Fuel under transfer pump pressure flows through the center of the transfer pump rotor shaft past the rotor retainers into an annular groove on the rotor. It next passes through a connecting passage in the head to the advance cylinder, up through a radial passage, and then through a duct to the metering valve. The rotational position of the metering valve, which is directly controlled by the governor, regulates fuel flow to the radial charging passage, which incorporates the hydraulic head charging ports.

As the rotor revolves, the two rotor inlet passages register with charging ports in the hydraulic head, allowing fuel to flow into the pumping chamber. Fuel flowing into the pump chamber spreads the pumping plungers outward. The extent to which they spread outward depends entirely on the fuel quantity metered into the pump chamber: This fact tends to mean that injection timing is advanced proportionate with load. With further rotation, the inlet passages move out of register and complete the metering phase. Next, the discharge port of the rotor is brought into register with one of the hydraulic head distribution outlets that connect the pump with an individual fuel injector. During the register of the discharge port with the rotor, the pumping phase takes place. The plunger-actuating rollers contact the lobes of the internal cam ring, forcing the opposed plungers inboard into the pump chamber.

The pumping element is shown in **Figure 23–3**. The greater the fuel load in the pump chamber, the more advanced the timing of this moment that begins delivery. Fuel trapped in the pump chamber between the plungers is pressurized and unloaded through the discharge port in the hydraulic head during the delivery phase. The discharge port is connected by a high-pressure pipe to a hydraulic injector nozzle located in the engine cylinder head. When fuel pump pressure exceeds the nozzle opening pressure (NOP), the injector nozzle valve unseats and fuel is injected. Most applications using the Roosa pump use indirect injection and pintle-type nozzle assemblies. Depending on the engine, NOPs are typically much lower than in today's engines, typically around 2,000 psi (138 bar).

Inlet-metering, opposed-plunger, distributor injection pumps are self-lubricating, and the

FIGURE 23–3 DB2 pumping element and rotor.

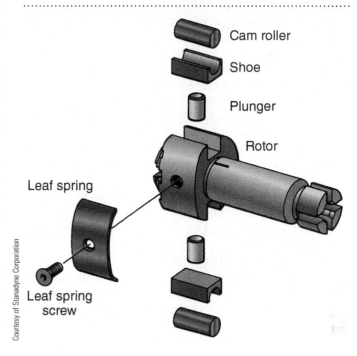

high-pressure injection circuit is self-priming. The lubricity of diesel fuel accomplishes the lubrication of the internal components of the pump. As fuel at transfer pump pressure reaches the charging ports, slots on the rotor shank allow fuel and any entrapped air to flow into the pump housing cavity. An air vent passage in the hydraulic head connects the outlet side of the transfer pump with the pump housing. This permits air and some fuel to bleed back to the fuel tank by means of a return line. Bypass fuel fills the pump housing, lubricates the internal components, acts as coolant, and purges the housing of small air bubbles. The pump is therefore designed to operate with the housing charged with fuel. During operation, there should be no air within the pump.

INLET-METERING DISTRIBUTOR PUMP CIRCUITS

There are nine subcircuits in an inlet-metering, opposed-plunger distributor injection pump. Technicians should understand the role of each circuit, as it will help isolate problems during troubleshooting.

Transfer Pump Circuit

The vane-type fuel transfer pump consists of a stationary liner and spring-loaded vanes or blades carried in slots in the rotor shaft. The inside diameter of the liner is eccentric to the rotor axis. Rotation creates centrifugal force that causes the blades to move outward in the rotor slots to hug the liner wall. As the pump rotates, the volume between the blade segments is varied, allowing the pump to discharge fuel to the outlet.

The transfer pump uses a positive displacement operating principle, which means that transfer pump output volume and pressure increase in direct proportion to pump driven speed. Displacement volumes of the transfer pump are designed to exceed injection requirements by a margin, so some of the fuel is recirculated by the pump regulator that routes it back to the inlet side of the transfer pump. **Figure 23–4** shows the vane-type transfer pump.

Figure 23–4 illustrates the pumping principle. Radial movement causes a volume increase in the quadrant between blades 1 and 2 (**Figure 23–4A**). In this position, the quadrant is in register with a kidney-shaped inlet slot in the top portion of the regulator assembly. The increasing volume causes fuel to be pulled through the inlet fitting and filter screen into the transfer pump liner. Volume between the two blades continues to increase until blade 2 passes out of register with the regulator slot. At this point,

the rotor is in a position in which there is little outward movement of blades 1 and 2 and the volume is not changing (**Figure 23–4B**). The slug of fuel between the blades is now carried to the bottom of the transfer pump liner.

As blade 1 passes the edge of the kidney-shaped groove in the lower region of the regulator assembly (**Figure 23–4C**), the eccentric liner wall compresses blades 1 and 2 in an inward direction (Figure 23–4A). This action reduces the volume available for fuel storage but not the quantity, so the fuel is pressurized. Pressurized fuel is unloaded through a groove in the regulator assembly and directed into a channel on the rotor leading to the hydraulic head. As the rotor continues with its rotation, volume between blades continues to decrease, pressurizing the fuel in the quadrant, until blade 2 passes the groove in the regulator assembly.

Regulator Assembly Circuit

The regulator prevents excessive vane pump pressures in the event of an engine overspeed condition. Fuel from the discharge side of the transfer pump forces the regulator piston against the regulator spring. As pump speed and therefore flow increase, the regulator spring is further compressed until the leading edge of the regulator piston starts to expose the pressure-regulating slot. Because fuel pressure acting on the regulator piston is opposed by the regulator spring, delivery pressure of the transfer pump is controlled by:

- Regulator spring tension
- Flow area defined by the regulating slot

Metering Circuit

Inlet metering refers to the fact that only fuel permitted to pass through the metering valve enters the pump chamber. The fuel delivered to the pump chamber during each pump cycle is the metered fuel quantity and defines the injection pulse duration. The metering valve rotates in the bore. It receives fuel from the charging passage. Because it is milled with a scrolled metering recess, it directs this fuel to the opposed-plunger injection pump through a charging passage. In other words, the rotational position of the metering valve controlled by the governor defines the flow area to the duct that feeds the pump chamber. This flow area must accommodate all the fuel requirements of the engine from no fuel to full fuel. The no-fuel rotational position of the

FIGURE 23–4 Roosa vane-type transfer pump: progression of one slug of fuel from inlet to outlet.

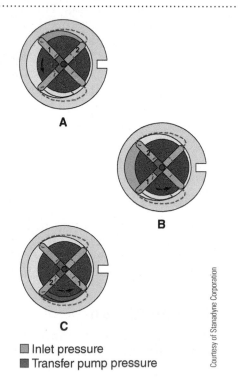

A

B

C

■ Inlet pressure
■ Transfer pump pressure

Courtesy of Stanadyne Corporation

FIGURE 23-5 Charging cycle.

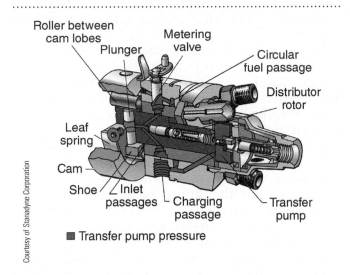

Courtesy of Stanadyne Corporation

■ Transfer pump pressure

FIGURE 23-6 Discharge cycle.

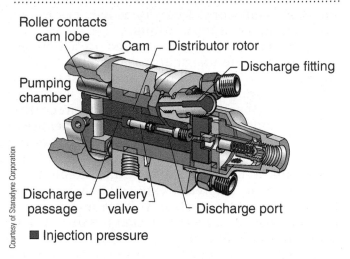

Courtesy of Stanadyne Corporation

■ Injection pressure

metering valve is achieved by moving a dedicated shutoff linkage or by an electrical solenoid.

Charging Circuit

The charging circuit determines the exact quantity of fuel that enters the pumping chamber. As the rotor revolves (**Figure 23-5**), the two inlet passages in the rotor register with charging passage ports. Fuel from the transfer pump, which is controlled by the opening of the metering valve, flows into the pumping chamber, thereby forcing the plungers apart.

The plungers move outward only to the extent required to accommodate the fuel required for injection on the following stroke. If only a small quantity of fuel is charged to the pumping chamber—for instance, that required to idle the engine—the plungers spread only a short distance. When engine fuel load is high, the plungers are forced outward further to accommodate the higher volume of fuel. Maximum plunger travel is limited by a leaf spring that contacts the edge of the roller shoes. Only when the engine is operating at full load will the plungers move to the most outward position.

Discharge Circuit

As the cycle continues, the inlet passages are moved out of register with the charging ports. Next, the rotor discharge port is brought into register with one of the outlets in the hydraulic head that will direct fuel to an injector. The plunger-actuating rollers then contact the cam profiles in the internal cam ring, driving the shoes against the plungers and forcing them

inboard into the pump chamber. This action begins the high-pressure pumping phase called the *discharge cycle*, shown in **Figure 23-6**.

The beginning of injection varies according to the required fuel load. Assuming that the internal cam ring remains stationary, the higher the fuel load admitted to the pump chamber, the more advanced the resultant injection timing. We can summarize this by stating that the cam ring geometry provides a *load-sensitive advance* feature.

During the discharge stroke, fuel trapped in the pump chamber between the plungers is forced through the axial passage of the rotor to the discharge port and out through the injection line to the injector nozzle. Fuel delivery continues until the plunger-actuating rollers are ramped beyond the highest point of the cam lobe and are allowed to move outward. Pressure in the axial passage is allowed to collapse, dropping line pressure and allowing the injector nozzle to close. Nozzle closure ends delivery.

Delivery Valve Circuit

Delivery valves are an option on most inlet-metering, opposed-plunger distributor pumps. The delivery valve accelerates injection line pressure drop after injection to a value approximately two-thirds of the specified nozzle closing pressure. This reduction in line pressure permits the nozzle valve to seat abruptly and minimizes the fuel injected during the collapse phase of injection. When larger droplets of fuel are injected to the engine cylinder during the collapse phase at the end of the injection pulse, there is insufficient time available to properly combust them, which causes higher hydrocarbon (HC) emissions. Delivery valves are found on most highway applications.

The delivery valve is located in a bore in the center of the distributor rotor. This type of delivery valve requires no seat and uses just a mechanical stop to limit travel. Sealing is accomplished by the close tolerance fit between the valve and bore. When injection begins, fuel pressure moves the delivery valve slightly out of its bore, adding its swept volume displacement to the spring chamber. Because at this moment the discharge port is already exposed to a hydraulic head outlet, the retraction volume and plunger displacement volume are discharged under high pressure to the nozzle.

Delivery ends when pressure on the plunger side of the delivery valve drops as the cam rollers ramp over the high point of the cam profile. Next, the rotor discharge port is closed off completely and a residual line pressure is sealed in the high-pressure injection pipe. The delivery valve seals only while the discharge port is open: Once the port is closed, residual line pressure is maintained by the close tolerance fit of the hydraulic head and rotor.

Fuel Return Circuit

Fuel under transfer pump pressure is discharged into a vent passage in the hydraulic head. Flow through the passage is restricted by a vent wire assembly to prevent excessive return fuel that could cause undue pressure loss. The actual amount of return fuel is controlled by the size of wire used in the vent bore assembly. The smaller the wire, the greater the return flow, and vice versa. Vent wires are available in several size options to meet differing specifications. The vent wire assembly can be accessed by removing the governor cover. The vent passage is located behind the metering valve bore and connects with a short vertical passage containing the vent wire assembly, leading to the governor housing.

Any air entering the transfer pump is routed to the vent passage as shown. Both air and fuel then flow from the housing to return to the fuel tank via the return line. Housing pressure is maintained by a spring-loaded ball check return fitting in the governor cover of the pump.

Mechanical Governor

The governor used can be classified as a variable-speed governor, also known as an *all-speed*
governor. This type of governor functions to maintain desired engine speed (requested rpm) and will do so within a certain window as load changes.

Speed sensing is performed by the flyweights, as shown in Figure 23–1 and indicated by arrow 11. Movement of the flyweights acting against the governor thrust sleeve rotates the metering valve in its bore by means of the governor arm and linkage hook. Rotation of the metering valve varies the register of the metering valve scroll to the passage from the transfer pump, thereby controlling how much fuel is metered to the pump element. Centrifugal force, which directly correlates with rotational speed, forces the flyweights outward, moving the governor thrust sleeve against the governor arm, actuating the linkages that rotate the metering valve. Force of the flyweights acting on the governor arm is balanced by the governor spring force. This spring force is variable and controlled by the manually positioned throttle lever. The throttle lever connects to the vehicle accelerator linkage.

LOAD DECREASE A variable speed governor defines a specific rpm value. In the event of a load reduction on the engine, engine speed would tend to increase. This would in turn increase the centrifugal force produced by the flyweights, which would act to rotate the metering valve clockwise to reduce engine fueling.

LOAD INCREASE When the load on the engine is increased, engine speed initially tends to drop. As engine speed reduces, centrifugal force generated by the weights drops, permitting the spring forces that oppose it to rotate the metering valve in the counterclockwise direction, increasing fuel metered to the pumping element. Engine speed at any point in the operating range of the engine is dependent on the combination of forces that act on the governor thrust lever. As with any mechanical governor, centrifugal force acting on the thrust lever will result in speed reduction (less fuel) and spring forces acting on the thrust lever will attempt to increase speed (more fuel).

GOVERNOR OPERATION SUMMARY A light idle spring is provided for more sensitive regulation when flyweight centrifugal force is low, such as when the engine is operating close to idle speeds. The limits of throttle travel are set by adjusting screws to define low-idle and high-idle speeds. A light tension spring on the linkage assembly

FIGURE 23–7 Advance circuit components and operating principle.

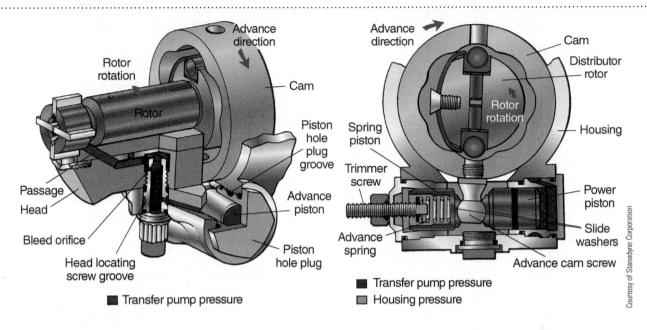

Courtesy of Stanadyne Corporation

takes up slack in the linkage joints and permits the shutoff mechanism to close the metering valve without having to overcome the governor spring force, which means that only a little force is required to rotate the metering valve to the closed position to shut the engine down.

The function of any variable speed governor is to attempt to hold engine rpm at a consistent value (based on a given throttle position) and let the governor adjust fueling to hold that rpm constant as engine load varies. Positioning the throttle lever simply defines a request for an rpm value, not a fuel quantity, which would be the case in a limiting speed governor.

Advance Circuit

Opposed-plunger, inlet-metering distributor pumps permit the use of a simple, direct-acting hydraulic mechanism powered by fuel pressure from the transfer pump to rotate the internal cam within the pump housing. This changes the phasing of injection pump stroke with that of the engine that drives the injection pump and varies delivery timing. The advance mechanism defaults to its most retarded position when there is no or low pressure developed by the vane-type transfer pump. As vane pump pressure increases, fuel pressure acting on the advance piston overcomes the advance spring pressure and rotates the internal cam ring to advance the start of fuel delivery. Total movement of the cam is limited by the piston length. A trimmer screw is provided to adjust the

advance spring tension, which essentially determines how much fuel pressure is required (that is, the specific rpm) to begin the advance. It can be incorporated at either side of the advance mechanism and may be adjusted on the test bench while running. Because the extent of advance depends on vane pump pressure, it is speed sensitive. **Figure 23–7** shows the advance circuit components and operating principle.

Advancing fuel injection timing compensates for inherent injection lag and greatly improves high-speed engine performance. Beginning the injection pulse earlier when the engine is operating at higher speeds ensures that peak cylinder combustion pressures are developed when the piston is ideally positioned in its downstroke to optimize torque transfer to the crankshaft. Advancing the beginning of the injection pulse results in the plungers' completing their pumping stroke earlier.

OPPOSED-PLUNGER, INLET-METERING PUMP SUMMARY

The worldwide success of Roosa's injection pump design is a testament to its low initial cost, ease of maintenance, and ability to manage a range of engines. Though not seen in anything but light-duty trucks, opposed-plunger, inlet-metering, rotary distributor pumps are found in many small diesel engine applications. They are especially prominent in agricultural equipment and are still used in South America, Asia, and Africa.

ELECTRONIC MANAGEMENT OF INLET-METERING PUMPS

The design of inlet-metering, opposed-plunger injection pumps lends itself to some limited enhancement by using **partial authority** computer controls, usually governing (ECM control of metering valve) and timing advance functions: In these, the critical mechanical components of the fuel pump are retained. The partial authority controls on these pumps were limited to controlling the cam ring (for ECM control of timing advance) and the metering valve. The sensing circuit feeding data back to the ECM could include engine temperature, throttle positions, engine shaft speed, road speed, and fluid pressure values. An example would be the DPA-EPIC systems that survive in some marine and agricultural diesel engines. With today's expectations for minimum emissions, better fuel economy, and higher longevity, this category of fuel injection pump has serious limitations, whether mechanically or electronically managed, and can be regarded as a disappearing technology, at least in North America. A full treatment of engine computer controls is provided in Chapter 34 of this textbook.

SUMMARY

- The inlet-metering, opposed-plunger, rotary distributor pump was invented by Vernon Roosa. For this reason, these pumps are often known as Roosa Master pumps.
- Inlet-metering rotary distributor pumps were widely used on older, small-bore diesel engines up until the mid-1990s. They were manufactured by two companies: Stanadyne in the United States and Delphi Lucas CAV in the United Kingdom.
- The main components of an inlet-metering distributor injection pump are the vane pump, rotor and hydraulic head assembly, internal cam ring, opposed plungers, inlet-metering valve, governor assembly, and timing advance.
- An opposed-plunger, inlet-metering injection pump is driven through one full revolution per full cycle on the engine or two complete revolutions.
- An opposed-plunger, inlet-metering injection pump has a single pump chamber actuated by a pair of opposed plungers. Fuel quantity metered into the pump chamber determines the outward travel of the plungers, advancing fuel injection timing in respect of load.

- Fuel is moved through the fuel subsystem by a vane-type transfer pump, integral with the pump housing. This fuel is then routed through the fuel pump circuitry, directed to the metering valve, and from there to the pumping chamber. Pressure rise to injection pressures is developed in the pump chamber and unloaded to the rotor, from which it is distributed to the injectors.
- When adapted for control by electronics, all of the pump's main circuits remain unchanged. The ECM controls are limited to control over the advance piston that moves the cam ring and control of the metering valve. For this reason, it is classified as a partial authority system.
- Inlet-metering, opposed-plunger pumps were used in some U.S.-built automotive diesels (found mostly in pickup trucks) before the introduction of common rail systems.

REVIEW QUESTIONS

1. If a four-stroke cycle diesel engine fueled by an inlet-metering, opposed-plunger fuel pump is rotated through a complete cycle, how many times is the pump rotated?
   a. One-half revolution
   b. One revolution
   c. Two revolutions
   d. Four revolutions

2. What actuates the plungers of an inlet-metering, opposed-plunger fuel injection pump to create fuel injection pressures?
   a. Metered fuel quantity
   b. Charging fuel pressure
   c. External cam profile
   d. Internal cam ring

3. In an inlet-metering, opposed-plunger fuel pump, what causes the outward movement of the opposed plungers in the pump chamber during metering?
   a. Centrifugal force
   b. Metered fuel quantity
   c. Spring force
   d. Pump housing backpressure

4. How is an inlet-metering, opposed-plunger fuel pump lubricated?
   a. With a dedicated supply of engine lubricating oil
   b. With pressurized engine lubrication oil
   c. With fuel from the vane pump
   d. Prelubed on assembly

5. Technician A states that when a mechanical governor is used on an inlet-metering, opposed-plunger fuel pump, metering valve rotational position determines how much fuel is metered to the pump element. Technician B states that the metering valve determines the pressure value developed by the vane-type transfer pump. Who is correct?
   a. Technician A only
   b. Technician B only
   c. Both A and B
   d. Neither A nor B

6. When an inlet-metering, opposed-plunger fuel pump fuels an automotive eight-cylinder diesel engine, how many delivery valves would be used?
   a. One
   b. Two
   c. Four
   d. Eight

7. Technician A states that on an inlet-metering, opposed-plunger fuel pump, plunger actual stroke is constant regardless of fuel requirement. Technician B states that in the same pump, plunger effective stroke is determined by vane pump pressure. Who is correct?
   a. Technician A only
   b. Technician B only
   c. Both A and B
   d. Neither A nor B

8. How is the timing advance mechanism on a hydromechanical, inlet-metering, opposed-plunger fuel pump actuated?
   a. Hydraulically by the vane pump fuel pressure
   b. Hydraulically by engine oil pressure
   c. Pneumatically by manifold boost
   d. By manifold vacuum

9. What limits the maximum fuel metered to the pump chamber in an inlet-metering, opposed-plunger fuel pump?
   a. Vane pump pressure
   b. Metering valve flow area
   c. Leaf spring stops
   d. Roller outboard travel

10. Technician A states that pintle-type injector nozzles are commonly used with an inlet-metering, opposed-plunger fuel pump system. Technician B states that this type of fuel system is more likely used on indirect-injected diesel engines rather than direct-injected engines. Who is correct?
    a. Technician A only
    b. Technician B only
    c. Both A and B
    d. Neither A nor B

24

Prerequisites: Familiarity with Section 1
and Chapters 19, 20, and 21

SLEEVE-METERING ROTARY DISTRIBUTOR PUMPS

OBJECTIVES

After studying this chapter, you should be able to:

- Identify the main components of a sleeve-metering, distributor injection pump.
- Describe the operating principles of a sleeve-metering, distributor injection pump.
- Explain how fuel is routed, pumped, and metered from the fuel pump to the injector during a sleeve-metering, distributor injection pump cycle.
- Outline the circuits in a sleeve-metering, distributor injection pump.
- Describe the operating principles of a Bosch VE rotary injection pump.
- Identify Bosch VE electronically controlled rotary distributor pump systems.
- Trace fuel flow routing from tank to injector on electronically controlled, rotary distributor pump-fueled diesel engines.
- Identify Bosch Electronic Diesel Control (EDC) system components used to manage its rotary distributor pump injection systems.

KEY TERMS

cam plate

distributor head

distributor plunger

Electronic Diesel Control (EDC)

nozzle valve motion sensor (NVMS)

partial authority

sleeve-metering

thrust collar

INTRODUCTION

In the days before electronic engine management systems, a significant disadvantage of port-helix metering injection pumps was up-front cost, due to the requirement for close tolerance manufacture and a pump/metering element for each cylinder on the engine. In the quest for lower-cost alternatives, manufacturers looked at rotary distributor pumps that used a single pump element in combination with a distributor head to fuel all the engine cylinders. Among the advantages offered by rotary distributor injection pumps are:

- Lower up-front cost
- Simple disassembly and reassembly (for purposes of cleaning) not requiring costly calibration equipment
- Hard value phasing of injection pulse not influenced by wear
- Balanced cylinder fueling

Rotary distributor injection pumps have a significant initial cost savings advantage over equivalent port-helix metering pumps, but they also have the disadvantage of overall reduced longevity. Over the years, rotary distributor pumps have used a number of different operating principles, but only a couple of designs have survived in North American applications. Today, rotary distributor pumps are mostly associated with small-bore diesel engines of the 1990s and earlier, and the Bosch sleeve-metering rotary distributor pump is limited to fueling six engine cylinders.

Bosch sleeve-metering rotary distributor pumps are simple in construction, but unlike inlet-metering rotary distributor pumps (see Chapter 23), they have achieved most of their sales in Europe and only to a lesser extent in North America. They were less successful in third-world markets due to the more complex design and the fact that a comparitor bench is required to verify any trim adjustments.

SLEEVE-METERING, SINGLE PLUNGER DISTRIBUTOR PUMPS

Bosch hydromechanical, **sleeve-metering** distributor injection pumps use a single plunger pumping element. In describing this technology,

the popular VE pump is used as our primary reference. The VE pump has been used in a number of offshore small-bore engines, including Volkswagen, and was an option on some early versions of the Cummins B series engine. These pumps manage fueling for engines with up to six cylinders. A VE pump has four primary circuits:

1. Fuel-supply pump
2. High-pressure pump
3. Governor
4. Variable timing

The VE distributor pump has been used in passenger cars, commercial vehicles, agricultural tractors, and stationary engines.

SUBASSEMBLIES

The VE distributor pump uses only one pump cylinder and a single plunger. It is designed to fuel multicylinder engines. The general layout of a typical VE fuel system is shown in **Figure 24–1**.

All movement through the fuel subsystem is the responsibility of a vane-type transfer pump integral with the VE pump assembly. Once fuel from the vehicle tank enters the VE pump, fuel is pressurized to injection pressures and routed to the engine cylinders by means of high-pressure pipes. Injection pressures are created by a single plunger-type pump. Fuel delivered by the pump plunger is routed by a distributor groove to the outlet ports, which connect to hydraulic injectors located at each engine cylinder. The VE distributor pump housing contains the following subcircuits:

- High-pressure (injection) pump with distributor
- Mechanical (flyweight) governor
- Hydraulic timing device
- Vane-type fuel supply pump
- Shutoff device
- Engine-specific add-on modules

Figure 24–2 shows a cutaway view of the subcircuits used on a typical VE pump. Add-on modules, some of which are described later in the chapter, allow the pump to be adapted to the requirements of specific diesel engines.

DESIGN AND CONSTRUCTION

The pump drive shaft is supported by bearings in the pump housing and drives the vane-type fuel supply pump. A roller ring is located

FIGURE 24–1 VE distributor pump fuel system layout.

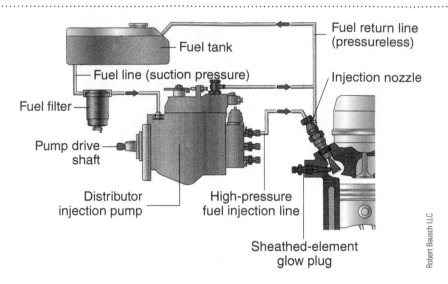

Fuel return line (pressureless)

Fuel tank

Fuel line (suction pressure)

Injection nozzle

Fuel filter

Pump drive shaft

Distributor injection pump

High-pressure fuel injection line

Sheathed-element glow plug

Robert Bausch LLC

FIGURE 24–2 Location of pump subcircuits.

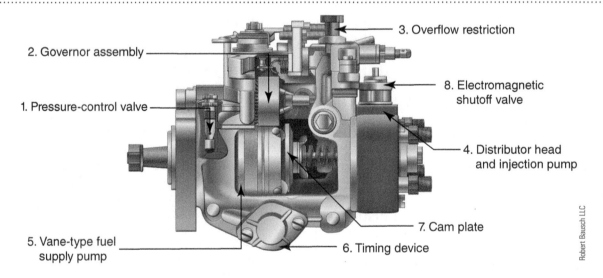

2. Governor assembly

1. Pressure-control valve

5. Vane-type fuel supply pump

3. Overflow restriction

8. Electromagnetic shutoff valve

4. Distributor head and injection pump

7. Cam plate

6. Timing device

Robert Bausch LLC

inside the pump at the end of the drive shaft, although it is not connected to the shaft. **Figure 24–3** shows the arrangement of the pump drive shaft and components in the front section of the pump. A rotating-reciprocating movement is imparted to the distributor plunger by means of a **cam plate** driven by the input shaft that rides on the rollers of the roller ring. The plunger moves inside the distributor head, which is itself bolted to the pump housing. Located in the distributor head are the electric fuel shutdown, a screw plug with vent screw, and the delivery valves. If the distributor

pump is also equipped with a mechanical fuel shutdown, it is mounted to the governor cover.

The governor assembly, which includes flyweights and the control sleeve, is driven by the drive shaft. The governor linkage, made up of control, starting, and tensioning levers, pivots in the housing. The governor shifts the position of the control sleeve on the pump plunger and in this way defines plunger effective stroke. Located above the governor mechanism is the governor spring that connects with the external control lever by means of the control-lever shaft, itself held in bearings in the governor cover.

FIGURE 24–3 Interaction of fuel supply pump, pressure control valve, and overflow restriction valve.

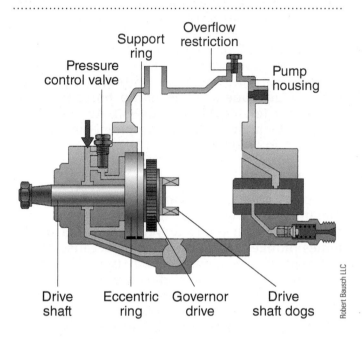

The control sleeve is used to control pump output. The governor assembly is located at the top of the pump, and it contains the full-load adjusting screw, the overflow restriction or the overflow valve, and the engine speed adjusting screw. The variable timing device is located under the pump assembly; it functions to advance pump timing based on fuel pressure developed by the internal vane pump.

Pump Drive

The sleeve-metering, distributor injection pump is direct-driven by the engine it manages, and it must be driven through one complete rotation per full engine cycle. This means that on a four-stroke cycle engine, the pump is driven through one complete revolution per two crankshaft revolutions; in other words, at camshaft speed. In common with most other injection pumps, a sleeve-metering injection pump must be precisely timed to the engine it manages.

The injection pump can be driven by toothed timing belts, a pinion, gear wheel, or chain. The direction of rotation can be either clockwise or counterclockwise, depending on the engine manufacturer requirements. The fuel delivery outlets in the **distributor head** are supplied with fuel in rotational geometric sequence and each is identified with a letter, beginning with A and following through with B, C, D, and so on,

up to the total number of engine cylinders. This is done to avoid confusion with engine cylinder numbering. VE distributor pumps will fuel an engine with up to six cylinders.

FUEL SUBSYSTEM

The fuel subsystem of a sleeve-metering, distributor injection pump is also known as the *low-pressure circuit*. It consists of a fuel tank, fuel lines, fuel filter, vane-type fuel supply pump, pressure control valve, and overflow restriction. The vane-type supply pump is responsible for all movement of fuel in the fuel subsystem. It pulls fuel from the fuel tank and routes it through a filter before it enters the injection pump. The vane pump is positive displacement in operating principle, so the volume of fuel it pumps is directly related to rotational speed. A pressure control valve ensures that injection pump internal pressure is managed as a function of vane pump speed. This valve sets a defined internal pressure for any given speed, meaning that pump internal pressure rises directly in proportion to engine speed. In operation, some fuel flows through the pressure-regulating valve and is routed back to the suction side of the vane pump. Some fuel also flows through the overflow restriction located at the top of the governor housing, and this fuel is routed back to the fuel tank. By flowing excess fuel through the injection pump, fuel is used for cooling and venting the injection pump housing.

In some applications, an overflow valve is fitted instead of the overflow restriction. The interaction between the supply pump, pressure control valve, and overflow restriction valve is shown in Figure 24–3. In some applications, the vane pump exerts insufficient suction to pull fuel through the fuel subsystem, so in these applications a presupply pump is required. This pump is usually located in or close to the fuel tank.

Supply Pump Operation

The vane-type transfer pump, which is the prime mover of the fuel subsystem, is located on the injection pump drive shaft. The pump impeller assembly is concentric with the shaft and lugged to it by means of a Woodruff key. The impeller assembly rotates within an eccentric liner. When the drive shaft rotates, centrifugal force throws the four vanes in the impeller outward against the wall of the eccentric liner. Fuel enters the impeller assembly through an inlet passage and a kidney-shaped recess in the pump housing and charges the cavity formed between the vanes and the liner wall. As the pump rotates, fuel between adjacent vanes is forced into the outlet kidney-shaped recess and from there is directed to the injection pump circuitry. Some discharge fuel is also directed to the pressure control valve, a spring-loaded spool valve, which options fuel to the return circuit when pressure exceeds a specified value.

DEVELOPING INJECTION PRESSURES

Fuel injection pressures are produced by the high-pressure stage of injection pump assembly. High-pressure fuel is then routed to delivery valves, and from there to injection nozzles located at each engine cylinder, by means of high-pressure pipes.

Distributor Plunger Drive

Rotary movement of the drive shaft is transferred to the **distributor plunger** by a coupling unit as shown in **Figure 24–4**. Here, drive lugs or dogs on the cam plate engage with the recesses in a yoke, located between the end of the drive shaft and the cam plate. The cam plate is loaded onto the roller ring by a spring, so when it rotates, the cam lobes riding on the ring rollers convert the rotational movement of the drive shaft into a rotating-reciprocating movement of the cam plate.

The distributor plunger is locked into position relative to the cam plate by a pin. The distributor plunger is actuated upward through its stroke by cams on the cam plate; a pair of symmetric return springs forces it back downward. Because the plunger is actuated by cam profile

FIGURE 24–4 High-pressure pump components.

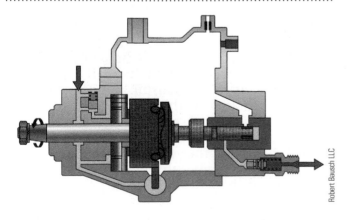

Robert Bausch LLC

and loaded to ride that profile by springs, its actual stroke does not vary.

The plunger return springs contact the distributor head at one end, and at the other act on the plunger by a link element. These springs also have a dampening effect and can prevent the cam plate from jumping off the rollers during sudden speed change. Return spring length must be carefully matched so that the plunger is not side-loaded in the pump bore. (See the lower portion of **Figure 24–5**.) An exploded view of the high-pressure pumping components is shown in Figure 24–5.

Cam Plates

The cam plate and its cam contour help define fuel injection pressure values and injection duration, along with pump-driven speed that determines plunger actuation velocity. Because of the different requirements of each type of engine, fuel injection factors produced by an injection pump are distinct to each engine. That means a specific cam plate profile is required for each engine type; technicians should remember that cam plates are generally not interchangeable because of the engine-specific machining of each.

Distributor Head Assembly

The distributor plunger, the distributor head bushing, and the control collar are each precisely fitted by lapping into the distributor head. These components are required to seal at injection pressure values. Some internal leakage losses do occur and serve to lubricate the plunger. In common with other components that are lap finished in manufacture, the distributor head should always be replaced as a complete assembly.

Metering

Metering and the development of injection pressures take place in four distinct phases shown in **Figure 24–6**. In a four-cylinder engine, the distributor plunger has to rotate through 90 degrees for a complete pumping stroke to occur. A complete pump stroke means that the plunger has to be stroked from bottom dead center (BDC) to top dead center (TDC) and back again. In the case of a six-cylinder engine, the plunger has to complete a pumping stroke within 60 degrees of pump rotation.

Use Figure 24–6 and correlate the text with the four phases of a complete pumping stroke. As the distributor plunger is forced down from TDC to BDC, fuel flows through the open inlet passage and passes into the pumping chamber

FIGURE 24–5 Exploded view of the high-pressure pump components.

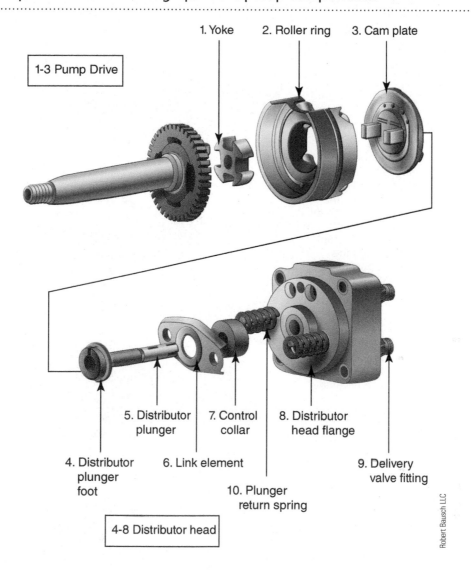

1-3 Pump Drive

1. Yoke 2. Roller ring 3. Cam plate

4. Distributor plunger foot
5. Distributor plunger
6. Link element
7. Control collar
8. Distributor head flange
9. Delivery valve fitting
10. Plunger return spring

4-8 Distributor head

Robert Bausch LLC

located above the plunger. At BDC, plunger rotational movement takes the plunger out of register with the inlet passage and exposes the distributor slot for one of the outlet ports, as shown in Figure 24–6A. The plunger now reverses direction and is driven upward to begin the working stroke. Pressure rise is created in the pump chamber above the plunger and when sufficient, opens the delivery valve and forces fuel through the high-pressure pipe to the injector nozzle. The working (delivery) stroke is shown in Figure 24–6B. The delivery stroke is complete when the plunger transverse cutoff bore (cross drilling) protrudes beyond the metering sleeve, collapsing the pressure. When collapse is initiated, pressure drops in the high-pressure line and pump chamber until there is no longer sufficient pressure to hold the nozzle valve open. Injection ceases the instant the nozzle valve closes.

As the plunger continues to move upward to TDC, fuel spills backward through the cutoff bore to the pump housing. During this collapse phase, the inlet passage is again exposed, ready for the next pump working cycle, as shown in Figure 24–6C. As the plunger is forced back down by the return springs from TDC to BDC, the transverse cutoff bore is taken out of register by the plunger rotational movement, and the pump chamber is again charged with fuel through the now exposed inlet passage, as shown in Figure 24–6D. **Figure 24–7** shows a complete distributor head and high-pressure pumping assembly in cutaway view.

Delivery Valve

The delivery valve seals the high-pressure pipe from the injection pump chamber. It therefore retains dead volume fuel (static fuel in the pipe)

FIGURE 24–6 Distributor plunger stroke and delivery phases.

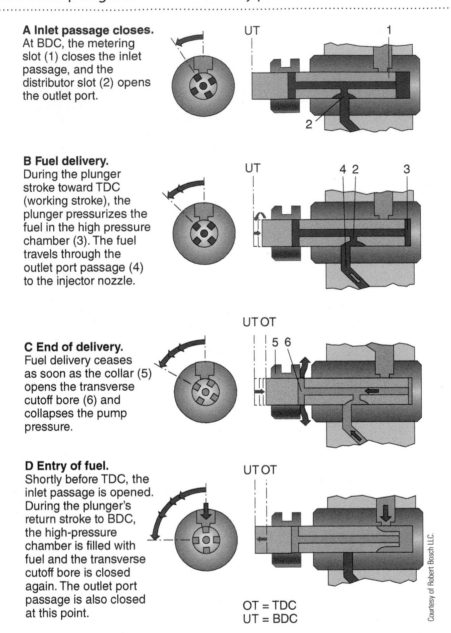

A Inlet passage closes. At BDC, the metering slot (1) closes the inlet passage, and the distributor slot (2) opens the outlet port.

B Fuel delivery. During the plunger stroke toward TDC (working stroke), the plunger pressurizes the fuel in the high pressure chamber (3). The fuel travels through the outlet port passage (4) to the injector nozzle.

C End of delivery. Fuel delivery ceases as soon as the collar (5) opens the transverse cutoff bore (6) and collapses the pump pressure.

D Entry of fuel. Shortly before TDC, the inlet passage is opened. During the plunger's return stroke to BDC, the high-pressure chamber is filled with fuel and the transverse cutoff bore is closed again. The outlet port passage is also closed at this point.

OT = TDC
UT = BDC

Courtesy of Robert Bosch LLC.

at a value well above that in the pump chamber, but comfortably below that required to open the injector nozzle. This static pressure is known as *residual line pressure*, and it ensures precise closure of the injector nozzle at the end of injection. It also ensures that a stable pressure is maintained in the high-pressure pipe between injection pulses, regardless of injected fuel quantity.

One delivery valve is used per engine cylinder. The delivery valve is a spring-loaded plunger. It is opened by delivery pressure developed in the injection pump chamber and closed by a return spring. Between injection pulses, the delivery valve remains closed. Its function can

be most simply described by stating that it separates the high-pressure pipe from the distributor head outlet port for the larger portion of the cycle when no fuel is being pumped to a given engine cylinder.

DELIVERY VALVE OPERATION The construction of each delivery valve is identical to that used on port-helix metering pumps: You may wish to consult Chapter 22, in which the operation of delivery valves is covered in greater detail. The valve core consists of a stem, seat, retraction piston, and flutes. Subject to pressure rise created during the injection pump delivery stroke,

FIGURE 24–7 Distributor head with pump chamber.

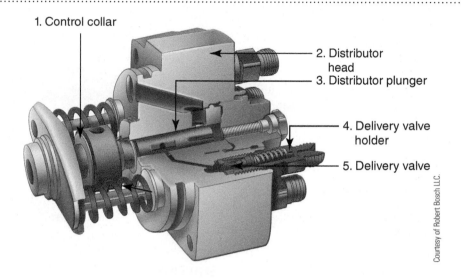

1. Control collar
2. Distributor head
3. Distributor plunger
4. Delivery valve holder
5. Delivery valve

Courtesy of Robert Bosch LLC.

the piston is hydraulically opened when pump chamber pressure exceeds the combined forces acting to load it on its seat: spring force and line pressure. Initially, the delivery valve acts as a hydraulically actuated plunger, compressing the fuel retained in the high-pressure pipe. Once the retraction piston of the delivery valve exits above the seat in the delivery valve body, fuel in the pump chamber is united with that in the high- pressure pipe and the valve can be considered open.

Following the injection pump delivery stroke, line pressure is collapsed by the spill taking place at the control sleeve: The instant there is insufficient hydraulic pressure to hold the delivery valve open, it begins to retract toward its seat. However, the moment the retraction piston passes the delivery valve seat, dead volume fuel quantity is defined, the injector nozzle having sealed. Because the delivery valve has to retract further before it physically seats, the defined dead volume fuel is given a fraction more space, so the pressure is further reduced. This reduction in pressure establishes the residual line pressure value, usually about two-thirds of that required to open the injector nozzle.

DELIVERY VALVE WITH RETURN-FLOW RESTRICTION
Pressure drop-off to a precise value in the high-pressure pipes is desirable at the end of injection. However, the high-speed, high-pressure switching that the high-pressure pipe is subject to creates pressure waves that are reflected between the delivery valve and injector nozzle seat. This pressure wave reflection causes local spiking of line pressure and may cause undesirable nozzle

opening (known as *secondary injection*) or vacuum phases in the high-pressure pipe, causing cavitation.

Using a delivery valve with a restriction bore that is only a factor in the direction of return (spill) fuel flow can minimize pressure wave reflection. The return-flow restriction consists of a valve plate and a pressure spring arranged so that the restriction is only effective in the return direction when it dampens pressure spikes and vacuum phases.

Constant-Pressure Valve

Another means of dealing with the problems associated with pressure wave reflection (pressure spikes and vacuum phases) is to use a constant-pressure-type delivery valve. These are usually found on high-speed engines using direct-injected (DI) engines. Constant-pressure valves relieve the high-pressure pipe pressure by means of a single-acting, nonreturn valve set to a specific pressure. The specific pressure would define the residual line pressure. A diagram of a constant-pressure delivery valve is shown in **Figure 24–8**.

GOVERNING

Bosch sleeve-metering rotary distributor pumps are available with both variable speed and limiting speed governing options. These are usually described by Bosch using the British terms:

- Variable speed governor = all-speed governor
- Limiting speed governor = min-max governor

FIGURE 24–8 Constant-pressure delivery valve.

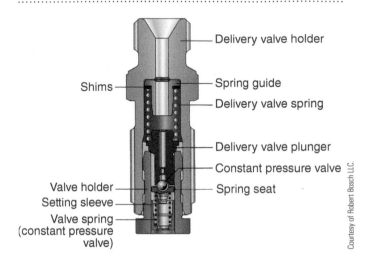

- Delivery valve holder
- Shims
- Spring guide
- Delivery valve spring
- Delivery valve plunger
- Constant pressure valve
- Valve holder
- Spring seat
- Setting sleeve
- Valve spring (constant pressure valve)

Courtesy of Robert Bosch LLC.

FIGURE 24–9 VE governor assembly.

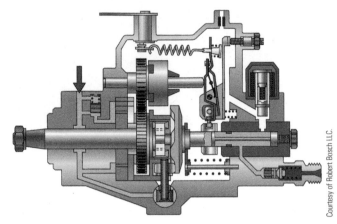

Courtesy of Robert Bosch LLC.

In addressing the governors used on Bosch sleeve-metering distributor pumps, this book uses the U.S. terms, and a variable speed governor will be referenced. Remember, regardless of governor type, the position of the sleeve-metering collar defines the injection pump effective stroke, so engine output is entirely dependent on this.

Governor Design

The governor assembly is attached to the governor drive shaft located in the governor housing. It consists of a flyweight carrier, **thrust collar**, and tensioning lever. When the flyweights rotate, they are forced outward due to centrifugal force. This radial outward movement is converted to axial movement of the thrust collar or what Bosch describes as a *sliding sleeve*. Thrust collar travel is allowed to act on the governor lever assembly, which is made up of a start lever, tensioning lever, and adjusting lever.

As in any mechanical governor, spring forces defined at the governor lever assembly act in opposition to the centrifugal force produced by the flyweights. Centrifugal force tends to reduce fueling/rpm, whereas spring force tends to increase fueling/rpm. Therefore, the interaction of spring forces and centrifugal force acting on the thrust collar (sliding sleeve) defines the positioning of the governor lever assembly. The governor lever assembly controls the position of the control sleeve or collar. As we learned earlier, the position of the control sleeve determines the plunger effective stroke that defines the quantity of fuel to be delivered. The governor assembly on a VE distributor pump is shown in **Figure 24–9**.

Startup Fueling

When the engine is stationary, the flyweights and thrust collar are in their initial position. This results in the start lever being forced into the start position by the starting spring, moving the control sleeve on the distributor plunger to its start fuel position. When the engine is cranked, the distributor plunger travels through a complete working stroke before the cutoff cross-drilling is exposed to end delivery. The result is a full-fuel delivery pulse.

Low-Idle Operation

Once the engine is running with the accelerator pedal released, the engine speed control lever shifts to the idle position. This positions the control sleeve to provide a short plunger effective pumping stroke and represents the lowest fuel delivery condition of a running engine. Idle speed can be adjusted independent of the accelerator pedal setting and can be increased or decreased if temperature or load conditions require it.

Operation under Load

During actual operation, the driver requests the required engine speed by accelerator pedal angle. If higher engine speeds are required, the driver pushes harder on the pedal, increasing the angle and, therefore, the governor spring force. If a lower engine speed is required, the driver reduces the pedal angle. At any engine speed above idle, the start and idle springs are compressed completely, so they do not influence governing. Governed speed becomes the responsibility of the governor spring.

Under load, the driver increases the pedal angle to set the accelerator pedal at a specific position. If a higher engine speed is required, the pedal angle has to be further increased. As a result, the governor spring is tensioned, increasing the spring force available to counter the centrifugal force produced by the flyweights. This acts through the thrust collar governor levers to shift the control sleeve toward the full-fuel direction, increasing the injection pump effective stroke. As a result, both injected fuel quantity and engine speed increase.

The control collar remains in the full-fuel position until equilibrium is established once again between the centrifugal force generated by the flyweights (now greater) and the governor spring forces that oppose it. Should engine speed continue to increase, the flyweights extend further, resulting in governor thrust collar movement that forces the control sleeve toward the no-fuel direction, trimming back fueling. The governor can reduce delivery fueling to no fuel, ensuring that engine speed limitation takes place.

During operation, assuming the engine is not overloaded, every position of the engine speed control lever relates to a specific engine speed: The governor manages that speed by having the ability to control the control sleeve in any position between full fuel and no fuel. In this way, the governor maintains the desired speed. The speed at which the governor responds to a change in engine load in order to maintain desired engine speed is known as *droop*.

If, during engine operation, engine load increases to the extent that when the control sleeve is in full-fuel position engine speed continues to drop, the engine can be assumed to be overloaded and the driver has no option but to downshift.

Governor Break

During the downhill operation of a vehicle, the engine is driven by vehicle momentum and engine speed tends to increase. This results in the governor flyweights moving outward, causing the governor thrust collar to press against the tensioning and start levers. Both levers react by changing position and pushing the control sleeve toward the no-fuel position until a reduced fuel equilibrium is established in the governor that corresponds to the new load/speed condition. At engine overspeed, the governor can always no-fuel the engine. With a variable speed governor, any control sleeve position can be set by the governor in order to maintain desired speed.

VARIABLE TIMING DEVICE

A hydraulically actuated timing device is located under the main pump housing at right angles to the pump longitudinal axis, as shown in **Figure 24–10**. The variable timing device is a speed-sensitive advance mechanism that defaults to the most retarded delivery position in the absence of hydraulic (fuel) pressure.

The timing device housing is closed with a cover on either side. A passage is located in one end of the timing device that allows fuel from the vane pump to enter. This fuel is allowed to act on the sectional area of the advance piston. On the opposite side of the piston, spring force opposes the hydraulic pressure of the fuel. The piston is connected to the roller ring by means of a sliding block and pin, enabling piston linear movement to be converted to rotational movement of the roller ring.

Timing Device Operation

The timing device is held in its initial or default position by the timing device spring as shown in **Figure 24–11A**. When the engine is started, the pressure control valve regulates fuel pressure so that it is exactly proportional to engine speed. As a result, this engine-speed-dependent fuel pressure is applied to the end of the timing device piston in opposition to the spring force acting on the other side of it.

FIGURE 24–10 VE variable timing device.

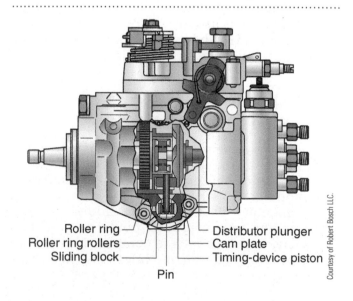

Roller ring
Roller ring rollers
Sliding block
Pin
Distributor plunger
Cam plate
Timing-device piston

FIGURE 24–11 Timing device operating principle.

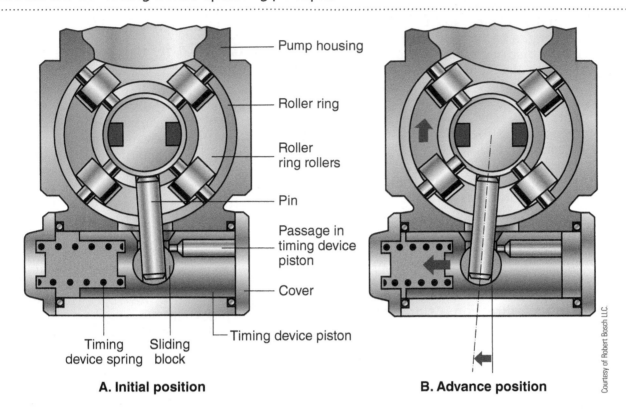

Pump housing

Roller ring

Roller ring rollers

Pin

Passage in timing device piston

Cover

Timing device piston

Timing device spring   Sliding block

A. Initial position

B. Advance position

At a predetermined vane pump fuel pressure, the advance piston overcomes the spring preload and shifts the sliding block and the pin that engages with the roller ring. The roller ring is rotated, moving its relative position with the cam plate, which results in the rollers lifting the rotating cam plate earlier. This action means that the actuation of the injection plunger is advanced. The maximum advance angle achievable in Bosch sleeve-metering distributor injection pumps is limited by timing piston linear movement and is usually 24 crank angle degrees. **Figure 24–11B** shows the maximum timing angle location of the advance piston.

ADD-ON MODULES AND SHUTDOWN DEVICES

Bosch sleeve-metering, distributor injection pumps are available with a variety of add-on modules and shutdown devices. Because of the modular construction of the pump, these supplementary devices can be added to optimize engine torque profile, power output, fuel economy, and exhaust gas composition. A brief description of add-on modules and how they affect engine operation follows. **Figure 24–12** is a schematic that shows how these add-on modules interact with the basic distributor pump.

Torque Control

Torque control relates to how fuel delivery is managed with respect to engine speed and the engine load requirement characteristic. Generally, engine fuel requirement increases when a request for higher engine speed is made; that is, when the driver pushes harder on the accelerator pedal. Fueling should then level off as actual engine speed approximates desired engine speed.

Note that the same position of the fuel control sleeve will result in slightly more fuel delivery at higher engine speeds than at lower rpm, due to the throttling effect that occurs at the distributor plunger cutoff port. This means that if the fuel trim settings were set to produce maximum torque at low engine speeds, the engine would be overfueling at high engine speeds, resulting in smoking and possible engine overheat.

Conversely, if the fuel trim settings were set to produce optimum performance at rated speed, the engine would not be able to develop sufficient power at lower-than-rated speeds. Getting fueling quantities optimized throughout the engine-operating range is known as *torque control*.

FIGURE 24-12 VE add-on modules.

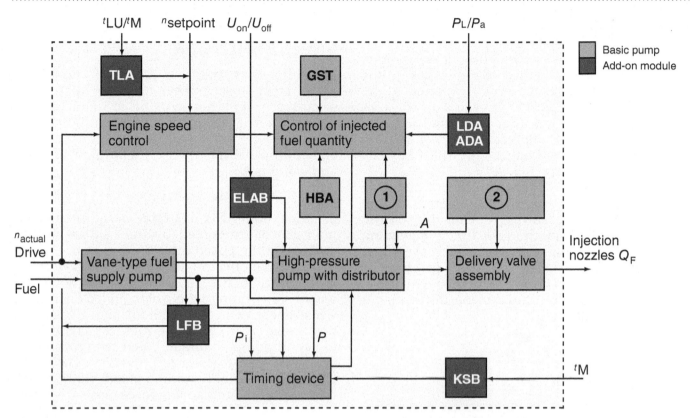

LDA Manifold pressure compensator.
Controls the delivery quantity as a function of the change-air pressure.

HBA Hydraulically controlled torque control.
Controls the delivery quantity as a function of the engine speed (not for pressure-charged engines with LDA).

LFB Load-dependent start of delivery.
Adaptation of pump delivery to load. For reduction of noise and exhaust gas emissions.

ADA Altitude pressure compensator.
Controls the delivery quantity as a function of atmospheric pressure.

KSB Cold-start accelerator.
Improves cold-start behavior by changing the start of delivery.

GST Graded (or variable) start quantity.
Prevents excessive start quantity during warm start.

TLA Temperature-controlled idle speed increase.
Improves engine warmup and smooth running when the engine is cold.

ELAB Electrical shutoff device.

A Cutoff port, n_{actual} Actual engine speed (controlled variable), $n_{setpoint}$ Desired engine speed (reference variable). Q_F Delivery quarterly, t_M Engine temperature, t_{LU} Ambient air temperature, P_L Change-air pressure, p_i Pump interior pressure.

①Full-load torque control with governor lever assembly.
②Hydraulic full-load torque control.

Positive Torque Control

Positive torque control would be required on a pump that delivers excess fuel at higher speeds. Positive torque control limits engine fueling in the upper portion of torque rise. This can be achieved by using a lower tension spring in the delivery valve, altering the cutoff port geometry and producing a throttling effect, or by using additional torque control springs in the governor.

Negative Torque Control

Negative torque control would be required in an engine that overfueled in the lower speed ranges but produced satisfactory performance at speeds closer to the rated speed of the engine. Negative torque control limits fueling in the lower portion of torque rise speed. It achieves this by governor spring-pack trim or hydraulically, using pump housing fuel pressure.

ANEROID

The manifold pressure compensator (known by Bosch as an LDA, a German acronym) is a simple aneroid device. As such, it reacts to the manifold boost pressure generated by the turbocharger and essentially limits fueling until there is sufficient air in the engine cylinder to properly combust it.

Charge air is ported directly to the LDA assembly. The LDA is divided into two separate airtight chambers divided by a diaphragm. Manifold boost is applied to one side of the diaphragm while spring force is applied to the other. The diaphragm is connected to the LDA sliding pin, which has a taper in the form of a control cone. This is contacted by a guide pin through which levers act on the full-fuel stop setting for the control sleeve.

At lower engine loads, insufficient manifold boost is developed to effect movement on the diaphragm, so the spring remains in control, with the result that the LDA limits maximum fueling. When engine load is increased and a predetermined manifold boost pressure is achieved, the LDA spring pressure is overcome, allowing the control sleeve to permit a longer pump effective stroke.

ALTITUDE-PRESSURE COMPENSATOR

The objective of an altitude-pressure compensator (known by Bosch as ADA, a German acronym) is to limit engine fueling when the vehicle is operated at high altitudes and the oxygen density in air is reduced. A reduction in *air* density means that a lower number of oxygen molecules are charged to the engine cylinder per cycle, resulting in overfueling that can cause smoking.

All altitude compensators are deration devices; that is, they reduce engine fueling and power output at altitude to eliminate smoking. The construction of an ADA is somewhat similar to that of the LDA. The major difference is that the ADA is equipped with a barometric capsule that connects to a vacuum system somewhere on the vehicle (for instance, a power-assisted brake system circuit will do).

ADA Operation

Atmospheric pressure is applied to the upper side of the ADA diaphragm. A reference pressure from the barometric capsule is applied to the lower chamber in the ADA. The two chambers are separated by a diaphragm. Should a drop in atmospheric pressure occur, such as would be experienced by driving a vehicle up a mountain, the barometric capsule (constant pressure) would be at higher pressure than that on the opposing side of the diaphragm. This pressure

would cause the diaphragm to move the sliding bolt vertically away from the lower fuel stop and reduce engine fueling.

ENGINE SHUTOFF

Diesel engines are shut down by no-fueling them. Most Bosch sleeve-metering distributor pumps are shut down using a solenoid-operated shutoff (ELAB). A few of these pumps are equipped with a mechanical shutoff device, but you will probably only see them in off-highway applications.

Electrical Shutoff Device

Electrical shutoff is desirable because the solenoid can be energized by the vehicle ignition circuit. On the Bosch distributor pump, the fuel shutoff solenoid (the acronym ELAB is German) is installed in the distributor head. When the engine is running, the solenoid is energized. When energized, the solenoid shutoff valve is positioned open, allowing fuel to pass into the injection pump chamber. When the ignition circuit is opened (turned off), current flow to the shutdown solenoid winding is cut, its magnetic field collapses, and spring force closes the shutdown valve. This seals off the inlet passage to the injection pump chamber, resulting in no fuel delivery. The shutoff solenoid is energized to run and does not latch. In the event of unwanted interruption of the electrical circuit, the engine will shut down.

Mechanical Shutoff Device

The mechanical shutoff device is located in the governor cover and has an outer and inner stop lever. The outer lever can be actuated by the driver from inside the vehicle. When the shutdown cable is actuated, both inner and outer levers swivel around a common pivot, causing the inner stop lever to push against the start lever of the governor-lever mechanism. This in turn moves the control sleeve to the no-fuel position; therefore, the distributor plungers cutoff port remains open throughout plunger stroke and no fuel can be pressurized.

VE PUMP ELECTRONIC CONTROLS

Because Bosch catered to a European market that embraced small-bore diesels to a greater extent than in North America, it had a little more success in adapting its VE pump to electronic controls than other rotary distributor pumps. In this section, we will take a brief look at how a VE pump is adapted for **partial authority** computer controls. The Bosch term for its electronic management controls is **Electronic Diesel Control (EDC)**, the core system used on a wide range of different Bosch fuel systems. EDC is looked at in more detail in Chapter 40.

NOZZLE VALVE MOTION SENSOR

EDC-managed VE pumps use pintle-type nozzles with a **nozzle valve motion sensor (NVMS)**, shown in **Figure 24–13**. It consists of a coil and pressure pin. Pressure pin movement through the coil winding changes the coil reluctance, inducing a signal voltage proportional to the valve's speed of movement. The NVMS enables the ECU to determine the precise moment of start of injection, which helps build the algorithms required for injection timing and exhaust gas

recirculation (EGR) management. It is designed to detect and signal nozzle valve movement (at nozzle opening) because the pressure pin moves with the nozzle valve. In **Figure 24–14**, tracking waves #1 and #2 show a graphic representation of the NVMS waveforms, unconditioned (#1) and conditioned (#2). **Figure 24–15** shows a block schematic of a Bosch EDC-managed VE injection pump.

EDC CONTROL OF VE PUMPS

The ECM processes input circuit data and plots output commands that are sent to the output circuit. The hardware that converts the results of ECM processing into mechanical action is the actuator components. In a Bosch sleeve-metering, single plunger injection pump, there are two critical actuators that manage injected fuel quantity and fuel injection timing:

- Injected fuel quantity control
- Start of injection control

Figure 24–16 shows a cutaway view of a Bosch EDC VE pump, highlighting the electronic controls that make it different from its hydromechanical predecessor.

FIGURE 24–13 Pintle-type nozzle equipped with an NVMS.

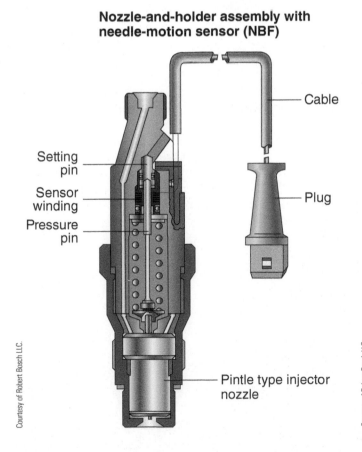

Nozzle-and-holder assembly with needle-motion sensor (NBF)

Setting pin
Sensor winding
Pressure pin
Cable
Plug
Pintle type injector nozzle

Courtesy of Robert Bosch LLC.

FIGURE 24–14 NVMS tracking waves #1 and #2 show a graphic representation of the NVMS waveforms, unconditioned (#1) and conditioned (#2).

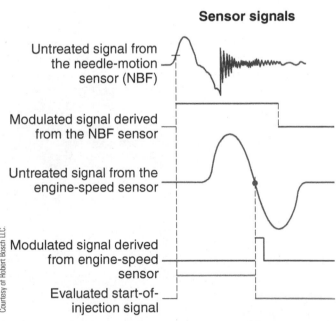

Sensor signals

Untreated signal from the needle-motion sensor (NBF)

Modulated signal derived from the NBF sensor

Untreated signal from the engine-speed sensor

Modulated signal derived from engine-speed sensor

Evaluated start-of-injection signal

Courtesy of Robert Bosch LLC.

FIGURE 24–15 Schematic of how output algorithms are mapped in a typical Bosch EDC-managed VE pump.

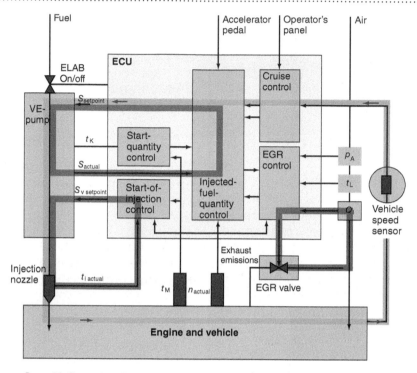

Q	Air-flow quantity	$s_{v\,set}$	Timing-device signal (setpoint)
n_{act}	Engine speed (actual)		
p_A	Atmospheric pressure	t_K	Fuel temperature
s_{set}	Control-collar signal (setpoint)	t_L	Intake-air temperature
		t_M	Engine temperature
s_{act}	Control-collar position (actual)	$t_{i\,act}$	Start of injection (actual)

Robert Bausch LLC

FIGURE 24–16 Partial authority VE distributor injection pump adapted for electronic control.

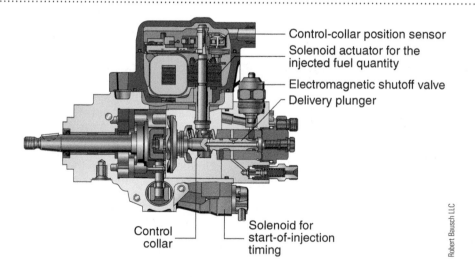

- Control-collar position sensor
- Solenoid actuator for the injected fuel quantity
- Electromagnetic shutoff valve
- Delivery plunger
- Control collar
- Solenoid for start-of-injection timing

Robert Bausch LLC

Injected Fuel Quantity Control

The solenoid actuator (rotary actuator) engages with the control collar or metering sleeve by means of a shaft, as shown in Figure 24–16. In a manner similar to the mechanically governed version of the pump, the spill/cutoff ports are opened or closed depending on control sleeve position. In this way, injected fuel quantity can be varied between zero and maximum because the control sleeve will define how much of the plunger stroke will be effective. By using a potentiometer-type sensor, the position of the control sleeve or collar is continually reported back to the ECM. In this way, the ECM has complete control over plunger effective stroke and, therefore, engine output. When no voltage is applied to the sleeve actuator, return springs position it to reduce injected fuel quantity to zero. In other words, in the event of a system electrical malfunction or solenoid failure, the fuel management system is designed to default to no-fuel and shut the engine down.

Start-of-Injection Control

The pump is charged by a positive displacement-type transfer pump unloaded into a defined flow area, so pump internal pressure is dependent on engine speed. Similar to the timing device used on the mechanical version of the pump, this pressure is applied to the timing-device piston as shown in Figure 24–16 (#5). In the EDC-controlled version, fuel pressure acting on the timing device, pressure side, is modulated by a linear proportioning solenoid valve.

When the solenoid valve is electrically open (pressure reduction phase), the start of injection is at its most retarded location. When fully energized (pressure increase), the timing solenoid will locate start of injection to the most advanced position. Because solenoid position can be proportioned by ECM, any timing location between the two extreme values can be achieved by the EDC. If the solenoid were to fail, the system is designed to default to the most retarded timing value.

EDC Performance Outcomes

Improved control over injected fuel quantity influences vehicle starting, idling, power output, and drivability characteristics, but perhaps most significantly improves engine particulate emissions. Driver input is delivered to the ECM by means of the accelerator sensor, and the ECM will plot outcome responses in terms of speed, power, and torque based on pedal angle. Factoring programmed fuel map data, and the actual input values from the sensors, a set point is calculated for locating the control sleeve actuator in the pump. Check-back signaling ensures that the control sleeve/collar is correctly positioned in any given moment of operation.

Injection timing (start of injection) has a decisive influence on startup, engine noise, fuel consumption, and exhaust emissions. Start-of-injection maps programmed to the ECM take these interdependencies into account to optimize engine operation. The NVMS in the nozzle assembly signals the actual start of injection to the ECM and compares this with the desired or programmed start of injection. Any deviation in actual and desired timing values will result in a change to the on/off ratio of the timing solenoid valve.

ECU Failure Strategies

Consistent with early-generation vehicle computer-controlled systems, EDC can be programmed with a limited range of failure compensation strategies. Some of these are shown in **Table 24–1**.

TABLE 24–1 EDC VE Failure Responses

Failure	Monitoring	Output Response	Warning Lamp	Fault Code
Correction sensors	Signal range	Engine derate	No	Yes
System sensors	Signal range	Limp home mode	Yes	Yes
ECU	Self-test	Limp home mode	Yes	Yes
Fuel quantity actuator	Permanent deviation	Engine shutdown	Yes	Yes

SUMMARY

- The main components of a Bosch sleeve-metering, distributor injection pump are a vane-type transfer pump, cam plate, single plunger–actuated pump chamber, distributor head, delivery valves, control sleeve, governor assembly, and advance mechanism.
- A sleeve-metering, distributor injection pump uses axial movement of a sleeve on the pumping plunger to alter the effective pumping stroke: The plunger both rotates and reciprocates to pressurize and distribute fuel to outlets in the distributor head.
- Movement of fuel through the fuel subsystem in a sleeve-metering, distributor injection pump is the responsibility of a vane-type transfer pump. Actual pump plunger stroke is defined by the actuating cam geometry, and the position of the metering or control sleeve determines the actual fuel pumped.

- EDC-managed VE injection pumps use hydraulic injectors with pintle nozzles. Sometimes these pintle nozzles are equipped with nozzle valve motion sensors (NVMSs).
- An NVMS consists of a coil and nozzle valve–actuated pressure pin. Movement of the nozzle valve–actuated pressure pin through the coil winding changes the coil reluctance, inducing a signal voltage proportional to the valve's speed of movement.
- The NVMS enables the ECU to determine the precise moment of start of injection, which helps build the algorithms required for injection timing and EGR management.
- The key actuator circuit components in a partial authority VE pump are the control sleeve solenoid (controls effective pump stroke/fuel quantity) and the start-of-injection solenoid valve (controls timing).

REVIEW QUESTIONS

1. When a Bosch sleeve-metering rotary distributor pump is used to fuel a four-stroke cycle engine, at what speed is the fuel pump driven?
   a. Engine camshaft speed
   b. Engine crankshaft speed
   c. Two times engine speed
   d. Four times engine speed

2. Technician A states that Bosch sleeve-metering rotary injection pumps can be used to fuel high-speed diesel engines of up to eight engine cylinders. Technician B states that when this type of pump is used on a V-configured engine, two distributor heads are used. Who is correct?
   a. Technician A only
   b. Technician B only
   c. Both A and B
   d. Neither A nor B

3. When a Bosch sleeve-metering rotary distributor pump is used on a six-cylinder, four-stroke cycle diesel engine, how many delivery valves would be required?
   a. One
   b. Two
   c. Four
   d. Six

4. Technician A states that the pumping plunger used on a Bosch sleeve-metering rotary distributor pump reciprocates. Technician B states that the pumping plunger used in this fuel system rotates. Who is correct?
   a. Technician A only
   b. Technician B only
   c. Both A and B
   d. Neither A nor B

5. What determines plunger stroke in a Bosch sleeve-metering rotary distributor pump?
   a. Position of the sleeve-metering collar
   b. Cam geometry
   c. Rotational speed of the pump
   d. Metered fuel quantity

6. Technician A states that the cam geometry used on a Bosch sleeve-metering rotary distributor pump is specific to the engine that it fuels. Referring to the same pump, Technician B states that the cam ring rotates at engine camshaft speed. Who is correct?
   a. Technician A only
   b. Technician B only
   c. Both A and B
   d. Neither A nor B

7. How is timing advance achieved in a Bosch hydromechanical, sleeve-metering rotary distributor pump?
   a. Centrifugal force generated by flyweights
   b. Hydraulic pressure generated by the vane pump
   c. Spring force relayed by the governor
   d. Mechanical force from the accelerator linkage

8. Technician A states that a variable speed governor on a Bosch sleeve-metering rotary distributor pump functions by defining a specific fuel quantity that corresponds to throttle lever angle. Technician B states that a variable speed governor will attempt to maintain a specific rpm value as engine load changes. Who is correct?
   a. Technician A only
   b. Technician B only
   c. Both A and B
   d. Neither A nor B

9. Technician A states that most Bosch sleeve-metering rotary distributor pumps use a shutoff solenoid known as an ELAB. Technician B states that an ELAB does not latch, so in the event of a loss of electrical power, the fuel system will shut the engine down. Who is correct?
   a. Technician A only
   b. Technician B only
   c. Both A and B
   d. Neither A nor B

10. Which of the following could address the problem of a Bosch sleeve-metering rotary distributor pump fueled engine that functioned well at peak torque but was overfueling and smoking when run at rated speed?
   a. Positive torque control
   b. Negative torque control
   c. Trim back maximum speed stop screw
   d. Replace the aneroid

Prerequisites: Chapters 19, 20, and 21; additional reference Chapters 34 and 35

SINGLE-ACTUATOR EUI SYSTEMS

OBJECTIVES

After studying this chapter, you should be able to:

- Describe the system layout and the primary components in a typical single-actuator, EUI, electronic management system.
- Describe the operating principles of a two-terminal EUI.
- Define the role of input circuit components.
- Describe how the ECM manages EUI duty cycle to control engine fueling.
- Outline some of the factors that govern the ECM fueling and engine management algorithm.
- Describe the importance of programming EUI calibration data to the ECM.
- Define the terms *pilot injection* and *multipulse injection* and their application to managing combustion.
- Explain injector response time (IRT).
- Perform some basic troubleshooting on EUI-fueled engines.
- Troubleshoot EUI malfunctions using OEM diagnostic routines.

KEY TERMS

advanced combustion and emissions reduction technology (ACERT)

advanced diesel engine management (ADEM)

algorithm

audit trail

beginning of energizing (BOE)

beginning of injection (BOI)

calibration codes

CELECT Plus

check engine light (CEL)

control cartridge

Detroit Diesel (DD)

Detroit Diesel Electronic Controls (DDEC)

digital diagnostic reader (DDR)

duty cycle

electronic distributor unit (EDU)

electronic unit injectors (EUIs)

ending of energizing (EOE)

ending of injection (EOI)

engine control module (ECM)

E-Trim

flash programming

fuel map

full authority

injector driver

injector response time (IRT)

mechanically actuated, electronically controlled unit injector (MEUI)

nozzle opening pressure (NOP)

personality module

pilot injection

pulse width (PW)

snapshot test

spill circuit

split-shot injection

throttle position sensor (TPS)

two-terminal EUI

valve closing pressure (VCP)

VECTRO

INTRODUCTION

Detroit Diesel Corporation (DDC) was the first diesel engine manufacturer to offer an electronically managed diesel engine in the North American truck and bus markets. The earliest version was introduced in 1985 and made generally available in 1987 on two-stroke cycle, Series 92 engines (displacement of 92 cubic inches per cylinder). DDC used single-actuator **electronic unit injectors (EUIs)** that were computer-controlled and cam-actuated. The computer control on DDEC I was by a dash-located **engine control module (ECM)** and an engine-mounted **injector driver** unit called an **electronic distributor unit (EDU)**. The injector drivers are the ECM actuators responsible for effecting its fueling commands by switching the EUI duty cycle. This first generation of diesel engine computer controls was supplied to the transit bus industry, DDC's primary market at the time. However, it inaugurated the electronic age in commercial diesel engine controls, and DDC's main competitors, Caterpillar and Cummins, were quick to follow with their own EUI-fueled, four-stroke cycle engines.

Single-actuator EUI fuel systems were the dominant fuel system found on medium- and heavy-duty highway-compliant diesel engines from the 1990s until 2007, when the age of single-actuator EUIs on highway diesel engines came to an abrupt halt. In 2007, the major engine original equipment manufacturers (OEMs) either adopted common rail fuel systems or opted to use dual-actuator EUIs, the subject matter of Chapter 26.

SECOND GENERATION OF EUIs

Because of the dominance of single-actuator EUIs for much of the recent past, there are more engines on our roads today using this fuel system than any other. At the time of writing, you can also expect to find more questions on this fuel system than any other in certification testing. The single actuator is always a solenoid. This category of EUIs is known by the following terms:

- Single-actuator EUIs
- **Two-terminal EUIs**
- **Mechanically actuated, electronically controlled unit injectors (MEUIs)** (Caterpillar)

Our choice will generally be to use the term *single-actuator EUI* unless we are specifically referencing Caterpillar MEUIs.

FULL AUTHORITY

The term **full authority** management can be applied to any engines fueled by EUIs. The term means that the engine management electronics have full control over engine fueling. Because EUI fueling was the first full authority diesel engine management option and it has been around for more than two decades, current fuel systems have considerably greater control over fueling. EUIs are actuated by cam profile—that is, the integral pump that creates injection pressures is actuated by cam profile. This meant that the fueling window available to the ECM within which it could select injection was limited to cam geometry. In other words, for injection to occur, the EUI pumping plunger has to be moving downward into the EUI pump chamber.

MANUFACTURERS OF SINGLE-ACTUATOR EUIs

In North America, single-actuator EUIs are manufactured by:

- Rochester Fuels (DDEC)
- Delphi Lucas (Caterpillar, DDEC, Volvo)
- Caterpillar (for in-house Cat engines only)
- Cummins (for in-house Cummins engines only)
- Robert Bosch (VW and off-highway engines)

The good news is that regardless of manufacturer, most EUIs work on almost identical principles. The exception is those manufactured by Cummins, which use slightly different operating principles. In this chapter, we will look at typical EUIs and toward the end, examine the slightly different Cummins EUI.

MANAGING EUIs

The electronic controls used to manage EUI fuel systems will be examined in more detail in later chapters in this textbook. However, the OEM systems that do the managing should be identified here:

- Detroit Diesel (DD) engine management system is known as **Detroit Diesel Electronic Controls (DDEC)**. DDEC has passed through several generations as the engine technology has changed. Versions of DDEC up to DDEC V were used to manage single-actuator EUIs. DDC recently changed their corporate name to **Detroit Diesel (DD)**: this term will be used in this chapter. DD engines using single-actuator EUIs include the Series 92 (two-stroke cycle),

Series 60 (11.1 liter, 12.7 liter, and 14.0 liter), and Series 50 (8.5 liter) families.

- Caterpillar engine management is known as **advanced diesel engine management (ADEM)** system electronics. ADEM has evolved through a number of software and hardware generations and more recent (post-2004) low-emissions engines were additionally categorized as **advanced combustion and emissions reduction technology (ACERT)**. ACERT engines are identified by the absence of a hyphen between the C and displacement: for instance, a C15 is a Caterpillar 15-liter ACERT engine. Engines using ADEM include 3176B, 3196B, 3406E, C-10, C-12, C-15, C-16, C11, C13, and C15 families.
- Cummins engine management of EUIs is known as CELECT (Cummins Electronics), or **CELECT Plus** (later version). CELECT management was used on L-10 (late versions), N-14, and M-11 (early versions). The M-11 engine outlived its predecessors and later versions used Interact Management and were known as ISM engines. Production of ISM engines ceased in 2009.
- Volvo **VECTRO** (Volvo electronics) is used to manage the pre-2007 VDE-12 engine using single-actuator EUIs manufactured by Delphi Lucas.
- Bosch management systems are known as Electronic Diesel Controls (EDC), and they are designed to bus into vehicle management electronics. EDC management of EUIs is not used in any North American highway trucks, but is used in VW EUI fuel systems and other offshore engines used in heavy equipment, marine, and mining applications.

SYSTEM OVERVIEW

All full authority electronic engines provide the ECM with at least some ability to control the fueling pulse. EUIs have an effective pumping stroke managed and switched by the ECM. However, because EUIs are cam-actuated, the physical movement of the plunger through its stroke is cam-actuated. In short, this means that the ECM can only select an effective stroke while the plunger is being forced through its downstroke by the cam responsible for actuating it. The result is that the ECM is confined to the hard limit window represented by cam profile when that is correlated to crank angle degrees. The actual fueling windows depend on the specific engine and the cam profile geometry used on

FIGURE 25–1 Location of key components on a CELECT-managed, EUI-fueled engine.

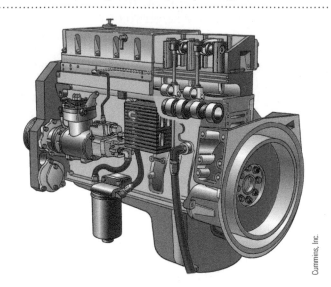

Cummins, Inc.

that engine. **Figure 25–1** shows the location of the key components on a Cummins CELECT-managed, EUI-fueled engine.

EUI-fueled engines with full authority management systems may be divided into four subsystems for purposes of study:

- Fuel subsystem (Chapter 19)
- Electronic input circuit (Chapter 34)
- ECM (Chapter 34)
- Output circuit

The focus of this chapter will be the output circuit of an EUI fuel system. The other three subsystems are dealt with in detail elsewhere in this textbook, so they will only be briefly addressed here.

FUEL SUBSYSTEM

The fuel subsystem incorporates those components that enable the transfer of fuel from the fuel tank to the EUIs, as shown in **Figure 25–2**. A fixed clearance gear pump such as the one shown in **Figure 25–3** is responsible for fuel movement through the supply circuit. This gear pump is flange mounted and is driven by the engine camshaft by means of a pair of helical gears. The circuit incorporates a check valve and pressure relief valve. The Caterpillar EUI fuel system shown in Figure 25–2 uses a hand-actuated, plunger-type, priming pump located on the secondary fuel filter mounting pad; not all EUI fuel systems will be similarly equipped.

Fuel from the fuel subsystem is delivered to the fuel supply and return manifold or

FIGURE 25–2 Fuel system schematic for a typical EUI-fueled diesel engine.

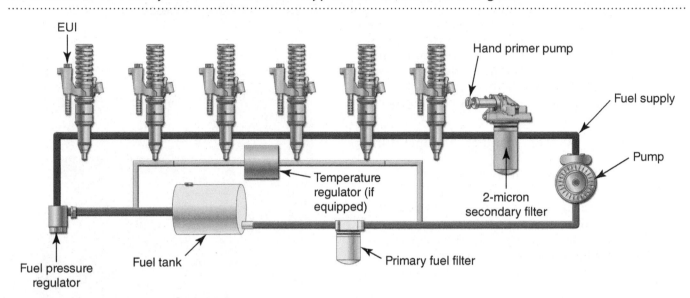

FIGURE 25–3 The hydromechanical fuel subsystem used on a Cummins CELECT-managed, EUI-fueled engine.

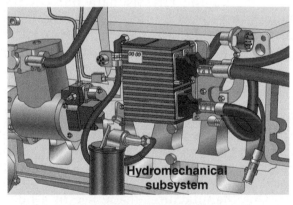

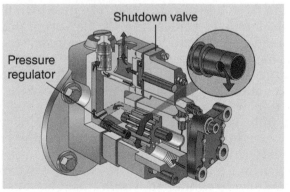

Cummins, Inc.

manifolds. An adapter or siphon-break prevents fuel drain-back from the manifold when the engine is not running. While the engine is running, fuel is continually circulated through the system. In some EUI fuel systems, charge fuel is routed through a heat exchanger on which the ECM is mounted. This fuel acts as coolant for the heat generated by the microprocessor and injector drivers in the ECM. System charging pressure is maintained at values typically 60 to 150 psi (4 to 10.3 bar), but in single-actuator EUI systems, the pressures tend to be closer to the lower end of this window. The fuel subsystem is usually equipped with additional devices such as pressure regulators, anti-siphon valves, shutdown valves, and various sensors.

ELECTRONIC INPUT CIRCUIT

Command and monitoring sensors and switches in EUI fuel systems are similar regardless of manufacturer. The function of the input circuit is to feed monitoring data such as temperature, pressure, and position data to the ECM, along with command data such as accelerator position. Medium- and heavy-duty trucks have used drive by wire for more than two decades with no mechanical default mode. Most of the OEMs opted to use potentiometer-type **throttle position sensors (TPSs)** supplied with V-Ref from the onset, but Caterpillar is an exception so if you are working on Cat engines you should consult Chapter 41 or Cat service literature. Potentiometer-type sensors output an analog signal, so unless that signal is digitized using a printed circuit, an analog V-DC signal is returned to the ECM. Almost all single-actuator EUI fuel systems use potentiometer-type TPS and not the noncontact, Hall-effect type TPS which have been adopted by OEMs since 2007. A full treatment of sensor circuits is provided in Chapter 34.

ECM

The ECM is responsible for engine governing, the fuel map, self-diagnostics, and system monitoring, creating data audit trails, and controlling all the exhaust aftertreatment devices. The **fuel map** (some OEMs use the term *fuel algorithm*) is what results from the ECM processing cycle, which consists of:

- Monitoring sensor inputs (temperature/pressure/rpm/etc.)
- Command sensor and switch inputs (accelerator position/cruise controls/etc.)
- Program command protocols (proprietary data programming)
- Customer data programming (governor type/road speed governing/etc.)
- Inhibit commands such as trimback and fault code inhibitors
- Output device status (EUI response time/temperature/etc.)
- EUI fuel flow calibration programming

Early-generation EUI engines were managed by ECMs networked to the J1587 bus. In 1991, the faster J1939 CAN platform bus (see Chapter 37) was introduced, and by 1997 most truck diesel engine had ECMs with addresses on both the J1587 and J1939 CAN buses. A current J1939 bus network can accommodate up to 30 nodes or addresses. This allows the engine computer to "speak" to any other chassis system computer with a network address.

Electronic service tool (EST) access is by means of a data connector, either six- or nine-pin Deutsch socket, connected to the chassis data bus. Some systems may be accessed wirelessly, but this did not become common practice until after 2007 when single-actuator EUIs ceased to be a factor in on-highway diesel engines. Engine and emissions controls on the generations of engines using single-actuator EUIs were managed by a single ECM using the SA 00/MID 128 address on the chassis data bus. In some instances, the engine electronics could be accessed by directly connecting to the ECM

FIGURE 25–4 The CELECT ECM showing the sensor and actuator harnesses.

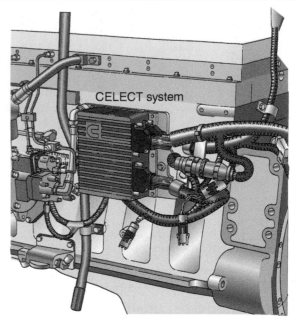

CELECT system

Cummins, Inc.

rather than to the chassis data bus: In these instances, access is limited to the engine electronics. **Figure 25–4** shows the ECM used on a Cummins CELECT-managed, EUI-fueled engine.

ECM HARDWARE

After DDEC I, truck engine OEMs were inclined to use single-module controllers almost exclusively. In some first-generation systems, the only means of effecting programming changes was by changing out programmable read-only memory (PROM) chips. One manufacturer made use of a bolt-on (to the ECM) **personality module** on which both PROM and electronically erasable, programmable read-only memory (EEPROM) memory retention hardware were embedded. The personality module was loaded by external **flash programming** and ECM-driven write-to-self capability, but this evolved into a personality module that was fully integrated into the ECM housing and flash-programmed at factory initialization—and thereafter on an as-required basis. The processing hardware and all of the output switching apparatus are contained within the ECM housing.

ECM DRIVERS

After processing the input data, ECMs have to put the results of that processing into action. They do this by using drivers to convert processing outcomes into action that is effected by actuators.

FIGURE 25–5 Single module Caterpillar ECM with integral memory and drivers.

ECMs incorporate all of the required system drivers within the ECM housing. The various drivers are responsible for outputting system reference voltages, powering up sensors, switching the EUIs, and governing all the emissions control hardware. The switching of EUIs is the responsibility of injector drivers. Almost all ECMs are "one-box" systems that house all the processing, memory banks, and drivers into a single housing, such as the Caterpillar ECM shown in **Figure 25–5**.

INJECTOR DRIVERS

Injector drivers are built into the ECM in all but the earliest versions of EUI fuel systems. They are the switching mechanism that energizes the actuator, a solenoid, in the EUI. Energizing the actuator in the EUI closes a poppet control valve in the unit so that fuel becomes trapped in the EUI pump chamber, making an effective pumping stroke possible. Some OEMs use the term **control cartridge** to describe the solenoid and control valve assembly. To shut down an engine, the ECM does not energize the control cartridge, meaning that no effective stroke is possible and the engine is no-fueled.

Depending on the OEM, different DC voltage values are used to energize solenoids in the EUIs. Most OEMs other than DD use voltage values that extend from a low of around 60 V-DC to a high of up to 120 V-DC. The reason for stepping the voltage to higher voltages is to kick the EUI solenoid into a faster response than could be achieved using a lower voltage pressure. It also helps compensate for variables such as lower circuit conductivity when the solenoid

coil is hot. OEMs tend to be specific about the actuation voltages of EUIs. Cummins states that it actuates its CELECT EUIs at 78 V-DC, whereas Caterpillar specifies that the average actuation voltage for its MEUIs is 108 V-DC.

The injector driver unit steps the voltage to these values using induction coils. The high voltage spike is initial and following this, the circuit holds at 12 volts. The inductive kick produced by the EUI coil when its magnetic field collapses as the ECM opens the circuit to switch it off is suppressed to prevent back-feed spikes.

Command pulses from the injector drivers to the EUIs can be referred to as **duty cycle** or **pulse width (PW)** and are usually measured in milliseconds. ESTs may display PW in either milliseconds or crank angle degrees. The software control algorithm determines the desired duty cycle in any given moment of operation, which is converted to an *effective* EUI pumping stroke by the length of time the solenoid cartridge in the EUI is energized.

DDEC DRIVERS

Detroit Diesel single-actuator EUIs are energized at a 12 V-DC electrical pressure. Because DDEC uses this lower voltage value, the ECM monitors the EUI solenoid response by analyzing the voltage wave and expresses this as **injector response time (IRT)**. By monitoring IRT, DDEC can compensate for small electrical resistance variables in the circuit to help balance timing and engine fueling. IRT is measured in tenths of milliseconds, and an out-of-spec value indicates a problem in the EUI or its electrical circuit. We will take a closer look at IRT toward the end of this chapter.

EUI OPERATION

Since their introduction in the late 1980s, single-actuator EUIs have undergone few changes, other than a trend toward becoming slimmer and lighter in weight. As indicated earlier, all EUIs are cam-actuated. Depending on the engine family, the actuating cam may be overhead or cylinder block–mounted. If an EUI is actuated by a cylinder block–mounted camshaft, the actuation train consists of a rocker, pushrod, roller tappet, and cam profile as shown when the camshaft is cylinder block located. **Figure 25–6** shows the injector actuation train used in a Caterpillar engine equipped with a cylinder block–mounted camshaft.

In an engine with an overhead camshaft, a rocker is still used to actuate the EUI. Using

FIGURE 25–6 Cutaway showing a Caterpillar MEUI actuation train driven by a cylinder block–mounted camshaft.

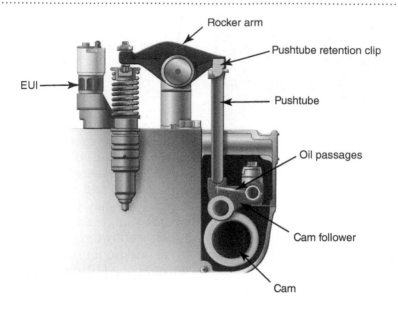

the rocker can reduce cam profile unit loading and amplify mechanical movement. This is required because extreme pumping pressures of EUIs require considerable mechanical force. The overhead camshaft actually simplifies the injector actuation train, as shown for the Volvo example in **Figure 25–7**.

OVERVIEW

An EUI has three basic functions:

- **Pump.** The EUI receives relatively low pressure from the charging circuit in the fuel subsystem, and converts this into injection pressures that can be as high as 30,000 psi

FIGURE 25–7 Volvo EUI actuated by an overhead cam.

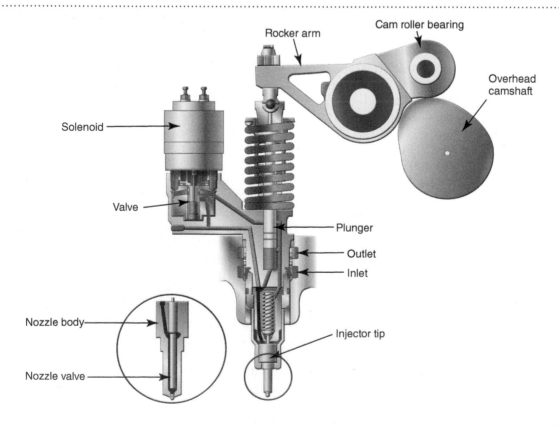

(2,2068 bar). Pumping is achieved by a cam-actuated plunger that reciprocates within a stationary barrel. This is known as the *EUI pump chamber.*

- **Control.** The EUI has an ECM-controlled solenoid valve. Fuel from the fuel subsystem flows through the EUI circuitry charging the EUI pump chamber. Initially, when the EUI plunger is forced downward in the pump chamber by cam profile, fuel in the chamber is simply displaced into the return circuit. However, when the EUI control cartridge is energized, a control valve snaps closed, trapping fuel in the EUI pump chamber. The fuel can no longer escape from the pump chamber, so a rapid pressure rise results: the instant the control valve closes, effective stroke begins. Rapid pressure rise results, producing injection-sized pressures sufficient to open the nozzle valve and begin injection. Injection continues as the EUI plunger is driven downward into the pump chamber. Injection ends when the EUI solenoid circuit opens, allowing fuel in the EUI pump chamber to escape to a **spill circuit**. As fuel escapes into the spill circuit, pressure rapidly collapses until it is insufficient to hold the nozzle valve open. When the nozzle valve closes, injection ceases. Fuel in the spill circuit is routed to a return gallery.

- **Atomization.** The EUI is equipped with an integral multiple orifice injector nozzle. This nozzle is a hydraulic switch consisting of a nozzle body, nozzle valve, and spring. It functions exactly like the multiple orifice injector nozzles studied in Chapter 21. The nozzle valve is subject to whatever pressure is in the EUI pump chamber. During EUI effective stroke, the instant the fuel pressure exceeds the **nozzle opening pressure (NOP)** of the valve, it opens to begin the injection pulse. The valve remains open and injecting fuel while pressure in the EUI pump chamber exceeds NOP. At the completion of effective stroke, the instant the EUI internal pressure is insufficient to hold the nozzle valve open, it closes, ending injection. Because NOP is defined by nozzle spring tension, it does not change: it can therefore be described as a *hard* value in a single-actuator EUI.

TWO-TERMINAL EUI SUBCOMPONENTS

Figure 25-8 shows a sectional view of a two-terminal Delphi EUI used in pre-2007 Caterpillar

and Volvo engines. It should be pointed out that the single-actuator EUIs used by DD function identically. Reference the callout codes in the description that follows.

1. Terminals. Connect to the injector drivers in the ECM.
2. Control cartridge. A solenoid consisting of a coil and armature with an integral poppet control valve (4). A spring loads the armature open. Energizing the solenoid closes the armature/poppet control valve.
3. EUI tappet spring. Loads the EUI tappet upward. This enables the tappet/plunger actuation train to ride the cam profile and raise the tappet after a cam-actuated mechanical stroke.
4. Poppet control valve. A valve integral with the solenoid armature. In Figure 25-8 the control valve is shown closed (solenoid energized). This prevents fuel from exiting through the spill port, trapping it in the EUI circuitry, enabling the effective stroke.
5. Plunger. The reciprocating member of the pump element, the plunger, is lugged to the tappet, so it reciprocates with it. In Figure 25-8 the plunger is shown in its upward position.
6. Barrel. The stationary member of the EUI pumping element containing the fill port, pump chamber, and duct connecting the pump chamber with the injector nozzle.
7. Upper O-ring. Seals the upper fuel charging gallery.
8. Lower O-ring. Seals the lower fuel charging gallery.
9. Nozzle spring. Defines the NOP value, which is typically around 5,000 psi (344 bar). NOP is initial and rebuild set by shims acting on the nozzle spring.
10. Spacer or shims. Define nozzle spring tension and, therefore, the specific NOP value.
11. Upper nozzle body. Machined with the ducting that feeds fuel to the pressure chamber of the nozzle valve.
12. Nozzle valve. The nozzle assembly is a hydraulically actuated, multi-orifii, valve closes orifice (VCO) nozzle. A full description of the operating principles of this type of nozzle is provided in Chapter 21.
13. Tappet. Cam-actuated by injector train.
14. Spill duct. The exit path of fuel from the control circuit.
15. Spill control circuit. This is open when the control solenoid is de-energized, allowing fuel to spill from the EUI. When the ECM

FIGURE 25–8 Sectional view of a Delphi EUI identifying the internal components.

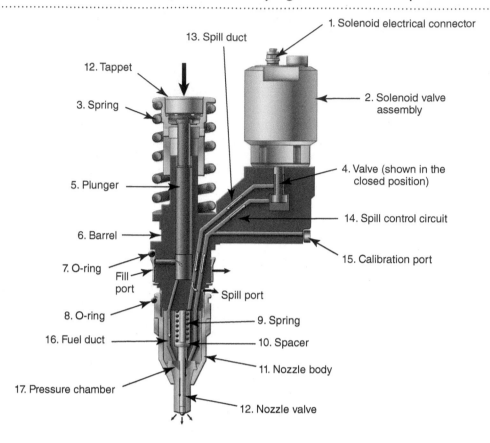

injector driver energizes the control solenoid, the spill circuit is closed off at the control plunger, trapping fuel in the MEUI. At this point, fuel is trapped in the EUI circuit so that plunger effective stroke can take place.

16. Calibration port. Used only for bench calibration to determine the fuel flow values.
17. Fuel duct. Connects the EUI pump chamber with the injector circuit.
18. Pressure chamber. The sectional area of the nozzle valve over which pressurized fuel acts to open the nozzle valve and begin injection.

TWO-TERMINAL EUI PERFORMANCE

Two-terminal EUI NOP values are typically around 5,000 psi (345 bar), sometimes a little more, sometimes a little less. When nozzle valve pressure differential ratio is factored (see Chapter 21), nozzle closing pressure values are typically 4,000 psi (275 bar). Anytime the nozzle valve is open, the EUI is injecting fuel. At the point the EUI actuating cam achieves peak

lift, the injector train unloads and the tappet ramps down the cam flank toward cam base circle. Simultaneously, the EUI spring lifts the plunger within the barrel, returning it to its fully retracted position and thereby exposing the fill port. Charging pressure fuel is then permitted to circulate throughout the MEUI passages for purposes of cooling the assembly and charging the pump chamber.

Charge pressure fuel flows through the EUI internal circuit and exits the spill port until the effective cycle is once again repeated. **Figure 25–9** shows the four operating stages of a Caterpillar MEUI. Caterpillar states that peak injection pressures in C-10 and C-12 engines reach values of 25,500 psi (1,758 bar). Peak injection pressures can achieve values exceeding 30,000 psi (2,068 bar) in pre-2007 C-15, C-16, and C15 engines.

Once you have understood the operating principles of the Delphi Lucas EUI we have just described, you will learn that the operating principles of other EUIs are nearly identical. **Figure 25–10** shows two types of DD single-actuator EUI known as the N2 and N3. The earlier N2 is heavier and bulkier than the

FIGURE 25–9 Operating phases of a Caterpillar MEUI.

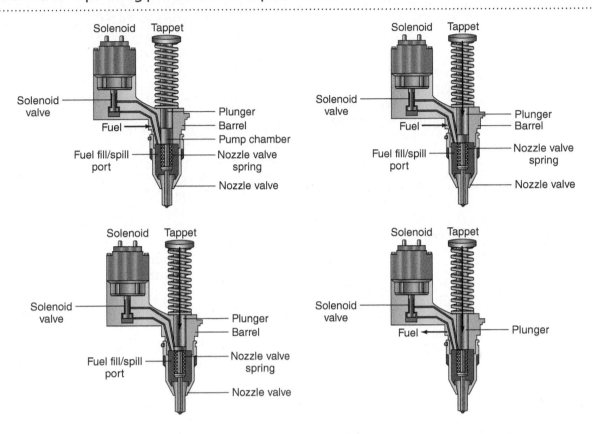

FIGURE 25–10 Component identification on single-actuator DDEC N2 and N3 EUIs.

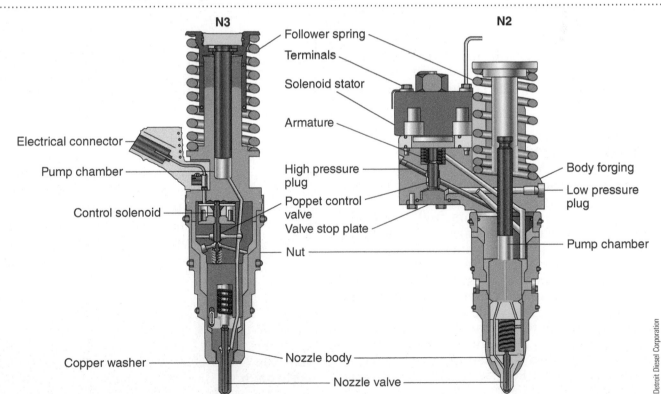

Detroit Diesel Corporation

N3 that replaced it; in addition, the lighter N3 was capable of producing higher peak injection pressures.

Peak Pressure

Peak pressure is the highest pressure an EUI can achieve. Unlike the NOP in an EUI, peak pressure is a *soft* value because it varies considerably depending on the length of the plunger effective stroke. Some single-actuator EUIs are rated to produce peak pressures of 30,000 psi (2,068 bar), but they will only do this during high engine loads when maximum fuel is required. When that same engine is being idled, the pressure may rise only slightly above the typical NOP value of 5,000 psi (345 bar).

Collapse Phase

Any hydraulically switched nozzle is subject to a collapse phase. The hydraulic injector nozzles used on single-actuator EUIs have hard opening and closing values. A nozzle with an NOP of 5,000 psi (345 bar) typically closes at a value at least 1,000 psi (69 bar) below NOP. Given that any time the nozzle is open, fuel is being injected—and that the size of the injected droplets depends on pressure—the largest droplets, requiring the most time to completely combust, are injected at the end of the injection pulse. The duration of the collapse phase of injection increases as peak pressure increases: simply, the higher the peak pressure, the longer (in real-time units) the collapse phase. The main reason that no hydraulically switched injector nozzles are used on post-2007 compliant, EUI-fueled diesel engines is the collapse phase characteristic.

CALIBRATION CODES

Most EUIs are graded with **calibration codes**. A calibration code is a bench test fuel flow rating of an individual EUI. This fuel flow code must be programmed into the ECM managing the engine so that it can balance fueling to the engine cylinders. Failure to reprogram calibration codes to the ECM can result in unbalancing engine fueling. Calibration codes may have to be alpha or numerically reprogrammed to the engine ECM by the technician when the changeout is completed or by connection online to the OEM data hub. Always consult the OEM service literature whenever EUIs are changed out from an engine.

DDEC CODES

The first generation of DDEC EUIs was not specified with calibration codes. DDEC then introduced three alpha codes rating EUIs with an A, B, or C code that had to be programmed to the ECM; A denoted the least fuel flow and C the most fuel flow. As time progressed, the need for more precise calibration coding meant that DDEC single-actuator EUIs began using codes that ranged from 00 to 99. DDEC calibration code reprogramming requires the use of an EST known as a **digital diagnostic reader (DDR)** in early versions of DDEC and of DDEC PC software in later versions. The programming of calibration codes is achieved in the customer data programming field. The injector cylinder number has to be selected first, after which digital calibration code is input.

CATERPILLAR E-TRIM

Caterpillar **E-Trim** is the Caterpillar means of evaluating how each MEUI flows fuel during operation. Typically, E-Trim is a four-digit number printed on either the solenoid or the upper face of the MEUI tappet flange (pre-2004 engines) or a flash file that must be downloaded using Caterpillar's Electronic Technician (ET) software (post-2004 engines). **Figure 25–11** is a graphic representation of the fuel flow differential that would be found in a set of injectors when subjected to factory bench flow testing. After this test, each MEUI is assigned an E-Trim code. After the E-Trim code has been programmed to the ADEM ECM, the fueling algorithm can adjust the duty cycle of each MEUI so that it can compensate for fueling variables.

Numeric E-Trim codes for each injector must be programmed to the engine ECM using Electronic Technician (ET) software each time an EUI is changed out. In post-2004 (ACERT engines), E-trim codes are downloaded online, then flashed to the ECM using ET: this is said to ensure greater accuracy and an assurance that the procedure is actually performed each time an injector is changed out.

> **TECH TIP:**
> Whenever an EUI or set of EUIs is replaced, the fuel flow code(s) must be reprogrammed. Failure to perform this critical step can result in unbalanced engine fueling.

FIGURE 25-11 Caterpillar E-Trim balancing of MEUI fuel flow rates.

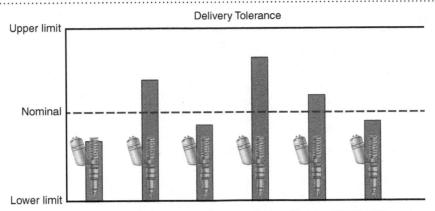

Calibration codes or E-Trim programming enables the ECM to either increase or decrease the actuation pulse width (PW) to each individual injector to balance engine fueling.
The calibration code or E-Trim value is determined by injector performance during final bench testing.

UNDERSTANDING IRT

DDEC EUIs are switched at 12 V, unlike most other EUI systems that spike the application voltage to values around 100 V. This means that the time lag between **beginning of energizing (BOE)** or the instant that the EDU initiates current flow to the EUI solenoid and **beginning of injection (BOI)** is to some extent variable. DDEC electronics are programmed to measure the response time between BOE and BOI by studying the actuation voltage wave of the previous two actuations of each EUI on a continual basis. Injector response time (IRT) is essentially the time lag between the output of the actuating signal at the EDU and the moment the EUI poppet control valve actually closes. It is measured in tenths of milliseconds and displayed on an EST. Because IRT is monitored, DDEC is capable of adjusting to minor electrical circuit resistance variations within a certain window to maintain balanced fueling and timing.

It should also be noted that there is a fractional lag between EUI control valve closure (BOI) and the actual opening of the EUI hydraulic nozzle valve (NOP), which truly begins injection. Similarly, at the completion of the switched duty cycle or PW known as **ending of energizing (EOE)**, there is not an immediate cessation of injected fuel because some fraction of time is required to drop the pressure in the EUI pump chamber to the **valve closing pressure (VCP)** value at which point the injection pulse truly ceases—**ending of injection (EOI)**. DD claims that this collapse phase is of shorter duration in N3 injectors than in N2s.

GRAPHING BOI, IRT, AND PW

If you are not intimidated by graphs, maybe the best way of understanding IRT is to look at what happens using a graph. **Figure 25-12** and **Figure 25-13** show the time and electrical waveforms that define IRT and PW, while **Figure 25-14** shows real-time representations of IRT.

MULTIPLE INJECTION EVENTS

As emissions controls and the requirement for fuel economy became more demanding, combustion in diesel engines had to be managed with a higher level of precision. A key to making this happen was to break up an injection pulse into more than one event. The extent to which a single-actuator EUI was able to achieve this was limited because of its hydraulically actuated nozzle. The following are some examples of how OEMs were able to achieve multiple injection events.

SPLIT-SHOT INJECTION

DDEC electronics, in conjunction with N2 and N3 single-actuator EUIs, could manage **pilot injection**, which DD commonly referred to as **split-shot injection**. This technology was a forerunner of the multipulse capability that became commonplace toward the end of the 1990s. The objective of split-shot injection was to manage ECM cold-start strategy designed to eliminate diesel knock and minimize startup smoke emission. Pilot injection in a single-actuator EUI breaks up the fueling pulse by switching the EUI at high speeds.

FIGURE 25–12 DDEC injection cycle time graph.

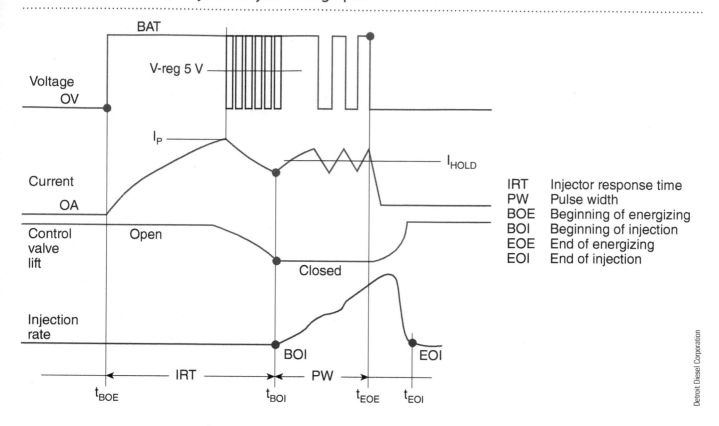

IRT	Injector response time
PW	Pulse width
BOE	Beginning of energizing
BOI	Beginning of injection
EOE	End of energizing
EOI	End of injection

FIGURE 25–13 DDEC injection cycle electrical waveform to time graph.

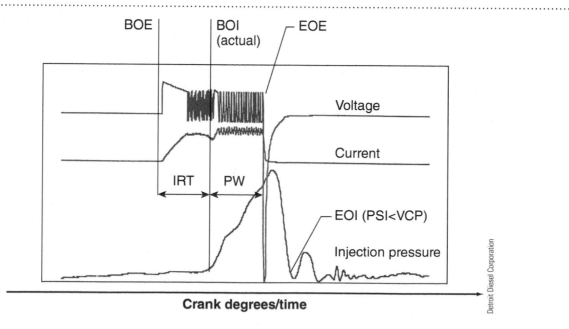

FIGURE 25–14 Response time effect on the injection cycle.

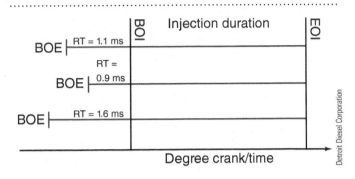

Degree crank/time

Detroit Diesel Corporation

Cold-Start Pilot Pulse

Using split-shot injection under cold-start conditions means delivering a short "priming" pulse of fuel to the engine cylinder, interrupting injection while the ECM then calculates the moment of ignition, and then resuming fueling with the main EUI fuel pulse. Priming the main pulse achieved two objectives:

- Lowered HC emissions during startup
- Eliminated diesel knock

Diesel knock is a cold-start detonation condition. It is caused by delayed ignition, resulting in an excess of fuel in the cylinder at the actual moment of ignition. When pilot injection is controlled by the ECM, it can be used to help manage the combustion process. Besides cold-start fueling, it is also used at low-speed, high-load lug. In addition to reducing engine wear, pilot injection also greatly lowers cold-start emissions.

MULTIPULSE INJECTION

A natural progression from pilot injection for engine management systems was to further increase the number of injection pulses per cycle. By breaking up the injection pulse, the engine management system is better able to manage the in-cylinder combustion process. Managing combustion gives the ECM better control of cylinder pressures along with the added bonus of reducing emissions. Because single-actuator EUIs use solenoid control cartridges that have to build and collapse magnetic fields in order to move their control valves, most are limited to a maximum of 3 pulses per injection cycle in engines run at rpms from 2,000 to 3,000 rpm. This limitation meant that single-actuator EUIs could not meet fuel economy and Environmental Protection Agency (EPA) emission standards for model year (MY) 2007.

OPTIMIZED IDLE

Some EUI-fueled engines from the mid-1990s can be programmed with optimized idle (OI). It should be noted that its use is illegal in many states. Optimized idle functions a little like a home heating thermostat: in jurisdictions where it is legal, OI can automatically start and shut off the engine to:

- Maintain a preset cab/bunk temperature
- Maintain battery charge
- Keep the engine warm

SERVICING AND DIAGNOSTICS

Single-actuator EUI self-diagnostics depend on the generation of management hardware and software used on the engine. The self-diagnostic capabilities of each system may be accessed by a range of means, beginning with simple flash codes and extending through a number of PC-based software, data management, and analysis programs. In the event of electronic system or component failure, the operator is alerted by the dash-mounted **check engine light (CEL)**. Codes may be flashed on CELs using the required switches (cruise control/dedicated toggle switch, etc.), or by using off-vehicle ESTs.

DIAGNOSTIC RECORDER

All EUI electronic management systems of the past decade have a built-in diagnostic recorder. This diagnostic recorder provides a continuous snapshot of engine operating parameters, state of health (SOH) broadcasts, and fault codes, known as an **audit trail**. Although fault codes can usually be blinked/flashed by diagnostic lights, more advanced ESTs are required to read audit trails.

Some more recent engine management systems can analyze sets of conditions logged into an audit trail and point the technician toward solutions to either a failure or potential failure. In addition, a technician can run a **snapshot test**. This is commonly used to diagnose intermittent problems in electronic management systems. The test is triggered by an event such as a trouble code and records data frames at the instant of, before, and after the event. These data frames display all the critical system parameters for analysis: The data immediately prior to the event can be critical in determining the cause of the code.

While the technician troubleshooting an electronically managed engine must not overlook the fact that an engine does have systems that are not electronic, most more recent engines require that diagnostic routines be driven electronically even if the problem is a mechanical one. For this reason, whenever diagnosing any problem on an engine, the manufacturer's sequential troubleshooting sequence must be observed.

INJECTOR CUTOUT TESTS

There is no appropriate way to mechanically short out any type of EUI. Doing so can damage the EUI and create fault codes. When a cylinder misfire has to be diagnosed, the ECM electronics are designed to perform this task in conjunction with EST-driven diagnostic routines. The diagnostic routines electronically cut out the EUIs in sequence and analyze the performance effect. Injector cutout tests have been used since the introduction of the first EUIs. Initially, they functioned to do little more than identify a *dead* EUI or engine cylinder. More recent injector cutout tests are known by descriptions such as:

- Cylinder cutout test
- Cylinder contribution test
- Engine balance test

SINGLE-CYLINDER CUTOUT

When an ECM commands an engine to run at a specific rpm and an injector cutout test is performed, first the average duty cycle of the EUI in milliseconds with all cylinders firing is displayed. If the set engine rpm is to be maintained during the test (this test is normally run at idle or 1,000 rpm depending on software generation), as each EUI is cut out electronically by the ECM, the PW of the remainder of the injectors will have to be lengthened if engine rpm is held at the test value. This would be true until a defective EUI was cut out; in this case, there would be no increase in the average PW of the operating EUIs, because average PW was initially established with that one dead cylinder.

Test Logic

If the example of a Series 60 engine with a dead EUI is used, the following would occur if an injector cutout test sequence were set with the engine running at 1,000 rpm. To run the engine at 1,000 rpm, the five functioning EUIs would

FIGURE 25–15 DDDL screen display identifying the results of an injector cutout test that has failed out the #2 cylinder.

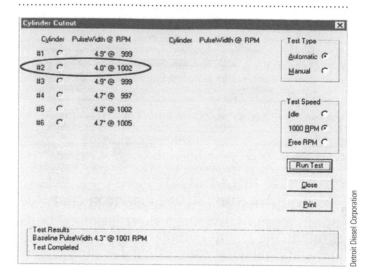

produce fueling values in PW milliseconds, which would be averaged on the initial display. When one of the five functioning EUIs is electronically cut out by the ECM, only four EUIs would be available to run the engine at the test speed of 1,000 rpm, causing the average PW to increase. As each functioning EUI is cut out in sequence, the average PW of the firing EUIs has to increase in order to maintain the test rotational speed of 1,000 rpm. However, when the defective EUI is cut out, there would be no change in the average PW because this specification was based on the engine running on these five cylinders at the beginning of the test. **Figure 25–15** shows the Detroit Diesel diagnostic link (DDDL) screen display following an injector cutout test that has identified a defective #2 EUI.

Multicylinder Cutout

Multicylinder cutout tests can do much more than simply identify a cylinder misfire. They achieve this by electronically cutting out cylinders in pairs, and in some cases, up to five EUIs in a six-cylinder engine. This type of testing matches each EUI individually against the others in the engine: this provides accurate data on exactly how each EUI contributes to fueling the engine. In addition, some ECM software diagnostic algorithms based on the cutout feedback can calculate such things as cylinder leakage. Although five-cylinder cutout diagnostic routines are unusual (some engines will not run on one cylinder alone), four-cylinder cutout

FIGURE 25–16 The Caterpillar ET GUI displayed following a cylinder cutout test that has identified a defective #5 EUI.

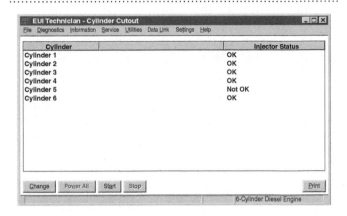

FIGURE 25–17 Delphi Lucas single-actuator EUI.

is commonly used. A four-cylinder cutout test focuses on each EUI in sequence, pairing it with each other EUI in sequence. This matching while running the engine on just two cylinders provides accurate data on exactly how much each injector contributes while achieving the no-load test rpm. **Figure 25–16** shows the ET screen display following a cylinder cutout test procedure: The test indicates that performance on engine cylinder #5 is *not OK.*

> ### TECH TIP:
> When performing cylinder cutout tests, especially multi-cylinder testing, it is not unusual for an engine to vibrate severely. In cases where there is an EUI, fuel, or cylinder problem, it is possible for an engine to stall.

EUI Solenoid Test

Some management systems run a solenoid state of health (SOH) before startup when the ignition circuit is activated. This test sequentially cycles the EUI solenoids, producing a rhythmic clicking noise. A dysfunctional solenoid is indicated by a pause between clicks. **Figure 25–17** shows a Delphi single-actuator EUI.

Interpreting Test Data

When working with electronic engines, it is sometimes easy to forget that the diesel engine is a complex hydromechanical assembly of interacting systems and that not all failures are electronic—or that some system failures cannot be easily identified by electronic troubleshooting.

In the event a cylinder cutout test has identified a cylinder misfire before changing out an EUI, it makes sense to perform the following routine:

1. Check for air in fuel. This can sometimes create a vapor lock in the system.
2. Remove the rocker housing cover. Visually check for damage. Check for evidence of damage to the EUI wires and perform a pull-check. Remove the EUI terminal connector and check for arcing.
3. Check the valve lash setting on the suspect cylinder. Adjust if marginally out of spec. Inspect the actuation train for the cause of valve lash well outside specification.
4. Ensure that the EUI hold-down bolt is properly torqued. Check the OEM service literature for the specification.
5. If steps 1 through 4 check out OK, remove the EUI and check for engine coolant exposure. Inspect the nozzle assembly for brown discoloration (indicates a fuel quality problem) or coking on the tip orifii.
6. If all the preceding checks are OK, you can assume that the cutout test identified an internal EUI failure and that it can be changed out. Some OEMs permit suspect EUIs to be swapped within the engine or with a known good injector; always check the OEM service literature before doing this and remember the variability factor of calibration code programming.

> ## CAUTION:
> Always observe OEM instructions for draining the fuel charging rail when removing EUIs from an engine cylinder head. When an EUI is removed, the contents of the fuel charging rail can end up in the engine cylinder if the cylinder head fuel gallery is not first drained.

CAUTION:

Some EUI-fueled engines are designed to cycle the engine on as few as three cylinders under certain conditions, with the objective of saving fuel and lowering emissions. This produces a clearly audible, multicylinder engine miss, which of course is exactly what it is. The instant the engine is required to perform any work, all six cylinders kick in and the engine runs normally. Do not be too hasty to diagnose an engine miss on an engine that produces a rough idle but otherwise functions well.

VALVE SET AND INJECTOR TIMING

A detailed account of adjusting cylinder valves is provided elsewhere in this textbook. When preparing to perform an overhead adjustment (set valves/time injectors) on an electronic engine, the first step should be to consult the OEM service literature. In describing this procedure, we are going to use the example of a DD Series 60 engine. Because this engine has evolved through three distinct generations of EUIs, it is essential to identify the engine you are working on, then reference the appropriate DD service literature.

DD prefers the use of go/no-go gauges when checking and adjusting valve lash. The procedure used to set EUI follower height requires a test tram, shown in **Figure 25–18**. However, it is important to identify the injector generation because the methods vary with each.

- N2 and earlier: Injector height set with follower up.
- N3 (2004–2007): Injector set with follower down.

We now describe the procedures required for adjusting and servicing the N2 and earlier EUIs.

DDEC N2 AND EARLIER EUI FAMILIES

This procedure essentially synchronizes the actuating cam geometry with the EUI plunger.

FIGURE 25–18 DDEC EUI timing tool.

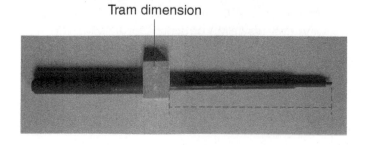

Tram dimension

The correct height adjustment gauge must be selected by consulting the DD specifications. Timing dimension tools of 78.2 mm, 78.8 mm, 80.3 mm, and 81.0 mm are commonly used with engines using N2 injectors, so ensure that you select the specified tool.

You can use the overlap method of navigating the overhead adjustment procedure on engines with DDEC N2 injectors. Identify valve overlap on any engine cylinder in the firing order. Adjust the valves and EUI height over that cylinder as indicated in **Table 25–1**. Then proceed to the next cylinder in the firing order until all the overhead adjustments have been either checked or adjusted.

1. Insert the dowel of the EUI height adjustment tool into the gauge hole in the EUI. Place a drop of the same engine oil used in the engine on top of the EUI follower; the lower ledge of the T on the height adjustment tool should just wipe the oil as it is rotated.
2. If the follower flange-to-EUI body height is incorrect, loosen the locknut on the injector rocker and, using a ⁣³⁄₁₆ Allen socket, adjust the rocker train to obtain the exact specified height dimension. Torque the locknut to specification and recheck the EUI body-to-follower height. Because this procedure sets a dimension, in an emergency—that is, when the correct EUI height dimension tool is not available—an accurate electronic Vernier caliper can be used to check or adjust this setting.

TECH TIP:

Consult the engine data plate before performing an overhead adjustment. This identifies the injector types, injector height setting, and required valve lash dimension.

TABLE 25–1 Series 60 with N2 EUIs Tune-Up Chart

Valve Overlap	Set Valves on Cylinder Number	Set EUI Height Dimension on Cylinder Number
#6	1	5
#2	5	3
#4	3	6
#1	6	2
#5	2	4
#3	4	1

EUI *Removal*

When the troubleshooting sequencing indicates that an EUI must be removed, it is essential that fuel be drained from the cylinder head fuel supply gallery before attempting the removal, using the following procedure:

1. First, clean off the exterior of the valve housing cover and remove it.
2. Drain the cylinder head fuel gallery by removing the supply hose from the inlet fitting (upper port) at the rear of the cylinder head. Collect the fuel that drains from the cylinder head in a vessel and then remove the outlet hose (lower port) from the fitting at the cylinder head.
3. Use regulated shop air (around 30 psi [2 bar]) and an air nozzle to blow out any remaining fuel from the fuel supply gallery.

WARNING:

Failure to observe the foregoing procedure will result in fuel from the galleries flowing into the EUI bore the instant it is removed; this fuel will drain onto the piston crown and may cause a hydrostatic lock and other problems in the affected cylinder.

4. Remove the two rocker shaft through bolts and remove the rocker assembly from the engine.
5. Loosen the EUI terminal screws. The EUI connectors have keyhole slots that permit them to fit over the terminal screw caps. Avoid attempting to remove the terminal screws, because this will damage the solenoid housing threads.
6. Use an injector heel bar to lift the EUI from its seated position.
7. Cap the EUI bore to prevent dirt from entering the engine. Handle the EUI with care.

EUI INSTALLATION

1. Install the O-rings dry onto the EUI body, ensuring that they do not roll or get cut. Then lightly lubricate the exposed area of the O-rings with engine oil and carefully install them on the EUI body. Lubing the O-rings before installing them onto the EUI body can make them more likely to roll. Lubricate the injector O-rings just prior to installation; doing this ahead of time may cause them to swell.
2. Insert the EUI into the injector tube. Visually align the EUI body between the valve springs. The EUI is seated by pressing it firmly into

position using the heel of one hand; usually this will produce a metallic pop if it seats properly. Ensure that the injector is centered on the alignment dowel.
3. The EUI is retained by a hold-down crab; position the hold-down crab and install the hold-down fastener. Ensure that the hold-down crab does not interfere with either the EUI follower spring or the valve springs; difficulty here indicates that the injector is not centered on the alignment dowel. Torque the hold-down fastener to the required specification.

WARNING:

The hold-down washer must be installed with the hemispherical side located downward, or the washer will be damaged.

4. Install the EUI wires by positioning the keyhole terminal over the terminal screw; next, position the terminal so that the narrow slot is immediately below the terminal screw and torque to the DD specification.
5. Install the rocker shaft assemblies.

TECH TIP:

The front and rear rocker shaft assemblies look similar, but are not identical due to different bolt hole center distance. Identify the rocker shaft assemblies on removal and take care to return each to the proper location on reassembly

6. Set the valve lash and EUI height dimension to specification.
7. Reinstall the fuel inlet and outlet lines to the cylinder head fittings and replace the valve housing cover.

N2 EUI SOLENOID REPLACEMENT

DDEC N2 injector solenoids are serviceable without removing the EUI assembly from the cylinder head.

1. Loosen the EUI terminal screws. The EUI connectors have keyhole slots that permit them to fit over the terminal screw caps. Avoid attempting to remove the terminal screws, because this will damage the solenoid housing threads.
2. Remove the four solenoid hex capscrews to remove the solenoid. The solenoid, load

plate, follower retainer, and capscrews should be discarded. DD stresses that the capscrews should always be replaced when undertaking this procedure.

3. Remove the spacer and seals from the EUI body. The seals may be discarded but the spacer *must* be reused. The spacer is matched to the EUI armature and cannot be interchanged.
4. Install a new seal in the spacer groove and position the spacer on the body with the seal facing downward. Lightly coating the seal with grease will help retain it during assembly.
5. Install a new seal in the solenoid groove and assemble the solenoid on the spacer.
6. Install the new solenoid capscrews through the load plate, follower retainer, solenoid, and spacer, threading the screws into the EUI body.

WARNING:

Do not reuse the used load plate, follower retainer, capscrews, and washers, or damage to the solenoids or screws may result.

7. Torque the capscrews in the correct sequence to the DD specification.
8. Using an electric etching pencil, write the final four digits of the injector part number on the load plate.
9. Pressurize the fuel system and visually check for leaks.

TIMING N3 EUIs

The N3 EUIs were introduced for the Tier 2 generation (EPA model year 2004) of DD Series 60 engines. The general procedure for timing both N3 and the post-2007 DDEC E3 EUIs (used from 2007 until 2010) is similar and is outlined here, but remember to consult the DD service procedure before performing this task.

1. Disable engine startup.
2. Remove the rocker housing covers.
3. Bar the engine in its correct direction of rotation. Identify a cylinder in which an injector actuating rocker is just beginning to depress the EUI follower: At this point and on this cylinder, both intake and exhaust valves should be closed, which is indicated by valve lash.
4. Fit a magnetic base dial indicator so that it can monitor the upward lift of the injector cam profile on that cylinder. You should set the pedestal of the dial indicator on top of the injector cam roller and adjust so that it is capable of measuring the full cam lift dimension.
5. Now continue to bar the engine in its correct direction of rotation until the indicator stops registering any further lift. At this point, the injector can be set.

CAUTION:

If you rotate the engine beyond this set point (i.e., the indicator needle begins to descend), you will have to back the engine up and repeat steps 3 through 5 because of engine geartrain backlash variables.

6. Beginning at the cylinder you have been working on, use **Table 25–2** to adjust both the valves and injectors.
7. Set the injector. Loosen the jam nut on the adjusting screw by backing off two turns.
8. Tighten the adjusting screw until the injector plunger bottoms out: Torque to 40 lb-in. (4.50 N • m).
9. Next, back off the adjusting screw ¾ turn. Now torque the jam nut to 30–35 lb-ft. (41–47 N • m).
10. The EUI is now adjusted. Next, set the valves on the corresponding cylinders identified in Table 25–2.

Injector Cups

Injector cups provide the means for seating and cooling EUIs. The injector cup is inserted into the injector bore in the cylinder head and has direct contact with the water jacket. As a consequence, this can be a source of coolant leakage to the combustion chamber. Injector

TABLE 25–2 Setting Valves and Injectors on N3 and E3 Series 60 Engines

Maximum EUI Cam Lobe Travel on Cylinder #	Adjust EUI on Cylinder #	Adjust Valves on Cylinder #
6	6	2
2	2	4
4	4	1
1	1	5
5	5	3
3	3	6

cup sealing integrity should be hydrostatically checked (see Chapter 9) when cylinder heads are serviced. **Figure 25–19** shows a sectional view of a Series 60 injector cup, but other OEM versions are similar. Caterpillar uses brass injector cups in older engines and stainless steel cups in more recent ones.

FIGURE 25–19 DD Series 60 injector cup.

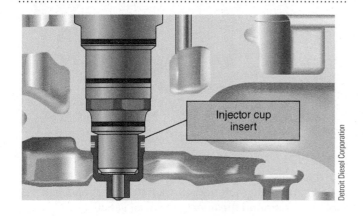

Injector cup insert

Detroit Diesel Corporation

CELECT PLUS EUIs

Cummins CELECT and CELECT Plus injectors use similar operating principles. The CELECT Plus injector (see **Figure 25–20**) is referenced in the following description.

CELECT injectors differ in metering and timing principles. CELECT injectors are fitted to cylindrical bores in the engine cylinder head. They circulate fuel at any time the engine is running and the gear supply pump is rotating. Fuel enters and exits the injector by means of annular recesses sealed by rubber O-rings. The lower annular recess is exposed to the supply gallery in the cylinder head and receives fuel at charging pressure (150 psi [10 bar]). Fuel passes from the lower annular recess to the internal injector circuitry, through the metering spill port, and is circulated through the injector and solenoid control valve ducting. It exits through a fuel drain in the upper external annulus. To properly understand the operation of this injector assembly, it is necessary to refer to the sequence of diagrams shown in **Figure 25–21**. Figure 25–21

FIGURE 25–20 Sectional view of the key CELECT injector components.

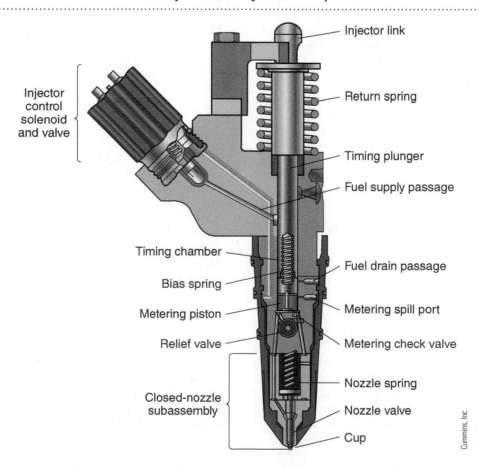

Injector control solenoid and valve

Injector link

Return spring

Timing plunger

Fuel supply passage

Timing chamber

Bias spring

Metering piston

Relief valve

Fuel drain passage

Metering spill port

Metering check valve

Nozzle spring

Nozzle valve

Cup

Closed-nozzle subassembly

Cummins, Inc.

FIGURE 25–21 The CELECT Plus injector operating cycle on an M11 engine.

Metering

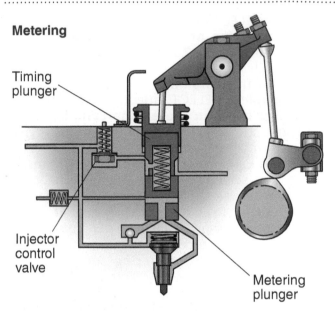

Metering

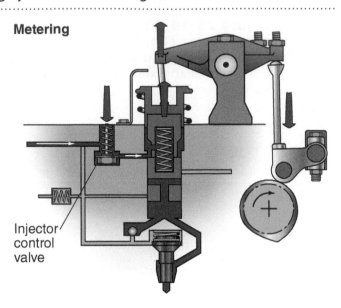

1. At the start of metering, both the metering plunger and the timing plunger are at their lower travel limit, as their actuating cam is at peak lift. The injector control valve closes, actuated by a 78-V induction coil derived spike delivered from the CELECT injector driver unit.

3. The ECM will determine the end of metering by switching the injector control valve to its open position. This action causes the metering check ball to seat and permits fuel to pass around the injector control valve.

Metering

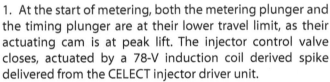
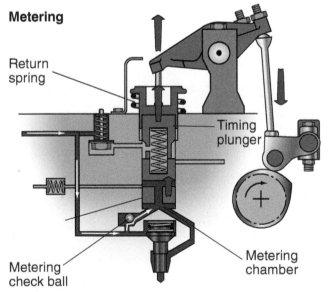

Metering

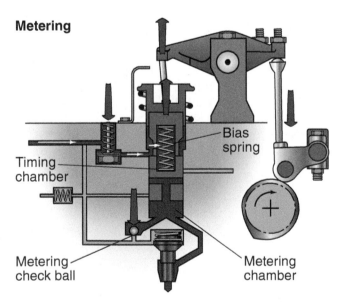

2. As the cycle continues, the cam ramps off the nose toward base circle, unloading the injector train and permitting the timing plunger return spring to lift the timing plunger. This enables fuel to flow past the metering check ball into the metering chamber. This flow continues as long as the timing plunger is moving upward and the injector control valve is closed. Supply pressure acting on the bottom of the metering piston forces it to maintain contact with the timing plunger.

4. Fuel at supply pressure then flows into the timing chamber, stopping metering piston travel. The bias spring ensures that the metering plunger remains stationary, preventing it from drifting upward as the timing plunger moves upward. This same force against the metering plunger results in sufficient fuel pressure below the metering piston to keep the metering check ball seated. The result is a precisely metered quantity of fuel in the metering chamber.

FIGURE 25–21 *(Continued)*

Timing

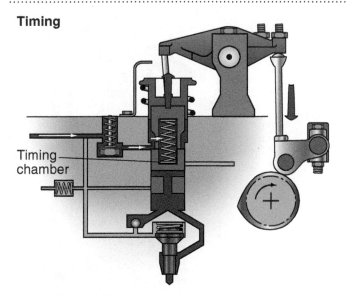

5. As the cycle continues, the injector train continues to ride toward cam inner base circle, permitting the timing chamber to fill with fuel.

Timing

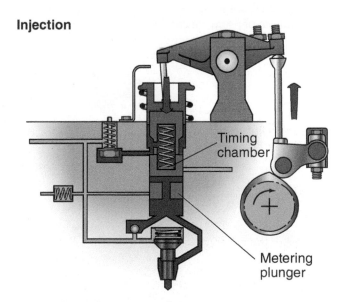

7. The delivery sequence begins when the ECM switches the injector control valve to its closed position, trapping fuel in the timing chamber. This trapped fuel acts as a hydraulic link between the timing plunger and the metering plunger; this forces the metering plunger downward with the timing plunger.

Timing

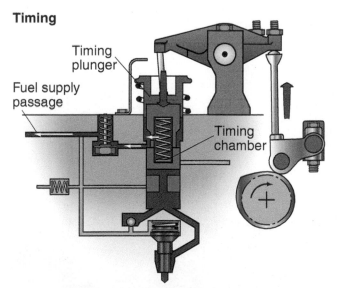

6. Next, the injector cam passes over the inner base circle location and begins ramping toward outer base circle. This action loads the injector train and consequently the timing plunger begins its downstroke. Initially the injector control valve remains open, allowing fuel to spill from the timing chamber and reverse-flowing it through the fuel supply passage.

Injection

8. Because the metering plunger is being driven downward (hydraulically), rapid pressure rise begins in the metering chamber.

FIGURE 25–21 (Continued)

Injection

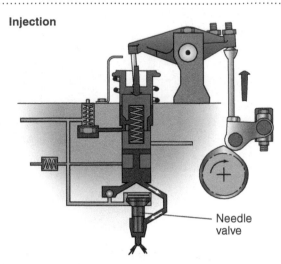

Needle valve

9. Ducting connects the metering chamber with the pressure chamber of the hydraulic, multi-orifii injector nozzle located at the base of the CELECT injector. When the pressure in the metering chamber (and therefore in the nozzle pressure chamber) reaches the NOP value, approximately 5,000 psi (340 atms or 34.442 MPa), the nozzle valve opens and injection begins. Fuel is forced through the nozzle orifii and is atomized directly into the engine cylinder. The minute size of the nozzle orifii means that they are unable to relieve the pressure as fast as it is created, and peak pressure is capable of rising well above the NOP value depending on the length of the effective stroke.

Injection

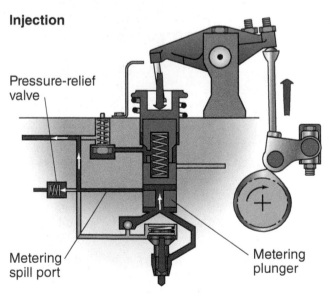

Pressure-relief valve

Metering spill port

Metering plunger

10. Injection continues until the metering plunger passes the spill passage. This action causes a collapse of metering chamber pressure, permitting abrupt nozzle valve closure. At this moment, the pressure relief valve will relieve, minimizing the effect of the high pressure spike that occurs at metering spill: The relief valve passage connects to the fuel drain line.

Injection

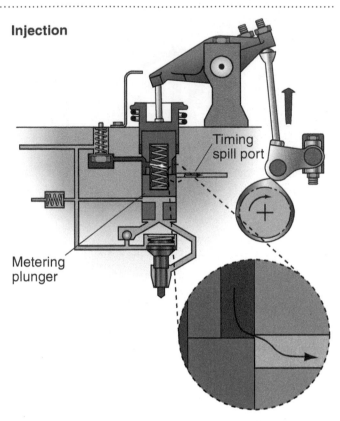

Timing spill port

Metering plunger

11. Immediately after the metering spill port is exposed by the downward travel of the metering plunger, its upper edge exposes the timing spill port.

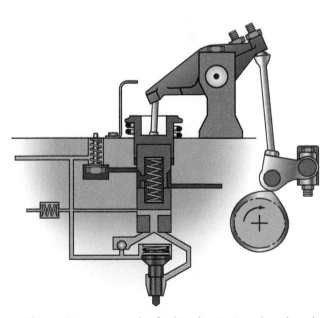

12. This action permits the fuel in the timing chamber that was used as hydraulic medium to spill to the fuel drain. This completes the cycle.

FIGURE 25–22 CELECT Plus injector.

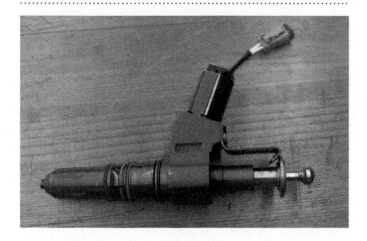

references the procedure on an M11 in which the camshaft rotates clockwise (CW) orientated from the front of the engine. The procedure for an N14 is similar, but you should note that the N-series camshaft rotates counterclockwise (CCW). **Figure 25–22** shows a CELECT Plus injector.

TECH TIP:

CELECT and CELECT Plus injectors, while sharing operating principles, are *not* interchangeable, as the latter incorporates increased orifii sizing, modified spray angles, and other performance enhancements.

BENCH TESTING EUIs

The vast number of single-actuator EUIs in circulation has resulted in a service repair infrastructure rather than of testing and repair. Some shops are equipped to bench-test EUIs for serviceability and designate failed units for replacement or repair at a fuel injection pump specialty shop. Repairing failed EUIs goes beyond the scope of this textbook, but diesel technicians should understand the service routines for bench-testing injectors for serviceability. It is good practice to run EUI test routines when reconditioning an engine that has a failure that is not related to the fuel system.

EUI TEST ROUTINE

Although the bench test fixtures are user friendly and the test profiles are software

managed, it helps to have some fuel injection shop experience to ensure that diagnoses are accurate. An EUI test bench fixture is required to mechanically actuate the EUI through its pumping stroke as well as to electrically energize the EUI control cartridge. The test bench fixture shown here is the DieseLogic ITU-101, but there are other simple-to-operate units available. First the unit should be mechanically installed into the test mounting fixture, as shown in **Figure 25–23**.

After mechanically installing the EUI bench to test fixture, it must then be electrically connected as shown in **Figure 25–24**. This allows the test bench to switch the EUI control cartridge to enable the unit to produce an effective stroke.

Usually, at minimum an EUI bench test fixture is required to evaluate the following data:

- NOP
- EUI output pressure

FIGURE 25–23 The EUI should first be mechanically installed to the test fixture. This figure shows a DDEC N2 injector installed into a DieseLogic ITU-101.

FIGURE 25–24 After mounting the EUI into the test fixture, it must be electrically connected by placing electrical connections onto the control cartridge terminals.

- Metered fuel quantity
- Back-leakage fuel quantity

Figure 25–25 shows the DieseLogic calibration graduates (vials) used to measure metered (sprayed) fuel quantity and the back-leakage factor, along with the bench fixture controls.

FIGURE 25–25 The DieseLogic EUI test fixture calibration graduates used to measure metered fuel and back-leakage volume.

SUMMARY

- All single-actuator EUIs share common operating principles.
- The fuel subsystems supplying the EUIs use either a gear- or plunger-type transfer pump to create charging pressures ranging from 60 to 150 psi (4 to 10.3 bar).
- Most single-actuator, EUI-fueled engines are managed by ECMs housed in a single module. The ECM incorporates the processing capability and output drivers required by the engine and emissions control system.
- EUI actuation voltage values range from 12 V-DC up to 120 V-DC depending on the OEM system.
- Single-actuator EUIs have three primary functions: pumping fuel to injection pressures, controlling effective stroke (fuel quantity), and atomizing fuel into the engine cylinder by means of a nozzle.
- All single-actuator EUIs are equipped with hard value, hydraulic injector nozzles. This means that NOP is set at a constant value.
- Some later EUIs are capable of pilot and multipulse injection events and can achieve peak pressures exceeding 30,000 psi (2,068 bar).
- Calibration codes are a bench test rating of how an individual EUI flows fuel. Cal codes must be programmed to the ECM each time an EUI is changed. Failure to reprogram the correct cal code can result in seriously unbalancing engine fueling.
- Electronic cylinder cutout tests can be used to identify a dead engine cylinder.
- More advanced cylinder cutout tests can provide an accurate assessment of engine cylinder performance balance. This is achieved by multicylinder cutout tests in which each EUI's contribution is matched against the other five in the engine.

- Cummins CELECT injectors differ slightly from other EUIs because they meter and time fuel delivery in a distinct manner.
- EUIs are not usually repaired in truck service facilities, but they are commonly tested using a bench test fixture. Bench-testing of EUIs

is good practice before reinstallation into a reconditioned engine that has failed for non-fuel injection system related reasons, as well as for diagnosing problems that the vehicle onboard diagnostic routines have failed to identify.

REVIEW QUESTIONS

1. Which of the following sets of pressure values would be typical of fuel subsystem charging pressure in a single-actuator EUI fuel system?
   a. 15–45 psi (100–300 kPa)
   b. 60–125 psi (400–862 kPa)
   c. 500–600 psi (3.4–4.14 MPa)
   d. 1,200–5,000 psi (8.3–35 MPa)

2. Which of the following tests would be most likely to identify a functional but weak EUI that was causing a cylinder balance problem?
   a. Single-cylinder cutout
   b. Sequential mechanical EUI train shortout
   c. Four-cylinder cutout
   d. Solenoid SOH

3. How many actuators are used on a two-terminal EUI?
   a. One
   b. Two
   c. Three
   d. Four

4. What force creates injection pressure values in a two-terminal EUI?
   a. Electrical
   b. Hydraulic
   c. Spring
   d. Mechanical

5. What defines the hard limit window available to the engine ECM managing an EUI fuel system within which an effective stroke must occur?
   a. Accelerator position
   b. Road speed
   c. Cam geometry
   d. Engine rpm

6. Where would you expect to find the injector drivers in most single-actuator EUI fuel systems?
   a. Integral with the ECM
   b. On the firewall bulkhead
   c. Under the dash
   d. Integral with each EUI

7. Which of the following values would represent a typical EUI hydraulic nozzle NOP?
   a. 60 psi (400 kPa)
   b. 120 psi (800 kPa)
   c. 3,700 psi (255 bar)
   d. 5,000 psi (345 bar)

8. Peak injection pressures from a typical two-terminal EUI may reach:
   a. 5,000 psi (345 bar).
   b. 15,000 psi (1,034 bar).
   c. 25,000 psi (1,724 bar).
   d. 30,000 psi (2,000 bar).

9. Caterpillar MEUIs are switched by the injector drivers at:
   a. 5 V-DC.
   b. 12 V-DC.
   c. 24 V-DC.
   d. 108 V-DC.

10. Technician A states that peak injection pressures produced by an EUI are a hard value. Technician B states that EUI nozzle opening pressure (NOP) in single-actuator EUIs is a soft value. Who is correct?
    a. Technician A only
    b. Technician B only
    c. Both A and B
    d. Neither A nor B

11. A single-actuator, EUI-fueled engine is at its usual operating temperature but at idle rpm appears to have an audible engine miss. Under load the engine appears to function normally. Technician A states that an EST should be connected to the data bus to identify the misfiring cylinder. Technician B states that the condition is probably normal, as the management electronics are sometimes designed to cycle the engine on three cylinders under certain conditions. Who is correct?
    a. Technician A only
    b. Technician B only
    c. Both A and B
    d. Neither A nor B

12. Technician A states that the force that creates injection pumping pressures in a two-terminal EUI-fueled engine is electrical. Technician B states that the nozzle valve in a two-terminal EUI is opened hydraulically. Who is correct?
    a. Technician A only
    b. Technician B only
    c. Both A and B
    d. Neither A nor B

13. After an EUI is identified as "Not OK" after performing a four-cylinder cutout test, what should be the next step?
    a. Immediately change out the EUI.
    b. Check that there is no other reason for the EUI failure.
    c. Reprogram the E-Trim code.
    d. Change out all six EUIs.

14. If an EUI is removed without first draining the charge rail supply gallery, where is the fuel in the gallery likely to drain?
    a. Directly to the oil pan
    b. Into the cylinder head water jacket
    c. Directly into the engine cylinder
    d. Into the lube oil circuit

15. Which of the following must occur to no-fuel and therefore shut down a single-actuator, EUI-fueled engine?
    a. Control cartridge in the EUI is not energized.
    b. Cylinder valves are held open by the engine brake.
    c. Control cartridge in the EUI is energized.
    d. Fuel supply at charge pump is shut off.

26

DUAL-ACTUATOR EUI SYSTEMS

Prerequisites: Chapter 18; additional reference Chapters 29, 34, and 35

OBJECTIVES

After studying this chapter, you should be able to:

- Identify the engine families and OEMs that have used dual-actuator EUIs.
- Describe the system layout and the primary components in a full authority, dual-actuator EUI-fueled, engine management system.
- Identify the truck engines using dual-actuator EUI fueling from 2007 to 2010.
- Identify the truck engines that currently (post-2010) use dual-actuator EUI fueling.
- Outline the role that the four primary subsystems play in managing a dual-actuator EUI-fueled engine.
- Describe the operating principles of a four-terminal (dual-actuator) Delphi EUI.
- Sequence the injection phases of a Delphi E3 injector.
- Describe how the ECM manages duty cycle in dual-actuator EUIs to control engine fueling.
- Outline some of the factors that govern the ECM fueling and engine management algorithm.
- Perform some basic troubleshooting on VECTRO III and V-MAC IV EUI-fueled engines.

KEY TERMS

advanced combustion and emissions reduction technology (ACERT)

advanced diesel engine management system (ADEM)

algorithm

clean gas induction (CGI)

common platform

common powertrain controller (CPC)

control cartridge

Delphi E3 injector

driver information display (DID)

electrohydraulic injector (EHI)

electronic engine control unit (EECU)

electronic unit injector (EUI)

engine management system (EMS)

four-terminal EUI

four-terminal MEUI

injector driver

motor control module (MCM)

nozzle control valve (NCV) actuator

pulse width modulation (PWM)

spill valve (SV) actuator

variable valve timing (VVT)

VECTRO

vehicle control unit (VCU)

vehicle management and control IV (V-MAC IV)

V-MAC

Volvo electronics III (VECTRO III)

INTRODUCTION

The dominant fuel system of commercial truck diesel engines was the single-actuator **electronic unit injector (EUI)** system, but by 2007, more precise management of combustion was required. At the launch of the Environmental Protection Agency (EPA) model year 2007, three diesel engine original equipment manufacturers (OEMs) adopted dual-actuator EUIs on engines that had previously used single-actuator EUI fueling:

- Volvo Trucks
- Detroit Diesel (DDC)
- Caterpillar

DDC

Detroit Diesel used the dual-actuator EUI on its post-2007, 14-liter Series 60 engine, the only version of this engine family available after 2007. The Series 60 was phased out of production in 2009, replaced by DDC's common rail fueled, DD family of engines.

CATERPILLAR

Caterpillar used the dual-actuator EUI fuel system on its post-2007, C11, C13, and C15 engines. However, Caterpillar—the market leader in commercial medium- and heavy-duty, on-highway diesel engines in 2006—announced that it would no longer be supplying highway truck diesel engines to the United States and Canada after 2010. The announcement fractioned Caterpillar sales to North American markets, though the company continued to supply offshore markets. As a consequence, it is not so easy to find examples of dual-actuator EUI-fueled Cat engines. **Figure 26-1** shows a left-side view of a post-2007 Caterpillar C15 engine.

VOLVO AND MACK TRUCKS

Volvo and Mack Trucks also adopted the dual-actuator EUI fuel system for their **common platform** engines, introduced in the 2007 model year. Volvo Trucks has a long history of using Delphi EUIs, so using them for the common platform families of engines was obvious. However, unlike DDC and Caterpillar, Volvo and Mack Truck engines continued to use dual-actuator EUIs after the EPA 2010 model year, so it is now the fuel system used in all of their current engine lineup. For this reason, as the dual-actuator fuel system is described, the primary reference will be the Volvo and Mack Trucks use of this fuel system. **Figure 26-2** shows a 2010 Volvo engine fueled with dual-actuator EUIs.

Volvo and Mack Engine Families

There are few real differences between the stable of common platform engines badged as either Volvo or Mack Trucks. The primary differences are those of paint color and name. In this chapter we reference the management systems used by Volvo and Mack Trucks to control their post-2007 product only. These are:

- Volvo dual-actuator EUI-fueled engines: VECTRO III
- Mack Trucks dual-actuator EUI-fueled engines: V-MAC IV

The Volvo-Mack common platform engines are:

Volvo VE D11 (11-liter)	Mack Trucks MP7 (700 cu. in.)
Volvo VE D13 (13-liter)	Mack Trucks MP8 (800 cu. in.)
Volvo VE D16 (16.1-liter)	Mack Trucks MP10 (1,000 cu. in.)

Although the Volvo engines are designated by metric specifications and the Mack engines by standard specs, both engines are fully engineered in the metric system. Because the OEM biases Volvo badging toward linehaul applications and Mack Trucks toward vocational (though this is by no means exclusive), there are some differences in the way torque and power are mapped into the engine electronics, along with how the exhaust aftertreatment system is handled.

Post-2007 versions of both Volvo and Mack Trucks engines adopted steel trunk (Monotherm) pistons and are equipped with standard internal and external (exhaust) compression brakes. All post-2010 versions of both these engines incorporated selective catalytic reduction (SCR) in the exhaust aftertreatment hardware. At the top end of the power range of the common platform engines, the 16-liter (1,000 cu. in.) engine can produce 625 BHP (465 kW) and up to 2,250 lb-ft. (3,350 N • m) of torque.

VECTRO and V-MAC

The electronics used to manage the EUI fueling on the Volvo and Mack Trucks common platform engines are nearly identical. The Volvo engine and chassis management system is known as **VECTRO**, a loose acronym for *Volvo electronic*

FIGURE 26–1 View of the left side of a dual-actuator EUI-fueled Caterpillar C15 engine.

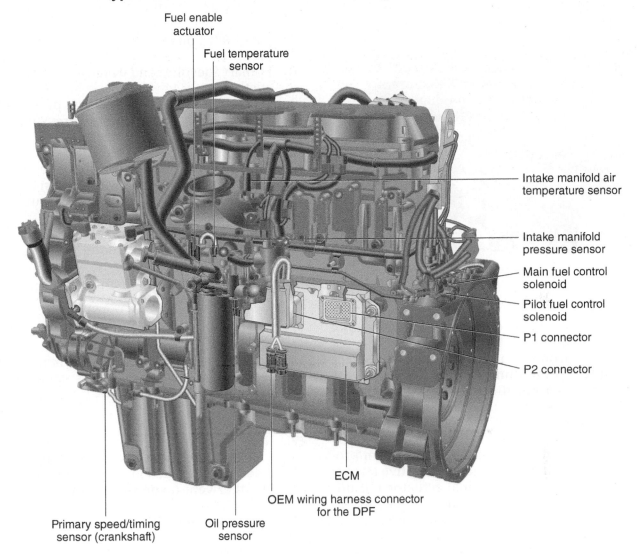

Typical view of the left side of the engine

Fuel enable actuator

Fuel temperature sensor

Intake manifold air temperature sensor

Intake manifold pressure sensor

Main fuel control solenoid

Pilot fuel control solenoid

P1 connector

P2 connector

ECM

OEM wiring harness connector for the DPF

Primary speed/timing sensor (crankshaft)

Oil pressure sensor

controls. The post-2007 version is known as **Volvo electronics III (VECTRO III)** or **engine management system (EMS)** to describe its chassis electronics.

The Mack Trucks engine and chassis management system is known as **V-MAC**, an acronym for **vehicle management and control**. The post-2007 version is known as **V-MAC IV**. Although the current VECTRO III shares a high degree of commonality with its previous versions, it is important to remember that V-MAC IV has almost nothing in common with previous versions of V-MAC.

Corporate Identity

As indicated earlier, Volvo and Mack Trucks have attempted to maintain some degree of corporate identity when describing each badged set of engines in the common platform family. This may be effective from a marketing viewpoint, but it makes it a little confusing for technicians learning the technology. It means that separate terminology and acronyms are required to describe exactly the same components depending on whether the engine is called a Volvo or a Mack. We can begin by stating that Volvo badged engines have their usual forest green paint job. In contrast, if the engine is Mack Trucks badged, the engine gets a brand new scarlet paint job. Engine color is the easy part. In dealing with this subject matter in this book, there is little option but to use both the Mack and Volvo terms and hope it does not create confusion.

FIGURE 26-2 2010 Volvo dual-actuator EUI-fueled engine. This engine is a show engine and is dressed in a blue paint job in place of the usual Volvo forest green.

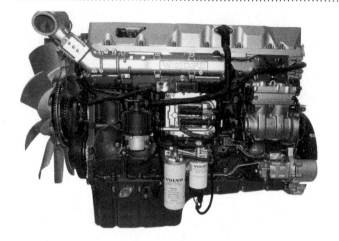

SYSTEM OVERVIEW

Mechanically actuated, dual-actuator EUIs have an effective pumping stroke managed and switched by the electronic control module (ECM) or **electronic engine control unit (EECU).** In this respect, they do not differ from single-actuator EUIs. Also in common with other EUI-fueled engines, the actual EUI plunger stroke is cam actuated. This means that the ECM is confined to a hard limit window (represented by cam profile) within which it can select an effective stroke. However, what makes the dual-actuator EUI different from single-actuator EUIs is the ability to control nozzle opening timing and pressure.

Dual-actuator EUI-fueled engines can be divided into the following subsystems for purposes of studying fueling control:

- Fuel subsystem
- Electronic input circuit
- Management electronics
- Output circuit

FUEL SUBSYSTEM

The fuel subsystem incorporates those components that enable the transfer of fuel from the fuel tank to the EUIs. However, because the fuel subsystem incorporates a return circuit, it is best introduced by looking at the schematic shown in **Figure 26-3** showing a current Mack EUI-fueled engine. If you follow the directional flow arrows in this figure it will make it easier to understand the description in the text.

Callouts for Figure 26-3:

1. Supply pump (external gear type)
2. Fuel tank
3. EECU (SA00 / MID128) mounted on fuel-cooled heat sink
4. Fuel filter housing pad
5. Pre-filter
6. Primary fuel filter and water separator (under suction)
7. Secondary filter (under charge pressure)
8. Fuel gallery (under charge pressure: supplies and returns fuel from EUIs)
9. Electronic unit injectors (EUIs)
10. Charging pressure control valve: defines charging pressures at around 60 psi (400 kPa)
11. Safety check valve: if tripped, routes fuel back to tank
12. Non-return valve: a siphon-break to check fuel drain-back during hand priming
13. Hand primer pump
14. Water-in-fuel (WIF) sensor
15. Dash-mounted water drain switch
16. Water separator drain valve
17. Bleeder valve (used in event of loss of prime)
18. Charging pressure test measuring point
19. Fuel pressure sensor (signals *actual* charge pressure to EECU)
20. Optional fuel heater
21. Valve peg (lock-off for servicing)
22. Non-return valve: a siphon-break that traps fuel in the primary circuit on shutdown
23. Bleeder valve (used in event of loss of prime)
24. Breather vent (aspirates fuel tank as fuel is pulled out)
25. Fuel return pipe

SUBSYSTEM ROUTING

For purposes of this description, we are going to assume that you are familiar with Chapter 19 in this textbook. Use the callouts in Figure 26–3 to follow the fuel from the tank, through the fuel circuit, and back to the tank again. A fixed clearance gear pump (1) is responsible for all movement of fuel through the fuel subsystem, so identify this first. For purposes of teaching the system, the fuel subsystem is divided into primary and secondary circuits with the supply pump dividing them.

Primary Circuit

Begin by locating the fuel tank (2). When the fuel pump is rotated, low pressure is created at its inlet and in the circuit upstream from it.

FIGURE 26–3 Fuel subsystem on a Mack Trucks EUI-fueled engine.

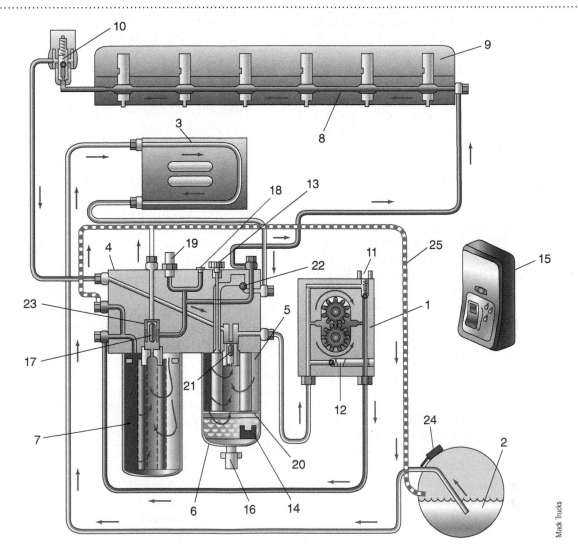

Mack Trucks

This lower-than-atmospheric pressure allows atmospheric pressure to act on the fuel in the fuel tank and push it through the primary circuit. We often (incorrectly) describe the primary circuit as the *suction* circuit, but you should nevertheless remember the term because it is commonly used. By following the arrows, you can see that fuel is pulled through a heat sink on which the EECU (3) is mounted: This helps cool the EECU and perhaps warm the fuel a little. Fuel is next pulled through a primary filter assembly that can have up to three functions:

- Primary filter
- Water separator
- Optional fuel heater

The primary fuel filter assembly is equipped with a water-in-fuel (WIF) sensor and a drain valve to remove any accumulated water. It uses a positive-type filter element to entrap larger particles suspended in the fuel and a centrifuge to separate water and deposit in the sump at its base. A one-way check valve known as a non-return valve (22) prevents fuel siphon from the primary circuit when the engine is shut down. The downstream circuit from the primary filter connects to the supply pump (1).

Supply Pump

The supply pump (1) is an external gear pump. The supply pump is usually flange mounted to the power steering hydraulic pump, which is driven by an auxiliary drive gear in the engine timing geartrain. Providing the supply pump is primed, when rotated it pushes fuel to its exit outlet and in doing so creates lower-than-atmospheric pressure in the circuit upstream from its inlet. Atmospheric pressure acting on the fuel stored in the fuel tank pushes fuel toward the inlet of the supply pump. Because fuel from the supply pump is discharged to the secondary circuit, you can say that it produces charging pressures. Actual charge pressure values are defined by the fuel pressure supply control valve (10), which represents the most restricted portion of the circuit. Charge pressure values are approximately 60 psi (400 kPa).

Secondary Circuit

Fuel discharged by the supply pump is routed within the fuel filter housing to the secondary filter (7). The secondary filter uses a positive filtration principle and is rated at 2 microns. Filtered fuel exits through the center of the secondary filter and proceeds to the fuel gallery that runs through the cylinder head. The fuel gallery supplies the 6 EUIs with fuel at the charging pressure. Charging pressure is regulated by the fuel pressure supply control (10) located at the fuel gallery exit on the cylinder head. Charging pressures to the EUIs are controlled at around 60 psi (400 kPa).

Auxiliary Fuel Subsystem Components

Volvo and Mack fuel subsystems are equipped with a range of auxiliary components that are designed to eliminate common maintenance problems. Some of these are described here, but you should note that not all engines are equipped with them.

AUTOMATIC BLEEDING An automatic bleeding valve (23) eliminates any air in the fuel charge circuit on startup. During bleeding, any air in the charge circuit is routed to the return line (25).

PRESSURE SAFETY VALVE A pressure safety valve (11) is a relief valve located in the supply pump. It is designed to trip in the event of a blockage or partial restriction in the secondary circuit. When the pressure safety valve trips, it diverts the fuel back to the pump inlet.

FUEL PUMP NON-RETURN VALVE The fuel pump non-return valve (12) is designed to act as a one-way check valve any time the hand primer pump is used. If you take a look at the circuitry surrounding the transfer pump, you will be able to see why this is required: When the hand primer pump is actuated, it creates low pressure in a portion of the circuit that is normally under charge.

WATER DRAINAGE VALVE The water drainage valve (16) is located in the water separator (6).

When water is detected by the WIF sensor (WIF sensor operation is explained in Chapter 19), the dash water drainage switch (15) illuminates and an alert is posted on the **driver information display (DID)**. When this occurs, the driver may activate the water drainage switch in the dash providing the following conditions are met:

- The ignition key is *on.*
- The engine is not running.
- The parking brake is applied.

When the dash switch is depressed, the drain valve (16) opens for about 15 seconds to drain any water in the sump of the water separator. In cases where additional drainage is required, it is necessary to wait for a minimum of 6 minutes before attempting to repeat the drain cycle.

MANUAL HAND PRIMER A manually actuated, hand primer pump (13) is located on top of the combination filter housing assembly. This should be used only when the engine is not running and is intended for use following repair work in which the fuel system has been drained or when the system has run dry. When priming the circuit using the hand primer, the inlet side of the charge fuel line to the cylinder head should be cracked loose.

FILTER PAD VALVE PEGS Filter pad valve pegs are used on both the primary (21) and secondary (17) filter mounts. The valve pegs are spring-loaded lock-offs that prevent fuel siphoning when the filters are removed for servicing.

INPUT CIRCUIT

Command and monitoring sensors and switches in the dual-actuator, EUI-fueled engines are consistent with other contemporary, electronically controlled engines. This subject matter is dealt with in some detail later, in Chapter 34. **Figure 26–4** shows a schematic of the Caterpillar C15 dual-actuator EUI-fueled electronic circuit.

MANAGEMENT ELECTRONICS

The architecture and organization of the chassis data bus and functions of the controllers networked to it have become considerably more complex as engines have had to accommodate better control over the in-cylinder combustion dynamics to reduce emissions and manage after-treatment systems such as diesel particulate

FIGURE 26-4 Block diagram of the dual-actuator EUI-fueled C15 engine electronic circuit.

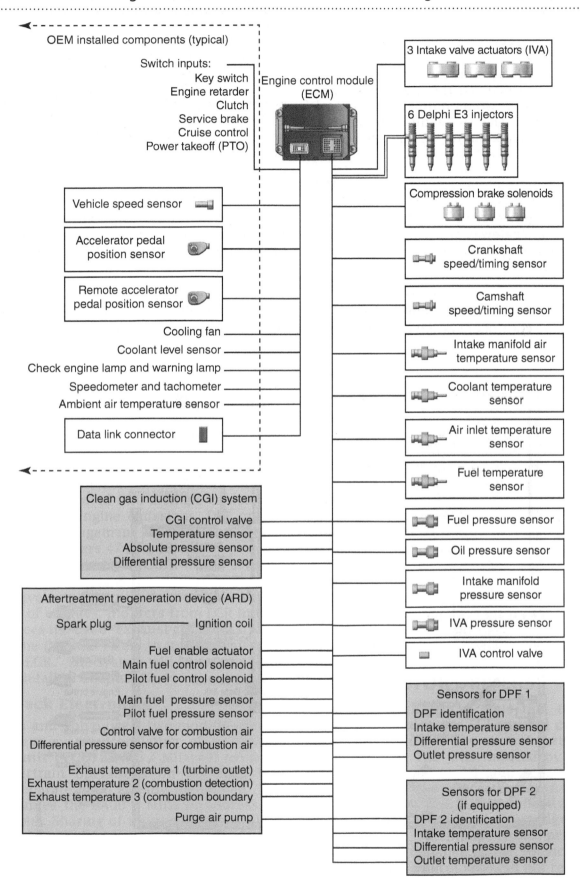

FIGURE 26–6 Engine wiring harness from a Volvo VE-D16 engine.

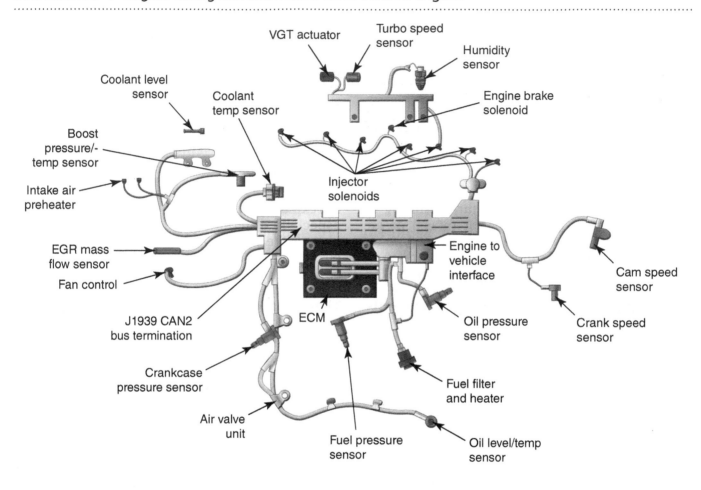

TABLE 26–1 List of Inputs to EECU (SA00 / MID128)

Fan speed %
EGR position 1
Vehicle speed
Accelerator position
Fuel supply pressure
WIF sensor
Engine oil pressure
Boost pressure
Battery Voltage
Ambient temperature
SIDs 1–6, EUIs 1–6
Engine rpm, flywheel sensor
V-Ref
Idle validation switch
J1939 control link

TABLE 26–2 Inputs to VCU (SA71 / MID144)

Vehicle speed
Accelerator position, percentage position
PTO output
Output shaft speed (tailshaft of transmission)
Retarder switches Volvo engines only
Idle validation switch, Volvo engines only
Cruise control and engine brake supply voltage
VECU power supply
Idle validation switch circuit
SAE J1939 control data link
Program memory
Cruise control set switch
Data exchange link to J1587/1708
Engine brake stalk for Cummins ISX option
Engine timeout

FIGURE 26–7 The ECM used on a dual-actuator EUI injection system.

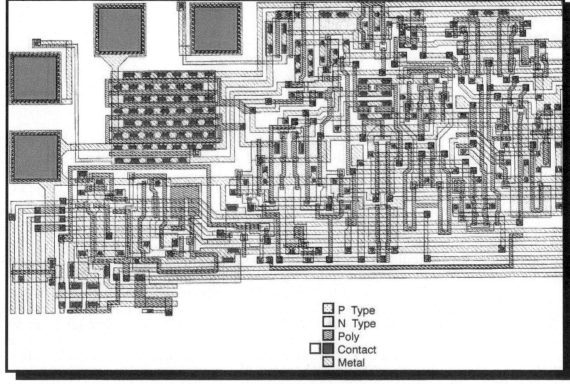

P Type
N Type
Poly
Contact
Metal

any kind of troubleshooting, you can use training or test engines to observe the **pulse width modulation (PWM)** voltage profile by connecting a lab scope to the actuator terminals, then run the engine. If you plan to do this, actuation frequency should be set for a maximum of 5 ms and voltage peaks set for a maximum of 130 V-DC.

OUTPUT CIRCUIT

Output circuit devices put the results of the computer processing cycle into action. In an EUI fuel system, the primary engine outputs are the EUIs and commands to the exhaust aftertreatment hardware. Other outputs are V-Ref and any information broadcast to the data backbone, such as instrument cluster displays and powertrain management.

DUAL-ACTUATOR EUIS

All three OEMs using dual-actuator EUIs use the **Delphi E3 injector**. This will be referred to exclusively in the descriptions that follow. The Delphi E3 EUI is sometimes referred to as a **four-terminal EUI**. The Delphi E3 is required to be mechanically actuated by an injector train in the same way cylinder valves are actuated. In an engine with an overhead camshaft, a rocker is used to actuate the EUI. Effective stroke of the EUI is electronically controlled by the ECM or EECU, specifically by the injector drivers. Additional ECM/EECU drivers are required to actuate the nozzle control solenoid.

Delphi E3

Because Volvo-Mack is the only OEM using dual-actuator EUIs in post-2010 engines, their terminology is going to be used in the description that follows. Caterpillar and DDC use different terminology but their EUIs function identically. The four-terminal Delphi E3 injector has a pair of actuators with quite different functions:

- **Spill valve (SV) actuator**: The ECM/EECU switched control cartridge that fulfills the same role as the control solenoid in the two-terminal EUI. In other words, it opens and closes the spill circuit to manage EUI effective stroke. For an effective stroke to take place, the actuating cam must be in the process of driving the E3 injector plunger downward, so this can only occur when the cam is ramping from IBC to OBC.
- **Nozzle control valve (NCV) actuator**: The NCV is what makes the E3 distinct from all other EUIs. The NCV actuator is integrated into the EUI body, as shown in **Figure 26–8**. The NCV actuator is an electrohydraulic nozzle that allows a soft nozzle opening pressure (NOP) value.

E3 Construction

Four-terminal EUIs have eliminated three of the major disadvantages of earlier generations of EUIs. They have the following advantages in comparison with their predecessors:

- Slim, lightweight assembly with no protruding control cartridge.
- Soft value NOPs allowing the ECM complete control over injection timing and injection pressure.
- Cessation of injection at high delivery pressure, allowing for the smallest size droplets to be delivered at the end of the injection pulse. This results in eliminating the prolonged pressure collapse phase at the end of injection that disadvantaged single-actuator EUIs.

Despite their increased complexity, four-terminal EUIs weigh about one-half of an equivalent two-terminal EUI. In addition, the obstruction to the injector and valve trains created by the protruding control solenoid cartridge has been significantly reduced. Figure 26–8 shows the nomenclature Volvo-Mack uses to describe the E3 injector: Use this to guide you through the following description of its operating principles.

E4 Operating Principles

In terms of general operating principles, four-terminal EUIs such as the Delphi E3 injectors are essentially a "two-terminal EUI" fitted with an ECM/EECU-controlled **electrohydraulic injector (EHI)** nozzle. EHI nozzles are the subject of some detailed study in Chapter 21, so you may want to reference that chapter again. We are referencing **Figure 26–9**, **Figure 26–10**, and **Figure 26–11** with the assumption that you have a good understanding of how EHIs operate.

AT REST For most of the cycle, the E3 will appear as it is shown in Figure 26–9. Fuel at the charge pressure flows into the EUI and circulates through the pump chamber and nozzle assembly, exiting through the spill circuit. Note that both the actuators are de-energized and that the EUI pump plunger is in its raised position because the injector cam is on its IBC. In this phase, the nozzle needle valve is held seated by spring force. For the larger portion of the cycle, the E3 injector will be in this at rest position.

Actuator status:

SV actuator:	de-energized
NCV actuator:	de-energized

FIGURE 26–8 E3 EUI nomenclature.

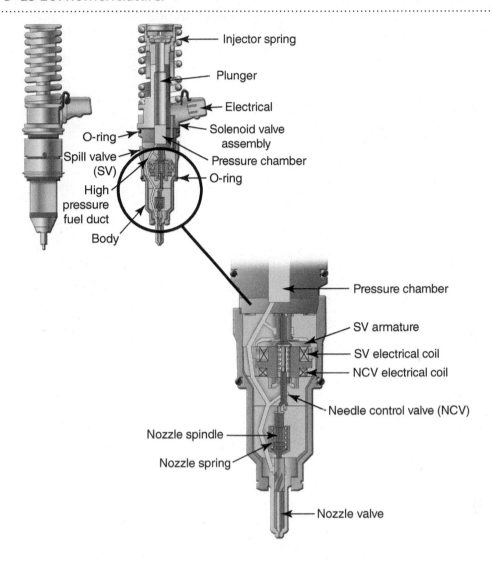

PRESSURIZING Pressurizing begins when the injector cam profile begins to ramp off its IBC: This actuates the EUI plunger, driving it downward in its bore. When the ECM/EECU energizes the SV actuator, the spill circuit closes, trapping fuel in the pump chamber underneath the plunger. As pressure rise is created by the descending plunger, identical pressure acts on both the upper and lower pressure fields. However, because the sectional area of the upper pressure field (acting on the nozzle control piston) exceeds that of the lower pressure field (acting on the needle pressure chamber sectional area), the nozzle needle valve remains firmly seated. In this phase the nozzle needle valve is held seated by a combination of spring force and hydraulic force acting on the needle control piston. In the pressurizing phase, pressure rise is taking place

within the E3 but no fuel is being injected. In this way, pressures can be driven up to values that greatly exceed those achieved in single-actuator EUIs before the injection pulse begins. Figure 26–10 shows the E3 pressurizing phase.

Actuator status:

SV actuator:	energized
NCV actuator:	de-energized

INJECTION When the desired NOP is achieved within the E3 circuit, the ECM/EECU energizes the NCV actuator. This pulls the NCV valve into the NCV actuator, collapsing the upper pressure chamber field. Because the upper pressure chamber field collapses and the lower pressure chamber field remains the same, hydraulic force lifts the nozzle needle valve, beginning injection. While injection

FIGURE 26–9 E3 EUI: At rest phase.

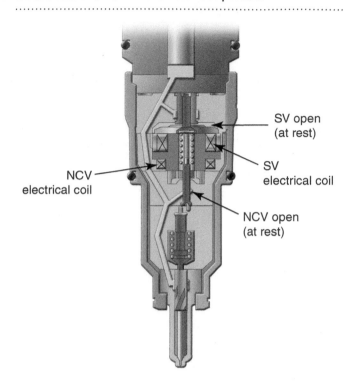

NCV electrical coil

SV open (at rest)

SV electrical coil

NCV open (at rest)

FIGURE 26–10 E3 EUI: Pressurizing phase.

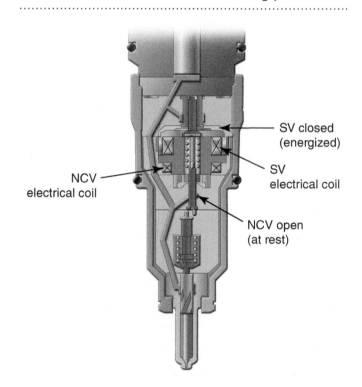

NCV electrical coil

SV closed (energized)

SV electrical coil

NCV open (at rest)

continues, the NCV valve remains lifted, which means no pressure can build in the upper pressure chamber: The exit flow area spilling fuel from the upper chamber is very small, so spilling fuel

FIGURE 26–11 Four-terminal EUI: Injection phase.

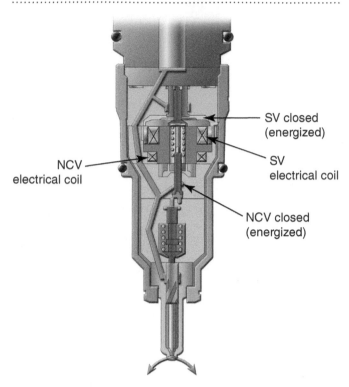

NCV electrical coil

SV closed (energized)

SV electrical coil

NCV closed (energized)

from the upper pressure field has little effect on the pressure in the remainder of the E3 circuit. Figure 26–11 shows a four-terminal EUI during injection: Note that both actuators are energized.

Actuator status:

SV actuator:	energized
NCV actuator:	energized

END OF INJECTION PULSE The EECU ends an injection pulse by de-energizing the NCV. Spring force slams the NCV downward, closing the NCV spill passage, and consequently permits almost instant reestablishment of the upper pressure field. Hydraulic force acting on the nozzle needle control piston abruptly closes the nozzle needle valve, ending the injection pulse.

Actuator status:

SV actuator:	energized
NCV actuator:	de-energized

MULTIPULSE INJECTION The dual-actuator, four-terminal EUI lends itself to multipulse injection. For multipulse injection to take place, the NCV actuator is energized multiple times during a single mechanical downstroke of the EUI plunger. The advantages of multipulse injection relate to better combustion efficiency and lower emissions. Four-terminal EUIs better suit multiple pulse injection events because the NOP can be made to rise incrementally with each successive pulse, producing the smallest droplets late in the combustion phase.

Actuator status:

SV actuator:	energized
NCV actuator:	cycling ON and OFF

END OF INJECTION PHASE The injection phase ends when both the SV and NCV actuators are de-energized by the ECM/EECU drivers. This necessarily must occur before peak lift is attained by the injector actuation cam. Because EUIs are mechanically actuated by cam profile, the ECM/EECU can only switch effective strokes while the EUI plunger is descending. So, in cases where the EECU **algorithm** requires multiple injection pulses during one cycle (that is, one injection phase), these must occur within a hard window defined by cam profile. Thus, at the completion of the injection phase, the actuating cam profile ramps down to IBC and both actuators are de-energized: The "at rest" status resumes.

Actuator status:

SV actuator:	de-energized
NCV actuator:	de-energized

Advantages of the E3 EUI

The key advantage of the E3 EUI over the two-terminal versions it replaced is the incorporation of the EHI nozzle. This allows ECM/EECU complete control over the NOP. Remember that pressure at the nozzle's orifii determines the size of the fuel droplets that exit the nozzle. Because the ECM/EECU can control the pressure, it removes the disadvantages associated with the hard opening and closing values in the two-terminal version. Additionally, the E3 uses more advanced manufacturing technology to make it lighter and much less bulky.

Fuel Calibration Codes

In common with other EUIs, E3 EUIs have to be calibration programmed to the ECM/EECU managing the engine. Volvo and Mack Trucks four-terminal injectors have a fuel flow code printed on the side of the unit. The code numeric value is established when an EUI is factory bench-tested and a precise determination is made of how the injector flows fuel. This data is required by the

FIGURE 26–12 Mack Trucks 2010 MP8 engine with the cylinder head cut away to show a sectioned E3 injector.

ECM/EECU to ensure that the fueling to each engine cylinder is balanced by compensating for minor hydraulic differences between injectors. A new fuel calibration code for an EUI must be programmed to the EECU when it is changed out. **Figure 26–12** shows a Mack Trucks MP8 engine with the cylinder head cut away to display the E3 injector.

CAUTION:

Failure to reprogram fuel calibration codes when EUIs are replaced will result in the ECM/EECU using fuel flow data of the previous injector programming, which can result in engine fueling balance problems.

CAUTION:

Always observe OEM instructions for draining the fuel manifold when removing EUIs from an engine cylinder head. When an EUI is removed, the contents of the fuel charging rail end up in the engine cylinder if the cylinder head fuel gallery is not first drained.

INSTALLATION OF A DELPHI E3 EUI

In describing the installation of an E3 dual-actuator EUI, we are going to use a DDC post-2007 Series 60 engine as our example. However, the procedure differs little from that of the other two OEMs using this fuel system.

PRE-INSTALLATION CHECKS

If it is suspected that the fuel system is contaminated (depends on why the EUI was pulled), perform the following steps:

1. Drain the fuel tanks and refill with clean fuel.
2. Replace the fuel filter(s) and clean the fuel/water separator.
3. Visually inspect the EUIs for damage and replace as required. **Figure 26–13** shows an E3 injector.

Once the injector has been evaluated as being fit for reinstallation, use the following procedure:

1. Remove any leftover fuel from the injector bore. If fuel is trapped between the top of the injector bore tube and the lower injector O-ring seal, it may seep into the injector bore tube sealing ring, causing it to swell and leak.
2. Make sure to replace the EUI O-rings, washers, and hold-down clamp bolts, all of which are considered one-off use items. Failure to do this can result in leaks.
3. Make sure the injector bore is thoroughly clean. When cleaning the injector sleeves in the cylinder head, ensure that dirt and debris do not enter the fuel supply and return galleries. Avoid using power tools to clean the injector sleeves, because these may remove material.

FIGURE 26–13 An out-of-engine Delphi E3 injector.

FIGURE 26–14 The external seals used on a DDC Delphi E3 injector.

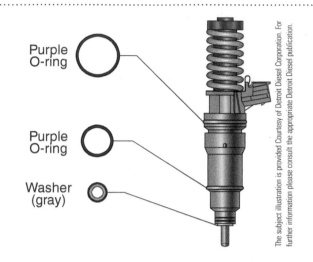

Purple O-ring

Purple O-ring

Washer (gray)

The subject illustration is provided Courtesy of Detroit Diesel Corporation. For further information please consult the appropriate Detroit Diesel publication.

4. Install a new washer on the EUI nozzle seat.
5. The E3 external O-rings must be lubricated with diesel fuel prior to installation into the cylinder head. Install onto the injector body dry, ensuring that they are not rolled, then smear with fuel. **Figure 26–14** shows the two E3 O-rings and the nozzle sealing washer.
6. Make a note of the injector calibration code, because this will have to be programmed to the ECM after installation of the E3. **Figure 26–15** shows the location of the calibration code on a DDEC E3 injector.
7. If the E3 is new or reconditioned, remove nozzle tip protector.

FIGURE 26–15 Location of the calibration code on a DDC Delphi E3 injector. 1. Injector body. 2. Calibration code. The cal code must be programmed to the ECM any time an injector is changed out.

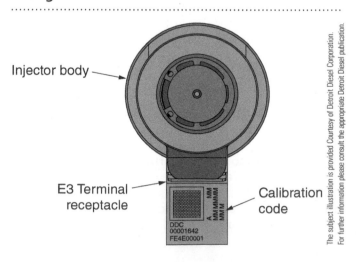

Injector body

E3 Terminal receptacle

Calibration code

DDC
00001642
FE4E00001

The subject illustration is provided Courtesy of Detroit Diesel Corporation. For further information please consult the appropriate Detroit Diesel publication.

FIGURE 26–16 Hold-down hardware used on an E3 injector: 1. Hold-down clamp. 2. Hold-down washer. 3. E3 injector body.

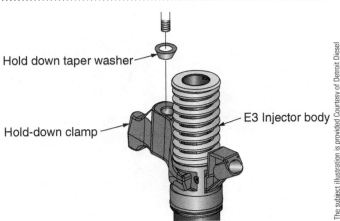

Hold down taper washer

Hold-down clamp

E3 Injector body

FIGURE 26–17 Installation of an E3 into a DDC Series 60 cylinder head. 1. Hold-down clamp. 2. Injector hold-down bolt. 3. Hold-down washer. 4. E3 terminal connector. 5. E3 injector (installed).

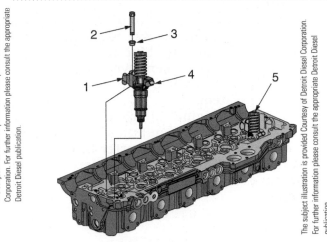

The subject illustration is provided Courtesy of Detroit Diesel Corporation. For further information please consult the appropriate Detroit Diesel publication.

The subject illustration is provided Courtesy of Detroit Diesel Corporation. For further information please consult the appropriate Detroit Diesel publication.

8. Install a new injector hold-down clamp washer. The curved side of the washer fits into a corresponding curved cup located in the injector hold-down clamp, as shown in **Figure 26–16**.

9. Using a new injector hold-down clamp bolt, align the hold-down clamp over the retaining bolt hole and torque using the following procedure:
   - Torque the hold-down bolt to 37 lb-ft (50 N • m).
   - Back off the hold-down bolt exactly 60 degrees ($\frac{1}{6}$ of a turn, or 1 hex flat). Do not fully loosen the bolt.
   - **Re-torque the bolt to 26 lb-ft (35 N • m).**
   - Now turn the bolt another 90 degrees (¼ of a turn).
   - No further adjustment is required.

   Figure 26–17 shows a Series 60 cylinder head equipped with E3 injectors.

10. Ensure that the injector wiring harness connector is installed into the lower rocker cover with the notch facing upward. Unless the harness connector is properly installed, its mating connector cannot be installed. **Figure 26–18** shows an E3 injector.

11. Insert the E3 EUI harness plug into the E3 connector, making sure that the locking tang clicks into place.

12. Apply a small amount of clean engine oil to the plunger area of the fuel injector, as indicated in **Figure 26–19**.

13. With the E3 injector installed, you can adjust the intake and exhaust valve clearances and set the injector clearance.

FIGURE 26–18 E3 injector.

FIGURE 26–19 Apply a small amount of clean engine oil to the oil hole in the plunger of the E3 injector as indicated by the arrow. 1. Follower. 2. Plunger. 3. Actuator module. 4. E3 body. 5. Nozzle supply duct. 6. Nozzle valve.

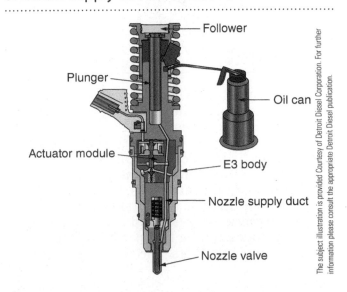

Follower

Plunger

Oil can

Actuator module

E3 body

Nozzle supply duct

Nozzle valve

The subject illustration is provided Courtesy of Detroit Diesel Corporation. For further information please consult the appropriate Detroit Diesel publication.

14. Install the Jake brakes.
15. Using the appropriate EST, program the calibration codes recorded in step 6, ensuring that you get the cylinder location correct and observe the OEM programming routine.
16. Bar the engine over for two complete revolutions, observing the way each EUI is actuated and checking for binding.
17. Install the valve rocker cover assembly.
18. Reconnect the vehicle batteries and prime the fuel system.
19. Crank the engine in 15-second cycles, allowing a couple of minutes between each cranking cycle for the starter to cool. The system is self-priming and you are unlikely to have to do this for more than three cycles.

BENCH-TESTING E3 INJECTORS

At the time of writing, the only test bench capable of running proper test profiles on Delphi E3 injectors is the Hartridge AVM2-PC, an advanced PC-based diesel fuel pump test stand capable of testing most current EHIs used on CR, EUP, and EUI fuel systems—along with just about any other type of diesel fuel system in the marketplace. The AVM2-PC uses a modular design, which means that functionality can be added on as and when necessary. The test bench is equipped with an LCD display and Hartridge's in-house Magmah software. Magmah software uses a Windows operating environment. The test bench fixture uses a pneumatic-over-hydraulic system to replicate

FIGURE 26–20 A Hartridge AVM2-PC equipped with Magmah software; required to test Delphi E3 injectors.

Courtesy of Hartridge Limited

the required mechanical actuation of the EUI and can simulate the OEM ECM driver signals to activate the two E3 electronic circuits. **Figure 26–20** shows the Hartridge test bench fixture. However, because of its cost you are likely to see this only in specialty fuel injection shops. It is anticipated that aftermarket E3 test benches will be available in the near future. This means that, at the time of writing, suspect E3 injectors should be returned to the OEM.

SUMMARY

- Dual-actuator EUIs were introduced in 2007 and were used by Caterpillar in C11, C13, and C15 ACERT engines; by DDC in its 14-liter Series 60, and by the entire range of Volvo and Mack Trucks common platform engines.
- The only OEM using Delphi E3 injectors for highway engines after EPA model year 2010 (in the U.S./Canada markets) is Volvo-Mack.
- The numeric values used in Volvo engine family codes can be interpreted as the engine displacement in liters. The VE-D11 code can be

interpreted as follows: V = Volvo, E = electronic, D = diesel, 11 = engine displacement in liters.
- The numeric values used in Mack Trucks engine family codes can be interpreted as the engine displacement to the nearest 100 cubic inches displacement. The MP-10 code can be interpreted as follows: M = Mack, P = power, 10 = engine displacement in 100s of cubic inches. So the 10 is equivalent to 1,000 cubic inches, which is close to the 16.1 liters the engine displaces.

- The common platform Volvo engines are the VE-D11 (11-liter), VE-D13 (13-liter), and VE-D15 (15-liter) engines.
- The common platform Mack Trucks engines are the MP7 (700 cu. in.), MP8 (800 cu. in.) and MP10 (1,000 cu. in.) engines.
- It should be noted that the Volvo-Mack common platform engines correlate as 11-liter/ 700 cu. in., 13-liter/800 cu. in., and 15-liter/ 1,000 cu. in. They are all metrically engineered and are differentiated primarily by paint job.
- Dual-actuator EUIs are also known as four-terminal EUIs. They are manufactured by Delphi and described as E3 injectors.
- The fuel subsystems supplying E3 injectors regardless of manufacturer use a gear-type transfer pump to create charging pressures. However, because the fuel subsystem is used by some OEMs to supply aftertreatment dosing injectors, the charging pressures vary from a low of around 60 psi (415 kPa) to a high of 250 psi (1,724 kPa).
- ECM functions in Volvo and Mack Trucks E3-fueled engines are divided between two modules. A VCU (SA71 / MID144) interacts with the EECU (SA00 / MID128) to produce engine powertrain outcomes. The EECU incorporates both the processing capability and output switching apparatus required to manage fueling and emissions controls on 2007 to 2010 engines. Post-2010 engines use an aftertreatment module to manage DPF and SCR functions.
- The Volvo-Mack ECM/EECU houses the injector drivers and uses induction coils to spike the EUI actuation voltage to values around 100 V-DC in post-2007 engines.
- The control cartridge in an E3 injector is known as a spill valve (SV) actuator. It is an ECM-controlled solenoid and valve that controls effective stroke either by trapping fuel in the EUI or by optioning it to the spill circuit.
- The nozzle control valve (NCV) actuator enables the ECM to precisely manage the nozzle opening pressure (NOP).
- The E3 NCV enables soft value NOPs, permitting much higher NOP and nozzle closure pressures than would be possible with the hard value NOPs of single-actuator EUIs.
- The E3 pressurizing phase requires the SV actuator to be energized. During the pressurizing phase, fuel is not necessarily injected into the engine.
- For fuel injection to take place, both the NCV and SV actuators must be energized.
- The E3 SV actuator may be energized several times during an injection pulse. This enables multipulse injection.

REVIEW QUESTIONS

1. What is a typical charging pressure used by Volvo in its EUI fuel subsystem?
   a. 15 psi (105 kPa)
   b. 60 psi (415 kPa)
   c. 300 psi (2,070 kPa)
   d. 1,200 psi (8,270 kPa)

2. Which type of injector is required in all post-2007 Volvo and Mack Trucks EUI-fueled engines?
   a. Two-terminal EUI
   b. Two-terminal EUP
   c. Four-terminal EUI
   d. Four-terminal EUP

3. How many actuators are used in a four-terminal EUI?
   a. None
   b. One
   c. Two
   d. Four

4. Which of the following is the closest common platform relative of the Volvo VE-D16 engine?
   a. Volvo VE-D11
   b. Volvo VE-D13
   c. Mack Trucks MP-8
   d. Mack Trucks MP-10

5. Which of the following metric values would be closest to the engine displacement of a Mack MP-7 engine?
   a. 7 liters
   b. 10 liters
   c. 11 liters
   d. 13 liters

6. Which of the following correctly describes the two engine controllers used in an E3-fueled Series 60 with DDEC VI electronics?
   a. CPC and MCM
   b. ECM and EECU
   c. ECU and VPM
   d. DDEC and DDC

7. Where is the fuel pressure sensor located in a Mack Trucks MP-8 engine?
   a. In the fuel tank
   b. Upstream from the primary filter
   c. Upstream from the secondary filter
   d. Downstream from the secondary filter

8. What does the fuel pressure sensor on a MP-8 measure?
   a. Fuel inlet restriction
   b. Charging pressure to the EUIs
   c. Injection pressure
   d. EUI pump chamber pressure

9. Dual-actuator E3 injectors in Volvo-Mack applications are switched by the injector drivers at:
   a. 5 V.
   b. 12 V.
   c. 24 V.
   d. ±100 V.

10. Which of the following values would represent a typical NOP for an E3 injector equipped with an electrohydraulic nozzle?
    a. E3 injectors use soft value NOPs
    b. 3,800 psi (262 bar)
    c. 5,000 psi (345 bar)
    d. 22,000 psi (1517 bar)

11. Technician A states that when a four-terminal EUI is injecting fuel into the engine cylinder, the SV actuator must be energized. Technician B states that for fuel injection to take place in an E3 injector, the NCV actuator must be energized. Who is correct?
    a. Technician A only
    b. Technician B only
    c. Both A and B
    d. Neither A nor B

12. Technician A states that E3 EUI calibration codes must be reprogrammed to the ECM/EECU whenever one is changed out. Technician B states that the four-terminal EUI NCV control cartridge is located outside the cylindrical body of the injector. Who is correct?
    a. Technician A only
    b. Technician B only
    c. Both A and B
    d. Neither A nor B

13. When the WIF sensor alerts the driver that there is water in the fuel, what should be done?
    a. Stop the truck and depress the dash water separator purge switch.
    b. Pull over to the side of the road and manually purge the separator.
    c. Pull over to the side of the road and await mechanical assistance.
    d. Pull over to the side of the road and pour a pint of alcohol into the fuel tanks.

14. Technician A states that if the NCV actuator fails on a four-terminal EUI, fuel injection can still take place because the SV actuator provides redundancy. Technician B states that the EUI pump chamber cannot produce injection pressures until the SV actuator is energized. Who is correct?
    a. Technician A only
    b. Technician B only
    c. Both A and B
    d. Neither A nor B

15. Technician A says that failure to reprogram E3 calibration codes to the ECM/EECU following an injector change-out can result in unbalanced cylinder fueling. Technician B says that the E3 EUI is a "smart" injector that automatically reprograms its cal codes to the ECM/EECU following a change-out. Who is correct?
    a. Technician A only
    b. Technician B only
    c. Both A and B
    d. Neither A nor B

27

CATERPILLAR AND NAVISTAR HEUI

OBJECTIVES

After studying this chapter, you should be able to:

- Describe the HEUI system layout and the primary components.
- Outline the role of the four primary HEUI subsystems.
- Describe the operating principles of an injection pressure regulator (IPR).
- Describe the operating principles and subcomponents of Caterpillar-manufactured HEUI injector units.
- Outline the operating principles of 2004 Siemens-manufactured HEUI injector units.
- Define the role played by the ECM input circuit and the factors that govern ECM processing logic.
- Describe how the ECM switches output devices to control engine fueling and manage combustion.
- Describe the role of the consolidated engine controller.
- Perform basic electronic troubleshooting on an HEUI system.
- Outline the procedure required to perform proprietary data reprogramming of an ECM.
- Perform customer data programming using an EST.

Prerequisites: Chapter 19; additional reference Chapters 34, 35, 41, and 44

KEY TERMS

advanced combustion and emissions reduction technology (ACERT)

advanced diesel engine management (ADEM)

amplifier piston

calibration parameters

camshaft position sensor (CPS)

consolidated engine controller (CEC)

Diamond Logic

Electronic Technician (ET)

engine family rating code (EFRC)

EZ-Tech

fuel demand command signal (FDCS)

fuel rate

hydraulically actuated electronic unit injector (HEUI)

injection pressure regulator (IPR)

injector driver module (IDM)

intensifier piston

International Service Information System (ISIS)

keep-alive memory (KAM)

Master Diagnostics (MD)

pilot injection

pre-injection metering (PRIME)

reference voltage (V-Ref)

self-test input (STI)

service information system (SIS)

ServiceMaxx

swash plate

valve closes orifice (VCO)

vehicle personality module (VPM)

INTRODUCTION

When it was introduced in 1994, **hydraulically actuated electronic unit injector (HEUI)** technology represented a new direction for the Caterpillar Engine Division because, for the first time, it launched the business of supplying fuel system engineering and components to competitor engine original equipment manufacturers (OEMs). The HEUI story began in 1987 when Caterpillar and International Trucks signed a joint development agreement. This resulted in the introduction of HEUI on the light-duty, International Trucks 7.3-liter engine (444E) in 1994, an engine widely marketed as a Ford 7.3-liter engine. The fuel system appeared a little later on Caterpillar's 3126 engine.

HISTORY

HEUI was developed in Caterpillar's Pontiac, Illinois, fuel systems production plant, and Caterpillar manufactured the system exclusively until the 2004 model year (MY). It is important to note that many 2004 model year engines were released in October of 2002. For Environmental Protection Agency (EPA) MY 2004, Navistar International (and the engines it supplied to Ford) adopted HEUI injectors manufactured by Siemens in Germany. In this chapter we take a look at HEUI principles of operation, which are common to all HEUI injectors. We follow that by looking at some of the more recent models.

Caterpillar incorporated its **advanced combustion and emissions reduction technology (ACERT)** into HEUI-fueled engines built from 2004 to 2007. Caterpillar abandoned HEUI in preference for common rail (CR) technology on its small- and medium-bore highway engines beginning in 2007. Navistar continues to manufacture updated versions of its DT466 and DT using HEUI fueling.

ENGINES USING HEUI

HEUI engine management has been used in the following highway engines:

- Navistar International 444E (7.3 liter)
- Caterpillar 3126B
- Navistar International VT365 (6.0 liter)
- Navistar International 466E, 530E, and 570E
- Caterpillar C7 and C9

HEUI engine management is currently used in the following post-2010 highway engines:

- Navistar MaxxForce DT (466 cu. in./7.6 liter) max 300 BHP
- Navistar MaxxForce 9 (570 cu. in./9.3 liter) max 330 BHP
- Navistar MaxxForce 10 (570 cu. in./9.3 liter) max 350 BHP

The MaxxForce DT is the latest reincarnation of the DT 466 engine, which debuted in 1971 and has been through various fuel systems. It is probably the best known mid-size diesel engine sold in America today. MaxxForce 9 and MaxxForce 10 are evolved from the former 570 engine. The two engines share a common platform and identical displacement. They differ only in that the MaxxForce 10 has slightly higher horsepower and peak torque.

ADVANTAGES AND LIMITATIONS OF HEUI

The HEUI fuel system was the first to offer significant control over injection rate and duration. It could do this because its injectors were actuated not by cam profile but hydraulically, using oil pressure. This meant it did not have to rely on high engine rpm to produce high fueling pressures. The electronics that manage HEUI fueling controls were able to set HEUI actuation oil pressures over a wide range of pressure values, resulting in precise control of injected fuel pressure entirely independent of engine speed. This rate-shaping ability was unique during the 1990s, but since then has given way to the more recently introduced CR fuel systems, which offer even more precise fueling controls. **Figure 27–1**, **Figure 27–2**, and **Figure 27–3** show some views of both International and Caterpillar engines using the HEUI fuel management system.

SCOPE OF THIS CHAPTER

We are going to take a look at the evolution of HEUI systems, beginning with the earliest Caterpillar systems and working up to the latest generation of Siemens-manufactured HEUIs that are featured on Navistar International diesel engines. Although the physical appearance changed somewhat as HEUI systems evolved, the operating principles remained unchanged.

FIGURE 27-1 Component locations on an International Trucks I-6 engine with the HEUI fuel system.

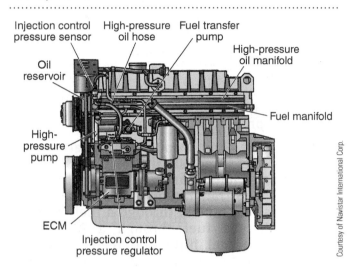

Injection control pressure sensor

High-pressure oil hose

Fuel transfer pump

High-pressure oil manifold

Oil reservoir

Fuel manifold

High-pressure pump

ECM

Injection control pressure regulator

Courtesy of Navistar International Corp.

FIGURE 27-2 Cutaway view of an International Trucks I-6 engine with HEUI: Note the location of the HEUI injectors.

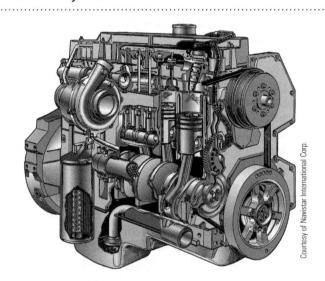

Courtesy of Navistar International Corp.

FIGURE 27-3 Side and overhead views of a Caterpillar 3126 engine with HEUI showing the electronic component and sensor locations.

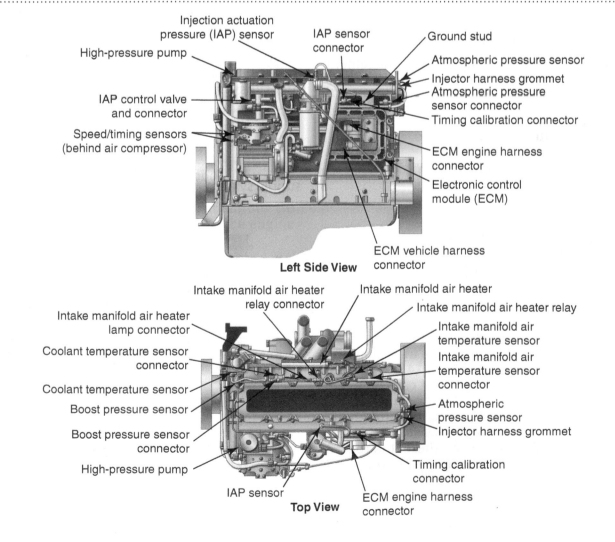

Injection actuation pressure (IAP) sensor

IAP sensor connector

Ground stud

High-pressure pump

Atmospheric pressure sensor

Injector harness grommet

Atmospheric pressure sensor connector

IAP control valve and connector

Timing calibration connector

Speed/timing sensors (behind air compressor)

ECM engine harness connector

Electronic control module (ECM)

ECM vehicle harness connector

Left Side View

Intake manifold air heater relay connector

Intake manifold air heater

Intake manifold air heater lamp connector

Intake manifold air heater relay

Coolant temperature sensor connector

Intake manifold air temperature sensor

Coolant temperature sensor

Intake manifold air temperature sensor connector

Boost pressure sensor

Atmospheric pressure sensor

Boost pressure sensor connector

Injector harness grommet

High-pressure pump

Timing calibration connector

IAP sensor

ECM engine harness connector

Top View

FIGURE 27–6 Operation of the International Trucks IPR valve.

Engine Off

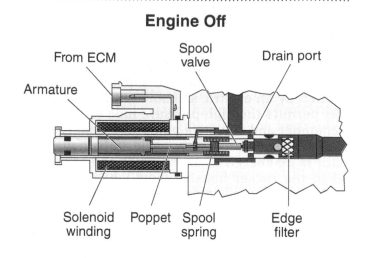

Engine Running

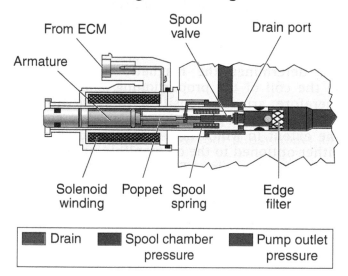

| Drain | Spool chamber pressure | Pump outlet pressure |

shows a Navistar International IPR in engine off and engine on positions.

HEUI INJECTOR

The HEUI injector is an integral pumping, metering, and atomizing unit controlled by ECM drivers. The unit is best understood if you think of it as being an EUI that is actuated hydraulically rather than by cam profile. At the base of the HEUI is a hydraulically actuated, multi-orifii nozzle, almost identical to what you will find in an EUI. Control of an HEUI is by the ECM-switched control cartridge. This spends most of the cycle de-energized and therefore closed. The instant the control cartridge is energized, the HEUI actuation circuit opens, admitting high-pressure oil into the unit.

AMPLIFIER OR INTENSIFIER PISTON

The **amplifier** (International) or **intensifier** (Caterpillar) **piston** is responsible for creating injection pressure values. Because each of the OEMs that use this system prefers different terms, we use *amplifier piston* generally in this text except when specifically addressing a Caterpillar system. When the HEUI is energized, high-pressure actuation oil supplied by a stepper pump is admitted to an HEUI circuit where it acts on the amplifier piston. This drives its integral plunger downward into the fuel in the pumping chamber, creating the fuel pumping stroke.

HEUI EFFECTIVE STROKE

A duct connects the pump chamber with the pressure chamber of the injector nozzle valve. The moment the HEUI is de-energized, the oil pressure acting on the amplifier piston collapses, and the amplifier piston return spring plus the high-pressure fuel in the pump chamber retract the amplifier piston, causing the almost immediate collapse of the pressure holding the nozzle valve open. This results in rapid ending of the injection pulse. In fact, the real time period between the moment the HEUI solenoid is de-energized and the point that droplets cease to exit the injector nozzle orifii is claimed to be significantly less with HEUI than with equivalent EUI systems.

HEUIs typically have hard value nozzle opening pressures (NOPs) of 5,000 psi (345 bar), with a potential for peak pressures rising to 28,000 psi (1,931 bar). Actual NOPs and peak pressures vary by OEM and specific engines. Oil pressure acting on the HEUI amplifier piston is "amplified" (or "intensified") by seven times in the fuel pump chamber. This amplification is achieved because the sectional area of the amplifier piston is seven times that of the injection plunger. The descent velocity of the injection plunger into the HEUI pump chamber is variable and dependent on the specific actuation oil pressure value at a given moment of operation.

Because the ECM directly controls the actuation oil pressure value, it can therefore control injection pressure. The injection pressure determines the emitted droplet size. The higher the injection pressure, the smaller the droplets emitted from the HEUI. Control over droplet size provides what is known as the *rate-shaping* ability of the HEUI. In short, rate shaping provides the ECM with the ability to determine the extent of atomization to best suit the combustion conditions at any given moment of operation.

Collapse Phase

When the ECM de-energizes the HEUI control solenoid, the oil actuation pressure collapses as oil vents the HEUI to the rocker housing. Compared with an EUI with an older hydraulic injector nozzle, the fuel injection collapse phase in an HEUI is accelerated. This rapid pressure collapse reduces the injection of larger-sized droplets toward the end of an injection pulse.

Mechanical Pilot Injection

In the late 1990s, some versions of Caterpillar-built HEUIs were manufactured with plunger and barrel geometry that provided **pilot injection**. The term *pilot injection* is used to describe an injection pulse that is broken into two separate phases. In a pilot injection fueling pulse, the initial phase injects a short-duration pulse of fuel into the engine cylinder; ceases until close to the moment of ignition; then resumes injection, pumping the remainder of the fuel pulse into the engine cylinder. Pilot injection is used as a cold-start and warmup strategy in most current fuel systems to avoid an excess of fuel in the engine cylinder at the point of ignition. This is important in diesel engines to minimize cold-start detonation. HEUI systems with the pilot injection feature are designed to produce a pilot pulse for each injection. The feature is mechanical and achieved by machined center and cross-drillings in the plunger to an annular recess. Caterpillar uses the term **PRIME** to describe its mechanical pilot injection feature. PRIME is a loose acronym for **pre-injection metering**.

HEUI Oil and Fuel Manifold

Actuation oil and fuel at charging pressure are routed to the HEUI units by means of an oil/fuel manifold on the cylinder head. The HEUIs are inserted into cylindrical bores in the cylinder head. Each HEUI has a dedicated external annulus separated by O-rings to access the oil and fuel rifles illustrated in **Figure 27–7**. Figure 27–7 also shows a cylinder head cross-section indicating how the oil/fuel manifold and the ducts connect to the individual HEUIs.

FIGURE 27–7 International Trucks HEUI I-6 oil and fuel manifolds and HEUI cross-section in the cylinder head.

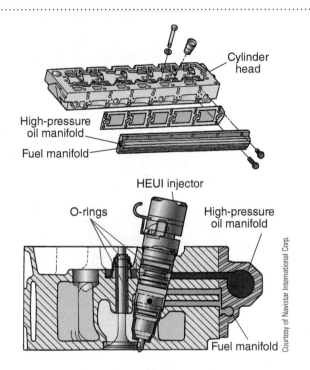

Courtesy of Navistar International Corp.

HEUI SUBCOMPONENTS

As mentioned a little earlier, there are some differences between the Caterpillar- and Siemens-built HEUIs. We focus first on the Caterpillar HEUIs that were used in both Caterpillar and International Navistar HEUI-fueled engines until 2004. We will look at the Siemens HEUIs in the next section. A Caterpillar HEUI injector assembly can be subdivided as shown in **Figure 27–8**.

Solenoid

The solenoid is switched by the ECM using a 115 V-DC coil-induced voltage. The HEUI electrical terminals connect the solenoid coil with wiring to the ECM injector drivers.

Poppet Valve

The HEUI poppet valve is integral with the solenoid armature. It is machined with an upper and a lower seat. For most of the cycle, the poppet valve seat loads the lower seat into a closed position, preventing high-pressure engine oil from entering the HEUI. Any time the solenoid is de-energized, the poppet valve upper seat is open, venting the oil actuation spill ducting. When the HEUI solenoid is energized, the poppet valve is drawn into the solenoid, opening the lower seat

FIGURE 27–8 International Trucks HEUI internal component identification and operating phases.

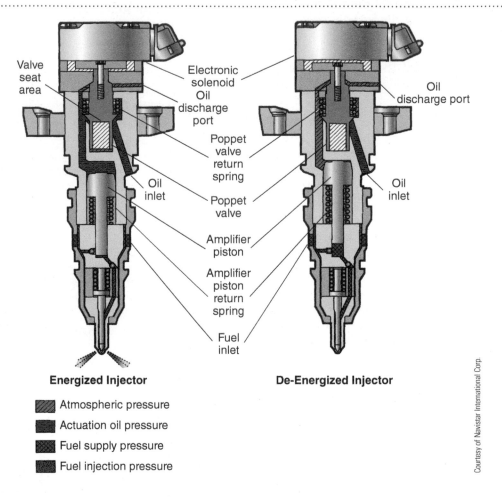

Energized Injector   De-Energized Injector

Atmospheric pressure
Actuation oil pressure
Fuel supply pressure
Fuel injection pressure

Courtesy of Navistar International Corp.

and admitting high-pressure oil from the IPR. When the poppet valve is fully open, the upper seat seals, preventing the oil from exiting the HEUI through the spill passage.

Intensifier or Amplifier Piston

The intensifier/amplifier piston is designed to actuate the injection plunger, which is located below it. When the poppet control valve is switched by the ECM to admit high-pressure oil into the HEUI, the oil pressure acts on the sectional area of the amplifier piston. The actual oil pressure (managed by the ECM) determines the velocity at which the plunger located below the amplifier piston is driven into the injection pump chamber. The sectional area of the amplifier piston determines how much the actuating oil pressure is multiplied in the injection pump chamber. This value is specified as seven times in current HEUI systems. In other words, an actuating oil pressure of 3,000 psi (207 bar) produces an injection pressure potential of 21,000 psi (1448 bar). The amplifier piston and

injection plunger are loaded into their retracted position by a spring. **Figure 27–9** is a cutaway of a HEUI injector highlighting the high-pressure oil circuit.

Plunger and Barrel

The plunger and barrel form the HEUI pump element. The first versions of the HEUI injectors did not offer the pilot injection feature. This description references second-generation HEUI with the PRIME feature. The injection cycle shown in Figure 27–11 shows an HEUI with the PRIME feature we referenced a little earlier. As the injection plunger is driven into the pump chamber, fuel is pressurized for a short portion of the stroke, actuating and opening the injector nozzle. The pressure rise is of short duration because when the PRIME recess in the plunger registers with the PRIME spill port in the barrel, the pressure in the pump chamber collapses as fuel spills through the PRIME spill port. This closes the injector nozzle and injection ceases. However, the moment the PRIME recess in the

FIGURE 27–9 Relationship between Intensifier Piston and the Plunger and Barrel: Yellow is used to identify the oil actuation circuit; purple identifies the actuation chamber, which is vented in this image because the actuation solenoid is not energized.

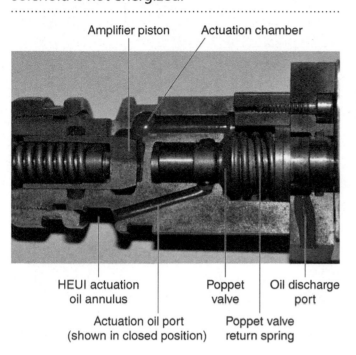

Amplifier piston   Actuation chamber

HEUI actuation oil annulus   Poppet valve   Oil discharge port

Actuation oil port (shown in closed position)   Poppet valve return spring

FIGURE 27–10 Cutaway of a HEUI injector showing the high-pressure fuel plunger and barrel, and the injector nozzle circuit.

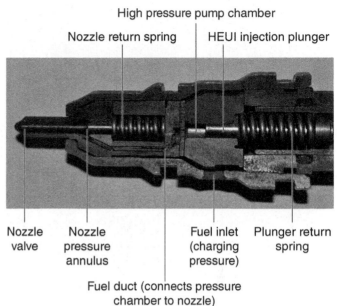

High pressure pump chamber

Nozzle return spring   HEUI injection plunger

Nozzle valve   Nozzle pressure annulus   Fuel inlet (charging pressure)   Plunger return spring

Fuel duct (connects pressure chamber to nozzle)

plunger passes beyond the spill port, fuel is once again trapped in the pump chamber and pressure rise resumes. This results in the injector nozzle being opened for the delivery of the main portion of the fuel pulse.

The fueling pulse continues until the ECM ends the effective stroke by de-energizing the HEUI solenoid. At this point, the poppet control valve is driven onto its lower seat, opening the upper seat and permitting the actuating oil to be vented. With no force acting on the amplifier piston, the plunger is driven upward by the combined force of the high-pressure fuel in the pump chamber and the plunger return spring. This causes an almost immediate collapse of pump chamber pressure and results in almost instantaneous nozzle closure. A feature of the HEUI is its ability to almost instantly close the nozzle at the end of the plunger effective stroke.

Injector Nozzle

The HEUI injector nozzle is a multi-orifii injector nozzle of the **valve closes orifice (VCO)** type that is a little different from any other injector nozzle used in an electronic unit injector (EUI) assembly.

A duct connects the nozzle pressure chamber with the HEUI pump chamber. A spring loads the injector nozzle valve onto its seat. The spring tension defines the NOP value. When the hydraulic pressure acting on the sectional area of the nozzle valve is sufficient to overcome the spring pressure, the nozzle valve unseats, permitting fuel to pass around the nozzle seat and through the nozzle orifii. The nozzle valve functions as a simple hydraulic switch. Because of the nozzle differential ratio, the nozzle closure pressure is always lower than the NOP. For instance, a Caterpillar version of the HEUI with an NOP identified at 4,500 psi (310 bar) will not close until the pressure drops to 4,000 psi (275 bar). A full explanation of hydraulic injector nozzle performance is found in Chapter 21. **Figure 27–10** is a cutaway of a HEUI injector highlighting the fuel injection circuit.

STAGES OF INJECTION

When PRIME HEUIs are used, the injection pulse can be divided into five distinct stages. The text in this section describes the stages, and you should use this and **Figure 27–11** to follow it through.

Pre-Injection

The HEUI internal components are all located in their retracted positions as shown in **Figure 27–11A**. In fact, they are in the

FIGURE 27–11 The HEUI injection cycle.

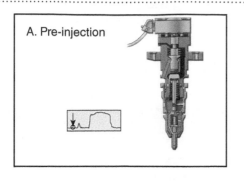

A. Pre-injection

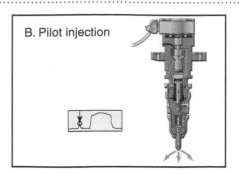

B. Pilot injection

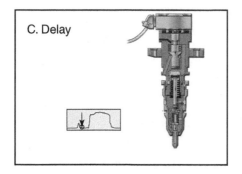

C. Delay

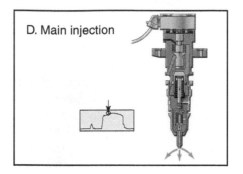

D. Main injection

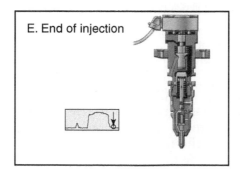

E. End of injection

pre-injection position for most of the cycle. The poppet valve seat is spring-loaded into the lower seat, preventing the high-pressure actuating oil from entering the HEUI, and the amplifier piston and plunger are both in their raised position. Fuel enters the HEUI to charge the pump chamber at the charging pressure.

Pilot Injection

The pilot injection phase begins when the plunger is first moved downward into the HEUI pump chamber by actuation oil as it enters the HEUI circuit. The pressure rise created opens the injector nozzle to deliver a short pulse of fuel. The pilot injection phase ends when the PRIME recess in the HEUI plunger is driven downward enough to register with the PRIME spill port, causing the pump chamber pressure to collapse and the nozzle valve to close. **Figure 27–11B** shows the pilot injection stage.

Delay

The delay phase occurs between the ending of the pilot injection phase and restart of the fuel pulse. As the PRIME recess registers with the PRIME port in the pump barrel, pressure collapses. This pressure collapse results in nozzle closure. The objective is to cease fueling the engine cylinder while the prime pulse of fuel is vaporized and heated to its ignition point. It is important to note that the plunger is still being driven through its stroke during this phase because the HEUI poppet control valve is in the open position, and oil pressure continues to drive the amplifier piston downward. **Figure 27–11C** shows the delay stage of HEUI injection.

Main Injection

When the PRIME recess in the plunger passes beyond the PRIME spill port, fuel is once again trapped in the HEUI pump chamber because it can no longer exit through the spill port. The resulting pressure rise opens the injector nozzle a second time to deliver the main volume of fuel to be delivered in the cycle. In an HEUI injector with no PRIME feature, the plunger has no cross or center drillings and PRIME recess, so main injection begins when the plunger leading edge passes the spill port on its downward stroke, as shown in **Figure 27–11D**.

End of Injection

The end of injection begins with the de-energizing of the HEUI solenoid. The armature is released by the solenoid coil and a spring drives the poppet valve downward to seat on its lower seat. The instant the poppet valve starts to move downward, the upper seat is exposed, permitting the actuating oil inside the HEUI to spill. When the actuating oil pressure acting on the amplifier piston is relieved, the fuel pressure in the HEUI pump chamber combined with the plunger return spring collapses the fuel pressure almost instantly. Injection ends when there is insufficient pressure to hold the nozzle valve in its open position, and the three moving assemblies (poppet valve, amplifier/plunger, and nozzle valve) in the HEUI are all in their return positions outlined in the pre-injection phase. **Figure 27–11E** shows a PRIME HEUI injector during the end of injection stage.

> ### TECH TIP:
> The importance of the engine oil type and condition in an HEUI-fueled engine cannot be overemphasized. Because engine oil is the HEUI actuation medium, it should meet OEM temperature and operating condition specifications. Contaminated, high mileage, and degraded engine oil can cause HEUI injector malfunctions.

SIEMENS HEUI

As mentioned earlier, Navistar International began using the Siemens HEUI system for the 2004 model year. Some refer to this version of HEUI as generation II. This included all the Navistar engines, including those it supplied to Ford as Powerstroke 6.0-liter engines. The operating principles of Caterpillar and Siemens HEUIs are identical, but the packaging of the Siemens model is a little different. The Siemens injectors use dual integral actuators built into the HEUI cylinder, as shown in **Figure 27–12**. This provides for a sleeker design and a reduced actuation potential of 48 volts. The actuator coils are located on either side of the single armature with integral spool valve. The spool valve shuttles horizontally between the pair of coils to either an *on* or an *off* position. For most of the cycle, the spool valve is held in its *off* position, meaning that oil from the actuation circuit cannot enter the HEUI. When the on-coil is energized by its ECM driver, the spool shuttles transversely to its *on* position, which aligns an

FIGURE 27–12 Siemens HEUI.

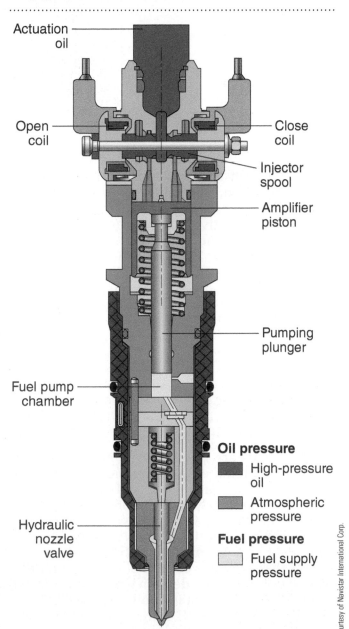

Actuation oil
Open coil
Close coil
Injector spool
Amplifier piston
Pumping plunger
Fuel pump chamber
Hydraulic nozzle valve

Oil pressure
- High-pressure oil
- Atmospheric pressure

Fuel pressure
- Fuel supply pressure

FIGURE 27–13 ECM switching of the spool valve in a Siemens HEUI.

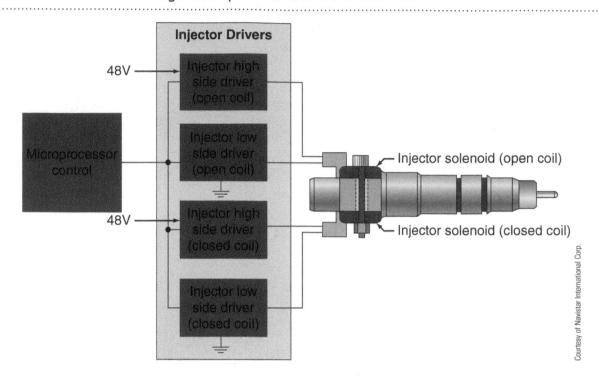

Courtesy of Navistar International Corp.

inlet port with the HEUI actuation oil inlet. In the *on* position, actuation oil is permitted to enter the HEUI and act on the amplifier piston. To end an effective stroke, the off-coil at its opposite side is energized to return the spool to the *off* position, taking the spool inlet port out of register. You can see how the ECM controls the shuttle action of the Siemens spool valve in **Figure 27–13**. **Figure 27–14** is a photograph of the Siemens HEUI injector.

HEUI ELECTRONIC MANAGEMENT AND SWITCHING

HEUI systems are full authority electronic management systems with comprehensive monitoring, vehicle management, and self-diagnostic capabilities. In early International Trucks applications, logging of fault codes was the responsibility of nonvolatile RAM (NV-RAM), which is described as **KAM** or **keep-alive memory**. The circuit that provides continuous power (in other words, it is not dependent on the ignition circuit) to maintain KAM data is known as KAMPWR.

Additionally, the HEUI management ECM, the vehicle personality module, and the switching

FIGURE 27–14 A Siemens HEUI injector.

apparatus are housed separately in some International Trucks engines, depending on the engine series and generation. Caterpillar has always located the HEUI switching apparatus in a single ECM housing with no fuel cooling. In the late 1990s, International Trucks introduced its **consolidated engine controller (CEC)**, which basically consolidated the microprocessing and switching functions of the ECM, the personality module, and the **injector driver module (IDM)** into a single engine-mounted unit. As with Caterpillar, this housing is simply referred to as the ECM, but it was not used on all engines.

ECM FUNCTIONS

According to Navistar service literature, ECM functions can be divided as follows (**Figure 27–15**):

1. Reference voltage regulator
2. Input conditioning
3. Microcomputer
4. Outputs

Reference Voltage

Reference voltage (V-Ref) is delivered to system sensors that return a percentage of it as a signal to the ECM. Thermistors (temperature sensors) and potentiometers (TPS) are examples of sensors requiring reference voltage. Reference voltage values used are at 5 V-DC pressure and the flow is limited by a current-limiting resistor to safeguard against a dead short to ground. Reference voltage is also used to power up the circuitry in Hall-effect sensors used in the system, such as the **camshaft position sensor (CPS)** (International Trucks). There is a full explanation of the electrical principles of input circuit components in Chapter 34.

Input Conditioning

Signal conditioning consists of converting analog signals to digital signals, squaring up sine wave signals, and amplifying low-intensity signals for processing. Part of this process includes cleaning up electronic noise induced in the circuit wiring.

FIGURE 27–15 ECM processing cycle.

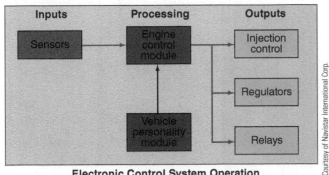

Electronic Control System Operation

Courtesy of Navistar International Corp.

Microcomputer

Both Caterpillar and International Trucks HEUI microprocessors function similarly to other vehicle system management computers. It stores operating instructions, control strategies, and tables of values, which are **calibration parameters**. It compares sensor monitoring and command inputs with the logged control strategies and calibration parameters and then computes the appropriate operating strategy for any given set of conditions. Late-generation ECMs use a 32-bit processor for fully integral units used by both Caterpillar and Navistar. Early HEUI systems were managed by 16-bit and 8-bit processors used in Navistar and Ford multiple module units. In multiple module units, a proprietary data bus connects the ECM with the personality and injector driver modules. For a full description of ECM processing, refer to Chapter 34.

Personality Module

Both Caterpillar and International Trucks describe their combined programmable read-only memory (PROM) and electronically erasable, programmable read-only memory (EEPROM) as a **vehicle personality module (VPM)**. The VPM is customer and proprietary data programmable. The function of the VPM is to trim engine management to a specific chassis application and customer requirements. The **engine family rating code (EFRC)** is located in the VPM calibration list and can be read with an EST; this identifies the engine power and emissions calibration of the engine.

Caterpillar ADEM

Caterpillar's **advanced diesel engine management (ADEM)** system is used to manage the Caterpillar family of HEUI-fueled engines. This is the core software that drives ECM functions at the SA 00/MID 128 address on the chassis data bus. All Caterpillar's generations of HEUI use a single module that is designed to interface with Caterpillar's CA, ET, and service information system (SIS).

International Diamond Logic

Navistar's **Diamond Logic** system is a comprehensive chassis management system used to drive all data bus networking. The Navistar HEUI management system is integrated into the chassis data bus and the engine ECM uses the SA 00/MID 128 address on the bus. The Navistar ECM is designed to interact with the **EZ-Tech** EST, which coordinates **Master Diagnostics (MD)** and the online **International Service Information System (ISIS)** software. **ServiceMaxx**, the more recent Navistar diagnostic software, was introduced for post-2007 systems, but it should be noted that this software is designed to function with HEUI fuel systems using MD protocols. MD and ISIS are described a little later. International went through three generations of management for its HEUI-fueled engines, usually known by the number of modules used. Most Navistar techs refer to the modules as *boxes*:

- Three-box system: three separate modules consisting of an ECM, injector driver module (IDM), and personality module (PM).
- One-box system: a single module incorporating the ECM, IDM, and PM.
- Two-box system: two modules, one incorporating the ECM and PM, the other the IDM.

INJECTION DRIVER MODULE (IDM)

The IDM is responsible for switching the HEUIs. In all Caterpillar and some Navistar HEUI systems, the IDM is integral with the ECM. The IDM is housed separately in some Navistar HEUI-managed engines, including those supplied to Ford. When a single module is used by Navistar, it is known as a consolidated engine controller (CEC). The IDM has four functions:

1. Electronic distributor for the HEUIs
2. HEUI power-up
3. Output driver for the HEUIs
4. IDM and HEUI diagnostics

Electronic Distributor for the HEUIs

The ECM calculates engine position from the CMP sensor located at the engine front cover. The ECM uses this signal to determine cylinder firing sequence and then delivers this command data to the IDM by means of a **fuel demand command signal (FDCS)**. The FDCS contains injection timing and fuel quantity data. **Figure 27–16** shows the relationship between the IDM, VPM, and the ECM on a Navistar three-module HEUI. Note how the FDCS and cylinder ID signals are communicated between the IDM and ECM. These communications are transacted on a proprietary bus.

HEUI Power-Up

The IDM supplies:

- A constant 115 + V-DC supply or
- A constant 48 + V-DC supply

Which voltage value is used depends on whether a Caterpillar or Siemens HEUI injector is used in

FIGURE 27–16 IDM operation.

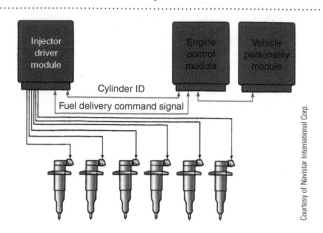

Courtesy of Navistar International Corp.

the system: We refer to this as *actuation voltage*. The actuation voltage is created in the IDM by making and breaking a 12 V-DC source potential across a coil, using the same principles employed by the ignition coil in a spark-ignited (SI) engine. The resultant voltage induced by the coil is stored in capacitors until discharged to the HEUIs. **Figure 27–17** is a graphic showing the relationship between an HEUI, capacitors, a coil, and switching.

Output Driver for the HEUIs

The IDM is responsible for switching the HEUIs. The unit controls the effective stroke of the HEUI

FIGURE 27–17 IDM: The relationship between an HEUI, capacitors, a coil, and switching.

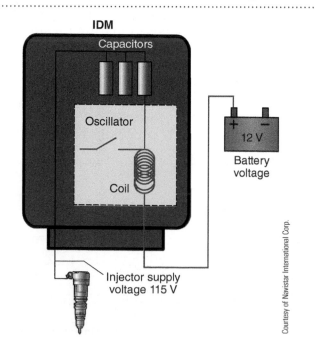

Courtesy of Navistar International Corp.

FIGURE 27–18 Injector driver module operation: output driver operation.

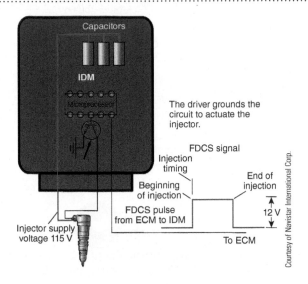

by closing the circuit to ground. The direct control of the HEUI is managed by an output driver transistor in the IDM. When the FDCS signal is delivered from the ECM processing cycle, the beginning of injection (timing) and fuel quantity are determined. **Figure 27–18** shows the role of the output drivers and **Figure 27–19** the role of the timing sensor.

FIGURE 27–19 IDM and ECM communications signals and relationship with CMP input.

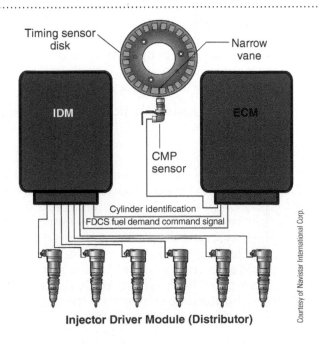

Injector Driver Module (Distributor)

IDM and HEUI Diagnostics

In common with other engine ECM-driven systems, the software is capable of identifying faults within its electronic circuitry and can determine whether an HEUI solenoid or its wiring circuit is drawing too much (or too little) current. In the event of such an electronic malfunction, a fault code is logged. The self-diagnostics can also set an ECM code indicating a module failure.

INJECTION ACTUATION PRESSURE

The ECM is responsible for maintaining the correct injection actuation pressure (IAP) during operation. This means monitoring and continually adjusting the high-pressure oil circuit responsible for actuating HEUI fueling. It does this by comparing *actual* injection pressure with *desired* injection pressure and using the injection actuation pressure solenoid valve to attempt to keep the two values close to each other.

- Actual IAP: measured by IAP sensor and signaled to ECM
- Desired IAP: calculated by ECM

Actual injection pressure is measured by a variable capacitance pressure sensor and signaled to the ECM. Desired injection actuation pressure is based on the fueling algorithm (computed by ECM) effective at any given moment of operation. In the processing loop, the ECM will evaluate any differential between actual and desired actuation pressures and will modulate an output signal to the injection actuation control solenoid valve to keep the values close. **Figure 27–20** shows a Caterpillar HEUI schematic. Note the location of the high-pressure pump, the IAP control valve, and the IAP sensor a little downstream from the IAP control valve solenoid.

HEUI DIAGNOSTICS

Diagnostic procedures for Caterpillar and International versions of HEUI are distinct, as each has developed its own management software. Caterpillar uses Electronic Technician (ET) to read, diagnose, and program its systems. ET should be used in conjunction with the Caterpillar Service Information System (SIS). Early versions of Navistar HEUI were accessed using ProLink and a dedicated cartridge or its Ford

FIGURE 27-20 Caterpillar HEUI schematic.

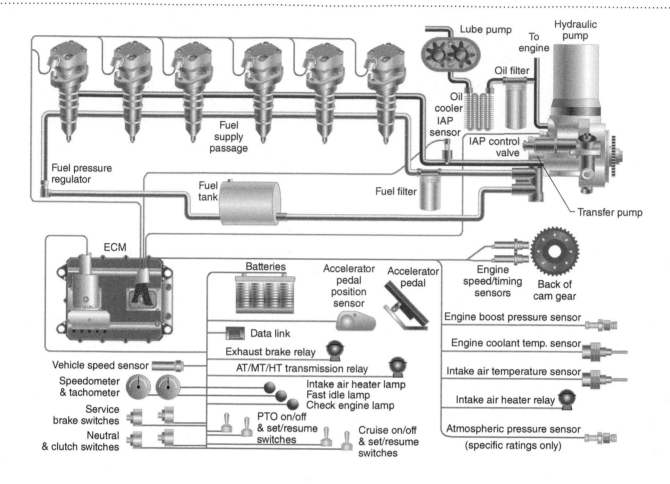

equivalent. More recent versions require the use of Navistar's MD or SM (Windows-driven software) and ISIS. We will refer to the troubleshooting software as *diagnostic software* and use the generic term **service information system (SIS)** to refer to online service information.

DIAGNOSTIC SOFTWARE

Electronic Technician (ET) and MD/SM are the software platforms required to read, program, and troubleshoot HEUI systems. Navistar states that its software is best run on a dedicated EZ-Tech notebook computer. ET and MD/SM are not interchangeable and can only work with each OEM's specific product. To access the ECM, the appropriate communications adapter (CA) must be used (see Chapter 35). ET and MD/SM will do the following on their respective systems:

- Test injector solenoid
- Test IAP

- Perform cylinder cutout tests
- Identify active faults
- Identify logged faults
- Identify logged events
- Display engine configuration data
- Rewrite customer programmable parameters
- Flash new software
- Print configuration and test results

Three typical tests distinct to HEUI systems are described here.

Injector Cutout Test

ET and MD/SM can perform injector cutout tests on HEUI-managed engines. Cylinder cutout testing on HEUI-fueled engines is not unlike that used on other EUI or EUP systems. Caterpillar HEUI systems only offer a single cylinder cutout option, whereas SM can perform multiple cylinder cutout and produce a more comprehensive cylinder balance analysis. The test sequence should be performed with the engine at operating temperature and with intermittent parasitic loads such as the A/C disconnected. The test sequence for single cylinder cutout is described here:

1. Governor maintains programmed idle speed.
2. The diagnostic software turns off one HEUI injector at a time: This means the five functioning HEUIs must increase their duty cycle if the specified engine rpm is to be maintained.
3. The diagnostic software measures the average duty cycle of the five functioning HEUIs at each stage of the cutout test.
4. A test value is assigned for each HEUI tested.
5. The cutout test cycle is then repeated.

Figure 27–21 shows an ET screen capture for an injector cutout test. The data in the cycle fields is fuel position in millimeters.

TECH TIP:

When making a warranty claim for a defective HEUI, a printout of the injector cutout test profile is usually required to ensure that the warranty claim is processed.

Injection Actuation Pressure Test

The IAP test checks the high-pressure oil pump performance and IAP valve operation. The test described here is once again the Caterpillar version, but the Navistar and Ford versions are similar. The test is performed at low idle. It functions by having ET read *desired* IAP pressure versus actual IAP pressure using ADEM

FIGURE 27–21 ET graphical user interface (Windows) during a cylinder cutout test.

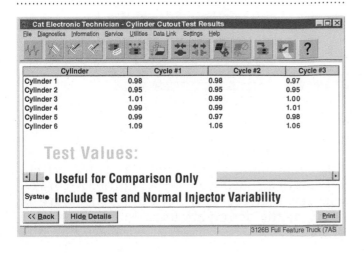

[3126B Full Feature Truck (7AS]

ECM data. The IAP test sequence uses four desired pressure values:

1. 870 psi (60 bar)
2. 1,450 psi (100 bar)
3. 2,100 psi (145 bar)
4. 3,300 psi (228 bar)

and compares these with actual IAP values read by the IAP pressure sensor.

Fuel Rate Test

The **fuel rate** test can be used to identify a marginally defective injector and sometimes one with intermittent performance. Fuel rate is reported by the software in gal/p-hr and the technician is looking to identify a deviation factor in one or more of the HEUIs. Correlate the original complaint and the test results to OEM service literature before changing out an HEUI based on this test.

Navistar Self-Test

Navistar's HEUI electronics are capable of performing self-test procedures. When the dash-mounted **self-test input (STI)** button is depressed and the ignition circuit is key-on, engine-off (KOEO) (**Figure 27–22**), the ECM begins the self-test cycle. When complete, the oil/water and warn engine dash lights are used to signal fault codes. All Navistar in-house (as opposed to SAE) fault codes are three digits. Following is the sequence:

1. Oil/water light flashes once, indicating the beginning of the active faults display.
2. Warn engine light flashes each digit of the active fault code, pausing between each. The oil/water light will flash once between each active code readout when multiple codes are logged. Code 111 indicates no active fault codes.
3. Oil/water light flashes twice to indicate that inactive fault codes will be displayed. Inactive fault codes are then blinked out in the same manner as active fault codes.
4. When all codes have been displayed, the oil/water light will flash three times.
5. Test sequence can be repeated by retracing the preceding steps, but all active faults should be repaired before progressing to later tests.

Troubleshooting Navistar HEUI is made easier by using a Hickok breakout box (ZTSE 4346) and breakout "T" (ZTSE 4347), both used in conjunction with a DMM. Figure 27–22 shows the

FIGURE 27–22 International Trucks self-test button location and troubleshooting with a DMM and breakout box.

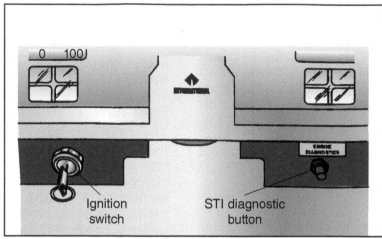

Self-Test Button Location

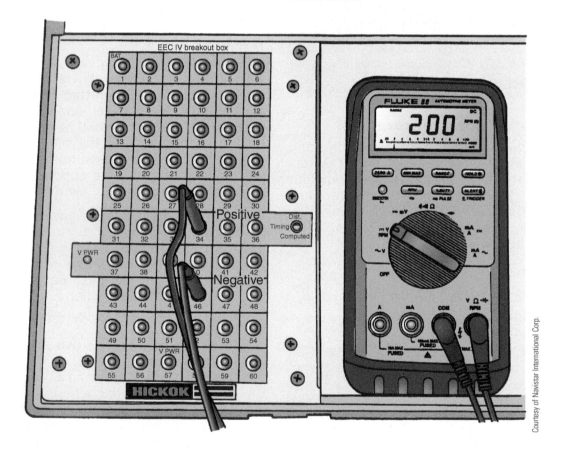

location of a dash STI and a DMM used with a breakout box.

International Trucks HEUI Circuit Schematic

Figure 27–23 is a schematic showing the Navistar HEUI system as it is used on its DT 466E and DT 530E engines. If you compare this schematic with the Caterpillar HEUI schematics shown earlier in Figure 27–20, you will see that the only real differences are in some of the acronyms used to describe each system.

FIGURE 27–23 International Trucks I-6 HEUI circuit schematics.

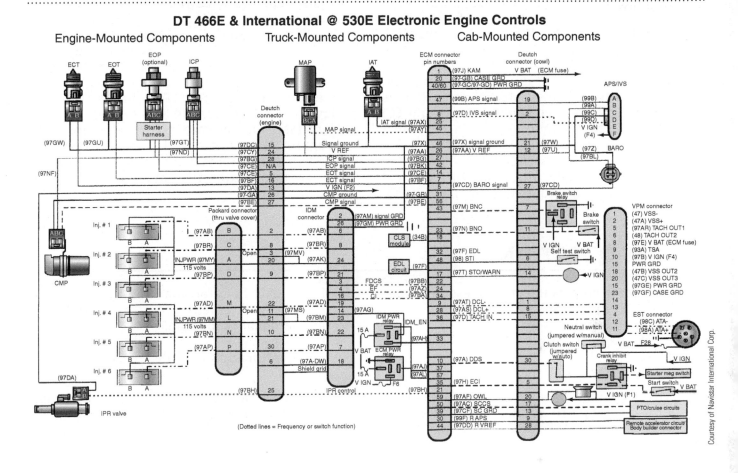

DT 466E & International @ 530E Electronic Engine Controls

SUMMARY

- The HEUI engine management system was the first to use electronically controlled, hydraulically actuated injection pump units. Until the introduction of HEUI technology, pumping of fuel to diesel injection pressure values was always achieved mechanically.
- Effective injection pumping stroke in HEUI units is not confined by the hard limits of cam geometry, as in other full authority electronic management systems.
- Fuel charging pressure to the HEUIs is at values between 30 psi (2 bar) and 60 psi (4 bar).
- Engine-lubricating oil is used as the hydraulic actuating medium for the HEUIs. The pressure is boosted to values of up to 4,000 psi (276 bar) by a swash plate–type hydraulic pump.
- Actual HEUI-actuating oil pressure values are precisely controlled by the ECM, which switches the IPR to achieve oil pressure values of between 485 psi (33 bar) and 4,000 psi (276 bar).

- The IPR is a spool valve positionally controlled by a pulse width modulated ECM signal.
- The actuating oil pressure value defines the descent (actuation) velocity of the HEUI pumping plunger. This determines the pumping pressure and therefore the injection rate and the emitted atomized droplet sizing.
- The HEUI solenoid controls a poppet valve that, when energized, admits high-pressure oil so that it acts on the amplifier piston.
- In Caterpillar-manufactured HEUI, when the control solenoid is energized, actuation oil is admitted to the HEUI to create a pumping stroke. When the control solenoid is de-energized, the high-pressure oil is spilled to the rocker housing.
- In the more recent Siemens HEUI, a transverse spool actuated by a pair of coils controls the entry of oil to the HEUI internal circuit.
- HEUIs use multi-orifii, hydraulic injector nozzles of the VCO type.

- HEUI NOP values are typically 5,000 psi (345 bar), with peak system values rising to between 18,000 and 28,000 psi (1,241 and 1,931 bar).
- The HEUI ECM uses an IDM to switch the HEUI control solenoids.
- Some Navistar ECMs use three-module architecture consisting of an ECM, an IDM, and a personality module. Most later versions adopted a consolidated engine controller (CEC) in which the three modules were incorporated into a single housing.
- Caterpillar has always used an integral ECM, incorporating all of the processing, memory, and switching functions required by its HEUI system.

- The IDM used to drive Caterpillar-manufactured HEUIs steps the actuation voltage to 115 V-DC using induction coils.
- The IDM used to drive Siemens-manufactured HEUIs used in Navistar applications after 2004 steps the actuation voltage to 48 V-DC using induction coils.
- Caterpillar's Electronic Technician (ET) and Navistar's Master Diagnostics (MD) or Service-Maxx (SM) software are used to diagnose and program HEUI engines. ET and MD/SM are used in conjunction with each OEM's online service information system (SIS).

REVIEW QUESTIONS

1. What force creates injection pressure values in an HEUI injector?
   a. Pneumatic
   b. Mechanical
   c. Electrical
   d. Hydraulic

2. What type of pump is used to increase engine lube oil pressure to the values required by HEUI?
   a. Gear
   b. Plunger
   c. Swash plate
   d. Diaphragm

3. Oil pressure values within the HEUI actuation circuit are controlled by a(n):
   a. pressure relief valve.
   b. IPR.
   c. accumulator.
   d. IDM.

4. What type of injector nozzle is used in an HEUI?
   a. Pintle type
   b. Poppet type
   c. Multi-orifii, VCO
   d. Electrohydraulic

5. Which of the following components is used by HEUI electronics to signal the actuating oil pressure to the ECM?
   a. Transducer
   b. IPR spool valve
   c. Relief valve
   d. IAP sensor

6. PROM data in Caterpillar and Navistar HEUI systems is retained in the:
   a. personality module.
   b. IDM.
   c. identification module.
   d. ICR.

7. The HEUI amplifier piston increases actuation pressures by approximately how many times in the injection pump chamber of the unit?
   a. 2
   b. 3
   c. 7
   d. 10

8. Siemens-manufactured HEUIs are switched at:
   a. 12 V-DC.
   b. 48 V-DC.
   c. 90 V-AC.
   d. 115 V-AC.

9. Navistar fault codes may be read from the vehicle dash when the STI button is depressed using which lights?
   a. Check engine and Stop engine
   b. Warn engine and Oil/water
   c. Electronic malfunction and Shutdown engine

10. Technician A states that the actual oil pressure acting on the HEUI amplifier piston will influence the sizing of droplets emitted from the injector nozzle. Technician B states that the HEUI effective stroke is not limited by any hard parameters such as those that limit effective stroke in EUIs. Who is correct?
    a. Technician A only
    b. Technician B only
    c. Both A and B
    d. Neither A nor B

11. Technician A states that Caterpillar has always used a three-module controller system on its ACERT C7 engine with HEUI fueling. Technician B states that the Navistar single-module controller is known as a CEC. Who is correct?
    a. Technician A only
    b. Technician B only
    c. Both A and B
    d. Neither A nor B

12. Technician A states that Siemens-manufactured HEUIs use a transverse spool valve shuttled from side to side by a pair of coils. Technician B states that Siemens-manufactured HEUIs use an external control cartridge to actuate the spool. Who is correct?
    a. Technician A only
    b. Technician B only
    c. Both A and B
    d. Neither A nor B

13. Technician A states that Ford HEUI-fueled engines used up to 2010 are manufactured by Navistar. Technician B states that Caterpillar stopped using the HEUI system on highway diesel engines after 2007. Who is correct?
    a. Technician A only
    b. Technician B only
    c. Both A and B
    d. Neither A nor B

14. Technician A states that the Caterpillar *intensifier* piston and the Navistar *amplifier* piston both refer to the same HEUI component. Technician B states that an amplifier piston will produce fuel pressures seven times the value of the actuating oil pressure. Who is correct?
    a. Technician A only
    b. Technician B only
    c. Both A and B
    d. Neither A nor B

15. Technician A states that a swash plate–type pump and ECM-controlled pressure regulator are used to supply the HEUIs with the engine oil used as hydraulic medium. Technician B states that the hydraulic medium used to actuate the HEUI pumping plunger is high-pressure diesel fuel. Who is correct?
    a. Technician A only
    b. Technician B only
    c. Both A and B
    d. Neither A nor B

28

Prerequisites: Chapters 19, 20, and 21

ELECTRONIC UNIT PUMP (EUP) SYSTEMS

OBJECTIVES

After studying this chapter, you should be able to:

- Define the acronym EUP.
- Identify the similarities between EUP-fueled engines and those using EUI systems.
- Explain the differences between full authority EUP and EUI diesel engine management.
- Identify the OEMs and engine series using EUP fuel systems.
- Outline the EUP fuel system layout.
- Describe the principles of operation of the EUP.
- Describe how an EUP converts charging pressure fuel to injection pressure values.
- Explain how the EUP fuel system was adapted to meet 2007 and 2010 emissions standards.
- Safely remove and re-install EUPs.
- Reprogram EUP calibration codes to an ECM.

KEY TERMS

beginning of energizing (BOE)	electrohydraulic injector (EHI)	MBE-900	SMART injector
beginning of injection (BOI)	electronic control unit (ECU)	MBE-4000	V-MAC III
E-7	E-Tech	Paccar MX-Series	
		PLD module	

INTRODUCTION

Electronic unit pump (EUP) technology was introduced into highway diesel engines by Mack Trucks with its **E-Tech** engine, which debuted in 1997, and the short-lived Detroit Diesel Corporation (DDC) Series 55. The Mack Trucks E-Tech remained in production up until the 2007 model year (MY), when Mack abandoned the EUP system and introduced its EUI family of engines based on the Volvo V-series. In 2000, Mercedes-Benz (MB) introduced EUP technology on the **MBE-900** series (4.2 to 6.4 liter) engine family into light-duty Freightliner chassis, and this was joined by the **MBE-4000** (12.8 liter) in 2002. MB, Freightliner Trucks, and Detroit Diesel have common ownership by the Daimler-Benz group, so from the onset MB-badged engines were marketed and supported by Detroit Diesel dealerships.

Mack Trucks opted to use the Bosch EUP system on its V-MAC III E-Tech engines because it proved to be a good fit with a moderately re-engineered **E-7**, 12-liter engine that would come to be known as E-Tech. Those familiar with both E-7 and E-Tech quickly identify that the combustion dynamics and the components that determine this (cylinder head, injector-type, piston geometry) are not so different between the two series. Mack Trucks manages E-Tech EUP using **V-MAC III** electronics, a two-module management system in which the chassis management "commands" an engine/fuel system controller. **Figure 28–1** is an image of a PACCAR MX 13, which used EUP fueling until MY 2013.

The MB engines were given some help in establishing a presence in the North American market by becoming the default specification in many Freightliner, Sterling, and Western Star trucks. When first introduced, the MB family of engines boasted some innovative features such as cracked connecting rods (these are now commonplace in diesels) and a constant-throttle engine brake. The electronic controls used on the engine are similar to those used by Mack Trucks, with a vehicle control unit (VCU) mastering an engine-mounted control unit known as a **PLD module** (German acronym for ECM).

At the onset of the 2007 model year, the MB-4000 was designated as a vocational engine by the MB/DDC organization and boasted 450 BHP and 1650 lb-ft. (2237 N.m) of torque. The management system used on this final version of the MB-4000 is DDEC VI. The engine ceased

FIGURE 28–1 2011 PACCAR MX with an EUP fuel system.

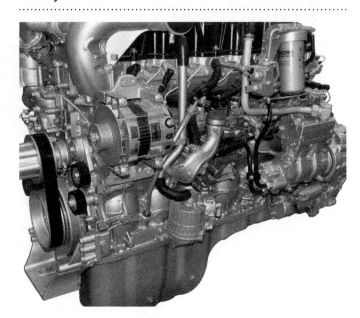

production at the end of 2009. All post-2007 versions of the MBE-4000 and MBE-900 engines use exhaust gas recirculation (EGR) and diesel particulate filters (DPFs). In addition, all post-2007 compliant EUP engines have replaced the multi-orifii hydraulic injector with an ECM-controlled **electrohydraulic injector (EHI)** unit. This is sometimes referred to as a **SMART injector**.

SYSTEM OVERVIEW

If you have already studied electronic unit injector systems, you will know much of what there is to know about EUP systems. In an EUP system, the functions of pumping and control are separated from that of the atomizing function of the nozzle. The pumping and control unit are hydraulically connected to a remotely located injector. The injector used on all Mack and MB EUP systems up until 2007 was a hydraulic multi-orifii nozzle. The injectors used on all post-2007 EUP engines, including the current **Paccar MX-Series** engines, is the EHI.

If we begin by outlining the functions of a diesel engine EUI, they can be divided into three subsystems:

1. Solenoid control
2. Cam-actuated pumping
3. Hydraulic injector nozzle (before 2007) or EHI (after 2007)

FIGURE 28–2 Side view of the E-Tech engine showing the location of the ECM and EUPs.

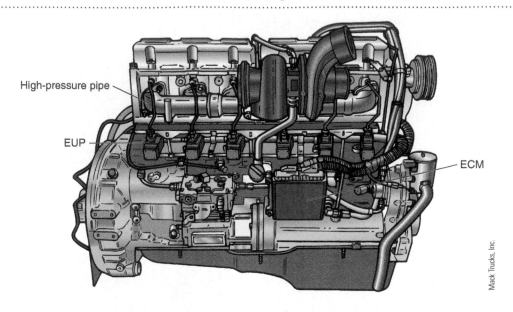

High-pressure pipe

EUP

ECM

Mack Trucks, Inc.

Bosch EUP technology incorporates the first two EUI functions in a single unit, flange mounted directly over the engine camshaft that actuates the pumping stroke. One EUP manages fueling for a single engine cylinder. The EUP is connected by means of a high-pressure pipe to the injector.

Figure 28–2 shows a broadside view of the Mack Trucks E-Tech engine. Compare this view with the fuel system schematic in **Figure 28–3**,

FIGURE 28–3 Schematic of the EUP fuel system.

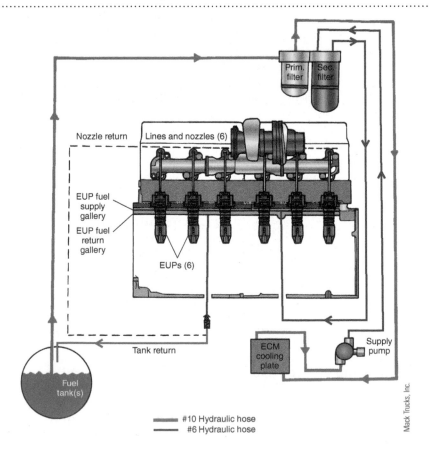

Prim. filter   Sec. filter

Nozzle return   Lines and nozzles (6)

EUP fuel supply gallery

EUP fuel return gallery

EUPs (6)

Tank return

ECM cooling plate

Supply pump

Fuel tank(s)

Mack Trucks, Inc.

— #10 Hydraulic hose
— #6 Hydraulic hose

which shows how fuel is routed through the system, and note the location of the EUP units, high-pressure pipes, and the engine controller ECU. All six high-pressure pipes are of equal length and shape, and quite a bit shorter than those found on an inline port-helix metering injection pump.

FUEL SUBSYSTEM

The fuel subsystem required to fuel the EUPs is fairly standard in that it can be divided into primary and secondary circuits regardless of the original equipment manufacturer (OEM).

MACK E-TECH FUEL ROUTING

Typically, a gear pump is used to move fuel through the fuel subsystem. The gear pump is required to produce the charging pressures of 100 psi (7 bar) and up to 100 gph (gallons per hour) (378 liters per hour) flow required by the EUPs. Fuel is drawn from the fuel tank by a gear-type transfer pump and pulled through a primary filter and (depending on the OEM) the ECM cooling plate. When fuel is routed through the ECM heat exchanger, it acts as the cooling medium for the heat generated by the microprocessor and switching units. Fuel exits the transfer pump at the charging pressure and flows through the secondary filter.

Fuel exiting the secondary filter is then fed to the fuel supply gallery in the cylinder block, which runs the length of the cylinder block. This enables charging pressure fuel to be made available to the EUPs, which are located in cylindrical bores in the cylinder block. The EUPs are manufactured with exterior annular inlet and output recesses, which are separated and sealed with O-rings. In this way, charge fuel is pumped into the EUPs; it is circulated within (where some is used for fueling the engine), and then returned to the fuel tank by means of the cylinder block return gallery, which runs parallel with the supply gallery, as illustrated in Figure 28–3 and **Figure 28–4**.

The filtering requirements of EUP-fueled engines that use SMART injectors or EHIs are generally more exacting. EHIs are especially vulnerable to even minute particulate contamination. For this reason, it is recommended that only OEM-recommended filters be used.

PRIMING THE FUEL SUBSYSTEM

This procedure should only be required when the fuel system has run completely dry. Mack Trucks stresses that when loss of prime occurs, using a hand primer pump is the only acceptable method of priming. The following method should be used when the fuel subsystem has to be primed:

1. Fill both the primary and secondary fuel filters with filtered fuel, pouring it into the inlet side of the filter.
2. Loosen the inlet hose fitting on the secondary filter mounting pad.

FIGURE 28–4 Fuel routing in the E-Tech fuel circuit.

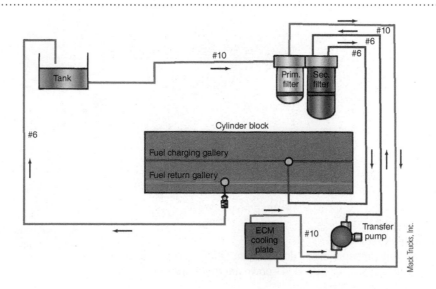

3. Actuate the hand primer pump until bubble-free fuel exits at the inlet fitting on the secondary filter mounting pad. No more than 50 strokes should be required. Tighten the hose line nut and crank the engine.

TECH TIP:

Do not crank an EUP-fueled engine for more than 30 continuous seconds. Allow 2 minutes between each 30-second cranking cycle.

WARNING:

Applying air pressure to the fuel tank to prime the fuel system can blow out the transfer pump seals and pump fuel into the crankcase, contaminating the engine oil.

Figure 28–5 is a schematic of the MB fuel system showing both the fuel subsystem and the high-pressure circuit. In addition, the test points for verifying system performance pressures are indicated.

INPUT CIRCUIT

Bosch EUP-fueled engines are full authority, electronic management systems with comprehensive engine/chassis monitoring and command circuits. The input circuit components used are similar regardless of engine OEM. Until recently, it has been both a Bosch and MB preference to retain the original German acronyms in translation, and this can cause some confusion. For instance, the engine controller module was a PLD control unit rather than an ECM. This confusing approach appears to have changed somewhat for the better with MB's adoption of DDEC as its engine management system. In common with other full authority management systems, every critical engine function is monitored by the input circuit. The locations of some of the key sensors on a Mack Trucks E-Tech engine using EUP fueling are shown in **Figure 28–6.**

FIGURE 28–5 EUP fuel circuit flow.

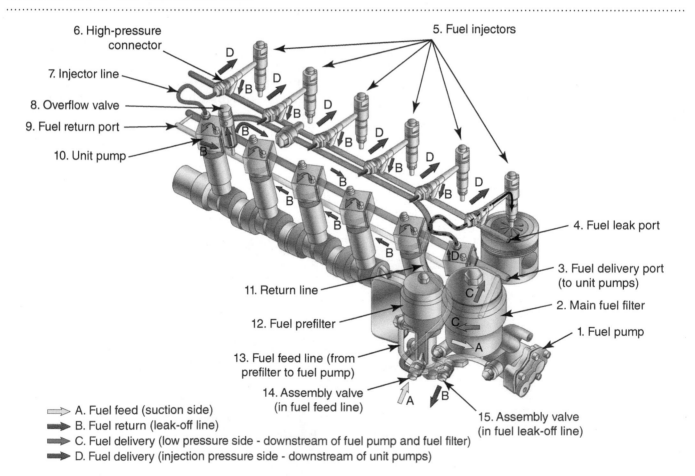

6. High-pressure connector
7. Injector line
8. Overflow valve
9. Fuel return port
10. Unit pump
5. Fuel injectors
4. Fuel leak port
3. Fuel delivery port (to unit pumps)
2. Main fuel filter
1. Fuel pump
11. Return line
12. Fuel prefilter
13. Fuel feed line (from prefilter to fuel pump)
14. Assembly valve (in fuel feed line)
15. Assembly valve (in fuel leak-off line)

A. Fuel feed (suction side)
B. Fuel return (leak-off line)
C. Fuel delivery (low pressure side - downstream of fuel pump and fuel filter)
D. Fuel delivery (injection pressure side - downstream of unit pumps)

FIGURE 28–6 Location of V-MAC III input circuit components.

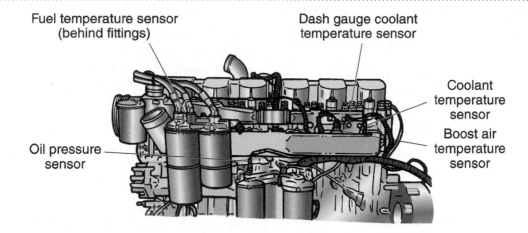

Fuel temperature sensor
(behind fittings)

Dash gauge coolant
temperature sensor

Coolant
temperature
sensor

Boost air
temperature
sensor

Oil pressure
sensor

Not shown
- Engine speed sensor (on left side of flywheel housing)
- Engine position sensor (on engine front cover)
- Dash gauge oil temperature sensor (on left side of oil pan)

Mack Trucks, Inc.

MERCEDES-BENZ INPUTS

The locations of the sensors used on a six-cylinder version of a MBE-900 engine are shown in **Figure 28–7**. The electrical principles on which these sensors operate are discussed in Chapter 34.

ENGINE CONTROLLERS AND MANAGEMENT ELECTRONICS

The way in which Mack Trucks, MB, and Paccar electronically manage their EUP systems is similar. All use a chassis management module with a

FIGURE 28–7 Location of sensors on the MBE-900 engine.

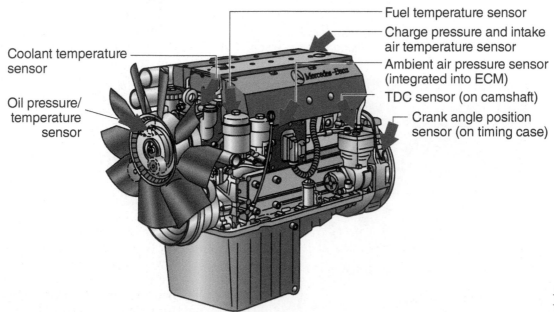

Coolant temperature
sensor

Oil pressure/
temperature
sensor

Fuel temperature sensor

Charge pressure and intake
air temperature sensor

Ambient air pressure sensor
(integrated into ECM)

TDC sensor (on camshaft)

Crank angle position
sensor (on timing case)

Mack Trucks, Inc.

Note: The 6-cylinder engine is shown; sensor locations are similar on the 4-cylinder engine.

proprietary control area network (CAN) connection to an engine management module (see Chapter 37). In each case, the chassis and engine management modules can receive and broadcast data over the J1587 and J1939 data backbones.

V-MAC III ELECTRONICS

Mack Trucks V-MAC III on E-Tech returns to a two-module system, separating vehicle control functions from engine control functions. Mack Trucks uses the acronym **electronic control unit (ECU)** to describe its modules. The engine controller module is located on the right side of the engine, mounted on a fuel-cooled heat exchanger as shown in **Figure 28–8**. Because the engine control module is located close to the engine exhaust manifold, a heat shield helps protect the device from exhaust heat. Removal of this heat shield has resulted in ECU overheat failures. The engine controller is multiplexed to the vehicle control module, which is mounted under the dash in the cab.

MERCEDES-BENZ ELECTRONICS

The two-controller module system used by most versions of the MB EUP system is known as:

- PLD—German acronym for engine-mounted control unit or ECM. It is located on the left side of the engine and does not need to be mounted on a heat sink.

FIGURE 28–8 The Mack Trucks E-Tech ECU.

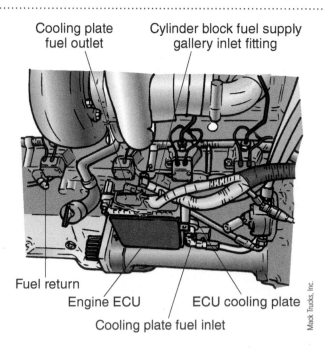

Cooling plate fuel outlet

Cylinder block fuel supply gallery inlet fitting

Fuel return

Engine ECU

ECU cooling plate

Cooling plate fuel inlet

Mack Trucks, Inc.

- VCU—the vehicle control unit that fulfills the same function as the V-MAC III module on the Mack Trucks system.

The two modules are multiplexed by a proprietary CAN bus. Input data signaled to the PLD module can be broadcast to the J1587 and J1939 data backbones only by first routing it through the VCU module. For first-generation EUPs, the MB electronics had to be accessed for read, reprogram, and diagnostic operations. The EST connection was by chassis data link, the appropriate communications adapter, and Freightliner ServiceLink, PC-based software. More recent versions with DDEC management are accessed using DDC software. For read-only purposes, the electronics can be interpreted through the standard SAE SAs, MIDs, SIDs, PGNs, PIDs, and FMIs. With the 2007 model year, almost all of the language and terms used to describe the MB system and its components are DDEC in origin, so the system has become much easier to work with. **Figure 28–9** shows a simplification of the multiplexing architecture used by an MB-powered chassis: The EST is shown using Freightliner ServiceLink software.

ELECTRONIC UNIT PUMPS

The EUPs are flange mounted to the engine cylinder block directly over the engine camshaft, as shown in cutaway format in Figure 28–5. An EUP roller tappet rides the center lobe of each triple set of cam profiles, one per engine cylinder. In other words, a separate EUP is required for each engine cylinder. Each is connected electrically to the ECM and hydraulically to an injector nozzle. You can see how the EUPs are arranged on a six-cylinder engine in **Figure 28–10**: The pipes connect each EUP with a cylinder head located injector.

PUMPING ACTION

Pumping action in the EUP is dictated by the actuating cam geometry. As the engine-driven cam rotates off its base circle ramping toward the nose, the roller lifter drives the EUP plunger into the pump chamber. Fuel is routed at charging pressure through the pump chamber at any time the engine is running, entering through an upper exterior annulus, circulating through the EUP internal ducting, and exiting through a lower exterior annulus. **Figure 28–11** is a cutaway

FIGURE 28–9 Daimler Trucks multiplexing architecture.

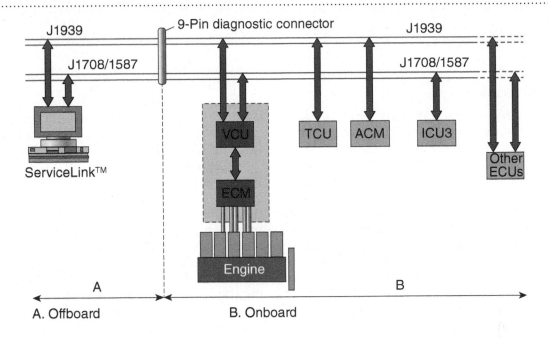

A. Offboard

B. Onboard

FIGURE 28–10 The E-Tech engine showing the EUP line connection to the hydraulic injectors.

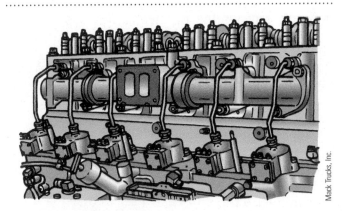

Mack Trucks, Inc.

view showing the relationship between the EUP, a hydraulic injector, and the engine cylinder.

Control of the injection pulse is the responsibility of the EUP solenoid, which is itself switched by the engine-mounted control module. When the EUP plunger is driven into the pump chamber by the actuating cam profile, fuel is merely displaced; however, the moment the EUP solenoid is energized, fuel is trapped in the pump chamber and pressure rise occurs. Connected to the EUP pump chamber by a high-pressure pipe is the injector, either a hydraulic

FIGURE 28–11 Sectional view of the Mercedes-Benz EUP-fueled engine showing the hydraulic connection between the EUP and injector.

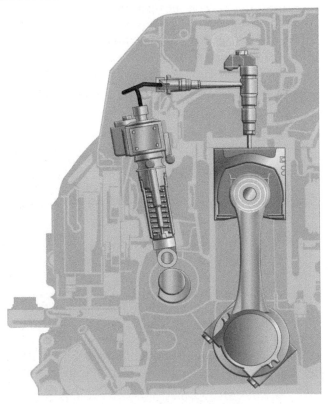

multi-orifii or an electrohydraulic nozzle. Actual injection to the engine cylinder begins when:

- The preset, hard value, nozzle opening pressure (NOP) is achieved with hydraulic injectors
- The ECM energizes the electrohydraulic injector (soft value opening and closing) in post-2007 versions

The EUP plunger has a 10 mm diameter and the potential for an 18 mm stroke. Actual plunger stroke is determined by the cam profile. Peak injection pressures of up to 26,000 psi (1,793 bar) are possible on pre-2007 engines, with pressures rising to above 30,000 psi on the post-2010 Paccar engines. The EUPs are supplied with low-pressure (charging pressure) fuel by a fuel supply gallery machined into the engine block. High-pressure fuel is routed from the EUP to the injectors in the cylinder head by a relatively short (compared with earlier pump-line-nozzle [PLN] engines) high-pressure pipe. Each high-pressure pipe is of equal length and has an identical part number regardless of which engine cylinder it is used to fuel.

CONTROL OF EFFECTIVE STROKE

Controlling effective stroke is the responsibility of the ECM. Operation of the EUP almost identically parallels that of any typical diesel engine EUI system, with one exception. Because the EUP is connected to the injector by means of a high-pressure pipe and in the EUI system the nozzle is integral, the lag time between the **beginning of energizing (BOE)**

and **beginning of injection (BOI)** is obviously extended in the EUP-managed engine when compared to the typical EUI system.

Hydraulic nozzles, which are set to a specified NOP value (around 5,000 psi/345 bar), are serviced as units in the same manner as any other hydraulic injector nozzles; these procedures are covered elsewhere in this textbook. The EHIs used with the post-2007 MB and post-2010 Paccar must be serviced by a Bosch dealership, although this will likely change in the near future.

Effective stroke can only take place within the ramp window between cam inner base circle and outer base circle. When the ECM switches the EUP control solenoid, fuel is trapped in the pump chamber as shown in **Figure 28–12**, creating pressure rise in the feed circuit to the injector. Effective stroke ends when the engine controller de-energizes the EUP solenoid, opening the spill circuit and resulting in pressure collapse. Where hydraulic injectors are used, when there is no longer sufficient pressure to hold the nozzle valve open, it closes. Where EHIs are used, the ECM is responsible for signaling both the opening and closing of the nozzle valve.

REMOVAL AND INSTALLATION OF EUPS

As with any engine or electronics system procedure, the appropriate OEM technical service literature is required before starting the work. The procedure is outlined here as a model so that the student has a general awareness of what is

FIGURE 28–12 EUP operating principle.

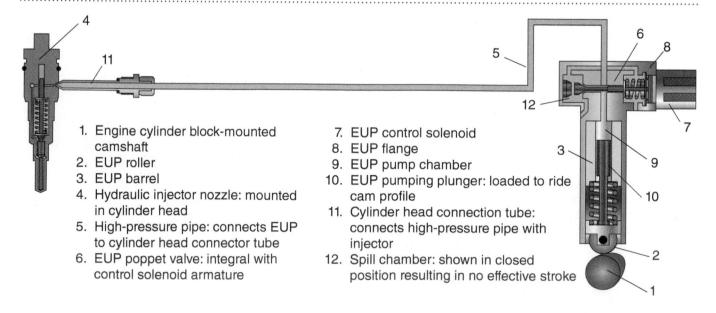

1. Engine cylinder block-mounted camshaft
2. EUP roller
3. EUP barrel
4. Hydraulic injector nozzle: mounted in cylinder head
5. High-pressure pipe: connects EUP to cylinder head connector tube
6. EUP poppet valve: integral with control solenoid armature
7. EUP control solenoid
8. EUP flange
9. EUP pump chamber
10. EUP pumping plunger: loaded to ride cam profile
11. Cylinder head connection tube: connects high-pressure pipe with injector
12. Spill chamber: shown in closed position resulting in no effective stroke

required to remove and replace the distinct components on this fuel system. **Figure 28–13** shows a view of a Paccar EUP manifold located above the engine fuel module. **Figure 28–14** shows an overhead view of the same engine: Note the routing of the high-pressure pipe connecting the EUP with the injector within the cylinder head.

Removal

When more than one EUP has to be removed from an engine, use a paint stick to mark each

EUP with the engine cylinder number. This will eliminate the need to reprogram the EUP calibration data to the ECU on reinstallation.

1. Remove the heat shields if fitted and thoroughly clean the exposed portion of the EUP and the cylinder block. Any dirt or debris that drops into the EUP bores will enter the crankcase of the engine, so this step is critical.
2. Drain fuel from the cylinder block fuel supply gallery. Consult the OEM service literature to determine how to do this most effectively on the specific engine on which the procedure is being performed. In some cases, the filter pad assembly will have to be drained. It is important to remember that if the fuel supply gallery is not drained, all of the fuel in this gallery will drain into the crankcase when the first EUP is pulled. If this happens, the engine oil will be diluted to a level in which engine damage will result, so the oil must be changed.
3. Remove the high-pressure pipe from the EUP (see **Figure 28–15**) and discard it. This is a torque-to-yield component designed for one-time use.
4. Remove the electrical terminals from the EUP solenoid (see **Figure 28–16**).
5. Remove the EUP inboard screw and loosen and back out the outboard screw to about ½ inch (13 mm).

FIGURE 28–13 View of the EUP manifold and fuel module on a 2011 Paccar MX385 engine.

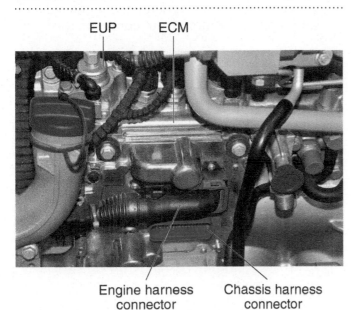

Engine harness connector   Chassis harness connector

FIGURE 28–14 Overhead view of a Paccar EUP-fueled engine's external subcomponents.

FIGURE 28–15 When removing EUPs from the engine, the high-pressure pipe should be removed and discarded and the EUP electrical connector separated before attempting to remove the two hold-down fasteners.

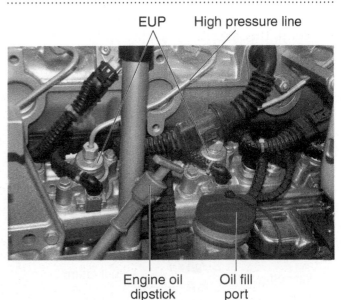

Engine oil dipstick   Oil fill port

FIGURE 28–16 EUP with terminal wires removed.

High pressure
discharge port
to injector

Engine harness
terminals

EUP terminals

6. Insert an injector heel bar under each of the EUP bolt bosses and lever on the EUP flange until the assembly stops on the outboard capscrew. **Figure 28–17** shows an external view of an EUP after removal from the engine.

FIGURE 28–17 EUP external subcomponents.

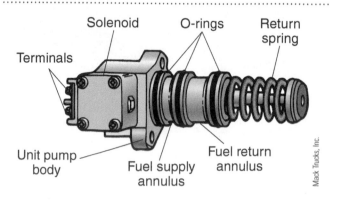

Solenoid

O-rings

Return
spring

Terminals

Unit pump
body

Fuel supply
annulus

Fuel return
annulus

Mack Trucks, Inc.

CAUTION:

The EUP assembly may be loaded with considerable spring force depending on the position of the actuating cam profile under it. For this reason, it is essential that the outboard capscrew be backed out no more than ½ inch (13 mm).

7. Back out the outboard EUP capscrew and remove the EUP assembly from the bore.
8. Remove the roller tappet by hand. It is important not to use any tool that could result in damage to the bore. Take precautions to ensure that dirt does not enter the engine through the exposed EUP bore. Protect the removed EUP and tappet assembly from contamination.

Tappet and EUP Installation

1. Clean the cylinder block at the EUP bore. Lubricate the tappet assembly using the same engine oil used in the engine.
2. Install the roller tappet assembly into the bore, being sure to orient it with the guide pin, and check that the tappet slides freely in the bore.

WARNING:

Tappet guide pins are factory installed and should not be removed.

3. Install a set of new O-rings (3) on the EUP. The center O-ring is color-coded to identify it; it is a different size from the upper and lower O-rings.
4. Lubricate the O-rings with the same engine oil to be used in the engine. Press into position by hand. You can see the fuel inlet (supply) and return annuli (see return gland) in **Figure 28–18**.

TECH TIP:

The cam profile under the EUP being installed must be on its base circle, that is, in its unactuated position. Manually bar the engine to ensure that the engine camshaft is correctly positioned. Using the starter may result in fuel being pushed through the supply gallery and ending up in the crankcase, so this should be avoided.

5. Install the EUP capscrews and torque to the required specification.

FIGURE 28–18 Sectional view of an EUP.

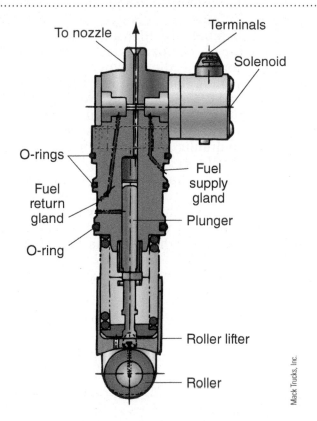

Mack Trucks, Inc.

FIGURE 28–19 A typical nozzle test bench.

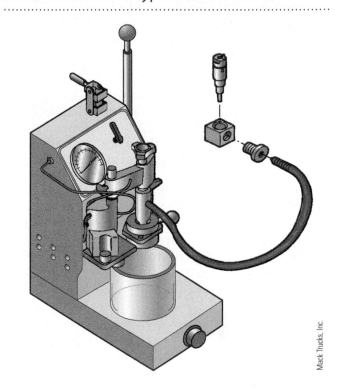

Mack Trucks, Inc.

6. Install a *new* high-pressure pipe (connects the EUP with the injector: see warning below) and torque the line nut to specification.
7. Reinstall the EUP connector or wire terminals and torque to specification.
8. Identify the calibration code, usually recorded on the EUP nameplate. This is a four-digit code with a CAL prefix. Program the calibration code to the ECU using an electronic service tool (EST), with the appropriate software. At the time of writing, when working with Paccar engines, this can only be done with DAVIE software and a Paccar communications adapter (not RP1210 A/B compatible).
9. Install the heat shields on engines that use them. *Never* omit these, as heat may affect the operation of the EUP solenoid coils and may damage the ECM.

WARNING:

Some OEMs have issued service bulletins requiring that the high-pressure pipes that connect the EUPs with the injectors be replaced and not reused. The reason stated is that the seat on the pipe nipple sets (deforms) when it is first torqued to spec. Check with OEM service literature to identify the correct procedure for either reusing or replacing EUP high-pressure pipes.

TESTING HYDRAULIC INJECTORS

EUP engines use multi-orifii or electrohydraulic injectors. Make sure you identify which you are working with, because what you are permitted to do with each type varies. Electrohydraulic nozzles can be identified by the fact that they have both electrical and hydraulic connections: At present, MB and Paccar regard EHIs as non-field serviceable. However, field test benches do exist and may be found in larger service facilities. The hydraulic nozzles used up until 2007 are fully hydromechanical devices that can be tested and set up according to the procedures outlined in Chapter 21. **Figure 28–19** shows a typical nozzle testing tool recommended for bench-testing hydraulic injector nozzles.

ELECTROHYDRAULIC NOZZLES

In order to meet 2007 emissions requirements, MB adapted its EUP fuel system to use EHIs, and all post-2010 Paccar engines use them. EHIs are ECM pulse width modulation (PWM) controlled: The pulse is delivered to a solenoid actuator in current versions. The reasons for adopting EHIs can be briefly summarized as follows:

- Soft NOPs (nozzle can be opened at whatever pressure the ECM requires within the EUP pressure capability range)

- Multipulse injection events (required to provide the ECM with better control of combustion to meet emissions requirements)
- Soft (ECM-controlled) nozzle closure (this removes the collapse phase of injection that disadvantages hydraulically switched injector nozzles)

A full treatment of EHIs was provided in Chapter 21; EHI operation is rapidly reviewed here. Referencing **Figure 28–20**, fuel at rail pressure is supplied to the high-pressure connection (4), to the nozzle through the fuel duct (10), and to the control chamber (8) through the feed orifice (7). The control chamber is connected to the fuel return (1) via a bleed orifice (6) that is opened by the actuator valve. With the bleed orifice closed, hydraulic force acts on the valve control plunger (9), exceeding that at the nozzle-needle pressure chamber (located between the

shank and the needle of the nozzle valve). Although the hydraulic pressure values acting on the top of the nozzle valve and that in the pressure chamber are identical, the sectional area at the top of the nozzle valve is greater. As a result, the nozzle needle is loaded into its seated position, meaning that the injector is closed.

When an ECM signal triggers the actuator valve, the bleed orifice opens. This immediately drops the control-chamber pressure and, as a result, the hydraulic pressure acting on the top of the nozzle valve (11) also drops. When hydraulic force acting on top of the nozzle valve drops below the force acting on the nozzle-needle pressure shoulder, the nozzle valve lifts and allows fuel to pass around the seat to be injected through orifii into the combustion chamber. The hydraulic assist and amplification factor are required in this system because the forces

FIGURE 28–20 Key components on an EHI.

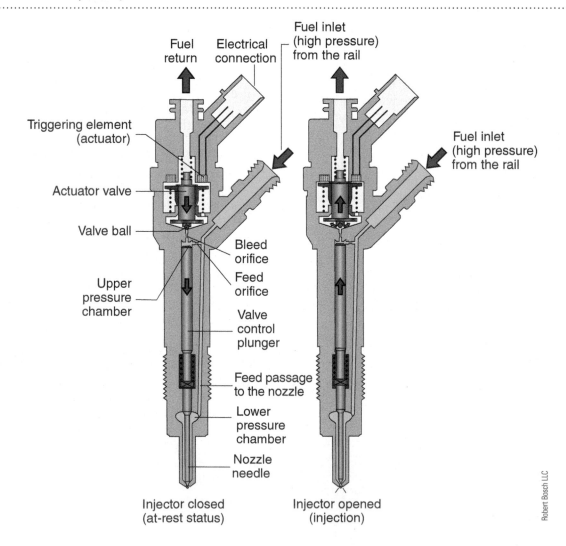

Injector closed (at-rest status)

Injector opened (injection)

Triggering element (actuator)

Actuator valve

Valve ball

Upper pressure chamber

Fuel return

Electrical connection

Fuel inlet (high pressure) from the rail

Fuel inlet (high pressure) from the rail

Bleed orifice

Feed orifice

Valve control plunger

Feed passage to the nozzle

Lower pressure chamber

Nozzle needle

Robert Bosch LLC

necessary for rapid nozzle valve opening cannot be directly generated by the actuator valve alone. Fuel used as hydraulic media to open the nozzle valve is in addition to the injected fuel quantity, so this excess fuel is routed back to the tank. In addition to this fuel, some leak-by fuel losses occur at the nozzle valve-to-body clearance and the valve-plunger guide clearance.

FUTURE OF EUPS

Although EUP-fueled engines have been widely used in Europe, no American engines are currently using this fuel system for on-highway applications. The first generation of Paccar MX engines using EUP fueling was discontinued at the beginning of MY 2013 in favor of re-engineered second-generation engines managed by CR fueling. That said, technicians should be aware that there are a lot of EUP engines still out there, Paccar, MB, and Mack Trucks branded, and that these engines will not simply disappear overnight. In addition, the post-2013 Paccar MX-11 and MX-13 engines use a pair of cam-actuated EUPs to generate the rail pressures required for their CR system. **Figure 28–21** shows a left-side view of a PACCAR MX13 engine with an EUP fuel system feeding EHI injectors.

FIGURE 28–21 Left-side view of a 2011 PACCAR MX series engine; this engine series used EUP fuel systems until MY 2013.

High pressure pipes: connect EUPs to EHIs.

EUPs   Fuel transfer pump

SUMMARY

- The Bosch EUP system may be classified as a full authority electronic management system.
- Since EPA MY 2103, no current American-built diesel engines use EUP fueling. The most recent engines using this fuel system were the first-generation Paccar MX Series engines manufactured from 2010 to 2013.
- MB engines manufactured between 2007 and 2010, and Paccar MX Series engines manufactured between 2010 and 2013, used EUPs in conjunction with EHIs, often referred to as SMART injectors.
- EUP-fueled diesel engine series manufactured for the North American market prior to EPA MY 2007 were the Mack Trucks E-Tech and Mercedes-Benz MBE-900 and MBE-4000 Series. This generation of engines used hydraulic injectors.
- EUP engines sold into the North American markets used a two-module management system. In most cases these required a separate module to manage the fueling and some engine functions.

- The Mack E-Tech V-MAC III is a two-module system; the engine controller (ECU) is mounted on a fuel-cooled heat exchanger located on the right side of the engine. It is multiplexed to the vehicle control module located in the cab under the dash.
- The Mercedes-Benz MBE-900 and MBE-4000 engines also use a two-module system, and what it calls the modules depends on the generation. The PLD or ECM (DDEC VI) manages fuel and engine management functions, while a multiplexed VCU takes care of command inputs and communications with other on-chassis systems on the J1587 and J1939 data backbones.
- The EUPs are supplied with fuel from the fuel subsystem at charging pressure. Fuel is constantly cycled through the system circuitry and the EUPs, following which it is returned to the tank.
- Actual EUP plunger stroke is dictated by cam geometry. Plunger effective stroke is controlled by the engine electronics by switching the EUP solenoids.

- The EUP plunger is a simple cylindrical piston with no milled recesses or drillings. It is spring-loaded to ride the cam profile and reciprocates within the EUP barrel.
- A high-pressure pipe connects each EUP unit with either a multi-orifii hydraulic injector (pre-2007) or an ECM-controlled EHI (post-2007).
- It is important to observe OEM procedure when replacing EUPs. Fuel should be drained from the charging gallery in the cylinder block or it will spill into the engine oil. It should be remembered that EUPs can be under considerable tension if the actuating cam profile is at or close to outer base circle during removal.

- The injectors used with EUP-fueled engines are connected to the EUPs by a high-pressure pipe and cylinder head connection tube. Hydraulic injectors are tested similarly to any other types of hydraulic injectors.
- Although there is a wide range of aftermarket options, OEMs recommend that EHIs be serviced only by authorized dealers.
- EHI opening and closing events are controlled by the ECM and are not dependent on hydraulic pressure. They are also capable of multipulse injection events that are required to meet post-2007 emissions.

REVIEW QUESTIONS

1. What force creates injection pressure values in an EUP-managed engine?
   a. Electrical
   b. Hydraulic
   c. Spring
   d. Mechanical

2. What defines the fueling window available to the ECM within which it can select an effective EUP stroke?
   a. Engine rpm
   b. Accelerator position
   c. Road speed
   d. Cam profile

3. In which of the following engines would you be likely to find an EUP-fueling system equipped with EHI injectors?
   a. Pre-2007 Mack E-Tech
   b. Pre-2007 MBE-900
   c. Pre-2007 MBE-4000
   d. 2010–2013 Paccar MX 375

4. How is EUP effective stroke controlled?
   a. By varying the pump plunger stroke
   b. By switching the EUP solenoid
   c. By varying the EUP charging pressure
   d. By controlling the rotational position of the plunger

5. Peak injection pressure values in EUP-fueled engines up to 2007 may reach:
   a. 4,700 psi (324 bar).
   b. 12,500 psi (862 bar).
   c. 18,000 psi (1,241 bar).
   d. 26,000 psi (1,793 bar).

6. Where is the TDC sensor located in a MB-900 Series EUP-fueled engine?
   a. camshaft
   b. crankshaft
   c. fuel pump
   d. flywheel

7. Fuel is delivered to the EUP by the transfer pump at what pressure?
   a. 5,000 psi (345 bar)
   b. Charging pressure
   c. 26,000 psi (1,793 bar)
   d. Peak pressure

8. Technician A states that Bosch EUPs are mounted above and actuated directly by the engine camshaft. Technician B states that duty cycle in an EUP is controlled by the ECM. Who is correct?
   a. Technician A only
   b. Technician B only
   c. Both A and B
   d. Neither A nor B

9. Technician A states that the EUP functions similarly to an EUI, with the exception that the injector function is remote. Technician B states that the EUP-to-nozzle lines on a multicylinder engine must be of identical length. Who is correct?
   a. Technician A only
   b. Technician B only
   c. Both A and B
   d. Neither A nor B

10. When removing a set of EUPs from an engine that you intend to reinstall, which of the following should be performed first?
    a. Mark the EUPs by cylinder number with a paint stick.
    b. Reprogram the fuel flow code.
    c. Ensure that the actuating cam profile under the EUP is on an inner base circle.
    d. Drain the fuel supply gallery.

11. Technician A states that hydraulic injectors used with pre-2007 EUP-fueled engines have soft opening and closing pressure values. Technician B states that hydraulic injectors used with pre-2007 EUP-fueled engines are not serviceable using standard shop equipment. Who is correct?
    a. Technician A only
    b. Technician B only
    c. Both A and B
    d. Neither A nor B

12. What software is required to read, program, and troubleshoot the first generation of Mercedes-Benz 900 and 4000 engines?
    a. ServiceLink
    b. Electronic Technician
    c. INSITE
    d. MackNet

13. Which of the following is required to actuate an EHI?
    a. NOP pressure
    b. ECM control pulse
    c. EHI actuating cam ramping to OBC
    d. EHI actuating cam ramping to IBC

14. Which of the following is an advantage of using EHIs in place of hydraulic injectors?
    a. Soft NOPs
    b. Rapid-response multipulse injection events
    c. Elimination of collapse phase
    d. All of the above

15. Which of the following OEMs uses the EUP fuel system on highway diesel engines sold after the U.S. 2010 Environmental Protection Agency (EPA) model year?
    a. Mercedes-Benz
    b. Detroit Diesel
    c. Mack Trucks
    d. Paccar

29

Prerequisites: Chapters 19 and 20

CUMMINS HPI-TP

OBJECTIVES

After studying this chapter, you should be able to:

- Identify the engine family using the HPI-TP fuel system.
- Outline the changes required by ISX to meet 2004, 2007, and 2010 EPA emissions standards.
- Describe the HPI-TP fuel subsystem.
- Trace fuel flow routing from tank to injector in a typical HPI-TP-fueled engine.
- Identify the components of an IFSM module.
- Describe the operation of timing and metering actuators.
- Understand the operating principles of the HPI-TP system.
- Outline some of the features of an ISX engine.
- Set the valves on a Cummins HPI-TP ISX engine
- Adjust HPI-TP injectors to Cummins specifications
- Outline the camshaft timing procedure used on twin OHC ISX engines

KEY TERMS

high-pressure injection-time pressure (HPI-TP)

hydrocarbon injector

INSITE

Intebrake

integrated fuel system module (IFSM)

Interact System (IS)

ISX-TP

metering actuator

Monotherm™ pistons

QuickServe Online (QSOL)

Signature Series

timing actuator

trapped volume spill (TVS)

water-in-fuel (WIF) sensor

CHAPTER 29 CUMMINS HPI-TP 613

INTRODUCTION

The current Cummins **high-pressure injection-time pressure (HPI-TP)** fuel system was used on the successful ISX series engines until 2010. In 2010, Cummins re-engineered the ISX to use a standard common rail (CR) fuel system it calls XPI. There are few similarities between the HPI-TP and XPI fuel systems, so it is important that they not be confused. At the time of writing, HPI-TP fueled ISX engines are still being supplied to markets outside the United States and Canada.

HPI-TP is a common rail, open-nozzle system with some similarities to the now-obsolete pressure-time or PT system. If you have previously worked with and understand the PT system, it might be a good idea for you to make the connection between the PT and TP system. However, in describing the TP system here, this is not done, because the reality is that truck technicians today will seldom encounter the PT system. The HPI-TP fuel system is used on Cummins's ISX family of engines, so this engine family will be the primary reference in this chapter. In addition, the HPI-TP fuel system is found on the following engines:

- Scania 12-liter (Euro and other offshore markets)
- Cummins QS-K series (off highway)
- Cummins QS-T series (off highway)

EVOLUTION OF THE ISX

Although the ISX engine has only been around since 1998, it has undergone extensive development since its introduction. Some of the changes have been driven by Environmental Protection Agency (EPA) emissions standards, but along the way, many technical improvements have been made to the engine. The original ISX was notable for its clean, uncluttered appearance. However, the addition of exhaust gas recirculation (EGR) to meet 2004 emissions standards, positive crankcase ventilation (PCV) (2007), and diesel particulate filter (DPF) (2007) contributed to changing the appearance of Cummins's flagship, high-powered engine over the years up to 2010.

The Cummins HPI-TP system was launched on the ISX **Signature Series** engine introduced in 1998. The ISX is an inline 6-cylinder, 15-liter engine that was initially rated at 600 horsepower (447 kW) with the capability of a little over 2,000 lb-ft. (2,712 N•m) of torque output. This became the platform for a broader range of **ISX-TP** engine series with BHP ratings that extend from 385 to 600 horsepower (287 to 447 kW). The ISX-TP engine used up to 2010 was unique in that it used a pair of overhead camshafts mounted on a single slab cylinder head. Both camshafts were gear-driven by the engine timing geartrain. Later versions of the double overhead camshaft (DOHC) engine used single-piece **Monotherm™ pistons** (see Chapter 7), variable-geometry turbocharging (VGT), EGR, and DPF.

ISX-TP FEATURES

The pre-2010 ISX engine uses one camshaft to actuate the TP injectors and drive the fuel pump assembly. The other camshaft is dedicated to the valve trains and engine brake. An internal engine compression brake known as **Intebrake** is capable of six stages of progressive braking by retarding on one through six cylinders. The engine uses a variable-geometry turbocharger, and for 2004 EPA emissions (became effective October 2002) used cooled exhaust gas recirculation (C-EGR). The original articulating pistons with steel crowns gave way to steel trunk-type pistons (Monotherm, see Chapter 7). The engine uses midstop wet-dry liners installed in a lightweight compacted graphite iron (CGI) cylinder block. Cummins introduced a fleet version of this engine, the ISX 385 ST (smart torque), to enable the phase-out of the much older N-14 engine and more recent ISM engines with CELECT Plus fueling. The lower horsepower fleet versions of the ISX engine have fuel map algorithms trimmed for fuel economy, making them suitable for linehaul fleet applications.

TP HYDRAULIC EQUATION

In describing the TP system, note that the letters *TP* refer to two of the three factors of a hydraulic equation whose product is a volume of fuel flow. If you recall from earlier chapters, several times we have made the statement that the output of a diesel engine is determined by the volume of fuel metered into its cylinders. It follows that the specific fuel quantity (i.e., *volume of flow*) emitted per fueling pulse is critical: It defines how the engine is being run. So, if we construct a hydraulic equation whose product is a volume of flow, it has three factors:

1. Flow area
2. Pressure
3. Time of flow

Change any of the values and the product—that is, the volume of flow—will also change. In the Cummins TP hydraulic equation, both the critical flow areas and the pressure are designed to remain constant, so the variable used to control the "product" of the equation or metered fuel quantity is time. Because time is the control variable, it is the first letter in the acronym TP. The control variable in the older Cummins PT system was pressure, so P was the first letter in the acronym PT.

CONTROL VARIABLE

The time factor in the TP system is precisely controlled by the engine control module (ECM). It accomplishes this by switching a pair of actuators for each bank of the engine, front and rear, which are four in all. The actuators are pulse width modulation (PWM)–controlled solenoid gate valves that either open or close. These gate valves are located on the fuel CR that is charged at a more or less constant pressure. When energized, the actuator opens and permits fuel to be routed to a mechanical open-nozzle injector by means of riflings in the cylinder head. The timing actuator uses CR fuel as hydraulic media to establish a timing value for the fuel pulse (this fuel is not injected), while the metering actuator feeds CR fuel to the metering chamber in the TP injector. TP injectors are open-nozzle mechanical injectors. Although the fuel that is supplied to its timing and metering chambers is precisely controlled by the ECM, no electronic components are integral with the TP injector. These injectors are actuated mechanically by an overhead camshaft.

ENGINE MANAGEMENT ELECTRONICS

ISX engine management electronics use Cummins common platform ECM architecture known as **Interact System** or **IS**. Engine performance and engine subsystems are precisely monitored and managed and the engine electronics connect to the J1939 data bus. Engine protection, extensively programmable customer and proprietary data programming options, and guided troubleshooting (in conjunction with **INSITE** software) are all features of the ISX Series. The engine uses a double overhead camshaft design: The camshafts are parallel mounted on a single slab

cylinder head. The left-side camshaft is responsible for actuating the HPI-TP injectors. The right-side camshaft is responsible for actuating the intake and exhaust valves and the engine brake. The ISX engine has a built-in engine brake known as *Intebrake*. The ECM-actuated Intebrake uses three solenoids to permit progressive braking using from one to all six engine cylinders.

FUEL SYSTEM COMPONENTS

The Cummins HPI-TP CR system is designed to manage the hydraulic fueling equation by holding the flow area constant, holding the pressure value constant, and using the time factor as the control variable. **Figure 29–1** shows a schematic of the Cummins HPI-TP system before the 2004 EGR version. Although the basics of the HPI-TP fuel system did not change that much during the years 1998 to 2010, there are some differences in each generation that you should be aware of. The following components make up the HPI-TP system.

INTEGRATED FUEL SYSTEM MODULE

The **integrated fuel system module** or **IFSM** acts as the hydraulic command center of the fuel system. The fuel routing and plumbing have undergone some modifications through each generation of the HPI-TP fuel system, so you should always consult QuickServe Online (QSOL) to reference the specific system you are working on. An IFSM consists of the following subcomponents.

Check Valve

Fuel enters the IFSM through a check valve located behind the inlet. This prevents fuel from flowing out of the IFSM.

Fuel Filter/Water Separator

Fuel from the check valve is directed to a combination fuel filter and water separator with an integral **water-in-fuel (WIF) sensor** and drain. The filter medium uses a Stratapore™ 10-micron filtration medium. The combination fuel filter/water separator strips water out of the fuel using a centrifuge and drains the water to a sump. The WIF sensor is located in the sump, and it signals the dash maintenance lamp when it detects water. The electrical operation of WIF sensors is

FIGURE 29–1 Heavy-duty HPI-TP fuel system schematic.

Heavy Duty HPI-TP Fuel System Schematic

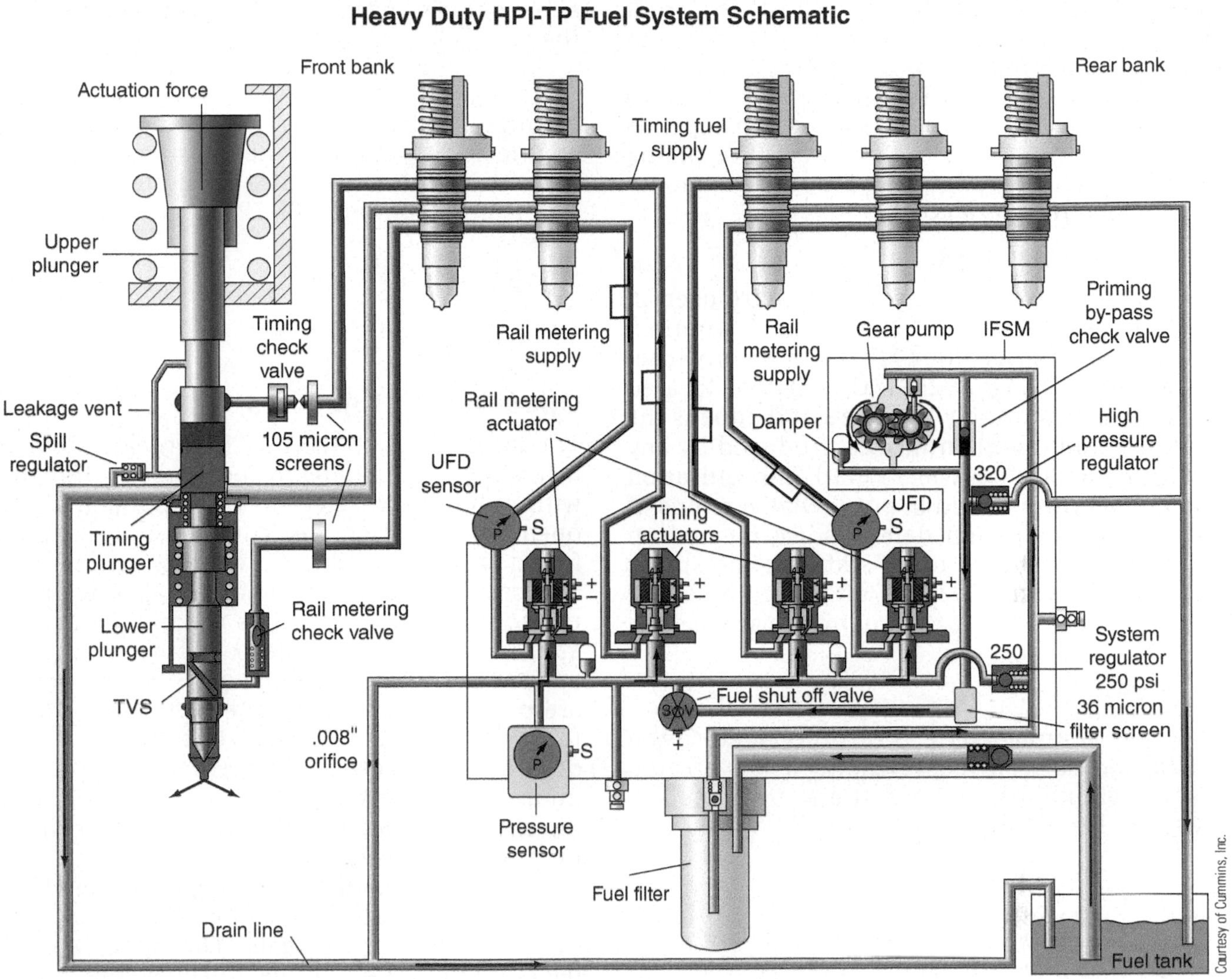

explained in Chapter 34. Note that sometimes a WIF can produce a service alert immediately after draining the water sump: The reason is that water-resident bacteria can coat the probes after draining and trigger a false signal.

Gear Pump

The gear pump moves the fuel through the fuel subsystem; depending on the generation of ISX, it may also be assisted by an electric lift pump. The gear pump uses an external gear pumping principle to push fuel downstream and charge the actuator rail. The resulting lower pressure upstream from the pump pulls more fuel into the inlet of the gear pump. The gear pump charges the IFSM. The gear pump is driven by a gear on the injector camshaft at 1.12 times crankshaft speed.

Lift Pumps

Depending on the generation of ISX, an electric lift pump may be incorporated. The first generation of HPI-TP used a lift pump and these have been reintroduced in the post-2004 EGR engines. The role of the lift pump is to initiate and maintain prime to the HPI-TP transfer pump and the IFSM.

Actuators

The system uses four externally mounted actuators: two **metering actuators** and two **timing actuators**. They are electrohydraulic solenoid valves. One timing actuator and one metering actuator manage separate fueling and timing events for each bank of the engine. The front bank consists of engine cylinders 1, 2, and 3 and the rear bank consists of cylinders 4, 5, and 6. The four actuators are fed by the engine actuator rail, so any fuel that passes by them depends on the duration (*time*) of actuation. The timing actuators are controlled by a pulse width modulated signal from the ECM.

Pulsation Dampers

Up to three fuel pulsation dampers are used in the HPI-TP system depending on the generation. You can see the location of these in the schematic shown in Figure 29–1. One may be located at the gear pump and when used, it dampens the pressure nodes and antinodes produced by any positive displacement gear pump. This pulsation damper was eliminated in post-2004 versions of HPI-TP. Two pulsation dampers are located on the actuator rail and act to stabilize the spikes produced by high-speed on/off switching of the actuators. The actuator rail dampers are used in all versions of HPI-TP.

Fuel Shutoff Valve

The fuel shutoff valve is an energized-to-run (ETR), normally closed solenoid. It has a rapid restart feature and is opened any time the key switch is turned on.

Fuel Pressure Sensor

The fuel pressure sensor is installed in the bottom of the IFSM close to the fuel filter pad. It signals fuel pressure values to the ECM. It uses a variable capacitance operating principle and is supplied with V-Ref. The return signal it sends to the ECM is V-DC and proportionally increases with fuel pressure.

Unintended Fueling Sensors

Two unintended fueling sensors (UFSs) may be used in the IFSM, one located on the front bank rail, the other on the rear. They were used in all early versions of ISX. They are designed to detect a problem with the actuators, specifically when they fail to seal the rail. A UFS signals the ECM in the event of actuator leakage. They were eliminated in later versions of IFSM because of improved monitoring logic.

IFSM Ports

There are two ports located on the IFSM used to test the fuel system. The front port is used to check the actuator rail pressure. The rear port is designed to test fuel subsystem inlet restriction. Both are equipped with quick couplers that allow speedy insertion of pressure gauges into the circuit.

Fuel Manifold

A single slab cylinder head is used on ISX engines. The cylinder head is manufactured with three internal rifles designed to direct fuel to and from the HPI-TP injectors. The three rifles are:

1. Timing
2. Drain
3. Metering

Open-Nozzle Injectors

The injectors used in an HPI-TP fuel system are mechanically actuated, open-nozzle injectors with no integral electronic components. The open-nozzle principle eliminates leak paths found in many hydraulic injector nozzles and can be used to bring about an abrupt ending to the injection pulse. The collapse phase created in hydraulic nozzles used by most other current systems is eliminated. HPI-TP injectors are designed to deliver injection pressures up to 35,000 psi (2,415 bar), resulting in smaller droplet size, better combustion control, and improved emissions. The plungers within the injector are coated with titanium nitride for high scuff resistance.

Fuel is directed into and out of the HPI-TP injectors by means of three exterior annuli separated by four O-ring seals. The upper annulus feeds timing fuel to the injector, the middle annulus discharges drain/spill fuel, and the lower annulus receives the metering fuel. The operation and internal components of an HPI-TP injector are described in detail a little later in this chapter.

IFSM Covers

Three nylon covers snap on over the IFSM and other exterior fuel system components by means of clips.

FUEL FLOW

Figure 29–2 shows the fuel flow through the HPI-TP system on a pre-2004 ISX engine. However, the fuel flow routing has changed with successive generations of HPI-TP. The description here applies to the pre-2004 circuit illustrated in Figure 29–1. You can use the following list and the system schematics (Figure 29–1,

FIGURE 29–2 Fuel flow schematic.

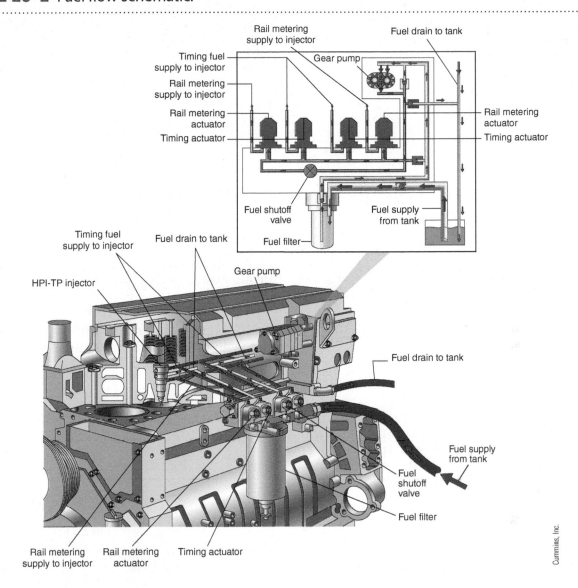

Cummins, Inc.

Figure 29–2) to follow the fuel flow routing through the engine:

1. Fuel is drawn by the gear pump from the fuel tank, through the fuel filter/water separator.

CAUTION:

In post-2004 ISX-TP engines, the filter flow routing changed and became subject to charging pressure; these later filters are smaller in size and more robust in construction.

2. The fuel filter is specified as 98% efficient and capable of 10 microns entrapment. System test specifications will vary according to the generation of the HPI-TP fuel system. Filter efficiencies are said to be slightly better in post-2004 versions of ISX-TP engines.

3. Fuel is charged to the IFSM by the gear pump. A 320 psi (22 bar) high-pressure regulator is located upstream from the IFSM circuitry. If a fuel pressure exceeding 320 psi (22 bar) is achieved, the high-pressure regulator valve is tripped to route fuel back to the tank.

4. Fuel is next routed through a 36-micron screen within the IFSM. The screen is used to prevent a cutting from the teeth in the gear pump passing through the rest of the circuit.

5. Fuel is next flowed through a fuel shutoff valve. The shutoff valve is ETR and controlled by the key switch.

FIGURE 29–3 Timing and metering actuators.

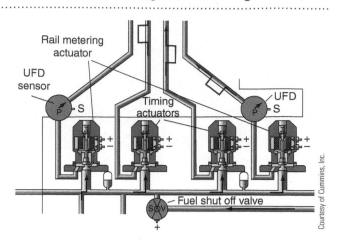

Courtesy of Cummins, Inc.

6. Fuel is next charged to the rail, where it is made available to the two timing and two metering actuators. The four actuators used are shown in **Figure 29–3**. Two rail dampers suppress spiking created by high-pressure, high-speed switching of the actuators.

7. A 250 psi (17 bar) fuel system low-pressure regulator is located in the rail. It attempts to maintain a residual pressure in the rail circuit on engine shutdown. In earlier versions of ISX-TP, during hot weather conditions the residual pressure could increase, and in cases where a TP injector was enabled by the positioning of its actuator train, discharge fuel into the engine cylinder. Although this siphoned insufficient fuel to create a hydrostatic lock, it could cause hard starting and greater cranking resistance. In later versions, Cummins incorporated a drain orifice in each metering actuator; these function to relieve rail pressure during shutdown.

8. The actuators are spring-loaded to normally closed position. The ECM controls the actuators by means of PWM signals. This means that the four actuators are normally closed, on/off devices that only allow fuel to pass by them from the rail when energized by ECM signal.

9. Passages from the timing and metering rails connect to rifles in the cylinder head that, in turn, connect to the exterior annuli in the injectors. The injectors are inserted into cylindrical bores in the cylinder head and each annulus is sealed by rubber O-rings.

HPI-TP INJECTORS

HPI-TP injectors are mechanical with no integral electronic components. **Figure 29–4** shows an internal view of the injector, and **Figure 29–5** shows an external view. Each injector consists of the following subcomponents.

Upper Plunger/Tappet

The integral tappet and upper plunger assembly is loaded by the injector retraction spring into the injector actuation train to achieve zero

FIGURE 29–4 HPI-TP internal components.

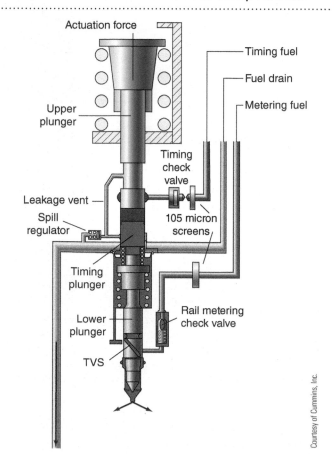

Courtesy of Cummins, Inc.

FIGURE 29–5 External view of an HPI-TP injector.

lash. When actuation force drives the tappet downward, the upper plunger is driven into the timing chamber. A leakage vent directs plunger bleed-back fuel into the return circuit following each downstroke of the upper plunger.

Injector Retraction Spring

The injector retraction spring serves two purposes. It loads the upper plunger tappet assembly into the injector actuation train, and it returns the upper plunger to allow fuel to enter the timing chamber when the injection train ramps off outer base circle.

Inlet Screen

The inlet screen is designed to entrap any larger particulates that may have been created downstream from the gear pump responsible for moving fuel through the fuel subsystem. It is a simple screen rated at 105 microns entrapment.

Timing Check Valve

The timing check valve prevents back pressurization of the fuel circuit from the injector timing chamber to the timing actuator. This permits the slug of fuel to be trapped under the upper plunger that defines injection timing value in any cycle.

Timing Plunger

The timing plunger is positioned by the amount of fuel charged into the timing chamber (by the timing actuator) immediately above it. The more fuel charged to the timing chamber, the more advanced the timing of the injection pulse. At the completion of each injection pulse, the timing plunger is mechanically trapped between the upper and lower plungers of the HPI-TP injector.

Timing Plunger Spring

When the injector actuation cam ramps off outer base circle, the main injector spring lifts the

upper plunger, and the timing plunger spring does likewise for the timing plunger. This means that the spring permits the timing plunger to be loaded against the slug volume of fuel metered into the timing chamber. Because the hydraulic pressure of the fuel metered into the timing chamber is much higher, timing plunger spring tension plays no role in determining the volume of fuel charged to the timing chamber.

Timing Chamber

The timing chamber is charged by fuel that passes through the timing actuator. The actual volume of fuel charged to the timing chamber depends on:

- Time duration the timing actuator is energized, which is controlled by the ECM
- Rail fuel pressure (designed to be held relatively constant in the HPI-TP system)

The amount of fuel in the timing chamber positions the timing plunger. This slug of fuel acts as a hydraulic lock when the HPI-TP injector is mechanically actuated by the injector train.

Spill Regulator

The spill regulator is responsible for directing timing chamber fuel back into the return circuit at the completion of the injection pulse. As the injector train drives the upper plunger downward into the timing chamber following the injection pulse (that is, after the metering plunger has bottomed into the cup), the fuel trapped in the timing chamber has no place to go other than through the spill regulator. Pressure rise causes the spill regulator to trip (open) and it spills fuel until the upper plunger mechanically contacts the timing plunger.

Lower Plunger/Annular Groove

The lower plunger is machined with an annular groove. This routes leak-by fuel upward to hydraulically center the lower plunger. It also prevents side loading of the lower plunger and lubricates it. The lower plunger is mechanically actuated by the timing plunger located directly above it. Remember, this is positioned by the slug of fuel charged to the timing chamber. Fuel is directed by the metering actuator into the cup of the HPI-TP injector. Once again, the amount of fuel metered to the cup depends on:

- Time duration the metering actuator is energized, which is controlled by the ECM
- Rail fuel pressure (designed to be held relatively constant in the HPI-TP system)

Lower Plunger Spring

The lower plunger spring serves to load the lower plunger against the timing plunger. When the injector train is ramped off outer base circle, the lower plunger spring lifts the lower plunger to make it possible for metering to take place.

Metering Chamber

The metering chamber is located under the lower plunger in the cup. HPI-TP injectors use an open-nozzle principle, so fuel directed into the cup is subject to whatever is happening in the engine cylinder. At high engine speeds, this is unlikely to affect the metering process, because there is little time for cylinder pressure bleed through, but at lower engine speeds there is more time for cylinder gas leakage into the cup, which can influence metering.

Rail Metering Check Valve

The metering check valve isolates the cup whenever cup pressures exceed the actual metering pressure. Because metering fuel pressures are designed to be a little less than 300 psi (21 bar) and cylinder pressures tend to be more than twice that value, it is possible at lower engine speeds to raise cup pressure above metering pressure. In this event, the metering check valve locks off to isolate the cup. Also, when the lower plunger is actuated to deliver a fuel pulse, fuel in the cup is effectively trapped in the metering cup when the metering check valve locks off, preventing back pressurization of the metering circuit. For those students familiar with the older Cummins PT system, the metering check valve fulfills the same function as the lock-off ball in the PT injector.

Trapped Volume Spill Port

The **trapped volume spill** port or **TVS** is designed to provide an escape route for fuel just as the lower plunger bottoms into the cup at the completion of an injection stroke. This helps provide a more abrupt closure to the injection pulse. When the TVS passage aligns with the TVS port, fuel is optioned to the return circuit rather than to the cup orifii.

Cup Orifii

The cup orifii define the flow area through which all metered fuel has to pass. Their actual sizes, combined with the pressure developed in the metering chamber, determine the exact sizing of the metered fuel droplets.

INJECTION CYCLE

The injection cycle begins with all three plungers loaded into the cup by mechanical crush created by the injector camshaft, which is on outer base circle (OBC). When the injector cam ramps off OBC toward the inner base circle (IBC), springs lift all three plungers as the injector train is unloaded. As the lower plunger moves upward, it exposes the metering port. However, no fuel enters the metering chamber at this point. The lower plunger rises until it contacts the lower stop. The upper and timing plungers continue to move upward by spring pressure until the timing plunger exposes the timing feed port. The upper plunger continues to move upward until the tappet contacts the top stop. With the plungers in this position, both timing and metering ports are exposed, but no fuel feeds into the timing and metering chambers until the actuators are switched by the ECM.

The timing and metering actuators are opened at the appropriate time and duration to charge the injector timing and metering chambers. By varying the open time, the ECM controls the amount of fuel charged to the timing and metering chambers. The longer the metering actuator is open, the more fuel is charged to the cup, also known as the *metering chamber*. Fuel is charged to the timing chamber between the upper plunger and timing plunger, forcing the latter downward. Next, when the injector cam ramps off base circle, the upper plunger is driven downward. The slug of fuel in the timing chamber now acts as a hydraulic lock because the timing check valve prevents fuel from flowing back to the rail; as a result, the upper plunger and timing plunger move downward in unison. The more fuel charged to the timing chamber, the lower the position of the timing plunger at the beginning of travel, resulting in more advanced injection timing. The less fuel metered to the timing chamber, the higher the position of the timing plunger at the beginning of travel, resulting in more retarded timing.

When the timing plunger mechanically contacts the lower plunger, all three now move downward in unison. The metering check valve prevents fuel backflow from the metering chamber to the rail. When the lower plunger contacts fuel in the cup, pressure rise is created in the metering chamber, forcing fuel through the cup orifii. Injection continues until the annular groove in the lower plunger aligns with the

FIGURE 29–6 Left-side view of an ISX engine.

TVS port. This permits the small amount of fuel remaining in the cup to flow out of the injector into the drain rifle, providing an almost immediate cessation of injection. At the same time, the timing spill port is open to the drain, allowing fuel in the timing chamber to spill. As the lower plunger seats, a ring valve (exterior drain annulus) flexes to regulate the timing spill drain, preventing pressure from dropping too rapidly in the timing chamber; this holds the lower plunger seated until the injector cam is fully ramped to OBC.

The cycle is completed when all three plungers are loaded into the cup with mechanical crush created by the injector train. The fuel injector drain flows fuel back into the IFSM and from there is returned to the tank. **Figure 29–6** shows a left-side view of an ISX engine featuring the IFSM and electrical harnesses.

OVERHEAD ADJUSTMENTS

For truck technicians familiar with setting valves and injectors, the procedure on the HPI-TP versions of ISX is straightforward. When performing any service work, including overhead adjustments, use the Cummins online service literature known as QSOL and always reference specifications and check for technical service bulletins. This referencing of QSOL is especially important because the overhead adjustment procedure varies with the generation of the engine. Bar the engine clockwise as seen from the front during the procedure.

ENGINE LOCATION SET POINTS

Overhead valve and injector setting marks are indicated on the vibration damper as A, B, and C. The alpha designations are used because the piston location at the set point is not at top dead center (TDC) but at 90 degrees ATDC on the power stroke. Use the following table as a reference for location. Note that in a set position on the valve timing index known as *valve set (VS) position*, both the injector and valves are adjusted on the *same* cylinder. In some versions of ISX-TP, the engine brake over the VS cylinder being checked may also be adjusted. However, this is not always the case, so in engines with an engine brake set point the engine must be rotated beyond the VS position. This emphasizes the importance of checking the service literature whenever performing overhead adjustments. The firing order is 1-5-3-6-2-4.

Pulley Position	Set Injector	Set Valves
A	1	1
B	5	5
C	3	3
A	6	6
B	2	2
C	4	4

SETTING VALVES AND INJECTORS

Bar the engine to align the A VS index with the pointer on the front timing gear cover. Check the valve rockers on the #1 engine cylinder: Both should move easily, indicating lash. That is, the valves on #1 should be fully closed.

Adjust HPI-TP Injectors

Back off the #1 injector adjusting screw locknut and back out the adjusting screw a couple of turns. Next, turn the adjusting screw clockwise and torque to 70 in.-lb. Continue to hold the adjusting screw in position and torque the locknut. Next, bar the engine over to the B setting and adjust the injector over the #5 cylinder, using the same procedure. Continue the in-engine firing sequence until all the injectors have been adjusted.

Adjust ISX-TP Valves

The valves and injectors may be adjusted simultaneously on ISX engines. Position the engine with VS index A and aligned with the pointer on the timing gear cover. In this position, both the intake and exhaust valves should show lash. To verify intake valve lash, insert a 0.014" (0.35 mm) thickness gauge between the rocker pallet and the valve crosshead. It should indicate minimal drag. If not, back off the rocker adjusting screw locknut, and reset the valve lash. Use the same procedure to set exhaust valve lash, which is specified at 0.027". Progress through the firing order in sequence, checking the valve lash: Adjust only where necessary.

CAUTION:

When setting injectors and valves on an ISX engine, both are checked/adjusted on the same cylinder at one timing location. Always consult Cummins specifications and check for technical service bulletins (TSBs) before attempting the procedure.

INTEBRAKE OPERATING PRINCIPLE

A general explanation of engine brake operation is provided in Chapter 13. Cummins ISX-TP engines use an enhanced internal engine brake operating principle that is explained here because it has some unique features not addressed in Chapter 13. The retarder assembly is equipped with a hydraulic locking plunger that holds the rocker in neutral when Intebrake is not activated. When actuated during retarding cycles, it functions to open the exhaust valves close to TDC at the completion of the compression stroke, negating the power stroke. Engine braking enhancement is provided by adding a additional lobe on the brake rocker, which reopens the exhaust valve to recharge the engine cylinder with pressurized gas dumped from the other cylinders on the intake stroke, thus increasing the cylinder pressure.

ISX-TP Intebrake Management

ISX-TP engines use six-stage engine braking achieved by using three engine brake solenoids that function as follows:

Solenoid 1: Actuates braking on #1 cylinder only.

Solenoid 2: Actuates braking on cylinders #2 and #3.

Solenoid 3: Actuates braking on cylinders #4, #5, and #6.

In this way, engine braking is possible on one, all six, or any number of cylinders in-between, depending on which solenoids are energized by the ECM. For instance, to achieve maximum engine braking, all three solenoids would be energized. Engine braking is not enabled when cruise control is active, when an engine fault code is active, or when engine speed drops below 850 rpm. The engine brake should immediately deactivate when the accelerator pedal is depressed.

ISX ELECTRONICS AND ENGINE FEATURES

The electronic input circuit used on the ISX engine is consistent with those on a late-generation, large-bore truck diesel engine. Sensors requiring reference voltage are fed a 5-DC V-Ref signal, precisely modulated by the ECM. The ECM is vented to atmosphere and either air-cooled or mounted on a fuel-cooled heat sink depending on the generation. ISX ECMs incorporate a unique method of sealing ambient moisture away from the circuit board: A Gore-Tex™ seal is used in a vent port, so the ECM housing is aspirated to atmosphere (as the unit heats, warm air is discharged; as it cools, moisture-free air is pulled in), eliminating a vacuum seal that could fail in time.

Early versions of the ISX engine package were trim and uncluttered. This changed as the engine evolved through 2001, 2004, and 2007 emissions standards. The 2007 ISX is notably light for its class of horsepower ratings up to 600 BHP and torque ratings exceeding 2,000 lb-ft. of torque. Engine electronics are simple to diagnose using QSOL- and INSITE-guided, sequential electronic troubleshooting. The acronym IS, or Interact System, means that the electronic management architecture has plenty in common with other Cummins electronic management systems. The IS ECM is networked to the J1939 powertrain data bus with an SA 00 address.

Cam Timing

Engine rebuilds and servicing tend to be relatively straightforward, with the possible exception of timing the double overhead camshafts: The Cummins procedure for timing the camshafts must be followed. This is accomplished by working through the engine timing geartrain, beginning at the crankshaft drive gear and working up to the camshaft gears, which are physically wedged to position them for the procedure. First, the engine vibration damper must be positioned to enable insertion of the timing pin at the VS #1 and #6 locations. Ensure that the engine is on the correct cycle: that is, the valves over the #6 cylinder should show lash. At this point, the timing wedges can be inserted. ISX timing wedges are machined at different angles, so these should be checked using Cummins service literature and corroborated on the engine data plate.

CAUTION:

Do not attempt to time ISX overhead camshafts without the Cummins special tool timing wedges. The consequence of out-of-time camshafts can be a lost engine!

Generational Changes in ISX-TP Engines

Early ISX engines used articulating piston assemblies (**Figure 29–7**), but Cummins was the first

FIGURE 29–7 First-generation ISX articulating piston assembly.

major original equipment manufacturer (OEM) to adopt Monotherm forged steel trunk pistons (refer to Chapter 7). Monotherm pistons were introduced for the EPA 2004 model year.

For engines meeting 2004 emissions standards (manufactured after October 2002), cooled EGR (C-EGR) was introduced to minimize NO_x emissions. Second-generation C-EGR appeared on 2007 engines. This permits higher EGR mix ratios and improved cooling. The EGR system uses a pressure differential-type mass airflow (MAF) sensor (see Chapter 34) and electronically controlled variable-geometry turbocharger. All 2007 Cummins ISX engines are equipped with a DPF: This requires that the DPF be inspected for damage whenever a turbocharger failure occurs, and after a high oil consumption problem has been diagnosed and repaired.

Post-2007 engines use DPF diesel fuel dosing by means of a dedicated injector. Cummins refers to this as a **hydrocarbon injector**. The injector receives its supply of fuel at IFSM rail pressure and is ECM controlled by PWM signal. The hydrocarbon injector has a drain shutoff valve on one side and a pressure sensor and shutoff on the other. Using INSITE, the injector can be tested for both flow volume and leakage. The power range of ISX TP-fueled engines runs from 375 up to 600 BHP. Power upgrades within this range are possible, but some mechanical considerations are the turbocharger, camshafts, TP injectors, and lube oil cooler.

TROUBLESHOOTING ISX

Troubleshooting problems in all electronically managed engines should always be performed by technicians with OEM training using guided software and service literature, specifically INSITE and QSOL when working on ISX engines. Be very sure that the information you are using applies to the specific engine model you are working on.

QUICKSERVE ONLINE

Cummins **QuickServe Online (QSOL** or just QS) is required for work on all Cummins electronically controlled engines. QSOL is updated daily. Learn how to use the integrated website search engine. Information searches on QSOL are by engine serial number and include searches of the parts data if you use the full text search feature (in the upper right-hand corner of the screen). If you add double quotes on either side of a search term such as "piston ring," QS will locate all documents containing both words. QSOL also supports engines manufactured before the website existed, so make a habit of using it.

ISX HPI-TP SPECS

The following data is intended to give technicians some broad guidelines for diagnosing performance complaints.

Gear pump pressure:	**Cranking**: 50 psi (3.4 bar) min.
	Idle: 245 to 275 psi (17 to 19 bar) min.
	High idle: 245 to 320 psi (17 to 22 bar) min.
Maximum fuel inlet temp.:	160°F (71°C)
Maximum air intake restriction:	10 in. (254 mm) H_2O at rated/new filter
	20 in. (508 mm) H_2O at rated/used filter
Maximum exhaust restriction:	3 in. (76 mm) Hg at rated power

SUMMARY

- The 1998–2010 ISX engines exclusively used the HPI-TP fuel system. This generation of engines is rated between 385 to 600 BHP, with peak torque values slightly exceeding 2,000 lb-ft. of torque.
- The HPI-TP fuel subsystem uses a gear pump as the primary means of moving fuel through from the tank to the integrated fuel system module (IFSM). Depending on the generation of the HPI-TP system, an electric lift pump may also complement the fuel subsystem.
- Fuel is pulled through the HPI-TP fueled engine by a gear pump, charged to a common rail, and from there metered by timing and metering actuators to mechanically actuated injectors.
- The IFSM module houses the electronics required to manage the fuel system and routes fuel to the common rail used to make fuel available to the timing and metering actuators.
- The timing and metering actuators are electro-hydraulic solenoids controlled by PWM actuation by the ECM. One timing actuator and one metering actuator are used to manage three engine cylinders. A six-cylinder ISX engine uses a total of four actuators: one timing actuator and one metering actuator to manage the front engine cylinders, and another pair to manage the rear cylinders. When energized, each actuator opens to permit rail-pressure fuel to pass into the circuit it controls.

- The HPI-TP system uses computer-controlled actuators to feed fuel to the timing and metering chambers of an entirely mechanically actuated, open-nozzle–type injector.
- Two overhead camshafts are used in an ISX engine with HPI-TP fuel system. The left-side camshaft is responsible for actuating the HPI-TP injectors, while the right-side camshaft is responsible for actuating the valves and the six-stage engine brake.
- The ISX engine series that uses HPI-TP injectors is a 15-liter displacement engine that can produce up to 600 BHP (447 kW) and more than 2,000 lb-ft. (2,712 N•m) of torque in its current trim. These engines weighed less than many competitors that output 30% less power. It uses a single slab cylinder head equipped with double overhead camshafts, dedicated to actuating the HPI-TP injectors and the actuation and operation of a six-stage engine brake and the cylinder head valves.
- Engines manufactured after October 2002 use cooled EGR to reduce NO_x emissions. Those meeting 2007 emissions standards use DPFs to minimize PM emissions.
- All current versions of the ISX use steel trunk-type (Monotherm) pistons.
- The fuel flow routing through the IFSM varies with the generation of ISX, so technicians should always consult the service literature in QSOL when troubleshooting.
- HPI-TP fueled ISX engines ceased production for North American markets at the end of 2009.

REVIEW QUESTIONS

1. How is a Cummins HPI-TP injector actuated?
   a. Hydraulically
   b. Electrically
   c. Electronically
   d. Mechanically

2. Which of the following describes how an ISX ECM prevents moisture from entering the housing?
   a. Vacuum sealed
   b. WeatherPac sealed
   c. Vented with a Gore-Tex seal
   d. WeatherProof II technology

3. Which of the following would approximate actuator rail pressure in an HPI-TP fuel system?
   a. 50 psi (3.4 bar)
   b. 150 psi (10.3 bar)
   c. 285 psi (19.6 bar)
   d. 5,000 psi (344 bar)

4. How many timing actuators are used on the HPI-TP system in an ISX engine?
   a. One
   b. Two
   c. Four
   d. Six

5. How many metering actuators are used on the HPI-TP system in an ISX engine?
   a. One
   b. Two
   c. Four
   d. Six

6. What happens to fuel charged to the HPI-TP injector timing chamber following an effective pumping stroke?
   a. It is spilled to the rocker housing.
   b. It is directed to the drain circuit.
   c. It is flowed into the injector cup.
   d. It is routed back to the transfer pump.

7. What component in an ISX engine is used to impart drive to the HPI-TP external gear transfer pump?
   a. Flywheel ring gear
   b. Idler concept gear
   c. Right-side camshaft
   d. Left-side camshaft

8. Which of the following is true of the moving components of an HPI-TP injector after the actuating cam profile has been ramped to OBC?
   a. They are returned by the injector spring.
   b. They are loaded into the cup with mechanical crush.
   c. Timing and pumping plungers are separated by fuel in the timing chamber.
   d. The injector push tube is under compression.

9. Technician A states that the timing actuator on an HPI-TP fuel system determines injected fuel quantity by the amount of time it is energized and held open. Technician B states that each metering actuator used on the same engine is responsible for fueling three engine cylinders. Who is correct?
   a. Technician A only
   b. Technician B only
   c. Both A and B
   d. Neither A nor B

10. Fuel that passes through the metering actuator is routed to what component on the HPI-TP injector?
    a. Hydraulic nozzle assembly
    b. Timing chamber
    c. Cup
    d. Accumulator

11. Which of the following best describes an HPI-TP injector?
    a. Open-nozzle, mechanically actuated
    b. Closed-nozzle, electronically actuated
    c. Mechanically actuated, hydraulic nozzle
    d. PWM controlled and actuated

12. What type of fuel transfer pump is used on the HPI-TP system in ISX engines?
    a. External gear
    b. Double-acting plunger
    c. Vane
    d. Single-acting plunger

13. What software is used by Cummins to troubleshoot an ISX, HPI-TP fueled engine?
    a. Electronic Technician
    b. INSITE
    c. DeNet
    d. ServiceLink

14. What is the function of the pulsation dampers used in the HPI-TP actuator rail circuit?
    a. Dampens pressure waves produced by actuator switching and the transfer pump
    b. Insulates the ECM from vibration
    c. Dampens drive torque oscillation produced by the gear pump
    d. Protects the transfer pump from shock loading

15. What defines the window, measured in crank angle degrees, within which the ISX ECM can select an effective stroke of an HPI-TP injector?
    a. Infinitely variable
    b. Cam profile
    c. Engine rpm
    d. Injector timing height

16. How is the mechanical stroke of an HPI-TP injector actuated?
    a. Lobes on the left-side camshaft
    b. Lobes on the right-side camshaft
    c. Front bank by the left-side camshaft, rear bank by the right side
    d. Front bank by the right-side camshaft, rear bank by the left side

17. What type of pistons do the later generations of HPI-TP fueled ISX engines use?
    a. Aluminum trunk type
    b. Two-piece, articulating
    c. Crosshead (Ferrotherm)
    d. Steel trunk-type (Monotherm)

18. Which of the following best explains why ISX, HPI-TP fueled engines use cooled EGR?
    a. To improve fuel economy
    b. To improve power
    c. To reduce HC emissions
    d. To reduce NO_x emissions

19. Technician A states that the lower plunger seals the cup orifii at the completion of each injection stroke in an HPI-TP injector. Technician B states that at the completion of the injection cycle, the HPI-TP lower plunger is loaded into the cup with mechanical crush created by the injection train. Who is correct?
    a. Technician A only
    b. Technician B only
    c. Both A and B
    d. Neither A nor B

20. Technician A states that the ISX Intebrake on HPI-TP fueled engines is actuated by the injector cam profile on the right-side camshaft. Technician B states that intake and exhaust valves are both actuated by the right-side camshaft. Who is correct?
    a. Technician A only
    b. Technician B only
    c. Both A and B
    d. Neither A nor B

30

Prerequisites: Chapters 19, 20, and 21; additional references Chapters 34 and 37

COMMON RAIL SYSTEMS

OBJECTIVES

After studying this chapter, you should be able to:

- Identify current engines using common rail (CR) diesel fuel systems.
- Identify some of the diesel engines currently using common rail diesel fuel injection.
- Outline the fuel subsystems in a typical CR system.
- Trace fuel flow routing from tank to injector in common rail, diesel-fueled engines.
- Describe the electronic management circuit components used in common rail fuel systems.
- Describe the operation of the inline and radial piston pumps used to achieve sufficient flow to produce rail and injection pressures in a typical CR system.
- Understand how rail pressures are managed in electronically managed, common rail diesel fuel systems.
- Detail the phases of operation of an electrohydraulic injector (EHI).
- Identify some of the characteristics of different OEM common rail diesel fuel injection systems.
- Diagnose some typical CR fuel system malfunctions.
- Outline the procedure required to time a CR pump to an engine.
- Test EHI actuator resistance to OEM specifications.

KEY TERMS

accumulator

adaptive trim

A-trim

common rail (CR)

electrohydraulic
injectors (EHIs)

engine control
module (ECM)

E-trim

Extreme Pressure
Injection (XPI)

high-pressure heavy-
duty diesel common rail
(HPHDDCR)

injection quantity
calibration data

Injector Verification
Test (IVT)

quick response (QR) code

radial piston pump

rail

rail pressure control valve

rail pressure sensor

ultra high-pressure
heavy-duty common rail
fuel injection (UPCRI)

INTRODUCTION

Electronically controlled, **common rail (CR)** diesel fuel injection systems were introduced on small-bore and automobile diesel engines in the late 1990s. These systems were manufactured by Robert Bosch and Delphi Lucas, and both had similar operating principles. The first-generation CR systems typically had lower peak pressures than those we associate with medium- and large-bore diesels. Maximum pressures were typically just over 20,000 psi (1,379 bar). Bosch and Delphi CR systems have been joined by Siemens, Caterpillar, Cummins, and Denso in recent years.

However, since the earliest generation of CR diesel fuel systems, peak system pressure potential has crept upward and today can exceed 40,000 psi (2,758 bar) in some systems. By Environmental Protection Agency (EPA) model year (MY) 2010, almost every major diesel original equipment manufacturer (OEM) was using a CR system on at least one of its engine families to meet emissions and performance standards.

WHAT IS CR?

For purposes of defining CR diesel fuel injection, the term *CR* is used to refer to only those systems in which fuel injection pressure values are held in the **rail** that directly feeds the injectors. For instance, some texts refer to the hydraulically actuated electronic unit injector (HEUI) system as a CR system, but because injection pressures are not developed in the manifold supplying the HEUIs (this is held relatively constant at a low charge pressure), this cannot be considered a CR system, at least in the way we use the term. Beginning in 2008, a second generation of CR fueling in which rail pressures are amplified at the injector prior to injection was introduced: This system is described in Chapter 31. **Figure 30–1** shows a current Bosch CR system, which you should reference during this introductory explanation.

FUNCTION OF THE RAIL

In this text, the term *rail* is used to describe the supply manifold or gallery that directly feeds all of the diesel fuel injectors. The basic principle of diesel CR can be compared to the way in which automotive gasoline fuel injection (GFI) systems operate. The major differences between GFI and diesel CR is that the diesel systems:

- Operate at much higher pressures, some exceeding 35,000 psi (2,413 bar)

FIGURE 30–1 Common rail injection system on a four-cylinder diesel engine.

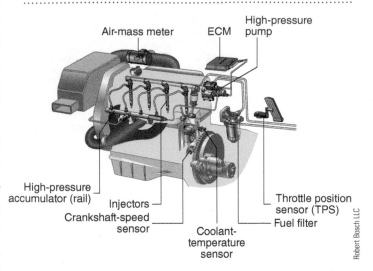

- Precisely manage rail pressure within a wide range of values

In terms of managing and switching the injectors, there are many commonalities between diesel and gasoline CR injection. The similarities increase when the comparison is made between diesel CR and current direct injection (DI) gasoline fuel injection systems.

ENGINES USING CR DIESEL SYSTEMS

As indicated earlier, CR diesel fuel systems have been used since the end of the 1990s. This means that diesel engine manufacturers have already progressed through a first generation of the technology. Some current applications of diesel CR fuel systems are shown in **Table 30–1**.

Table 30–1 does not include some well-established pre-2007 engines such as the 5.9-liter Cummins ISB and the Mack Trucks E-3 engine: These engines are no longer in production. Initially, most commercial diesel engines with CR fueling were small bore, but this has changed. Navistar International MaxxForce N13 engines (using Bosch CR), the two versions of the post-2010 Cummins ISX (using Cummins CR known as **Extreme Pressure Injection [XPI]**), and the post-2013 Paccar MX-Series engines (using Delphi CR) are examples of high-horsepower CR fuel systems. The Detroit Diesel/Mercedes-Benz common platform engine family introduced in 2008 (DD15) through to 2010 (13- to 16-liter versions) uses the amplified CR fueling described in Chapter 31. **Figure 30–2** shows a schematic layout of a Bosch CR fuel system.

TABLE 30–1 Examples of Current Engines with CR Fuel Systems

OEM	Series	Displacement	Peak Power BHP (kW)	Maximum Torque lb-ft. (N•m)
Caterpillar	C7 ACERT	7.2 liters	330 BHP (246 kW)	860 lb-ft. (1,166 N•m)
Caterpillar	C9 ACERT	9.3 liters	350 BHP (260 kW)	1,250 lb-ft. (1,695 N•m)
Cummins	ISB	6.7 liters	325 BHP (242 kW)	750 lb-ft. (1,017 N•m)
Cummins	ISC	8.3 liters	325 BHP (242 kW)	1,000 lb-ft. (1,356 N•m)
Cummins	ISL	8.9 liters	325 BHP (242 kW)	750 lb-ft. (1,017 N•m)
Cummins	ISX-XPI	11.9 liters	425 BHP (317 kW)	1,650 lb-ft. (2,237 N•m)
Cummins	ISX-XPI	15 liters	600 BHP (448 kW)	2,050 lb-ft. (2,780 N•m)
Deere	Power Tech 6.8	6.8 liters	200 BHP (150 kW)	500 lb-ft. (678 N•m)
Ford	PowerStroke	6.7 liters	400 BHP (298 kW)	800 lb-ft. (1,085 N•m)
GM Isuzu	6600 V-8	6.6 liters	360 BHP (268 kW)	650 lb-ft. (880 N•m)
GM Isuzu	7800	7.8 liters	300 BHP (224 kW)	860 lb-ft. (1,156 N•m)
Hino	J08E TB	7.7 liters	260 BHP (193 kW)	585 lb-ft. (794 N•m)
Navistar	N13	12.4 liters	475 BHP (354 kW)	1,700 lb-ft. (2,305 N•m)
Paccar	PX-6	6.7 liters	325 BHP (242 kW)	750 lb-ft. (1,017 N•m)
Paccar	PX-8	8.3 liters	325 BHP (242 kW)	1,000 lb-ft. (1,356 N•m)
Paccar	MX-11	10.8 liters	430 BHP (320 kW)	1,550 lb-ft. (2100 N•m)
Paccar	MX-13	12.9 liters	510 BHP (375 kW)	1,845 lb-ft. (2500 N•m)

FIGURE 30–2 Schematic layout of a Bosch common rail diesel fuel system.

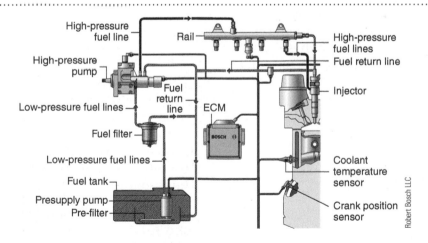

Robert Bosch LLC

CAUTION:

Do not confuse post-2007 and post-2010 engines with their earlier versions even if they are nominally the same series. In most cases, the fuel system, engine displacement, and emissions control apparatus are completely different.

CR SYSTEM MANUFACTURERS

CR fuel system technology was launched by Bosch and Delphi Lucas, but these companies have been joined by others. In most cases, diesel engine OEMs have opted to use one of the CR systems manufactured by a specialty diesel fuel system manufacturer rather than develop their own, but Caterpillar and Cummins are notable exceptions. Current systems are manufactured by:

- Bosch
- Caterpillar
- Cummins (large-bore engines)
- Delphi Lucas
- Denso
- Siemens

ADVANTAGES OF CR DIESEL FUEL SYSTEMS

If you have studied the many different diesel fuel management systems that appear in this textbook up to this chapter, you might conclude that many of them were pretty complicated. One of the primary advantages of CR diesel fuel systems is simplicity. A technically less complex fuel system results in less potential for failures as the system ages. Not only is CR diesel fueling less complex, it also allows the engine control electronics much more precise management of cylinder combustion. This precise management of combustion results in:

- Lower emissions
- Improved fuel economy
- Lower engine noise levels
- Optimization of cylinder pressures

In fact, the CR system is in many ways so much superior to its predecessors you might well ask why it has taken so long for diesel engine OEMs to adopt it. Two key innovations have made the current generation of CR diesel fuel systems possible:

- Metals technology allowing containment of large volumes of ultra-high injection pressure fuel in the rail and rail-to-injector lines
- Electrohydraulic injectors (EHIs) permitting superfast open and close events at the injector nozzle

CR SUBSYSTEMS AND COMPONENTS

A typical diesel CR system consists of the following key components:

- Fuel subsystem: Stores and supplies fuel to the high-pressure rail pump.
- High-pressure pump: An engine-driven pump capable of producing flow sufficient to produce injection pressures up to, and exceeding,

40,000 psi (2,758 bar). Either a radial piston or multicylinder inline piston pump is used.
- ECM-controlled **rail pressure control valve**: A linear proportioning solenoid with an integral spool valve is typically used. The linear proportioning solenoid is an ECM output. Its function is detailed a little later in this chapter.
- A V-Ref supplied **rail pressure sensor**: A variable capacitance electronic device that signals "actual" rail pressure to the ECM at any given moment of operation.
- CR: Stores fuel at injection pressures. Distribution lines or pipes connect the rail with EHIs. The rail can also be known as the high-pressure **accumulator** (Bosch).
- EHIs: These function as ECM-switched hydraulic valves that inject fuel directly into the engine cylinders at pressure values close to the rail pressure value.

CR FEATURES

The reasons for the rapid and nearly universal acceptance of CR diesel fuel systems by diesel engine OEMs are:

- Their ability to achieve high injection pressures entirely independent of engine speed.
- Their ability to control the emitted droplet size to optimize engine performance under almost any temperature, load, or speed condition.
- Their ability to switch EHIs at high speed. In current systems, there can be up to seven injection "events" during a single power stroke.

These features translate into much better management of fuel, providing improved fuel economy, reduced exhaust emissions, and improved response to a request for a change in engine output. CR diesel fuel systems also provide superior cold-start performance and dramatically reduced cold-start emissions because of their capability of producing finely atomized fuel during cranking and cold idle conditions.

ENGINE CONTROLLER ACRONYM

Because diesel CR systems are used by the smallest to the largest diesel engines on our highways, some of the automobile diesel OEMs use acronyms such as ECU (electronic control unit) or PCM (powertrain control module) in preference to **ECM (engine control module)**. In addition, some of these fuel systems are manufactured offshore and, for whatever reasons, continue to use a foreign acronym on the product marketed here. For the sake of consistency when dealing with this system, we use the acronym *ECM* when referring to engine system controllers except when making reference to a specific OEM that prefers one of the other terms.

CR MANAGEMENT ELECTRONICS

CR fuel systems feature full authority electronic controls that really do not differ too much regardless of OEM. While attempting to be somewhat generic in our approach to diesel CR systems, we nevertheless reference the Bosch CR system used by Cummins (small-bore engines), Paccar (small-bore engines), and others, as well as making some references to the other OEM systems.

In all CR fuel systems, injected fuel quantity is defined by the engine management computer based on a range of input variables and output requirements that include accelerator pedal angle, operating temperatures, and emissions requirements. As in all full authority engine management systems, the ECM monitors ambient, chassis, and engine conditions and is capable of detecting both electronic and hydromechanical faults. Depending upon the severity of any faults identified, the ECM can strategize countermeasures such as torque limitation, power-derate, and limp-home operating modes. All the CR systems identified in this chapter are networked to the J1939 data bus and can therefore interface with other powertrain and chassis components. Some also interface with the CAN-C light-duty data bus; an example is the Cummins ISB 6.7 used in Dodge pickups along with a wide range of commercial vehicle applications.

INPUT CIRCUIT

The sensor circuit inputs data to the ECM by means of dedicated circuitry, and most current systems are equipped with electronic signal transducers, electronic signal amplifiers, and fluid pressure transducers. The specific components used to input data to the ECM are no different from other engine management systems and are covered in Chapter 34. Both analog and digital signals are inputted to the processing cycle.

Analog Inputs

Mass airflow, engine fluid and intake air temperatures, engine pressure values, diesel particulate filter (DPF) pyrometers, and battery voltage are examples of analog signals that have to be converted to digital values by an A/D converter in the ECM. When fluid pressure values are transduced to electrical values, these are signaled in an analog format, but some systems transduce directly to digital.

Digital Inputs

Digital input signals include *on/off* switching signals and digital sensor signals such as rotational speed/ position pulses from Hall-effect sensors; these bypass the A/D unit to be processed directly by the microprocessor. Depending on the manufacturer, the throttle position sensor (TPS) signal may use an older style analog signature or may produce a digital signal using one of two types of devices:

- Hall-effect (noncontact) TPS broadcasting pulse width modulated (PWM) signal
- Potentiometer with built-in integrated circuit (I/C) broadcasting PWM signal

SIGNAL CONDITIONING

In many current systems where alternating current (AC) inductive pulse generators are used to measure shaft speeds (such as crank and camshaft speed/position sensors), the signal is transduced to a digital format to suppress interference pulses and other electronic noise. In engines designed to run at higher speeds (especially automotive diesels), the likelihood that Hall-effect shaft speed/position sensors are used increases: These are entirely digital devices. In most current systems, shaft speed sensor inputs are delivered to the ECM in a square-wave form.

This means that, depending upon the level of integration, some signal conditioning can take place either completely or partially in the sensor. Protective circuitry is used to limit the incoming signals to a maximum voltage level. Inputted signals are freed of superimposed interference signals by filtering, and then amplified to match them to the ECM working voltage.

PROCESSING CYCLE

The ECMs used to manage CR fuel systems function using a selection of operational maps (algorithms) stored in memory that can be modified within certain limits by the OEM or by the technician. Engine-specific curves and engine-management maps are also written to ECM memory and include data such as failure strategies, calibration data, and power trim/ derate programming. All OEM ECMs used on post-2007 products have a write-to-self capability that will log fault codes and audit trails to electronically erasable, programmable read-only memory (EEPROM). In addition, the ECM is networked to the J1939 data bus, which permits it to interface with other chassis electronic systems.

Fueling Algorithm

The key processing transaction that concerns engine fueling is the "closed" loop cycle between *desired* rail pressure and *actual* rail pressure. This can be summarized as follows:

- **Desired rail pressure:** Computed by the ECM based on sensor inputs, emissions monitoring, and stored instructions in memory. The ECM then attempts to maintain desired rail pressure by controlling the rail pressure control valve.
- **Actual rail pressure:** Measured by pressure sensor (a piezoresistive or variable capacitance type) and signaled to the ECM.

A major function of the ECM is to monitor and manage engine emissions, so every fueling algorithm is mapped around the requirement to minimize emissions. The operation of emission controls is studied in Chapter 47: The CR systems used in post-2010 products may use exhaust gas recirculation (EGR), catalytic converters, diesel particulate filters (DPFs), and selective catalytic reduction (SCR) systems. For a more detailed look at vehicle engine management computers and how a logic processing cycle functions, refer to Chapter 34.

OUTPUT CIRCUIT

Insofar as the fuel system management is concerned, the output driver system is not that complex. However, in keeping with most post-2010 engines, the driver apparatus for EGR, DPF, and SCR systems tends to be a little more complicated; some OEMs use a separate module to manage the emissions controls (see Chapter 48). The two ECM driver outputs that manage fueling are the rail management pressure control valve(s) and the injector drivers.

Rail Pressure Management Control

The rail pressure management control (RPMC) valve, as its name suggests, manages rail pressure. Though each OEM has its own terms to describe this valve and some use two of them (Caterpillar, where one backs up the other), they

all perform the same function. It is necessarily located downstream from the high-pressure pump and upstream from the rail. RPMC valves are PWM to control their linear position. The valve is spring-loaded to default to no-fuel status; this means that in the event of a RPMC electrical malfunction, all fuel exiting the high-pressure pump circuit is optioned to bypass the rail, shutting the engine down. Depending on the current flowed through its coil, an RPMC spool options fuel from the high-pressure pump to either the rail or the fuel return circuit. To precisely maintain desired rail pressure, it is typically capable of linear correction at high frequency (60 kHz).

Injector Drivers

ECM-located injector drivers are used to switch the EHIs. They function similarly to drivers used to switch other comparable EUI, electronic unit pump (EUP), or HEUI injectors. The ECM outputs a PWM control pulse spiked to around 100 V-DC to systems using solenoid actuators, sometimes less when piezoelectric actuators are used. Current draw during actuation also depends on whether solenoid or piezoelectric actuators are used, with the latter requiring less current draw.

MULTIPLEXING

Communication between the CR ECM and the vehicle data bus uses serial CAN 2.0 protocols. However, these are not necessarily J1939 and depend on the weight classification of the vehicle. The current CAN 2.0 version used on light-duty vehicles is CAN-C. Multiplexing technology is studied in Chapter 37, but at this point, we can say that CAN-C can be summarized by stating that it is nearly identical to J1939. However, unlike J1939 it tends to be less accessible, because automotive OEMs do their utmost to keep anyone without their proprietary software off their data bus. In general, the only automotive bus data that can be read with nonproprietary software is that falling under onboard diagnostics II (OBD II). OBD II fields relate specifically to emissions and are required to be accessible using generic electronic service tools (ESTs).

CR FUEL ROUTING CIRCUIT

The CR fuel routing system is modular, so for purposes of study, we can divide it up as follows:

- Fuel subsystem
- High-pressure pump

FIGURE 30–3 Key components of the Caterpillar CR system used on C7 and C9 engines: The micron ratings shown are the fuel filtration requirements of the system.

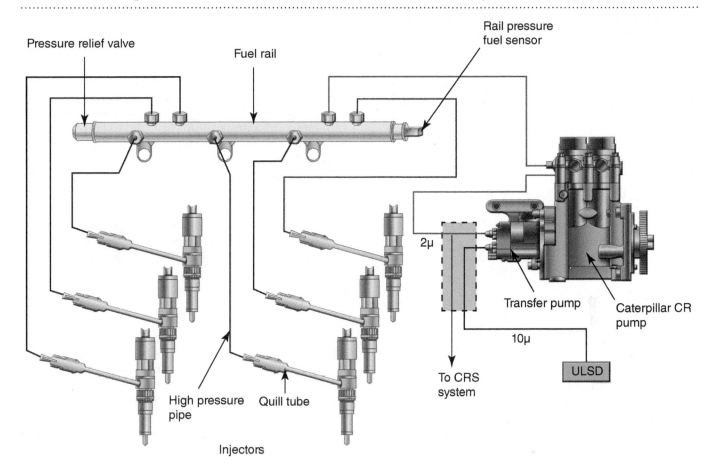

- Pressure accumulator or rail
- High-pressure distribution system
- Electrohydraulic injectors

Figure 30–3 shows the layout of the Caterpillar CR system used on its post-2007 C7 and C9 engines.

FUEL SUBSYSTEM

The fuel subsystem varies by OEM, but the Bosch example shown in Figure 30–2 is typical. All CR systems use a transfer pump, which Bosch calls a presupply pump; this may be located in the fuel tank, or (more commonly) on the rear of the CR high-pressure pump. The Caterpillar transfer pump (Figure 30–3) is a gear-type pump flange mounted to the CR high-pressure pump.

Fuel Tank

The fuel tank is an OEM responsibility, but Bosch recommends that it be manufactured of noncorroding materials and designed to be free from

leaks at double the normal operating pressure. Normal operating pressure, according to Bosch, is 2.5 psi (0.15 bar/17 kPa), so the required tank test pressures are 5 psi (0.3 bar/34 kPa). The tank should be properly vented (at the moment of writing, venting to atmosphere is permitted) and equipped with appropriate fittings for cycling fuel through the system.

Transfer Pump

The transfer or presupply pump may be located within the fuel tank or inline. At present, there are two possible versions:

- Electric roller-cell fuel pump located in the fuel tank. It functions similarly to the fuel supply pump in a gasoline-fueled automobile.
- External gear pump mechanically driven by the engine. The gear pump is often located behind, and driven by, the CR high-pressure pump.

In both cases, the fuel transfer pump is positive displacement and functions to push fuel through the fuel subsystem to deliver it to the high-pressure pump.

Fuel Filter(s)

The fuel filter is an OEM responsibility, but it should meet the specifications of the CR fuel system manufacturer. In a Bosch CR application, the fuel filter should have a nominal entrapment capability of 8 microns. Caterpillar requires the use of its high-efficiency secondary filter with a nominal entrapment capability of 2 microns. All fuel filtration must occur upstream from the high-pressure pump. Similar to other injection systems, CR fuel systems should either use a fuel filter with a water separator or integrate a separate water separator into the fuel subsystem. Collected water should be drained at regular intervals in systems equipped only with manual drains. Some water separators are equipped with a water-in-fuel (WIF) sensor that triggers a warning lamp, indicating that water should be drained.

HIGH-PRESSURE PUMPS

There are some differences between the types of high-pressure pump used by CR manufacturers, so we first describe the radial piston pumps used by Bosch and Denso, and follow with a description of the inline piston pumps used in Caterpillar systems and the single-element EUPs used by Delphi. The high-pressure pumps used in a CR diesel fuel system are simple in terms of the role they play. All they are required to do is create sufficiently high flow volume so that when subject to flow restriction, they achieve the specified window of rail pressures. Pump output is unloaded to the rail. The high-pressure pump plays no role in metering or timing of the fuel delivery. **Figure 30–4** shows all the high-pressure stage components in a typical CR diesel fuel injection system.

Radial Piston Pumps

Bosch and Denso use a three-cylinder **radial piston pump** to produce the injection pressures required for system operation. These pumps are responsible for developing rail pressures. Pressurized fuel from the high-pressure pump is unloaded by means of a high-pressure line into a tubular, high-pressure fuel accumulator that

FIGURE 30–4 Radial piston, high-pressure pump (schematic, longitudinal section).

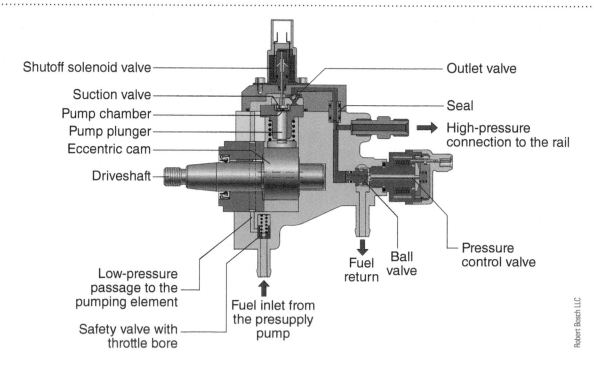

Shutoff solenoid valve
Suction valve
Pump chamber
Pump plunger
Eccentric cam
Driveshaft
Outlet valve
Seal
High-pressure connection to the rail
Pressure control valve
Fuel return
Ball valve
Low-pressure passage to the pumping element
Safety valve with throttle bore
Fuel inlet from the presupply pump

Robert Bosch LLC

we call the *rail*. The high-pressure pump continually attempts to maintain the ECM-desired pressure to the rail, with the result that in contrast to conventional systems, fuel does not have to be specially pressurized for each individual injection pulse. The advantage of using a radial piston pump is its compact design.

The high-pressure pump is installed on a diesel engine so that it can be driven by the engine timing geartrain. It may be driven at either camshaft or crankshaft speed, depending on the system, but camshaft speed is more common. The high-pressure pump is usually drive-coupled to the timing geartrain using a dedicated gear, but both chain and toothed belt drives may be used in light-duty applications. The pump is internally lubricated by the diesel fuel it pumps. **Figure 30–5** shows a schematic cross-section of a radial piston, high-pressure pump: Note how the pumping elements are actuated by the central camshaft.

Radial Piston Pump Components

Pressure rise is created in the high-pressure pump by three radially arranged piston-type pump elements that are evenly offset at an angle of 120 degrees around the pump drive shaft. This means that each pump element is actuated once during a single pump rotation, so the stress on the pump drive remains uniform. Each pump piston is actuated by eccentric cams machined to the drive shaft (see Figure 30–5) and discharged through an outlet valve.

FIGURE 30–5 Radial piston, high-pressure pump (schematic, cross-section).

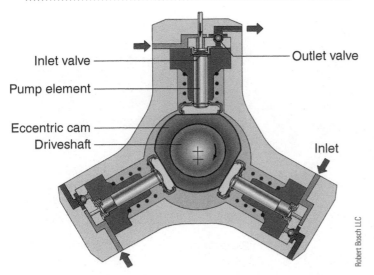

Inlet valve

Pump element

Eccentric cam

Driveshaft

Outlet valve

Inlet

Robert Bosch LLC

Operating Principle

Fuel forced through the fuel subsystem is delivered to each pump element through the fuel inlet (see Figure 30–4, item 13) and the safety valve. Fuel passes through the safety valve throttle bore (14) and enters the high-pressure pump lubrication and cooling circuit, charging the pump elements. As the drive shaft (1) machined with its eccentric cams (2) rotates, it sequentially actuates the three pump plungers (3). These, therefore, reciprocate in their bores because they ride the cam profiles.

Any time delivery pressure (created in the fuel subsystem) exceeds the safety valve opening pressure, usually from 5 to 25 psi (0.5 to 1.5 bar), the pumping-element chamber (4) is charged with fuel as the pump piston moves downward on its suction stroke. The pump element inlet valve closes when the piston passes through bottom dead center (BDC), and at this moment fuel is trapped in the pump chamber. As the piston is driven into the pump chamber, pressure rise is created; when the pump chamber pressure exceeds the rail pressure, the outlet valve (7) opens and compressed fuel is charged to the high-pressure circuit.

The pump piston continues to unload fuel through its outlet until it reaches top dead center (TDC) on the delivery stroke. At TDC, pressure collapses, causing the outlet valve to close. As the piston moves downward on the fill stroke, the moment pressure in the pumping-element chamber drops below fuel subsystem pressure, the inlet valve opens, and the pump element is charged with another slug of fuel ready for the next effective stroke.

Fuel Delivery Rate

Because the high-pressure pump is designed to comfortably deliver the required volume of fuel for rated speed and load performance, excess high-pressure fuel is delivered to the rail during idle and low-load operation. This excess fuel is returned to the tank by means of the rail pressure control valve, which routes the fuel back to the tank. This results in wasted energy because of the mechanical effort required to actuate the pumping elements. Some of this parasitic loss can be recovered by switching off one of the pumping elements.

ELEMENT SWITCH-OFF When one of the pumping elements (Figure 30–4, item 3) is switched off, the fuel volume delivered into the rail

FIGURE 30–6 Caterpillar CR system high-pressure pump.

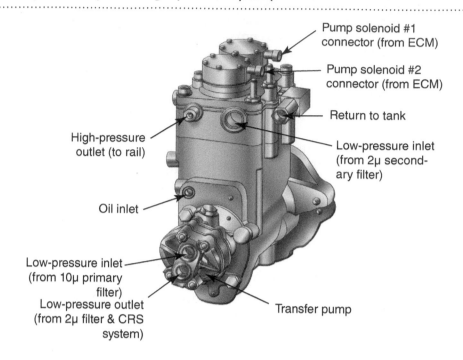

is reduced. Element switch-off is effected by holding the suction valve (5) open. When the solenoid valve of the pumping-element switch-off is triggered, a pin attached to its armature holds the inlet valve open, meaning that fuel drawn into the pumping element cannot be compressed because the pump element does not seal. Instead, fuel is pushed back into the low-pressure circuit. In essence, the result is similar to that of unloading an air compressor on a truck. With one pumping element switched off when lower engine output is required, the high-pressure pump operates on two cylinders.

Inline Piston Pumps

Caterpillar uses a two-cylinder inline piston pump to produce rail pressures in its post-2007 C7 and C9 engines. The pump is flange mounted and direct driven by an accessory drive gear. The pump is lubricated with engine oil. Fuel from the secondary filter is routed to an inlet on the upper outboard face of the pump. This fuel is then routed to the two high-pressure fuel pump elements. The transfer pump that moves fuel through the fuel subsystem is a gear-type pump coupled directly to the high-pressure pump. This low-pressure pump also supplies the fuel for dosing the Cat Regeneration System

(CRS). **Figure 30–6** shows an angled view of the Caterpillar CR system high-pressure pump: Note how the transfer pump is coupled to, and driven by, the high-pressure pump. **Figure 30–7** shows

FIGURE 30–7 Location of the Bosch inline CR pump used on a Navistar MaxxForce 13 engine.

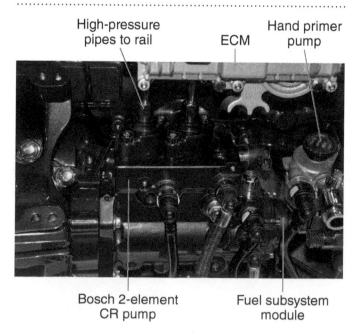

the twin-cylinder Bosch CR piston pump used on a post-2010 MaxxForce 13 engine.

RAIL PRESSURE CONTROL VALVES

The rail pressure control valve (RPCV) is PWM actuated by the ECM. The ECM uses it to define the "desired" pressure in the rail at any given moment of operation. As discussed earlier, the RPCV consists of a linear proportioning solenoid and spool valve that can option fuel unloaded by the high-pressure pump either to the rail or into the return circuit. Its operation can be summarized as follows:

- If *actual* rail pressure (signaled to the ECM by the rail pressure sensor) is higher than *desired* rail pressure, the RPCV opens to divert fuel from the rail, optioning it to the return circuit.
- If *actual* rail pressure is lower than *desired* rail pressure, the pressure control valve closes, sealing the rail and permitting pressure to rise.

A sectional view of the ECM-controlled rail pressure control valve is shown in **Figure 30-8**.

The Bosch rail pressure control valve is located on the high-pressure pump (see Figure 30-4, item 10) and is flange mounted to it. Some systems use a pressure control valve located at the rail inlet. To seal the high-pressure rail from the return circuit, the control valve armature forces a ball into a seat to create a seal. Two forces act on the armature. Mechanical force is provided by a spring, and opposing this, electromagnetic force is created by the solenoid coil when energized. Two control loops are used to manage pressure control valve operation:

- A slow-response electrical control loop for setting (variable) mean pressure in the rail
- A fast-response mechanical control loop to compensate for the high-frequency pressure fluctuations

Pressure Control Valve Nonenergized

When desired rail pressure is higher than actual rail pressure, the rail pressure control valve must drop rail pressure. High pressure at the rail or at the high-pressure pump outlet acts on the pressure control valve via the high-pressure input. Because the nonenergized electromagnet in the control valve exerts no force, high-pressure fuel exceeds the spring force, opening the control valve and spilling rail fuel to the return circuit.

Pressure Control Valve Energized

When desired rail pressure is lower than actual rail pressure, the pressure control valve must allow rail pressure to rise. If the pressure in the high-pressure circuit is to be increased, the force of the electromagnet must combine with the mechanical force of the spring. The ECM energizes the pressure control valve, causing it to close and remain closed until equilibrium is established between desired and actual rail pressures. This means that a balance is reached between the high-pressure fuel forces on the one side and the combined forces of the spring and the electromagnet on the other. The valve then remains open and maintains rail pressure constant. Any change in the pump delivery quantity/engine load is compensated for by the valve assuming a different setting.

CATERPILLAR RAIL PRESSURE CONTROLS

Rail pressure control in the Caterpillar high-pressure pump is achieved by a pair of solenoids located above the pump elements. The operating principle is simple. Depending on the solenoid status, fuel is either optioned to charge the rail or routed to the low-pressure fuel return circuit. **Figure 30-9** shows how the pump elements work in conjunction with the Caterpillar high-pressure pump.

FIGURE 30-8 Bosch type rail pressure control valve.

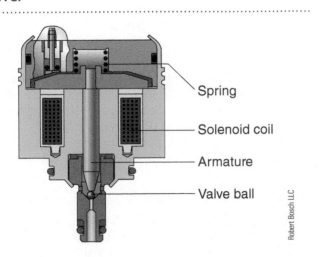

Spring

Solenoid coil

Armature

Valve ball

Robert Bosch LLC

FIGURE 30–9 Sectioned view of a Caterpillar CR high-pressure pump and the solenoids that act as rail pressure control valves.

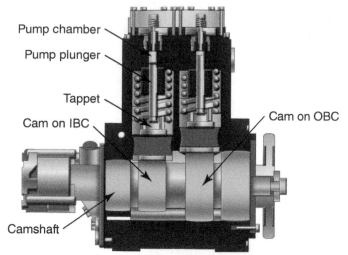

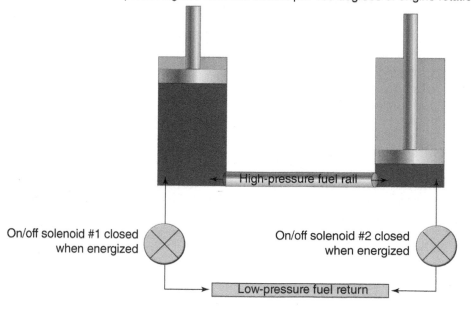

Each pump plunger is actuated four times per cam revolution producing two effective strokes per 180 degrees of engine rotation.

COMMON RAIL

The CR or accumulator receives fuel from the high-pressure pump, and by means of dedicated exit lines makes it available to the ECM-controlled EHIs. The accumulator feature of the rail means that even after an injector has discharged a pulse of fuel into the engine, the fuel pressure in the rail remains almost constant. The volume of fuel in the rail has a damping effect on the changes in rail pressure that occur as the injectors are actuated and the RPCV kicks in and out. The damping ability of the rail can be accounted for by its accumulator effect resulting from the compressibility factor of the fuel. **Figure 30–10** is a line drawing of the Bosch CR used on a four-cylinder engine, and **Figure 30–11** shows the Caterpillar CR used on a C7 engine.

Rail Pressure Limits

Rail pressure is monitored by the rail pressure sensor and maintained at the desired value by the ECM pressure control valve. A pressure

FIGURE 30–10 Bosch common rail.

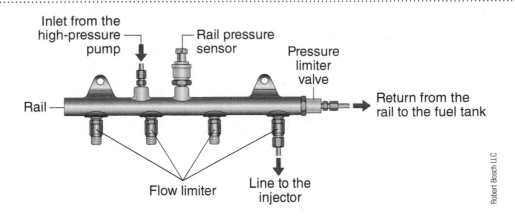

Inlet from the
high-pressure
pump

Rail pressure
sensor

Pressure
limiter
valve

Return from the
rail to the fuel tank

Rail

Flow limiter

Line to the
injector

Robert Bosch LLC

FIGURE 30–11 Common rail system layout on a Caterpillar C7 engine.

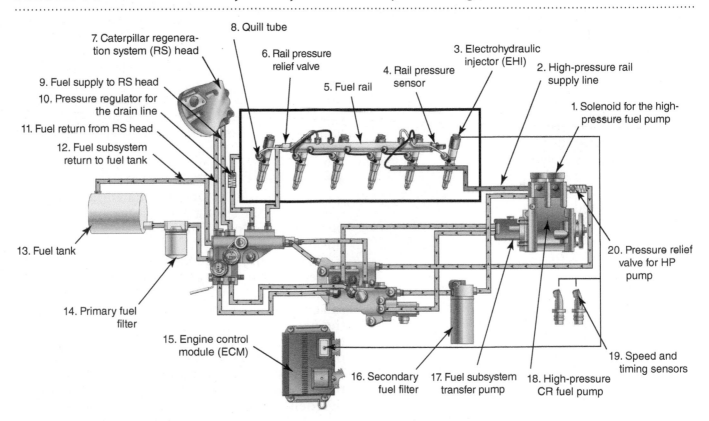

7. Caterpillar regenera-
tion system (RS) head

8. Quill tube

6. Rail pressure
relief valve

3. Electrohydraulic
injector (EHI)

4. Rail pressure
sensor

2. High-pressure rail
supply line

5. Fuel rail

9. Fuel supply to RS head

10. Pressure regulator for
the drain line

1. Solenoid for the high-
pressure fuel pump

11. Fuel return from RS head

12. Fuel subsystem
return to fuel tank

13. Fuel tank

14. Primary fuel
filter

15. Engine control
module (ECM)

16. Secondary
fuel filter

17. Fuel subsystem
transfer pump

18. High-pressure
CR fuel pump

19. Speed and
timing sensors

20. Pressure relief
valve for HP
pump

limiter valve acts to limit the maximum fuel pressure in the rail to a specification that usually exceeds the intended peak rail pressure by a small margin. For instance, in the current Caterpillar CR system the highest specified rail pressure is 27,550 psi (1,900 bar), so the pressure limiter valve is designed to trip at 33,300 psi (2,300 bar). Maximum rail pressure in the Cummins XPI system exceeds 35,000 (2,413 bar), so the pressure limiter valve is set to trip at a higher value, 42,000 psi (2,896 bar). Fuel in the rail is made available to the injectors by means of flow limiters, which prevent excess fuel from being injected. The rail and its critical components on a Bosch CR system are shown in Figure 30–10.

Rail Pressure Sensor

The rail pressure sensor consists of a sensor housing, integral printed circuit, and sensor element. A rail pressure sensor can use either a piezoresistive, Wheatstone bridge operating principle (most common), or a variable capacitance-type sensor. Both these types of sensors are usually supplied with a 5-volt V-Ref and are fully explained in Chapter 34. Here we review the more commonly used piezoresistive sensor.

Pressurized fuel acts on the sensor diaphragm through a blind hole and the sensor element (semiconductor device) is mounted on this diaphragm. When the diaphragm shape changes as a result of pressure acting on it, the electrical resistance of the layers attached to the diaphragm also changes. Sensing diaphragm deflection is approximately 0.040 inch at 21,750 psi (1 mm at 1,500 bar) and has the effect of altering its electrical resistance, causing a voltage change across the 5-V resistance bridge. The voltage change ranges between 0 and 70 mV (depending upon applied fuel pressure) and is then amplified by the evaluation circuit to a signal value of 0.5 to 4.5 V that increases proportionally with pressure values. A sectional view of a rail pressure sensor is shown in **Figure 30–12**.

Tight tolerances enable a high degree of accuracy to the resulting rail pressure sensor signals when measuring pressure. Measuring accuracy is stated to be around 2%. In the event of failure of a rail pressure sensor, the pressure control valve is triggered "blind" and defaults to a limp-home mode of operation.

Flow Limiter

The flow limiter (**Figure 30–13**) functions to prevent continuous injection in the event that one

FIGURE 30–12 Rail pressure sensor.

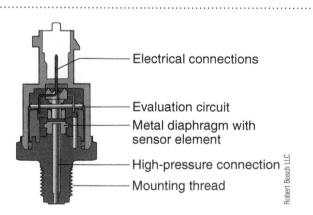

- Electrical connections
- Evaluation circuit
- Metal diaphragm with sensor element
- High-pressure connection
- Mounting thread

Robert Bosch LLC

FIGURE 30–13 Flow limiter.

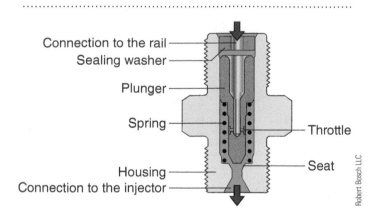

- Connection to the rail
- Sealing washer
- Plunger
- Spring
- Throttle
- Seat
- Housing
- Connection to the injector

Robert Bosch LLC

of the injectors sticks in the open position. Once the fuel quantity leaving the rail exceeds a predetermined volume, the flow limiter shuts off the line to the problem injector. The flow limiter consists of a metal housing with external threads for installation into the rail at one end and external threads at the other for connecting the injector lines. A plunger inside the flow limiter is forced toward the rail end by a spring. When fuel is injected, pressure drops at the injector end and causes the plunger to shift in the direction of the injector, compensating for the fuel volume that exited the rail during injection. At the completion of the injection pulse, the plunger moves to a mid-position away from its seat without closing off the outlet completely, having a throttling effect. Next, the spring forces it back to its at-rest position, allowing fuel to flow freely through the throttle bore.

The spring and throttle bore are dimensioned so that even at maximum injection fuel quantity, the plunger returns to the stop at the rail end of the flow limiter, where it remains until the next injection. When a leak occurs, the flow limiter plunger is forced away from its at-rest position up against the seal seat at the outlet. It remains in this position up against the stop at the injector end of the flow limiter and prevents fuel delivery to the injector.

High-Pressure Fuel Lines

The fuel lines or pipes used in CR systems (see **Figure 30–14**) have requirements similar to those of the high-pressure pipes used in other high-pressure diesel fuel injection systems. They must be capable of sustaining the maximum system pressures with a wide margin of safety and enduring the pressure wave reflections that result from high-speed hydraulic switching. In common with the high-pressure

FIGURE 30–14 Cummins ISX-XPI CR pump.

pipes used with older pump-line-nozzle (PLN) systems, the injection lines tend to be of identical length and internal diameter. Should this not be the case, however, there would be no consequences that could influence injection timing. The lines used with the most common Bosch CR systems have an outside diameter of 6 mm and an internal diameter of 2.4 mm. **Figure 30–15**

FIGURE 30–15 Cummins CR pump line routing to the rail.

Common rail   CR pump to rail line   High-pressure pipe to EHI

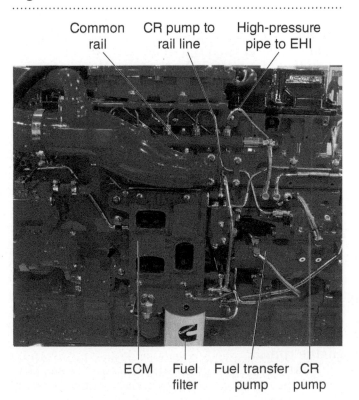

ECM   Fuel filter   Fuel transfer pump   CR pump

shows the routing of high-pressure lines from the Cummins XPI CR pump to the rail.

Caterpillar and Cummins High-Pressure Lines

The high-pressure lines used in CR diesel fuel systems (see **Figure 30–16** and **Figure 30–17**) may directly connect the rail with the injector or, in the case of Caterpillar and some Cummins applications, use a high-pressure pipe that connects with a quill (Caterpillar) or connector (Cummins) tube. Quill or connector tubes fit to cylindrical EHIs that are vertically positioned in the cylinder head. Rail fuel is routed into the EHI by machining a recess into the side of the injector: A nipple on the quill tube fits into and seals the inlet recess. You can see how this works by studying **Figure 30–18** and **Figure 30–19**. Alignment of the quill tube nut and incremental torque sequencing are critical and must be observed.

FIGURE 30–16 Cummins XPI high-pressure fuel lines that supply the injectors from the rail.

CR pump to rail line   High-pressure line from rail to EHI

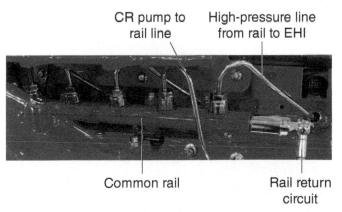

Common rail   Rail return circuit

FIGURE 30–17 PACCAR common rail system. This MX-13, and its smaller-bore sibling MX-11, engines use Delphi CR fueling.

FIGURE 30–18 Location of quill tube recess on a cylindrical Caterpillar EHI.

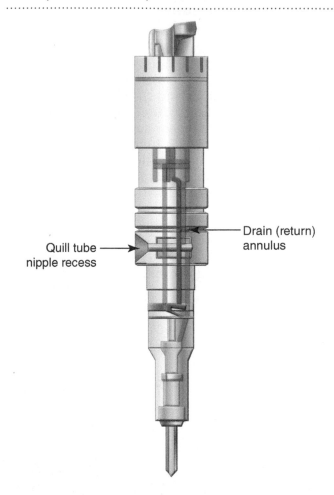

Quill tube nipple recess

Drain (return) annulus

FIGURE 30–19 Sectional view of a Caterpillar C9 engine showing how the fuel quill mates into the EHI recess: The rail pipe connects to the quill tube.

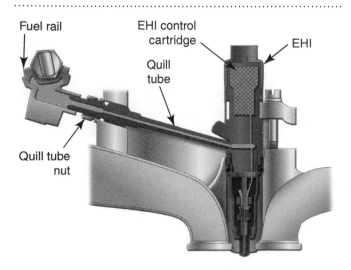

Fuel rail

EHI control cartridge

EHI

Quill tube

Quill tube nut

FIGURE 30–20 Left-side view of a Navistar MaxxForce 13 engine highlighting the CR system components.

WARNING:

Never crack the high-pressure pipe nuts attempting to bleed them. It could prove to be dangerous, and some OEMs prefer CR high-pressure lines to be single-use devices (they yield to deform on initial torque to form a better seal). CR fuel systems are designed to self-prime.

When all of the foregoing components are assembled on an engine, they may give a cluttered appearance. **Figure 30–20** shows a left-side view of a post-2010 Navistar MaxxForce 13 engine: most of the external CR components can be identified on this Bosch CR system.

ELECTROHYDRAULIC INJECTORS

Electrohydraulic injectors (EHIs) were first introduced in Chapter 21. Two general types of EHIs are used, differentiated by the type of actuator used. Some EHIs use a solenoid control valve (see **Figure 30–21**), whereas others use piezoelectric actuators. As a rule, piezoelectric-actuated EHIs can deliver a greater number of pulses per injection cycle, currently a maximum of seven. However, Denso and Cummins XPI EHIs with solenoid actuators are capable of delivering up to five separate shots of fuel per cycle, though they may only do this at lower engine rpms.

That said, the general principles used by each type remain identical; only the actuator mechanism differentiates them. We use a Bosch

FIGURE 30–21 Bosch CR injector.

EHI (**Figure 30–22**) for purposes of the description here. An EHI can be subdivided as follows:

- Nozzle assembly
- Hydraulic servo-system
- Actuator valve

Overview of Operation

Referencing Figure 30–22, fuel at rail pressure is supplied to the high-pressure connection (4), to the nozzle through the fuel duct (10), and to the control chamber (8) through the feed orifice (7). The control chamber is connected to the fuel return (1) via a bleed orifice (6) that is opened by the actuator valve. With the bleed orifice closed, hydraulic force acts on the valve control plunger (9) exceeding that at the nozzle needle pressure chamber (located between the shank and the needle of the nozzle valve). Although the hydraulic pressure values acting on the top of the nozzle valve and those in the pressure

FIGURE 30–22 EHI.

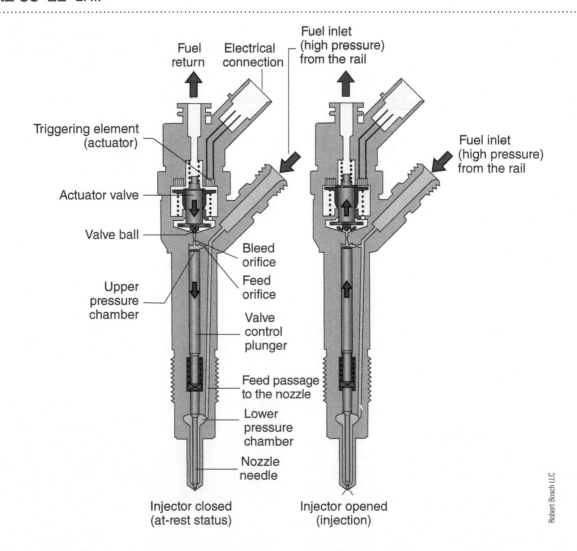

Injector closed (at-rest status)

Injector opened (injection)

chamber are identical, the sectional area at the top of the nozzle valve is greater. As a result, the nozzle needle is loaded into its seated position, meaning that the injector is closed.

When an ECM signal triggers the injector control actuator valve, the bleed orifice opens. This immediately drops the control chamber pressure and, as a result, the hydraulic pressure acting on the top of the nozzle valve (11) also drops. When hydraulic force acting on top of the nozzle valve drops below the force on the nozzle needle pressure shoulder, the nozzle valve retracts and allows fuel to pass around the seat to be injected through orifii into the engine cylinder. The hydraulic assist and amplification factor are required in this system because the forces necessary for rapid nozzle valve opening cannot be directly generated by an actuator valve alone.

Fuel used as hydraulic media to open the nozzle valve is in addition to the injected fuel quantity, so this excess fuel is routed back to the tank. In addition to this fuel, some leak-by fuel losses occur at the nozzle valve-to-body clearance and the valve-plunger guides clearance. This leak-off fuel volume is also returned to the fuel tank via the fuel return circuit.

Injector Operating Phases

When the engine is stopped, all injector nozzles are closed, meaning that their nozzle valves are loaded onto their seats by spring pressure. In a running engine, injector operation takes place in three phases.

INJECTOR CLOSED In the at-rest state, the actuator valve is not energized and, therefore, the nozzle valve is loaded onto its seat by the injector spring combined with hydraulic pressure (from the rail) acting on the sectional area of the valve control plunger. With the bleed orifice closed, the actuator valve spring forces the armature ball check onto the bleed orifice seat. Rail pressure builds in the injector control chamber, but identical pressure will be present in the nozzle pressure chamber. Given equal pressure acting on the larger sectional area of the nozzle control plunger (which is mechanically connected to the nozzle valve) and in the nozzle pressure chamber, this and the force of the nozzle spring combine to load the nozzle valve on its seat, holding the injector closed.

NOZZLE OPENING The injector actuator valve is PWM energized by the ECM injector driver. The actuation voltage varies by OEM, but typically is spiked at around 100 V-DC (although it may be lower, 48 V-DC, in some systems). The current draw during injector energization depends on whether a solenoid or piezoelectric actuator is used: Current draw is lower when piezoelectric actuators are used. Force exerted by the triggered actuator now exceeds that of the valve spring and the control valve opens the bleed orifice. Almost instantly, the high-level pickup current to the actuator drops off to a lower hold-in current flow. As the bleed orifice opens, fuel flows from the valve control chamber into the cavity above it and out to the return circuit. This collapses the hydraulic pressure acting on the valve control plunger that was helping to hold the nozzle valve closed. Now pressure in the valve control chamber is much lower than that in the nozzle pressure chamber that is maintained at the rail pressure. The result is a collapsing of the force that was holding the nozzle valve closed, causing the nozzle valve to open and beginning the injection pulse.

The nozzle needle opening velocity is determined by the difference in the flow rate through the bleed and feed orifices. When the control plunger reaches its upper stop, it is cushioned by fuel generated by flow between the bleed and feed orifices. When the injector nozzle valve has fully opened, fuel is injected into the combustion chamber at a pressure very close to that in the fuel rail.

NOZZLE CLOSING When the actuator valve is de-energized by the ECM, its spring forces the control valve downward and the check ball closes the bleed orifice. The closing of the bleed orifice creates pressure buildup in the control chamber via the input from the feed orifice. This pressure should be the same as that in the rail, and now it exerts an increased force on the nozzle valve control plunger through its end face. This force, combined with that of the nozzle spring, exceeds the hydraulic force acting on the nozzle valve sectional area and the nozzle valve closes, ending injection. Nozzle valve closing velocity is determined by the flow through the feed orifice. The injection pulse ceases the instant the nozzle valve seats.

CAUTION:

Never attempt to locate an engine miss by cracking open the high-pressure lines that feed the EHIs. Use OEM technical literature to troubleshoot engine as well as fuel system malfunctions.

Nozzle Hole Geometry

CR EHIs use both sac-chamber nozzles and what are generally referred to as valve closes orifice (VCO) nozzles. The latter tend to be used in engines required to meet North American emissions standards. Most CR injectors use a 4-mm nozzle valve diameter. Both sac-hole and seat-hole nozzles have the edges of each orifice rounded by hydroerosive (HE) machining. HE machining helps prevent edge wear caused by the abrasive particles in the fuel and carbon coking that can reduce flow and distort the spray geometry.

PHASES OF INJECTION

Solenoid-actuated CR fuel injection systems are capable of breaking up an injection pulse into two or three shots, whereas piezoelectric-actuated systems can manage up to seven shots per cycle. Multipulse injections require high-speed actuator switching, and this is better achieved by the more recently introduced piezoelectric EHIs. Start of injection (base timing) is plotted by the ECM using the running conditions of the chassis and engine factored with programmed fuel maps. This will result in the pilot pulse. The pilot pulse will then be followed by main pulses. You can see what this looks like in **Figure 30–23**, which graphically represents the events of a five-phase multipulse injection cycle.

Pilot Injection

Pilot injection has been used by diesel engine OEMs for a generation in other fuel systems, and

FIGURE 30–23 A Denso EHI five-phase multipulse injection cycle represented graphically. Note that the rail pressure is 1,600 bar (23,225 psi).

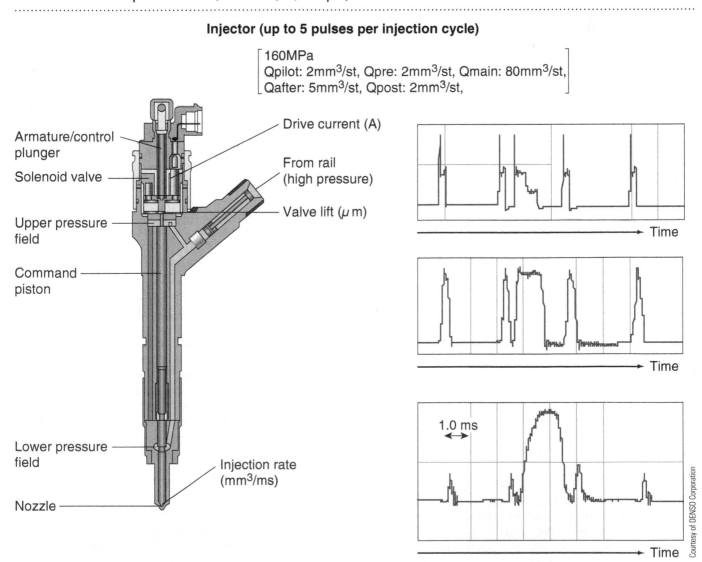

Injector (up to 5 pulses per injection cycle)

160MPa
Qpilot: 2mm^3/st, Qpre: 2mm^3/st, Qmain: 80mm^3/st, Qafter: 5mm^3/st, Qpost: 2mm^3/st,

Armature/control plunger

Solenoid valve

Upper pressure field

Command piston

Lower pressure field

Nozzle

Drive current (A)

From rail (high pressure)

Valve lift (μm)

Injection rate (mm^3/ms)

1.0 ms

Time

Time

Time

Courtesy of DENSO Corporation

on replacement components to enable rapid and accurate reprogramming of ECM files.

ADAPTIVE TRIM

Most CR management electronics complement injection quantity calibration data with **adaptive trim** logic. Adaptive trim evaluates the performance of each EHI at set engine-operating-hour intervals and "corrects" the fuel flow programming. The Caterpillar CR fuel system runs an **Injector Verification Test (IVT)** every 125 hours of engine operation to balance injector fueling. Adaptive trim is often abbreviated to **A-trim**.

TIMING PUMPS

Some CR high-pressure pumps have to be timed to the engine they fuel. Timing the pump is essential for reasons of dynamic mechanical balance and has nothing to do with fuel delivery phasing. You should consult OEM service literature when timing a pump to the engine. For example, Caterpillar requires technicians to use a variation of the timing pin method similar to that used on its new scroll port-helix metering pumps. The timing pin locks the pump into position so it can be mated up in complementary balance with the engine. **Figure 30–25** shows a timing pin locked into position in the pump.

EHI ADMISSION VALVES

A typical EHI has the disadvantage of having the rail pressure fuel constantly present at the nozzle valve seat. In the event that a nozzle valve becomes stuck completely open, a flow limiter would shut off the fuel supply to the EHI.

FIGURE 30–25 Caterpillar high-pressure pump timing pin locked into position.

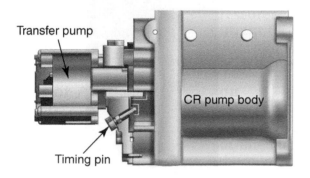

Transfer pump

CR pump body

Timing pin

However, as rail pressures become increasingly higher, if the nozzle valve were to remain in a partially open position insufficient to engage the flow limiter, the result would be fuel dribble to the engine cylinder. This type of leakage at the injector seat usually results in costly engine damage. One way around this problem is to incorporate an admission valve, typically a poppet valve. This valve is designed to hold rail supply fuel off the nozzle seat until energized. When integrated into EHI, it reduces both internal and external leakage frequencies.

DIAGNOSING CR SYSTEM PROBLEMS

If you have read this chapter, you will realize that CR fuel pumps are simple devices designed to push a sufficient volume of fuel through the high-pressure circuit to produce the highest specified injection pressures required by the system. At this juncture in the history of CR pumps, we can say that they do not commonly fail. When fuel system–related problems emerge, they are commonly related to the EHIs. The subject of EHIs, testing them, and reconditioning practices is covered in Chapter 21 in some detail, so only a brief account is provided here.

Until fairly recently, troubleshooting EHIs was usually a matter of using OEM software to identify a malfunctioning component, then replacing the defective unit. This has changed. The number of CR fuel systems in service has resulted in an extensive repair infrastructure. Some larger truck shops have made the investment in the equipment required to test and repair CR components and EHIs. However, most have not. This means that once OEM diagnostic troubleshooting routines have identified a defective component, the component is changed out. This has channeled repair work into the OEM repair infrastructure or the specialty diesel fuel injection shops.

DIAGNOSTIC ROUTINES

Most truck service facilities have focused on the accurate diagnosis of EHI failures rather than the repair of the injectors, leaving that to the specialty shops. A key on-engine diagnostic test is injector internal back leakage that can identify wear and sealing problems; the test is outlined in OEM service routines. It should be emphasized that the three requirements of accurately diagnosing CR problems are:

- Data bus connection hardware
- OEM diagnostic software
- Access to the OEM service information system (SIS)

Attempting to diagnose CR problems without these three elements is all but impossible. This may change when HD-OBD is finally adopted, when some emissions-related problems should theoretically be diagnosable using generic ESTs, but do not bet the barn on it. For the present, technicians should be aware that attempting to troubleshoot CR systems without OEM-supported equipment and software can end up creating costly damage.

REASONS EHIS FAIL

A high percentage of EHI failures are related to fuel quality, especially contaminants that find their way into fuel. Accordingly, the incidence of failures tends to be much higher in geographical areas where fuel quality is suspect. Caught early, bad fuel may require only disassembly, cleaning, and reassembly of the EHI. However, fuel-related problems are seldom caught early enough.

PROPRIETARY TESTING OF EHIs

The procedure for testing EHIs in-engine requires using manufacturer electronic service tools (ESTs) and software-driven diagnostic routines. The initial objective is to identify a defective EHI so it can be removed for further diagnosis, followed by replacement or repair.

After an EHI has been condemned in-engine, there are a number of OEM and generic test benches (see **Figure 30–26**) that may be used to identify the specific problem. In cases where contaminated fuel has caused the problem, disassembly and cleaning may be all that is required. This accounts for the fact that some shops are investing in the type of equipment shown in Figure 30–26 and covered in some detail back in Chapter 21.

GENERIC TESTING OF EHIs

There are a number of aftermarket test fixtures designed exclusively for testing EHIs, and the test procedure is designed to be simple to use. In all cases, the procedure is software-driven, so testing involves little more than following instructions. At the conclusion of the test

FIGURE 30–26 A Bosch EHI being prepped for testing in a relatively low-cost, DieseLogic bench test fixture.

sequence, the results leave no doubt as to how they should be interpreted. The outcome can only be one of:

- OK
- Not OK

WARNING:

When working with CR fuel systems, *never* crack the high-pressure pipe nuts attempting to bleed or troubleshoot problems. It could prove to be dangerous and result in costly system malfunctions. Note that most OEMs (but not all) prefer CR high-pressure lines to be single-use devices (they yield to deform to shape on initial torque). CR fuel systems are designed to self-prime, so there is no reason to crack the pipe nuts after initial torque.

Actuator Resistance

Although the odds are low of an EHI problem being actuator related, because you can perform this test on-engine with a digital multimeter (DMM) without pulling the injector, it helps to know what the specified resistance should be across the EHI terminals. Typical EHI with solenoids will have in-spec resistance of 0.3 to 2.5 ohms, with 1 ohm being typical in more recent systems and values over 1 ohm for earlier systems. **Figure 30–27** shows how easy it is to access the EHIs on a post-2010 Cummins ISB engine to perform a resistance test; however, these use a two-channel circuit, so you will have to use the service literature to identify the actuator circuit pins.

FIGURE 30–27 Easy-to-access location of the EHIs on a post-2010 Cummins ISB engine. When testing actuator resistance, consult the OEM specifications.

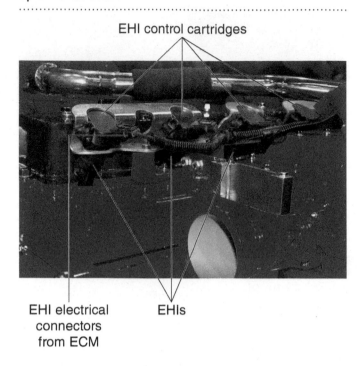

FIGURE 30–28 Cummins ISX-15 XPI CR injector.

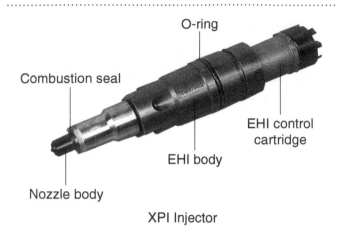

XPI Injector

Piezo actuators tend to have resistance specifications lower than 1 ohm. The resistance of the actuator wastes as heat a portion of the energy supplied to the injector, so as this rises, EHI performance is compromised. The most common type of piezo-actuated EHI states that resistance should measure between 0.3 and 0.6 ohms, so always check the OEM specifications. Indications of an actuator problem are excessive heat at the actuator body during bench-testing. Any reading over 2.5 ohms (you will only see resistances this high in older EHIs) suggests a problem, whereas readings in the high range of the OEM within-specification range can indicate an imminent failure. **Figure 30–28** shows a Cummins XPI CR injector used in its post-2015 ISX engines.

SUMMARY

- Common rail (CR) diesel fuel systems are currently used on a wide range of engines that extend from small- to large-bore highway diesels.
- CR diesel fuel systems have full authority engine management capability and are networked to J1939 data buses.
- The fuel subsystems that supply CR fuel systems have few functional differences when compared with other current fuel supply circuits.
- The electronic controls on a typical CR system consist of an input circuit, processing hardware, and actuator circuit.
- The primary outputs that manage fueling on a CR system are the rail pressure control valve and the switching of the EHI actuators.

- Bosch CR systems use either radial piston high-pressure pumps or inline piston pumps to produce rail pressures.
- The Caterpillar CR system on C7 and C9 engines uses an inline piston, high-pressure pump to produce rail pressures.
- The Paccar Delphi CR system on MX-11 and MX-13 engines uses a pair of engine camshaft-actuated EUPs to produce rail pressures.
- Rail pressures on CR diesel fuel systems are managed by the ECM using a rail pressure control valve. This applies flow restriction to fuel discharged by the high-pressure pump and options it to either the rail or the return circuit.

- The rail pressure control valve is a linear proportioning solenoid with an integral spool valve. It options fuel from the high-pressure pump outlet either to the rail or to the fuel return circuit.
- Actual rail pressures are signaled to the ECM by the rail pressure sensor. Rail pressure sensors use a piezoresistive operating principle.
- The ECM managing rail pressures in a typical CR system does so by computing *desired* rail pressure based on inputs and fuel map data monitoring. By monitoring *actual* rail pressure data, the ECM attempts to match desired and actual rail pressures.
- Electrohydraulic injectors or EHIs are used in CR systems because they can be switched at higher velocity and create fewer high-pressure

circuit variables than hydraulically actuated injectors.
- The actuators used in EHIs may be solenoid or piezo operated. Piezo actuators are used in the latest CR systems because of super-fast response times to ECM driver signals.
- The actuators in EHIs are PWM switched by the ECM.
- Most EHIs should have fuel flow codes programmed to the ECM. Programming may be done by keying in numeric data using an EST or by download from the OEM data hub of the flow codes. OEMs use different terms to describe EHI flow calibration data: Two of these are E-trim and QR codes.
- Some high-pressure pumps must be timed to the engine. The method Caterpillar uses for timing its pumps is pin timing.

REVIEW QUESTIONS

1. What type of fuel transfer pump is used on Caterpillar CR fuel systems that manage C7 and C9 engines?
   a. Reciprocating plunger
   b. Inline piston
   c. Vane
   d. External gear

2. Which of the following best describes the type of injectors used with CR fuel systems?
   a. Pintle injectors
   b. Electrohydraulic injectors (EHIs)
   c. Poppet injectors
   d. Electronic unit injectors (EUIs)

3. How many high-pressure pump elements are used on a Bosch radial piston pump fueling a six-cylinder engine with a CR (common rail) fuel system?
   a. One
   b. Two
   c. Three
   d. Six

4. In a typical CR fuel system, the rail could also be known as a(n):
   a. charging gallery.
   b. accumulator.
   c. jumper pipe.
   d. injector tube.

5. What is the normal peak rail pressure used by Caterpillar on its C7 and C9 CR-fueled engines when the system is functioning properly?
   a. 5,000 psi (345 bar)
   b. 12,000 psi (827 bar)
   c. 27,550 psi (1,900 bar)
   d. 33,300 psi (2,296 bar)

6. What is required to initiate the energization of a solenoid actuator on a typical CR EHI?
   a. Around 100 volts
   b. Around 12 volts
   c. V-Ref
   d. Less than 1.5 volts

7. Which of the following are advantages of multipulse injection cycles?
   a. Lower cold-start emissions
   b. Lower noise levels
   c. Better fuel economy
   d. All of the above

8. Which of the following best describes the means by which the ECM drivers control the actuation of CR EHIs?
   a. V-Ref signal
   b. V-Bat signal
   c. Distributor spike
   d. Pulse width modulation (PWM)

9. How many pumping elements are used on a Caterpillar CR high-pressure pump fueling a C7 engine?
   a. One
   b. Two
   c. Three
   d. Six

10. Which of the following is the key component used to signal actual rail pressure to the ECM?
   a. Rail pressure sensor
   b. Rail pressure control valve
   c. Pressure limiter valve
   d. Flow limiter valve

11. What device on a typical CR system prevents constant fueling of a cylinder if one of the EHIs sticks in the open position?
   a. Flow limiter
   b. Pressure limiter valve
   c. Pressure control valve
   d. Collapse of accumulator

12. Technician A states that most CR systems are capable of multipulse injection. Technician B states that although multipulse fuel injection events improve fuel economy, they tend to increase combustion noise, especially at startup. Who is correct?
   a. Technician A only
   b. Technician B only
   c. Both A and B
   d. Neither A nor B

13. Technician A states that first-generation CR diesel fuel systems used solenoid actuators on EHIs. Technician B states that some current CR diesel fuel systems use piezo injectors because they can be switched at higher speeds. Who is correct?
   a. Technician A only
   b. Technician B only
   c. Both A and B
   d. Neither A nor B

14. What force is used to hold a CR EHI nozzle valve in its closed and seated position?
   a. Spring force only
   b. Electrical force only
   c. Combined hydraulic and electrical forces
   d. Combined hydraulic and spring forces

15. When the control plunger in an EHI is energized, what should happen to the rail pressure charged to the injector?
   a. Significant decrease
   b. Significant increase
   c. Remains almost unchanged
   d. First increases, then drops off

16. What electronic principle is used in the rail pressure sensor fitted to most CR diesel fuel systems?
   a. Piezo resistive
   b. Thermistor
   c. Potentiometer
   d. Differential pressure

17. Technician A states that to purge a typical CR system, the line nuts on the pipes connecting the rail to the EHIs should be cracked and retorqued to spec after priming. Technician B states that some OEMs suggest that high-pressure pipes on CR systems be used once only, because the seats deform to seal when torqued. Who is correct?
   a. Technician A only
   b. Technician B only
   c. Both A and B
   d. Neither A nor B

18. Which of the following best describes the electrical principle that makes a piezo-type actuator on an EHI operate?
   a. Electromagnetism
   b. Piezoelectric effect
   c. Reversibility of piezoelectric effect
   d. Inductive capacitance

19. Which of the following is another way of saying *injection quantity calibration data*?
   a. Fuel flow codes
   b. E-trim codes
   c. Quick-response (QR) codes
   d. All of the above

20. Technician A states that CR systems that use adaptive trim do not require reprogramming of injection quantity calibration data when EHIs are replaced. Technician B states that CR systems with adaptive trim routinely evaluate EHIs performance and can make minor adjustments to the fuel trim. Who is correct?
   a. Technician A only
   b. Technician B only
   c. Both A and B
   d. Neither A nor B

31

Prerequisites: Chapters 18, 21 and 30

AMPLIFIED COMMON RAIL SYSTEMS

OBJECTIVES

After studying this chapter, you should be able to:

- Identify amplified common rail systems (ACRSs) on diesel engines.
- Identify diesel engines currently using ACRS.
- Track the fuel subsystems and fuel routing in ACRS from tank to injector.
- Describe the electronic management circuit components used in ACRS.
- Describe the operation of the ACRS inline piston pumps used to manage rail pressures.
- Outline how rail pressures are managed in ACRS.
- Outline the operation of the ACRS electrohydraulic injector.
- Perform some basic service routines on Detroit Diesel DD Series ACRS engines.
- Change out a HADI injector.
- Reprogram HADI fuel injection quantity calibration codes (IQCCs) using DDDL.

KEY TERMS

amplified common rail system (ACRS)

amplified pressure common rail (APCR)

DDEC 10

Detroit Diesel Customer Support Network (DDCSN)

Detroit Diesel Diagnostic Link (DDDL)

Detroit Diesel Electronic Controls (DDEC)

digital dash display (DDD)

fuel-amplified common rail (FACR) system

fuel filter module

hydraulically amplified diesel injector (HADI)

injection quantity compensation code (IQCC)

motor control module (MCM)

Power Service Literature (PSL)

pressure limiting valve (PLV)

quantity control valve (QCV)

rail

rail pressure sensor (RPS)

two-stage valve

INTRODUCTION

The **amplified common rail system (ACRS)** was introduced to North America on the Detroit Diesel (DD) DD15 engine in 2008. This engine was developed as the joint Mercedes-Benz (MB) and DD common platform engine. The DD15 has been joined by two siblings since its introduction. It is important to note that all DD designated engines are marketed as MB-badged engines outside the North American Free Trade Agreement (NAFTA) trade area. There are some minor differences in the location of ancillary components between the DD and MB engines, but none in the operating principles. **Figure 31–1** shows the left side of a DD15 engine where all of the critical fuel management components are located.

ACRS APPLICATIONS AND GENERATIONS

At the time of writing, this variation on the common rail (CR) fuel system is only used by DD on highway engines sold in North America. The fuel system is also known by the following terms:

- **Fuel-amplified common rail (FACR) system** (Bosch)
- **Amplified pressure common rail (APCR)** (original DD term)

However, in this chapter we will use the current preferred DD acronym, ACRS, to reference the system. In addition, we will generally reference the **Detroit Diesel Electronic Controls (DDEC)** generations VI (DDEC VI used after 2008) and 10 (**DDEC 10** used after 2010) management systems as simply DDEC.

At the time of writing, three generations of the APCR fuel system have been used on DD engines. The three generations are:

- V5
- V7
- GHG14

In dealing with the subject matter in this chapter, the three generations will not be distinguished, though generally the later GHG14 will be referenced. There will no doubt be additional versions of the fuel systems as time goes by, but this is unlikely to greatly change the operating principles of APCR as they are outlined here.

WHAT IS ACRS?

A disadvantage of a traditional CR system is the fact that each electrohydraulic injector (EHI) is pressure-loaded under whatever the rail pressure happens to be at any given moment of operation. The consequence is that the nozzle valve and internal seals must be capable of sustaining the peak rail pressures of the system, which often exceed 29,000 psi (2,000 bar). ACRS

FIGURE 31–1 Left-side view of a DD15 showing the location of the critical fuel management components.

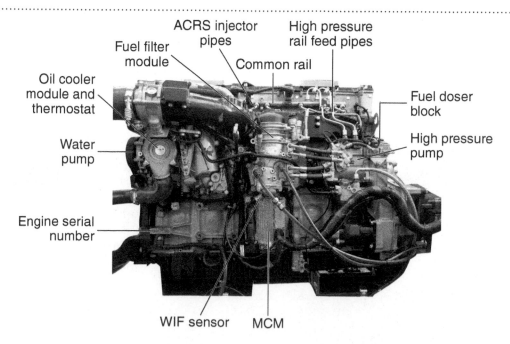

TABLE 31–1 Daimler Trucks North America (DTNA) DD Engines Using ACRS

OEM	Series	Displacement	Peak Power BHP (kW)	Maximum Torque lb-ft. (N•m)
DTNA-DD	DD13	12.8 liters	470 BHP (350 kW)	1,650 lb-ft. (2,237 N•m)
DTNA-DD	DD15	14.8 liters	560 BHP (418 kW)	1,850 lb-ft. (2,508 N•m)
DTNA-DD	DD16	15.6 liters	600 BHP (448 kW)	2,050 lb-ft. (2,780 N•m)

is a way of achieving injection pressures as high or higher than CR fuels systems while running a rail pressure of approximately one-half of the intended injection pressure. The key in enabling this is the ACRS **hydraulically amplified diesel injector (HADI)**, an electrohydraulic injector that is designed to amplify the supply rail pressure by more than doubling it. In this way, a rail pressure of 15,000 psi (1,034 bar) can result in an injection pressure of 30,000 psi (2,068 bar). The rail fulfills the same function as in a traditional CR system; however, the rail pressure is not necessarily the injection pressure in an ACRS.

When the DD Series was launched, a DD11 engine with 10.6 liters was planned, but it now appears that this will probably not be made available, at least in NAFTA markets. **Table 31–1** shows the MY 2015 DD line-up of ACRS fueled engines. The DD13 engine is also supplied to Mitsubishi Fuso trucks, a legacy of the now-dead Daimler-Chrysler-Mitsubishi connection.

AMPLIFICATION PRINCIPLE

In the ACRS HADI, a fuel pressure amplifier or intensifier piston within the injector body is actuated by CR-sourced fuel (pressure managed by ECM), and acts on fuel contained in a separate pump chamber (supplied by the rail) to amplify the pressure. In current systems, the amplification ratio is somewhat over 2:1, enabling the rail pressure to be more than doubled. The extent of amplification depends on the sectional area of the HADI-located amplifier piston, so in theory there is nothing to limit the current amplification ratio in future applications.

ACRS CIRCUIT LAYOUT

The general layout of an ACRS is not that different from any other CR system. Rail pressures are produced using an engine-driven, cam-actuated inline piston pump. A Bosch twin piston pump is

FIGURE 31–2 Bosch high-pressure pump used in an ACRS system.

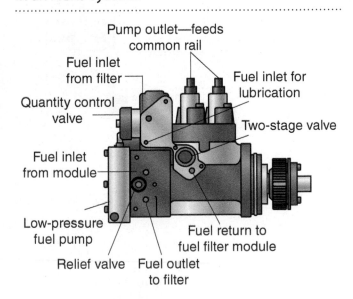

shown in **Figure 31–2**. The high-pressure pump feeds the **rail** by means of a pair of outlet pipes. The rail plays the same role in ACRS as it does in a standard CR fuel system, in that it acts as an accumulator for the high-pressure pump output, and as distributor channel to the injectors.

The illustration in **Figure 31–3** shows an ACRS system that uses a low-pressure **fuel filter module** (currently supplied by Racor) with the main components called out, including the transfer pump, multi-stage filtration, high-pressure pump, and common rail. The low-pressure fuel module moves fuel through the fuel subsystem to the high-pressure pump. **Figure 31–4** is a photographic image of the fuel module with the key components called out. **Figure 31–5** is a detail of the transfer piping between the fuel management module and the ACRS high-pressure pump.

FUEL FLOW ROUTING

The fuel flow routing of the ACRS takes fuel from the fuel subsystem, circulates it through

FIGURE 31-3 Components of a typical ACRS system.

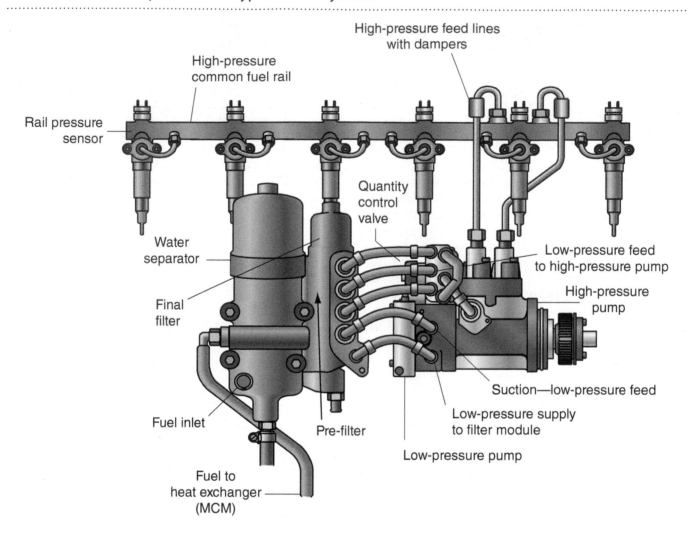

a fuel management module, delivers fuel to the high-pressure pump, and from there to the common rail and HADIs. Fuel movement through the fuel subsystem is produced by a gear pump driven by the ACRS high-pressure pump assembly. The fuel flow routing through an ACRS filter assembly is shown in the schematic illustration in **Figure 31-6**.

FUEL FILTER MODULE

DD Series engines are equipped with a fuel filter module whose primary function is to handle fuel through the fuel subsystem. The fuel filter module incorporates the following:

- Pre-filter
- Water separator
- Water-in-fuel (WIF) sensor
- Secondary filter
- Fuel cooler

Pre-Filter

Fuel pulled from the vehicle fuel tanks passes through the fuel inlet into the fuel pre-filter, pushing the inlet check valve off its seat. The inlet check valve (spring and ball) prevents fuel drain-back to the tank when the engine is shut down. Larger particles in the fuel are entrapped in the pre-filter element. Fuel is next routed to the transfer pump, which charges fuel to the water separator and secondary filter. The entrapment capability of the pre-filter is 100 microns.

Water Separator

The water separator also filters and has an entrapment capability of 10 microns. Fuel flow routing through the water separator is from the inside to the outside, as indicated in Figure 31-6, and this generates centrifugal force that propels the heavier water droplets to the outside of the separator canister. From there, gravity drops

FIGURE 31–4 Identifying the components of an ACRS fuel management module and the high-pressure CR pump.

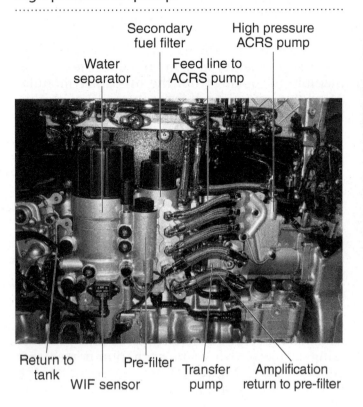

Water separator

Secondary fuel filter

High pressure ACRS pump

Feed line to ACRS pump

Return to tank

Pre-filter

WIF sensor

Transfer pump

Amplification return to pre-filter

FIGURE 31–5 Plumbing connections between the fuel module components and the ACRS low- and high-pressure pump components.

separated water droplets into the water collector at the base of the separator assembly. Water detected in the collector bowl at the base of the separator by the WIF sensor either illuminates an light-emitting diode (LED) on the face of the sensor or signals the **motor control module (MCM)**

FIGURE 31–6 Fuel flow routing through an ACRS fuel filtration module.

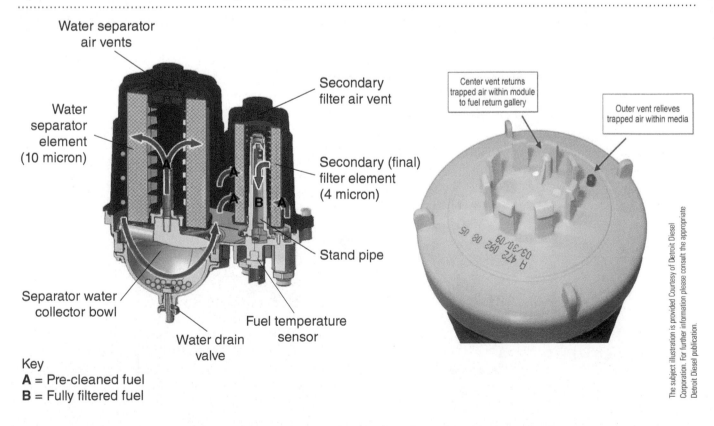

Water separator air vents

Water separator element (10 micron)

Separator water collector bowl

Water drain valve

Secondary filter air vent

Secondary (final) filter element (4 micron)

Stand pipe

Fuel temperature sensor

Center vent returns trapped air within module to fuel return gallery

Outer vent relieves trapped air within media

Key
A = Pre-cleaned fuel
B = Fully filtered fuel

so that it can broadcast a message to the **digital dash display (DDD)**.

A ventilation bore is located above the water separator element to divert any trapped air in the separator housing, routing it to the return line to the fuel tank. When the water separator element is removed, a drain circuit to the fuel collector is opened to allow fuel to flow out of the water separator housing.

Secondary Filter

The secondary or final filter (see Figure 31–6) has an entrapment capability of 4 microns. Flow routing is from the outside to the inside. Similar to the water separator canister, the secondary filter housing is equipped with a ventilation bore to ensure that fuel must pass through the filtration media before it can exit. Fuel exiting the secondary filter housing is routed to the high-pressure pump under charging pressure produced by the transfer pump. DD prefers that its service literature be consulted before attempting to change the secondary filter element.

Fuel PRO Filter Assembly

A Fuel PRO filter may also be fitted to the fuel subsystem. This is fitted upstream from the fuel filter module described in the previous section. This filter may be equipped with an optional fuel heater. The fuel heater runs off chassis 12 V-DC with an optional overnight 120 V-AC hookup. **Figure 31–7** shows the Fuel PRO

and a schematic of how it is plumbed into the fuel subsystem.

Fuel Cooler

A fuel cooler is located behind the fuel filter module. Its function is to cool fuel from the amplifiers in the HADIs. The fuel cooler uses a plate- or shell-type principle and the cooling medium is coolant from the oil cooler module. At engine operating temperatures, fuel exiting the HADI amplification circuit is typically in the region of 212°F (100°C). The temperature of this fuel is dropped so that it exits the heat exchanger at around 194°F (90°C).

High-Pressure Pump

The high-pressure pump **(Figure 31–8)** is a two-cylinder piston pump. The pistons are actuated by cam profile. The function of the high-pressure pump is to supply the rail and the HADIs it feeds with sufficient volume to maintain rail pressures. The actuating camshaft is machined with double cams, offset by 180 degrees so that each pump element is actuated twice during one camshaft revolution. The result is four pressurizing strokes (two from each pump element) per revolution. **Figure 31–9** is a cutaway of the Bosch high-pressure piston pump used with the DD Series ACRS.

Quantity Control Valve

The **quantity control valve (QCV)** regulates rail pressure by controlling the fuel admitted

FIGURE 31–7 Fuel PRO filter assembly and its plumbing schematic.

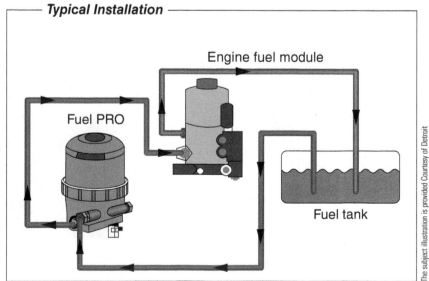

FIGURE 31–8 Bosch high-pressure piston pump used with DD Series ACRS.

into the high-pressure pump elements. The QCV is managed by the MCM using a pulse width modulated (PWM) signal. It functions as a proportioning solenoid valve (see Chapter 32) and at engine shutdown it immediately blocks flow into the high-pressure pump. **Figure 31–10** shows the operating characteristics of a QCV.

Two-Stage Valve

The **two-stage valve** functions to regulate fuel subsystem leak-off rates. It is used to avoid excessive charging circuit pressure (upstream from the rail pump) and is located on the inlet side of the high-pressure pump. It operates by:

- Sealing closed when charging pressure is below 43 psi (3 bar); this permits maximum cranking fuel pressure to the high-pressure pump elements.
- Gradually opening when charging pressure exceeds 43 psi (3 bar), opening a lubrication path to the high-pressure pump bearings.
- Fully opening the lubrication path at 51 psi (3.5 bar), maximizing flow to the high-pressure pump bearings.
- Exposing an overflow (backflow or leak-off) path when charge pressure exceeds 68 psi (4.7 bar). This backflow dump fuel is routed to the high-pressure pump cambox (where it will lubricate the cam rollers) before being rerouted to the return circuit.

The operation of the two-stage valve is critical in avoiding fuel subsystem charging pressures above the burst pressure of the filter module components when fuel demand is low but transfer pump output is high: in other words, at low load, high rpm. **Figure 31–11** shows the operating basics of a two-stage valve and **Figure 31–12** shows how it is configured in a hydraulic schematic.

FIGURE 31–9 Bosch high-pressure piston pump used with DD Series ACRS. One camshaft revolution results in four complete pumping strokes.

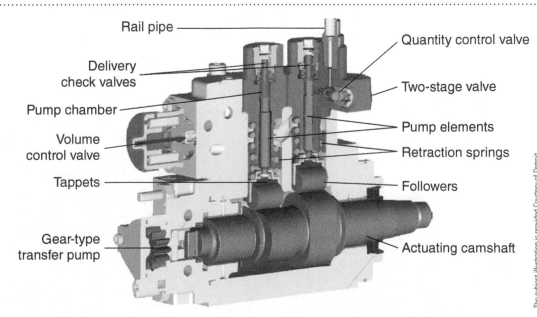

Rail pipe

Delivery check valves

Pump chamber

Volume control valve

Tappets

Gear-type transfer pump

Quantity control valve

Two-stage valve

Pump elements

Retraction springs

Followers

Actuating camshaft

FIGURE 31–10 Operating characteristics of a quantity control valve (QCV).

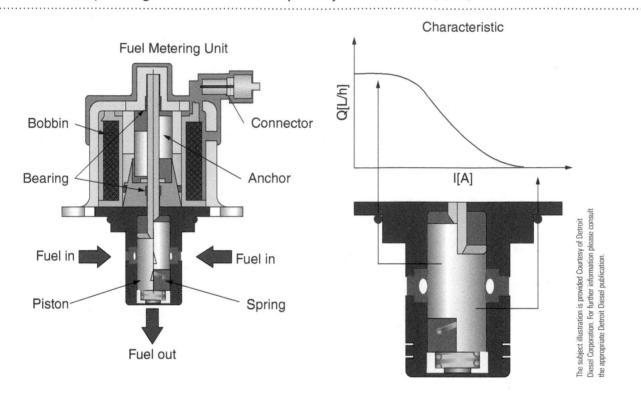

FIGURE 31–11 Operating basics of a two-stage valve.

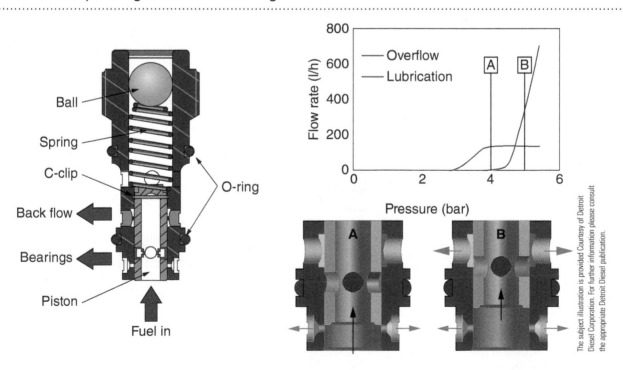

FIGURE 31–12 Hydraulic schematic showing the operation of a two-stage valve in the fuel subsystem.

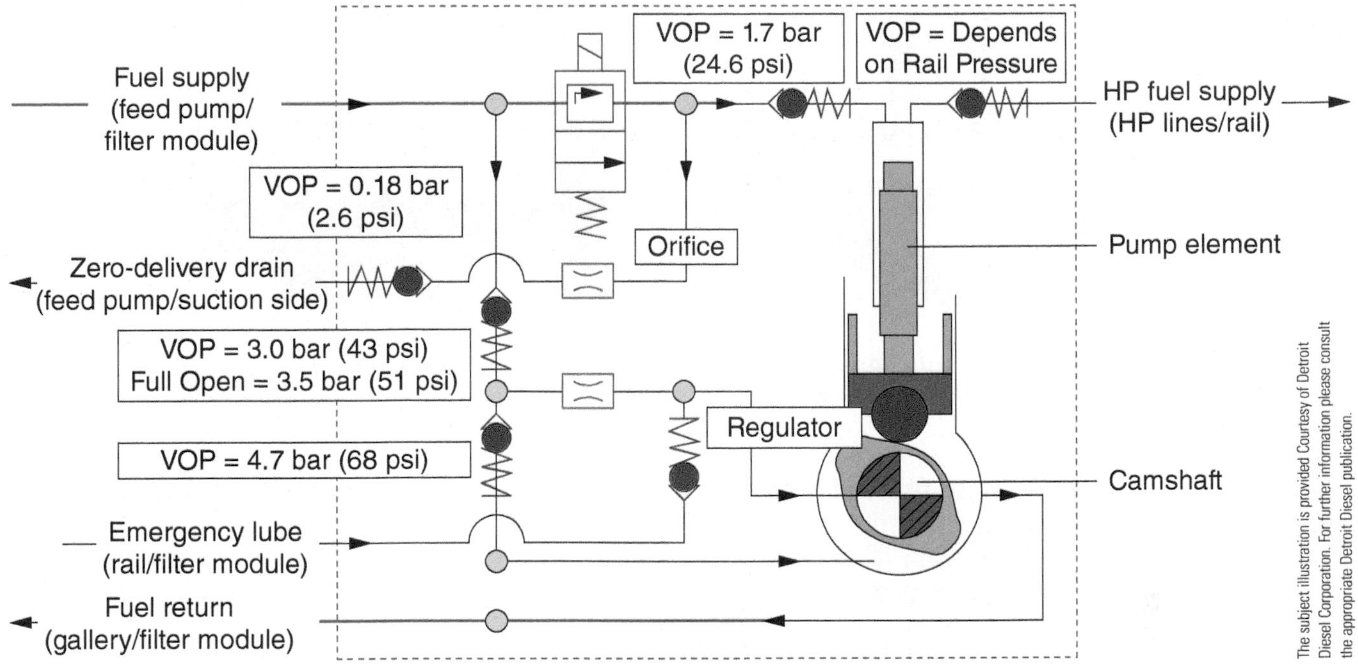

VOP = 1.7 bar (24.6 psi)

VOP = Depends on Rail Pressure

Fuel supply (feed pump/ filter module)

HP fuel supply (HP lines/rail)

VOP = 0.18 bar (2.6 psi)

Orifice

Pump element

Zero-delivery drain (feed pump/suction side)

VOP = 3.0 bar (43 psi)
Full Open = 3.5 bar (51 psi)

VOP = 4.7 bar (68 psi)

Regulator

Camshaft

Emergency lube (rail/filter module)

Fuel return (gallery/filter module)

The subject illustration is provided Courtesy of Detroit Diesel Corporation. For further information please consult the appropriate Detroit Diesel publication.

Rail Pressure Sensor

The **rail pressure sensor (RPS)** is located at the end of the fuel rail **(Figure 31–13)** in DD ACRS. It receives a V-Ref input and uses a variable capacitance principle to signal the MCM actual rail pressure at any given moment of operation. The schematic of the DDEC rail pressure sensor

FIGURE 31–13 Feed pipes from ACRS pump to rail and rail supply to injectors.

is shown in **Figure 31–14**, and a photographic image is in **Figure 31–15**.

Pressure Limiting Valve

The DD ACRS **pressure limiting valve (PLV)** is a safety valve that limits maximum rail pressure. It is a spring and check valve currently designed to trip at 20,015 psi (1,380 bar). If the PLV set pressure threshold is exceeded, it trips and routes rail fuel into the return circuit, immediately dropping rail pressure. Figure 31–14 shows a cutaway view of the PLV used in the DD ACRS.

ACRS HADI

The key difference in an ACRS system and a standard diesel CR system is in the hydraulically amplified diesel injector (HADI). The operation of an EHI in a standard CR system can be compared to that of a switch: When actuated by the ECM, it opens and permits whatever pressure is in the rail to pass through it for injection. An ACRS HADI receives a rail pressure supply in the same way, but it amplifies the rail pressure by approximately doubling it.

FIGURE 31–14 The DD Series fuel rail pressure sensor (left) and pressure limiting valve (right).

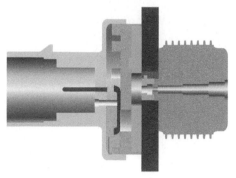

Fuel rail pressure sensor

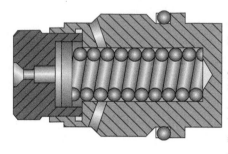

Pressure limiting valve

The subject illustration is provided Courtesy of Detroit Diesel Corporation. For further information please consult the appropriate Detroit Diesel publication.

FIGURE 31–15 The DD Series fuel rail pressure sensor.

FIGURE 31–16 Subcomponents of the ACRS HADI.

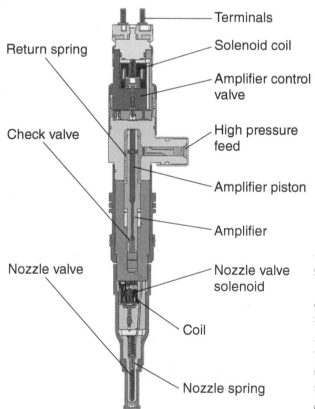

Return spring — Terminals — Solenoid coil — Amplifier control valve — Check valve — High pressure feed — Amplifier piston — Amplifier — Nozzle valve — Nozzle valve solenoid — Coil — Nozzle spring

The subject illustration is provided Courtesy of Detroit Diesel Corporation. For further information please consult the appropriate Detroit Diesel publication.

HADI COMPONENTS

The HADI subcomponents are called out in **Figure 31–16**, showing how the circuits within the injector assembly interconnect. The high-pressure feed is in the form of a direct pipe to the ACRS rail. Therefore, whatever injection pressures result from a HADI are dependent on rail pressure at any given moment of operation: The rail pressure is effectively doubled within the amplification circuit of the HADI.

HADI AMPLIFIER CIRCUIT

The ACRS HADI uses an electrohydraulic actuator to control the pressure amplifier. **Figure 31–17** should be referenced when following

the description here, which is limited to the HADI amplifier circuit. The components of the amplifier circuit are:

- High-pressure plunger
- Plunger retraction spring
- Intensifier piston
- High-pressure pump chamber

FIGURE 31–17 ACRS intensifier circuit in a 2:1 amplification HADI.

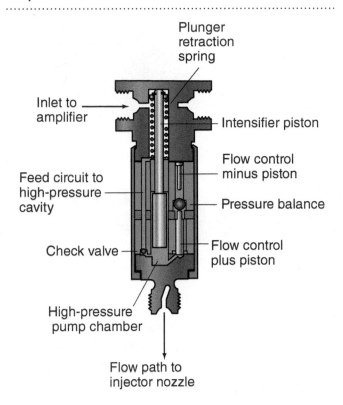

- Pump chamber check valve
- Flow control pressure ball
- Flow control minus piston
- Flow control plus piston

Operation of ACRS HADI

Injection is initiated when the HADI main actuator is energized: In current production this is a solenoid. This opens the HADI circuit and permits fuel to flow into the amplifier inlet (see Figure 31–17) to the high-pressure chamber. This flow generates a pressure drop at the lower end of the plus piston. The minus piston is charged with pressure downstream from this restriction. Because the minus and plus pistons are charged with different pressures, the flow control ball moves to its upper seat. The amplifier piston actuated by rail pressure then moves downward into the pump chamber, generating high (injection) pressure; the pump chamber check valve locks off the return path from the pump chamber to prevent back pressurization. High-pressure fuel is then charged to the fuel duct feeding the injector exit orifii from which it is injected to the engine cylinder.

The injection pulse ends when the actuator is de-energized. Flow to the nozzle abruptly stops and the plus and minus pistons are exposed to the same pressure. Because the plus piston has a slightly larger sectional area than the minus piston, the flow control pressure ball moves to its lower seat. At this point, the high-pressure chamber returns to the rail pressure value and the high-pressure plunger is retracted to its start position by its spring. A key advantage of an ACRS system is that it permits lower rail pressures while generating high injection pressures: This reduces the potential for both internal and external leakage.

Injection Pressure Management

The HADI can be managed in three operational modes:

- No-fuel (shutdown)
- Injection without amplification
- Injection with amplification

To no-fuel the HADI, neither actuator is energized, meaning that rail pressure is effectively blocked off at the injector. **Figure 31–18** shows the HADI circuits in a no-fuel status.

During injection without amplification, the injection pressure is roughly equivalent to whatever the rail pressure is being managed at: In this mode, the maximum injection pressure should be 13,053 psi (900 bar). **Figure 31–19** shows the HADI actuation circuits when in non-amplification mode.

In amplification mode, both actuators are energized and the rail pressures are more than doubled within the HADI. **Figure 31–20** shows the HADI in full amplification mode.

Actual Rail Pressure versus Desired Rail Pressure

The rail pressure is managed by the engine electronics, specifically the DDEC MCM. DDEC monitors the *actual* rail pressure by monitoring the signal receives from the rail pressure sensor. It then uses its programmed instructions in combination with command and monitoring sensors to compute *desired* rail pressure. Having done this, the engine electronics attempt to keep actual and desired rail pressures as close to each other as possible by using the available outputs, specifically the quantity control valve (QCV) and the HADIs. This process is covered in more detail in later chapters, but the idea is simple.

FIGURE 31–18 DD Series HADI with its circuits no-fueled: Rail fuel is blocked off at the injector.

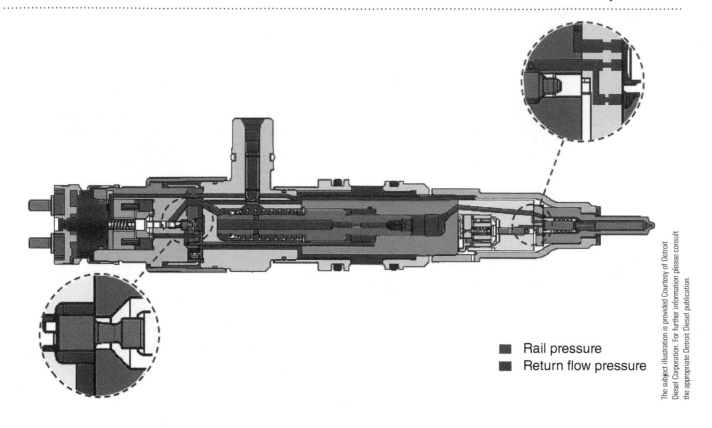

Rail pressure
Return flow pressure

The subject illustration is provided Courtesy of Detroit Diesel Corporation. For further information please consult the appropriate Detroit Diesel publication.

FIGURE 31–19 DD Series HADI with its circuits in non-amplification mode: Injection pressure would be equivalent to rail pressure.

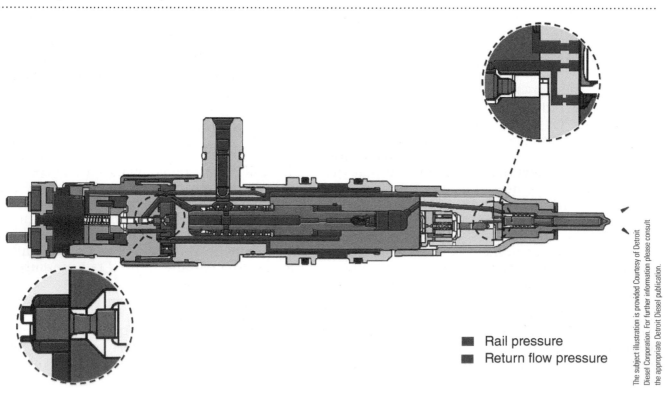

Rail pressure
Return flow pressure

The subject illustration is provided Courtesy of Detroit Diesel Corporation. For further information please consult the appropriate Detroit Diesel publication.

FIGURE 31–20 DD Series HADI with its circuits in amplification mode: Injection pressure more than doubles rail pressure.

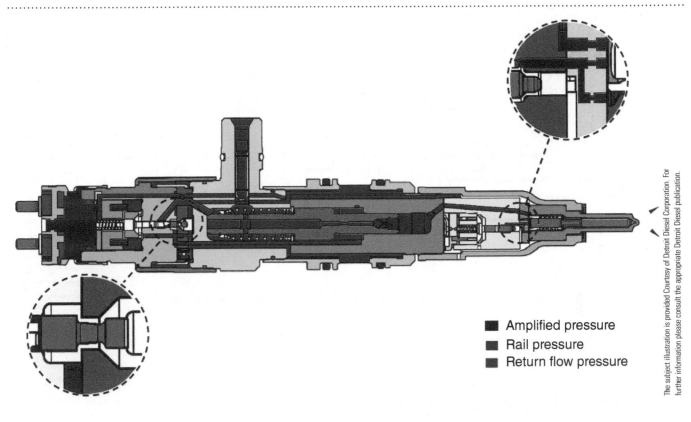

■ Amplified pressure
■ Rail pressure
■ Return flow pressure

The subject illustration is provided Courtesy of Detroit Diesel Corporation. For further information please consult the appropriate Detroit Diesel publication.

ACRS SERVICE PROCEDURES

ACRS is in its second generation (V7) at the time of writing, and will likely progress to others during the near future. **Figure 31–21** shows a full schematic of the DD Series (V7) fuel system. Technicians are reminded that OEM training is required to effectively work on an ACRS. Some simple service routines are outlined in this section, but DD service literature and diagnostic routines should always be consulted. The Detroit Diesel online SIS is currently known as the **Detroit Diesel Customer Support Network (DDCSN).** Within this portal is the service literature field known as **Power Service Literature (PSL),** and its diagnostic software and hardware package is known as **Detroit Diesel Diagnostic Link (DDDL).**

FUEL SUBSYSTEM PRIMING

Detroit Diesel states that DD Series engines should be primed using a DD priming canister (special tool J-47912), which is an air-actuated fuel charging vessel. Use the following DD procedure to prime after servicing the filter elements:

1. Ensure that the priming canister is at least ³/₄ full (minimum of 9 liters fuel).
2. Connect the priming canister to the priming port on the fuel filter module.
3. Make sure the canister shutoff valve is closed.
4. Connect the priming canister to shop air and pressurize to maximum pressure.
5. Slowly open the shutoff valve and allow the system to charge with fuel for approximately 60 seconds.
6. Close the shutoff valve.
7. Inspect for external fuel leaks.
8. Crank the engine for 20 seconds.
9. If the engine starts, proceed directly to step 12.
10. If the engine fails to start, allow a 1-minute cooldown, then repeat steps 4 through 8. This starting cycle can be repeated up to three times.
11. If the engine still does not start, use DDDL to check for fault codes and repair as necessary.

FIGURE 31–21 Fuel flow schematic of the V7 generation of DD Series ACRS.

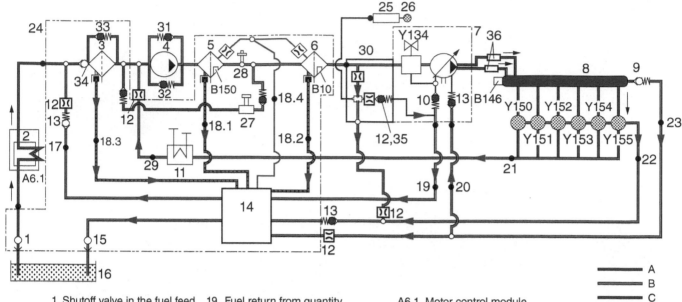

1. Shutoff valve in the fuel feed (locked in open position)
2. Fuel heat exchanger
3. Fuel prefilter
4. Low-pressure fuel pump
5. Water separator
6. Final filter
7. High-pressure fuel pump
8. Rail
9. Pressure limiting valve
10. Two-stage valve
11. Fuel cooler
12. Throttle valve
13. Regulator
14. Fuel accumulator
15. Shutoff valve in the fuel return (locked in open position)
16. Fuel tank
17. Fuel return bypass
18.1. Water separator drain
18.2. Final filter drain
18.3. Pre-filter drain
18.4. Air vents

19. Fuel return from quantity control valve
20. Emergency lubrication line
21. Fuel return from amplifiers
22. Fuel return from injector needle valves
23. Fuel return from pressure limiting valve
24. Fuel filter module
25. Doser block assembly
26. Fuel doser valve
27. Hand primer pump
28. Priming port
29. Amplifier return line (partially external to module)
30. High-pressure manifold
31. Pressure relief valve for low-pressure pump
32. Bypass valve
33. Bypass valve (pre-filter)
34. Check ball (pre-filter stand pipe)
35. Doser block pressure regulator
36. Fuel line dampers

A6.1. Motor control module (MCM)
B10. Fuel temperature sensor
B146. Rail pressure sensor
B150. Water level sensor
Y134. Quantity control valve
Y150. Injector (cylinder 1)
Y151. Injector (cylinder 2)
Y152. Injector (cylinder 3)
Y153. Injector (cylinder 4)
Y154. Injector (cylinder 5)
Y155. Injector (cylinder 6)

A. Fuel feed/suction side
B. Fuel feed (pressure side)
C. Fuel rail-pressure
D. Fuel return flow
E. Filter drain
F. Air vent passages

d470000i

12. Remove the priming canister hoses from the filter module.
13. Warm the engine to operating temperature (140°F/60°C).
14. Run the engine rpm to 1,800 and hold for 3 minutes.
15. Reduce the engine rpm to low idle. Check for leaks and fault codes.

RAIL PRESSURE BLEED-DOWN TEST

This procedure must be directed by DDDL software and can help identify a leak in the high-pressure circuit.

A leak in any of the following locations will result in accelerated bleed-down:

- High-pressure pump elements
- Pump to rail high-pressure lines
- High-pressure pipes from rail to HADIs
- Rail pressure sensor
- Pressure limiting valve
- Internal amplifier or nozzle needle

Use the following procedure to execute this test:

1. Connect the DDDL hardware to the data bus.
2. Boot the DDDL software.

3. Select the <Instrumentation> field, then <Chart>, then the parameter <rail pressure>.
4. Start the engine and run until it reaches its operating temperature of 140°F (60°C).
5. Shut down the engine.
6. Turn the ignition back on but do *not* start the engine. This must be done because the MCM will power down with the ignition circuit open.
7. Monitor the rail pressure; trace over time as shown in **Figure 31–22**.

8. A properly sealed high-pressure system (i.e., without leakage) should show a pressure bleed-down characteristic consistent with the pattern in the upper chart in Figure 31–22. Leakage in the high-pressure circuit will produce a profile similar to that shown in the lower chart in Figure 31–22. Record the time required for rail pressure to drop to 4,060 psi (280 bar). Record the time required for rail pressure to drop to 145 psi (10 bar). Then subtract the second time from the first.

FIGURE 31–22 Rail pressure bleed-down test profiles using DDDL software.

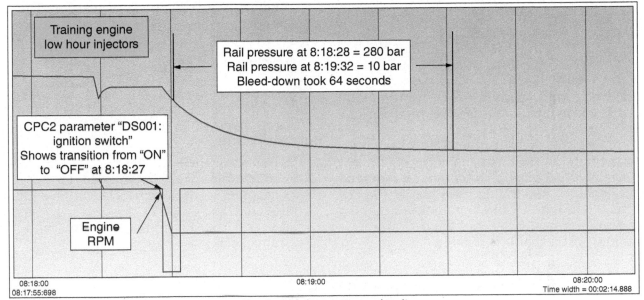

Sealed high-pressure circuit

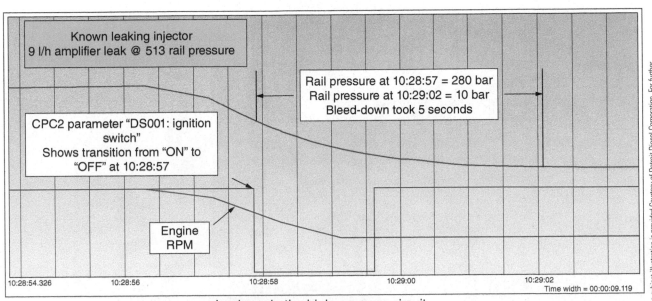

Leakage in the high-pressure circuit

9. If the bleed-down time required exceeds 35 seconds, the high-pressure circuit can be assumed to be sealed. If the drop-off occurs in less than 35 seconds, high-pressure circuit leakage should be suspected.

PLV LEAKAGE TEMPERATURE TEST

The PLV leakage temperature test procedure allows a technician to identify a leaking pressure limiting valve. A leaking PLV can result in fluctuating rail pressures, excessive cranking time, and logging of fault codes due to rail pressure deviation. Refer to Figure 31–22 while navigating the following sequence:

1. Start the engine and use an infrared temperature gun (callout #1 on **Figure 31–23**) to measure the surface temperature of the fuel rail between cylinders #4 and #5 (see callout #2 on Figure 31–23).
2. Make a second temperature measurement at the PLV line just above the fuel filter module (callout #3 in Figure 31–23).
3. Compare the pressure bleed-down readings to the data on the chart in Figure 31–22. In a normally operating engine, the rail temperature should read higher than that at the PLV line. When the PLV line temperature reading is higher than the fuel rail temperature, it is an indication that it is leaking.

DRAINING THE FUEL SYSTEM

Before attempting any type of servicing on the high-pressure circuit of an ACRS, the fuel system should be drained using the following procedure:

1. Remove the fuel supply line to the fuel filter module.
2. Install DD special tool J-48710 fuel pressure test kit onto the fuel supply line at the fuel filter module. Do not disconnect the return line from the module.
3. Using the J-48710 regulator, adjust the system pressure to 50 psi (3.5 bar).
4. After a period of 2 minutes, the system should be fully drained of fuel.
5. Remove the fuel pressure test kit. The system is now ready to be worked on.

INJECTOR REMOVAL

DD recommends that its own special tool J-47391 be used to pull HADIs. This is a bridge and bolt mechanical puller tool. Use the following procedure:

1. Disconnect the batteries.
2. Remove the rocker housing cover.
3. Disconnect the electrical contacts at the injector.
4. Release the high-pressure line and cam frame seal.

FIGURE 31–23 PLV temperature test procedure.

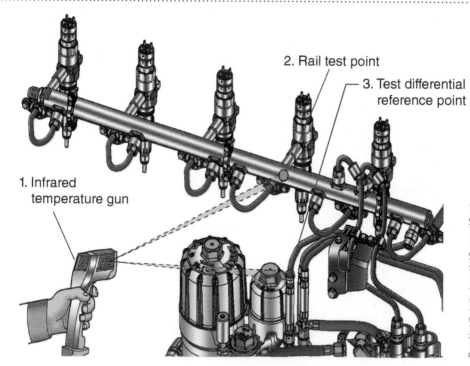

2. Rail test point

3. Test differential reference point

1. Infrared temperature gun

5. Remove the injector hold-down bolt.
6. Lift the clamp and injector from its seat in the cylinder head using the injector puller.

> **NOTE:**
>
> At present, Detroit Diesel considers the HADIs not to be field serviceable. Defective injectors should be changed out with DD replacements.

INJECTOR INSTALLATION

Prior to installing a HADI, the injector bore tube should be cleaned and visually inspected. In addition, ensure that the new injector is dry, clean, and free of lubricant. Use the following procedure:

1. Install a new copper washer on the injector.
2. Apply a thin coat of engine oil to the injector seal rings and insert them into the injector nut ring grooves. Ensure that they are properly seated.
3. Install the HADI and clamp into the injector bore.
4. Align the clamp over the retaining stud, install the hold-down bolt, and finger tighten.
5. Install the HADI high-pressure pipe from the rail and finger tighten the line nut.
6. Torque the injector hold-down bolt to specification: This uses a template torque method, so be sure to consult service literature.
7. Torque the high-pressure line nut to specification.
8. Install and tighten the electrical connector.
9. Tighten the cam frame seal at the high-pressure pipe.

> **TECH TIP:**
>
> Detroit Diesel permits the reuse of rail-to-HADI high-pressure pipes, but states that they should be carefully monitored after each retorque.

PROGRAMMING FUEL FLOW CODES

All HADIs have a 6-digit calibration code known as the **injector quantity compensation code (IQCC)**. This is recorded on the upper side of each injector. Each time an injector is changed out, the new IQCC must be programmed to the MCM, or the result will be imbalanced fueling. The IQCC can only be programmed to the MCM using DDDL.

DDDL DIAGNOSTIC ROUTINES

DDDL software is designed to run a wide range of semi-automated, technician-driven diagnostic routines, which include the following:

- Cylinder cutout tests
- High amplifier circuit return flow
- Idle speed balance

Figure 31–24 shows a left-side view of a Detroit Diesel DD15 featuring a cutaway view of one cylinder and highlighting of the ACRS.

FIGURE 31–24 Left-side view of a Detroit Diesel DD15 GHG14-generation engine featuring a cutaway of one cylinder and highlighting of the ACRS system.

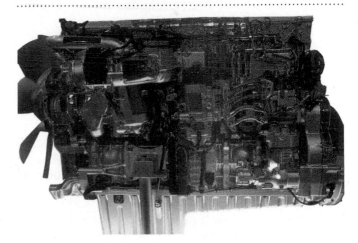

SUMMARY

- The Detroit Diesel ACRS is used to fuel its DD13, DD15, and DD16 engines.
- The system layout of the DD ACRS can be compared to most other types of CR diesel fuel systems.
- DD Series ACRS uses an inline, twin piston high-pressure pump to provide fuel flow to the rail.

- The ACRS is distinguished from other CR systems by its injectors. The HADIs can amplify the rail pressure when switched into amplification mode.
- In a typical ACRS system, the amplification ratio is just over 2:1, enabling the rail pressure to be approximately doubled prior to

injection. An ACRS system permits lower rail pressures while permitting high injection pressures; this reduces the potential for both internal and external leakage.

- In an ACRS HADI, an amplifier piston within the injector body is actuated by rail-sourced fuel to increase the rail pressure to much higher injection pressures.
- Peak ACRS injection pressures may exceed 29,000 psi (2,000 bar) when the HADIs are in amplification mode.
- A rail pressure sensor is used to signal actual rail pressure to the MCM.
- MCM logic monitors actual rail pressure, computes a desired rail pressure value, and manages its outputs to achieve a close match between actual and desired rail pressure value.

- The primary outputs that manage fueling on an ACRS are the quantity control valve (QCV) and the switching of the HADI actuators.
- The actuators in HADIs are PWM switched by the MCM.
- HADIs must have fuel flow codes programmed to the MCM. These are known as IQCCs in DD service literature.
- IQCCs are a 6-digit code recorded on the upper portion of each HADI.

REVIEW QUESTIONS

1. In an ACRS, which of the following is true of injection pressures?
   a. They are always one-half of the rail pressure.
   b. They are always more than double the rail pressure.
   c. They may be at either rail pressure or more than double rail pressure.
   d. They are not correlated with rail pressure.

2. What type of high-pressure pump is used on the DD Series ACRS?
   a. Twin piston, inline pump
   b. Triple piston, rotary pump
   c. Vane-type pump
   d. Single element, reciprocating pump

3. Technician A states that DD Series ACRS are capable of peak injection pressures as high as 29,000 psi (2,000 bar). Technician B states that the highest pressure attainable in a HADI in non-amplification mode is 13,053 psi (900 bar). Who is correct?
   a. Technician A only
   b. Technician B only
   c. Both A and B
   d. Neither A nor B

4. Technician A states that DD permits reuse of rail-to-HADI high-pressure pipes. Technician B states that when ACRS high-pressure pipes are reused, they must be carefully monitored after being torqued. Who is correct?
   a. Technician A only
   b. Technician B only
   c. Both A and B
   d. Neither A nor B

5. What is the entrapment rating of an ACRS pre-filter?
   a. 100 microns
   b. 50 microns
   c. 10 microns
   d. 3 to 5 microns

6. What means does the MCM use to energize HADI actuators?
   a. Hydraulic pressure rise
   b. AC voltage spike
   c. PWM signal
   d. DC system voltage

7. What electronic principle is used in the rail pressure sensor in the ACRS rail?
   a. Variable capacitance
   b. Thermistor
   c. Potentiometer
   d. Differential pressure

8. Technician A states that to purge an ACRS, the line nuts on the pipes connecting the rail to the HADIs should be cracked and retorqued after priming. Technician B states that DD prefers the use of a priming canister when reestablishing prime after servicing the fuel filter module. Who is correct?
   a. Technician A only
   b. Technician B only
   c. Both A and B
   d. Neither A nor B

9. How is the fuel quantity control valve controlled by the MCM?
   a. Directly from the accelerator pedal
   b. PWM signal
   c. V-Ref signal
   d. System voltage

10. What term is used by DD service literature to describe the rate at which a HADI flows fuel?
    a. Cal code
    b. E-trim code
    c. Quick response (QR) code
    d. Injector quantity compensation coding (IQCC)

11. If the IQCC was not reprogrammed after an injector change-out, which of the following would be the likely outcome?
    a. Engine runaway
    b. Misfire
    c. Unbalanced cylinder fueling
    d. Failure of the other five injectors

12. Where is the IQCC specification on a HADI?
    a. Upper side of the injector
    b. Lower side of the injector
    c. On the nozzle of the injector
    d. In the connector socket

13. How many digits are there in an IQCC?
    a. Two
    b. Four
    c. Six
    d. Eight

14. Which of the following must be used to reprogram an IQCC to the MCM?
    a. ProLink iQ
    b. DDDL
    c. An electric pencil
    d. A smart phone

15. Technician A says that HADIs are field-serviceable injectors. Technician B says that at present, all ACRS injectors should be returned to DD for reconditioning. Who is correct?
    a. Technician A only
    b. Technician B only
    c. Both A and B
    d. Neither A nor B

ENGINE MANAGEMENT, ALTERNATE POWER, AND EMISSIONS

Section 3 is dedicated to electronic engine management. It looks at engine management from a technician's perspective, so the fundamentals of electronics, networking, and multiplexing begin the section; we then continue with a look at the alternate fuel and hybrid technologies that are increasingly used in commercial vehicles. There follow dedicated chapters on each OEM management system and their service and diagnostic software, along with a couple of chapters on diesel emissions. The book concludes with chapters on failure analysis and diagnostics, which in many ways collate the learning objectives of all the chapters that precede them.

BRIEF HISTORY

All matter has some electrical properties, but it is only comparatively recently in history that humans have been able to make it work for them. The first type of electricity to be identified was **static electricity**, described by the Greeks more than 2,000 years ago when they observed that amber rubbed with fur would attract lightweight objects such as feathers. The Greek word for "amber" (a translucent, yellowish resin, derived from fossilized tree sap) is **electron**, from which the word *electricity* is derived. Probably the next significant step forward occurred toward the end of the sixteenth century when the English physicist William Gilbert (1544–1603) made the connection between electricity and magnetism. A hundred years later, Benjamin Franklin (1706–1790) proved the electrical nature of thunderstorms in his famous kite experiment, established the terms *positive* and *negative*, and formulated the conventional theory of current flow in a circuit. From this point forward, progress accelerated. In 1767, Joseph Priestly established that electrical charges attract with a force inversely proportional to distance, and in 1800, Alessandro Volta invented the first battery.

Michael Faraday (1791–1867) opened the doors of the science we now know as **electromagnetism** when he published his law of induction, which simply states that a magnetic field induces an electromotive force in a moving conductor. Thomas Edison (1847–1931) invented the incandescent lamp in 1879, but perhaps even more importantly built the first central power station and distribution system in New York City in 1881. This station provided a means of introducing electrical power into industry and the home. The discovery of the electron by J. J. Thomson (1856–1940) in 1897 introduced the science of electronics and quickly resulted in the invention of the diode (1904) and triode (1907).

DEFINITIONS

Electricity is a form of energy. This energy form can be observed in charged particles such as electrons or protons either statically, as accumulated charge, or dynamically, as current flow in a circuit. **Electronics** is a branch of electricity that addresses the behavior of flows of electrons through solids, liquids, gases, and across vacuums. However, in automotive technology, the terms *electronics* and *electronic engine management* are generally used to describe systems that are managed by computers.

ATOMIC STRUCTURE AND ELECTRON MOVEMENT

An **atom** is the smallest particle of a chemical element that can take part in a chemical reaction. An atom is usually made up of **protons**, **neutrons**, and electrons. Protons and neutrons form the center or **nucleus** of each atom, while the electrons orbit the nucleus in a manner similar to that of planets orbiting the sun in our solar system. The simplest atom is hydrogen. It has a single electron orbiting a nucleus consisting of a single proton: It has no neutron. A representation of the structure of a hydrogen atom is shown in **Figure 32–1**.

ELECTRONS AND PROTONS

Electrons orbit the nucleus of an atom in a concentric ring known as a *shell*. Electrons have a negative electrical charge. Protons and neutrons form the nucleus of all atoms, around which the electrons orbit. Protons have a positive electrical charge, whereas neutrons have no electrical charge. The nucleus of an atom comprises 99.9% of its mass. The number of protons in the nucleus is the atomic number of any given element; the sum of the neutrons and protons is the atomic mass number. In a balanced or electrically neutral atom, the nucleus is surrounded by as many electrons as there are protons.

All electrons are alike. All protons are alike. The number of protons in the nucleus of an atom identifies it as a specific element. Electrons have 5/10,000 (0.0005) of the mass of a proton. Under normal conditions, electrons are bound to the positively charged nuclei of atoms by the attraction between opposite electrical charges.

FIGURE 32–1 Hydrogen atom.

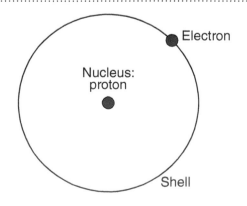

UNBALANCED ATOMS

Any atom may possess more or fewer electrons than protons. Such an atom would be described as negatively charged (an excess of electrons) or positively charged (a net deficit of electrons); a charged atom is known as an **ion**. The concentric orbital **shells** (a *shell* is an orbital path) of an atom proceed outward from the nucleus of the atom. The electrons in the shells closest to the nucleus of an atom are held most tightly: Those in the outermost shell are held more loosely.

Shell Occupation

The most complex atoms may have seven shells. The maximum number of electrons that can occupy shells one through seven are, in sequence: 2, 8, 18, 32, 50, 72, 98. The heaviest elements in their normal states have only the first four shells fully occupied with electrons; the outer three shells are only partially occupied. The outermost shell in any atom is known as its **valence**. The number of electrons in the valence will dictate some basic characteristics of an element. The chemical properties of atoms are defined by how the shells are occupied with electrons.

Charge Differential

An atom of the element helium, whose atomic number is 2, has a full inner shell. An atom of the element neon, with an atomic number of 10, has both a full first and a full second shell (2 and 8): Its second shell is its valence (**Figure 32–2**). Other more complex atoms that have eight electrons in their outermost shell, even though this shell might not be full, will resemble neon in terms of their chemical inertness. Remember that an ion is any atom with either a surplus or a deficit of electrons. Free electrons can rest on a surface or travel through matter (or a vacuum) at close to the speed of light. Electrons resting on a surface cause

it to be negatively charged. Because the electrons are not moving, that surface is described as having a negative static electrical charge. The extent of the charge is measured in **voltage** or **charge differential**. A stream of moving electrons is known as an *electrical current*. For instance, if a group of positive ions passes in close proximity to electrons resting on a surface, they will attract the resting electrons by causing them to fill the "holes" left by the missing electrons in the positive ions. Current flow is measured in **amperes**: 1 ampere equals 6.28×10^{18} electrons (a **coulomb**) passing a given point per second.

Factors of Charge Imbalance

A number of factors, such as friction, heat, light, and chemical reactions, can "steal" electrons from a surface, and when this occurs the surface becomes positively charged. If the positive ions remain at rest, the surface will have a positive static electrical charge differential. Every time a person walks across a carpet, electrons are "stolen" from the carpet surface, and this has an electrifying effect (electrification) on both the substance from which electrons are stolen (the carpet) and the moving body that performs the theft. When the moving body has accumulated a sufficient charge differential (measured in voltage), the excess electrons will be discharged through an arc and balance the charge.

Electrification results in both attractive and repulsive forces. In electricity, like charges repel and unlike charges attract. When a plastic comb is run through hair, electrons are stolen by the comb, giving it a negative charge. The comb may subsequently attract small pieces of paper as shown in **Figure 32–3**. The experiment always works better on a dry day because electrons can travel

FIGURE 32–3 Unlike charges attract.

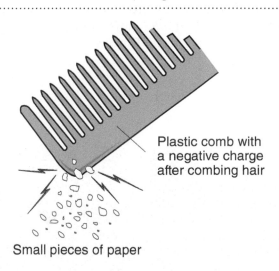

Plastic comb with a negative charge after combing hair

Small pieces of paper

FIGURE 32–2 Atomic structure of a neon atom: The outer shell is full.

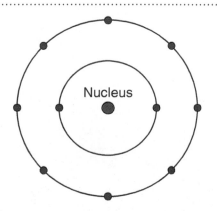

Nucleus

FIGURE 32–4 Balanced atom: The number of protons and electrons are equal.

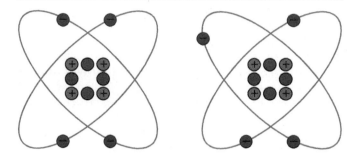

more easily through humid air and any accumulated charge will dissipate rapidly. Two balloons rubbed on a woolen fiber will both acquire a negative charge and therefore tend to repel each other. An atom is held together because of the electrical tendency of unlike charges attracting each other. Positively charged protons hold the negatively charged electrons in their orbital shells and, because like electrical charges repel each other, the electrons do not collide. All matter is composed of atoms. Electrical charge is a component of all atoms. When an atom is balanced—that is, when the number of protons matches the number of electrons (**Figure 32–4**)—the atom can be described as being in an electrically neutral state. So all matter is electrical in essence. The phenomenon we describe as electricity concerns the behavior of atoms that, for whatever reason, have become unbalanced or electrified.

CONDUCTORS AND INSULATORS

The ease with which an electron moves from one atom to another determines the conductivity of the material. **Conductance** is the ability of a material to carry electric current. To produce current flow, electrons must move from atom to atom, as shown in **Figure 32–5**. Materials that readily permit this flow of electrons from atom to atom are classified as **conductors**. A conductor is generally a metallic element that contains fewer than four electrons in its outer shell. Examples of conductors include copper, aluminum, gold, silver, iron, and platinum.

Materials that inhibit or perhaps prevent a flow of electrons are classified as **insulators**. An insulator is a nonmetallic substance that contains more than four electrons in the outer shell. Examples of insulators include glass, mica, rubber, and plastic.

Semiconductors are a group of materials that cannot be classified either as conductors or insulators: They have exactly four electrons in their outer shell. Silicon is an example of a semiconductor.

CONDUCTIVITY IN A CIRCUIT

Conductive metals, even when in an electrically neutral state, contain vast numbers of moving electrons that move at random from atom to atom. When a battery is placed at either end of a conductor, such as copper wire, and a complete circuit is formed, electrons are pumped from the more negative terminal to the more positive until either the charge differential ceases to exist or the circuit is opened. The number of electrons does not change.

CURRENT FLOW

Current flow occurs only when there is a path and a difference in electrical potential. This difference is known as *charge differential* and is measured in voltage. Charge differential exists when the electrical source has a "shortage" (deficit) of electrons and therefore is positively charged. Because electrons are negatively charged and unlike charges attract, electrons flow toward the positive source.

FIGURE 32–5 Electrons flow through a conductor.

Conductor

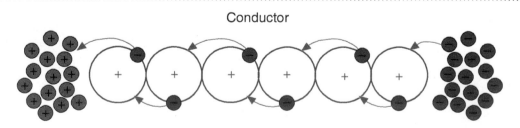

CONVENTIONAL AND ELECTRON THEORY OF CURRENT FLOW

Initially it was thought that current flow in an electrical circuit had one direction of flow, that is, from positive to negative. This idea is known as the **conventional theory** of current flow. When the electron was discovered, scientists revised the theory of current flow and called it **electron theory**. In studying electricity, the technician should be acquainted with both conventional and electron theories of current flow.

Creating an Electron Flow Path

A conductor, such as a piece of copper wire, contains billions of neutral atoms whose electrons move randomly from atom to atom, vibrating at high frequencies. When an external power source such as a battery is connected to the conductor, a deficit of electrons occurs at one end of the conductor and an excess of electrons occurs at the other end: The negative terminal repels free electrons from the conductor's atoms while the positive terminal attracts free electrons. This results in a flow of electrons through the conductor from the negative charge to the positive charge. The rate of flow depends on the charge differential (or **potential difference**/voltage). The charge differential or *voltage* is a measure of electrical pressure. **Figure 32–6**

FIGURE 32–6 Voltage or charge differential is the pressure that causes electrons to move.

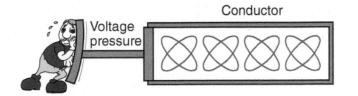

shows the effect of voltage on electron flow. The role of a battery, for instance, is to act as a sort of electron pump. In a closed electrical circuit, electrons move through a conductor, producing a displacement effect close to the speed of light.

The physical dimensions of a conductor are also a factor. The larger the sectional area (measured by wire gauge size), the more atoms there are over a given sectional area, therefore the more free electrons. This means that as wire cross-section size increases, so does the ability to flow more electrical current through the wire. The rate of electron flow is called **current** and it is measured in amperes. A current flow of 6.25 billion electrons per second is equal to 1 ampere, as shown in **Figure 32–7**.

HOLE THEORY

Rather than saying that the conventional theory of current flow is wrong and electron flow is right, you can think about current flow by comparing it with what happens in a lineup at a movie theater. As each person buys a ticket, the people remaining in the line move a step forward. This concept can be compared to what happens to each electron in an energized electrical circuit—it moves forward. However, as the line moves forward, the gap moves backward. You can compare this gap to the hole left by an electron in the electrical circuit as it moves forward. There is nothing different in what is happening in the movie theater line; the difference is just in whether you think of its movement from the point of view of a person in the line or the gap.

Terminals

The terminal from which electrons exit in an electrical device is known as the **anode** or positive terminal. The terminal through which electrons enter an electrical component is known as the **cathode** or negative terminal. The suffix

FIGURE 32–7 The rate of electron flow is measured in amperes.

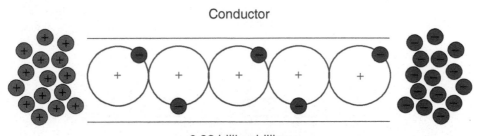

6.28 billion billion
electrons per second = 1 ampere

"-ode" is taken from the term *electrode.* It might help you to think of an electrode as a sort of gate in an electrical circuit.

MAGNETISM

The phenomenon of magnetism was first observed in lodestone (magnetite) and the way ferrous (iron-based) metals reacted to it. When a bar of lodestone was suspended by string, the same end would always rotate to point toward the earth's North Pole. The molecular theory of magnetism tends to be the most widely accepted: In most materials, the magnetic poles of the composite molecules are arranged randomly so there is no magnetic force. In certain metals such as iron, nickel, and cobalt, the molecules can be aligned so that their north or N poles all point in one direction and their south or S poles all point in the opposite direction. In lodestone, the molecules align themselves naturally. Some materials have good magnetic retention, which means that when they are magnetized they retain their molecular alignment. Other materials are only capable of maintaining their molecular alignment when positioned within a magnetic field; when the field is removed, the molecules disarrange themselves randomly and the substance's magnetic properties are lost.

All magnetism is essentially electromagnetism, in that it results from the kinetic energy of electrons. Whenever an electric current is flowed through a conductor, a magnetic field is created. When a bar-shaped permanent magnet is cut in two, each piece assumes the magnetic properties of the parent magnet with individual north and south poles. **Figure 32–8** shows some magnetic fields and how separate magnetic fields react when in proximity with one another.

The term **reluctance** describes resistance to the movement of magnetic lines of force. Reluctance can be reduced by using permeable (susceptible to penetration) materials within magnetic fields. The permeability of matter is rated by giving a rating of 1 for air, which is generally considered to be a poor conductor of magnetic lines of force. In contrast, iron is ascribed a permeability factor of 2,000, and certain ferrous alloys may have values exceeding 50,000.

The force field existing in the space around a magnet can be demonstrated when a piece of cardboard is placed over a magnet and iron filings are sprinkled on top of the cardboard. The pattern produced as the filings arrange themselves on the cardboard is referred to as *flux lines.* Flux lines are directional and exit from the magnet's north pole and enter through the south pole. Flux lines do not cross each other in a permanent magnet. Flux lines facing the same direction attract, whereas flux lines facing opposite directions tend to repel.

The flux density (concentration) determines the magnetic force. A powerful magnetic field

FIGURE 32–8 Magnetic principles: A. All magnets have poles. B. Unlike poles attract each other. C. Like poles repel each other.

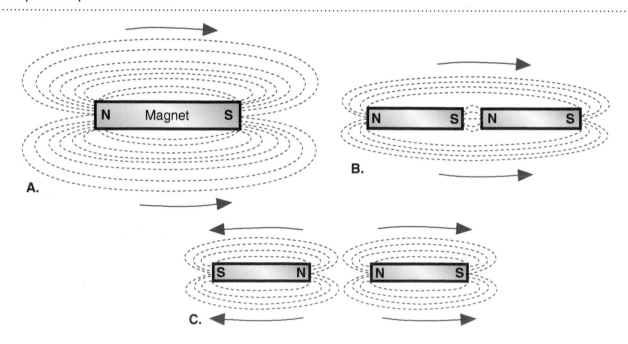

exhibits a dense flux field, whereas a weak magnetic field exhibits a low-density flux field. Flux density is always greatest at the poles of a magnet.

ATOMIC STRUCTURE AND MAGNETISM

In an atom, all of the electrons in their orbital shells also spin on their own axes in much the same way the planets orbit the sun. They rotate axially, each producing magnetic fields. Because of their axial rotation, each electron can be regarded as a tiny permanent magnet. In most atoms, pairs of electrons spinning in opposite directions produce magnetic fields that cancel each other out. An atom of iron has 26 electrons, 22 of which are paired. In the second from the outermost shell, four of the eight electrons are not paired, meaning that they rotate in the same direction and do not cancel each other out. This fact accounts for the magnetic character of the metal iron. A large number of vehicle electrical components use electromagnetic principles in some way or other, and magnetic field strength is the reason that **coils** and other electromagnetic devices contain iron cores.

ELECTROMAGNETISM

Electrical current flow through a conductor such as copper wire creates a magnetic field surrounding the wire. This effect can be observed by passing a copper wire through which current is flowing, which is lengthwise, over a compass needle: The needle will deflect from its north-south orientation when this occurs. Any magnetic field created by electrical current flow is known as *electromagnetism*. Study of the behavior of electromagnetic fields has proved the following:

- Magnetic lines of force do not move when current flow through a conductor remains constant. When current flowing through the conductor increases, the magnetic lines of force will extend farther away from the conductor.
- The intensity and strength of magnetic lines of force increase proportionally with an increase in current flow through a conductor. Similarly, they diminish proportionally with a decrease in current flow through the conductor.
- The right-hand rule is used to denote the direction of the magnetic lines of force: The right hand should enclose the wire with the thumb pointing in the direction of

conventional current flow (positive to negative), and the fingertips will then point in the direction of the magnetic lines of force, as shown in **Figure 32–9** and **Figure 32–10**.

FIGURE 32–9 Electromagnetic field characteristics.

FIGURE 32–10 A. Magnetic lines of force join together and attract each other. **B.** The right-hand rule.

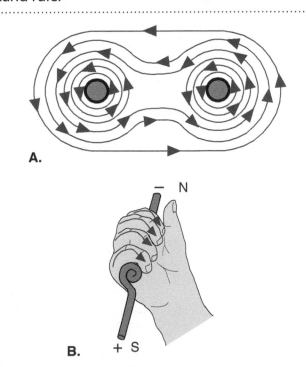

USING ELECTROMAGNETISM

When wire is coiled and electric current flows through it, the magnetic field that would be produced if the wire were straight combines to form a larger magnetic field identified by north and south poles. This effect can be amplified by placing an iron core through the center of the coil (**Figure 32–11**), which reduces the reluctance of the magnetic field. The polarity of the electromagnet created can be determined by the right-hand rule for coils: The coiled wire should be held with the fingers pointed in the direction of conventional current flow (positive to negative) and the thumb will point to the north pole of the coil (check out Figure 32–10 again). Electromagnetic field force is often described as magnetomotive force (mmf). The mmf is determined by two factors:

1. The amount of current flowing through the conductor
2. The number of turns of wire in a coil

Magnetomotive force is measured in **ampere-turns (At)**. Ampere-turn factors are the number of windings (complete turns of a wire conductor) and the quantity of current flowed (measured in amperes). Referencing **Figure 32–12**, if a coil with 100 windings has 1 ampere of current flowed through it, the result will be a magnetic

FIGURE 32–11 Magnetic field characteristics of coiled conductors: note how the field is intensified when an iron core is inserted.

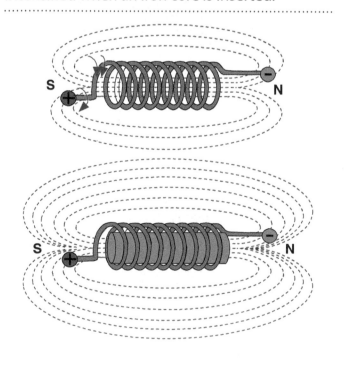

FIGURE 32–12 Magnetic field strength is determined by the amount of amperage and the number of coils.

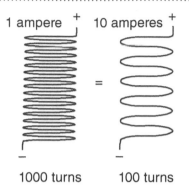

1 ampere + 10 amperes +

=

1000 turns   100 turns

field strength rated at 100 At. An identical magnetic field strength rating could be produced by a coil with 10 windings with a current flow of 10 amperes. The actual field strength would have to factor in reluctance. In other words, the actual field strength of both the foregoing coils would be increased if the coil windings were to be wrapped around an iron core.

Solenoids

A simple solenoid consists of a coil and an armature. The coil is usually stationary and the armature moves within it. The armature can be integral with devices such as hydraulic poppet valves, spool valves, and levers that effect mechanical movement. A simple solenoid has two status conditions: *off* or *on*. In most cases, the armature is spring-loaded to default to the mechanical *off* position when no current is flowed through the coil. When an electrical current energizes the coil, the magnetic field that builds mechanically moves the armature. This is the principle that is used to engage a starter motor or move the poppet valve in a solenoid-actuated injector.

An inherent disadvantage of a solenoid is response lag. Although the electrical trigger to the solenoid takes place almost instantly after switching, before mechanical movement can take place a magnetic field must build. Where an almost instant response to signal is required, devices such as stepper motors and piezoelectric actuators (see Chapter 34) may be used and are becoming more common.

Proportioning Solenoids

A proportioning solenoid functions similarly to a simple solenoid in that it produces mechanical movement in response to current flowed through a coil. However, a proportioning solenoid is capable of precise linear or rotary positioning determined by the amount of current flowed through its actuating coil.

ELECTRICAL CURRENT CHARACTERISTICS AND SOURCES OF ELECTRICITY

Electrical current is classified as either direct current (DC) or alternating current (AC). The technician should understand the basic characteristics of both because both are used in vehicles. Although most of the chassis electrical circuit uses DC, an alternator and an inductive pulse generator both produce AC. In fact, an alternator produces AC internally and rectifies it to DC externally.

DIRECT CURRENT

Electrical current can be made to flow in two directions through a conductor. If the current flows in one direction it is known as **direct current**, usually abbreviated as **DC**. The direction of flow can be expressed with respect to either the electron or conventional theories of current flow, but if the current characteristic is DC, then it does not alternate. The current flow may be steady or have a pulse characteristic. DC can be produced in a number of ways, as outlined later in this section. DC has many applications and it is extensively, if not quite exclusively, used in highway vehicles through most of the chassis electrical circuits.

ALTERNATING CURRENT

Alternating current or **AC** describes a flow of electrical charge that cyclically reverses due to a reversal in polarity at the voltage source. It is usually produced by rotating a coil in a magnetic field. AC is used in vehicle AC generators (perhaps more often called *alternators*) and in certain sensors (shaft speed) on modern vehicles: It is also better suited than DC for transmission through power lines. The frequency at which the current alternates is measured in **cycles**. A cycle is one complete reversal of current from zero through positive to negative and back to the zero point. Frequency is usually measured in cycles per second.

SOURCES OF ELECTRICITY

There are a number of ways of producing electricity and modern trucks use most of them in some way or another.

Chemical

Batteries are a means of producing DC from a chemical reaction. In the lead acid battery, a potential difference is created by the chemical interaction of lead and lead peroxide submerged in sulfuric acid electrolyte. When a circuit is connected to a charged battery (one in which there is a charge differential), the battery will pump electrons through the circuit from the negative terminal through the circuit load to the positive terminal. This process will continue until the charge differential ceases to exist. When the charge differential ceases to exist, there is no difference between the potential at either terminal and the battery can be said to be discharged.

TYPES OF BATTERY Batteries used in highway commercial vehicles whose primary power source is the diesel engine are standard lead acid or its gel cell relative:

- Standard lead acid battery. Suitable for providing short bursts of peak currents for cranking, but otherwise are not deeply discharged.
- Gel cell (recombinant) lead acid battery. Adapted for deep cycle applications such as for providing chassis power when the engine is not running.

NiMH BATTERIES The dominant battery used in hybrid electric vehicles (HEVs) is the **NiMH battery**, but this is changing due to the emergence of lithium battery technology. An aqueous solution of potassium hydroxide is used as the electrolyte and the electrodes are made from nickel oxide (positive) and a metal hydride (negative). The active element in the NiMH is hydrogen, which is absorbed/de-adsorbed as the battery is discharged and charged. The cell voltage is 1.2 volts. Banks of these batteries are used in many HEV buses.

LITHIUM-BASED BATTERIES Lithium has the highest electrochemical potential of any current batteries, producing a per-cell potential of between 2 and 5 volts. Their storage and power density features suit HEV applications, where they are rapidly replacing NiMh batteries. The common categories are cobalt based, lithium-ion (Li-on), and lithium-ion polymer (Li-po); there is more detailed coverage in Chapter 39.

Static Electricity

The term *static electricity* is somewhat misleading because it implies that it is unmoving. Perhaps it is more accurately expressed as frictional electricity, because it results from the contact of two surfaces. Chemical bonds are formed when any surfaces contact, and if the atoms on one surface tend to hold electrons more tightly, the result is a "theft" of electrons. Such contact produces a charge imbalance by pulling electrons of one surface from that of the other. As electrons are pulled away from a surface, the result is an excess of electrons in one surface (result = negative charge) and a deficit in the other (result = positive charge). The extent of the charge differential is measured in voltage. While the surfaces with opposite charges remain separate, the charge differential will exist. When the two polarities of charge are united, the charge imbalance will be canceled.

Static electricity is an everyday phenomenon, as described in examples earlier in this chapter. It usually involves voltages of more than 1,000 V and perhaps rising to as much as 50,000 V. A fuel tanker trailer towed by a highway tractor steals electrons from the air as it is hauled down the highway (as does any moving vehicle) and can accumulate a significant and potentially dangerous charge differential. This charge differential, which can be as high as 40,000 V, must be neutralized by grounding before any attempt is made to load or unload fuel that could otherwise be ignited by an electrostatic arc.

Electromagnetic Induction

Current flow can be created in any conductor that is moved through a magnetic field or alternatively by a mobile magnetic field and a stationary conductor. The voltage induced increases both with speed of movement and the number of conductors, so densely wound conductors tend to produce higher voltage values. Generators, alternators, cranking motors, and shaft speed sensors all use the principle of electromagnetic induction. **Figure 32–13** shows what happens when a conductor is moved through a magnetic field.

Thermoelectric

Electron flow can be created by applying heat to the connection point of two dissimilar metals in a device known as a **thermocouple**. This principle is used in the **pyrometer** to monitor exhaust

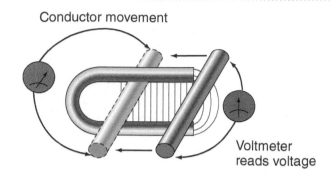

FIGURE 32–13 Moving a conductor through a magnetic field induces an electrical charge differential.

Conductor movement

Voltmeter reads voltage

gas temperature in recently introduced diesel particulate filters (DPFs). In addition, pyrometers were often used as a driver downshift alert device in diesel engines a generation ago. A thermocouple consists of two dissimilar metals (iron and constantin, a copper-tin alloy) joined at the "hot" end and connected to a sensitive voltmeter at the gauge end. As temperature increases at the hot end, the reading will increase at the display gauge, which functions like a millivoltmeter calibrated to display Celsius or Fahrenheit.

Photoelectric

When light contacts certain materials such as selenium and cesium, electron flow is stimulated. Photoelectric cells are used as sensors that can control headlight beams and automatic daylight/night mirrors.

Piezoelectricity

Piezoelectricity is a word taken from the Greek words meaning "pressure electricity." It was discovered in 1880 by the brothers Pierre and Jacques Curie. They observed that some crystals, notably quartz (in their original experiments), become electrified when subjected to direct pressure, the potential difference increasing with pressure increase. When mechanical force is applied across the opposite faces of certain nonconducting crystals, a voltage is generated. The actual voltage value that results is proportional to the applied stress. The Curie brothers also observed that the direction of the polarization reverses if the direction of applied stress changes, that is, from compression to tension.

Piezoelectrical effect is therefore reversible. If the opposite faces of the piezo crystal have a voltage applied to them, the crystal lattice (the way the crystals structurally bond to each other) changes almost instantly, resulting in either expansion or contraction. This change of shape produces a powerful force that can be used for actuating a valve in much the same way as a solenoid, but at much faster response speeds. Solenoids use electromagnetism and respond more slowly due to the time required to build and collapse electromagnetic fields.

USES OF PIEZOELECTRICITY Piezoelectricity can be used in both sensors and actuators in vehicle electronics. Piezoelectric sensors are used as detonation sensors in on spark-ignited (SI) electronically controlled engines. Reverse piezoelectric effect is becoming common in diesel engine actuators replacing solenoids as fuel injector switches. The reason for adopting piezoelectric actuators is faster response times along with lower electrical power draw.

ELECTRICAL CIRCUITS AND OHM'S LAW

The German physicist Georg Ohm (1787–1854) proved the relationship between electrical potential (pressure or voltage), electrical current flow (measured in amperes), and the **resistance** to the current flow. In order to understand the behavior of electricity in an electrical circuit, it is necessary to understand the terminology used to describe its characteristics. When introducing electricity, comparisons are often made between electrical circuits and hydraulic circuits: These analogies are used in the following explanations.

VOLTAGE

Voltage can be described in a number of different ways. Charge differential, electrical pressure, and potential difference are all correct ways of describing voltage. Using a hydraulic analogy, voltage in an electrical circuit can be compared to fluid water pressure. Similar to pressure in the hydraulic circuit, voltage may be present in an electrical circuit without any current flow. You measure voltage using a digital multimeter (DMM) on the V-DC or V-AC settings. You can measure voltage in both a closed (energized) and an open electrical circuit.

RESISTANCE

Resistance is the opposition to current flow. The resistance to the flow of electrons through a circuit is measured in **ohms**, the symbol for which

is Ω. The resistance to the flow of free electrons through a conductor results from the innumerable collisions that occur; generally, the greater the sectional area of the conductor (wire gauge size), the less resistance to current flow, simply because there are more available paths for free electrons.

Once again, using the hydraulic analogy, the resistance to fluid flow through a circuit would be defined by the pipe internal diameter or flow area. In an electrical circuit, resistance generally increases with temperature because of collisions between free electrons and vibrating atoms. As the temperature of a conductor increases, the tendency of the atoms to vibrate also increases and so does the incidence of colliding free electrons. The categories of resistance we see in vehicle electrical circuits are:

- Load—could mean lights, motors, anything that is powered electrically
- Corrosion—eats away from outside in reducing the effective surface contact area
- Wiring—size and material should provide as low resistance as possible to the electron flow

Resistance in an electrical circuit is measured with a DMM set in ohms. It can only be measured when the circuit is not electrically energized.

∞	=	infinite resistance, out of limit, open circuit
OL	=	infinite resistance, out of limit, open circuit
0Ω	=	zero or minimum circuit resistance, complete or **closed circuit**

There can be both voltage and resistance in an open electrical circuit. For current to flow in a circuit, both voltage (charge differential) and a physical circuit (resistance) must first exist. When such a circuit is closed, a path for current flow is provided.

Variable Resistance

We can use variable resistance devices in a number of ways to monitor parameters such as temperature and position status in modern engines. These will be examined in greater detail in later chapters of this book, but here are some examples.

- **Thermistors**: Designed to precisely vary resistance as temperature rises or falls. This means that when a constant value reference voltage is supplied to the thermistor, a signal can be output that exactly correlates with a temperature value.

- **Rheostats**: These are two-wire, mechanically variable resistors. A mechanical wiper into which the return signal path is integrated moves over a resistor. Its actual position determines how much of the electrical path has to pass through the resistor.
- **Potentiometers**: These are three-wire, mechanically variable voltage dividers. A reference voltage is supplied to the potentiometer. The mechanical position of a wiper on a resistor determines how the voltage is divided between the signal and ground paths.

CURRENT

Current flows when the conditions of voltage and a closed circuit are met. Current is specifically the flow of electrons measured in amperes. One ampere is equal to 6.28×1018 electrons passing a given point in an electrical circuit in 1 second (also known as 1 coulomb). If the comparison with a hydraulic circuit is used once again, amps can be compared to gallons per minute (gpm). If current flow is to be measured in an electric circuit, the circuit must be electrically active or closed, that is, actively flowing current.

CLOSED CIRCUIT

A complete electrical circuit is an arrangement that permits electrical current to flow. At its simplest, this arrangement would require a power source, a load, and a means of connecting supply and return paths to the power source. A circuit is described as closed when current is flowing and open when it is not. **Figure 32–14** shows the simplest type of electrical circuit.

SERIES CIRCUITS

A **series circuit** may have several components, such as switches, resistors, and lamps, but they are connected so that there is only one path for current flow through the circuit, such as that in Figure 32–14. In this figure, if the element in the lightbulb were to fail, the circuit would open and no current would flow.

PARALLEL CIRCUITS

A **parallel circuit** is one with multiple paths for current flow, meaning that the components in the circuit are connected so that current can flow through a component without having first flowed through other components in the circuit. **Figure 32–15** shows an example of a parallel circuit using three paths for current flow, each through a separate load.

SERIES-PARALLEL CIRCUIT

Many circuits are constructed using the principles of both series and parallel circuits. These are known as *series-parallel circuits*.

ELECTRICAL CIRCUIT TERMINOLOGY

The following terminology is used to describe both normal and abnormal behavior in electrical circuits.

Short Circuit

Short circuit is used to describe what occurs in an electrical circuit when a conductor is placed across the connections of a component and some or all of the circuit current flow takes a

FIGURE 32–14 Simplified series light circuit with 3-ohm resistance.

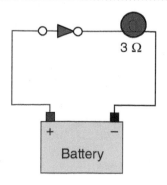

FIGURE 32–15 A parallel circuit with different resistances in each branch.

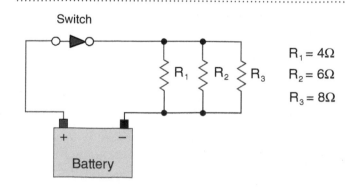

shortcut. Short circuits are generally undesirable and can quickly overheat electrical circuits. Electricity will generally choose to flow through the shortest possible path in order to complete a circuit.

Open Circuit

The term **open circuit** describes any electrical circuit through which there is no current flow. A switch is used in electrical circuits to intentionally open them. An electrical circuit may also be opened unintentionally, and this might occur when a fuse fails, a wire breaks, or connections corrode.

Ground

The term *ground* represents the point of a circuit with the lowest voltage potential. In vehicles, ground or chassis ground is integral in the electrical circuit, as it provides the return electrical path for all components in the circuit. Technicians used to working on vehicles always use the term *ground* to mean chassis ground. To power a lightbulb in a vehicle, a single wire can supply one terminal on the bulb with a feed from the positive terminal of the battery and the return path is completed by connecting the other bulb terminal directly to the chassis ground.

OHM'S LAW

Ohm's law tells us that an electrical pressure of 1 V is required to move 1 A of current through a resistance of 1 Ω.

- I = intensity = current in amperes
- E = EMF (electromotive force) = pressure in voltage
- R = resistance = resistance to current flow in ohms

$$E = I \times R \quad R = \frac{E}{I} \quad I = \frac{E}{R}$$

Ohm's law can also be expressed in the units of measurement used in the following formulas. See **Figure 32–16**. Better still, memorize it.

$$V = A \times \Omega \quad \Omega = \frac{V}{A} \quad A = \frac{V}{\Omega}$$

Ohm's Law Applied to Series Circuits

In a series circuit, all of the current flows through all of the resistances in that circuit, so the sum of the resistances in the circuit would

FIGURE 32–16 Ohm's law formula.

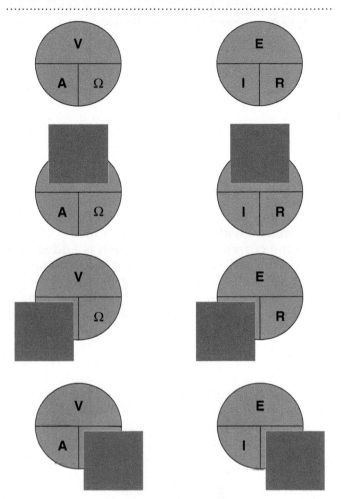

define the total circuit resistance. If a series circuit were to be constructed with 1-ohm and 2-ohm resistances (**Figure 32–17**), total circuit resistance (Rt) would be calculated as follows:

$$Rt = R_1 + R_2$$
$$Rt = 1\,\Omega + 2\,\Omega$$
$$Rt = 3\,\Omega$$

FIGURE 32–17 Series circuit calculation.

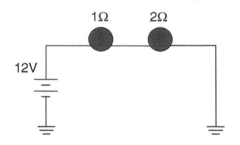

If the power source in the foregoing series circuit is a 12-V battery, then when the circuit is closed, current flow can be calculated using Ohm's law as follows:

$$I = \frac{E}{Rt}$$

$$I = \frac{12\,V}{3\,\Omega}$$

$$I = 4\text{ amps}$$

Ohm's Law Applied to Parallel Circuits

According to Kirchhoff's law of current (see the next section), current that is flowed through a parallel circuit divides into each path in the circuit. When the current flow in each path is added, the total current will equal the current flow leaving the power source. When calculating the current flow in parallel circuits, each current flow path must be treated as a series circuit or the total resistance of the circuit must be calculated before calculating total current. When performing calculation on a parallel circuit, it should be remembered that more current will always flow through the path with the least resistance. If a parallel circuit is constructed with 2 W and 6 W resistors in parallel fed by a 12-V power source (**Figure 32–18**), total current can be calculated by treating each current flow path separately, as follows:

$$h = \frac{12\,V}{2\,\Omega} = 6\text{ amps}$$

$$I_2 = \frac{12\,V}{6\,\Omega} = 2\text{ amps}$$

$$I_T = 8\text{ amps}$$

An alternative method would be to calculate *Rt* using the following formula:

$$Rt = \frac{R_1 \times R_2}{R_1 + R_2}$$

FIGURE 32–18 Parallel circuit calculation.

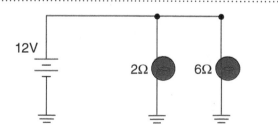

$$Rt = \frac{6\,\Omega \times 2\,\Omega}{6\,\Omega + 2\,\Omega} = \frac{12\,\Omega}{8} = 1.5\,\Omega$$

then

$$I = \frac{E}{R}$$

$$I = \frac{12\,V}{1.5\,\Omega} = 8\text{ amps}$$

RECIPROCAL FORMULA The inverse or reciprocal formula can be used to calculate resistance in a parallel circuit with more than two paths for current flow. Each resistance value is divided into 1 and expressed as follows:

$$\frac{1}{Rt} = \frac{1}{R_1} + \frac{1}{R_2} + \frac{1}{R_3} + \frac{1}{R_4}\ldots\text{etc}$$

Bear in mind when calculating resistance in parallel circuits that total circuit resistance always has to be less than the resistance in any individual path.

Most programs of study emphasize circuit calculations basically to get students of technology to "think" electrically. For that reason, you should remind yourself that the information in this section is presented more as a review guideline than a basic introduction. Many vehicle electrical circuits are of the series-parallel type, that is, they combine the characteristics of both the series circuit and the parallel circuit. When performing circuit analysis and calculation, it helps to visualize the circuit in terms of paths for current flow.

Kirchhoff's Law of Current (Kirchhoff's First Law)

Kirchhoff's law of current states that the current flowing into a junction or point in an electrical circuit must equal the current flowing out. High resistance anywhere in a closed circuit will choke down total current flow.

Kirchhoff's Law of Voltage Drops (Kirchhoff's Second Law)

Kirchhoff's law of **voltage drops** states that voltage will drop in exact proportion to the resistance and that the sum of the voltage drops must equal the voltage applied to the circuit. Technicians troubleshooting electrical circuits frequently measure or calculate voltage drop. If a series circuit is constructed with a 12-V power source and 2 Ω and 6 Ω resistors, the voltage drop across each resistor when the circuit is closed and subject to a current flow of 1.5 A can be calculated as:

Voltage drop for $R_1 \Omega$:

$$E_1 = I \times R_1$$

$$E_1 = 1.5\,\text{A} \times 2\,\Omega$$

$$E_1 = 3\,\text{V}$$

Voltage drop for R_2:

$$E_2 = I\,\Omega\,R$$

$$E_2 = 1.5\,\text{A} \times 6\,\Omega$$

$$E_2 = 9\,\text{V}$$

Total voltage drop through the circuit should equal that of the sum of the two calculations:

$$E_1 + E_2 = \text{source voltage}$$

$$3\,\text{V} + 9\,\text{V} = 12\,\text{V}$$

TECH TIP:

The importance of voltage drop testing cannot be over-emphasized in troubleshooting vehicle electrical systems. Voltage drop verifies active or energized electrical circuits. More detail on voltage drop testing is provided in Chapter 36.

POWER

Just as in the internal combustion engine, the unit for measuring electrical power is the **watt** (named for James Watt, 1736–1819), usually represented by the letter P. In engine technology, *power* is defined as the rate of accomplishing work and, therefore, it is always factored by time. Remember, the definition of an ampere is 6.28×10^{18} electrons (1 coulomb) passing a point in a circuit per *second*. So the formula for calculating electrical power is:

$$P = I \times E \text{ (spells "pie")}$$

Using the data from the previous formula, in which the circuit voltage was 12 V and the current flow was 1.5 A:

$$P = 1.5 \times 12 = 18\,\text{W} = \text{power consumed}$$

One HP = 746 watts, so calculated values can be compared to standard values used to rate power-producing or power-absorbing components.

CAPACITANCE

The term **capacitance** is used to describe the electron storage capability of a commonly used electrical component known as a **capacitor**.

Capacitors, which are also called **condensers**, all do the same thing—they store electrons. The simplest type of capacitor would consist of two conductors separated by some insulating material called **dielectric**. The conductor plates could be aluminum and the dielectric may be mica (silicate mineral). The greater the dielectric properties of the material, the greater the resistance to voltage leakage. When a capacitor is connected to an electrical power source, it is capable of storing electrons from that power source. When the capacitor's charge-storage capability is reached, it ceases to accept electrons from the power source. The charge is retained in the capacitor until the plates are connected to a lower voltage electrical circuit. At this point, the stored electrons are discharged from the capacitor into the lower potential (voltage) electrical circuit. **Figure 32–19** shows the operating principle of a capacitor.

FIGURE 32–19 Operating principle of a capacitor.

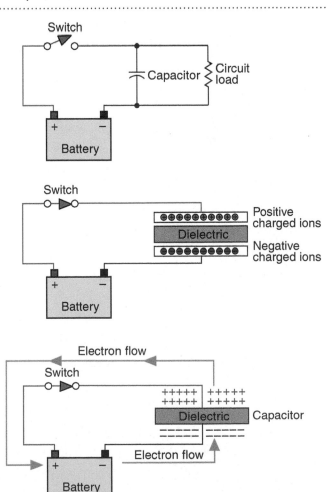

As a capacitor is electrified, for every electron removed from one plate, one is loaded onto the other plate. The number of electrons in a capacitor is identical when it is in both the electrified and neutral states. What changes is the location of the electrons. The electrons in a fully charged capacitor (**Figure 32–20**) will in time "leak" through the dielectric until both conductor plates have an equal charge: At this point, the capacitor would be described as being in a discharged condition. The ability to store electrons is known as *capacitance*, and this is measured in **farads** (named after Michael Faraday [1791–1867], the discoverer of the principle). One farad is the ability to store 6.28×10^{18} electrons at a 1-volt charge differential. Most capacitors have much less capacitance, so they are rated in picofarads (trillionths of a farad) and microfarads (millionths of a farad).

1 farad = 1 F
1 microfarad = 1 μF = 0.000001F
1 picofarad = 1 ρF = 0.000000000001F

FIGURE 32–20 Current flow with a fully charged capacitor.

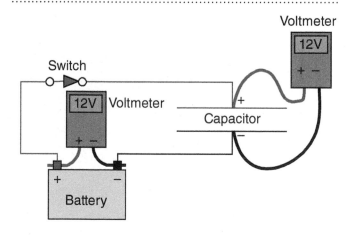

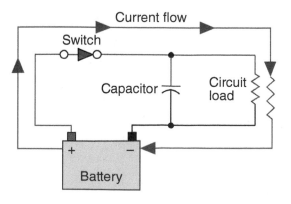

TYPES OF CAPACITORS

Many capacitors used in electric and electronic circuits are fixed value capacitors: These are coded by capacitance and voltage rating. Some capacitors have a variable capacity. These may have a combination of fixed and moving conductor plates, and the capacitance is varied by a shaft that rotates the moving plates. In some variable capacitance-type capacitors, the dielectric may be air. Electrolytic-type capacitors tend to have much higher capacitance ratings than nonelectrolytic types, and they are polarized, so they must be connected accordingly in a circuit. The dielectric in this type of capacitor is the oxide formed on the aluminum conductor plate. Ultracapacitors (UCs) and cassette technology have enabled capacitors to complement the battery banks in HEVs; these are addressed in some detail in Chapter 39.

When working on electrical circuits, it should be noted that capacitors can retain a charge for a considerable time after the circuit current flow has ceased. Accidental discharge can damage circuit components and cause personal injury through electrical shock.

Capacitors are used extensively in electronic circuits performing the following roles:

- AC-DC filter: Steadies a DC voltage wave offset sometimes caused by exposure to sunlight.
- Power supply filter: Smoothes a pulsating voltage supply into a steady DC voltage form.
- Spike suppressant: When digital circuiting is switched at high speed, transient (very brief) voltage reductions can occur. Capacitors can eliminate these spikes or glitches by compensating for them.
- Resistor-capacitor circuits (R-C circuits): Circuits that incorporate a resistor and a capacitor are used to reshape a voltage wave or pulse pattern from square wave to sawtooth shaping or to modify a wave to an alternating pattern.
- **Ultracapacitors**: These are double layers that function like two capacitors in series. They are in development as storage-assist devices in HEV applications.

> ## CAUTION:
> Because capacitors store a charge differential, they can discharge when given the opportunity, even when a circuit is supposedly open because a battery is disconnected. This can be dangerous in circuits such as air bag deployment circuits that are designed to be actuated by capacitors in event of the vehicle batteries being destroyed in a collision.

COILS AND TRANSFORMERS

When electrons are moved through a conductor, an electromagnetic field is created surrounding the conductor. When the conductor is a wire wound into a coil, the electromagnetic field created is stronger. Coils are the basis of electric solenoids and motors. They are used in electronic circuits to shape voltage waves because they tend to resist rapid fluctuations in current flow. Like capacitors, coils can be used in electrical circuits to reshape voltage waves. Also, the energy in the electromagnetic field surrounding a coil can be induced to any nearby conductor. If the nearby conductor happens to be a second coil, then a current flow can be induced in it. The principle of a transformer is essentially that of passing current through a primary coil and inducing current flow in a secondary or output coil, as shown in **Figure 32–21**. Variations on this principle would be coils constructed with a movable core, which permits their inductance to be varied, thereby altering output.

Transformers of various different types are used in vehicle electrical circuits, but they all fall into three general categories:

1. *Isolation transformers.* In an isolation transformer, the primary and secondary coils have the same number of windings, producing a 1:1 input to output ratio. Their objective is to "isolate" one portion of an electrical circuit from another: Secondary voltage and current equal the primary.
2. *Step-up transformer.* The objective of a step-up transformer is to multiply the primary coil voltage by the winding ratio of the primary coil versus that of the secondary coil. For instance, if the primary to secondary coil winding ratio is 1:10, 12 V through the primary coil will induce 120 V through the secondary with a similarly proportional drop in current flow. Examples of step-up transformers are automotive ignition coils and the injector driver units used on some diesel EUI systems.
3. *Step-down transformer.* Step-down transformers function oppositely from step-up transformers. The primary coil winding ratio exceeds that of the secondary coil, resulting in a diminished output voltage and increased output current.

SEMICONDUCTORS

Semiconductors are a group of materials with exactly four electrons in their outer shell. As such, they cannot be classified either as insulators or conductors. Silicon and germanium are semiconductor materials commonly used in the manufacture of electronics components. Both silicon and germanium have four electrons in their outer shells but would "prefer" to have eight: This means that silicon and germanium atoms readily unite in clusters called *crystals*, sharing electrons in their outer shells. Silicon and germanium can be grown into large crystals by applying heat to melting point followed by a period of cooling. Pure semiconductors are of little use in electronics components. For semiconductors to be useful, they must be doped, that is, have small quantities of impurities added to them. The doping agents are usually phosphorus and boron. The doping intensity defines the electrical behavior of the crystal. After doping, semiconductor crystals may be sliced into thin sections known as *wafers*.

The type of doping agent used to produce semiconductor crystals defines the electrical properties of the crystals produced. A boron atom has three electrons in its outer shell. The outer shell is known as the *valence* and an atom with three electrons in its outer shell is known as *trivalent*. A boron atom in a crystallized cluster of semiconductor atoms produces an outer shell with seven electrons instead of eight. This "vacant" electron opening is known as a *hole*. The hole makes it possible for an electron from a nearby atom to fall into the hole. In other words, the holes can move, permitting a flow of electrons. Semiconductor crystals doped with boron (or other elemental atoms with three electrons in the outer shell—trivalent) form a P-type semiconductor.

A phosphorus atom has five electrons in its outer shell. It is pentavalent. In the bonding between the semiconductors and the doping material, there is room for only eight electrons

FIGURE 32–21 Transformer operating principle.

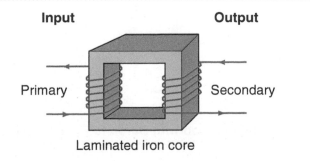

Input　　　　　　　**Output**

Primary　　　　　　Secondary

Laminated iron core

FIGURE 32–22 Structure of a germanium atom with four electrons in the outer shell, shown in a crystallized cluster with shared electrons.

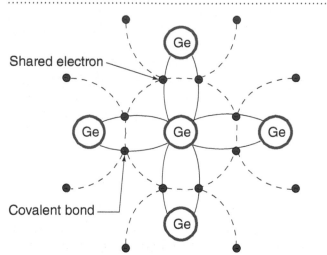

Germanium Semiconductor: 4 Electrons in the Outer Shell—Shown Crystallized with Shared Electrons

in the center shell. Even when the material is in an electrically neutral state, the extra electron can move through the crystal. When a semiconductor crystal is manufactured using a doping material with five electrons in the outer shell (pentavalent), it forms an N-type semiconductor. **Figure 32–22** shows a germanium atom in a crystallized cluster with shared electrons.

The doping of a semiconductor crystal will always define its electrical characteristics. In **Figure 32–23**, germanium is used once again to show how the element forms a P-type semiconductor when doped with arsenic and an N-type semiconductor when doped with boron. Semiconductor materials are classified as P type or N type. In different ways, P-type and N-type semiconductor crystals may permit an electrical current flow. In the P-type semiconductor, current flow is occasioned by a deficit of electrons, while in the N-type semiconductor, current flow takes place by an excess of electrons. Whenever a voltage is applied to a semiconductor, electrons flow toward the positive terminal and the "holes" move toward the negative terminal.

DIODES

The suffix "-ode" literally means "terminal." For instance, it is used as the suffix for cathode and anode. The word *diode* means, literally, having two terminals. In the previous section it was explained how both P-type and N-type semiconductor crystals can conduct electricity. The actual resistance of each type is determined by either the proportion of holes or surplus of electrons. When a chip is manufactured using both P-type and N-type semiconductors, electrons will flow in only one direction. The diode is used in electronic circuitry as a sort of one-way

FIGURE 32–23 Doped germanium semiconductor crystals of the N and P types.

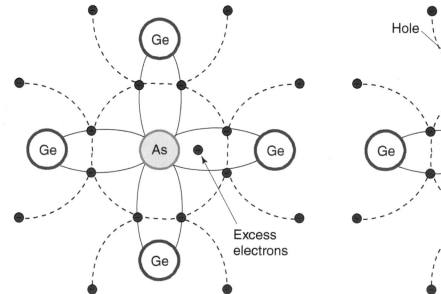

Germanium Doped with Arsenic to Form an N-Type Semiconductor

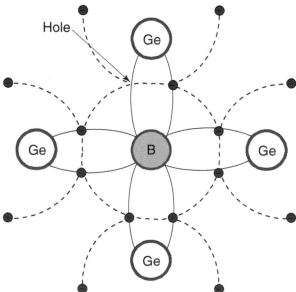

Germanium Doped with Boron to Form a P-Type Semiconductor

check valve that will conduct electricity in one direction (forward bias) and block it in the other (reverse bias). **Figure 32–24** shows how a diode operates in forward and reverse bias modes.

The positive terminal (+) is called the anode and the negative terminal (−) the cathode. As an electrical one-way check valve, diodes will permit current flow only when correctly polarized. Diodes are used in AC generators (alternators) to produce a DC characteristic from AC. They are also used extensively in electronic circuits.

Diodes may be destroyed when subjected to voltage or current values that exceed their rated capacity. Excessive reverse current may cause a diode to conduct in the wrong direction, and excessive heat can melt the semiconductor material. Diode voltage and current specifications are written as follows:

V_F = forward voltage I_F = forward current

V_R = reverse voltage I_R = reverse current

FIGURE 32–24 Diode operation and diodes in forward and reverse bias.

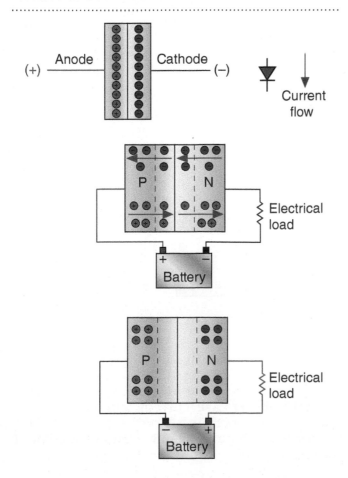

Numerous types of diodes play a variety of roles in electronic circuits. The following list gives examples of some of the more common types:

- Small signal. Small signal diodes are used to transform low current AC to DC (rectification), perform logic data flows, and absorb voltage spikes.
- Power rectifier. Power rectifier diodes function in the same manner as small signal diodes but are designed to permit much greater current flow. They are used in multiples and often mounted on a heat sink to dissipate excess heat caused by high current flow.
- Zener. A **zener diode** functions as a voltage-sensitive switch. Named after its inventor (Clarence Zener, who invented it in 1934), the zener diode is designed to block reverse bias current, but only up to a specific voltage value. When this reverse breakdown voltage is attained, it conducts the reverse bias current flow without damage to the semiconductor material. Zener diodes are manufactured from heavily doped semiconductor crystals. They are used in electronic voltage regulators and in other automotive electronic circuitry. Zener diodes are rated by breakdown voltage (VZ), which can range from 2 V to 200 V. A schematic of a zener diode is shown in **Figure 32–25**.
- Light-emitting diode. All diodes emit electromagnetic radiation when forward biased, but diodes manufactured from some semiconductors (notably gallium arsenide phosphide) emit it at much higher levels. **Light-emitting diodes (LEDs)** may be constructed to produce a variety of colors and are commonly used for digital data displays. For instance, a digital display with seven linear LED bars arranged in a bridged rectangle could display any single numeric digit

FIGURE 32–25 Zener diode.

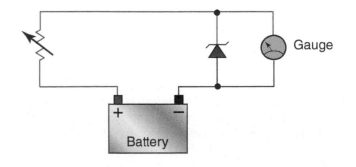

FIGURE 32–26 Light-emitting diode (LED).

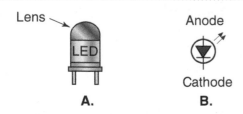

A.   B.

by energizing or not energizing each of the seven LEDs. LED arrangements constructed to display alpha characters are only slightly more complex. LEDs convert electrical current directly into light (photons) and therefore are highly efficient, as there are no heat losses. **Figure 32–26A** shows an LED and **Figure 32–26B** shows how one is represented on a schematic.

- Photo diode. All diodes produce some electrical response when subjected to light. A photo diode is designed to detect light and therefore has a clear window through which light can enter. Silicon is the usual semiconductor medium used in photo diodes. Diodes operate in either forward or reverse bias.
  - Forward bias: A positive voltage is applied to the P-type material and a negative voltage to the N-type material, permitting current flow.
  - Reverse bias: A positive voltage is applied to the N-type material and a negative voltage to the P-type material, meaning that current flow is blocked.

TRANSISTORS

Transistors are three-terminal semiconductor chips that are used extensively in electronic circuits. Transistors can be generally grouped into bipolar and field effect categories. Many of their functions are either directly or indirectly associated with circuit switching, and in this capacity they can be likened to relays in electrical circuits. **Figure 32–27** shows a transistor-operating principle.

BIPOLAR TRANSISTORS

A bipolar transistor functions as a sort of switched diode with three terminals known as collector, emitter, and base, each connected to semiconductor media in what is known as a silicon sandwich. The sandwich may either be NPN or PNP. The middle of the sandwich always acts as a *gate* capable of controlling the current flow

FIGURE 32–27 Transistor-operating principle

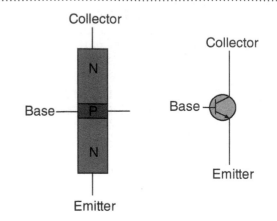

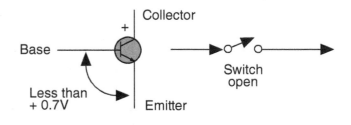

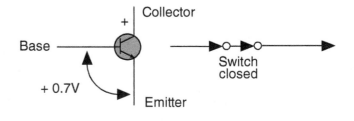

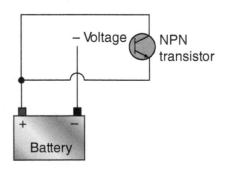

through all three layers. The base is fairly thin and it has comparatively fewer doping atoms than the semiconductor material on either side of it. Bipolar transistors are designed so that a small emitter-base current will "ungate" the transistor and permit a larger emitter-collector current flow. **Figure 32–28** shows the action of a PNP transistor.

FIGURE 32-28 Action of a PNP transistor.

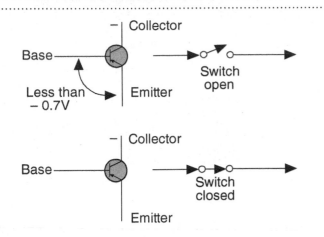

FIGURE 32-29 FET transistor: In order to conduct between source and drain, an FET requires a positive charge to the gate, which then creates a capacitive field to permit electron flow. It acts like a relay with no moving parts.

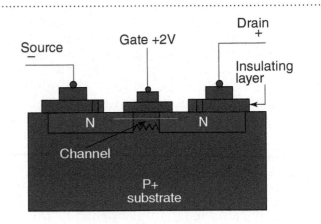

Facts about Bipolar Transistor Operation

- The base-emitter junctions will not conduct until the forward bias voltage exceeds ±0.6 V.
- Excessive current flow through a transistor will cause it to overheat or fail.
- Excessive voltage can destroy the semiconductor crystal media.

Small Signal Switching Transistors

Small signal transistors are used to amplify signals. They may be designed to fully gate current flow in their off position and others may both amplify and switch. These are used in many vehicle electronically controlled circuits and are often the ones you get to test and build into circuits in class projects.

Power Transistors

Used in power supply circuits, power transistors may conduct high current loads and may be mounted on heat sinks to enable them to dissipate heat. They are sometimes known as drivers because they serve as the final or output switch in an electronic circuit used to control a component such as a solenoid or pilot switch. The injector drivers used in many current diesel engine management systems use power transistors.

FIELD EFFECT TRANSISTORS

Field effect transistors or **FETs** are more commonly used than bipolar transistors largely because they are cheaper to manufacture. They may be divided into junction type and metal-oxide semiconductors. The FET has three terminals: source, drain, and gate. The source

supplies the electrons like the emitter in a bipolar transistor. The drain collects the current, so it can be compared to the collector in a bipolar transistor. The gate creates the electrostatic field that "switches" the FET and permits electron flow from the source to the drain, so it can be compared to the gate in a bipolar transistor.

Both junction-type and metal-oxide FETs are controlled by a very small input or gate voltage. They are used in many smart switch multiplexing circuits used today in trucks. An FET functions like a relay with no moving parts. It is connected into a circuit that uses the FET like a switch. **Figure 32-29** shows the operating principle of an FET.

Facts about FETs

- Gate-channel resistance is very high, so the device has almost no effect on external components connected to the gate.
- Almost no current flows in the gate circuit because the gate-channel resistance is so high. The gate and channel form a "diode," and as long as the input signal reverse biases this diode, the gate will show high resistance.

THYRISTOR

Thyristors are three-terminal, solid-state switches. A small current flow through one of the terminals will switch the thyristors on and permit a larger current flow between the other two terminals. Thyristors are switches, so they are in either an *on* or an *off* condition. They are classified by whether they switch AC or DC current.

Some thyristors are designed with two terminals only: They will conduct current when a specific trigger or breakdown voltage is achieved, functioning somewhat like a diode.

Silicon-Controlled Rectifiers

Silicon-controlled rectifiers (SCRs) are similar to a bipolar transistor with a fourth semiconductor layer added, as shown in the upper section of **Figure 32–30**. They are used to switch DC. When the anode of an SCR is made more positive than the cathode, the outer two PN junctions become forward biased: The middle PN junction is reverse biased and will block current flow. However, a small gate current will forward bias the middle PN junction, enabling a large current to flow through the thyristor. SCRs will remain *on* even when the gate current is removed: The *on* condition will remain until the anode-cathode circuit is opened or reversed biased. SCRs are used for switching circuits in vehicle electronic and ignition systems.

Darlington Pairs

A **Darlington pair** (named after the inventor) consists of a pair of transistors wired so that the emitter of one supplies the base signal to a second, through which a large current flows. The objective once again is to use a very small current to switch a much larger current. This type of application is known as **amplification**. Darlington pairs are used extensively in vehicle computer control systems. Figure 32–30 shows a Darlington pair relationship.

FIGURE 32–30 A forward direction SCR and Darlington pair relationship.

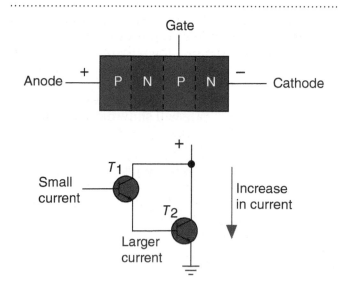

SUMMARY OF TRANSISTOR OPERATION

A transistor has three operating states:

- Cutoff: Reverse bias voltage is applied to the base terminal. In cutoff state, no current will flow through the semiconductor.
- Conduction: Bias voltage between the base and emitter has increased and switched the transistor to its *on* state. In its *on* state, the transistor is conducting, permitting electron flow. Output current is proportional to base current.
- Saturation: When collector-to-base voltage drops off to a near-zero value by voltage drop across the collector, the transistor enters saturation state.

TESTING SEMICONDUCTORS

Diodes and transistors are normally tested using a DMM. The semiconductor being tested should be isolated from the circuit. Diodes should produce a high-resistance reading with the DMM test leads in the reverse bias and low resistance when the leads are switched. Low-resistance readings both ways indicate a shorted diode. High resistance both ways indicates an open diode. Similarly, you can set the DMM to the diode test mode.

A functional transistor should test:

- Continuity between the emitter and base
- Continuity between the base and the collector when tested one way and high resistance when DMM test leads are reversed
- High resistance in either direction when tested across the emitter and collector terminals

Testing semiconductors is discussed in more detail in Chapter 35, which also supplies diagrams.

PHOTONIC DEVICES

Photonic semiconductors emit and detect light or photons. Photons are produced when certain electrons excited to a higher-than-normal energy level return to a more normal level. Photons behave like waves, and the distance between the wave nodes and antinodes (wave crests and valleys) is known as **wavelength**. Electrons excited to higher energy levels emit photons with shorter wavelengths than electrons excited to lower levels. Photons are not necessarily visible, and it is perhaps important

FIGURE 32–31 The optical spectrum.

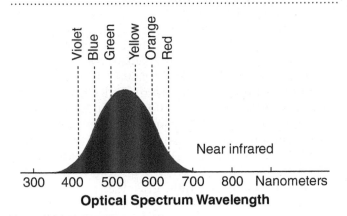

Optical Spectrum Wavelength

FIGURE 32–32 The electromagnetic spectrum.

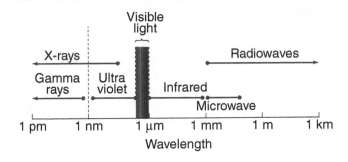

pm Picometer
nm Nanometer
μm Micrometer
mm Millimeter
m Meter
km Kilometer

to note that they may only truly be described as light when they are visible. Phototransistors are used in conjunction with an LED and slotted beam interrupter to accurately signal shaft/rotor speeds in vehicle electronics.

THE OPTICAL SPECTRUM

All visible light is classified as electromagnetic radiation. The specific wavelength of a light ray defines its characteristics. Light wavelengths are specified in nanometers, that is, billionths of a meter. The optical light spectrum includes ultraviolet, visible, and infrared radiation. Photonic semiconductors either emit or can detect near-infrared radiation, so near-infrared is usually referred to as light. As the computer age advances, technology is taking advantage of the ultrahigh frequencies of light waves and using them increasingly. **Figure 32–31** shows the optical spectrum.

OPTICAL COMPONENTS

Optical components may conduct, refract, or modify light. For instance, an audio or data compact disk (CD) retains data that has to be read optically, usually by a laser. Some of the more common optical components are:

- Filters. Filters transmit only a narrow band of the spectrum and block the remainder.
- Reflectors. In much the same way a mirror functions, reflectors bend back a light beam, or at least most of it.
- Beam splitters. Beam splitters transmit some of the optical wavelength and reflect back the rest of it.
- Lenses. Lenses bend light waves. They are often used in conjunction with semiconductor light sources and detectors. They are often used to collect and focus light onto a detector.

- Optical fibers. Increasingly used to transmit digital data by pulsing light, optical fibers are thin, flexible strands of glass or plastic that conduct light; the light travels through a core surrounded by conduit or cladding. The use of fiber optics is growing rapidly, and it is only a matter of time before they become extensively used in vehicle technology.
- Electromagnetic spectrum. The electromagnetic spectrum is shown in **Figure 32–32** so that you have an idea of the relative frequencies of the wavelengths. The higher the frequency, the higher the intensity of data that can be relayed (reason for shift to fiber optics), and we use frequency shift analysis in technologies such as the Doppler radar used in truck collision warning systems.
- Solar cells. A solar cell consists of a PN or NP silicon semiconductor junction built onto contact plates. A single silicon solar cell may generate up to 0.5 V in ideal light condition (bright sunlight), but output values are usually lower. Like battery cells, solar cells are normally arranged in series groups, in which case the output voltage would be the sum of cell voltages; or in parallel, where the output current would be the sum of the cell currents. They are used as battery chargers on vehicles.

USING ELECTRONIC SIGNALS

Simple electronic circuits can be designed to transmit relatively complex data by switching subcircuit components on or off, making use of the binary voltage or no-voltage features that are the essence of computer transactions. The idea is that a series of input signals works to produce a defined output signal. Signal processing includes filtering, amplification, and rectification performed by the devices presented earlier in this chapter. Digital circuits handle pulsed waveforms that can do things like add, subtract, and multiply and compare and perform logic processing. An example of a pulsed waveform is **pulse width modulation (PWM),** which is used frequently in truck digital electronics both for input signaling (Hall-effect TPS) and to drive electronic injector control cartridges or proportioning actuators used on computer-controlled engines. If you want to take a look at a graphical representation of a PWM signal, you get the best image using a PWM-actuated proportioning solenoid.

Gates are used to route signals. If a circuit consisting of a power source, lightbulb, and switch is constructed, the switch can be used to "pulse" the *on/off* time of the bulb. If you know Morse code, think of what can be expressed using the two Morse signals, a dot and a dash. This pulsing can be coded into many types of data, such as alpha or numeric values. *Pulses* are controlled immediate variations in current flow in a circuit: Ideally, the increase or decrease in current would be instantaneous. If this were to be so, the pulse could be represented graphically as in **Figure 32–33**.

However, true pulse shaping results in graduated rise when the circuit is switched to the *on* state and graduated fall when the circuit is switched to the *off* state. Waves are rhythmic fluctuations in circuit current or voltage: They are often represented graphically and are described by their graphic shapes. Some waveforms are shown in **Figure 32–34**. You can see

these waveform types in vehicle electronic circuits when you use scopes to display them.

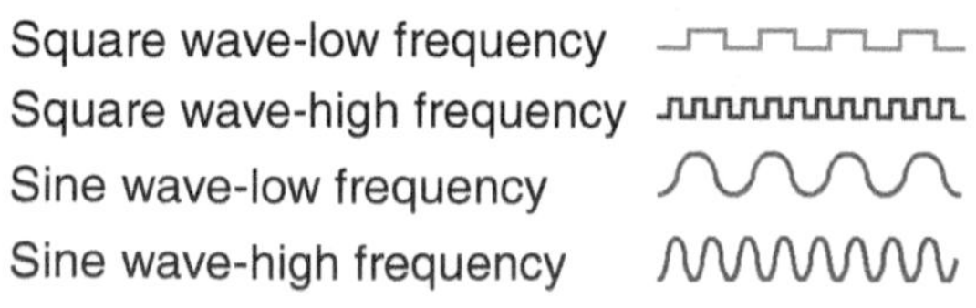

The term *signals* is used to describe pulses and waveforms that are shaped to transmit data. The mechanisms and processes used to shape data signals are called **modulation**. In vehicle electronics, the term *modulation* is more commonly used in reference to digital signaling.

Electronic noise is unwanted pulse or waveform interference that can scramble signals. All electrical and electronic components produce electromagnetic fields that may generate noise. All electronic circuits are vulnerable to magnetic and electromagnetic field effects.

COMPUTER BASICS

Computers process information (data). They do this using simple but long-winded methods of saying yes and no (presence of voltage versus no voltage) thousands, and sometimes millions, of times per second to express simple messages, using the means described in the previous section. But even though they use this long-winded process, the transactions occur at incredible speeds, that is, at very high frequencies. In this chapter, we begin to look at how computers function, a subject that is continued in Chapters 34 and 37. We also look at some of the hardware and data packaging used in computer technology.

INTEGRATED CIRCUITS

Integrated circuits or **I/Cs** are the hardware, the building blocks of computers. They consist of resistors, diodes, and transistors arranged in a circuit on a *chip* of silicon. The number of electronic components that comprise the I/C varies from a handful to hundreds of thousands, depending on the function of the chip. I/Cs have innumerable household, industrial, and automotive applications and are the basis of digital watches, electronic pulse wipers, and all computer systems. **Figure 32–35** shows a typical I/C.

I/Cs fall into two general categories. Analog I/Cs operate on variable voltage values: Electronic voltage regulators are a good vehicle example of an analog I/C. Digital I/Cs operate on two voltage values only, usually presence of voltage and no voltage. Digital I/Cs are the basis of most computer hardware, including processing units, main memory, and data retention chips. I/C chips can be fused into a motherboard (main circuit) or socketed: The latter has the advantage

FIGURE 32–33 Square sine waves.

....

FIGURE 32–34 Waveforms.

....

| Square wave-low frequency |
| Square wave-high frequency |
| Sine wave-low frequency |
| Sine wave-high frequency |

FIGURE 32–35 Integrated circuit.

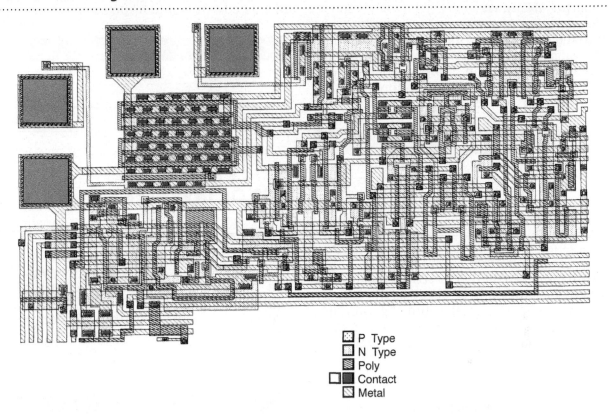

☒ P Type
☐ N Type
▨ Poly
◲ Contact
▨ Metal

of removal and replacement ability. A common chip package used in computer and vehicle engine control modules (ECMs) is the dual in-line package (DIP), a rectangular plastic-enclosed I/C with usually 14 to 16 pins arranged evenly on either side. DIPs may be fused (not removable) or socketed (removable) to the motherboard.

GATES AND TRUTH TABLES

In outlining the operation of transistors earlier in this chapter, the importance of **gates** was emphasized. *Gates* are the electronically controlled switching mechanisms that manage the operating mode of a transistor. Digital I/Cs are constructed by using thousands of gates. In most areas of electronics, gates can be either open or closed; in other words, in-between states do not exist. The terms used to describe the state of a gate are *on* or *off*. In a circuit, these states are identified as presence of voltage or no voltage. By saying yes or no through a number of channels, we can actually say quite a bit, as shown by what we can get a single byte of information to represent (shown a little later in this chapter).

The best way to learn to understand the operation of gates in a digital circuit is to observe the operation of some electromechanical switches in some simple electrical circuits such as the ones described next. Because these switches change state and therefore outcome on the simple basis of voltage *on*, voltage *off*, they adapt ideally to electronic digital circuits.

AND GATES

In **Figure 32–36**, a power source is used to supply a lightbulb in a series circuit. In the circuit, there are two push-button switches that are in the normally open state. In such a circuit, the lightbulb will only illuminate when

FIGURE 32–36 AND gate: Both switches are of the normally open type.

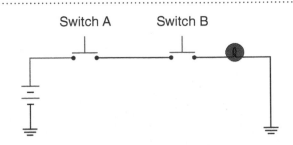

Switch A   Switch B

both switches are closed. This kind of switch is known as an **AND gate**.

The operation of the foregoing circuit can be summarized by looking at the circuit and coming to some logical conclusions: A table that assesses a gated circuit's operation is often called a **truth table**. A truth table applied to the foregoing circuit, an AND gate, would read as follows:

Switch A	Switch B	Outcome
Off	Off	Off
Off	On	Off
On	Off	Off
On	On	On

A truth table is usually constructed using the digits zero (0) and one (1) because the **binary system** (outlined in detail following this section on gates) is usually used to code data in digital electronics. A truth table that charts the outcomes of the same AND gate would appear as follows:

Switch A	Switch B	Outcome
0	0	0
0	1	0
1	0	0
1	1	1

OR GATES

If another circuit is constructed using two normally open electromechanical switches, but this time they are arranged in parallel, the result would be an **OR gate**. A schematic of an OR gate circuit is shown in **Figure 32–37**. A truth table

FIGURE 32–37 OR gate: Both switches are of the normally open type.

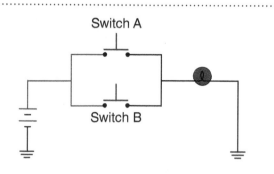

Switch A

Switch B

constructed to represent the possible outcomes of this circuit would appear as follows:

Switch A	Switch B	Outcome
0	0	0
1	0	1
0	1	1
1	1	1

NOT OR INVERTER GATES

A **NOT gated** circuit switch can be constructed by using a push-button switch that is in the normally closed state. This means that circuit current flow is interrupted when the button is pushed. In the series circuit shown in **Figure 32–38**, current will flow until the switch opens the circuit. A truth table constructed to graphically represent the outcomes of the NOT gated circuit shown in Figure 32–38 would look like the following:

In	Out
0	1
1	0

Although the examples presented here used electromechanical switches for ease of understanding, in digital electronics, circuit switching is performed electronically using diode and transistor gates. AND, OR, and NOT gates are three commonly used means of producing an outcome that depends on the switching status of components in the gate circuit. If you understood how transistors function (described earlier in this chapter), you should now begin to understand how they can function as the switches in gate circuits.

FIGURE 32–38 NOT gate: The single switch is of the normally closed type.

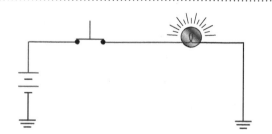

GATES, TRUTH TABLES, AND BASIC DATA PROCESSING

Figure 32–39 shows some simple two-input logic gates and the outcomes that can be produced from them. Logic gates are the basis of **data processing**.

Gates are normally used in complex networks in which they are connected by buses to form a logic circuit. Bits of data can be moved through the logic circuit or data highway to produce outcomes that evolve from inputs and retained memory. By massing hundreds of thousands of logic circuits, the processing of information becomes possible. A computer works simply by processing input data and generating logical outcomes based on the input data.

BINARY SYSTEM BASICS

The binary system is an arithmetic numeric system using two digits: It therefore has a base number of 2. The base number of a numeric system is the number of digits used in it. The decimal system is therefore a 10 base number system. The binary numeric system is often used in computer electronics, as it directly correlates to the *on* or *off* states of switches and circuits. In computer electronics, the binary system is the primary means of coding data, using the digits 0 and 1 to represent alpha, numeric, and any other data. Numeric data is normally represented using the decimal system: Again, this is simple coding. When we see the digit 3, it is a representation of a quantitative value that most of us have been accustomed to decoding since early childhood. If decimal system values were coded into binary values, they could look like this:

Decimal digit	Binary digit
0	0
1	1
2	10
3	11
4	100
5	101
6	110
7	111
8	1000
9	1001
10	1010

In digital electronics, a **bit** is the smallest piece of data that a computer can manipulate: It is simply the ability to represent one of two values: either *on* (1) or *off* (0). When groups of bits are arranged in patterns, they are collectively described as follows:

4 bits = nibble

8 bits = **byte**

Most data is referred to quantitatively as bytes. Computer systems are capable of processing and retaining vast quantities of data, so in most cases, millions (megabytes) and billions (gigabytes) of bytes are quantified. A byte is 8 bits of data, so it has the ability to represent up to 256 data possibilities. If a byte were to be used to code numeric data, it could appear as follows:

Decimal digit	Binary-coded digit
0	0000 0000
1	0000 0001
2	0000 0010
3	0000 0011
4	0000 0100
5	0000 0101
6	0000 0110
7	0000 0111
8	0000 1000

and so on.

FIGURE 32–39 Logic gates and truth tables showing the switching outcomes.

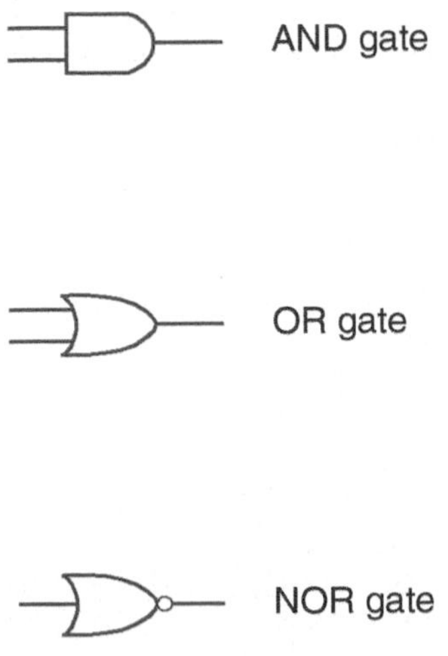

AND gate

A	B	Out
0	0	0
0	1	0
1	0	0
1	1	1

OR gate

A	B	Out
0	0	0
0	1	1
1	0	1
1	1	1

NOR gate

A	B	Out
0	0	1
0	1	0
1	0	0
1	1	0

FIGURE 32–40 Sequential switching of binary-coded numbers: serial link.

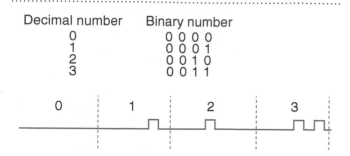

FIGURE 32–41 Parallel link: Transmission time is greatly reduced.

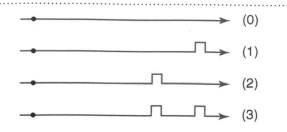

A number of methods are used to code data. If you are familiar with some computer basics, you may be acquainted with some American Standard Code for Information Interchange (ASCII) codes. This coding system has its own distinct method of coding values and would not be compatible with other coding systems without some kind of translation. Because on-off states can so easily be used to represent data, most digital computers and communications use this technology; it also is used in optical data processing, retention, and communications. Digital signals may be transmitted in series, one bit at a time, which tends to be slower; or in parallel, which is much faster. If the numbers 0 through 3 had to be transmitted through a serial link, they would be signaled sequentially, as shown in **Figure 32–40**. If the same numbers were to be transmitted through a parallel link, they would be outputted simultaneously, as shown in **Figure 32–41**.

CONCLUSION

If you have read through this chapter, you will see that electricity has some complex aspects. However, it may comfort you to know that there are only three types of faults that can occur in an electrical circuit:

- Opens
- Shorts
- High resistance

When you understand the operating principles of the electrical circuits you are working on, it makes finding and then classifying electrical circuit faults that much easier. Most of the remainder of this textbook requires some understanding of the electrical and electronic basics introduced in this chapter. Chapter 36 reiterates some of the theory you have learned in this chapter and gets you to use it by working on actual truck electronic circuits. Remember, you are not going to become an electrical or electronics specialist overnight; it is a process that takes some time. But if you really want to understand what makes the wheels roll on any recent-model truck, you have no choice but to become comfortable working with electricity and electronics.

TECH TIP:

When confronted with the most frustrating type of electrical problems, remember that the cause of the problem will be classified into one of just three categories: open, short, or high resistance.

SUMMARY

- All matter is composed of atoms.
- Electrical charge is a component of all atoms. When an atom is balanced, it can be described as being in an electrically neutral state.
- All matter is electrical. What we call *electricity* concerns the behavior of atoms that have become, for whatever reason, unbalanced or electrified.
- Electricity may be defined as the movement of free electrons from one atom to another.
- Current flow is measured by the number of free electrons passing a given point in an electrical circuit per second.
- Electrical pressure or charge differential is measured in *volts*, resistance in *ohms*, and current in *amperes*.

- If a hydraulic circuit analogy were used to describe an electrical circuit, *voltage* is equivalent to fluid pressure, *current* to the flow in gpm, and *resistance* to flow restriction.
- The magnetic properties of some metals, such as iron, are due to electron motion within the atomic structure.
- There is a direct relationship between electricity and magnetism.
- Magnetomotive force (mmf) is a measure of electromagnetic field strength. Its unit is ampere-turns.
- Ohm's law is used to perform circuit calculations on series, parallel, and series-parallel circuits.
- In a series circuit, there is a single path for current flow, and all of the current flows through each resistor in the circuit. As more resistors are added, current flow decreases.
- A parallel circuit has multiple paths for current flow. As more paths are added, total current flow in the circuit increases. The current flow in each branch of a circuit depends on the resistance of that particular branch.
- Kirchhoff's law of voltage drops states that the sum of voltage drops through resistors in a circuit must equal the source voltage.
- When current is flowed through a conductor, a magnetic field is created.
- Reluctance is resistance to the movement of magnetic lines of force. Iron cores have permeability and are used to reduce reluctance in electromagnetic fields. Air has high reluctance.
- Capacitors are used to store electrons. They consist of conductor plates separated by a dielectric.
- Capacitance is measured in farads. Capacitors are rated by voltage and by capacitance.
- When current is flowed through a wire conductor, an electromagnetic field is created. When the wire is wound into a coil, the electromagnetic field strength is intensified.
- The principle of a transformer can be summarized by describing it as flowing current through a primary coil and inducing current flow in a secondary or output coil.
- Transformers can be grouped into three categories: isolation, step-up, and step-down.
- Data can be transmitted electronically by means of electrical waveforms.
- Semiconductor elements have four electrons in their outer shells.
- Silicon is the most commonly used semiconductor material. Germanium is another.
- Semiconductors must be doped to provide them with the electrical properties that can make them useful as electronic components.
- After doping, semiconductor crystals may be classified as having N or P electrical properties.
- Diodes are two-terminal semiconductors that often function as a sort of electrical one-way check valve.
- Zener diodes are commonly used in vehicle electronic systems: They act as voltage-sensitive switches in a circuit.
- Transistors are three-terminal semiconductor chips.
- Transistors can be generally grouped into bipolar and field effect types.
- Essentially, a transistor is a semiconductor sandwich with the middle layer acting as a control gate: A small current flow through the base emitter will ungate the transistor and permit a much larger emitter-collector current flow.
- Many different types of transistors are used in vehicle electronic circuits, but their roles are primarily concerned with switching and amplification.
- The optical spectrum includes ultraviolet, visible, and infrared radiation.
- Optical components conduct, reflect, refract, or modify light. Fiber optics are increasingly being used in vehicle electronics, as are optical components, because of the higher frequency of light.
- Integrated circuits consist of resistors, diodes, and transistors arranged in a circuit on a chip of silicon.
- A common integrated circuit chip package used in computer and vehicle electronic systems is a DIP with either 14 or 16 terminals.
- Many different chips with different functions, including a central processing unit (CPU), are often arranged on a primary circuit board, also known as a motherboard.
- Gates are the foundation of digital integrated circuits.
- Gates are switched controls that channel flows of data through electronic circuitry.
- AND, OR, and NOT gates are examples of gates used in electronics. They produce outcomes based on the switching status of the input circuit.
- The binary numeric system is a two-digit arithmetic system often used in computer electronics because it directly correlates to the *on* or *off* states of switches and circuits.
- A bit is the smallest piece of data that a computer can manipulate. It has the ability to show one of two states, either ON or OFF.

- A byte consists of eight bits.
- A byte of data can represent up to 256 pieces of coded data simply by changing the two states of each of the eight bits of which it is composed.

- Never forget that there are only three types of electrical circuit faults: opens, shorts, and high resistance.

REVIEW QUESTIONS

1. A material described as an insulator would have how many electrons in its outer shell?
   a. Less than 4
   b. 4
   c. More than 4

2. Which of the following is a measure of electrical pressure?
   a. Amperes
   b. Ohms
   c. Voltage
   d. Watts

3. Which of the following units of measurement quantitatively expresses electron flow in a circuit factored with time?
   a. Coulombs
   b. Watts
   c. Farads

4. How many electrons does the element silicon have in its outer shell?
   a. 2
   b. 4
   c. 6
   d. 8

5. Who originated the branch of electricity generally described as electromagnetism?
   a. Franklin
   b. Gilbert
   c. Thomson
   d. Faraday

6. Which of the following elements could be described as being electrically inert?
   a. Oxygen
   b. Neon
   c. Carbon
   d. Iron

7. Which of the following is a measure of charge differential?
   a. Voltage
   b. Wattage
   c. Amperage
   d. Ohm

8. An element classified as a semiconductor would have how many electrons in its outer shell?
   a. Less than 4
   b. 4
   c. More than 4
   d. 8

9. Which of the following describes resistance to movement of magnetic lines of force?
   a. Reluctance
   b. Inductance
   c. Counterelectromotive force
   d. Capacitance

10. Use Ohm's law to calculate the current flow in a series circuit with a 12-V power source and a total circuit resistance of 6 ohms.

11. Calculate the power consumed in a circuit through which 3 amperes are flowed at a potential difference of 24 V.

12. A farad is a measure of:
    a. inductance.
    b. reluctance.
    c. charge differential.
    d. capacitance.

13. The term *pulse width modulation* refers to:
    a. waveforms shaped to transmit data.
    b. unwanted voltage spikes.
    c. electronic noise.

14. To form a P-type semiconductor crystal, the doping agent would be required to have how many electrons in its outer shell?
    a. 3
    b. 4
    c. 5
    d. 8

15. To form an N-type semiconductor crystal, the doping agent would be required to have how many electrons in its outer shell?
    a. 3
    b. 4
    c. 5
    d. 8

16. The positive terminal of a diode is correctly called a(n):
    a. electrode.
    b. cathode.
    c. anode.
    d. emitter.

17. Which of the following terms best describes the role of a typical transistor in an electronic circuit?
    a. Check valve
    b. Relay
    c. Rectifier
    d. Filter

18. When testing the operation of a typical transistor, which of the following should be true?
    a. High resistance across the emitter and base terminals
    b. Continuity across the emitter and collector terminals
    c. Continuity across the base and emitter terminals

19. What would be the outcome in an OR gate if one of two switches in the circuit was closed?
    a. Off
    b. On

20. How many different data codes could be represented by a byte?
    a. 2
    b. 8
    c. 64
    d. 256

21. A potentiometer is a:
    a. two-terminal, mechanically variable resistor.
    b. three-terminal, mechanically variable resistor.
    c. two-terminal, thermally variable resistor.
    d. three-terminal, thermally variable resistor.

22. Which of the following devices can be used to block AC and pass DC?
    a. Rheostat
    b. Inductor
    c. Capacitor
    d. Thermistor

23. Which of the following components is typically used in a half-wave rectifier?
    a. Rheostat
    b. Transformer
    c. Diode
    d. Zener diode

24. An N-type semiconductor crystal is doped with:
    a. trivalent atoms.
    b. pentavalent atoms.
    c. carbon atoms.
    d. germanium atoms.

25. A pulse width modulated (PWM) signal is:
    a. analog.
    b. digital.
    c. either analog or digital.
    d. neither analog or digital.

26. Which one of the following can store energy in the form of an electric charge?
    a. Thermocouple
    b. Induction coil
    c. Potentiometer
    d. Capacitor

27. Which of the following can store energy in the form of an electromagnetic charge?
    a. Thermocouple
    b. Induction coil
    c. Potentiometer
    d. Capacitor

28. In which of the following devices is polarity always important?
    a. Coil
    b. Capacitor
    c. Resistor
    d. Diode

29. Which of the following is a three-terminal device?
    a. Zener diode
    b. Transistor
    c. Capacitor
    d. Diode

30. Which of the following is a two-terminal device?
    a. Potentiometer
    b. Thermocouple pyrometer
    c. NPN transistor
    d. PNP transistor

building, it usually involves using telecommunications hardware and software.

A *modem* is a device used for converting the digital output of the computer to the analog signals required for transmission by the phone system. The speed at which a modem or network card can transmit data is specified by its **baud rate**. Baud rate indicates the number of times per second 1 bit can be transmitted. The baud rate specification is critical when considering the purchase of any equipment that must be networked. Truck engine original equipment manufacturers (OEMs) always specify a minimum baud rate for networking computers with their mainframe systems, and today usually recommend high-speed (large bandwidth) connections.

A **star network** is one that is constructed around a central computer with multiple terminals or **nodes**. *Node* is a term used to describe each user station. The central computer may be a mainframe, but it does not have to be. Often a star network will use **dumb nodes**, that is, stations that consist of a screen and keyboard but no processing or data storage capability independent of the central computer.

THE INTERNET

The Internet is a network of networks. It is very appropriately referred to as the World Wide Web or WWW. It now connects most of the countries in the world and is said to be used by nearly 5 billion people worldwide, a number that grows daily. Internet penetration in the United States is 86%. Most developed countries now have Internet penetration rates of close to 90%, but it should be noted that in Asia, there are three Internet users for every one in the United States, due to the enormous population of Asia. The following list outlines some of the ways we use the Internet system:

1. Sending e-mail (electronic mail). This is a highly efficient means of getting messages to users served by the Internet. It has the advantage of nearly immediate transfer and is made easier without the protocols (and delay) of hard-copy mail. Users are required to have an e-mail address and minimal computer skills: Some keyboarding ability is desirable.
2. File transfer. Files may be transferred from the Internet to a user PC system using a graphical user interface (GUI) and dragging the file title from the Internet menu to the user menu. Most files are exchanged with minimal security, but in cases where higher levels of security are required, this can be provided using the appropriate software.
3. Newsgroups and social networking. Internet users may belong to social networks, which are discussion groups linked by Facebook, Twitter, LinkedIn, and other accounts made up of Internet users with common interests. Messages on a newsgroup are titled and may consist of a single phrase or be pages long if the software will permit. An example of a subscription newsgroup is the International Automotive Technicians' Network (iatn.net). Message titles may be browsed and only those of interest downloaded for reading. People with some time on their hands can blog the world with their opinions.
4. Searching databases. Most government agencies and educational institutions make archives of information available on the Internet. Good search software makes accessing and sorting information easy, especially detailed, subject-specific data, which is certainly much easier than attempting to locate it by phoning bureaucrats or searching a public library with its limited "hard" resources. A variety of **search engines** are used on the Internet. Search engines will hunt down data on the Web using a key word or phrase; the best example is Google.
5. Gaming. Many different games may be played either online with other Internet users or downloaded to a PC and retained.
6. Researching a company. Few companies worldwide could conduct business today without having some kind of Web profile. The type of information you can access varies with the company. Some companies conduct business solely on the Internet.
7. Shopping. Thousands of products and services are advertised on the Internet and may be purchased using a credit card number. Although most are probably reputable, "buyer beware" should be exercised at all times.
8. Finding a job. More and more companies list job vacancies on the Internet. There are search engines dedicated exclusively to job search on the Internet. An example is monster.com.
9. Receiving online news. Magazines, newspapers, and other news services all make information available on the Web, and depending on the service it may be up to date. Sports scores throughout the world

are an example of data that is almost constantly updated. The scores are usually accompanied by stories that can be read or downloaded for printing. Major newspapers would lose status immediately if they did not maintain a Web version. Most magazines today offer electronic subscriptions and some are available exclusively online.

10. Public relations (PR). Almost every company, government agency, and organization in North America and Western Europe realizes the importance of the Internet as a communications tool. Connect to the White House website, for instance, and you may select anything from a pictorial tour to messages from the president and vice president. A presence on the Internet is essential for any major company transacting business in North America.

LANS AND INTRANET SYSTEMS

Local area network (LAN) and *intranet* are terms that usually describe private communications networks run by a corporation, government agency, or institution to handle the specific communications needs of their operations. Access is usually restricted, with passwords required for system entry and fields within the system. The protocols used are Internet derived, and while general access from the Internet may be to some extent blocked, access to it is usually enabled. A LAN could be housed in a single room and consist of two or three nodes, or it may be spread over the country and incorporate thousands of nodes. A LAN may use wireless connectivity or, for security

reasons (and reliability), retain a hardwired setup as shown in **Figure 33–2**.

THE TELECOMMUNICATIONS SYSTEM

Telephone systems are responsible for both the hard (wiring/switching/decoding) and soft (microwave/radio waves, and so forth) linkages that enable networking. Of the telecommunications systems available in the world today, the telephone system is probably the most used. The telephone system is continually being expanded, largely to handle the immense growth in data communications traffic over the past decade. **Figure 33–3** should give you an idea of some of the ways we use a telephone system today.

HOW A LANDLINE PHONE WORKS

A landline telephone consists of a transmitter, a receiver, and a push-button mechanism. The telephone transmits voice or sound waves by having them act to vibrate a thin metal diaphragm backed by carbon granules through which current flows; when a sound wave acts to pulse the diaphragm inward, the carbon granules pack closely, permitting higher current flow. Therefore, the current flow depends on sound waves. This fluctuating current flows to a receiver. The receiver earpiece consists of an annular armature located between a permanent magnet and a coil; attached to the armature is a plastic diaphragm. When fluctuating current flows into the coil, it becomes an electromagnet. This attracts the armature, causing it to vibrate and create waves that duplicate speech.

FIGURE 33–2 A LAN consists of multiple PCs connected to one another for purposes of sharing hardware and information.

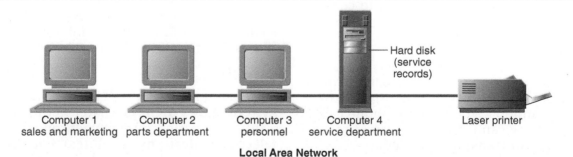

Computer 1
sales and marketing

Computer 2
parts department

Computer 3
personnel

Computer 4
service department

Hard disk
(service
records)

Laser printer

Local Area Network

FIGURE 33-3 The use of telephone lines, fiber optics, microwave transmission, and a communications satellite allows a PC to communicate with a large host computer, star network, or data hub.

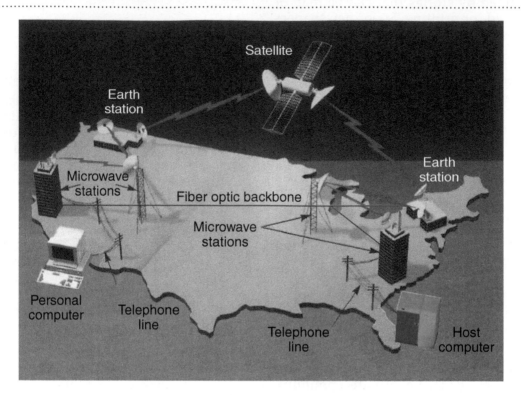

TARGETING A CALL

The telephone must also have a means of targeting calls. A touch-tone device is used and it sends a series of pulses to the switching network; when the number 5 is "dialed," current from the source set is interrupted five times. The dialing procedure creates a pattern of interruptions that is used to target the telephone signal to the correct location. With a touch-tone device, each numeric button produces a different *tone* or frequency, which is electronically decoded to target the telephone call.

Most current telephone switching is performed digitally. Incoming signals from a telephone set are first converted into digital signals, which are patterns of on/off pulses. These pulses are then processed by computer to search the shortest (and least overloaded) path to connect the target telephone.

TRANSMISSION MEDIA

Early telephone systems used exclusively hardwired transmission media to carry signals from one point to another. Today, a telephone call to a foreign country can involve the use of several different types of transmission media.

Copper Wire

Most local calls are carried over pairs of copper wires. Coaxial cable is also used; it can carry signals of higher frequency and allow more transmissions on a single line using multiple coaxial conductors.

Microwave

Microwave communications use the modulation of high-frequency radio signals. These radio signals are transmitted between antennae located on towers that are within sight of one another. Microwaves travel only in straight lines and do not refract from the ionosphere layer of the atmosphere.

Because they only travel short distances, multiple relays must be used. Microwaves have frequencies of many gigahertz, permitting large numbers of simultaneous transmissions on each frequency band. A typical microwave transaction is illustrated in **Figure 33–4**.

Satellites

Telecommunications satellites parked in **geosynchronous orbit** (see later in this section for a full explanation of geosynchronous orbit and telecommunications satellites) handle a large

FIGURE 33-4 Microwave transmission.

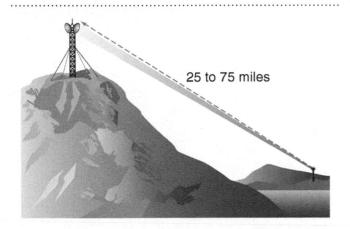

25 to 75 miles

but diminishing portion of transcontinental transmissions. The telecommunications satellite acts as a relay station for microwave signals, receiving a signal from a ground base and retransmitting it to another Earth-based station.

Cell Phones

Each geographic region is divided into "cells," each with its own transmitter-receiver. The cells are arranged so that the frequencies used in adjacent cell locations are different, although the same frequencies are reused many times over throughout the whole system. If a call is made from a cell phone in a car traveling over the boundary of one cell to another, the phone automatically switches frequencies, permitting a continuous phone conversation (**Figure 33-5**).

Wireless Data Connectivity

A majority of truck stops in the United States and Canada provide wireless connectivity as part of their service now that the industry has come to rely on the Internet. **Wireless fidelity**, almost always known as just **WiFi**, has become a key communications technology over the past few years. As far as the trucking industry is concerned, WiFi services adhering to TMC RP2402(T) standards should be used. WiFi client devices in trucks can be divided into:

- Driver devices. These include laptop computers, fixed cab PCs, and PDAs. Driver devices are used for both personal and fleet functions.
- Vehicle devices. These include a range of devices used to broadcast data bus data off-vehicle. For instance, truck chassis J1939 data backbone communications can be monitored at a central data hub. Many city transit buses use a separate data bus in addition to

J1939 (they interface) to drive such things as door, air conditioning (A/C), buzzers, lighting, video, and passenger security. By providing wireless connectivity, vehicle and passenger security can be increased, providing the signals are not breached. There are some concerns that the planned introduction of electronic onboard recorders (EOBRs) could put high-value truck loads at risk.

WiFi footprint is the geographical area over which client devices can network: This is usually known as a **hotspot**. When a client device enters a WiFi hotspot, more than one WiFi service may be provided. In cases of vehicle client devices, the selection of WiFi provider may be automatic, whereas with driver client devices, the user may have to select the provider. WiFi is more commonly used in trucking than Bluetooth because it functions on higher power, better security, and is capable of high volumes of data transfer. We will take a closer look at WiFi telematics and EOBRs at the end of this chapter. **Figure 33-6** illustrates how wireless connectivity can be made to work for the trucking industry, providing for personal communications, truck data bus communications, and trailer tracking.

BLUETOOTH **Bluetooth** is also a wireless network, but it is better suited to applications where lower volumes of data have to be transferred. It is used primarily for phones, headsets, and PDAs and suits situations in which two client devices are in close proximity. Bluetooth uses the same radio frequencies as WiFi, but is regarded as an "open" network: This makes it more accessible and less subject to permissions.

Fiber Optics

Fiber-optic technology is beginning to dominate the telecommunications industry because of the vast volume of transmissions it can handle. Optical fibers use light as the transmitting medium rather than radio waves. Because light has a frequency of around 100 THz (100 trillion hertz), it has the potential to handle (theoretically) almost infinite numbers of transmissions. Telephone signals are first digitized, then fed to semiconductor lasers, which produce pulses of light to a conduit of extremely thin glass fiber. At the receiving end of the optical fiber, photo detectors convert the optical signal to an electrical signal for local transmission. The fibers used to transmit the optical signals can be made almost transparent and the transmission volume can be increased simply by upgrading

FIGURE 33–5 Cellular phone operation.

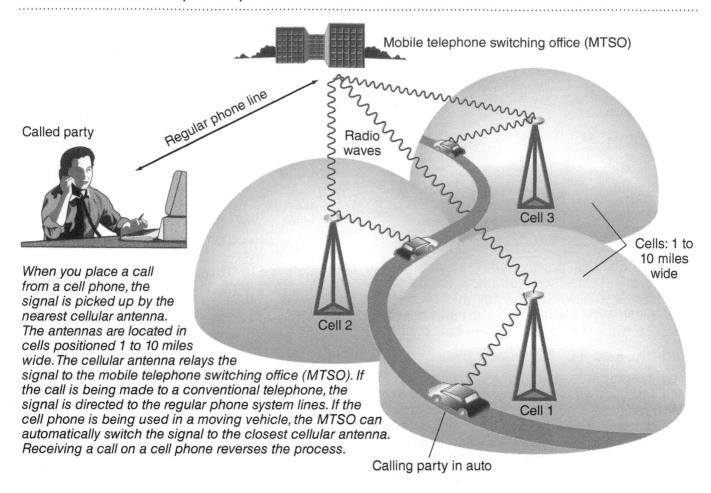

When you place a call from a cell phone, the signal is picked up by the nearest cellular antenna. The antennas are located in cells positioned 1 to 10 miles wide. The cellular antenna relays the signal to the mobile telephone switching office (MTSO). If the call is being made to a conventional telephone, the signal is directed to the regular phone system lines. If the cell phone is being used in a moving vehicle, the MTSO can automatically switch the signal to the closest cellular antenna. Receiving a call on a cell phone reverses the process.

FIGURE 33–6 How the trucking industry puts wireless connectivity to work, enabling such things as personal communications, truck data bus communications, and trailer tracking.

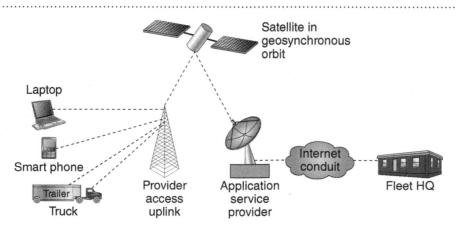

the transmission and receiving electronics and lasers. **Fiber optics** already handle a growing percentage of the world's transcontinental telecommunications; up-front expense is really the only thing hindering its rate of growth. In time, continental long-distance services and then local systems will adopt the technology. **Figure 33–7** compares the sectional size of a multistrand, copper wire cable with an equivalent (data volume) fiber-optic cable.

FIGURE 33–7 The fiber-optic cable (right) can transmit as much information as the 1,500-pair copper wire cable (left).

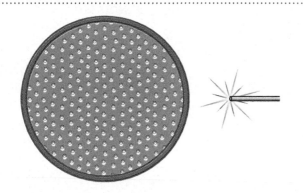

SECURITY ISSUES

Since the tragic events of September 11, 2001, truck operators are looking at vehicle location tracking and security in an entirely new light. Until that date, truck security usually meant theft avoidance. The realization that a truck could be used as a weapon of mass destruction (it has already been done offshore) or as a means of transporting illegal immigrants across borders (done frequently) has forced operators to think beyond load security. A variety of companies are competing for the business of addressing truck security, and most of these involve using communications systems coupled with fast response strategies.

Companies such as Qualcomm, Corp Ten, and Siemens are marketing systems designed to comprehensively enable driver and vehicle communications. These systems range from simple wireless panic buttons up to powerful broadband off-vehicle networking. This, in conjunction with sophisticated vehicle tracking technology, is being used by large fleets that can afford telecommunications networking. The major operators have been using asset protection systems of one kind or another for a generation now because they cannot afford not to have it. When a vehicle deviates from a preprogrammed dispatch route, most fleets like to know about the event immediately.

SATELLITE COMMUNICATIONS TECHNOLOGY

A *satellite* is by definition a small body that orbits a larger astronomical object; by this definition, the earth's moon is a natural satellite.

The first artificial satellite was launched into orbit in 1957 by the Soviet Union. It was called *Sputnik I*. Today, thousands of satellites orbit the earth; all but one are artificial, that is, manufactured on Earth. These satellites orbit the planet at altitudes of 100 miles (160 kilometers) or higher and are used for weather study, spying (military), navigation, and communications.

Geosynchronous Orbit

A communications satellite is often placed in geosynchronous orbit. The concept of geosynchronous orbit was conceived by a science fiction writer by the name of Arthur C. Clarke, whom you might have heard of because he wrote *2001: A Space Odyssey.* Anyway, to the irritation of many true scientists of the day, Clarke came up with the concept of geosynchronous orbit in 1945, and 15 years later, the telecom satellite was born. Clarke figured that the time that it takes for a satellite to orbit the earth once correlates exactly to its altitude. Accordingly, a satellite parked exactly 22,300 miles (35,900 km) above the earth's surface on the equator will be positioned at a fixed point above the earth's surface throughout the rotation. Such a satellite is said to be in *geostationary orbit.* If its altitude were to increase slightly, its orbit would cause it to fall behind the fixed point; if it descended below the geosynchronous altitude, the reverse would occur. **Figure 33–8** demonstrates the concept of the Clarke orbit.

FIGURE 33–8 The Clarke orbit: concept of geosynchronous orbit conceived by science fiction writer Arthur C. Clarke (*2001: A Space Odyssey*) in 1945.

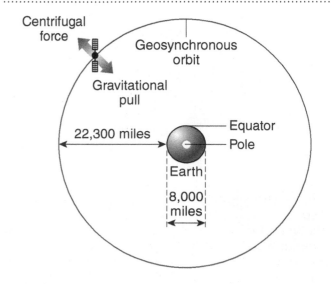

The first telecom satellite was launched by the United States in 1961; it was named *Telstar,* and it became the subject of a popular hit musical recording of the day. To maintain a geosynchronous orbit, satellites must have onboard rocket engines and a fuel supply, usually hydrazine, to adjust the orbit periodically. The power required to run the onboard electronics of a communications satellite is supplied by solar cells or nuclear-fueled thermoelectric generators. Onboard computers control the satellite's operation and orbit and manage the filtering, storing, and relaying of signals from and to ground stations.

Uplinks and Downlinks

To avoid signal interference, telecom satellites in geosynchronous orbit are parked 2 degrees apart from each other on the earth's equator. Therefore, there is limited parking space. The life of such a satellite is often governed by the fuel supply required to run the rockets that maintain the park position. The satellite receives ground signals from **uplinks** (ground-to-satellite communications hardware and software) on Earth that fall within its footprint. An *uplink* is any Earth-based station (including mobile units) capable of relaying signals to a telecom satellite. The satellite's footprint is the geographic area on Earth over which it can receive and send signals. **Figure 33–9** shows how uplinks and downlinks function in relation to a satellite in geostationary orbit.

FIGURE 33–9 Operating principle of a communications satellite in geosynchronous orbit.

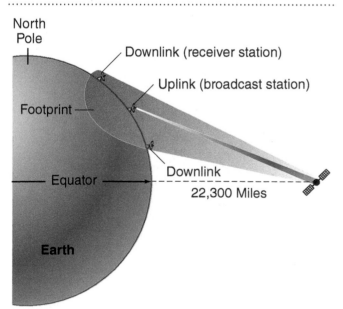

There are 32 telecom satellites parked with footprints directed on the American continents. Typically, a satellite receives a signal from an uplink, filters it, and rebroadcasts it to a **downlink**. A *downlink* is an Earth-based station equipped to receive signals from a telecom satellite. In such a way, a radio signal may be relayed through several satellites and ground stations. Until recently, television networks were the biggest users of telecom satellites. For instance, a baseball game that was televised in Seattle could be watched live in Montreal; the signal was relayed through a number of telecom satellites, uplinks, and downlinks. Today, many of the communications transactions that were formerly relayed using telecom satellites are undertaken by our fiber-optic networks, especially those created by big-money network TV. This fact has now made using telecom satellites much less costly for anyone else who might have a use for it. Telecommunications technology has been used by the trucking industry since the late 1980s, but its use has grown significantly since 2002. Satellite communications technology was first used mainly by major fleets, but now most OEMs offer a range of telecom options.

How Trucks Use Satellite Communications

Until fiber-optic networks took over, the television networks and cable network providers were the major consumers of telecommunications satellite air time, making air time most expensive during prime time television hours. Because a comprehensive fiber-optic network is now in place, television networks and telephone service providers rely less on satellite communications, meaning that the cost of air time for satellite communications has dropped. This has opened the door and made satellite communications technology affordable for the trucking industry as well as other potential users.

Satellite communications technology tracks a vehicle by placing an uplink, sometimes called a **transponder**, on the mirror brackets or cab roof of a truck. The uplink beams a signal to a telecom satellite, which may then relay it across the continent, if necessary, targeting a downlink at a data hub. Any data that can be transmitted digitally can be sent in this manner. **Figure 33–10** shows a dish-shaped Earth station designed for telecom transactions.

FIGURE 33-10 Earth stations use large dish-shaped antennae to communicate with satellites.

VEHICLE NAVIGATION

Vehicle navigation systems vary in complexity (and cost), but a comprehensive system consists of:

- Geographic positioning
- Target destination
- Route mapping, including real-time updates
- Route guidance, including real-time updates
- Map display

The detail that the navigation system offers in each of the foregoing categories depends on the stored data or telecommunications capability the system provider offers. Details such as real-time traffic reports and detour negotiation tend to be pretty expensive because of the cost of collating data, but maybe it is not so expensive when compared with the cost of a lost truck driver navigating Manhattan during rush hour. **Global positioning satellites (GPS)** are the key to vehicle navigation technology. In taking a look at GPS communications, remember that this is a one-way communications technology. To achieve two-way communications, GPS must be additionally supported by satellite communications or other wireless technologies such as WiFi or Bluetooth.

Trilateration

To understand how GPS functions, you have to understand a simple geometric principle called **trilateration**. Suppose you are completely lost somewhere in America. You pull into a truck stop to ask someone where you are, and the answer is

that he is not sure but he does know for sure that he is exactly 490 miles from Cleveland. At this point, you can get a map of the United States, find Cleveland, and draw a circle with a radius on a scale that equals 490 miles. You ask the next trucker, and you get the answer that he does not know exactly, but he has come directly from Houston and has traveled 710 miles. Now you can go back to the map and draw a circle with a radius representing 710 miles around Houston. At this point, you still cannot say exactly where you are until you approach a third trucker and ask him the same question. He informs you that he is exactly 520 miles from Jacksonville. Again, you draw a circle with a radius representing 520 miles around Jacksonville. Now if you look at your map (**Figure 33-11**), you will see that the three circles you have drawn all intersect at one point and you can determine your exact position.

GPS Location

If the world were flat, trilateration could be used to determine position. For the principle to work in three- dimensional space, you have to use spheres instead of circles, so in order to pinpoint exact position, four GPS satellites are required. If the GPS receiver can only locate three satellites, then its software creates a *virtual* sphere, which is a dummy sphere that allows it to use the coordinates established by the three satellites it has located. This means that your position can be calculated but not your altitude.

FIGURE 33-11 Position location by trilateration.

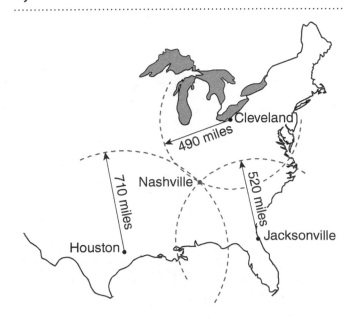

MEASURING DISTANCE   GPS satellites broadcast radio signals that a GPS receiver can detect. The receiver then calculates how long the signal has taken to travel from the satellite to the receiver. For a GPS system to function, 24 satellites are required so that there is a minimum of 4 on the horizon at any time or location during the day.

The signals received tend to be weak, so this technology works better driving through the countryside than it does in the middle of a large city. **Figure 33–12** shows how trilateration is put to use. Note that the term **triangulation** is used in place of trilateration; the two words are synonymous.

FIGURE 33–12 How GPS works.

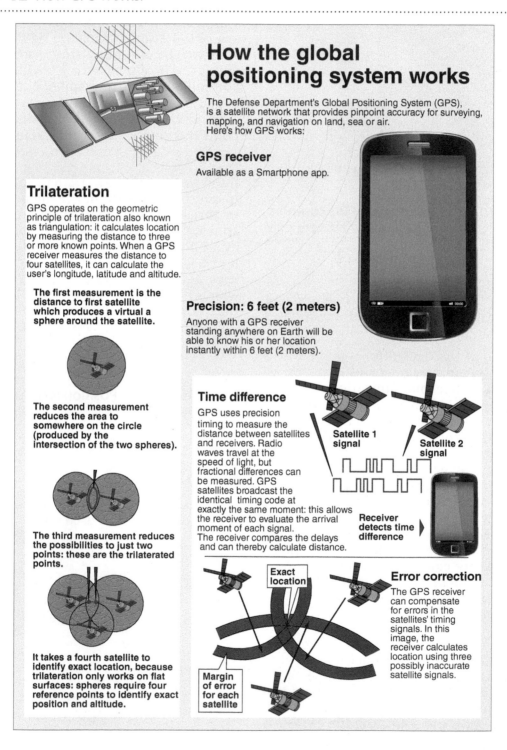

How the global positioning system works

The Defense Department's Global Positioning System (GPS), is a satellite network that provides pinpoint accuracy for surveying, mapping, and navigation on land, sea or air. Here's how GPS works:

GPS receiver
Available as a Smartphone app.

Trilateration
GPS operates on the geometric principle of trilateration also known as triangulation: it calculates location by measuring the distance to three or more known points. When a GPS receiver measures the distance to four satellites, it can calculate the user's longitude, latitude and altitude.

The first measurement is the distance to first satellite which produces a virtual a sphere around the satellite.

The second measurement reduces the area to somewhere on the circle (produced by the intersection of the two spheres).

The third measurement reduces the possibilities to just two points: these are the trilaterated points.

It takes a fourth satellite to identify exact location, because trilateration only works on flat surfaces: spheres require four reference points to identify exact position and altitude.

Precision: 6 feet (2 meters)
Anyone with a GPS receiver standing anywhere on Earth will be able to know his or her location instantly within 6 feet (2 meters).

Time difference
GPS uses precision timing to measure the distance between satellites and receivers. Radio waves travel at the speed of light, but fractional differences can be measured. GPS satellites broadcast the identical timing code at exactly the same moment: this allows the receiver to evaluate the arrival moment of each signal. The receiver compares the delays and can thereby calculate distance.

Satellite 1 signal

Satellite 2 signal

Receiver detects time difference

Exact location

Margin of error for each satellite

Error correction
The GPS receiver can compensate for errors in the satellites' timing signals. In this image, the receiver calculates location using three possibly inaccurate satellite signals.

MAPPING The raw positional data produced by the GPS receiver unit on your car or truck can next be connected to the geographic information retained in the memory of the GPS ECM. In a top-of-the-line system, the navigational display may produce color map readouts and provide detail on street addresses. The retained data may be on compact disk read-only memory (CD-ROM), but the system works best with a telecom link found on some trucks that can provide live data on such things as traffic congestion and road construction.

NAVIGATIONAL AIDS TO GPS Depending on the sophistication of the system, the effectiveness of a GPS unit can be improved by inputting data from the chassis electronics (road speed) and dedicated sensors such as a gyrometer to signal change-of-direction data. A top-of-the-line system uses the Doppler effect (frequency shift analysis) to constantly monitor directional and vehicle speed data.

VEHICLE CONTROL CENTER (VCC)

Keeping track of vehicle communications in modern trucks (and agricultural, off-road, and mining equipment) is complex and requires plenty of computing and networking capability. For this reason, a number of different vehicle-based communications management systems are available. We use the generic term **vehicle control center (VCC)** to describe these comprehensive networking systems. VCC telematics, satellite communications, and navigation systems enable external communications and, because each is networked to the truck chassis data bus (CAN 2.0/J1939, discussed in Chapter 37), permit any ECU with a bus address to both broadcast and receive data. The systems can accommodate both secure and open off-board communications and can be configured for GPS, WiFi, Bluetooth, two-way satellite, and proprietary communications systems.

A key feature of VCC systems is the driver display. This can be configured in many different ways according to how the vehicle owner wants the vehicle operated and may include features such as touch screen to minimally distract the operator. One OEM describes its VCC system as the "nerve center" of truck operations. VCC can be programmed for semicovert management operations. For instance, if the navigation system detects a forthcoming hill, VCC messages the chassis data bus to command an automated or automatic transmission to downshift

into an optimum gear just ahead of the climb. Perhaps the most cost-effective benefit of a VCC system is predictive remote diagnosis that allows a fleet data hub to be alerted the moment a potential problem is detected. This minimizes downtime and often avoids costly on-the-road breakdowns.

IRIS

A popular, low-cost method of transferring information from a truck to the land station is to use infrared. Detroit Diesel's infrared information system (IRIS) works in conjunction with DDEC, ProDriver, and ProManager software and can upload and download. IRIS requires a transceiver located on the truck and another at a stationary location such as a refueling island. A green dash light alerts the driver when an IRIS has made a connection: The system can be used by dispatch for logging outgoing and incoming vehicles along with other data bus uploads and downloads. **Figure 33–13** shows the horizontal and vertical window alignment required for infrared data exchange.

FIGURE 33–13 IRIS horizontal and vertical window alignment required for data exchange.

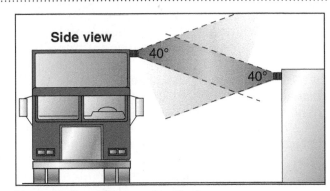

Vertical alignment is not critical

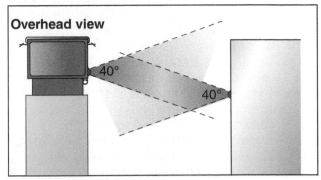

Horizontal alignment is not critical

Detroit Diesel

ELECTRONIC ONBOARD RECORDERS

Electronic onboard recorders (EOBRs) have recently been introduced by the **Federal Motor Carrier Safety Alliance (FMCSA)** to track data such as driver **hours of service (HOS)** for purposes of highway safety enforcement. Currently, any driver cited for a greater than 10% HOS infraction can be required to have an **electronic onboard recorder (EOBR)** installed in any vehicle he drives, but the FMCSA was aiming to have these devices installed in all line-haul commercial vehicles by 2015; at the time of writing, this had yet to be finalized. At present, these devices are only data downloadable by hardwired connectivity, but the intention is to make this a telematic device. Although some might say this is intrusive, the FMCSA argues that it is a less costly method of enforcing HOS and highway safety in general.

TRUCK INTELLIDRIVE FREIGHT MOBILITY INITIATIVE

The FMCSA-managed **Truck Intellidrive Freight Mobility Initiative** plans to make telematics part of all trucking operations. The aim is to develop an infrastructure in which trucks transmit data to a fixed inspection station or mobile Department of Transportation (DOT) or police vehicle. At this moment in time, *data* includes anything broadcast on the chassis data buses, and the objective of the **Smart Roadside Initiative (SRI)** is to make it possible to perform wireless mobile inspections. The status of this endeavor has yet to be decided; the current development of SRI is discussed in the last section of this chapter.

EOBR TELEMATICS

At present, there remain some questions as to what telematic protocol will be adopted when it becomes mandatory, but the betting is on **IEEE 802.11**, the WiFi standard using the 2.4, 3.6, and 5.0 GHz bands. The problem with IEEE 802.11 and **commercial mobile radio service (CMRS)** is security, because if GPS tracking and location electronics are to be communicated, it could endanger high-value loads. That said, as of the beginning of 2015, 28 states have adopted the CMRS IEEE 802.11 protocol that will be discussed a little later in this chapter. Other CMRS frequencies are under consideration because all support cell and satellite data transfer. At present, there is no agreement on a common OS for these devices. The following fields will likely be covered for telematic broadcast:

- Driver ID
- Road miles
- Yard miles
- Park time (pneumatic park brake sensor)
- Geographic location
- Error reporting
- Tamper detection

EOBR FAULT REPORTING

Phased implementation of EOBR began in 2015. The FMVSS now requires all trucks built after the EOBR implementation date to be equipped with EOBR: Those built before the implementation date will have the option of using paper or EOBR reporting. One of the problems is how to handle the loss of telematic communications in urban canyons, common for short periods in any large city environment. Urban canyon loss of signal in locations such as Manhattan and downtown Chicago may be prolonged.

Telematics Diagnostic Connector

As yet, there is no universal standard **telematics diagnostic connector (TDC)**, meaning that current data connectors and protocols will be used by the industry. These cover both hardware and wireless connection protocols for off-board vehicle telematics, and they will be looked at in more detail in the final section of this chapter. The communications it will be designed to handle can be categorized as:

- Vehicle to vehicle (V2V)
- Infrastructure to vehicle (I2V)
- Vehicle to infrastructure (V2I)

The objective will be to speed up state-by-state monitoring and enforcement of vehicle safety standards and will include:

- Wireless roadside inspection
- Universal truck ID
- Virtual weigh station
- Truck parking
- Intersection navigation safety

EOBR DOWNLOADS

At present, most enforcement agents and inspection stations are not equipped for log downloads. For this reason, telematic access to

EOBR would seem to make more sense than a hardwire alternative such as a USB connector or the vehicle data link (VDL). Another question not resolved is who would have access to any downloaded data apart from the FMCSA, for instance, state police.

DATA MINING USING TELEMATICS

With the introduction of super-high-speed wireless networking formats (WiMax) and Internet2, OEMs and fleets are already looking at using telematics for purposes of predictive and condition-based maintenance. Predictive maintenance uses historical data on component failure patterns to predict failures. The objective is to provide an optimum level of maintenance at the right time to avoid a breakdown—that is, to get away from the "driven to destruction," "if it ain't broke, don't fix it" maintenance profile. Condition-based maintenance (CBM) works a little differently, by closely monitoring component performance. A good example of CBM is a lab oil sample taken to determine whether an oil change is actually necessary. But taking the oil sample also assesses the condition of the internal engine based on the contents of the sample. Because of the comprehensive monitoring of engine components and status, telematics in combination with CBM software can be used to minimize unnecessary preventive maintenance (PM).

CBM DATA ANALYSIS

For CBM to work effectively, it should possess telematic access to the vehicle and use remote vehicle diagnostics to accurately assess pending failures. The telematic software can monitor driver habits along with component performance—a characteristic of a *smart* truck. CBM extends the boundaries of vehicle maintenance and enhances diagnostic techniques by combining trend analysis (i.e., predictive maintenance) with interactive maintenance. A database is required and CBM is likely to increase monitoring instrumentation on engines.

Data Mining for CBM

A current Cummins ISX engine is equipped with 28 sensors and 15 actuators. The engine electronics are multiplexed to J1939, so the technology for telematic broadcasting off the bus is already in place, and Cummins is already data-mining any ISX engines it can access. The U.S. military has for some years used telematic CBM software to reduce PM and optimize equipment performance, so trucking is looking to the military for CBM examples that work. Some additional CBM-specific sensors will be required. For example, battery-related problems account for a disproportionate amount of maintenance and unscheduled downtime. Much of this is eliminated with on-chassis battery performance monitoring, telematically communicated to a CBM data hub.

USING HD-OBD DATA MINING

Using no more than the existing engine monitoring sensors, significant maintenance data is already available, so it only requires mining that data and routing it into large databases to produce invaluable maintenance information. Combined with vehicle maintenance reporting standards (VMRS) software, this can provide the backbone for accurate CBM profiles.

Heavy-duty, onboard diagnostics (HD-OBD) is mapped to monitor vehicle performance and emissions and broadcast the monitored systems using the fault mode indicator (FMI) predictive fields to predict imminent failures. The degrees of service complexity can be categorized at three levels:

1. Field repairable
2. Field repairable with OEM support
3. Not field repairable

The problem with today's vehicles is that the percentage of level 2 and level 3 repair work is increasing while level 1 repairs diminish, so getting some advance warning is important to operators wanting to minimize downtime. Rising costs, along with the cutthroat competition that prevails in the trucking industry, mean that any technology that promises to reduce costs is likely to be adopted—and today, that means sooner rather than later. Before that happens, secure inter-vehicle wireless links will have to be installed, but that is not considered to be a major obstacle.

Proprietary Telematic Systems

While using over-the-road telematics for data mining is of great interest to OEMs, because of its potential as a prognostic tool, it has even more obvious benefits to fleets wanting to avoid costly breakdowns. Most of the engine OEMs are experimenting with in-house telematics, and many large fleets are implementing EOBR well ahead of its mandatory introduction. Some examples include:

- DDC-Freightliner **Virtual Technician (VT)**. Can be programmed for running data mining and mobile diagnostics. Capable of monitoring multiple vehicles and alerting a technician at a central data hub should a fault code be logged.
- Navistar **Aware**. Vehicle tracking and mapping telematics.
- Volvo-Mack **Sentry**. The Sentry system is fitted to all Volvo trucks since 2007. It is capable of remote diagnostics and data mining on mobile vehicles.

GEOFENCES

Today's newer connected vehicles are using the potential of telematics to maximize vehicle security, monitoring, and efficiency of operation. The telematics can be classified as **vehicle-to-vehicle (V2V)**, **infrastructure-to-vehicle (I2V)**, and **vehicle-to-infrastructure (V2I)**; they currently use CMRS, as discussed earlier in this chapter. Telematics are required to be installed on model year (MY) 2015 and newer highway vehicles, and now they are programmed to work with a range of communications protocols. Note that some OEM telematics software in earlier models would only function with a single service provider. The term **geofence** is a general, but much-used, term derived from the geographic area within which:

- A truck operates
- A jurisdiction has authority
- A fleet operates

Within a **dedicated short-range communications (DRSC)** geofence, a vehicle equipped with a transponder and the appropriate software can run tolls, bypass weigh scales, and even change lights (emergency vehicles and intracity transit buses).

E-SCREEN AND WRI

Electronic screening (E-Screen) and **wireless roadside inspection (WRI)** are enabled by geofence technology and have currently been adopted by 28 states, but obviously the vehicle has to be enabled to use it and at this time it is not mandatory. It is expected to be adopted in all states and provinces, but because of its potential to monitor both the vehicle and driver behavior, including HOS, some jurisdictions regard it as controversial. The major plus for operators is avoidance of the estimated cost of a state or provincial weigh station inspection stop, which is reckoned by FMCSA to be $8.68. This estimate factors in the cost of fuel and lost time created by a routine stop, and obviously the amount goes up significantly if the stop involves an inspection.

WRI Commands

When a connected vehicle crosses a geofence, its onboard data is immediately transferred to the jurisdiction's motor carrier operations center, initiating a **wireless inspection processing system (WIPS)** file. WIPS then triggers a wireless in-truck feedback message to the driver, broadcasting one of four color-coded commands on the driver display interface:

- **Red:** geo-triggered inspection. Options: 1. Self-test; 2. Login driver can investigate; 3. Officer-initiated inspection
- **Yellow:** pull in to inspection station. Options: 1. Random inspection; 2. Data analysis problem; 3. Actual problem
- **Green:** no problem with WRI: OK to bypass inspection site
- **No light:** WRI account not active or telematics communication problem

Speeding and Other Issues

One of the more controversial elements of IV2 telematics is that access to the vehicle data bus can monitor and potentially modulate driver behavior in ways that have never been possible previously. Can a stolen vehicle be immobilized from a fleet data hub? Would it be possible to electronically ticket a driver for speeding? The answer to both questions is yes, so the issue becomes one of driver autonomy and whether it should be managed. The fact that it is controversial is slowing the adoption of mandatory telematics technology in on-highway commercial vehicles.

DriveWyze

A no-frills weigh station bypass software package is **DriveWyze**. This is a subscription service (currently around $15 per month) software package that can operate from a smart phone or tablet that enables weigh or mobile station bypass in 33 states. It tends to be popular with owner-operators who may regard E-Screen and WRI monitoring to be undesirable. DriveWyze uses CMRS.

Aftermarket Wireless Connectivity

Some fleets identified the value of I2V and V2I wireless connectivity a number of years ago, and wanted to benefit from it throughout their fleet, including those vehicles that did not have built-in systems. For this reason, providers offer a number of aftermarket wireless hardware and software connection kits, such as SPX Ez-Tap.

Typically, one of these kits is made up of a vehicle bus interface that connects directly into a J1708 or J1939 DLC receptacle, from which it can broadcast wirelessly to the fleet data hub. The kit includes the PC hub telematics software, but note that to do much more than read bus status, OEM diagnostic software is required. The range of these systems is limited, but it can usually be expanded by using a signal intensifier located at the target PC; the signal intensifier used with the SPX system is known as Ez-Base. **Figure 33–14** shows an SPX Ez-Tap wireless vehicle connectivity kit.

FIGURE 33–14 An SPX Ez-Tap, aftermarket telematics kit. Typically this enables short-range telematic broadcasts from older vehicles with no integral system. A broadcast "tap" is installed into the J1708 or J1939 DLC and wirelessly connects with a fleet data hub.

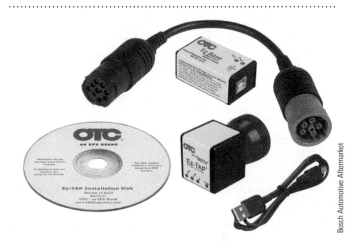

Bosch Automotive Aftermarket

SUMMARY

- Computers drive all communication systems today.
- The connection of a computer either to another single computer or to a network of computers can be referred to as a handshake.
- A network is a series of computers interconnected for purposes of data sharing, communication, and hardware sharing.
- The Internet is a network of networks, with millions of users spread all over the world. The Internet is used by private individuals, government agencies, and corporations.
- The telephone system is responsible for most of the hard and soft links that enable Internet transactions.
- Most local telephone system transactions use pairs of copper wires. Most long-distance telecommunications traffic uses a combination of microwave and fiber-optic transmissions with multiple relays.
- Most telecom satellites are parked in a geosynchronous orbit.
- Telecom satellites generally use microwave transmissions.
- An uplink is an Earth base that broadcasts a signal to a satellite. A downlink is an Earth base that receives a satellite signal.

- The uplink/downlink device on a truck is usually called a transponder.
- Telematics are common on today's trucks, and a variety of different systems are used.
- GPS technology is widely used in the trucking industry.
- GPS functions by adapting trilateration geometry to four spheres.
- GPS provides best functionality in trucking when combined with two-way telecom satellite communications.
- Infrared data transfer systems such as IRIS can be used to transmit data to and from trucks using a stationary transceiver located on a refueling island.
- Wireless EOBR is a means of monitoring driver HOS using telematics.
- Data mining of existing vehicle electronic systems using telematics and CBM software networked to data banks can reduce over-the-road breakdowns and unscheduled maintenance.
- Geofence technology is a key to enabling WRI, which as of 2015 is voluntarily enabled in 28 states and is expected to become mandatory sometime in the future. I2V telematics is controversial because driver autonomy is compromised. That said, most larger fleets have embraced the technology.

REVIEW QUESTIONS

1. Which of the following is best described as *a network of networks?*
   a. Internet
   b. Intranet
   c. E-mail
   d. LAN

2. Which of the following components can be used to condition the output of a computer for transmission through the telephone system?
   a. CPU
   b. Transponder
   c. CRT
   d. Modem

3. What is the transmission medium used by the telephone companies for local telephone service?
   a. Microwave
   b. Copper wire
   c. Radio waves
   d. Telecommunications satellites

4. In what format is data transmitted using fiber-optic technology?
   a. Analog
   b. Pulses of voltage
   c. Digital
   d. Nodes and antinodes

5. What altitude from the Earth's surface would describe a geosynchronous orbit?
   a. 160 miles (257 km)
   b. 22,300 miles (35,888 km)
   c. 35,900 miles (57,775 km)
   d. 56,700 miles (91,250 km)

6. The first telecommunications satellite was called:
   a. *Sputnik I.*
   b. *Apollo XI.*
   c. *Telstar.*
   d. *Discovery.*

7. The Earth-based station responsible for broadcasting microwave signals to a telecommunications satellite is called a(n):
   a. modem.
   b. uplink.
   c. downlink.
   d. footprint.

8. The uplink/downlink component used on trucks equipped with GPS technology is often called a(n):
   a. aerial.
   b. transponder.
   c. modem.
   d. footprint.

9. Technician A states that a telecommunications satellite orbits the earth at a distance of 35,900 (57,775 km) miles. Technician B states that all telecommunications satellites use fuel to maintain a fixed orbit on the earth's equator. Who is correct?
   a. Technician A only
   b. Technician B only
   c. Both A and B
   d. Neither A nor B

10. Technician A states that telecom satellites in geosynchronous orbit are required to park at about 2 degrees apart from one another. Technician B states that the earth surface geographic zone over which a telecom satellite's signals are effective is known as its footprint. Who is correct?
    a. Technician A only
    b. Technician B only
    c. Both A and B
    d. Neither A nor B

11. Technician A states that the hardwired telephone system can only handle analog transactions. Technician B states that most telecommunications systems in North America rely on hardwired mediums for at least some of the transmission. Who is correct?
    a. Technician A only
    b. Technician B only
    c. Both A and B
    d. Neither A nor B

12. Technician A states that a LAN is sometimes known as a network of networks. Technician B states that the Internet is owned by the Microsoft Corporation. Who is correct?
    a. Technician A only
    b. Technician B only
    c. Both A and B
    d. Neither A nor B

13. What is a transponder?
   a. An uplink/downlink device
   b. A satellite dish
   c. A footprint
   d. A CB antenna

14. Which of the following means the same thing as *network star*?
   a. Internet
   b. Intranet
   c. Remote node
   d. Data hub

15. Which of the following broadcast mediums relies on modulating high-frequency radio waves?
   a. Hardwired telephone system
   b. Microwave
   c. Fiber optics

16. The software tool capable of finding information on the Internet and on databases is known as a(n):
   a. search engine.
   b. operating system.
   c. mouse.
   d. scanner.

17. Technician A states that microwaves travel in geometrically straight lines. Technician B states that the point-to-point communications distance of microwaves is indefinite and a signal should be able to travel halfway around the world. Who is correct?
   a. Technician A only
   b. Technician B only
   c. Both A and B
   d. Neither A nor B

18. Which of the following mediums should be able to transmit the most data given a similar radial diameter of each?
   a. Aluminum wire
   b. Copper wire
   c. Coaxial cable
   d. Fiber-optic cable

19. What is the minimum number of GPS satellites a vehicle GPS system must locate to identify both vehicle position and altitude?
   a. One
   b. Two
   c. Three
   d. Four

20. To calculate a specific position on a flat map using trilateration geometry, what is the minimum number of coordinates required?
   a. One
   b. Two
   c. Three
   d. Four

21. Which telematics communications medium is currently favored by the trucking industry?
   a. CMRS IEEE 802.11
   b. J1939
   c. J1962
   d. CMRS 11121

22. During a WRI, the operator is alerted with a green light on the driver interface. What should be done?
   a. Pull over to the side of the pavement.
   b. Pull in to the next inspection station.
   c. OK to bypass the next inspection station.
   d. Prepare for an HOS citation.

23. Technician A says that DriveWyze is a subscription service that can be run from a smart phone. Technician B says that DriveWyze can enable weigh and inspection station bypass. Who is correct?
   a. Technician A only
   b. Technician B only
   c. Both A and B
   d. Neither A nor B

24. Which of the following technologies would permit a fleet data hub to communicate with a truck data bus?
   a. V2V
   b. V2I
   c. 2VV
   d. I2V

25. Technician A says that geofencing WRI can enable a truck to bypass a highway toll station. Technician B says that geofencing enables E-Screening of vehicles. Who is correct?
   a. Technician A only
   b. Technician B only
   c. Both A and B
   d. Neither A nor B

34

Prerequisites: Chapters 32 and 33

VEHICLE COMPUTER SYSTEMS

OBJECTIVES

After studying this chapter, you should be able to:

- Understand the language of computerized truck engine management systems.
- Describe the circuit layout of an electronically managed truck engine.
- Identify the differences between partial authority and full authority electronic engine management.
- Outline the stages of a computer processing cycle.
- Describe the data retention media used in vehicle ECMs.
- Describe the role played by the various memory components in a truck ECM.
- Identify the command and monitoring input circuits on a vehicle electronic system.
- Define the principles of operation of thermistors, variable capacitance sensors, Hall-effect sensors, potentiometers, induction pulse generators, and piezoresistive sensors.
- Describe how an ECM processes inputs and uses programmed data to generate outputs.
- Identify current computer-controlled engines by OEM and engine series.
- Define the role played by the injector driver unit in a typical full authority engine management system.
- Differentiate between customer and proprietary data reprogramming and identify the levels of access passwords used.
- Describe the processes used to reprogram a truck engine ECM with proprietary data.

KEY TERMS

actuator	critical flow venturi (CFV)	engine/electronic control unit (ECU)	hard parameter
algorithm	cybernetics		injector driver
background computations	diesel particulate filter (DPF)	failure mode indicator (FMI)	mass airflow (MAF) sensor
central gateway	download	failure strategy	master control module
central processing unit (CPU)	EEPROM	flash memory	microprocessor
chopper wheel	engine/electronic control module (ECM)	foreground computations	modular switch field (MSF)
		fuzzy logic	

multiplexing	potentiometer	SAE J standards	starpoint
negative temperature coefficient (NTC)	PROM	SAE J1587	strategy
NO$_x$ sensor	pulse wheel	SAE J1708	thermistor
parameter	pyrometer	SAE J1939	threshold value
platinum resistance thermometer (PRT)	RAM	sampling	tone wheel
polyswitch	reprogram	signal-detect and actuation module (SAM)	upload
positive temperature coefficient (PTC)	resistance temperature detector (RTD)	soft parameter	water-in-fuel (WIF) sensor
	ROM	source address (SA)	

INTRODUCTION

Most highway trucks and, increasingly, buses and off-highway equipment, use computers to manage engine and other onboard system functions. They are cybernetically controlled. **Cybernetics** is the science of computer control systems. The technician is required to trouble-shoot system problems and reprogram **parameters** (values), in most cases using software loaded to personal computers (PCs), laptops, or handheld units. Onboard vehicle computers are referred to as **engine/electronic control modules (ECMs)** or **electronic/engine control units (ECUs)**. ECM is the acronym used in this text except when discussing a product whose original equipment manufacturer (OEM) chooses to use the acronym ECU.

ENGINE CONTROLLER

An ECM is a modular housing containing a **microprocessor**, data retention media, and, usually, an output or switching apparatus. The ECM is the engine controller. It is usually but not always mounted somewhere on the engine. Other locations for mounting an ECM are the firewall or inside the vehicle cab. Although in the early days of vehicle computers the only system that was electronically managed was the engine, today most chassis systems are com-puter controlled. To enable the various chassis controllers to exchange data, each controller is assigned an address on a chassis data bus. The data bus is the information exchange backbone of the chassis. We use the term **multiplexing** to refer to communications on a vehicle data bus.

We will look at multiplexing in more detail a little later in Chapter 37. Technicians are required to have a basic understanding of both vehicle and personal computers to perform even the simplest chassis functions. This chapter introduces the essentials of electronic manage-ment of vehicle systems. The terms introduced in Chapter 32 are used extensively here, so if you do not understand a concept, you may wish to refer back to that chapter.

DATA PROCESSING

A vehicle computer (**Figure 34–1**) may be simple, such as that required to manage a pulse wiper circuit; or complex, such as that required to man-age a diesel engine and its emissions controls.

FIGURE 34–1 The ECM from a post-2013 PACCAR MX-13.

However, whether simple or complex, all chassis computers manage an information-processing cycle composed of three distinct stages:

1. Data input
2. Data processing
3. Outputs

Figure 34–2 shows a schematic layout of a more complex management system that is used on post-2007 Caterpillar ACERT C13 and C15 engines. This circuit is required to drive twin actuator injectors, variable valve timing, and an assortment of aftertreatment devices, including a diesel particulate filter.

Data Input

Data is simply raw information. Most of the data to be inputted to a truck diesel engine ECM comes from monitoring sensors, such as rpm signals, and command sensors, such as the throttle position sensor. This data may be in analog or digital formats. If the input data is in analog format, such as voltage values, it has to be digitized before it can be processed by the ECM. **Figure 34–3** shows some different types of input circuit devices: In this figure the switch status should be open in order to validate the pair of sensors above it.

Data Processing

A **central processing unit (CPU)** contains a control unit that executes program instructions and an arithmetic logic unit (ALU) to perform numeric calculations and logic processing such as comparing data. Random-access memory **(RAM)** is data that is electronically retained in the ECM; this data can be manipulated by the CPU because it can be accessed at high speed. RAM is often referred to as *main memory*. The ECM can also call up more permanent types of data that are retained magnetically or optically. Read-only memory **(ROM)**, programmable read-only memory **(PROM)**, and electronically erasable, programmable read-only memory **(EEPROM)** data can be transferred to RAM by the CPU for processing. Because RAM data is electronically retained, it is lost when its power-up circuit is opened. **Figure 34–4** is a simplified schematic of an ECM showing some of its basic functions: The output drivers shown in the schematic are transistors that convert processing logic into action such as switching injectors on and off.

Outputs

The results of processing operations must be converted to action by switching units and **actuators**. In most (but not all) truck/bus management ECMs, the switching units are integral with the ECM. In an ECM managing a full authority diesel engine, the **injector driver** unit would be one of the primary outputs to be switched. ECM commands would be converted to an electrical signal that would determine the pulse width or duty cycle of an electronic fuel injector (EUI) and define its effective pumping stroke. Note the output drivers in Figure 34–3 and Figure 34–4: It helps if you can develop a mental picture of what happens in an ECM rather than simply regarding it as a black box.

SAE HARDWARE AND SOFTWARE PROTOCOLS

Among the OEMs of truck and bus engines in the United States, there has been a generally higher degree of cooperation in establishing shared electronics hardware and software protocols than in the automobile manufacturing segment of the industry. To some extent this cooperation has been orchestrated by the SAE and ATA-TMC, but it is a cooperation that has been necessary due to the fact that truck chassis OEMs are usually obliged to provide more than one engine option, and that the powertrain electronics have to communicate with the brakes, collision warning systems, and so forth.

J-STANDARDS

Two primary powertrain data buses are used on current trucks. They are referred to as:

- SAE J1587/1708
- SAE J1939

In addition, manufacturers of truck chassis may use proprietary data buses. A proprietary data bus is usually designed to communicate with the powertrain bus by means of a gateway. Both hardwire and optical buses may be used. In some cases, such as in off-road hybrid rock trucks, optical buses may be used to handle some powertrain functions because more bandwidth is required. In this instance, a gateway connects the optical buses (used to manage hybrid electrical components) to J1939 (used to manage the diesel engine).

SAE J standards (surface vehicle recommended practice) dictate the hardware and software protocols that govern multiplexing data exchange between modules. These protocols are covered by the following J standards:

FIGURE 34–2 Schematic of a post-2007 Caterpillar ACERT system used to manage C13 and C15 engines.

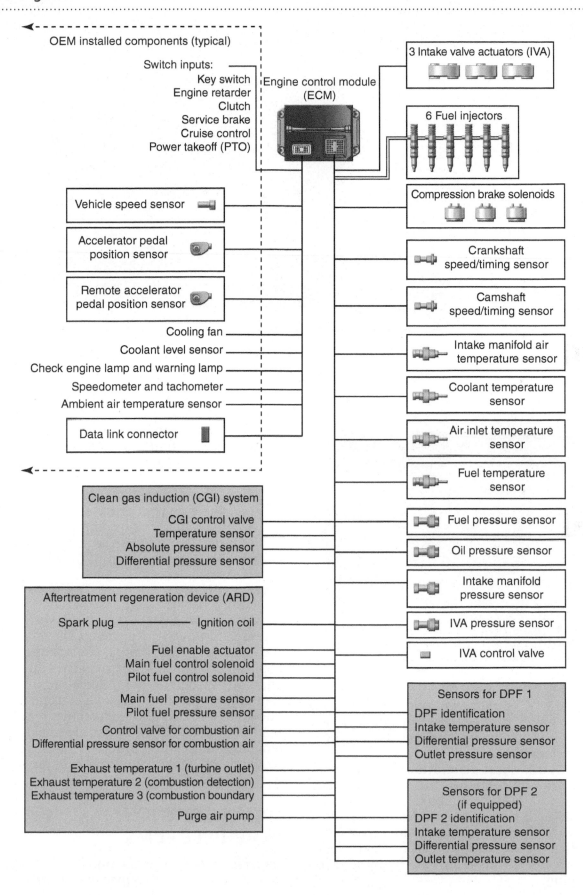

FIGURE 34–3 Types of ECM input signals.

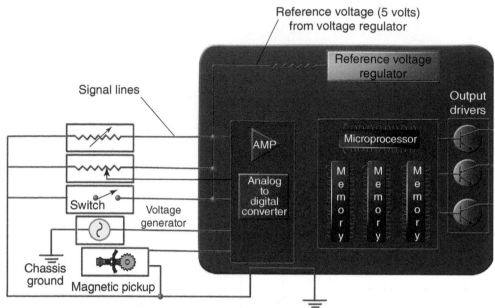

FIGURE 34–4 ECM functions.

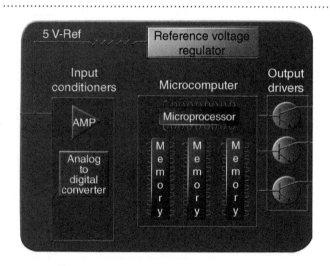

- **SAE J1587.** First-generation, multiplexing data exchange *protocols* used in data exchange between controllers networked on the powertrain data bus.
- **SAE J1708.** First-generation, multiplexing *hardware* compatibility for controllers networked to a J1587 data bus. In other words, on a J1587 bus the communication language is defined by J1587, but the hardware compatibility is dictated by J1708. That means data access to the J1587 bus is by a J1708 data plug.

- **SAE J1939.** The set of standards that incorporate both *software* and *hardware* protocols based on a high-speed Controller Area Network generation 2.0 (CAN 2.0) data bus—the current powertrain serial communication bus. We will take a close look at this in Chapter 37. When studying vehicle controllers, we often describe a controller by stating which of the two data buses it is compatible with. The light-duty/automotive equivalents of J1939 are J1850 and the current CAN-C.

Data Exchange

For data exchange to take place between two separate electronic control systems, they must "speak" the same language, that is, use common communication protocols. In many early systems, if the engine electronics were required to interact with transmission electronics, an electronic translator, known as an *interface module*, was required. Systems that are J1939 compatible speak the same language and can be plumbed into the data bus to share any information that is pumped through it. No interface module is required.

DATA RETENTION IN VEHICLE ECMS

Data is retained electronically, magnetically, and optically in current-generation truck, bus,

FIGURE 34–5 ECM from a 2015 John Deere engine.

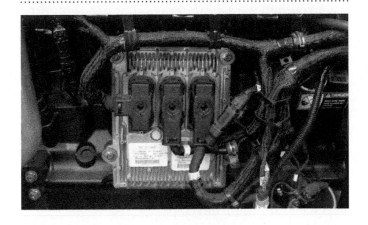

and heavy equipment ECMs. **Figure 34–5** shows the ECM used in a current John Deere engine. Optically retained data in laser-read systems, once common only in home computing, is now being used in vehicle computers. We categorize data in vehicle ECMs as follows.

Random-Access Memory

The amount of data that may be retained in RAM is a primary factor in quantifying the computing power of a system. It is also known as *main memory* because the CPU can only manipulate data when that data is retained electronically. At startup, RAM is electronically loaded along with the vehicle management operating system instructions and all necessary running data retained in other data categories (ROM/PROM/EEPROM) so that the CPU can access it at high speed.

VOLATILITY RAM data is electronically retained, which means that it is volatile. Another way of saying this is that RAM data storage is temporary. It requires power-up. If the circuit that supplies the RAM chip(s) is opened, the data in RAM is lost. Most truck ECMs use only fully volatile RAM; in other words, when the ignition circuit is opened, all RAM data is dumped.

Data such as coolant temperature, oil pressure, and boost pressure are also logged into RAM and, providing the values are within a threshold window defined in ROM/PROM/EEPROM, they only have significance at that specific moment; they can therefore be safely discarded when the ignition circuit is opened. This category of input data is continually monitored by a process known as **sampling**.

NV-RAM A second category of RAM is used in some truck and older automobile systems, usually ones that have no EEPROM capability. This is nonvolatile RAM (NV-RAM) (or KAM—keep-alive memory) in which data is retained until either the battery is disconnected or the ECM is reset, usually by depressing a computer reset button that temporarily opens the circuit. Like RAM, NV-RAM requires power-up to retain its memory. Often this is delivered outside the ignition circuit. For instance, in some vehicles the preset radio station selections are recorded in NV-RAM, so these have to be reestablished when you reconnect the vehicle battery. Codes and **failure strategy** (action sequence) are the type of things that could be written to NV-RAM in systems that use it.

Read-Only Memory

ROM data is magnetically or optically retained and designed not to be overwritten. It is "permanent," though it can be corrupted (rare), and may be susceptible to damage when exposed to powerful magnetic fields if it is magnetically retained. Low-level radiation, such as that routinely encountered driving on a highway from police radar and high-tension electrical wiring, will not affect any current ECMs. A majority of the total data retained in the ECM is logged in ROM. In an engine ECM, the master program for the system management is loaded into ROM. Production standardization is permitted by constructing ROM architecture so that it is written with common requisite data for a number of different systems. For example, identical ROM chips can be manufactured to run a group of different engines in a series—but to actually make an engine run in a specific chassis application, the ROM data would require further qualification from data loaded into PROM and EEPROM.

OPEN VS. CLOSED LOOP ROM contains all the protocols (rules and regulations) to master engine (or the system) management, including all the **threshold values** (limits). The term **hard parameters** is often used to describe values that are interpreted by the ECM in rigid terms. For instance, the temperature at which the ECM is programmed to identify an engine overheat condition is always a fixed value: At this specific value, a code and failure strategy are effected. Engine overspeed is another example of a hard parameter. In these examples, the processing loop is closed. The result is either OK or Not-OK.

A **soft parameter**/value is one that would be interpreted by the ECM with a cushion around the value (within a range). Soft parameters are those where the processing cycle may

730 SECTION 3 ENGINE MANAGEMENT, ALTERNATE POWER, AND EMISSIONS

use the input of many sensors to compute the output algorithm. When an engine or system is run under open loop conditions—and most current diesel engines are—the processing path to produce outcomes is sometimes known as a **fuzzy logic** path. In a truck you have a *hard cruise* option in which road speed is held at a set value. Or you can option *soft cruise* (a.k.a. *smart cruise*). In soft cruise mode, the objective might be to achieve the best fuel economy, so the ECM permits some latitude (both up and down) around the set road speed.

Programmable ROM

Programmable ROM (PROM) is magnetically retained data—usually a chip, set of chips, or card socketed into the ECM motherboard. PROM can sometimes be removed and replaced. The function of PROM is to qualify ROM to a specific chassis application. In the earliest truck engine management systems, programming options, such as idle shutdown time, could only be altered by replacing the PROM chip; in current systems, customer programmable options are written to EEPROM where they can easily be altered by flash programming. Some OEMs describe the PROM chip as a "personality module," which is an appropriate description of its actual function of trimming or fine-tuning the ROM data to a specific application.

Electronically Erasable PROM

The electronically erasable, programmable read-only memory (EEPROM) data category contains customer data programmable options and proprietary data that can be altered and modified using a variety of tools ranging from a generic reader programmer to a mainframe computer. EEPROM is usually magnetically retained in current systems, but this will probably change in the near future. EEPROM provides the ECM with a write-to-self capability. This allows it to log fault codes, audit trails, tattletales, and failure strategies in a way that is more permanent than NV-RAM. Other examples of the type of data programmed to EEPROM are tire rolling radius, governor options (LS or VS), cruise control limits, road speed limit, and many others. EEPROM data can be rewritten on an as-needed basis.

OEMs use passwords to protect programming fields and shield audit trails. Typically, passwords can be categorized at three levels:

- Customer: provides the minimum level of programming access and audit trail display. Provided to the owner of a vehicle. May or

may not be provided to the driver of the vehicle.
- Technician: OEM dealership technicians are provided with a higher level of programming and audit trail access.
- Factory: the highest level of programming and audit trail access. Depending on the specific OEM, factory passwords may be downloadable from the Internet as a start-of-message (SOM) on a reprogramming file, or be temporarily provided to an OEM dealership technician.

Usually only the customer (owner) or technician password is required to access EEPROM and make the changes required on a day-to-day service and repair basis.

Flash Memory

The term *flash programming* is commonly used to refer to both EEPROM and true flash memory. **Flash memory** is magnetically retained, nonvolatile, solid-state memory. We use it extensively for portable digital storage (such as camera memory) and increasingly in vehicle computers. It is faster to log and erase than EEPROM because memory segments are batched in large blocks of bytes rather than byte by byte. The term has become important because some OEMs are using it to describe any type of programmable onboard memory. For that reason, in this textbook the term *EEPROM* is used to describe both EEPROM and flash memory. Flash memory has also provided us with the verb *flash*: consequently, the term *flashing* is often used to describe any type of programming.

PROPRIETARY DATA Proprietary data logged into EEPROM is more complex both in character and methods of alteration. An example of proprietary EEPROM data is the fuel map in an engine ECM. The procedure here normally requires accessing a centrally located mainframe computer (usually at the OEM headquarters location) via the Internet; **downloading** the appropriate files to a PC; and finally **reprogramming** (altering or rewriting the original data) the ECM.

INPUT CIRCUIT

ECM inputs can be divided into sensor inputs and switched inputs. They are covered in this chapter in some detail because there is a high degree of input component commonality among the OEMs. When we deal with specific OEM management systems, we will assume that these input circuit components are understood. Inputs to the ECM can be divided into:

- Monitoring
- Command

Sensors and switches are used as input circuit components. A temperature signal to the ECM is an example of a monitoring input. The throttle position sensor is an example of a command input.

SENSORS

Anything that signals input data to a computer system can be described as a sensor. Sensors may be simple switches that an operator toggles open or closed to ground a reference voltage or modulate a reference voltage, or that are powered up either by V-Ref or require power-up outside of the V-Ref circuit.

Sensors Using a Reference Voltage to Produce an Analog or Digital Signal

These sensors receive a constant reference voltage (usually 5 V) and the ECM compares the return signals with values logged in its data retention banks. There are four types: thermistors, variable capacitance (pressure) sensors, piezoresistive pressure sensors, and signal-generating sensors.

THERMISTORS **Thermistors** precisely measure temperature. There are two types of thermistors, defined by whether resistance increases or decreases when temperature rise occurs:

- **Negative temperature coefficient (NTC)**: Temperature goes up, resistance goes down.
- **Positive temperature coefficient (PTC)**: Temperature goes up, resistance goes up.

The ECM receives temperature data from thermistors in the form of analog voltage values. The coolant temperature sensor, ambient temperature sensor, and oil temperature sensor are usually thermistors. Almost without exception, NTC-type temperature sensors are used on truck diesel engine systems, meaning that as temperature increases, resistance decreases, and therefore signal voltage (to the ECM) increases. Temperature sensors are critical inputs to the ECM when factoring injection timing and injection fuel quantity data. **Figure 34–6** is a schematic of a thermistor; **Figure 34–7** is an image of a coolant temperature sensor.

FIGURE 34–6 An engine coolant temperature sensor of the NTC thermistor type.

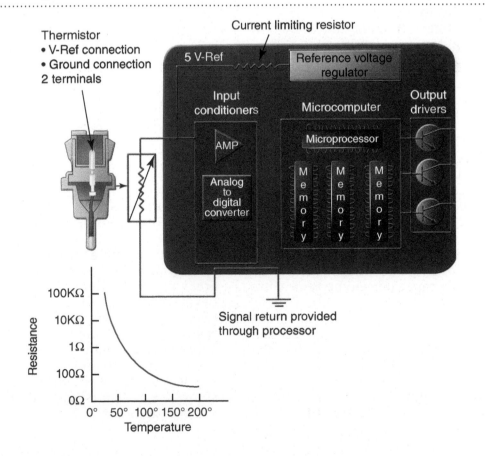

FIGURE 34–7 Coolant temperature sensor that uses a thermistor operating principle.

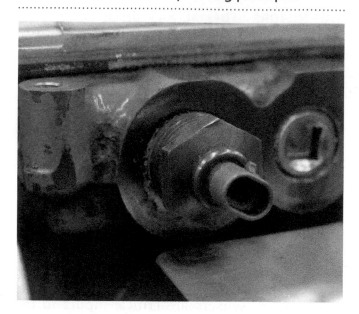

FIGURE 34–8 Fuel pressure sensor.

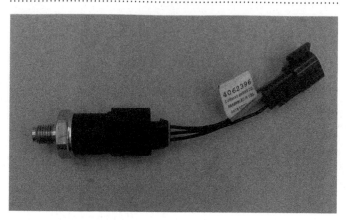

Functionality Test To check the functionality of an NTC thermistor, use these reference values:

Pin 1 = V-Ref (5 V-DC)
Pin 2 = GND
Pin 3 = Signal

Using a digital multimeter (DMM) on V-DC, the following voltage readings indicate a functional sensor:

Pin 1 to pin 2 = 5 V-DC
Pin 2 to pin 3 = 0.2–0.5 V-DC to 4.5–4.8 V-DC proportional with temperature rise

VARIABLE CAPACITANCE (PRESSURE) SENSORS These are three-wire sensors that are supplied with reference voltage and usually designed to measure pressure or linear position values. The medium whose pressure is to be measured acts on a ceramic disc and moves it either closer to or farther away from a steel disk, varying the capacitance of the device and thus the voltage value returned (signaled) to the ECM. **Figure 34–8** is an image of a variable capacitance-type sensor used to signal fuel pressure values.

Variable capacitance-type sensors can be used for oil pressure sensing, manifold actual pressure (MAP) sensing (turbo-boost pressure), barometric pressure sensing (BARO), and fuel pressure sensing. In addition, they can be used in pairs to measure mass airflow (these are described a little later in this chapter). **Figure 34–9** shows

an engine oil pressure sensor that uses a variable capacitance electrical operating principle. A variable capacitance principle has been used in the past by one OEM (Caterpillar) in a type of throttle position sensor (TPS); it was phased out in the mid-1990s. It should be noted that multiple types of sensors can be contained in a single device, such as the pressure-temperature sensor shown in **Figure 34–10**.

Functionality Test To check the functionality of a variable capacitance sensor, start with these values:

Pin 1 = V-Ref (5 V-DC)
Pin 2 = GND
Pin 3 = Signal

Using a DMM on V-DC, the following voltage readings indicate a functional sensor:

Pin 1 to pin 2 = 5 V-DC

Pin 2 to pin 3 = 0.2–0.5 V-DC to 4.5–4.8 V-DC proportional with pressure rise

POTENTIOMETERS The **potentiometer** is a three-wire (V-Ref, ground, and signal) variable resistor. Once again, these receive a reference voltage and output a signal proportional to the motion of a mechanical device. Potentiometers are voltage dividers. The moving mechanical device moves a contact wiper over a variable resistor. As the wiper is moved over the variable resistor, the resistance path is altered, with the supply voltage being divided between the signal (sent to the ECM) and ground. TPSs are a typical application for a potentiometer. **Figure 34–11** shows a TPS that uses a potentiometer principle of operation.

FIGURE 34–9 An engine oil pressure sensor of the variable capacitance type.

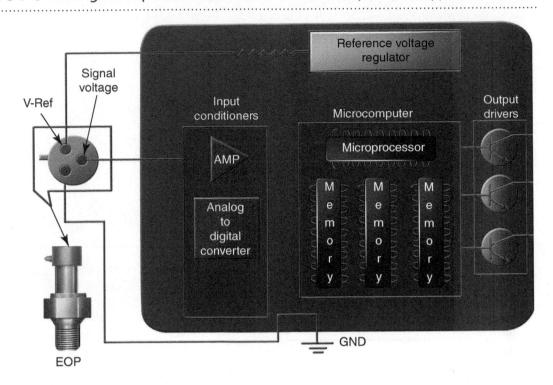

FIGURE 34–10 Combination pressure and temperature sensor.

Functionality Test To check the functionality of a potentiometer type TPS, use the following values. Note that Caterpillar TPSs are supplied with a power-up voltage of 8 V-DC to output a digital signal and should not be tested in this manner, nor should any noncontact, Hall-effect TPS.

Pin 1 = V-Ref (5 V-DC)

Pin 2 = GND

Pin 3 = Signal

Using a DMM on V-DC, the following voltage readings indicate a functional sensor:

Pin 1 to pin 2 = 5 V-DC

Pin 2 to pin 3 = 0.2–0.5 V-DC to 4.5–4.8 V-DC proportional with pedal angle

TECH TIP:

When a sensor logs an active fault code, try disconnecting the sensor and observing whether the fault mode indicator (FMI) changes. It there is no change, it suggests that the fault lies in the wiring circuit. If the FMI changes, it would suggest that the problem lies in the sensor.

PIEZORESISTIVE PRESSURE SENSOR This type of pressure sensor is often used to measure manifold pressure, especially where greater accuracy is required. In trucks it is used as a manifold boost sensor, and it is sometimes referred to as a *Wheatstone bridge sensor*. A doped silicon chip is formed in a diaphragm shape so that it measures 250 microns around the outside and reduces to about 25 microns at the center: This means that it forms a sort of drum skin that is 10 times thinner at its center. This permits the diaphragm to flex at that center when subjected to pressure. A set of sensing resistors is

FIGURE 34–11 An accelerator position sensor of the potentiometer type.

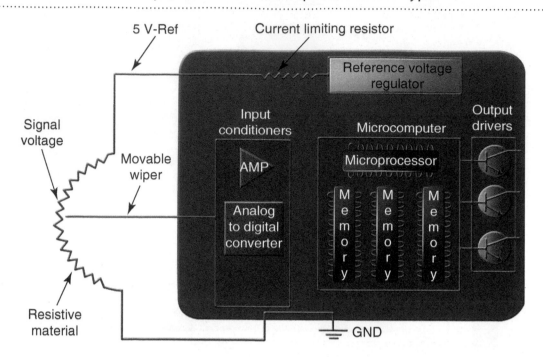

formed around the edge of a vacuum chamber over which the diaphragm is stretched. When subjected to pressure, the diaphragm deflects, causing the resistance of the sensing resistors to change in proportion to the increase in pressure.

Wheatstone Bridge An electrical signal proportional to pressure is produced by connecting the sensing resistors into a Wheatstone bridge circuit in which V-Ref is used to supply a constant DC voltage value across the bridge. When no pressure acts on the silicon diaphragm, all the sensing resistance will be equal and the bridge can be said to be balanced. When pressure causes the silicon diaphragm to deflect, resistance across the sensing resistors increases, unbalancing the bridge and creating a net voltage differential that can be relayed to the ECM as a signal. **Figure 34–12** shows the operating principle of a typical piezoresistive sensor.

Signal-Generating Sensors

Signal-generating sensors can be divided into three categories as follows:

- Sensors using V-Ref or other V-DC input to power-up but output a digital signal.
- Sensors with no electrical input that generate a V-AC output signal.
- Sensors with no electrical input that use a galvanic principle to output a V-DC output signal.

HALL-EFFECT SENSORS Hall-effect sensors generate a digital signal as timing windows or vanes on a rotating disc pass through a magnetic field. They can be used for both linear and rotary position signaling. In a rotary Hall-effect sensor, the rotating disc is known as a **pulse wheel** or **tone wheel**. Because these are terms

FIGURE 34–12 Piezoresistive sensor: Wheatstone bridge circuit, output signal is represented by Vs.

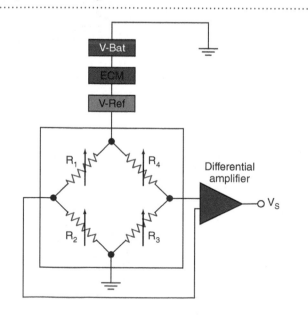

that are also used to describe the rotating members of induction pulse generators, care should be taken to avoid confusion. The frequency and width of the signal provide the ECM with speed and position data. The disc incorporates a narrow window or vane for relaying position data. The Hall-effect sensor outputs a digital signal by blocking a magnetic field with a vane from a semiconductor sensor.

Hall-effect sensors are used to input engine position data for purposes of event timing computations, such as the beginning and duration of the injection phase pulse width. Camshaft position sensors (CPSs), timing reference sensors (TRSs), and engine position sensors (EPSs) are examples. **Figure 34–13** shows the signal output of a Hall-effect sensor, and **Figure 34–14** is a schematic of the Hall-effect sensor when used to signal camshaft position information to an ECM.

Hall-Effect TPS Hall-effect sensors are also used as TPSs in some more recent chassis applications. The advantage of a Hall-effect TPS over a potentiometer TPS is that it lacks mechanical contact components. This feature eliminates one of the primary causes of potentiometer-type TPS failures: namely, that of wiper/resistor wear and corrosion. When the accelerator is depressed, the noncontact sliding shutter alternately blocks and exposes the Hall-effect

FIGURE 34–13 Hall-effect operating principle.

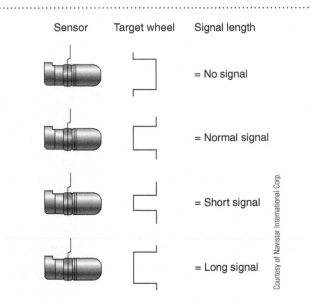

magnetic field to the signaling semiconductor sensor. The devices are configurable to digital or analog outputs depending on application. **Figure 34–15** shows an image of a typical electronic foot-pedal assembly with an integral TPS.

INDUCTION PULSE GENERATOR There is no electrical input to an induction pulse generator-type sensor. A toothed disc known as a *reluctor, pulse wheel,* or *tone wheel* (slang but commonly used:

FIGURE 34–14 Camshaft position sensor of the Hall-effect type.

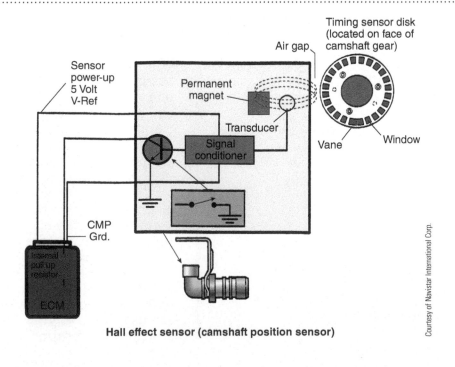

Hall effect sensor (camshaft position sensor)

FIGURE 34–15 A Williams electronic foot-pedal assembly (EFPA) commonly used by truck OEMs.

chopper wheel) with evenly spaced teeth or serrations is rotated through the magnetic field of a permanent stationary magnet. As the field builds and collapses, alternating current (AC) voltage pulses are generated and relayed to the ECM. The ECM uses the AC frequency to compute shaft speed. Reluctor-type sensors are used variously on modern truck chassis in applications such as antilock brake system (ABS) wheel speed sensors, vehicle speed sensors (VSS) located in the transmission tailshaft, and engine shaft speed sensors. **Figure 34–16** shows the operating principle of an induction pulse generator.

Functionality Test   When checking the functionality of a two-terminal shaft speed sensor, remember that this type of sensor generates an AC voltage; thus, the DMM should be set to V-AC. When the shaft is stationary, zero volts should

FIGURE 34–16 Induction pulse generator shaft speed sensor.

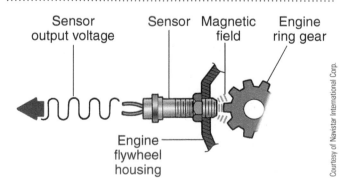

Sensor output voltage   Sensor   Magnetic field   Engine ring gear

Engine flywheel housing

Courtesy of Navistar International Corp.

be read across the terminals. When the shaft is rotated, V-AC voltage and frequency readings should increase proportionally with rpm.

GALVANIC SENSORS   Although used primarily on gasoline-fueled automotive engines, diesel technicians should have a rudimentary understanding of the operation of lambda (l) sensors (also known as *oxygen [O_2] sensors* or *exhaust gas sensors*). These sensors are used on natural gas (NG) adapted diesel engines and downstream from reduction converters (in the exhaust canister) in some post-2007, and most post-2010 and later, engines. A lambda sensor was used as the closed-loop driver on many spark-ignited (SI) engines and was the primary input reference the ECM used to monitor air-fuel ratio (AFR). Until the introduction of gas density-type O_2 sensors, galvanic-type sensors were used in most engines required to be fueled at close to stoichiometric ratios.

The most common lambda sensor is a galvanic device that produces an electric current by chemical action. In other words, it functions like a battery and does not require an electrical input. The lambda sensor is usually located in the exhaust piping, exposed to the engine exhaust gas on one side and ambient air on the other. When an O_2 sensor is used on a diesel engine, it plays a different role and is primarily a monitoring device for oxides of nitrogen (NO_x): The ECM calculates NO_x based on the O_2 present in the exhaust compared with the mass of air that entered the cylinder. When an O_2 sensor is used on an NG-fueled engine (Cummins, Mack, Caterpillar), it functions as a close-loop driver.

Construction   A typical O_2 sensor is constructed of a zirconium dioxide ceramic material with gas-permeable platinum electrodes exposed on one side to the exhaust gas (measuring electrode) and on the other to ambient air (reference electrode). The zirconium dioxide begins to conduct O_2 ions at a temperature value of around 550°F (300°C). At this temperature, as the O_2 proportion in the exhaust gas and that in the ambient air differ, a small voltage is generated due to the electrolytic properties of zirconium dioxide. The greater the *difference* in the oxygen proportions, the higher the voltage produced. These voltages range between 0.1 V and 1.0 V after the trigger temperature value is attained: In a majority of systems, a signal voltage of around 0.45 V-DC indicates a stoichiometric AFR. Lambda sensors are used in SI engines required to be fueled at stoichiometric ratios.

NO$_x$ SENSORS **NO$_x$ sensors** were introduced on 2007 products (notably some Mack vocational engines) and are used in most post-2010 diesel engines. They function by sampling the exhaust gas and calculating total NO$_x$ based on the sample. A NO$_x$ sensor consists of two chambers, which can be described as:

- Oxidation chamber: This is the first stage. Exhaust gas enters the oxidation cavity and a pair of platinum electrodes oxidize (HCs), (CO), and H$_2$. What remains then passes to the sampling chamber.
- Sampling chamber: This is the second stage. After the oxidation stage, all that remains of the exhaust gas is just a few ppm of O$_2$ and N$_2$. First, the O$_2$ is removed by catalytic reaction with the platinum electrodes; then the remaining NO$_x$ is electrolytically reduced to O$_2$ and N. In other words, NO$_x$ molecules are broken up into elemental nitrogen and oxygen. Finally, the O$_2$ is removed by catalytic reaction at the measuring electrode: The amount of current required to achieve this is directly proportional to the amount of NO$_x$ that first entered the sensor.

This type of NO$_x$ sensor requires contact with ambient O$_2$ in same way an O$_2$ sensor does. It references NO$_x$ with respect to the variability of atmospheric O$_2$ in proportion with increase in altitude. The operating temperature of these devices is about 1,200°F (650°C), so they usually incorporate a heater.

MAF Sensors

Mass airflow (MAF) sensors have only recently been introduced diesel engine manufacturers, although they have been used for decades in automobile applications. Their objective is to provide the ECM with accurate measurement of the air mass delivered to the engine cylinders. MAF sensors use either a "hot wire," critical flow venturi, or vortex flow operating principle.

HOT WIRE MAF In a hot wire MAF, a sensing element is heated and then maintained at a specified temperature. The sensing element is a film or wire positioned in the intake air stream to the engine and supplied with a constant voltage. Because of the applied voltage, the element is heated by the electrical current that the voltage produces. When intake air flows across the heated element, it has a cooling effect. The more air passing across the heated element, the greater the cooling effect. The heated wire or film element has a PTC electrical characteristic,

so its resistance decreases in proportion to any drop in temperature. As resistance decreases in the element, more current must flow through it in order to maintain the specified programmed temperature. The current flow at any given moment of operation is measured and transduced as an input signal to the ECM to be computed as airflow. A hot wire MAF works in conjunction with an inlet temperature sensor to ensure maximum accuracy.

CRITICAL FLOW VENTURI A **critical flow venturi (CFV)** MAF sensor is sometimes known as a *pressure differential flow sensor*. Its operating principle is based on the relationship between inlet pressure and flow rate through a venturi. By definition, a *venturi* is a gradually diminishing sectional area within a pipe designed to accelerate gas flow and decrease pressure: It is the flow principle that was used in carburetors. When the pressure is known both at the entry point to the venturi and at its exit point, the differential pressures can be used by the ECM to calculate the mass of the airflow. Some OEMs refer to these as *delta pressure sensors*. The venturi and pressure sensing points on a Detroit Diesel Series 60 are shown in **Figure 34–17**.

CFV Operation When air flows through the venturi, it reaches maximum velocity wherever the flow area is minimized. If you take a look at Figure 34–17, you will observe that the minimum flow area occurs at the throat of the venturi. When air (or a mixture of air and recirculated exhaust gas) is flowed through the venturi, a pressure differential is established between the P1 and P2. The differential readings will change as inlet pressure increases or decreases—or if the exit pressure increases or decreases. Whatever flow

FIGURE 34–17 Critical flow venturi, pressure differential MAF sensor.

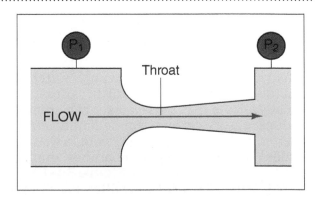

occurs is proportional to the differential pressure across it while the entrance pressure (P1) remains constant. For instance, if the exit pressure (P2) is reduced, the following occurs:

- Differential pressure increases.
- Flow increases.
- Air velocity at the throat increases.

These factors allow the ECM to compute the MAF with some degree of accuracy.

VORTEX AIRFLOW SENSOR These are sometimes known as Karman vortex flow sensors. The upper inlet of the sensor has an obstruction in the airflow. As air passes around the obstruction, it generates a stream of vortices (like mini-tornadoes) that increase as the airflow velocity increases. By locating an ultrasonic speaker and pickup (microphone) across the stream of vortices, which spin off in opposite directions, a frequency modulated shift can be signaled to the ECM. Frequency increases in proportion to air velocity, enabling the ECM to compute mass.

SUMMARY OF MAF OPERATION MAF sensors are designed to work in conjunction with other temperature and pressure sensors in the intake circuit. This permits the ECM to factor in variables such as ambient air temperature, humidity, barometric pressure, and manifold boost. For instance, cool air is denser than warm air, so the signal from an NTC-type ambient temperature sensor is used by the ECM to accurately compute actual airflow data. Humidity always affects air density because humid air is denser than dry air. However, because humid air has increased cooling effect on the sensing element, no other compensation is required. **Figure 34–18** shows a sensor cluster on a DD15 engine.

Water-in-Fuel Sensors

A **water-in-fuel (WIF) sensor** detects water contamination of fuel. A WIF sensor uses a couple of probes and a 12-volt supply. Because water has different electrical resistivity (known as *dielectric properties*) than fuel, a return signal is output from the sensor when the electrical path across the probes acts through water rather than fuel. At this point, the WIF broadcasts a service alert. Note that a WIF sensor can sometimes produce a service alert immediately after the water sump is drained: The reason is that water-resident bacteria can coat the probes after draining and trigger a false signal. **Figure 34–19** shows the WIF sensor on a FuelPRO filter assembly.

FIGURE 34–18 Sensor cluster on a 2015 DD15 engine.

FIGURE 34–19 WIF Sensor on a FuelPRO.

Thermocouple Pyrometers

In an earlier generation of truck diesel engines, a **pyrometer** was often located at a specified distance downstream from the turbocharger and used to provide the driver with engine loading information useful for shifting, especially down-shifting during prolonged loading. In post-2007 engines, one or more thermocouple pyrometers can be used to monitor the high temperatures produced in **diesel particulate filters (DPFs)**. DPFs will be studied in detail in Chapters 47 and 48 of this textbook, but we take a look at the electrical operating principles of thermocouple pyrometers here.

THERMOCOUPLE PRINCIPLE A thermocouple pyrometer consists of two dissimilar insulated wires (often pure iron and constantin [55% copper, 45% nickel]) connected at each end to form a continuous circuit. The two junctions are known as a *hot end*, which is located where temperature sensing is required; and a *reference end*, which is connected to a millivolt meter. Whenever the junctions are at different temperatures, there is current flow, the voltage increasing with temperature rise. Thermocouple pyrometers and their wiring circuit should be regarded as a complete unit: Never attempt to repair the wiring, and always replace it all as an integral unit. The practice of placing a thermocouple pyrometer in the exhaust tract of each engine cylinder is often used on large diesel engines to monitor cylinder balance. However, this type of pyrometer is not used as original equipment on any current truck diesel engines.

Resistance Thermometers

Resistance temperature detectors (RTDs) or resistive thermal devices measure the change in the electrical resistance of gases that occurs with temperature change. The detectors are made of platinum, so these devices are commonly known as **platinum resistance thermometers (PRTs)**. RTDs can replace thermocouple-type pyrometers where temperatures do not exceed 1,100°F (600°C): This is on the threshold of peak DPF temperatures, so some manufacturers have used RTDs in place of pyrometers because they produce more accurate signals.

SWITCHES

Switches complement the sensor circuit and can usually be classified as command inputs. Switches may be electromechanical or "smart"; that is, they use "messages" rather than analog voltage values to signal a change in status. Switches can be subdivided into three groups:

1. Switches grounding a reference signal (V-Ref). A good example is a coolant level sensor. This receives a reference signal from the ECM that grounds through the coolant in the upper radiator tank. Should the coolant level drop below the sensor level, the reference signal loses its ground after a preprogrammed time period (for example, 8 seconds). The time lag is required to prevent a temporary loss of ground caused by braking from opening the circuit and triggering an ECM response. The ECM responds with whatever action it is programmed with: electronic malfunction alert, deration, or engine shutdown. **Figure 34–20** and **Figure 34–21** show examples of switches used in a typical electronically managed engine circuit. The switch shown in Figure 34–20 is a driveline disengagement switch (DDS), which is located on the clutch pedal. This switch has to be closed to enable engine brake operation.
2. Manual switches controlling electrical circuit activity. Many versions of this type of switch are used by the operator to control vehicle functions. Some examples are the ignition key, engine retarder mode switches, and the cruise control switches. Switches that are controlled by the driver are sometimes called *command switches*.
3. Smart switches. Smart switches use digital signals to indicate a change in status. The signal produced by a smart switch may be automatically generated by a change in status condition or be generated by a mechanical action such as an operator toggling a switch. Smart switches are studied some detail in Chapter 37.

ECMS AND THE PROCESSING CYCLE

Figure 34–22 shows the location of an ECM and some sensors on a Navistar DT466E diesel engine. As mentioned a little earlier in this chapter, a diesel engine management ECM has four basic functions:

1. Regulation of reference voltage (V-Ref)
2. Input conditioning, amplification, and ADC
3. Processing
4. Management of output drivers

FIGURE 34–20 Switch-type input sensors.

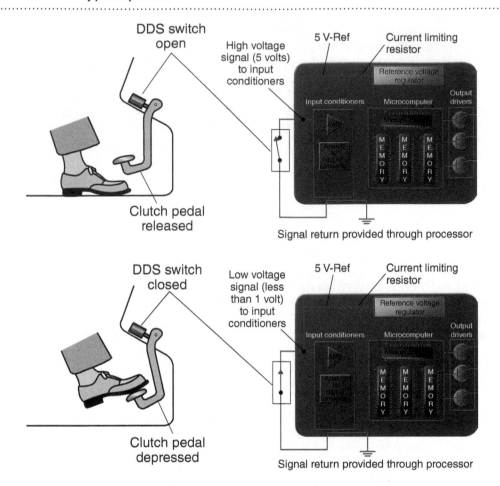

DDS switch open

High voltage signal (5 volts) to input conditioners

Clutch pedal released

Signal return provided through processor

DDS switch closed

Low voltage signal (less than 1 volt) to input conditioners

Clutch pedal depressed

Signal return provided through processor

FIGURE 34–21 Grounding-type switch operation.

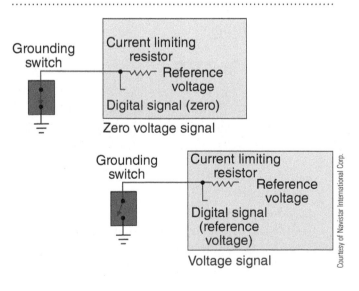

Grounding switch

Current limiting resistor
Reference voltage
Digital signal (zero)

Zero voltage signal

Grounding switch

Current limiting resistor
Reference voltage
Digital signal (reference voltage)

Voltage signal

ECM is the generic term for the unit housing the engine management electronics. It usually incorporates the complete computer assembly and some, if not all, of the output drivers or switching apparatus. ECM is also the SAE-recommended term for an engine controller. However, some engine OEMs choose to use their own terms. The ECM receives command and monitoring data from its input circuit. Inputs are responded to in the processing cycle and outputs are mapped. Among its outputs, the ECM manages V-Ref at a specific value. V-Ref is used both to power-up and to benchmark input signals.

The electronic subcircuit consists primarily of sensors located variously on the engine and chassis. Because the data they input is mostly in the form of analog voltage values, these must be converted to digital codes for processing by an ADC (analog to digital converter) integral with the ECM. Weak signals may be conditioned or strengthened before processing. Preparing input signals for processing is an ECM functions

FIGURE 34–22 Navistar DT466E seen from the left side and showing the location of the ECM and some sensors.

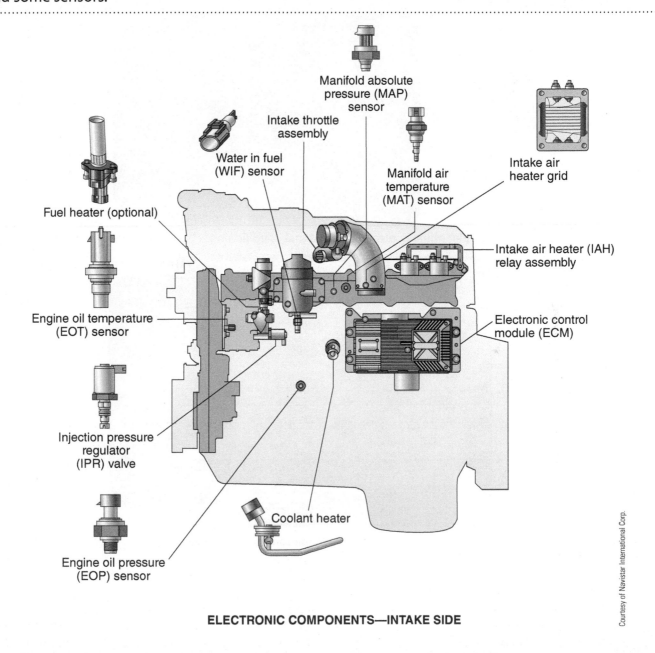

ELECTRONIC COMPONENTS—INTAKE SIDE

Courtesy of Navistar International Corp.

categorized as input conditioning. **Figure 34–23** outlines the role of V-Ref and signal conditioning in an ECM.

PROCESSING CYCLE

Processing in the ECM involves scanning the programmed fuel map data (in ROM, complemented or finally defined in PROM and EEPROM), engine and chassis monitoring sensors (such as engine coolant temperature [ECT], VSS, and so on) and command inputs (TPS, cruise control, engine brake, and so on), and subsequently plotting an actual fuel quantity to be delivered. **Figure 34–24** shows a typical Bosch ECM.

Processing Speeds

ECM processing may occur at different frequencies, classified as **foreground** and **background computations**. **Figure 34–25** shows an older ECM motherboard. Foreground operations include response to a critical command input such as the TPS, whose signal must be processed immediately to generate the appropriate

FIGURE 34–23 ECM input signal conditioning and data retention.

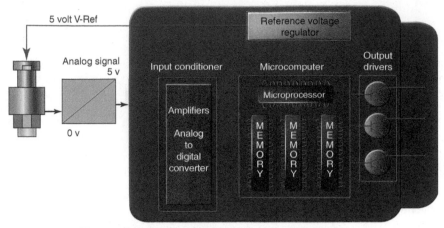

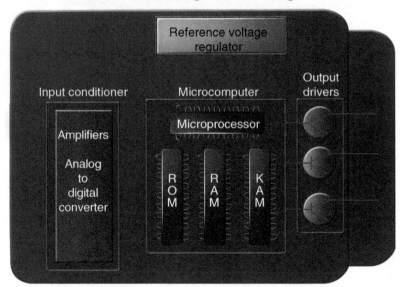

Electronic control module signal conditioning

Electronic control module microprocessor memory

FIGURE 34–24 The Bosch ECM used on a Navistar MaxxForce Series engine.

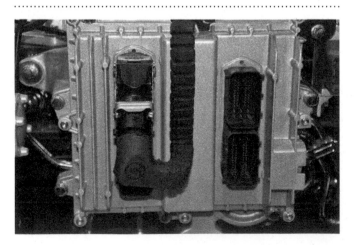

FIGURE 34–25 ECM motherboard.

FIGURE 34–26 A Volvo ECM.

outcome. The monitoring of engine oil temperature is often classified as a background operation. Although obviously valid, this signal does not require as immediate an adjustment to operating strategy as input from the accelerator. **Figure 34–26** shows the ECM used on a Volvo engine; this is known by Volvo as an EECU.

Engine controllers today use dual-core CPU architecture driven at speeds of at least 2 × 280 MHz. Clock speeds are likely to continue to increase as the number of smart devices on a chassis multiplies. CPU speeds and power rise as OEMs fully exploit the potential of multiplexing bandwidth and get serious about reducing the inputs and outputs (I/Os) on ECMs.

Generating Outputs

ECM outputs are switching functions. Switching functions are usually driven at system chassis voltage, although in some instances they are spiked to higher values. In this way, the ECM manages the cycles of fuel injection apparatus, exhaust gas recirculation (EGR), and diesel particulate filters (DPFs). In doing this, it also communicates with other chassis electronics by sharing data. **Figure 34–27** is a simplified example of the processing cycle in a three-module Navistar ECM assembly consisting of an ECM, personality module (PROM and EEPROM), and a separate injector driver module (IDM).

ECM Location

ECMs theoretically can be located anywhere on the vehicle chassis. Engine management ECMs are often mounted on the engine close to the devices they have to monitor and switch. While engine-mounted ECMs require better shock and vibration insulation, they have certain advantages in being close to both the sensors and actuators; where heat is a problem, they can be mounted on a heat exchanger with diesel fuel acting as the cooling medium. Another option is to locate the ECM under the dash inside the vehicle cab, reducing the requirement for shock and vibration insulation.

The following are examples of some OEM acronyms used to refer to engine and fuel system controllers:

EEC: Electronic engine control
EECU: Electronic engine control unit
ECI: Electronically controlled injection
ECU: Electronic control unit
FIC: Fuel injection control module
MCM: Motor control module
PCM: Powertrain control module
PLD: German acronym for ECM (Mercedes-Benz)

FIGURE 34–27 The processing cycle of an International Trucks HEUI, 3-module (3-box) controller system.

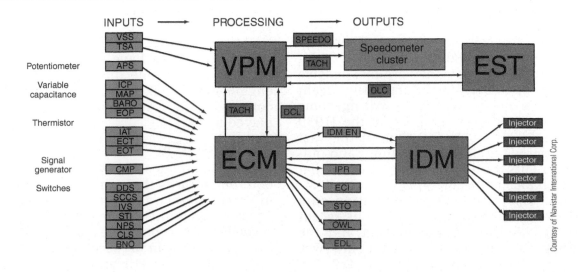

PROCESSING ALGORITHMS

The term **algorithm** is used to describe the sequence of processing events in an ECM, from the arrival of a signal to the switching of an outcome. The algorithm required to produce any computer outcome is the mapping of how the processing cycle uses inputs, program, instructions, and data bus (other chassis computers) data. Manufacturers use this term to describe all of the factors and preconditions required in processing to produce a specific outcome. For instance, if we say that $1 + 2 + 3 + 4 = 10$, we can say that we have used the rules of addition, applied the values, and come up with an outcome, 10, as the sum of the values. If any one of the values used in that example changes, the end result or outcome will change. So, if the number 1 is replaced by the number 6, the outcome or sum of the values has to change: When we apply the rules of addition, the outcome changes to 15.

The control algorithm used by an engine management system uses the same means to produce outcomes, except that there are hundreds of rules and thousands of values. The values are received into the processing cycle by the input circuit, from memory, and off the chassis data bus. The rules are logged into the ECM memory components known as ROM, PROM, and EEPROM. The computer then manipulates this data in main memory or RAM and computes an outcome.

Processing Power

Controllers networked to the J1939 bus run from 8-bit CPUs that perform straightforward tasks such as managing air bags or climate control to 32-bit diesel engine management CPUs. The industry is moving toward 64-bit controllers, largely because of the need to more precisely manage cylinder combustion and the complex emission control hardware. There is a disadvantage in using high-power 32- and 64-bit controllers (it is not cost, they are inexpensive today) in chassis that do not make significant use of multiplexing (at the time of writing, some current OEM chassis rely entirely on the J1939 and older J1587/1708 buses), due to the vast number of wires required for the input and output devices. This results in a wiring harness that looks like an anaconda emerging from the ECM.

If you compare the wiring congestion on a generously multiplexed chassis (such as recent versions of Navistar's Diamond Plus and the Freightliner Cascadia system) with the wiring on those that are not, it is easy to tell why multiplexing has become standard in the truck manufacturing industry.

ECM SELF-DIAGNOSTIC CAPABILITY

A major benefit of the truck and bus electronics systems manufacturers' compliance with SAE J1939 and J1587 powertrain data bus software protocols is the fact that current systems can at minimum be read by most electronic service tools (ESTs). This is achieved by industry standardized SAE bus standards using **source addresses (SAs)**, message identifiers (MIDs), system identifiers (SIDs), parameter group numbers (PGNs), parameter identifiers (PIDs), and **failure mode indicators (FMIs)**.

Self-diagnostic capability in diesel engine electronics systems can be grouped as onboard, in the form of flash codes or digital data displays; and EST-read, such as by handheld electronic service tools, and PC-based systems. The use of these instruments is covered in Chapter 35 and in chapters dealing with each specific system. The self-diagnostic capability of most current engines goes beyond just identifying electronic faults. Logic maps are used to identify many common hydromechanical faults, and post-2010 systems use an expanded suite of FMIs that can identify suspected pending failures.

TIME AND ELECTRONICALLY MANAGED ENGINES

Until the widespread use of electronics, engine technicians generally referred to timing and events within the engine cycle in terms of crank angle degrees. This tendency has shifted, as the data readouts produced by the onboard electronics in many systems tend to use time as well as crank angle to report engine events such as EUI response time and duty cycle. It may help the technician to have a basic understanding of some of the time dimensions within which engine events take place, especially when it comes to making sense of some of the data displayed by ESTs.

Time and RPM

If an engine rotates at a typical low idle speed of 600 rpm, it turns through 10 complete rotations in 1 second. When an engine rotates at 2,000 rpm, one rotation of the engine takes place in 30 milliseconds (0.03 second), the engine rotates through 33 revolutions in a second, and the typical fueling pulse of an EUI lasts about 3 milliseconds

(0.003 second). It should also be noted that a fuel pulse width (PW) of 3 milliseconds at 2,000 rpm results in fuel being injected for around 35 crank angle degrees, whereas a PW of 3 milliseconds at 600 rpm translates into fuel being injected for only around 10 crank angle degrees. The reason why a small variance in a factor such as injector response time is significant is that it can dramatically impact engine operation.

OUTPUT CIRCUIT

The switching apparatus used with each electronic management system is what truly differentiates each system from any other. Although the switching and pumping apparatus in full authority engine management systems have certain similarities regardless of the OEM system, it is more appropriate to address this technology by fuel system type rather than generally in this section. At the moment of writing, full authority engine management systems use EUIs, hydraulically actuated electronic unit injectors (HEUIs), EUPs, and common rail (CR) actuators that characterize each OEM system. Medium- and heavy-duty highway diesel engines certified for 2013 Environmental Protection Agency (EPA) highway compliance and beyond are using just four basic fuel systems:

- EUI with electrohydraulic nozzles
- CR with electrohydraulic injectors
- HEUI systems
- EUP with electrohydraulic injectors

The output circuit always begins in the ECM or in a module bussed to it. **Figure 34–28** shows the relationship of the ECM switching unit or output drivers within the processing cycle.

FIGURE 34–28 ECM actuator control.

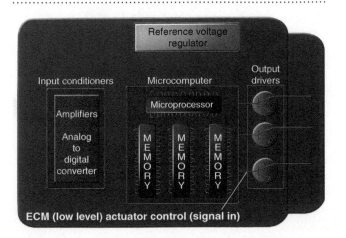

FIGURE 34–29 ECM to harness connectors.

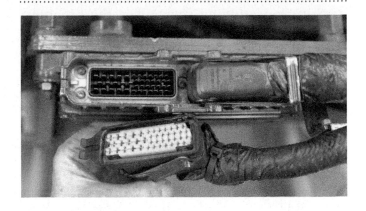

ACTUATORS

A wide range of actuators are used on diesel engine control systems. ECM signals are communicated to actuators via engine and chassis harnesses, as shown in **Figure 34–29**. Most actuators are fairly simple in terms of their operating principle. We take a brief look at some of them here.

Solenoids

A simple solenoid consists of a coil and an armature. The coil is usually stationary and the armature moves within it. The armature can be integral with devices such as hydraulic poppet valves, spool valves, and levers that effect mechanical movement. A simple solenoid has two status conditions: *off* or *on*. In most cases, the armature is spring-loaded to default to the mechanical *off* position when no current is flowed through the coil. When an ECM driver energizes the coil, the magnetic field that builds mechanically moves the armature. This is the principle used in the control cartridge of a solenoid-actuated injector. Because solenoids use electromagnetism, they respond more slowly due to the time required to build and collapse electromagnetic fields: This limits their use in applications that require fast response and frequent cycling.

Proportioning Solenoids

Proportioning solenoids are coil-and-armature devices that function similarly to a solenoid except that they are capable of precise linear or rotary positioning. To ensure the accuracy of the position, most proportioning solenoids are equipped with a means of signaling *actual* position while the ECM driver attempts to control current flow to the proportioning solenoid to maintain desired position: this results in a closed-loop correction cycle. An example of a rotary proportioning solenoid is the brushless torque motor (BTM) used in some early electronically managed Caterpillar engines. Examples of linear proportioning solenoids are the injection actuation pressure (IAP) oil control spool valve used in HEUI-fueled engines, or the rail pressure control valve used in the high-pressure pumps on CR fuel systems.

Piezo Actuators

Piezo actuators (see Chapter 32 for an explanation of operating principles) have an advantage over solenoids because of their super-fast response rates. The building and collapsing of magnetic fields is required to move an electromagnetic device such as a solenoid, but the mechanical response of a piezo actuator occurs the instant it is hit by an electrical trigger. The first generation of piezo actuators was bulky due to the size of the stack of piezo wafers required, but this is changing fast. Not only is the physical size of these actuators being reduced, but they also usually require lower electrical actuation pressures (voltages) and current draw. **Figure 34–30** shows the piezo actuator stack used in a typical piezo electrohydraulic injector.

FIGURE 34–30 Piezo actuator stack from an electrohydraulic injector (EHI) shown in de-energized and energized positions.

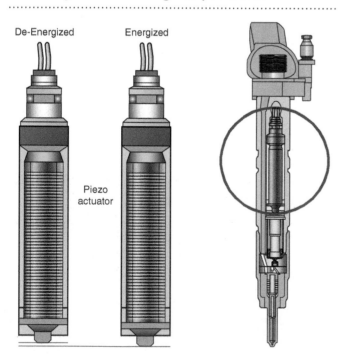

Stepper Motors

A *stepper motor* is a brushless electric motor capable of precision positioning of a shaft (and whatever is connected to it). A normal direct current (DC) electric motor spins when current is flowed through its electromagnetic fields. Stepper motors use multiple toothed electromagnets arranged around a rotor gear integral with the motor shaft. All but one of the toothed electromagnets are slightly offset from the gear teeth on the rotor: This means that when the rotor gear teeth are perfectly aligned with one of the toothed electromagnets, they are slightly offset from the teeth on the others. When the next electromagnet in the rotation is energized, the rotor gear moves slightly to realign the magnetic field and completes a "step." Typically, four electromagnets are used, spaced 90 degrees apart in the rotation. In this way, the rotor can be precisely aligned to any position in rotation. The precision increases with the number of teeth in the rotor and, correspondingly, on the electromagnets. **Figure 34–31** demonstrates the principle of a stepper motor.

ECM-controlled stepper motors are versatile positioning devices and have application in door/gate controls such as those used in EGR mixers. Controls are simple, and when driven by an 8-bit controller, outputs can be divided into up to 256 micro steps, providing some precision of placement. Because a constant DC current flow creates heat (and therefore resistance variables),

FIGURE 34–31 Principle of a stepper motor.

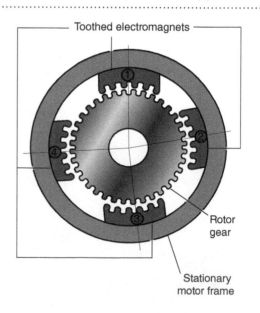

they are regulated by pulse width modulation (PWM) to reduce resistance-generated heat in the controller.

ECM PROGRAMMING

Vehicle ECM programming can be divided into two general categories: customer data programming and proprietary data programming. *Customer data programming* generally refers to any information that may have to be changed on a routine basis. It is usually concerned with day-to-day running parameters that the vehicle owner has ownership of. *Proprietary data programming* is that data that the engine manufacturer has ownership of. Typical proprietary data concerns the core system management algorithms that may require alteration in the lifetime of the system or perhaps may be vulnerable to corruption. Examples of proprietary data are the engine fuel map and maximum BHP.

CUSTOMER DATA PROGRAMMING

Most OEMs have designed their systems so that a wide range of running parameters can be altered to accommodate a change in chassis application and driver or owner preference. Usually all that is required to alter "customer data" is the ECM customer password. Fleets may sometimes not provide their drivers with the vehicle ECM password. Additionally, some fleets use an alpha password to either prevent or make difficult customer data programming changes with commonly available, generic HH-ESTs. Many customer data programming options are electronically toggled. This means you have no choice but to choose one option or the other. An example is the governor-type option. In this programming field you can either choose variable speed (VS) or limiting speed (LS) governing. We define this as a toggle option.

Typical Customer Programming Options

Other customer programming options would define limits, such as road speed limit (RSL) or idle shutdown time limit. Some examples of typical customer data programming options offered by OEMs are:

- **Governor type.** Any current truck engine management system can be programmed to governor type according to the preferences of the operator. The common options, LS and VS, are normally toggled options to ensure that one or the other is selected. See Chapter 20 for an explanation of governor options.

- **Power takeoff (PTO) governing/limits.** Precise isochronous (zero droop) governing was, before the electronic age, a costly governing option required in any engine driving a generator, in which application a change in engine load required an immediate governor response in fueling to maintain a constant speed and thus avoid variations in the electrical frequency. Isochronous governing in electronically managed engines is incorporated in the programmed software, and the term is used by some OEMs to describe the operation of the engine when driving PTO equipment such as pumps and compressors.

- **Cruise control parameters.** The upper and lower limits are programmable. Actual values are programmed by the driver operating the vehicle using dash switches. Smart cruise (flexible parameter) programming available in many current systems makes cruise control capable of producing fuel-to-mileage figures superior to those of hard (rigid parameter) cruise control. Smart cruise programming can also "reward" a driver who improves on projected vehicle fuel economy by increasing governed road speed.

- **Road speed limit (RSL).** Any observer of trucks driven on the highways will note that this is a popular option with large fleets that capitalize on the fuel-to-mileage and safety benefits of having a vehicle run at a lower maximum road speed. It is a programming option that most owner-operators choose not to take advantage of, but in some jurisdictions, it has recently become mandatory to have RSL enabled at a set speed.

- **Critical shutdown sensors.** A coolant level sensor can be programmed to a number of failure strategies if its ground (through the liquid coolant) is lost for a predetermined period. The failure strategies could vary from a simple warning alert to the driver, to ramping down to a default rpm/maximum load, or to shutting down the engine. The ECM could be programmed to neither shut down or derate the engine in an emergency vehicle such as a fire truck.

- **Tire size.** Tire size must be programmed using a tire specification manual that defines a tire's rolling radius. This is usually programmed to the ECM in revolutions per mile or revolutions per kilometer. It is important to note that two nominal 22.5-inch tires of different tread code ratings (even if they are manufactured by the same manufacturer) may have quite different dynamic rolling radii. Incorrectly programmed tire data (on the drive wheels) will result in false road speed data signaled to the ECM and, coincidentally, inaccurate speedometer and mileage information.

Additional examples of typical customer data programming options offered by OEMs include:

- Transmission ratio
- Carrier ratio
- Progressive shifting limits
- Idle speed
- Torque rise profile
- Peak brake power
- Idle shutdown duration

Customer data programming must fall within parameters defined in the ECM's data retention media. For instance, if the maximum high-idle speed in a given engine is defined by its management ECM as 2,000 rpm, this value cannot be reprogrammed to a higher value using the preceding methods. You can reference the typical reprogramming procedure that appears in Chapter 35 if you want to take a closer look at reprogramming right now.

> **TECH TIP:**
>
> Customer data programming fields may be first-level password protected to prevent unwanted rewriting of critical parameters. Unless properly authorized, avoid obliging fleet driver requests to reprogram data in such fields as progressive shifting and road speed limit, or you may lose a customer. After all, the fleet owns the truck and pays the fuel bills.

PROPRIETARY DATA PROGRAMMING

The technician enables proprietary data programming but in many cases does not actually perform the reprogramming. Proprietary data includes any ECM-programmed data that the OEM does not want the customer to alter. A good example is the fuel map. There are circumstances in which the fuel map might have to be rewritten or altered, but this would have to be accomplished by the OEM from its data hub. In the event that critical ECM files become damaged

or corrupted, proprietary data reprogramming may be required. Another example would be if the customer requested an increase in horsepower after purchase: this would require altering the fuel map. For this type of reprogramming, it is normal to charge the customer. Proprietary data programming normally takes place in three distinct stages: downloading, programming the ECM, and uploading verification.

Downloading

Downloading requires accessing the OEM's centrally located mainframe via a PC, the Internet, and OEM software. The vehicle is identified electronically, usually by its vehicle identification number (VIN), and the OEM software routes itself to the correct mainframe location of the system files. In some cases, the technician may be required to input passwords to enable this step. The mainframe computer can be viewed as a sort of filing cabinet. The function of the OEM software on your computer is to locate system files that pertain to the specific vehicle identified by its VIN. Having located these files, they are next downloaded to the PC's electronic memory, from which they can be copied to disks or transferred directly to the vehicle ECM. This step in the process does not require that the vehicle be electronically connected to whatever computer is being used. In fact, it could be out on the highway at the time of the transaction.

Programming the ECM

The system files that were copied to computer memory can now be transferred to the vehicle ECM. A portable PC (a laptop computer would be the instrument of choice) can be connected to the vehicle ECM by means of:

- A communications adapter (CA) and the data connector, a six-pin or nine-pin Deutsch connector
- A wireless handshake (if both the laptop and vehicle are wireless enabled)

Now, by adhering to some menu-driven sequencing, the downloaded files can be transferred to the ECM, usually by scan and overwrite so the procedure is fast. On completion, a verification file is created in computer (laptop) memory.

Before reprogramming, certain requirements usually must be met. For instance, the vehicle ignition circuit must usually be closed (switched *on*) with the engine stationary. All fault codes usually have to be cleared before reprogramming. Additionally, it would make sense to obtain a printout of all customer programmable options *before* reprogramming, because these may be erased by the process, depending on the system. Customer data sometimes has to be reprogrammed after a proprietary data reprogramming procedure. Some OEMs use the term *flashing* or *reflashing* ECM memory to describe programming.

CAUTION:

Most OEMs currently advise against wireless reprogramming of engine files using wireless technology. Should an unwanted interrupt take place, ECM files may become corrupted, requiring replacement.

Uploading

The term **upload** usually describes the transfer of data from one computer system to another, and in this sequence of events it is the final step in ECM reprogramming. The verification file created in computer memory by the vehicle ECM following reprogramming must, within a certain period of time, be uploaded to the OEM's data hub. This confirms that the reprogramming has been successful in the OEM mainframe computer's files on the vehicle. Once again, the Internet is used, so the verification file can be uploaded. Uploading verification files is a recordkeeping procedure.

Proprietary data reprogramming is a simple set of procedures. These require some familiarity with PCs. However, most of the sequencing is menu driven, and OEMs have designed the procedures to be as user friendly as possible. As each new software version is released, reprogramming becomes progressively simpler.

ENGINE MANAGEMENT SYSTEMS

Management systems for current truck and bus fuel systems tend to be classified by the degree of control they have over the fueling pulse. It should be noted that much of the language we use to describe truck computer systems was introduced in the early days of engine computer controls. Some of this language is out of date. However, the speed of the computer revolution in vehicles has been such that in a repair shop today you will still find entirely hydromechanically managed trucks alongside those that represent the very latest in electronic management.

FULL AUTHORITY SYSTEMS

For purposes of study, we will identify *full authority engine management systems* as those that were specifically designed for control by computer. This includes:

- EUIs
- EUPs
- HEUIs
- Time-pressure (TP) fuel systems
- CR fuel systems

The term *full authority* indicates that the system ECM has full control of the fueling pulse, but in the case of EUI, EUP, and TP systems not using EHIs, this necessarily occurs within a timing window established by the physical dimensions of the actuating cam profile. So, in reality, it can legitimately be argued that among the preceding systems some are "more full authority" than others.

PARTIAL AUTHORITY SYSTEMS

Partial authority systems are ECM-managed systems in which hydromechanical fueling apparatus has been adapted for computerized control. These are now obsolete; however, although they are not used on current systems, there are still a few examples in field operation, especially off-highway. The extent to which the ECM can control fueling in a partial authority system varies considerably, ranging from a limited function as a vehicle road speed governor to complex management of vehicle functions and engine fueling. Some partial authority management systems offer comprehensive onboard diagnostics, extensive customer data programming options, and proprietary data reprogramming capability. Examples of partial authority management systems are:

- Cat PEEC (3406C) based on a port-helix injection pump
- Mack V-MAC I and V-MAC II based on a port-helix injection pump
- Cummins PT PACE/PACER on NTC 855 based on PT pump fueling
- E-control of rotary distributor pumps: used exclusively on small-bore and off-highway engines

Some partial authority systems appeared on off-highway diesel engines up until 2004, but none appear to be used on larger equipment certified for 2008 and beyond. However, partial authority management systems continue to be manufactured for applications that are subject to lower levels of emissions regulation.

BODY CONTROLLERS

Because some truck OEMs have extensive chassis networking requirements, the powertrain J1939 bus no longer has sufficient bandwidth to handle the traffic. Today, a simple wake-up event can involve inputs from several modules that results in feeding data into the powertrain bus and the ECM before a vehicle can be started. This has led OEMs such as Freightliner to add proprietary buses to handle much of the traffic that is not powertrain related. This is done by "bussing" the J1939 network to a proprietary network. This subject matter is handled at a higher level of detail in Chapter 37, but some basics are introduced here.

Although the SAE has attempted to introduce standard terms and acronyms for components common in all OEM systems, it has been steadfastly ignored by industry, probably due to the significant European ownership of U.S. truck manufacturers. The SAE-recommended acronym for an engine controller is ECM. The SAE-recommended acronym for all other controllers is ECU.

STRANGE OEM NAMES FOR ECUs

Over recent years, our OEMs have come up with increasingly inventive (and confusing) acronyms for system controllers. This has occurred by directly translating a German acronym into English, such as PLD (ECM), or the latest from Freightliner, a SAM module. The acronym *SAM* is derived from the words **signal-detect and actuation module (SAM)**. This is just a clumsy way of describing what any electronic controller does.

There are a couple of SAMs (a body controller and a chassis controller) on any fully multiplexed Freightliner chassis, and because Freightliner is the current market leader, you might as well get used to the terms. However, the best way to understand what any controller with an address on a bus network actually does is to find out what its numeric SA is; when you do this with the SAMs on a Freightliner, you'll discover that one is a body controller and the other a chassis controller. SAs will be studied in more detail in Chapter 37, but SAMs are introduced here because they may incorporate a unique solid-state circuit protection device known as a *polyswitch*, which should be studied in this chapter.

POLYSWITCHES

Polyswitches are **positive temperature coefficient (PTC)** circuit protection devices that are built into some SAM chassis modules to handle certain kinds of intermittent faults. The objective is to provide circuit-breaker-like protection on trailer circuits that can affect the tractor electrical circuit. Polyswitches are auto-resetting, meaning that they can be classified as SAE #1 circuit protection devices.

Polyswitch Construction

The conductive element within a polyswitch is semi-crystalline polymer. The polymer conducts with low resistance until an over-current or short circuit occurs: the current overload causes the polymer medium to melt and expand, upon which its electrical resistance becomes high enough to choke down on excess current flow. This protects the load circuit in series with the polyswitch. The device is held in high-resistance mode until:

- The power source is removed, or:
- The over-current or short has been eliminated

After an overload event, the polymer within the polyswitch typically takes around 2 minutes to cool to its low-resistance state. This is known as *cycle time to reset*.

OTHER FUNCTIONS

The SAMs used on current Freightliner chassis have some other differences. A SAM incorporates a **modular switch field (MSF)**. The MSF is a system of multiplexed switches consisting of a master control module and one or more slave modules and sub-bus switches.

The **master control module** continuously monitors switch status. The switches on the steering wheel, stalk switch, and headlight switch are hard-wired (as opposed to multiplexed) to the master control module. The master control module has a cabin CAN network connection. The cabin CAN is a proprietary network that connects the **central gateway**, the MSF, the SAM Cab (body controller), and the SAM chassis (chassis controller). The function of the central gateway is to enable communication between those modules with addresses on J1939 and those on Freightliner's proprietary buses.

Sub-Buses

Switches located within the slave module communicate with, and connect to, the master control module using a proprietary sub-bus. The slave module is a passive device that can house up to four individual sub-bus switches. There are two types of sub-bus switches that connect to the master control module or slave module:

- Multiplex (signal/ message driven)
- Hard-wire (load interrupting)

The Freightliner **starpoint** junction block acts as a router that provides an electrical termination point to the cabin CAN. Note that SAMs also provide circuit protection to a number of circuits they feed in the form of virtual and hard-wire fuses.

SUMMARY

- All current on-highway trucks use computers to manage the engine and many other chassis systems.
- A truck with multiple ECM-managed systems usually networks them to a chassis data bus to optimize powertrain and vehicle control.
- A vehicle ECM information processing cycle comprises three stages: data input, data processing, and outputs.
- RAM or main memory is electronically retained and therefore volatile.
- The master program for engine management in an engine controller ECM is usually written to ROM.
- PROM data is used to qualify the ROM data to a specific chassis application.
- EEPROM is used for write-to-self capability, detailing customer and proprietary programming, holding failure strategy, logging codes, and recording audit trails and tattletales.
- Some OEMs describe their PROM and EEPROM component as a "personality module."
- *Multiplexing* is the term used to describe system network transactions in which two or more ECMs share data. Multiplexing reduces input hardware and optimizes vehicle operation.
- Input data is divided into *command* data and system *monitoring* data.
- Thermistors precisely measure temperature and operate on either an NTC or PTC principle.
- Variable capacitance-type sensors are often used to measure pressure values.
- Piezoresistive sensors using a Wheatstone bridge circuit can also be used for pressure measurement signaling.

- Throttle position sensors use either a potentiometer or Hall-effect operating principle.
- Hall-effect sensors generate a digital signal and are used to signal either rotating or linear position and speed data.
- Induction pulse generators are used to input shaft rotational speed data.
- Truck engine management ECMs are responsible for regulating reference voltage, conditioning input data, processing, and driving outputs.
- The ECM processes data at different frequencies that are known as foreground and background computations.
- Engine management ECMs can be mounted on the engine itself or in a remote location such as under the dash.
- ECM outputs require drivers to actuate a range of output devices. Output devices are known as *actuators*. Some examples of actuators are solenoids, proportioning solenoids, stepper motors, and piezo actuators.
- Customer data programming includes those parameters that may require change on a day-to-day basis, as well as those that may have to be reprogrammed if the vehicle application changes or critical components are changed.
- Proprietary data reprogramming is usually performed in these three stages: downloading system files, reprogramming the ECM, and uploading verification.
- Full authority engine management is used to describe the systems designed for management by the computer.

- The term *partial authority management* describes a system in which hydromechanical fueling apparatus has been adapted for computerized management of an engine.
- As multiplexing technology develops, the bandwidth of the J1939 powertrain bus becomes insufficient to handle the traffic for some of the more advanced vehicle systems. In these cases, OEM buses complement the powertrain bus and interact with it by means of a gateway.

REVIEW QUESTIONS

1. The acronym for the internal computer component that executes program instructions is:
   a. CRT.
   b. RAM.
   c. CPU.
   d. ROM.

2. Which of the following data retention media is electronically retained?
   a. RAM
   b. ROM
   c. PROM
   d. EEPROM

3. To which of the following memory categories would the master program for engine management be written in a typical truck engine ECM?
   a. RAM
   b. ROM
   c. PROM
   d. EEPROM

4. To which of the following memory categories would customer data programming be written from an electronic service tool?
   a. RAM
   b. ROM
   c. PROM
   d. EEPROM

5. Which of the following components conditions V-Ref?
   a. ECM
   b. Voltage regulator
   c. EUI
   d. Personality module

6. A thermistor is responsible for signaling data concerning:
   a. pressure.
   b. temperature.
   c. rotational speed.
   d. rotational position.

7. A Hall-effect sensor is usually responsible for signaling data concerning:
   a. pressure.
   b. temperature.
   c. fluid flow.
   d. rotational or linear position.

8. Induction pulse generators are used to input data concerning:
   a. pressure.
   b. temperature.
   c. rotational speed.
   d. altitude.

9. Which of the following components uses a voltage divider principle and can be used to signal accelerator pedal travel?
   a. Pulse generator
   b. Potentiometer
   c. Thermistor
   d. Galvanic sensor

10. Which of the following input components would more likely use a variable capacitance-type sensor?
    a. CPS
    b. TRS
    c. VSS
    d. MAP

11. In a full authority diesel engine management system, EUI switching is performed by:
    a. a personality module.
    b. injector drivers.
    c. V-Ref.
    d. FIC module.

12. Technician A states that a disadvantage of a piezo actuator is that it requires a much higher current draw than comparable solenoid actuators. Technician B states that an advantage of piezo actuators is that they are much less bulky than comparable solenoids. Who is correct?
    a. Technician A only
    b. Technician B only
    c. Both A and B
    d. Neither A nor B

13. Technician A states that Hall-effect TPSs use a noncontact principle that makes them more reliable than potentiometer types. Technician B states that a Hall-effect TPS does not require an input voltage to function. Who is correct?
    a. Technician A only
    b. Technician B only
    c. Both A and B
    d. Neither A nor B

14. Technician A states that V-Ref and the injector driver voltage are usually managed by the ECM to the same voltage values. Technician B states that V-Ref is controlled by the vehicle battery and is not conditioned by the ECM. Who is correct?
    a. Technician A only
    b. Technician B only
    c. Both A and B
    d. Neither A nor B

15. Technician A states that in some of the earliest engine management ECMs, the only method of changing customer options, such as idle shutdown duration and transmission ratios, was to replace the ECM PROM chip. Technician B states that in most current vehicle management systems, customer programmable options are written to ROM. Who is correct?
    a. Technician A only
    b. Technician B only
    c. Both A and B
    d. Neither A nor B

16. Technician A states that in most diesel engine ECMs, RAM data is lost whenever the engine is shut down. Technician B states that some systems write data to a special type of RAM that is nonvolatile because it connects directly to the battery. Who is correct?
    a. Technician A only
    b. Technician B only
    c. Both A and B
    d. Neither A nor B

17. Technician A states that engine overspeed rpm is usually programmed to the ECM as a hard value. Technician B states that the engine oil/coolant overheat temperature value was usually programmed to the ECM as a soft value because it would depend on the ambient temperatures. Who is correct?
    a. Technician A only
    b. Technician B only
    c. Both A and B
    d. Neither A nor B

18. Technician A states that it is not unusual for the vehicle maximum speed to be programmed at a lower speed than maximum cruise speed. Technician B states that because fuel economy is so important in trucking operations, soft cruise is a popular option. Who is correct?
    a. Technician A only
    b. Technician B only
    c. Both A and B
    d. Neither A nor B

19. Which of the following customer data programming fields could be described as a toggle option?
    a. Road speed limit
    b. Transmission ratios
    c. Tire rolling radii
    d. Governor type

20. When a Wheatstone bridge-type sensor is referred to, which of the following would correctly describe it?
    a. Hall-effect sensor
    b. Piezoresistive sensor
    c. Variable capacitance sensor
    d. Voltage divider

35

Prerequisites: Chapters 32, 33, and 34

ESTs AND SISs

OBJECTIVES

After studying this chapter, you should be able to:

- Define the acronyms EST and SIS.
- Identify the different types of EST in current usage and the levels of access and programming capability of each.
- Spec out a digital multimeter (DMM) that suits your objectives on the shop floor.
- Describe the operating principles of different types of DMM.
- Perform some basic electrical circuit diagnosis using a DMM.
- Test some everyday input circuit components such as thermistors and potentiometers.
- Identify and describe the functional capabilities of different types of handheld ESTs.
- Update a handheld electronic service tool by downloading online updates.
- Identify all of the major OEM online service information systems (SISs).
- Identify the diagnostic software used by each of the major OEMs.
- Define the objectives of a snapshot test.
- Outline the importance of completing each step when performing sequential trouble-shooting testing of electronic circuits.
- Connect a PC to a chassis data bus using the correct communications adapter (CA).
- Identify the importance of using an ABDC EST when connecting to any post-2014 J1939 data bus.
- Outline the procedures required to troubleshoot some simple electronic faults using proprietary ESTs running ET and MD software.
- Outline the procedure required to perform reprogramming of an ECM with customer and proprietary data.
- Interpret SAs, PG, PGNs, MIDs, PIDs, SIDs, and FMIs.
- Identify the prognostic fault mode indicators (FMIs).
- Explain how the implementation of HD-OBD might impact service procedures.
- Respond appropriately to all critical dash warning alerts including CEL, MIL, and SEL events.

KEY TERMS

active codes

assembly line data link (ALDL)

auto-baud detect capable (ABDC)

blink codes

breakout box

breakout T

check engine light (CEL)

clip points

continuity

current transformers

data communications link (DCL)

data link connector (DLC)

Deutsch connector

diagnostic link connector (DLC)

diagnostic trouble code (DTC)

digital multimeter (DMM)

electronic data recorder (EDR)

electronic logging device (ELD)

electronic onboard data recorder (EOBR)

electronic service tool (EST)

fault mode indicator (FMI)

flash codes

ground strap

Hall-effect probe

handheld (HH)

handheld electronic service tools (HH-ESTs)

handshake

heavy-duty, onboard diagnostics (HD-OBD)

historic codes

inactive codes

malfunction indicator light (MIL)

message identifier (MID)

meter resolution

onboard diagnostics II (OBD II)

open circuit

parameter group (PG)

parameter group number (PGN)

parameter identifier (PID)

Power Service Literature (PSL)

predictive repair logic

Pro-Link iQ

reader-programmer

Right-to-Repair

root mean square (rms)

SAE J1587

SAE J1708

SAE J1939

scopemeter

snapshot test

source address (SA)

stop engine light (SEL)

stop engine override (SEO or STEO)

subsystem identifier (SID)

thermistors

vehicle data link (VDL)

wireless vehicle link 2 (WVL2)

INTRODUCTION

The acronym **EST (electronic service tool)** is generally used in the trucking industry to cover a range of electronic service instruments ranging from onboard diagnostic/malfunction lights to sophisticated computer-based communications equipment. The study of ESTs should always begin with an introduction to digital multimeters (DMMs), which continue to be the workhorse of electrical and electronics troubleshooting. One of the first tools that a truck technician should purchase is a good quality DMM. This chapter will help a technician understand how a DMM works and explain its features in some detail.

Generic diagnostic ESTs are reviewed in this chapter because they are much used by fleet technicians and those working in independent service garages. This category of EST can either be handheld or computer based. Proprietary ESTs are designed to work with an original equipment manufacturer's (OEM's) specific electronics. The handheld proprietary EST has become a thing of the past for diesel engine technicians, with OEMs generally opting for low-cost, powerful personal computers (usually laptops) whose hardware and software can be cheaply upgraded. Some OEMs bundle their software into a portable PC hardware package such as a Panasonic Toughbook, known for its ruggedness on shop floor environments—along with a recommendation that the laptop be exclusively used with that manufacturer's product. This helps avoid file clashes that may occur when a single Windows platform is loaded with multiple OEM software.

DATA CONNECTOR STANDARDS

ESTs capable of reading engine control module (ECM) data are connected to the onboard electronics by means of a **data link connector (DLC)**, a **diagnostic link connector (DLC)**, or a **data communications link (DCL)**. The actual term used varies with the OEM; for purposes of this text, the term *DLC* will be used. DLCs are standardized by Society of Automotive Engineers (SAE) J-standards, but they vary by generation. The following are used today:

- J1587/J1708 six-pin Deutsch
- J1939 black nine-pin Deutsch (pre-2014)
- J1939 green nine-pin Deutsch (post-2014)
- J1962 sixteen-pin (ALDL) (post-2014 Volvo-Mack)

Standardized connectors and the adherence by the engine electronics OEMs to SAE data bus software protocols enable proprietary software of one manufacturer to at least read the parameters and conditions of its competitors using standardized software known as *heavy-duty reader*. This means that if a Cummins-powered truck has an electronic failure in a location where the only service dealer is Detroit Diesel Corporation (DDC), some first-level problem diagnosis can be undertaken using the DDC electronic diagnostic software.

More advanced access to a truck data bus may be possible using generic **handheld (HH)** ESTs loaded with OEM subscription software, but truck OEMs have generally been unwilling to share the software required for anything but basic troubleshooting. At the moment of writing, truck OEMs have limited full access to their electronic networks to their dealerships and fleet customers. It remains to be seen what will result from **Right-to-Repair** initiatives being enacted by a number of states.

The Technology and Maintenance Council (TMC) is in the process of establishing standard **clip points** agreed to by all OEMs. *Clip points* are locations on a data bus onto which ESTs can be physically connected for **handshake** access. The term *handshake* is often used in computer technology to describe two-way communication. The pending implementation of HD-OBD promises to o pen up any OEM chassis data bus for nonproprietary access to at least any emissions-related problems; this is addressed in further detail toward the end of this chapter.

DEVELOPMENT OF ESTs

Electronic service tools (ESTs) have developed since trucks entered the electronic age just over two decades ago and although they have evolved, they have added to rather than shed the more primitive predecessors. We will take a look at some of the ESTs used today and their capabilities. Today's EST categories can be grouped as follows:

- Flash codes: Recalled by using a paper clip, button, or ignition key cycling to signal blink codes.
- Scanners: Simple read-only devices that could do little more than analyze parametric data.
- Handheld (HH) reader-programmers: Generic and proprietary devices that could both "scan" and perform some of the diagnostics and programming required of truck diagnostic systems.
- Intelligent HH reader-programmers: Compact devices with online, wireless, and interactive capability.
- PC-based software with CAs (pass-through capability): In the world of truck engines, this has been the primary EST from the beginning. Only these can analyze and diagnose parametric data, along with providing online capability that affords dynamic feedback to OEM data hubs and structured/interactive diagnostic logic.

The latest EST software, in conjunction with an SIS and diagnostic software, can identify potential developing problems (**predictive repair logic** capability) before real-world problems impact vehicle operation. In addition, data fed back to an OEM data hub can be used for prognostic analysis. In fact, data feedback to an OEM data hub goes way beyond mere diagnostics: It includes such things as GPS, mileage, fuel usage, prognostic data mining, and driver evaluation, which some fleets might argue is their propriety information rather than that of the OEM.

ONBOARD DIAGNOSTIC LIGHTS

Blink or **flash codes** (OEMs use both terms) are an onboard means of troubleshooting using a dash or ECM-mounted electronic malfunction light or check engine light (CEL). Usually only **active codes** (ones that indicate a malfunction at the time of reading) can be read in truck (engine) ECMs, but some also read historic (inactive) codes.

DIGITAL DASH DISPLAY

Depending on the OEM and the chassis options, a digital dash display can be enabled to broadcast fault codes. In fact, it has the potential to display any data communicated over bus lines, though most operators are careful about how much distracting data actually gets displayed, especially while a truck is mobile. Most of the OEMs provide options that enable reading of at least some bus data on a dash display.

DIGITAL MULTIMETERS

The **digital multimeter (DMM)** is an essential diagnostic instrument that should be part of every truck technician's tool chest. It is used to troubleshoot electronic circuits and test components. We take a close look at how to use a DMM in this chapter, including some information on what to look for when purchasing one.

SCANNERS

Scanners were originally read-only tools capable of reading active and **historic** or **inactive** (logged but not currently indicating a malfunction) **codes** and sometimes system parameters, but little else. They are obsolete as a truck/bus diesel engine diagnostic tool, but the term is sometimes used to describe any type of handheld (HH) electronic service tool (EST). The term has lingered on in automotive technology (although in today's world they do much more than "scan") and for that reason, it is sometimes used by truck technicians.

GRAPHING METERS

Graphing meters or **scopemeters** are designed to display waveforms produced by a variety of electrical signals. They are not often used on the shop floor today because OEM diagnostic software will do the same job much more rapidly when it is important to interpret a waveform anomaly. However, they are useful instruments in a learning environment, because they can help students create a visual image of an electrical waveform and background versus real time. In addition, they can be used to verify (but not interpret) bus node activity, so they can be used to confirm whether a bus address is active or not, something we will take a closer look at in Chapter 37.

GENERIC ESTs

Generic ESTs capable of communicating with truck data buses were originally known as **reader-programmers**. Today, we more commonly refer to them as generic **handheld electronic service tools (HH-ESTs)**. Generic HH-ESTs are microcomputer-based and designed to read and reprogram customer data so long as they are loaded with the appropriate software. They are usually tough and portable.

For some time, the Pro-Link 9000 was the industry standard, and there are still plenty of these basic ESTs around despite the fact that they have limited functionality with today's electronic systems. The current versions of the Nexiq Pro-Link family capable of working with post-2013 engines, along with a couple of competitor HH-ESTs, are:

- Pro-Link iQ
- Pocket iQ
- Noregon J-Pro
- Dearborn Group DPA

Some generic HH-ESTs are available with more advanced suites of options, but what they can do depends on how well they are supported with software by the OEM.

PROPRIETARY EST SOFTWARE

These are PC-based diagnostic and programming software packages engineered by an OEM for use on its specific system. These programs are designed to run on a personal computer (PC) in a Windows environment with web access. There are many advantages to using PCs: They are cheap, easy to upgrade, and universal. PCs can be connected to a vehicle data bus either wirelessly or by means of a hardwire connection.

In order to use a PC as a truck EST, it must be loaded with the appropriate software, usually supplied by the chassis OEM on a subscription or license basis. In addition, key pieces of hardware are required, including a serial link communications adapter that provides pass-through capability and means of connecting to the truck electronics. We will cover how the software is used and connections are made in some detail later in this chapter.

All the OEMs offer comprehensive courses on their own management systems. Although navigation of OEM software has become progressively more user friendly, technicians are advised to take OEM courses so they can get the best out of the system. Most of these courses can be taken online with subscription-managed, OEM data hub access.

As OEMs increasingly adopt high-speed control area networks (CANs), more powerful PC systems will be required to diagnose and reprogram electronic management systems. The result is that while proprietary HH-ESTs may continue to have a role in scanning the data bus, any meaningful troubleshooting or diagnostics requires more computing power.

GENERIC EST SOFTWARE

In addition to OEM PC-based software, companies such as Noregon and Mitchell One offer

FIGURE 35–4 DMM push buttons.

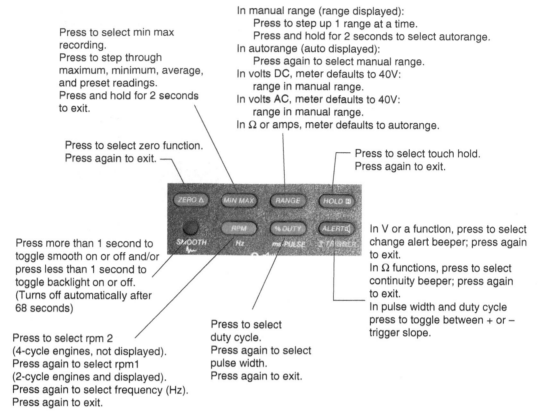

The pushbuttons are used to select meter operations. When a button is pushed, a display symbol will appear and the beeper will sound. Changing the rotary switch setting will reset all pushbuttons to their default settings.

Press to select min max recording.
Press to step through maximum, minimum, average, and preset readings.
Press and hold for 2 seconds to exit.

Press to select zero function.
Press again to exit.

In manual range (range displayed):
Press to step up 1 range at a time.
Press and hold for 2 seconds to select autorange.
In autorange (auto displayed):
Press again to select manual range.
In volts DC, meter defaults to 40V: range in manual range.
In volts AC, meter defaults to 40V: range in manual range.
In Ω or amps, meter defaults to autorange.

Press to select touch hold.
Press again to exit.

Press more than 1 second to toggle smooth on or off and/or press less than 1 second to toggle backlight on or off. (Turns off automatically after 68 seconds)

In V or a function, press to select change alert beeper; press again to exit.
In Ω functions, press to select continuity beeper; press again to exit.
In pulse width and duty cycle press to toggle between + or – trigger slope.

Press to select rpm 2 (4-cycle engines, not displayed).
Press again to select rpm1 (2-cycle engines and displayed).
Press again to select frequency (Hz).
Press again to exit.

Press to select duty cycle.
Press again to select pulse width.
Press again to exit.

Data Display

The data display is the means used to read the measurements made by the DMM. **Figure 35–5** shows the data display used on a high-end DMM. Many current DMMs have the ability to display both digital and analog readings. The analog display is simply an analog representation of the digital reading made by the meter, but it is often easier to interpret. The digital display should be used for stable input values, while the analog display should be used for frequently changing inputs. The acronym OL used in the display means overloaded or out of range.

RESOLUTION

Resolution specifications are often misunderstood. They tell you how fine a measurement can be made with the instrument. Digits and counts are used to describe the resolution capability of a DMM. A $3\frac{1}{2}$-digit meter can display three full digits ranging from 0 to 9 and one-half digit that displays either 1 or is left blank. A $3\frac{1}{2}$-digit meter therefore displays 1,999 counts

of resolution. A $4\frac{1}{2}$-digit DMM can display up to 19,999 counts of resolution.

However, many DMMs have enhanced resolution, so the meter's reading power is usually expressed in counts rather than digits. For instance, a $3\frac{1}{2}$-digit meter may have enhanced resolution of 4,000 counts. Basically, **meter resolution** is expressed in counts rather than digits. For example, a $3\frac{1}{2}$-digit or 1,999-count meter will not measure down to 0.1 V when measuring 200 V or higher. However, a 3,200-count meter will display 0.1 V up to 320 V, giving it the same resolution as a $4\frac{1}{2}$-digit, 19,999-count meter until the voltage exceeds 320 V.

ACCURACY

Accuracy tells you how close the displayed reading on the DMM is to the actual value of the measured signal. This is usually expressed as a percentage of the reading. An accuracy rating of ±1% in a DMM reading a voltage value of 10 V means the actual value could range between 9.9 V and 10.1 V. DMM accuracy can be extended

FIGURE 35–5 DMM data display.

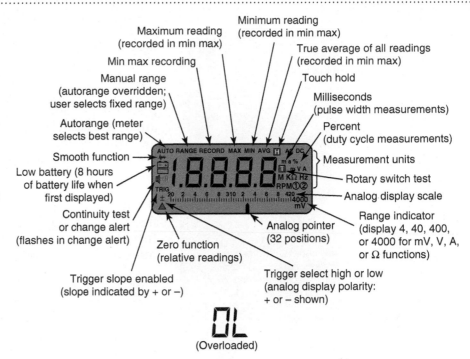

Display

The DMM has a digital and analog display capability. The digital display should be used for stable input values, while the analog display should be used for continuously changing input value. "OL" indicates a value too large to be shown on the digital display.

by indicating how many counts the right display digit may vary. So, an accuracy rating of ± (1% +2) means that a displayed voltage of 10 V could have an actual value range between 9.88 V and 10.12 V. Analog multimeters have accuracy ratings that vary between 2% and 3% of full scale. DMM accuracy ratings range between ± (0.07% + 1) and ± (0.1% + 1) of the *reading*.

OPERATING PRINCIPLES

In any electrical circuit, voltage, current flow, and resistance can be calculated using Ohm's law. A DMM makes use of Ohm's law to measure and display values in an electrical circuit. A typical DMM has the following selection options, which are chosen by rotating the selector to one of the following:

off: Shuts down the DMM

V~: Enables AC voltage readings

V–: Enables DC voltage readings

mV-: Enables low-pressure DC voltage readings

Ω: Enables component or circuit resistance readings

α: Enables **continuity** (a circuit capable of being closed) testing. Identifies an open/closed circuit

A~: Checks current flow (amperage) in an AC circuit

A–: Checks current flow (amperage) in a DC circuit

MEASURING VOLTAGE

Checking circuit supply voltage is usually one of the first steps in troubleshooting. This is performed in a vehicle DC circuit by selecting the V-DC setting and checking for voltage present or high-voltage/low-voltage values. Most electronic equipment is powered by DC voltage. For example, home electronic apparatus such as computers, televisions, and stereos use rectifiers to convert main supply AC voltage to DC voltage.

The waveforms produced by AC voltages can either be sinusoidal (sine waves) or nonsinusoidal (sawtooth, square, ripple). A DMM displays the **root mean square (rms)** value of these voltage waveforms. The rms value is the effective or equivalent DC value of the AC voltage. Meters described as "average responding" give accurate rms readings only if the AC voltage signal is a pure sine wave; they will not accurately measure nonsinusoidal signals. DMMs described as "true-rms" measure the correct rms value regardless of waveform and should be used for nonsinusoidal signals.

FIGURE 35–6 DMM set up for making DC voltage measurements.

12.60
RANGE
DC
mV
=mV
=V
RPM
mA
A
OFF
A
mA
COM
V Ω
RPM
10A MAX FUSED
400 mA MAX FUSED
1000V MAX
+
−

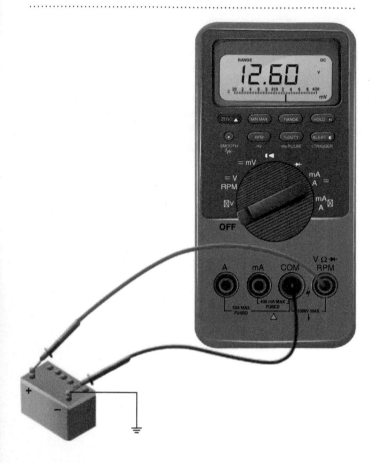

A DMM's ability to measure voltage can be limited by the signal frequency. The DMM specifications for AC voltage and current will identify the frequency range the instrument can accurately measure. Voltage measurements determine:

- Source voltage
- Voltage drop
- Voltage imbalance
- Ripple voltage
- Sensor voltages

Figure 35–6 shows a DMM set up to read DC voltage.

MEASURING RESISTANCE

Most DMMs measure resistance values as low as 0.1 Ω, and some measure high-resistance values up to 300 MΩ (megaohms). Infinite resistance or resistance greater than the instrument can measure is indicated as "OL" or flashing digits on the display. Resistance measurements test the continuity of a circuit when the circuit is not energized. Resistance tests will identify an **open circuit** (one in which there is no path for current flow and would read "OL" on the display) and high circuit resistance.

Resistance and continuity measurements should only be made on unenergized circuits (**Figure 35–7**). Using the resistance or continuity settings to check a circuit or component that is energized will result in damage to the test instrument. Some DMMs are protected against such "accidental" abuse and the extent of damage will depend on the model. For accurate low-resistance measurement, test lead resistance, typically between 0.2 Ω and 0.5 Ω depending on quality and length, must be subtracted from the display reading. Test lead resistance should never exceed 1 W. Some DMMs have a <zero> function that factors test lead resistance to produce a more accurate reading.

If a DMM supplies less than 0.3 V-DC test voltage for measuring resistance, it is capable of testing resistors isolated in a circuit by diodes or semiconductor junctions, meaning that they do not have to be removed from the circuit board. Resistance measurements determine:

- Resistance of a load
- Resistance of conductors
- Value of a resistor
- Operation of variable resistors

FIGURE 35–7 DMM set up for measuring resistance.

Measuring Resistance
To measure resistance, set the DMM rotary switch to Ω to power up the meter. Plug the black (negative) lead into the COM input jack and the red (positive) lead into the VΩ input jack. Because the DMM measures resistance by passing a small current through the component, source voltage must not be present in the circuit. The meter should be in parallel with the component as shown.
002.3
AUTO
OFF
COM
Ignition coil

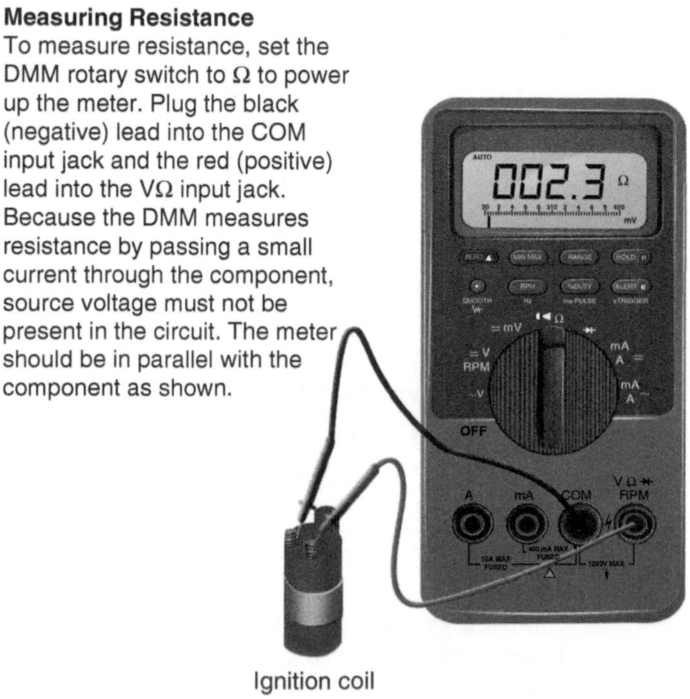

Continuity

Continuity is a quick resistance check that distinguishes between an open and a closed circuit. Most DMMs have audible continuity beepers that beep when they detect a closed circuit, permitting the test to be performed without looking at the meter display. The actual level of resistance required to trigger the beeper varies from model to model. Continuity tests determine:

- Fuse integrity
- Open conductors
- Shorted conductors
- Switch operation
- Circuit paths

Diode Testing

A *diode* is an electronic switch that can conduct electricity in one direction while blocking current flow in the opposite direction. It functions like a one-way electrical check valve. Diodes are commonly enclosed in glass cylinders; a dark band identifies the cathode or blocking terminal. Current flows when the anode is more positive than the cathode. Additionally, a diode will not conduct until the forward voltage pressure reaches a certain value, which is 0.3 V in a silicon diode. Some meters have a diode test mode. When testing a diode with the DMM in this mode, 0.6 V is delivered through the device to indicate continuity; reversing the test leads should indicate an open circuit in a properly functioning diode. If both readings indicate an open circuit condition, the diode is "open." If both readings indicate continuity, the diode is shorted.

MEASURING CURRENT

Current measurements can only be made in series, unlike voltage and resistance readings, which can be made in series or parallel. This means that the circuit electrical path is interrupted and routed right through the DMM. The test leads are plugged into a separate set of input jacks as shown in **Figure 35–8**. Make sure you have an approximate idea of the current you are testing. Get it wrong, and you will be replacing fuses in your DMM. Current measurements determine:

- Circuit overloads
- Circuit operating current
- Current in different branches of a circuit

When the test leads are plugged into the current input jacks and they are used to measure

FIGURE 35–8 DMM set up for measuring current flow.

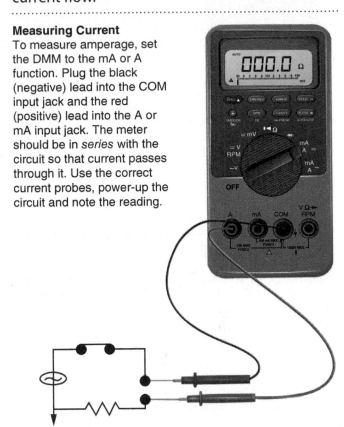

Measuring Current
To measure amperage, set the DMM to the mA or A function. Plug the black (negative) lead into the COM input jack and the red (positive) lead into the A or mA input jack. The meter should be in *series* with the circuit so that current passes through it. Use the correct current probes, power-up the circuit and note the reading.

voltage, this causes a direct short across the source voltage through a low-value resistor inside the DMM called a *current shunt*. If an excessively high current flow is routed through an unprotected meter, both the meter and the circuit can be damaged. A DMM should have current input fuse protection of high enough capacity for the circuit being tested. This protection is mainly of importance when working with high-pressure (220 V +) circuits, but you can also blow a DMM fuse by connecting to a circuit in parallel instead of in series.

CURRENT PROBE ACCESSORIES

When making current measurements that exceed the DMM's rated capacity, a current probe can be used. There are two types.

Current Transformers

Current transformers measure AC current only. Their output is 1 mA per 1 A. Therefore, a current flow of 100 A is reduced to 100 mA, which can be handled by most DMMs. The test leads would be connected to the mA and common input jacks and the meter function switch set to "mA AC." This is not a very accurate circuit test and is used for ballpark reckoning only. There are no applications for this tool in truck electrical systems.

Hall-Effect Probe

The output of a **Hall-effect probe** is 1 mV per ampere. It measures AC or DC. The test leads are connected to the V and common input jacks. The DMM function switch should be set to the V or mV scale, selecting V-AC for AC current and V-DC for DC current measurements; this is not especially accurate. The Hall-effect probe is commonly used to measure cranking motor current draw.

MEASURING FREQUENCY

Frequency is the number of cycles per second (cps) of an AC voltage wave, and it is measured in Hertz (Hz). A complete cycle is the node or positive portion of the AC sine wave, plus the antinode or negative portion of the wave. If you are using this book because you are studying in a Power Generation Technician program, then you should make sure that you obtain a DMM with a frequency counter.

Frequency Measurement Procedure

Most DMMs power up in Autorange voltage mode, which automatically selects range based on the voltage present. If the DMM has no Autorange feature, select the highest voltage first and work downward.

1. Set the function switch to Hz or, in DMMs that have a Hz button, select AC voltage.
2. Plug the black lead into the common jack and the red lead into the voltage jack.
3. Connect the test leads anywhere into the AC circuit.
4. Frequency is displayed providing <Hz> is displayed to the right of the reading on a DMM with a function switch. In DMMs with an Hz button, read the AC voltage first, then press the Hz button to read frequency.

DMM FEATURES

When purchasing a DMM, the following features should be considered:

- Fused current inputs
- Use of high-potential fuses (600 V +)
- High-voltage protection in resistance mode
- Protection against high-voltage transients
- High input impedance (greater than 10 M)
- Insulated test lead handles
- Ammeter (required)
- Ability to measure frequency
- Autorange capability
- Cost of replacement fuses

SOME TYPICAL DMM TESTS

Always perform tests in accordance with truck and bus OEM specifications; never jump sequence or skip steps in sequential troubleshooting charts. Most DMM tests on truck and bus electronic systems will be used in conjunction with a generic reader-programmer or PC. The following tests assume the use of a Fluke 88 DMM.

Engine Position (Fuel Injection Pump Camshaft), Cam, and Crank Position Sensors

This procedure tests Hall-effect sensors, so make sure to correctly identify the sensor (it could be an inductive pulse generator):

a. Cycle the ignition key, then off.
b. Switch the meter to measure V-DC/rpm.
c. Identify the ground and signal terminals at the Hall sensor. Connect the positive (+) test lead to the signal terminal and the negative (−) test lead to the ground terminal. Crank the engine. At cranking speeds, the analog bar graph should pulse; at idle speeds or above, the pulses are too fast for bar graph readout.
d. Press the duty cycle button once. Duty cycle can indicate square wave quality, with poor quality signals having a low duty cycle. Functioning Hall sensors should have a duty cycle of around 50% depending on the sensor. Check to specifications.

Potentiometer-Type TPS

Resistance test:

a. Key off.
b. Disconnect the throttle position sensor (TPS).
c. Select W on the DMM. Connect the test probes to the signal and ground terminals. Next, move the accelerator through its stroke while observing the DMM display.
d. The analog bar should move smoothly without jumps or steps. If it steps, there may be a bad spot in the sensor.

Voltage test:

a. Key on, engine off.
b. Set the meter to read V-DC. Connect the negative lead to ground.
c. Separate the TPS connector and use the vehicle wiring schematic to identify the V-Ref terminal on the harness side. With the positive lead, check the V-Ref voltage value and compare to specifications. Reconnect the TPS electrical connector. Next, check the signal voltage (to the ECM) value through the accelerator pedal stroke. Check values to specification. Also observe the analog pointer; as with the resistance test, this should move smoothly through the accelerator stroke.

NOTE:

This test will not work on those systems that digitize the signal to produce a pulse width modulation (PWM) input to the ECM.

Inductive Pulse Generator Sensors

Inductive pulse generator–type sensors are often used as shaft speed and position sensors. They may also be known as magnetic or variable reluctance sensors function. They function similarly to a magneto. A toothed wheel cuts through a magnetic field, which induces an AC signal voltage in the signal (output) terminal: The ECM reads the frequency of the AC signal to determine a shaft speed. The AC voltage rises proportionally with rotational speed increase, and ranges from 0.1 V up to 5.0 V-AC. Vehicle speed sensors (VSSs), engine speed sensors (ESSs), and antilock brake system (ABS) wheel speed sensors all use this method of determining rotational speed. Test using V-AC switch setting and locating test leads across the appropriate terminals: Then spin up the device.

Min/Max Average Test for Lambda (λ) (O₂) Sensors

a. Key on, engine running, DMM set at V-DC. Select the correct voltage range.
b. Connect the negative test lead to a chassis ground and the positive test lead to the signal wire from the lambda sensor. Press the DMM min/max button.
c. Ensure that the engine is warm enough to be in closed-loop mode (100 mV–900 mV oxygen [O₂] sensor output). Run for several

minutes to give the meter time to sample a scatter of readings.

d. Press the min/max button slowly three times while watching the DMM display. A maximum of 800 mV and a minimum of less than 200 mV should be observed. The average should be around 450 mV.
e. Next, disconnect a large vacuum hose to simulate a lean burn condition. Repeat steps c and d to read the average voltage. Average voltage should be lower, indicating a lean condition.
f. The same test can be performed using propane enrichment to produce a rich air-fuel ratio (AFR) condition and therefore higher voltage values.
g. Lambda sensor tests can be performed while road-testing the vehicle; 450 mV normally indicates stoichiometric fueling (λ= 1), but check to specifications.

Thermistors

Most **thermistors** used in computerized engine systems are supplied with V-Ref (5 V) and have a negative temperature coefficient (NTC), meaning that as the sensor temperature increases, its resistance decreases. They should be checked to specifications using the DMM ohmmeter function and an accurate temperature measurement instrument.

Applying DMM Tests

OEMs seldom suggest random testing of suspect components. The preceding tests are typical procedures. Circuit testing in today's computerized engine management systems is highly structured and part of a sequential troubleshooting procedure. It is important to perform each step in the sequence precisely; skipping a step can invalidate every step that follows.

BREAKOUT BOXES AND BREAKOUT TS

The DMM is often used in conjunction with a **breakout box** or **breakout T**. Breakout devices are designed to be teed into an electrical circuit to enable circuit measurements to be made on both closed (active) and de-energized circuits. The objective is to access a circuit with a test instrument without interrupting the circuit. A breakout T is a simpler diagnostic device that is inserted into a simple two- or three-wire circuit such as that used to connect an individual sensor, whereas a breakout box accesses multiple wire circuits for diagnostic analyses of circuit conditions.

Most of the electronic engine management system OEMs use a breakout box that is often inserted into the interface connection between the engine electronics and chassis electronics harnesses. The face of the breakout box displays a number of coded sockets into which the probes of a DMM can be safely inserted to read circuit conditions. Electronic troubleshooting sequencing is often structured based on the data read by a DMM accessing a circuit. A primary advantage of breakout diagnostic devices is the fact that they permit the reading of an active electronic circuit, for instance, while an engine is running.

WARNING:

When a troubleshooting sequence calls for the use of breakout devices, always use the recommended tool. Never puncture wiring or electrical harnesses to enable readings in active or open electronic circuits. The corrosion damage that results from damaging wiring insulation will create problems later on, and the electrical damage potential can be extensive.

Connector Dummies and Spoons

Diagnostic connector dummies are used to read a set of circuit conditions in a circuit that has been opened by separating a pair of connectors. The dummies are manufactured by the electrical/ electronic connector manufacturer as a means of accessing the circuitry with a DMM without damaging the connector sockets and pins. Diagnostic spoons are curved and designed to be inserted behind a connector without damaging the insulation boot. When the correct dummies and spoons are used, energized circuits can be tested without inflicting damage, providing some care is exercised.

TECH TIP:

When performing a multiple-step, electronic troubleshooting sequence on a large multiterminal connector, photocopy the coded face of the connector(s) from the service manual and use it as a template. The alphanumeric codes used on many connectors can be difficult to read, and using a template is a good method of orienting the test procedure.

DMM CIRCUIT TESTING

Many truck technicians learn to use DMMs on the fly, that is, they acquire their understanding on an as-needed basis, with the consequence that most do not properly understand the potential of a high-end DMM. It does not make sense to spend $500 on a complex DMM that will never be used to perform tasks that a DMM one-fifth of the cost will handle. This next section introduces some simple tasks that can be performed by low-end DMMs using components readily available in introductory electricity/ electronics labs.

Testing Resistors

Most carbon resistors used in electronic circuits are color-coded. Although individual resistors would seldom be tested in the real world of the truck shop, testing them in a teaching/learning environment can be a great way of getting to know the ohmmeter function of your DMM. You can grab a pile of resistors and check the color-coded resistance value against the actual measurement. First, you have to understand the color codes:

Color	Value
Black	0
Brown	1
Red	2
Orange	3
Yellow	4
Green	5
Blue	6
Violet	7
Gray	8
White	9

In the left-hand column of this list, note that the darkest colors like black and brown are used for the lowest numeric values (0 and 9), moving up to white, which is given the highest numeric value. These codes are standardized by the Electronics Industries Association (EIA) and are also used for capacitors. In addition, the colors gold and silver are used to rate tolerance or the percentage amount that similarly rated resistors can differ from each other and still function within specification. Gold indicates 5% and silver 10% tolerance. **Figure 35–9** shows the significance of each band used on a resistor.

FIGURE 35–9 Interpreting bands on a carbon resistor.

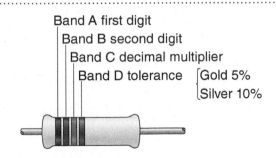

Next, we can look at two actual examples, shown in **Figure 35–10**. In **Figure 35–10A** the arrangement is:

1st stripe = red = 2

2nd stripe = green = 5

3rd stripe = red = multiplier to power of 2 or 10^2, so you *add* 2 zeros = 2,500 Ω

4th stripe = gold = tolerance rated at within 5%

At first glance, **Figure 35–10B** does not appear to be unlike the previous resistor:

1st stripe = red = 2

2nd stripe = green = 5

FIGURE 35–10 Interpreting band resistance codes.

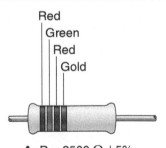

A: R = 2500 Ω ±5%

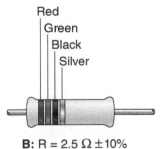

B: R = 2.5 Ω ±10%

3rd stripe = black = multiplier is zero, so the value is 25 Ω

4th stripe = silver = tolerance rated at within 10%

SCOPEMETERS

Scopemeters and graphing meters may be used to determine whether activity on a communications bus line falls within its specified range or whether injector driver actuation pulses spread a normal or abnormal profile. In addition, scopemeters are useful instruments in a learning environment because they help students "see" electrical signals.

As a learning tool, a scopemeter provides a visual image to the waveform produced by a PWM driver command for an injector. Because most of us are visual learners, this can help retention. A Pico scopemeter is used in Chapter 37 to display bus waveforms to verify node activity. The Pico scopemeter consists of a serial link adapter and PC-based software to display waveforms.

GENERIC EST

The Nexiq **Pro-Link iQ** is the most popular example of a handheld generic EST. Its predecessor versions have been widely used in the trucking industry, and over the years Pro-Link ESTs have advanced to the full color graphical display and touch screen of the iQ. The Pro-Link iQ is updated by online downloads and when a **wireless vehicle link 2 (WVL2)** is connected, can access vehicle data buses wirelessly. Any EST connecting to a post-2014 J1939 data bus must be **auto-baud detect capable (ABDC)**. Attempting to connect an EST that is not ABDC compliant can take down the entire bus. **Figure 35–11** is a Nexiq iQ screen display showing some engine parameters.

The Nexiq Pro-Link iQ will do the following depending on what software it is loaded with and how well the OEM supports the EST:

- Access active and inactive/historic codes; erase inactive historic codes
- Monitor all system identification data
- View data on engine operation with the engine running
- Perform diagnostic tests on system subcomponents such as electronic fuel injectors
- Reprogram customer data parameters on engine and chassis systems

FIGURE 35–11 Nexiq iQ screen display showing engine parameters.

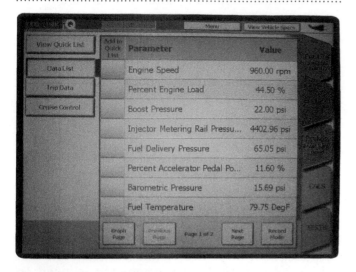

- Display and analyze trip data
- Take snapshots of system data parameters to assist in finding intermittent faults
- Store data in PDF or text format

ADVANTAGES AND DISADVANTAGES

The Nexiq Pro-Link iQ has the following advantages:

- User friendly. Technicians require very little time to develop a working knowledge of these tools. The best method of becoming familiar with them is simply to use them. Menus can be selected, data can be scrolled through. Stuck? Simply unplug and reconnect. This can be done at any time without sustaining physical or electronic damage.
- Universality. Pro-Link ESTs have a long track record in the truck service industry and can be used extensively even on systems that require the use of PCs for more detailed diagnostic and programming functions. The preloaded heavy-duty reader software will read most diesel engine and other onboard systems along with automobile systems.
- Easily updated. Updated by fast online data downloads that have replaced the cards and cartridges used by older versions.
- Durable. The latest generation of Pro-Link ESTs with their larger and touch screens are arguably not as tough as the older, more primitive Pro-Link 9000 and Pro-Link MPCs, but they are built to withstand life on the shop floor.

- Ideal for the general access to chassis data buses required by independent service providers planning to work with the more open bus access that comes with HD-OBD.

The disadvantages of generic HH-ESTs are:

- As truck ECMs become more powerful and networking speeds increase, the limitations of generic ESTs become more evident. PC-based systems are more often required to properly troubleshoot electronic problems.
- The effectiveness of generic ESTs is determined by an OEM's willingness to support the EST manufacturer with software. Experience will soon tell you that some OEMs do this a lot better than others: Use online feedback and the iATN website HD/Fleet forum to evaluate whether such an EST will work for you.

As we stated earlier, generic ESTs are connected to the chassis data bus either by means of a data connector or wirelessly. If a hardwire connection is to be made, either a six-, nine-, or 16-pin DLC may be used. If a wireless connection is to be used, a wireless CA such as a Nexiq WVL2 should be used. This should accommodate any multiple applications and multiple clients, which was the original intention of RP1210.

WARNING:

Attempting to connect to a post-2014 J1939 with an EST that is not ABDC compliant can take down the entire bus and incur costly repairs. Ensure that you select the correct EST for the chassis you are working on.

COMMUNICATIONS ADAPTERS

Most ESTs designed to access data on a truck chassis data bus require the use of a communications adapter (CA), which is also known as a *serial data link transducer*. Although all CAs theoretically meet the same TMC RP 1210 communications protocols, some of the OEM versions only function with their own specific system, for the simple reason that they are not tested on other manufacturer's systems. However, with the adoption of HD-OBD, the likelihood is that OEM CAs will evolve to support multiple applications and multiple clients, which was the original intention of RP1210. **Figure 35–12** shows a Navistar NavLink CA designed to access Navistar's DiamondLogic bus.

FIGURE 35–12 Navistar NavLink CA used to communicate with the DiamondLogic bus.

....

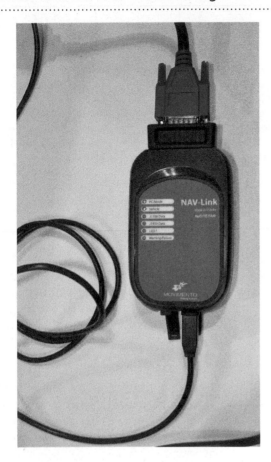

TECH TIP:

Bus accessibility is contentious, and although RP1210 was intended to standardize bus access hardware, many OEMs' CAs function only on their own systems. Generic CAs will usually function with the established U.S.-built systems, but there are some exceptions. That said, if you are working with multiple chassis and engine OEM products, the best bet is to invest in a known-brand generic CA that specifies that it is RP1210 compliant.

TECH TIP:

The Paccar CA required to work on MYs 2010 to 2013 MX engine electronics was not RP1210 compliant (see Chapter 45). Accessing this generation of MX engines could only be achieved using Paccar's in-house product.

VEHICLE DATA LINKS

There are three general categories of **vehicle data links (VDLs)** in use today:

- J1939: Current heavy-duty standard
- J1708: Older heavy-duty standard
- J1962: Light-duty (automotive) OBD II standard

In addition, it may be possible to connect directly to the engine electronics via a J1939 three-pin or proprietary connector. This can be done with most Caterpillar engines, but it may be difficult to actually locate the connector on the harness. Access also depends on the generation of ECM software: Cummins ISB electronics used on Dodge chassis could be accessed using Cummins InSite prior to Environmental Protection Agency (EPA) model year 2004, but not after that date.

J1587

The J1587 protocol was the original truck data bus backbone. It is accessed using a six-pin **Deutsch connector** that conforms to J1708 standards or by more recent J1939 connectors that support J1587. J1587 is an SAE standard that governs the software communication protocols (i.e., the "language") used for data transactions; this is explained in more detail in Chapter 37. J1708 governs all the hardware standards used on a J1587 data bus. Until 2010, all heavy-duty, data bus–equipped chassis were equipped with J1587 compliancy, but since then some OEMs (Cummins and DDC) have ceased to support it. That said, it is still used. A post-2010 truck with a Cummins engine and J1587-equipped cab electronics requires a gateway (usually the instrument cluster unit [ICU]) to permit the two buses to network. **Figure 35–13** shows the cavity pin assignments used on a J1708 data connector.

FIGURE 35–13 J1587/1708 connector cavity pin assignments.

....

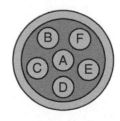

6-Pin J1587/1708 Connector

A. Data bus, dominant high (+)
B. Data bus, dominant low (–)
C. Battery positive
D. Dummy
E. Battery negative
F. Dummy

J1939 CONNECTOR

The J1939 data bus is more recent and a lot faster. It covers both hardware and software standards used on the bus. Because a current truck chassis equipped with a J1939 data bus is also equipped with the older J1587/1708 data bus, the data connector used has some extra pins. A J1939 connector is a nine-pin connector with the cavity pin assignments shown in **Figure 35–14**. High bus connections within the data bus backbone are made on a three-pin connector (also known as *stubs*) with cavity pin assignments as shown in Figure 37–7, whereas low bus connections use a two-pin connector.

J1962 CONNECTOR

The standard light-duty data bus connector is usually known by automobile technicians as a data communications link (DLC), and the current version and standard OBD II data link are an **assembly line data link (ALDL)**. J1962 is a 16-pin connector. The connector is designed to accommodate various generations of data bus technology, including the latest CAN-C based on CAN 2.0, as are the later versions of J1939. The J1962 connector is used in some light-duty commercial vehicles and in 2014 was adopted by all Volvo-Mack trucks, so it is outlined here. A J1962 data connector and its cavity pin assignments as designated by Volvo-Mack are shown in **Table 35–1**, with the J1939 high and low pins bolded.

MAKING THE CONNECTION

You will need an EST loaded with the appropriate software, connectors, and cabling. Most basic

TABLE 35–1 J1962 Cavity Pin Assignments

1	2	3	4	5	**6**	7	8
9	10	11	12	13	**14**	15	16

1. Manufacturer discretion	9. Blank (OEM discretion)
2. Bus positive + J1587/1708	10. Bus negative—for J1587/1708
3. DCL +	11. DCL
4. Chassis ground	12. Blank (OEM discretion)
5. Signal ground	13. Blank (OEM discretion)
6. **J1939 high (J2284 and ISO 15765-4)**	14. **J1939 low (J2284 and ISO 15765-4)**
7. K-line of ISO 9141 and ISO 14230	15. L line of ISO 9141 and ISO 14230-4
8. Blank (OEM discretion)	16. V-Bat (battery positive)

FIGURE 35–14 J1939 connector cavity pin assignments.

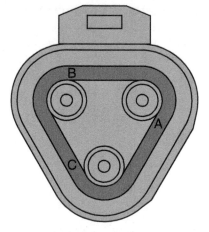

3-Pin J1939 Connector

A. CAN busline, dominant high (+)
B. CAN busline, dominant low (−)
C. CAN shield

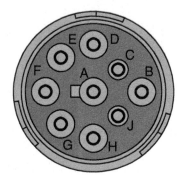

9-Pin J1939 Connector

A. Battery negative
B. Battery positive
C. J1939 CAN busline, dominant high (+)
D. J1939 CAN busline, dominant low (−)
E. CAN shield
F. J1587 busline, dominant high (+)
G. J1587 busline, dominant low (−)

transactions can be undertaken without network access. Examples of ESTs and levels of access are:

- HH-EST loaded with standard heavy-duty reader software
- HH-EST equipped with OEM-specific cartridge
- Laptop/notebook personal computer (PC) and OEM software
- PC station and OEM software

Connection Sequence

In this walk-through of the connection procedure, the assumption is made that you are using a laptop PC loaded with generic heavy-duty reader software. The procedure for connecting a PC loaded with OEM proprietary software to a data bus is covered a little later in this chapter. Note that standard heavy-duty reader software is read-only.

1. Boot up the laptop. Wait until OS is loaded into main memory and online updates are checked/downloaded.
2. Select and start the access software you are going to use. Examples are Nexiq, Noregon, Bosch, and so on.
3. Connect a RP1210 (A, B, or C) compliant CA to a USB port on the PC. Connect a J1939 cable to the CA.
4. Ensure that the truck parking brakes are engaged, the transmission is in neutral, and the wheels are chocked.
5. Locate the chassis data bus connector and connect the J1939 connector into the bus socket.
6. Key-on the truck chassis but do not start. The PC should display all of the modules with an address on J1939. These controllers are described in more detail in the next section. The flashing light on the CA will indicate whether J1939 or J1587 is being used; the default is the faster (J1939) bus to which the handshake can be made.
7. Scroll to the controller system you wish to work with and click. This will enable you to read all data not blocked by the OEM, including such fields as engine parameters and fault codes.

SA/MID Selection

Each major electronic system on the data bus is assigned a **source address (SA)** (J1939) or **message identifier (MID)** (J1587), and this must be selected before information in that system can be accessed. It actually sounds more complicated than it is. After connecting an EST to the data bus, all of the SAs/MIDs with an address on the data bus will be displayed. An SA or MID is any system controller (computer) networked to the chassis data bus. If you want to work on the engine SA/MID, use the EST to select this from the menu. Some examples of common SAs and MIDs used on a truck data bus are listed a little later in this chapter.

Identify FMIs

If you were troubleshooting a fault in the engine, you would be routed through the appropriate PGNs, SPGs, PIDs and SIDs to locate the specific FMI that had triggered the fault code. There are a limited number of malfunction categories that are assigned as FMIs, and these are listed a little later in this chapter. Most proprietary and generic troubleshooting software identifies FMIs numerically and by description, so it is not necessary to memorize these.

CONNECTING OEM ESTS TO THE DATA BUS

For purposes of illustrating this simple procedure, we are going to use the example of connecting to a chassis equipped with a Caterpillar electronic engine. We will also assume that the data bus connector is J1939, there are multiple ECMs networked to the chassis data backbone, and your objective is to communicate with the engine ECM. The hardware required for this operation consists of:

- A PC loaded with Cat Electronic Technician (ET) software
- A Cat communications adapter (CA) meeting 171-4401 or 275-5121 Cat and RP 1210A/B compatibilities
- Appropriate connection cables and a J1939 data connector

The connections should be made as indicated in **Figure 35–15**.

Use the following sequential procedure to make and verify the CA connection.

1. Boot the PC and wait until the OS is loaded. Turn the dash key switch *on*, and launch ET.
2. Connect the CA (4) to a communication port on the PC by using one of the following methods:
   a. Connect cables (3) and (2) between the *computer* end of the CA (4) and a universal serial bus (USB) port on the PC (1).
   b. Connect cable (3) between the *computer* end of the CA (4) and the RS232 serial port of the PC (1).

FIGURE 35–15 How a communications adapter (CA) is connected as a serial link between a notebook PC and vehicle data bus.

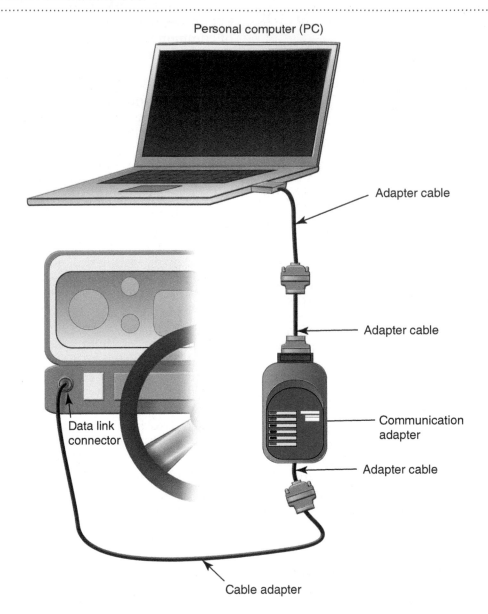

Personal computer (PC)

Adapter cable

Adapter cable

Data link connector

Communication adapter

Adapter cable

Cable adapter

3. Connect cables (5) and (6) between the *data link* end of the CA (4) and the service tool connector.
4. Turn the ignition *on*. Most engine OEMs use software and hardware that will only recognize their proprietary bus address, so they will ignore other modules on the bus. Therefore, Cat ET will attempt to communicate directly with the ECM and not option other chassis data bus modules.
5. Observe the CA and Cat ET graphical user interface (GUI). If both the "J1939/DeviceNet" and the "J1708" indicator light-emitting diodes (LEDs) are flashing and Cat ET does not display a message that refers to a communications problem, Cat ET is communicating with the engine ECM on both data links. This is important: Cat electronics broadcast to, and receive messages from, both data buses. If this is not the case, you will have to troubleshoot the EST using Cat SIS.

EST WIRELESS CONNECTIVITY

Both OEMs and the generic EST providers are increasingly making use of ESTs equipped with wireless connectivity to the chassis data bus.

The current generation of wireless ESTs tends to produce certain communications glitches, so although some troubleshooting operations are made easier and pose little risk, when performing programming it is best to ensure that you have a hardwire backup in the event of a communications failure. The consequence of not taking this precaution could be a downed vehicle.

REPROGRAM SEQUENCE

We will now switch systems and use Detroit Diesel Diagnostic Link (DDDL) as a model to perform a reprogramming sequence with the objective of a calibration update. The procedure is similar to that of other OEMs, and it requires an online connection to DDC's online SIS known as **Power Service Literature (PSL)**. **Figure 35–16** shows a technician using Freightliner's ServicePro software to access DDDL.

1. Connect the communications adapter (CA) and verify the connection with the data bus. Note: Several engine OEMs (DD and Cummins are two examples) only support J1939 on post-2010 systems.
2. Select the engine SA 00 or MID 128.
3. From menu, select <file, print inputs, and outputs>.
4. Select <calibration>, then <ECM accumulators file print>.
5. Select <injector calibration> and record the numbers.

6. Next select <program update customer calibration at DDC>. Cycle the ignition key to log this into the laptop memory.
7. Close the window for <DDEC reprogramming>.
8. Select <DDC mainframe> to connect to the DDC data hub.
9. Select <upload history> and key in the password. This transfers ECM history to mainframe files.
10. Select <download engine serial calibration>.
11. Clear the units, then key in the unit serial number, then hit <download>.
12. Close the window for the DDC mainframe.
13. Select <DDEC reprogramming>.
14. Now choose the <program ECM with mainframe data> option.
15. The display for <overwriting data> now appears: Select OK.
16. Identify the serial number, highlight, and click OK.
17. Select <no change> or <repair order #> and <enter>. This will initiate the programming.
18. When the programming is complete, the display shows the serial number and inputs/outputs (I/Os). Close the window.
19. Select <update customer calibration>. Check all parameters and change if required.
20. Check the ECM accumulators and set to previous values. Check the injector settings. Close.

ELECTRONIC TROUBLESHOOTING

As we have progressed through this textbook, we have taken a look at some of the characteristics of mechanical failures in diesel engines, and technicians who have grown up in the computer age should remind themselves from time to time that diesel engines sometimes malfunction mechanically. Technicians must not assume that every problem is electronically based. That said, modern electronic troubleshooting programs are usually interactive and are capable of identifying many problems that have nothing to do with the vehicle electronics.

When undertaking troubleshooting, the approach should be methodical. We know this as *sequential troubleshooting*. Sequential troubleshooting takes place in stages. It is critical that the instructions in each stage be precisely undertaken before proceeding to the next; subsequent stages will generally be rendered

FIGURE 35–16 Technician using Freightliner's ServicePro to access DDDL to troubleshoot a DDC engine problem.

FIGURE 35–17 A NEXIQ serial communications adaptor.

meaningless if a stage is skipped. Most OEMs also prefer that you use PC- or online-based sequential troubleshooting programs for their systems. These simplify the sequencing of the troubleshooting stages and save a lot of page turning. **Figure 35–17** shows another example of a typical serial communications adaptor (CA).

ONLINE SERVICE INFORMATION SYSTEMS

As mentioned a number of times earlier in this book, most OEMs prefer that the first step in any troubleshooting procedure be to log on to their online service information system (SIS), whether the technician is working on an electronic engine or one of an earlier vintage. Some examples of engine OEM SISs are:

- Caterpillar Service Information System or SIS
- Cummins QuickServe Online or QSOL
- Detroit Diesel/Mercedes-Benz Detroit Diesel Customer Support Network (DDCSN): Power Service Literature (PSL)
- Mack Trucks Electrical Information System (EIS)
- Navistar International Service Information System or ISIS (pre-2007)
- Navistar Service Information or NSI (post-2007)
- Paccar ServiceNet (chassis)
- Paccar DAVIE (engine)
- Volvo IMPACT

Most OEM service information systems are updated daily. They tend to be easy to navigate. Technicians should learn how to use the website search engines. In most cases, information searches are by engine serial number and may include searches of the parts data. It is important to note that most online SISs support engines manufactured before the OEM Web service existed, so try to make a habit of using it. In addition to the OEM subscription SIS, there are generic subscription, online SISs, which are described later in this chapter.

TROUBLESHOOTING TOOLS

In order to effectively use electronic troubleshooting methods, the technician should be capable of using:

- The OEM online service information system (SIS)
- The OEM diagnostic software
- The appropriate electronic service tool (EST) and communication adapter (CA)
- A DMM (and have a basic understanding of electrical and electronic circuitry)
- Electrical schematics
- The correct tools, including terminal spoons, breakout Ts, and breakout boxes

Using the correct tools is often overlooked. When the use of a breakout box is mandated, make sure that it is used. Also, it should be remembered that electrostatic discharge can damage solid-state components, so it is good practice to wear a **ground strap** when opening up any housing containing a microprocessor. When testing separated Deutsch, Weather Pack, and any other type of sealed connectors with a DMM, ensure that the sockets have been identified before inserting test leads, terminal spoons, or breakout Ts. Use socket adapters/spoons where necessary to avoid damaging terminal cavities. Never spike wires when testing circuits.

DIAGNOSTIC SOFTWARE

Each engine OEM produces its own diagnostic software, and if the technician has to do anything more than just scan a data bus, this software, along with the appropriate EST, must be used. Exceptions to this may occur when HD-OBD becomes mandatory in 2014. Some examples of engine OEM diagnostic software are listed here; the terms normally used on the shop floor are in bold:

- Caterpillar Electronic Technician (ET)
- Cummins InSite
- Detroit Diesel/Mercedes-Benz: Detroit Diesel Diagnostic Link DDDL (Version 5.0 or higher required for both DDC and MB applications)
- Detroit Diesel Reprogramming Station (DDRS) DDEC10 DD-Series (post-2010)
- Mack Trucks Premium Tech Tool (PTT)
- Navistar Master Diagnostics (MD) (up to 2007) or ServiceMaxx (after 2007)
- Paccar **Rapido** (embedded within the DAVIE website)
- Volvo **V-Cads Pro** (Volvo computer-aided diagnostic system and programming)

It should be noted that some versions of the software listed here may have limited functionality: Software for dealerships, body-builders, and fleet applications may all be different, depending on the level of programming required. For instance, a Volvo dealership uses V-Cads Pro (full function), whereas fleets would be restricted to V-Cads Elite, which cannot enable proprietary (Volvo) data programming.

Master Diagnostics and ServiceMaxx

Master Diagnostics (MD) and ServiceMaxx (SM) are Navistar International's diagnostic software packages. We use this software to show the functions and capabilities of one OEM's software. Most OEM diagnostic software has a lot in common, but the objective of using MD/SM is to give some shape to this section. MD/SM functions best if the computer onto which it is loaded is dedicated to use on Navistar International trucks and the Navistar data hub. This minimizes the chances of producing time-consuming software file clashes. If you purchase an EZ-Tech laptop computer from International Trucks, all the required Navistar software, including ISIS, MD, and SM, are loaded onto a Panasonic Toughbook, which is a notebook computer that adapts well to the truck shop floor. In common with all the OEMs, the functionality of the computer and its

FIGURE 35–18 Navistar EZ-Tech GUI.

Courtesy of Navistar International Corp.

software is designed to be as user friendly as is possible. Avoid loading competitor software onto an EZ-Tech laptop, because doing so may cause software file clashes that can result in communication problems. The EZ-Tech GUI is shown in **Figure 35–18**.

MD/SM Functions

MD/SM software is an umbrella program that houses all the software required to trouble-shoot Navistar International Trucks' and its partners' subsystem electronics by directing the user into their online SISs. MD/SM is designed to handshake directly to the vehicle data bus and access Navistar's Diamond Logic Controller (chassis control module) on the truck or bus. The MD/SM software is designed to perform the following:

1. Display engine parameters in text format.
2. Display engine parameters in graphical format.
3. Snapshot test engine parameters.
4. Perform off-chassis diagnostics.
5. View and edit programmable parameters.
6. Display and clear **diagnostic trouble codes (DTCs)**.
7. Display engine and chassis information.

Launching MD/SM

The procedure for launching MD is similar to that for other OEM diagnostic software packages. Because the software requires the technician to crank, start, and run the engine during the tests, perform the following before beginning:

1. Block the wheels on two axles.
2. Ensure that the parking brake is engaged.
3. Place the transmission in neutral.

Then follow this sequence to connect to the chassis data bus:

1. Boot the EZ-Tech computer.
2. Connect the EZ-Tech CA (NavCom or NavLink) to a serial or USB port on the EZ-Tech computer.
3. Connect the J1939 connector to the vehicle J1939 data connector.
4. Turn the ignition to key-on (do not start the engine).
5. Open the COM port. When the J1939 connection is established, all of the controllers (SAs and MIDs) on the chassis data bus will be identified. Select the one you want to work with. At any time, the <Sniffer> menu bar will identify other SAs/MIDs networked to the data bus. We will assume it is the engine electronics and that the engine is manufactured by Navistar.
6. Three MD/SM icon options will appear when the engine selection is made; each addresses a different family or generation of engines. This will change with time and as new engine families are introduced.

Opening a Session

Click on the <Session> text bar to begin a session. This will immediately:

- Open a pair of parameter graphical views (blank) on the left side of the display
- Open a text display of engine parameters on the right side of the display
- Display all DTCs on the lower part of the display window

You can select parameters that you want monitored during the diagnostic session by double-clicking. This means you can view selected parameters in graphical format and text/numeric formats. Note some of the following features:

- Double-clicking a DTC will drop down a <Help> dialog box with navigating suggestions. Close a text box by clicking on X.
- Placing the display cursor over a parameter and right-clicking will drop down advanced features. These vary with the parameter selected.
- Clicking on the <Diagnostics> pull-down menu will enable you to run diagnostic tests. Just click on the drop-down radio bar to run a specific test.

- Tests are divided into <Key-Off> and <Key-On> tests.
- Left-clicking over a value will change it from English to metric and vice versa.
- You can open a graphical display at any time by clicking on the <Graphics> icon.

Graphical Display

When you select a graphical display, a black screen will be displayed until you select parameter data to be displayed. Selected display parameters will be identified at the top of the graph, each assigned with a different color. This is done so you can identify parameter data as it is displayed on the graph in actual specification plus real time. On the graph:

- Vertical axis: Min and Max values are shown with maximum at top.
- Horizontal axis: Real time is displayed with each gradient representing 1 second.
- The color used to display the acronym of a selected parameter at the top of the graph is that used to plot the parameter values on the graph itself.

Using OEM Diagnostic Software

The guidelines for using Navistar International's MD/SM software are close to what you might expect to see on its competitors' diagnostic software. Today's versions of diagnostic software are user friendly; providing you have a little knowledge of navigating OEM software, you should be able learn the ins and outs by simply experimenting. It is difficult to create problems if you use a little common sense, but be careful when entering programming fields: When altering customer data programming, it is preferable that you have received the OEM-specific training.

SNAPSHOT TESTS

Most systems will accommodate a **snapshot test** readout from the ECM to facilitate troubleshooting intermittent problems that either do not generate codes or log a code with no clear reason. Snapshot mode troubleshooting can be triggered by a variety of methods (codes, conditions, manually) and will record data frames before and after the trigger; these can be recorded to an HH-EST, tablet PC, or laptop PC while the vehicle is running. Because frames can be snapped both before and after the trigger, it is possible to analyze a wide spectrum of data that may have contributed to a problem; each data frame can be examined individually after the event. The portability of HH-ESTs is ideal for this sort of test, and the HH-ESTs create less of a distraction than an open laptop.

DATA BUS CODES AND PROTOCOLS

The following is a partial listing of SAE codes that have been adopted by all the North American truck engine/electronics OEMs using a data bus network (explained in Chapter 37). The first-generation serial bus used in trucks adhered to SAE J1587. This slower serial bus was divided as follows:

- **SAE J1587** covered common software protocols used on the bus.
- **SAE J1708** covered common hardware protocols.

The more recent **SAE J1939** covers both hardware and software protocols. The acceptance and widespread usage of these J1587 and J1939 protocols enable the interfacing of electronic systems manufactured by different OEMs on truck and bus chassis, and additionally provide generic software with some ability to at least read competitor electronic systems. The accessibility of both truck data buses will increase when HD-OBD becomes universal in 2014.

Earlier we identified the procedure required to access modules with an address on the data bus known as SAs or MIDs. Each SA or MID is a major vehicle electronic system with processing and messaging capabilities. Here are some of the common SAs used on a current truck, bus, or mobile off-road heavy equipment.

Source Address (SA)	Description
00	Engine Controller (ECM)
01	ECM for secondary engine (e.g., crane)
03	Transmission controller
05	Shift console controller
11	Brakes and traction control
23	Instrument cluster
33	Body controller
61	Exhaust emissions controller
71	Vehicle/chassis controller

PGNs, PIDs, AND SIDs

A J1939 **parameter group (PG)** is a set of reportable values sourced from a sensor or electronic circuit. The acronyms **PGN (parameter group number)**, **PID (parameter identifier)**, and **SID (subsystem identifier)** are used to code components and systems within an SA or MID address. They are best sourced by using the OEM service literature, because some OEMs using J1939 are continuing to use many of the J1587 terms and acronyms. It is not necessary to remember the numeric codes for any of these buses, because access software programs today are user friendly and use alpha text displays.

FAULT MODE INDICATORS

FMIs (fault mode indicators) are designed to describe the electronic characteristics of a failed component or system once a diagnostic trouble code (DTC) has been logged. Because in most cases the OEM diagnostic software is designed to guide the technician through the troubleshooting path without having to memorize a sequence of meaningless numeric values, the technician will usually be routed directly to the FMI after a DTC has been logged.

When diagnosing circuit malfunctions, the technician will access the chassis data bus first, then be guided to the SA or MID that requires investigation. At that point, the subcircuit electronic troubleshooting is launched; the troubleshooting path routes through the PGNs, PIDs, and SIDs to identify a specific malfunctioning component(s).

FMIs Are Common to All Truck Systems

If every engine OEM were allowed to come up with coding for the ways in which one of its components could fail, there would be a scary number of options, most overlapping or slightly differentiating similar failure modes. FMIs are SAE defined and common to all OEMs. That means that when the diagnostic path has been completed, the failed component must be assigned to one FMI. An FMI is a specific failure mode.

Predictive FMIs

From 2007 onward, the number of FMIs was extended so that categories of predicted imminent failure could be identified. A *predictive* or *imminent failure* is one in which a controller is receiving low-quality data or performance from a component or circuit. The new FMIs are useful data-mining tools for fleets and OEMs who are establishing profiles for prognostics and condition base maintenance, often using telematics to communicate with OEM data hubs. Essentially, this new category of FMIs can help flag potential problems before they result in a breakdown. In addition, they can really help technicians locate marginal and intermittent problems in electronic circuits. The following is a *current* listing of FMIs. FMIs 15 through 31 were added in 2007:

Fault Mode Indicators (FMIs)	Description
00	Data valid but above normal operating range (most severe)
01	Data valid but below normal operating range
02	Data erratic, intermittent, or incorrect
03	Voltage above normal or shorted high
04	Voltage below normal or shorted low
05	Current below normal or open circuit
06	Current above normal or grounded circuit
07	Mechanical system not responding properly
08	Abnormal frequency, pulse width, or period
09	Abnormal update rate
10	Abnormal rate of change
11	Failure mode not identifiable
12	Bad intelligent device or component
13	Out of calibration
14	Special instructions
15	Data valid but above normal (least severe)
16	Data valid but above normal (moderate severity)
17	Data valid but below normal (least severe)
18	Data valid but below normal (moderate severity)
19	Received network data in error
20	Data drifted high
31	Not available

The graph in **Figure 35–19** shows how the new FMIs configure with the definition of "operating range," using the example of a temperature-sensing thermistor. Note that by adding the new FMIs, some distinction can be made in the severity of a failure.

FIGURE 35–19 New FMIs: Distinguishing the severity of a failure in a thermistor.

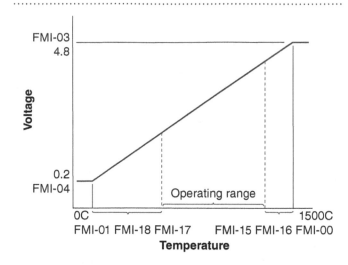

TABLE 35–2 PGNs, PIDs, SIDs, and FMI Display

Chassis Data Bus	PGNs, SIDs and PIDs	SFMI
J1587/1708	XXX	XX
J1939	XXXXXX	XX

Diagnostic Display Reporting

As mentioned, the way a problem is displayed by ECM diagnostics is common to all OEMs. So, once an SA or MID controller has been accessed, the numeric structure of the diagnostic path appears as a five-digit display on the J1587 bus and as an eight-digit display on the J1939 bus. **Table 35–2** shows how the numeric values of SAs, MIDs, and FMIs are sequenced in the display: five-digit on J1587, eight-digit on J1939.

HD-OBD

Since 1996, automobile OEMs have been compelled to make any diagnostic codes that relate to emissions accessible for display with nonproprietary ESTs, along with providing access to repair the systems. This was covered by **onboard diagnostics** (generation) **II**, known as **OBD II**. Beginning in 2010, the EPA required a phased implementation of **heavy-duty, onboard diagnostics (HD-OBD)**. For model year 2010, OEMs were required to produce one engine family that met HD-OBD requirements, progressing to mandatory HD-OBD on all commercial vehicles. HD-OBD only applies to failure conditions either directly or indirectly relating to emissions controls. In an HD-OBD-compliant vehicle, emissions-related failures will be required to be displayed by generic ESTs. There is more detail on the HD-OBD protocol in Chapter 50 of this book.

EOBRs AND EDRs

The terms **electronic onboard recorders (EOBRs)** and **electronic data recorders (EDRs)** both refer to vehicle data storage devices capable of capturing real-time data and storing it after shutdown or for telematic broadcast. The terms are generally used to refer to data that is pertinent following an accident or engine/ chassis problem event, or data that relates to driver hours of service.

MONITORED FIELDS

Any system that either directly or indirectly impacts on engine emissions will require HD-OBD monitoring and reporting. The list will vary according to type of fuel system and the specific exhaust gas aftertreatment devices the vehicle is equipped with, but will include:

- Misfire detection
- Fuel system efficiency
- Injector balance
- Exhaust gas recirculation (EGR) monitor
- Catalytic efficiency
- Manifold boost pressure
- Oxides of nitrogen (NO_x) adsorber monitor
- Selective catalytic reduction (SCR) efficiency
- DEF (for SCR) level
- Glow plug monitor
- Diesel particulate filter (DPF) monitor
- DPF efficiency
- O_2 and NO_x level reports

GENERIC SISs, ESTs, AND DIAGNOSTIC SOFTWARE

Perhaps in anticipation of HD-OBD, some OEMs have been more amenable to opening up access to their vehicle data buses for purposes of troubleshooting by supporting independent software developers. This has opened the door for companies such as Mitchell, Nexiq, and Noregon to develop PC diagnostic software that will perform most of what the proprietary software is capable of achieving. However, it is recommended that anyone intending to invest in this category of generic software fully research the product

before making the purchase: The scope of the software offered can be dated and repair procedures incomplete. That said, such software may be cost-effective for independent service facilities focusing on low-level repairs on a wide range of OEM chassis. Depending on what software options are used with the system, generic PC diagnostic software can be used for the following:

- Connecting to J1587/1708 buses
- Connecting to J1939
- Accessing repair guidelines
- Accessing wiring schematics
- Connecting to automotive buses
- Connecting directly to trailers
- Accessing labor time guides

NOREGON JPRO® KIT

For purposes of keeping things simple, we will base our description on the Noregon JPRO® kit, which can be tailored in terms of both hardware and software to suit an independent service facility or fleet. If money is no object, the kit can be purchased as follows:

- Laptop computer. One Noregon option is the Panasonic Toughbook CF-30, a costly but nearly indestructible laptop that will withstand handling by the most savage technicians working in the industry. Other options include touchscreen tablet notebooks and low-cost general purpose notebooks. An advantage of purchasing the laptop/PC directly from Noregon is that it comes custom preloaded with whatever software is required by the service facility to access their trucks. **Figure 35–20** shows the Noregon Windows environment software screen interface: The CA provides for hardwire

FIGURE 35–20 Noregon Windows environment software GUI.

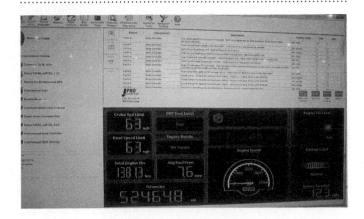

or wireless connectivity with most OEM chassis data buses.

- Cables and connectors. The typical cable and connector options are:
  - J1587/1708 six-pin Deutsch connector
  - J1939 Green nine-pin Deutsch connector
  - J1939 Black nine-pin Deutsch connector
  - J1939 three-pin Deutsch connector for Cummins light duty
  - J1962 for Volvo-Mack and light-duty/automotive CAN access
  - J560 (seven-pin) for trailer PLC access
- Communications adapter (CA). The JPRO® CA is J1210 compliant, so theoretically it can act as the CA for any OEM electronic subsystems.
- Wireless adapter. A J1210-compliant adapter using 802.11 wireless telematics protocols (WiFi).
- Software. The JPRO® Fleet Diagnostics package currently supports most basic troubleshooting with all but Paccar MX engines, and in addition can launch some OEM diagnostic routines and service literature. Also, depending on the OEM, some graphing display is possible. Updates to the software are online accessible.

TECH TIP:

Thinking of investing in a generic SIS and diagnostic software suite? Log on to the iATN heavy-duty forum and find out what truck technicians really think about the package you are considering purchasing. This can save you from making costly purchases that turn out to be of little use.

OTHER GENERIC SISs AND ESTs

There are other subscription-based SIS, EST, and diagnostic software packages that are worth consideration—but like all generic service packages, they should be well researched prior to investing in them. **Figure 35–21** shows the Snap-On service information and diagnostic screen interface. This type of generic software may be ideal for general service facilities that never get involved in in-depth repairs. The problems encountered are usually a considerable lag in updating content, and lack of comprehensiveness in troubleshooting and repair detail. Examples are:

- Motor E-tech online
- Mitchell 1 online
- All Data online (light duty only)

FIGURE 35–21 Snap-On diagnostic and service information station

INTERPRETING DASH WARNING LIGHTS

Vehicles today use an extensive suite of dash warning lights that do vary somewhat by OEM. However, from an operational and troubleshooting perspective, three of these warning lights are universal:

- Check engine light (CEL)
- Malfunction indicator light (MIL)
- Stop engine light (SEL)

Table 35–3 shows some typical dash warning lights used on post-2010 trucks, buses, and off-road equipment.

CHECK ENGINE LIGHT

When a **check engine light (CEL)** is illuminated, the engine requires servicing at the first opportunity. The CEL is colored amber (see Table 35–3):

TABLE 35–3 Interpreting Dash Warning Lights

Symbol Name	Symbol	Color
Active Warning, Exclamation Point	!	Red
Active Warnings, Number	1	Yellow
Alternator	ALT	Red
Anti-Lock Brake System (ABS)	((ABS))	Yellow
Anti-Lock Brake System (ABS), Trailer	((ABS))	Yellow
Axle, Inter-Axle Differential Locked (Tandem Axles)		Yellow
Emissions, Diesel Particulate Filter (DPF)		Yellow
Emissions, High Exhaust System Temperture (HEST)		Yellow
Malfunction Indicator Lamp (MIL)		Yellow
Diesel Exhaust Fluid Lamp (see chapter 48)		Yellow
Check Engine Light (CEL)		Yellow
Ether Start		Green
Engine, Heater		Yellow

Symbol Name	Symbol	Color
Engine, Low Coolant Level		Yellow
Engine Overspeed	RPM	Red
Engine Retarder (Brake)		Green
Stop Engine		Red
Engine, Wait To Start	WAIT	Yellow
Message Waiting		Green
Park Brake	((P))	Red
Power Take-off (PTO)	PTO	Green
Suspension Dump		Yellow
Tire Inflation		Yellow
Transmission, Do Not Shift		Red
Transmission, Oil Filter		Yellow
Transmission, Oil Temperature High		Yellow

it usually features the image of an engine and may have a wrench symbol or "warning" imposed over the engine. CELs alert the operator to the requirement for maintenance: When the CEL is illuminated, the driver/operator should be instructed to refer the vehicle to assessment by a technician. In most cases, CEL illumination does not require an immediate service intervention or shutting the engine down. A secondary function of the CEL is to alert the operator to other vehicle conditions that may affect its operation, by flashing at key-on. Examples are:

- Real clock time has been interrupted (usually generated by a battery-disconnect event)
- Coolant level is low but not enough to create problems
- Engine oil level is low but not enough to create problems

MALFUNCTION INDICATOR LIGHT

When a **malfunction indicator light (MIL)** is illuminated, the engine electronics are identifying problems with the emission controls. The MIL is amber (yellow) colored, and may use a silhouette of an engine with a graphic of exhaust gas (see Table 35–3). When the MIL is illuminated, it means that the engine is either producing a higher level of emissions or operating in a way that can damage emissions control hardware. A service facility is obliged to troubleshoot, or refer for troubleshooting, an engine condition that has illuminated the MIL. In most cases, when an MIL is ignored, the consequence is the illumination of other dash warning lights (see Table 35–3), including the stop engine light.

STOP ENGINE LIGHT

When a **stop engine light (SEL)** is illuminated, the engine should be shut down at the earliest safe opportunity. After shutdown, the engine should not be started until the problem has been identified using the appropriate EST. The SEL is always red (see Table 35–3) and when illuminated, it is often accompanied by a text alert on the driver information display. When the SEL is illuminated, the default programming is usually set to shut down the engine after a preset time period (30 seconds is typical); this programming may be defeated on certain applications such as emergency vehicles. In addition, most chassis provide the driver/operator with a manual **stop engine override (SEO or STEO);** each SEO depress event provides a further 30 seconds of operation before a programmed shutdown is initiated.

WARNING LIGHT AUDIT TRAILS

Operators and technicians should be aware that when any dash alert is broadcast, the event is logged in real time, and the operator response is tracked, also in real time. Ignoring CEL, MIL, and SEL alerts can result in costly engine damage and denial of warranty. In addition, STEO events are also logged and can be used to deny warranty.

ELECTRONIC LOGGING DEVICE (ELD)

Much used by fleets but not yet mandatory, onboard **electronic logging devices (ELDs)** that monitor driver hours-of-service (HOS) and geo-positioning will soon be a fact of life in trucks. Because ELDs are not yet legislated, their functions are often combined with those we have attributed to EOBRs in other chapters of this book. When the ELD final rule is established, it may be that ELD functions are stand-alone or combined with the chassis telematics. At issue are the usual problems of who has access to the data and how enforcement is structured.

SUMMARY

- The ESTs used to service, diagnose, and reprogram truck engine management systems are onboard diagnostic lights, DMMs, scanners, HH-ESTs, and PCs with the appropriate software.
- Flash codes are an onboard method of accessing diagnostic codes. Most systems display active codes only, but some display both active and historic (inactive) codes.
- A DMM is one of the most important ESTs available to the technician. You should understand how to spec one out and use it to perform electrical and electronic troubleshooting.
- A continuity test is a quick resistance test that distinguishes between an open and a closed circuit.
- A dark band identifies the cathode on a diode.
- Circuit resistance and voltage are measured with the test leads positioned in parallel with the circuit.
- Direct measurement of current flow is performed with the test leads located in series with the circuit. In other words, during the test, current flow is routed through the DMM.
- A Hall-effect probe can be used to approximate high current flow through a DC circuit.

- Pro-Link 9000 with the appropriate OEM software cartridge or data card was, for many years, the industry standard, portable shop floor diagnostic and customer data programming EST. Although still in use, there are a variety of more user-friendly and powerful HH-ESTs capable of online updates and wireless connectivity.
- Most OEMs are currently using the PC and proprietary software as their primary diagnostic and programming EST.
- ESTs designed to connect with the vehicle ECM(s) do so via a six- or nine-pin DLC. J1708 uses a six-pin and J1939 a nine-pin, green or black Deutsch connector. For post-2014 Volvo/Mack applications, a 16-pin J1962 DLC is required to access the chassis electronics.
- Most ESTs require the use of a CA serial link to make the connection between the chassis data bus and the EST unit. Wireless EST-to-data bus communications are also enabled when the appropriate land-to-chassis hardware and software are used.
- HH-ESTs may be updated by replacing PROM chips, by replacing a data card, or by downloads using the Internet.

- A snapshot test is performed to analyze multiple data frames before and after a trigger, which is usually a fault code or manually keyed.
- All OEMs require the use of their online SISs to produce accurate results when using their diagnostic software.
- SAE J1587 and J1939 protocols numerically code all onboard electronic subsystems, parameters, and failure modes.
- PGN, SID, and PID failures are identified by FMIs, making circuit diagnosis easier. The number of FMIs was increased for the 2007 model year to accommodate a category of predictive failures; these consist of components and/or systems that have not actually failed but are producing low-quality data. The new FMIs are also useful to OEMs for data mining via telemetry.
- Beginning with EPA model year 2010, some engine OEMs ceased to support the J1587/1708 data bus, meaning that if one is used on a current chassis, a gateway (transducer) module is required.

- HD-OBD-compliant diesel truck engines are required to generically broadcast all emissions-related failure codes.
- An illuminated CEL indicates that the engine soon requires servicing. A flashing CEL may indicate a possible problem such as a power-interrupt event (battery disconnect) or low engine fluid(s).
- An illuminated MIL indicates a problem with the engine emissions system that should be investigated as soon as possible. An ignored MIL usually results in other, more serious engine alerts and problems.
- An illuminated SEL alerts the operator to a condition that can result in serious engine damage if ignored. The default programming usually shuts the engine off after a preset period, such as 30 seconds after SEL illumination.
- Most OEMs provide an SEO button designed to provide a further 30 seconds of operation before shutdown occurs. The objective is to allow the operator to bring the vehicle to a safe stop.

REVIEW QUESTIONS

1. Which EST is used to read blink/flash codes?
   a. Dash diagnostic lights
   b. HH-ESTs
   c. Diagnostic fork
   d. PCs

2. The appropriate EST for performing a hardwire resistance test on a potentiometer-type TPS isolated from its circuit is a:
   a. DMM.
   b. scanner.
   c. generic HH-EST.
   d. PC.

3. Which of the following is usually required to hardwire-connect a diagnostic PC with a truck data bus?
   a. Modem
   b. Jumper wires
   c. Data connector and CA
   d. Parallel link connector

4. When resistance and continuity tests are made on electronic circuit components, the circuit should be:
   a. energized.
   b. not energized.

5. DMM test lead resistance should never exceed:
   a. 0.2 ohm.
   b. 1.0 ohm.
   c. 10 ohms per inch.
   d. 100 ohms per inch.

6. The output (signal) of an inductive pulse generator, shaft speed sensor is measured in:
   a. V-DC.
   b. ohms.
   c. V-AC.
   d. amperes.

7. Which of the following cannot be performed by an HH-EST?
   a. Erase historic fault codes
   b. Customer data programming
   c. Snapshot testing
   d. Proprietary data programming

8. Which of the following procedures cannot be performed using a PC and the OEM software?
   a. Erasing historic fault codes
   b. Customer data programming
   c. Erasing active fault codes
   d. EUI cutout tests

9. *Technician A* states that when a laptop is hardwire-connected to a chassis data bus, a CA is required. *Technician B* states that a PC with appropriate OEM software and wireless connectivity can communicate with a truck data bus. Who is correct?
   a. Technician A only
   b. Technician B only
   c. Both A and B
   d. Neither A nor B

10. When reading an open TPS circuit, which FMI would be broadcast to the data bus?
    a. 0
    b. 3
    c. 5
    d. 9

11. How many counts of resolution can be displayed by a 4½-digit DMM?
    a. 1,999
    b. 19,999
    c. 49,995
    d. 99,995

12. The specification that indicates how fine a measurement can be made by a DMM is known as:
    a. rms (root mean square).
    b. percentage deviation.
    c. resolution.
    d. hysteresis.

13. A DMM is set to read AC. Which is the term used to describe the averaging of potential difference to produce a reading?
    a. rms (root mean square)
    b. Percentage averaging
    c. Resolution
    d. Sawtoothing

14. What was the main reason for the addition of FMI fields in 2007?
    a. To make system access easier
    b. To accommodate increased numbers of sensors
    c. To make life tougher for technicians
    d. To forecast imminent failures

15. Which of the following components is used to test energized circuit conditions without risk of damaging the wiring?
    a. Cycling breakers
    b. Alligator clips and jumper wire
    c. Breakout boxes
    d. Test light with a sharp probe

16. Which electrical pressure value does a DMM output when in diode test mode?
    a. 0.3 V
    b. 0.6 V
    c. 0.9 V
    d. 1.1 V

17. Technician A states that the accuracy of an analog meter is usually no better than 3%. Technician B states that most DMMs have an accuracy factor that is within 0.1% of the reading. Who is correct?
    a. Technician A only
    b. Technician B only
    c. Both A and B
    d. Neither A nor B

18. Which of the following is the preferred source for service literature covering a repair procedure?
    a. Hard-copy service manual
    b. Technical service bulletin
    c. Online SIS
    d. DVD-based service literature

19. Technician A states that using the snapshot test mode on an EST to troubleshoot an intermittently occurring fault code could help identify the conditions that produced the code. Technician B states that the snapshot test mode can only analyze historic codes on an audit trail. Who is correct?
    a. Technician A only
    b. Technician B only
    c. Both A and B
    d. Neither A nor B

20. Which of the following is the correct address for an engine ECM on a chassis data bus?
    a. SA 00
    b. SA 03
    c. SA 37
    d. SA 71

21. To confirm the signal produced by a powered-up potentiometer-type TPS, the DMM test mode selected should be:
    a. V-AC.
    b. V-DC.
    c. diode test.
    d. resistance.

22. Which of the following is/are HD-OBD monitored field(s)?
    a. DEF level
    b. Manifold boost pressure
    c. SCR efficiency
    d. All of the above

23. When a CEL is illuminated, what should the operator do?
    a. Refer the vehicle for servicing as soon as possible.
    b. Shut down the vehicle immediately.
    c. Safely pull to the side of the road and shut the engine off.
    d. Depress the STEO.

24. When an SEL is illuminated, what should the operator do?
    a. Refer the vehicle for servicing as soon as possible.
    b. Shut down the vehicle immediately.
    c. Safely pull to the side of the road and shut the engine off.
    d. Depress the STEO.

25. Which of the following dash warning lights relates specifically to emissions monitored fields?
    a. CEL
    b. MIL
    c. SEL
    d. ABS

36

Prerequisites: Chapters 34 and 35

ELECTRICAL WIRING, CONNECTOR, AND TERMINAL REPAIR

OBJECTIVES

After studying this chapter, you should be able to:

- Identify SAE standard wiring colors and codes as outlined by SAE J2191 and TMC RP146.
- Interpret SAE standard wiring codes.
- Identify the Weather Pack-type and Deutsch-type terminals and connectors.
- Assemble sealed connectors using the correct methods and crimping tools.
- Disassemble sealed connectors without damaging components.
- Splice wires where necessary in circuits where the practice is permitted.
- Identify standard and virtual circuit protection devices, including fuses and cycling and noncycling circuit breakers.
- Explain how a standard SAE relay functions and interpret the terminal assignments using both older and new SAE codes.
- Identify some common circuit schematic symbols.
- Navigate a basic wiring schematic.
- Diagnose simple circuit malfunctions.
- Correlate DMM readings to normal and abnormal circuit conditions.

KEY TERMS

butt splice	locking tang	relay	three-way splice
crimping pliers	Metri-Pack connector	RP146	virtual protection device
cycling circuit breaker	multiple splice	SAE J2191	
Deutsch connector	noncycling circuit breaker	tang release tool	

INTRODUCTION

There has been a move toward standardizing the wiring used by the different truck original equipment manufacturers (OEMs). Since 2007, some truck OEMs have been bringing wiring color and codes into line with **SAE J2191** and Technology and Maintenance Council (TMC) **RP146** standards. Though this has some potential to initially create grief for truck technicians who have to learn yet another system, in the long run it will be beneficial, especially for those who have to work on multiple OEM products. We begin this chapter by outlining the basics of J2191 and RP146 wiring systems for heavy-duty trucks.

One of the reasons that today's truck electronically managed engines present relatively few wiring and terminal-related circuit problems is the overall quality of the weather-sealed components used. In a drive-by-wire chassis, it is crucial that wiring and connector repairs, when required, duplicate the original standards. Terminals may be platinum or gold coated to minimize resistance, so it is always important to observe OEM guidelines when undertaking any circuit repairs. The following instructions demonstrate general correct practices.

SAE WIRING STANDARDS

Any truck technician working in a service facility in which multiple OEM trucks are repaired will likely identify tracing electrical and electronic problems as a major challenge. Part of this challenge is that until recently, OEMs have each had their own way of coding and coloring the wiring in their electrical systems. Beginning in 2007, truck OEMs began a process of adhering to what will probably become known as SAE wiring codes; that said, not all chassis have converted to this at the time of writing. SAE wiring codes are based on an SAE J-standard known as J2191 and a later TMC-recommended practice (RP) known as RP146. We offer a primer in SAE wiring codes in this chapter, but note that some of the OEMs provide a more detailed introduction in their service information systems (SISs), including software-guided navigation of schematics.

COLOR CODES

Gone are the 100 different colors packed into a wiring harness—colors that faded with age and time into a fraction of that number. SAE wiring codes use just three colors, as follows:

- *Red:* Used for any unprotected (by fuse or breaker) wire. Specific wires are identified by *black* codes spaced every 4 in. (10 cm) apart.
- *White* with *orange* tracer: Used in any protected circuit. Most of the wiring on the chassis will fall into this category. Specific wires are identified by *black* codes spaced every 4 in. (10 cm) apart.
- *Gray:* Used for ground circuits. Specific wires are identified by *black* codes spaced every 4 in. (10 cm) apart.

WIRE IDENTIFICATION

Although this may seem complicated at first, the codes used to identify each wire in a circuit make navigating wiring schematics easier because each wire is identified by an alphanumeric code in black print spaced every 4 in. (10 cm) apart. **Figure 36–1** shows a typical SAE alphanumeric code, which we will decode in this section, then explain some of the terms used.

System Identifier

The system identifier is the first alpha character in the code. At the time of writing, 16 system identifiers are used, as shown in **Table 36–1**. In Figure 36–1, you will see that the system identifier alpha code is H, which tells us that the system we are working with is the instrumentation system.

Circuit Identifiers

The circuit identifier indicates what section of the system you are working with: This is often a connector. In cases where the circuit originates at a connector, the cavity number follows. Alternatively, where a circuit originates at a protection device such as a breaker or fuse, the number(s) that follow indicate the protection device number. In Figure 36–1, the circuit identifier is B12, so the B connector is at cavity number 12.

FIGURE 36–1 SAE wiring code interpretation.

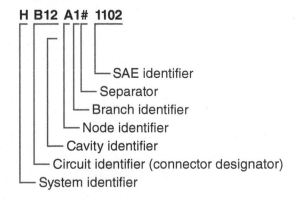

TABLE 36–1 SAE Wiring System Identifiers

Character Designation	System Identifier
A	Braking/traction control/centralized tire inflation
B	Electrical charging circuit
C	Control and management circuits: fuel, engine, security
D	Emergency/vision
E	Engine accessories
F	Protected circuits
G	HVAC
H	Instrumentation/monitoring/warning systems
I	Lighting systems
J	Serial data bus communications (J1939)
K	Protected power
L	Operator conveniences (GPS, WiFi, Satellite com, entertainment)
M	Trailer systems
N	Transmission, drivetrain, and drive axle carriers
U	Unprotected power
X	Ground

Node and Branch Identifiers

The node identifier is the first alpha character following the circuit identifier: It indicates which power node of the circuit the wire(s) form. By definition, a *node* is any unswitched portion of a circuit transmitting electrical current from a driving device to a load. This means that the node identifier must change every time it passes through a switching device such as a relay, switch, or field effect transistor (FET). Each time the node ID changes, the next available alpha is used. An example of how this occurs appears in **Figure 36–2**, which shows a continuation of the circuit presented in Figure 36–1.

The branch identifier is the number located immediately after the node ID. A *branch* describes a wire that electrically connects to a node and permits uninterrupted current flow. The specific branch id number is the next sequential number on the node, as you can see by referencing Figure 36–2. A splice or double terminal in the circuit is treated as a branch.

Separators and SAE Identifiers

The separator is simply the # symbol, and it is used to keep the circuit identifier separate from the SAE supplementary identifier. The SAE supplementary ID is also known as the *suffix*. **Table 36–2**, **Table 36–3**, **Table 36–4**, and **Table 36–5** list a sampling of some of the SAE IDs that you would be likely to encounter while working with the engine electronics. A complete list is provided in the Student Guide that accompanies this textbook.

Data Bus Identification

The operating principles of chassis data buses are discussed in some detail in Chapter 37, so our objective here is simply to identify how the circuit appears in SAE code format. **Figure 36–3** shows how this will appear on a schematic, while Table 36–5 shows the SAE supplementary IDs.

This should give you a general idea of how to navigate SAE wiring schematics. It is worth spending some time getting familiar with them,

FIGURE 36–2 Node ID changes.

TABLE 36–2 Power Circuit SAE Supplementary IDs

SAE Suffix	Subsystem Description	Circuit Function
1101	Power	Battery bus feed
1102	Power	Ignition bus feed
1103	Power	Battery disconnect
1104	Power	Key switch feed
1105	Power	Cab feed
1106	Power	Accessory bus feed
1107	Power	Battery cable
1108	Power	Ignition spare
1109	Power	Battery spare
1110	Power	Accessory spare
1111	Power	Ignition bus control: chassis engine control module (ECM)

TABLE 36–3 Ground Circuit SAE Supplementary IDs

SAE Suffix	Subsystem Description	Circuit Function
1201	Ground	Instrument ground
1202	Ground	Starter ground
1203	Ground	Lighting ground
1204	Ground	Cab ground
1205	Ground	Engine ground
1206	Ground	Electronic circuit ground
1207	Ground	Alternator ground
1208	Ground	Chassis ground
1209	Ground	Battery ground

because the objective is for all OEMs to eventually adopt them. **Figure 36–4** shows you how an SAE code appears on an actual section of wire, and **Figure 36–5** shows the source address (SA) topology of a Mack Trucks data bus using the new SAE wiring schematic architecture. What appears as figure-of-eight loops indicates twisted wire pairs.

CONNECTOR ASSEMBLY AND REPAIR

Most of the wiring and connectors used on electronically managed diesel engines in North America are manufactured by a couple of manufacturers, so although the procedures outlined in this section are specific to one OEM, they are representative of those required for all the major OEMs.

WEATHERPROOF CONNECTORS

The following sequences demonstrate the disassembly, repair, and reassembly procedure required for the Weather-Pack and **Metri-Pack connectors** used in truck electronic circuits. This procedure is similar to that required for the assembly and repair of most electronic wiring and connectors.

TABLE 36–4 Control Circuit SAE Supplementary IDs

SAE Suffix	Subsystem Description	Circuit Function
1501	Control: fuel and engine system	Engine shutdown
1502	Control: fuel and engine system	Engine retarder/brake
1503	Control: fuel and engine system	Idle shutdown timer
1504	Control: fuel and engine system	Cruise control on/off
1505	Control: fuel and engine system	Idle verification
1506	Control: fuel and engine system	rpm throttle set
1507	Control: fuel and engine system	Clutch/driveline disengage
1508	Control: fuel and engine system	Cruise set resume
1509	Control: fuel and engine system	Engine overspeed protection
1510	Control: fuel and engine system	(PTO) controls
1511	Control: fuel and engine system	Stop switch signals
1512	Control: fuel and engine system	Electronic/engine control
1513	Control: fuel and engine system	Spare relay: controlled by chassis ECU
1514	Control: fuel and engine system	Customer option: controlled by ECU
1515	Control: fuel and engine system	Air management control

TABLE 36–5 Data Bus SAE Supplementary IDs

SAE Suffix	Subsystem Description	Circuit Function
1601	Serial data communications	J1587/J1708
1602	Serial data communications	J922
1603	Serial data communications	J1939

Installation of Weatherproof Square Connectors

Weather-Pack and Metri-Pack connectors use a pull-to-seat design. The cable is pushed through the seal and correct cavity of the connector before crimping the terminal to the cable. It should be stripped of insulation *after* it is placed through the seal and connector body. The procedure required to assemble a Weather-Pack connector is demonstrated in the DVD/online video that accompanies this textbook. Use the following instructions for terminal installation:

1. Position the cable through the seal and the correct cavity of the connector (**Figure 36–6**).
2. Using wire strippers, strip the end of the cable to leave 0.2 ± 0.02 in. (5.0 ± 0.5 mm) of bare conductor.
3. Squeeze the handles of the crimping tool together firmly to cause the jaws to automatically open.
4. Hold the "wire side" facing you.
5. Push the terminal holder to the open position and insert the terminal until the wire-attaching portion of the terminal rests on the 20-22 anvil of the tool. Be sure that the wire core wings and the insulation wings of the terminal are pointing toward the upper jaw of the crimping tool (**Figure 36–7**).
6. Insert the cable into the terminal until the stripped portion is positioned in the wire core wings and the insulation portion ends just forward of the insulation wings (**Figure 36–8**).
7. Compress the handles of the crimping tool until the ratchet automatically releases and the crimp is complete.

FIGURE 36–3 J1939 data bus identifier.

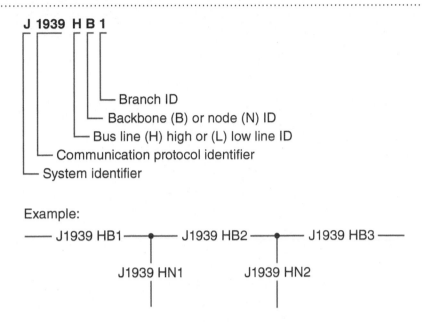

J 1939 H B 1

Branch ID
Backbone (B) or node (N) ID
Bus line (H) high or (L) low line ID
Communication protocol identifier
System identifier

Example:

── J1939 HB1 ──●── J1939 HB2 ──●── J1939 HB3 ──

J1939 HN1   J1939 HN2

FIGURE 36–4 SAE codes printed on J2191/RP146 chassis wiring.

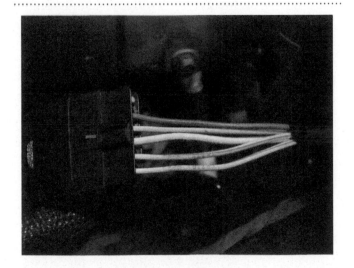

> **NOTE:**
> For a faster, more efficient crimping operation, a bracket or bench rest may be used to cradle one handle of the tool. The operator can apply the terminals by grasping and actuating only one handle of the tool (**Figure 36–9**).

8. Release the crimping tool with the lock lever located between the handles in case of jamming.

9. Align the **locking tang** of the terminal with the lettered side of the connector.
10. Pull the cable back through the connector until a click is heard (**Figure 36–10**). Position the seal into the connector.

> **NOTE:**
> For ECM 30-pin connectors, put the locking tang opposite the lettered side.

Removal and Repair

A tang on the terminal locks into a tab molded into the plastic connector to retain the cable assembly. Remove Metri-Pack 150 terminals using the following instructions.

1. Insert the **tang release tool** into the cavity of the connector, placing the tip of the tool between the locking tang of the terminal and the wall of the cavity (**Figure 36–11**).
2. Depress the tang of the terminal to release it from the connector.
3. Push the cable forward through the terminal until the complete crimp is exposed.
4. Cut the cable immediately behind the damaged terminal to repair it.
5. Follow the installation instructions for crimping the terminal and inserting it into the connector.

FIGURE 36–5 SAE wiring schematic showing the SA bus topology of a Mack Trucks powertrain bus.

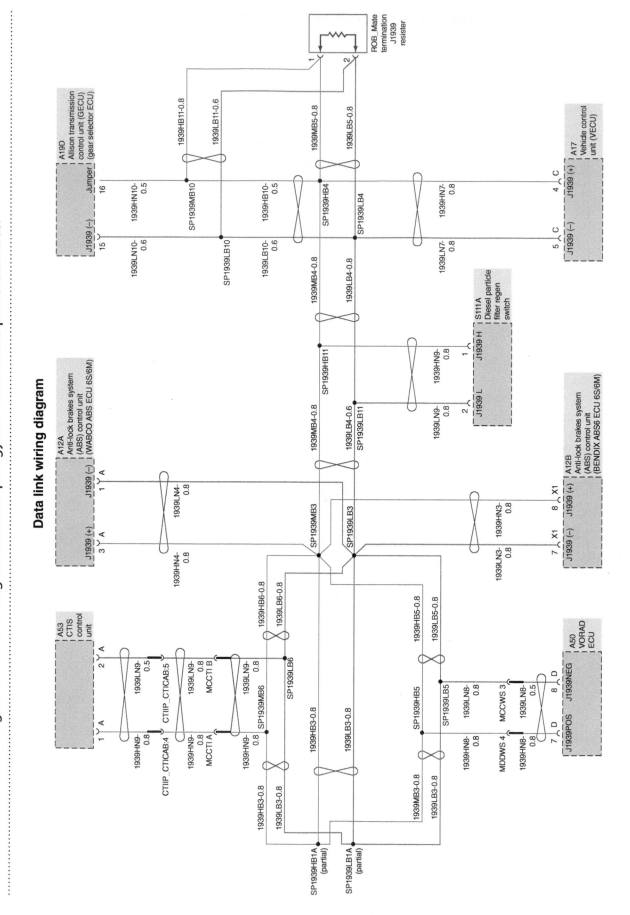

FIGURE 36–6 Inserting wire in the connector.

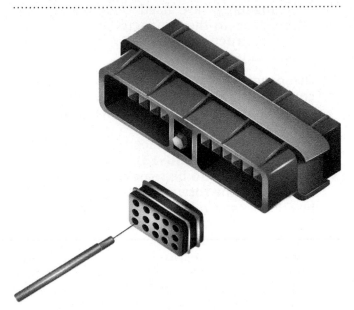

FIGURE 36–7 Terminal and crimping tool position.

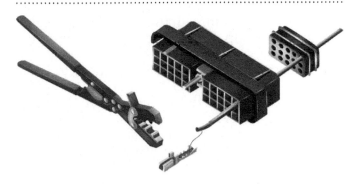

FIGURE 36–8 Cable-to-terminal alignment.

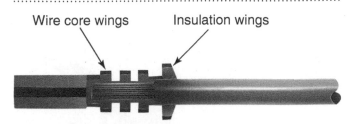

Wire core wings   Insulation wings

Assembly of Metri-Pack Round Connectors

Use the following instructions for terminal installation:

1. Insert the terminal into the locating hole of the crimping tool, using the proper hole according to the gauge of the cable to be used (**Figure 36–12**).
2. Insert the cable into the terminal until the stripped portion is positioned in the cable

FIGURE 36–9 Crimping operation.

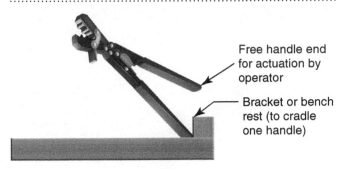

Free handle end for actuation by operator

Bracket or bench rest (to cradle one handle)

FIGURE 36–10 Pulling the terminal to seat.

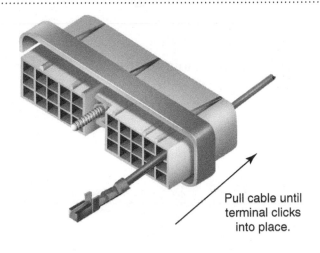

Pull cable until terminal clicks into place.

FIGURE 36–11 Terminal removal.

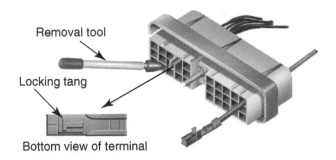

Removal tool

Locking tang

Bottom view of terminal

core wings, and the seal and insulated portion of the cable are in the insulation wings (**Figure 36–13**).
3. Compress the handles of the crimping tool until the ratchet automatically releases and the crimp is complete. A properly crimped terminal is shown in Figure 36–13.
4. Release the crimping tool with the lock lever located between the handles in case of jamming.
5. Push the crimped terminal into the connector until it clicks into place. Gently tug on the cable to make sure it is secure (**Figure 36–14**).

FIGURE 36–12 Terminal position.

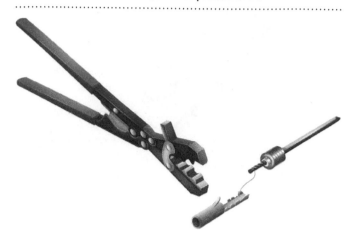

FIGURE 36–13 Cable and terminal position before and after crimping.

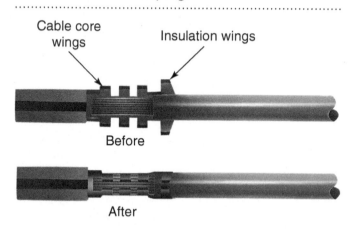

Cable core wings

Insulation wings

Before

After

FIGURE 36–14 Inserting the terminal in the connector.

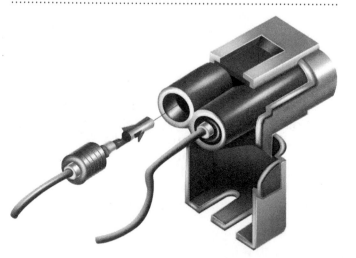

Removal and Repair

Two locking tangs are used on the terminals to secure them to the connector body. Use the following instructions for removing terminals from the connector body:

1. Disengage the locking tang, securing the connector bodies to each other. Grasp one half of the connector in each hand and gently pull apart.
2. Unlatch and open the secondary lock on the connector (**Figure 36–15**).
3. Grasp the cable to be removed and push the terminal to the forward position.
4. Insert the tang release tool straight into the front of the connector cavity until it resists on the cavity shoulder.
5. Grasp the cable and push it forward through the connector cavity into the tool while holding the tool securely in place (**Figure 36–16**).
6. The tool will press the locking tangs of the terminal. Pull the cable rearward (back through the connector). Remove the tool from the connector cavity.
7. Cut the wire immediately behind the cable seat and slip the new cable seal onto the wire.
8. Strip the end of the cable strippers to leave 0.2 ± 0.02 in. (5.0 ± 0.5 mm) of bare conductor. Position the cable seal as shown in **Figure 36–17**.
9. Crimp the new terminal onto the wire, using the crimp tool (**Figure 36–18**).

FIGURE 36–15 Unlatched secondary lock.

FIGURE 36–16 Removal tool procedure.

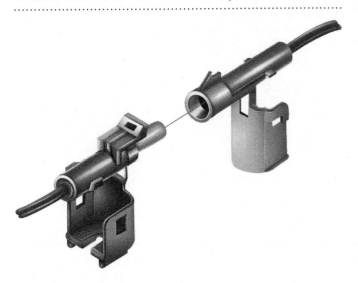

FIGURE 36–17 Proper cable seal position.

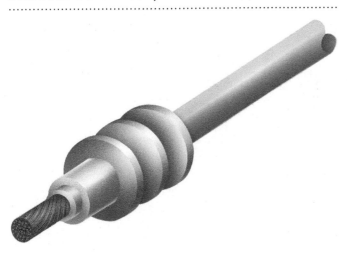

FIGURE 36–18 Crimping procedure.

DEUTSCH CONNECTORS

Deutsch connectors are used on the chassis data bus, including the six- or nine-pin data connector. Deutsch connectors have cable seals that are integrally molded into the connector. They are push-to-seat connectors with cylindrical terminals. The diagnostic terminal connectors are gold plated.

Assembly of Deutsch Connectors

Use the following instructions for installation:

1. Strip approximately $\frac{1}{4}$ inch (6 mm) of insulation from the cable.
2. Remove the lock clip, raise the wire gauge selector, and rotate the knob to the number matching the gauge of the wire that is being used.
3. Lower the selector and insert the lock clip.
4. Position the contact so that the crimp barrel is $\frac{1}{32}$ of an inch (0.75 mm) above the four indenters (**Figure 36–19**). Crimp the cable.
5. Grasp the contact approximately 1 in. (25 mm) behind the contact crimp barrel.
6. Hold the connector with the rear grommet facing you (**Figure 36–20**).
7. Push the contact into the grommet until a positive stop is felt (**Figure 36–21**). A slight tug will confirm that it is properly locked into place.

Removal

The appropriate size removal tool should be used when removing cables from connectors.

FIGURE 36–19 Setting wire gauge selector and positioning the contact.

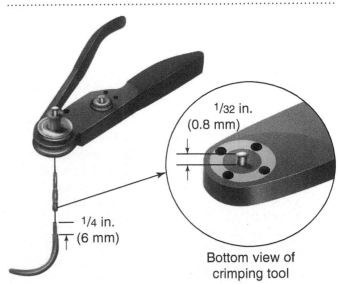

1/32 in. (0.8 mm)

1/4 in. (6 mm)

Bottom view of crimping tool

FIGURE 36–20 Pushing the contact into the grommet.

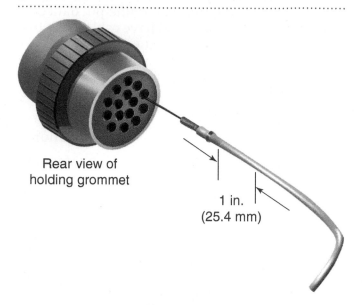

Rear view of
holding grommet

1 in.
(25.4 mm)

FIGURE 36–21 Locking the terminal into the connector.

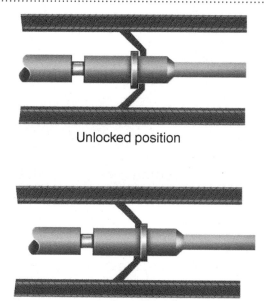

Unlocked position

Locked position

1. With the rear insert toward you, snap the appropriate size remover tool over the cable of the contact to be removed (**Figure 36–22**).
2. Slide the tool along the cable into the insert cavity until it engages and resistance is felt. Do not twist or insert the tool at an angle.
3. Pull the contact cable assembly out of the connector. Keep reverse tension on the cable and forward tension on the tool (**Figure 36–23**).

FIGURE 36–22 Removal tool positioned for removal.

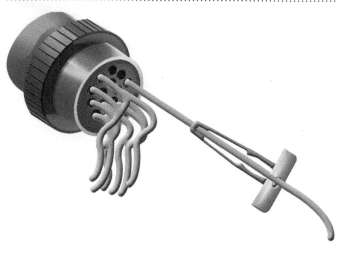

FIGURE 36–23 Removal tool and wire withdrawn.

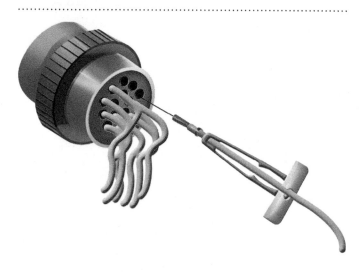

TECH TIP:

When replacing connectors, ensure that each wire is labeled by cavity location to facilitate reassembly. Use strips of masking tape on wires to record each cavity code on if you have to: This is usually easier than reassembling a multiwire connector using the OEM wiring schematic.

SPLICING GUIDELINES

Not all wiring in electronic circuits can be spliced, so always refer to the OEM service literature before attempting such a procedure.

The following may be used as a general guideline. The objective is to produce a high-quality, tight splice with durable insulation that should outlast the life of the vehicle. The selection of crimping tools and splice connectors will depend on the exact repair being performed.

TOOLS REQUIRED

- Soldering iron
- Rosin core solder
- Wire strippers
- Heat-shrink tubing
- Splice clips
- **Crimping pliers**

STRAIGHT LEADS

To splice straight leads:

1. Locate the broken wire.
2. Remove the insulation as required; be sure the exposed wire is clean and not corroded.
3. Slide a sleeve of shrink wrap on the wire long enough to cover the splice and overlap the wire insulation by about ¼ in. (6 mm) on both sides.
4. Insert one wire into the splice clip and crimp.
5. Insert the other wire into the splice and crimp (**Figure 36–24**).

Solder

Soldering splice connectors is optional. To solder splice connectors:

1. You must use rosin core solder.
2. Check the exposed wire before the splice is crimped in its connector. The exposed wire must be clean before the splice is crimped.
3. Use a suitable electronic soldering iron to heat the wires. Apply the solder to the heated wire (not to the soldering iron), allowing sufficient solder flow into the splice joint.
4. Pull on the connection to ensure crimping and soldering integrity.

Shrink Wrap

Shrink wrap is required. Alpha FIT-300, Raychem TAT 125, or any equivalent heat-shrink dual-wall epoxy encapsulating adhesive polyolefin is required.

To heat-shrink wrap a splice:

1. Select the correct diameter to allow a tight wrap when heated. The heated shrink wrap must be long enough to overlap the wire insulation about ¼ in. (6 mm) on both sides of the splice.
2. Heat the shrink wrap with a heat gun; do not concentrate the heat in one location, but play the heat over the entire length of the shrink wrap until the joint is complete.

MULTIPLE BROKEN WIRES

To create a **multiple splice** from broken wires:

1. Stagger the position of each splice as illustrated in **Figure 36–25**.
2. You *must* stagger positions to prevent a large bulge in the harness and to prevent the wires from chafing against each other.

FIGURE 36–24 Spliced wire.

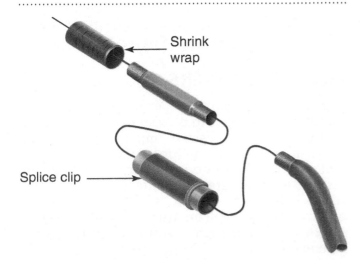

Shrink wrap

Splice clip

FIGURE 36–25 Multiple splices.

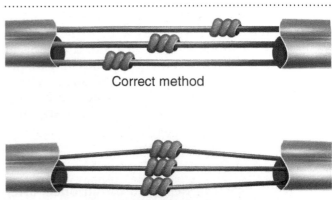

Correct method

Incorrect method

FIGURE 36–26 Three-way splice.

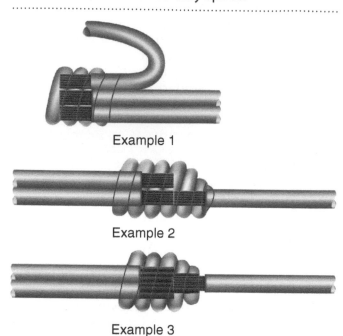

Example 1

Example 2

Example 3

Three-Wire Splice

Three-way splice connectors are commercially available to accommodate three-wire splices. The technique is the same as with a single **butt splice** connector (**Figure 36–26**).

CIRCUIT PROTECTION DEVICES

Circuit protection components are designed to limit current flow through a circuit. Almost all truck electrical circuits are protected by either a fuse or a circuit breaker. Many current chassis use **virtual protection devices**. An electrical virtual protection device is tripped by logic analysis of the circuit operating values: Its effect on the circuit is identical to an electromechanical tripping device such as a fuse or breaker. When troubleshooting electrical circuits, one of the first steps is to identify the location of the circuit protection device on any suspect wiring path. In SAE standard wiring codes, the color white with an orange tracer is used for any protected circuit.

FUSES

Hard wire fuses are designed to fail once, after which they have to be replaced. A typical fuse

FIGURE 36–27 Location of a maxi fuse on a Freightliner Columbia firewall.

consists of a wire bridge through which circuit current is routed. The bridge is rated for specific maximum amperage. If the specified amperage is exceeded, the bridge overheats and melts. Fuses have made something of a comeback during recent years. This is due to the sensitivity of low-potential electronic circuits to current overload discharge. A number of different types of fuses are used in current truck electrical circuits. **Figure 36–27** shows the location of maxi fuse on a Freightliner chassis firewall. The symbol for a fuse is shown in **Figure 36–28**.

CIRCUIT BREAKERS

A mechanical circuit breaker is designed not to fail when subjected to a circuit overload. When a circuit draws excessive amperage, the circuit breaker is designed to open the circuit, after which it will reset. A typical circuit breaker consists of an armature and contacts: The contacts "break" when the circuit is overloaded. There are two types used on trucks: Refer to Figure 36–28 to see how each is represented in a circuit schematic.

FIGURE 36–28 Circuit protection devices.

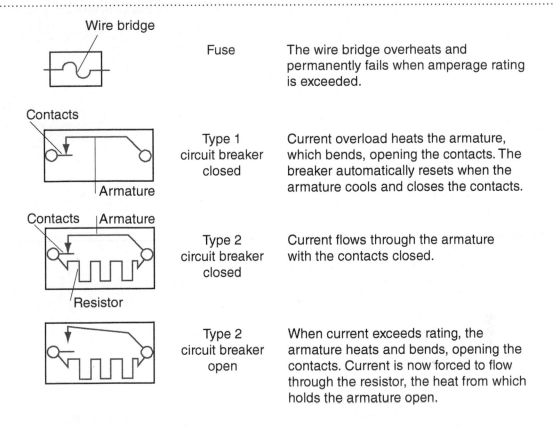

Wire bridge	Fuse	The wire bridge overheats and permanently fails when amperage rating is exceeded.
Contacts / Armature	Type 1 circuit breaker closed	Current overload heats the armature, which bends, opening the contacts. The breaker automatically resets when the armature cools and closes the contacts.
Contacts / Armature / Resistor	Type 2 circuit breaker closed	Current flows through the armature with the contacts closed.
	Type 2 circuit breaker open	When current exceeds rating, the armature heats and bends, opening the contacts. Current is now forced to flow through the resistor, the heat from which holds the armature open.

Cycling Circuit Breakers

Cycling circuit breakers are known as SAE type 1 circuit breakers. The symbol for a type 1 circuit is shown in Figure 36–28. When current flowed through the armature exceeds the specified rating, the armature heats up and bends away from the contact point shown by the arrow: This immediately opens the circuit. With the circuit open, no current flows through the armature, so it cools and as it straightens closes the circuit as the contacts connect. Typical circuits that use SAE type 1 breakers are headlights, fog lights, electric windshield wiper circuits, and so forth.

Noncycling Circuit Breakers

Noncycling circuit breakers are known as SAE type 2 circuit breakers. The symbol for a type 2 circuit breaker is shown in Figure 36–28: In this figure, you can see the breaker in both closed and tripped conditions. A type 2 circuit breaker functions similarly to the type 1 except that it has a resistor below the armature. When

the circuit it is protecting is closed (energized), there are two possible current paths through the breaker, but because electricity will use the path of least resistance, most of the current will flow through the armature. If the specified amperage of the circuit breaker is exceeded, the armature heats up and bends away from the contacts, opening the circuit: At this point, circuit current has no choice but to flow through the resistor. The current flowed through the resistor is converted to heat that acts to keep the armature warm enough so that the contacts do not meet. When a noncycling circuit breaker trips, the current load can only pass through the resistor, resulting in greatly reduced current and voltage loss to the circuit.

So long as the circuit is energized, the only path for current flow through a noncycling circuit breaker is through the resistor. To "reset" a noncycling circuit breaker, the circuit must be switched open. This allows the circuit breaker resistor and armature to cool and close the breaker contacts. Noncycling circuit breakers are used extensively in truck electrical circuits.

RELAYS

A **relay** is an electromechanical switch. They are used extensively on truck electrical circuits and every technician should know exactly how one functions. A relay consists of two electrically isolated circuits. One circuit (coil) is used to electromagnetically change the switch status of the power circuit, either opening or closing it. Relays enable a low-current circuit (coil) to control high-current ("power") circuits. Take a look at **Figure 36–29** and **Figure 36–30**, showing SAE standard relay terminal assignments, when following the explanation in the text.

COIL CIRCUIT

The relays shown in Figure 36–29 and Figure 36–30 are used in all OEM electrical systems. Two sets of terminal assignment numeric codes are used. The control or coil circuit is indicated by terminals 85 (2) and 86 (1). The polarity usually does not matter—but it might. For instance, Volvo Trucks uses a diode on some of its control circuits, so on these terminal 85 (2) must always be chassis ground. When no current flows through the coil circuit, the status of the switching circuit is in NC, or normally closed. In most cases (depending on how the relay is being used), this will mean that the output is open. When current flows through the control coil, an electromagnetic field is created and the movable

FIGURE 36–30 Newer-style standard SAE relay terminal assignments.

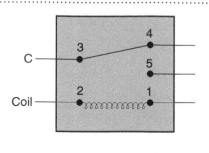

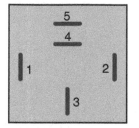

switch is pulled toward the coil, opening the 30–87a (3–4) circuit and closing the 30–87 (3–5) circuit.

CAUTION:

The wiring designations outlined here are the most common. If you take a look at Figure 36–29 and Figure 36–30, you can see that other wiring options are available depending on how the coil circuit is switched. Take nothing for granted, and use the OEM wiring schematics.

SWITCHED CIRCUIT

Referencing Figure 36–29 and Figure 36–30 once again, you will see that the switched circuit of the relay is represented by terminals 30 (3), 87 (5), and 87a (4). Terminal 30 (3) is common. This means that a voltage reading could normally be measured at terminal 30 (3) regardless of the status of the switch. When the coil circuit of the switch is not energized, 30 (3) would close on the NC terminal 87a (4). In most cases, this would mean that the switching status of the relay is open so that no current flows through the switch circuit. When the control coil is energized, the switch is moved from the 87a (4) normally closed pole to the 87 (5) normally open (NO) pole: This action permits current to flow from common terminal 30 (3) to the NO terminal 87 (5).

FIGURE 36–29 Older-style standard SAE relay terminal assignments.

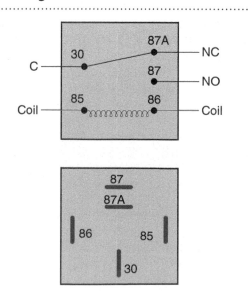

TABLE 36–6 SAE Relay Terminal Assignments

Terminal Designation	Former Number	Revised Number
Coil (control current positive) often stamped +	86	1
Coil (control current ground: direct or switched)	85	2
Common (supply current in)	30	3
Normally closed (NC)	87a	4
Normally open (NO)	87	5

Terminal Assignments

Standard SAE designations were recently revised by the SAE, with the result that two numbering systems are in use. For instance, some OEMs continue to use the older numbering system even on their current products. However, we can say that one of the following methods of numbering relays is standard through the industry, so it will pay you to commit the terminal designations to memory (**Table 36–6**).

Check these terminal assignments by referencing Figure 36–29 and Figure 36–30 again. Relays are simple switches that only cause confusion if you do not know how one operates. Take a little time to memorize the terminal assignments; it will pay off in troubleshooting time saved many times over.

Relay Functionality

A good method of remembering the function of each relay terminal is shown in **Table 36–7**.

Microrelays

Microrelays have become more commonly used in recent years. They use the same numbering codes as standard relays: Both the old and new numbering codes are used. Microrelays are compact and accordingly are specified to lower maximum current loads.

Four-Terminal Relays

Four-terminal relays are now widely used in truck electrical circuits because they are more compact. A four-terminal relay retains the coil circuit (terminals 1 and 2) and eliminates the NC option on the power circuit. Operation is simple. The common terminal (3) is the power in. When the coil circuit (terminals 1 and 2) is energized, the power circuit closes so that current can flow from terminal 3 to terminal 5.

TROUBLESHOOTING TECHNIQUES

In an earlier chapter, we said that there were only three types of electrical circuit faults: namely, opens, shorts, and high resistance. This said, locating a circuit fault can often be a tough task. The technician can make this task easier by understanding electrical basics and the actual circuit being diagnosed. Learn to rely on your digital multimeter (DMM) and make double-checking a habit.

TABLE 36–7 Relay Terminal Functions

New SAE #	Old SAE #	Function
1	86	Control current (usually positive, especially when a diode is used)
2	85	Control current out (usually to ground but could be switched)
3	30	Supply current in
4	87a	High current out—normally closed
5	87	High current out—normally open

WIRE GAUGE FACTORS

The larger the sectional area of wire, the more current carrying capability it will have, because there are more free electrons available to carry it. If too much current is forced down a wire with too small a sectional area, the wire will overheat due to the molecular friction created. Because some North American manufacturers are using metric wire gauge specifications, you should be able to convert them to American wire gauge (AWG) standards. Metric wire is identified by cross-sectional area expressed in square millimeters (mm²) and not by diameter. To calculate cross-sectional area:

wire sectional area = radius × radius × π (3.1416)*

Metric to AWG Conversion

The following list correlates metric wire size to its approximate AWG equivalent:

Metric Size	AWG
00,22	24 gauge
00,35	22 gauge
00,5	20 gauge
00,8	18 gauge
01,0	16 gauge
02,0	14 gauge
03,0	12 gauge
05,0	10 gauge
13,0	6 gauge
32,0	2 gauge
62,0	0 gauge

When selecting wire gauge, the sectional area is obviously a factor, but so is the length of the wire. As wire length increases, so will voltage losses when current is pumped through the wire. This means that the wire gauge size must be increased if the current destination is far away from the source. **Figure 36–31** shows how wire length and amperage affect voltage drop.

CIRCUIT VOLTAGE BEHAVIOR

When a discharged battery tested at 8 volts is connected to a battery charger with voltage measured at 16 volts, initially there will be high amperage flow from the charger to the battery. As the electrical pressure in the battery builds during charging, the rate of current transfer will slow due to the drop in charge differential,

FIGURE 36–31 Voltage drop and wire length chart.

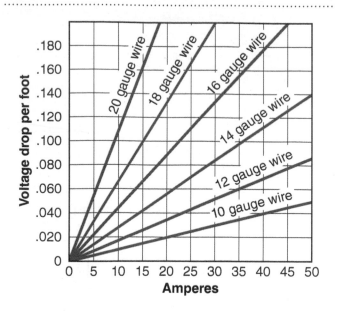

which is caused by battery voltage rising. The result is that as battery voltage rises to its fully charged level, the rate of amperage flow from the charger to the battery drops.

Basic circuit theory (see Chapter 32) tells us that the sum of voltage drops must always equal source voltage. In a perfect electrical circuit, voltage should be dropped only across the intended loads in that circuit. Should voltage be dropped elsewhere in the circuit due to high resistances, there will be insufficient voltage to allow the intended load in a circuit to operate properly.

Voltage Drop versus Resistance

Every technician should understand the importance of voltage drop testing, and that means understanding the limitations of the ohmmeter. If a copper starter motor cable has deteriorated to the extent that only 10% of its wire strands remain intact, an ohmmeter measurement will indicate that it checks out with a resistance reading similar to that of a cable in perfect condition. This is because the ohmmeter is forcing a very small current through the test circuit. However, if a voltage drop test were to be performed on the cable while cranking the engine, the voltage drop would immediately indicate the problem. Understanding voltage drop testing is essential for any vehicle technician, and the concept can be applied to any energized electrical circuit. The procedure is demonstrated in the DVD video that accompanies this textbook.

FIGURE 36–32 LOADpro Dynamic Test Leads. **A:** The LOADpro leads replace the leads on any DMM. **B:** When the LOADpro button is depressed, a 25-ohm resistance is added to the test circuit, which can identify high-resistance circuits when performing voltage drop tests.

A

LOADpro® CIRCUIT TESTING

LOADpro DMM leads are a replacement set of DMM leads with added circuitry that helps locate corrosion in some electrical circuits using digital voltmeter mode. The tool functions best when used on standard 12 V-DC circuits. The hardware consists of a set of normal DMM test leads connected through the LOADpro module, which is a small plastic case with a trigger button, shown in **Figure 36–32A** and **B**. Until the button is depressed (Figure 36–32B), the LOADpro leads function exactly like regular DMM test leads. When the LOADpro trigger button is depressed, a 25-ohm resistance is placed across the test leads. This means that a component can be removed from its circuit, and then be subjected to a dynamic load test. Because of the nearly universal adoption of sealed weatherproof connectors in truck electrical circuits making access to the wires difficult without damaging them, this permits voltage drop testing for corrosion in the wiring itself.

LOADpro® Test Procedure

The LOADpro testing sequence, which follows, is simple. The leads function as normal DMM test leads until the trigger button is depressed, so they are designed to replace the original set of leads.

1. Open the circuit at the component, for instance, a relay.
2. Connect the voltmeter in the exact place where the load component was. The negative (black) lead should be placed on the ground terminal, not to chassis ground.
3. Take a standard voltage reading with the circuit energized.
4. If nominal (system) voltage exists, depress the LOADpro trigger button.
5. If voltage remains nominal (does not drop more than 0.5 V), the circuit can be regarded as clean and the test can be concluded (**Figure 36–33A**).

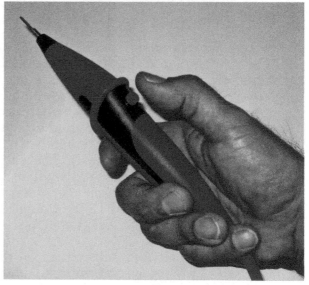

B

6. If the intended load in the circuit produces no voltage drop (**Figure 36–33B**), the load can be assumed to be defective.
7. If voltage drop exceeds 0.5 V, corrosion is present. Proceed to the next steps in the test procedure.
8. Move the negative lead to a good chassis ground and depress the LOADpro trigger.

FIGURE 36–33 Circuit analysis: DMM readings indicating normal and defective conditions.

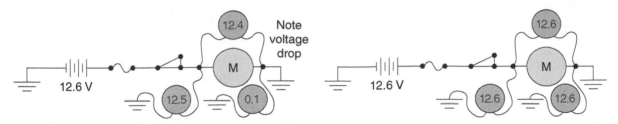

A. Circuit functioning properly

B. Defective load

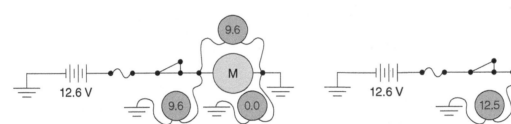

C. Defect on positive side

D. Defect on ground side

9. If voltage remains low, the corrosion is in the positive wire (**Figure 36–33C**).
10. If voltage rises to nominal, the corrosion is in the negative wire (**Figure 36–33D**).

CIRCUIT ANALYSIS

Getting familiar with using your DMM on real-world circuits should mean testing properly functioning circuits. Too often, a technician tests a circuit for a defect without knowing how that circuit would test if it were fully functional. Try to make a practice of testing good circuits as well as bad. It is important to remember that your DMM is capable of making exact measurements and that the specific value is significant. When evaluating circuit performance, there is a difference between 12.6 and 12.5 volts. Make a habit of writing down the results of circuit testing.

Figure 36–33 shows four schematics. In the first, Figure 36–33A, the circuit voltage values show what to expect when the circuit is energized and functioning properly. This is probably the most important of the four, so make sure you understand exactly what is going on. The next three schematics show typical measurements made when the load is defective (Figure 36–33B), there is a defect on the positive side (Figure 36–33C), and a defect on the ground side of the circuit (Figure 36–33D).

CIRCUIT SYMBOLS

Although there may be similarities, most engine manufacturers like to use their own wiring schematic symbols. This may change if OEMs decide to embrace SAE standard symbols. Despite some commonality, there are enough differences to make these symbols confusing if you are working with a variety of different manufacturers' products. However, you will almost always find that these symbols are deciphered somewhere in the service literature or online service link. **Figure 36–34** shows some examples of typical circuit symbols in current use.

INTERPRETING CIRCUIT SCHEMATICS

Until the recent move toward establishing SAE standard electrical schematics (introduced at the beginning of this chapter), there was no universal set of standards for wiring schematics. This can make the interpretation of schematics challenging. Even if the new SAE standards become embraced by all OEMs, it will take a generation to make obsolete the many different types of schematics used up until 2007. **Figure 36–35** shows a Navistar International wiring schematic: See if you can navigate it to determine how the injector driver module (IDM) and ECM are powered up.

FIGURE 36–34 Circuit symbols.

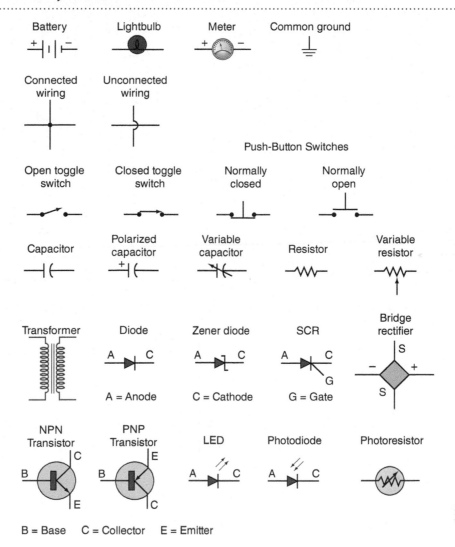

Virtual Schematics

OEMs do not usually produce hard-copy paper wiring schematics anymore. The reason is that electrical and electronic systems have simply become too complex to represent on a single sheet of paper, however large it opens up to. Most technicians today use schematics that have been downloaded off an SIS. You must be able to navigate schematics to identify the specific section of the electrical or electronic circuit you wish to work with. You can then display this on a laptop computer. Many OEMs today offer a variety of navigational options, including colorization and animation. This means you should get used to using them on the computer display and not waste time and paper by printing them out. **Figure 36–36** shows a subsection of a schematic exiting a Mack chassis power distribution module, downloaded from Mack's online electrical information system (EIS).

FIGURE 36–35 Electrical circuit schematic: mid-generation Navistar HEUI.

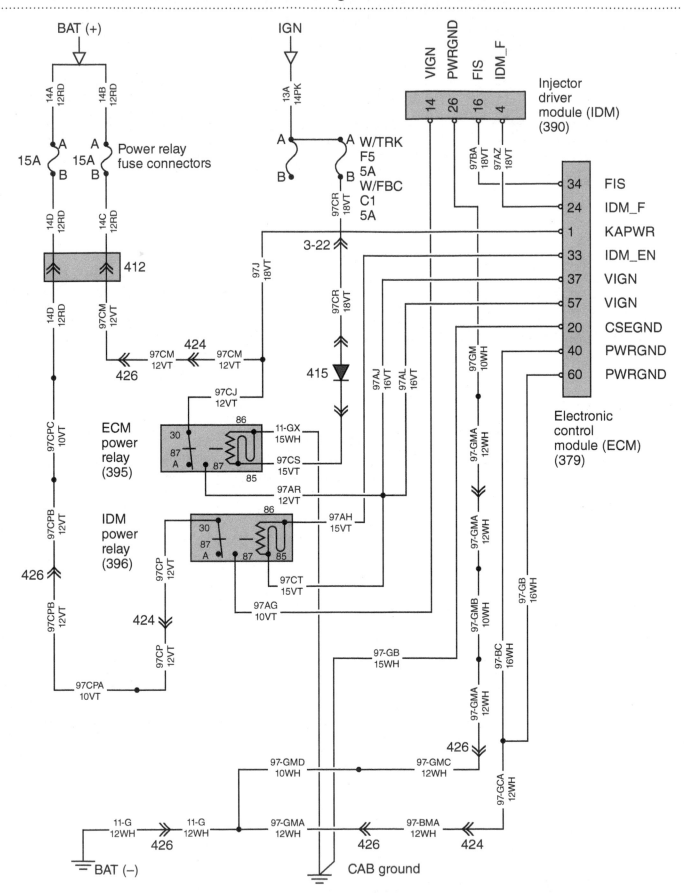

FIGURE 36–36 Subsection of a schematic exiting a Mack chassis power distribution module.

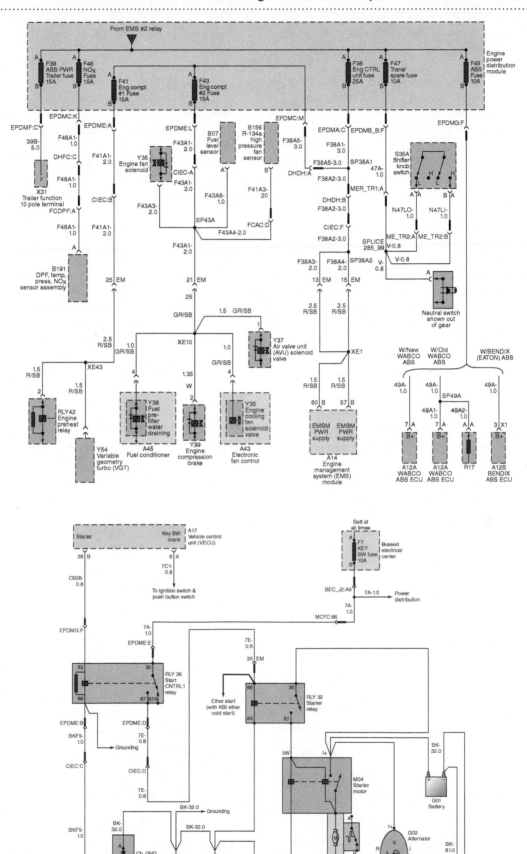

SUMMARY

- SAE standard wiring practice requires that all OEMs use common wiring color codes and descriptors.
- All SAE codes must be printed in black onto chassis wiring spaced 4 in. (10 cm) apart.
- SAE code requires that wires used in any unprotected circuit use red insulation.
- SAE code requires that wires used in any protected circuit use insulation that is white with an orange chaser.
- SAE code requires that all ground wires use gray insulation.
- SAE code requires that wires use structured system, circuit, cavity, node, branch, and path identifiers.
- Almost all electronic circuits in today's trucks and heavy equipment use weather-sealed connectors. These connectors usually require special tools and a set procedure to disassemble and reassemble them.
- Always use the correct terminals and connector units, and avoid "temporary" repairs.

- As much as possible, duplicate the original standards.
- It is important for truck technicians to be able to navigate standard wiring schematics. This requires knowing the symbols for common electrical and electronic components.
- It is essential to understand how a standard SAE relay functions: Technicians should memorize the terminal assignments of standard relays.
- Common electromechanical circuit protection devices used in today's chassis are fuses and both cycling and noncycling circuit breakers.
- Virtual circuit protection devices use logic analysis of circuit conditions; however, when they trip, they produce the same effect as an electromechanical protection device.
- Most OEMs no longer produce hard-copy wiring schematics. Virtual wiring schematics, usually devoted to small subsections of electrical circuits, have to be downloaded from OEM online SISs.

REVIEW QUESTIONS

1. What color is used to designate a ground circuit in a standard SAE-coded wiring harness?
   a. Red
   b. Gray
   c. White with an orange chaser
   d. Black

2. What color is used to designate an unprotected circuit in a standard SAE-coded wiring harness?
   a. Red
   b. Gray
   c. White with an orange chaser
   d. Black

3. What color is used to designate a protected circuit in a standard SAE-coded wiring harness?
   a. Red
   b. Gray
   c. White with an orange chaser
   d. Black

4. When an SAE code is used on a wire, where is the system identifier located?
   a. First letter
   b. Second letter
   c. Last alpha character in the sequence
   d. Last numeric character in the sequence

5. When the letter E appears as the system identifier in a standard SAE code, what system is being referred to?
   a. Electronics
   b. Air conditioning
   c. Diesel particulate filter
   d. Engine accessories

6. Weather-Pack terminals are retained in the connector unit by:
   a. a clamp.
   b. a jam bridge.
   c. a locking tang.
   d. silicone.

7. The correct tool for installing Weather-Pack terminals to the wiring is:
   a. a crimping tool.
   b. electrical pliers.
   c. wire strippers.
   d. a tang release tool.

8. Which type of connector is the industry standard data link connector?
   a. Weather-Pack
   b. Metri-Pack
   c. Siemens
   d. Deutsch

9. When using solder to splice repair wiring, which type should be used?
   a. 50/50
   b. Rosin core
   c. Silver solder
   d. Liquid set

10. When repairing a break through a section of a multiple-wire cable, which of the following would be good practice?
    a. Use shrink cable on each individual wire.
    b. Stagger the splices.
    c. Twist the bared wires at each connection before soldering.
    d. Write "temporary repair" on the work order hard copy.

11. What numeric code is used to represent the common terminal on a standard relay?
    a. 30 (3)
    b. 85 (1)
    c. 86 (2)
    d. 87 (5)

12. Which of the following describes the function of numeric code 87a on a standard relay?
    a. Common
    b. Coil
    c. Normally open
    d. Normally closed

13. Which metric wire gauge size is equivalent to 18-gauge AWG?
    a. 18 mm
    b. 00,22
    c. 00,8
    d. 05,0

14. When testing a 12-volt truck electrical circuit component, 12.5 volts are measured immediately on the positive side of the load, 8.9 volts are dropped across the load, and 3.6 volts are measured on the negative side of the load. Which of the following is *true*?
    a. The circuit is functioning properly.
    b. The load component is defective.
    c. There is a defect on the positive side of the circuit.
    d. There is a defect on the negative side of the circuit.

37

MULTIPLEXING

OBJECTIVES

After studying this chapter, you should be able to:

- Describe a typical truck data bus.
- List the key data bus hardware components.
- Define the word *multiplexing*.
- Describe how multiplexing can make data exchange more efficient.
- Outline how a J1939/CAN 2.0 data bus functions.
- Access J1587/1708 and J1939 data buses using a data connector.
- Explain how a "smart" ladder switch operates.
- List the seven essential fields that make up a data frame on a truck data bus transaction.
- Explain how FETs are used as relays to affect data bus outcomes.
- Access a module with a source address (SA) on a truck chassis data bus with multiple networked electronic systems.
- Outline the procedure required to access a data bus source address (SA) and navigate to fault mode indicator (FMI) fields using electronic service tools (ESTs).
- Interpret predictive FMIs.
- Correlate J1587 fields with J1939 terminology.
- Identify the DLCs required to connect to pre-2014 and post-2014 J1939 chassis data buses.
- Define the role played by proprietary CAN buses that gateway into J1939.
- Identify the role played by the SAM modules in Freightliner multiplexing.
- Troubleshoot some simple problems on a J1939 CAN bus.
- Isolate a failure-to-communicate problem from one and multiple bus addresses.
- Identify the common SAs that relate to engine performance on J1939.
- Use a scopemeter to verify normal and abnormal bus activity.

KEY TERMS

algorithm	bandwidth	CAN-C	cluster heartbeat
auto-baud detect capable (ABDC)	bus systems	central gateway	controller area network (CAN)
	bus topology	client	

data bus	ISO 9141	parameter identifier (PID)	soft (smart) cruise
data bus communications	ISO 15765	polyswitch	source address (SA)
data connector (DC)	J1587/1708	positive temperature coefficient (PTC)	specific PGN
data frame	J1939		starpoint
data link connector (DLC)	ladder switch	power distribution module (PDM)	state of health (SOH)
Deutsch connector	master control module	power line carrier (PLC)	subsystem identifier (SID)
diagnostic link connector (DLC)	message identifier (MID)	programmable logic controller (PLC)	suspect parameter group (SPG)
electromagnetic interference (EMI)	modular switch field (MSF)	proprietary bus	suspect parameter number (SPN)
gateway module	multiplexing	protocols	system-detect and actuation module (SAM)
global PGN	neural network	server	
hard cruise	packet	silicon-controlled rectifier (SCR)	terminating resistor
hexadecimal message code	parameter group (PG)	smart switch	twisted wire pair
	parameter group number (PGN)		

INTRODUCTION

In the days of sailing ships, there existed a chain of command that extended from a captain through a first mate and lieutenants, and ended up with sailors at the bottom of the chain, who would actually put into effect the instructions that began with a captain's whim. Communication was verbal. The captain delegated to subordinates. At the end of the chain of command were the sailors. They were entrusted with specific tasks such as raising a sail, turning the tiller, or dropping an anchor. Each task would probably be specialized to some extent and require training. In this way, the critical functions of the ship were relayed and undertaken by word-of-mouth communications.

If we go back a generation and take a look at a highway truck of that era, most of the critical functions were managed directly by the driver using mechanical, pneumatic, hydraulic, and electrical signals. An accelerator pedal required a mechanical linkage to connect the driver's boot with the engine fuel control mechanism. Likewise, every electrical function on the chassis had to be hardwired from the dash switch through to the relay to whatever type of actuator was being controlled. Over the years, as chassis systems became more complex, more and more miles of wire were required to enable the electrical and mechanical outcomes required to manage the vehicle. That is, until **data bus communications** were introduced.

Data bus communications make managing a modern truck chassis similar to the way a large sailboat was managed a couple of hundred years ago. Instead of having a ship's captain bellow out some orders to be passed down a chain of command, a module broadcasts digital signals to a data backbone. These signals can either be read and responded to by other modules connected to the data backbone or ignored if the message does not fall within that module's realm of responsibility.

Data bus communications make use of a technology called **multiplexing**, which has been used in truck computer control systems since the first electronic control modules (ECMs) were introduced on trucks in the late 1980s. In those early days, multiplexing was usually module to module and truck technicians did not have to have much of an understanding of what it was all about. For instance, one engine manufacturer used this type of communication to allow a chassis management module to "talk" to the fuel injection control module: This was a dedicated bus connection that meant the technician could not troubleshoot bus malfunctions. Today, technicians regularly access the truck data bus to troubleshoot, reprogram, and read the systems within it.

NEURAL NETWORK

Simply put, multiplexing means data sharing between multiple system control modules. Our definition of a control module is one that has both processing and outcome-switching capability. If you set up a chassis computer system so that all of the control modules "speak" the same language and provide a common, shared, communication path between them, then you have a multiplexed system. Today, most trucks use multiplexing systems that communicate using just a couple of "language" systems. Some manufacturers use the term **neural network** to describe a comprehensively multiplexed truck chassis: This analogy compares a multiplexed chassis to a human body's central nervous system. This is not really a fair comparison, because a multiplexed truck chassis is much less complex and more logically organized than a human body.

Although the term sounds complex, multiplexing actually simplifies truck electronics. It does this by giving electronic subsystems a common communication language, and, by using a **data bus** or information highway, allows data signals to take the place of hard wire in the electronic input and output circuits. More recently, truck technicians have necessarily become more aware of the term *multiplexing* because some truck manufacturers are making increasing use of the technology in truck chassis.

SECOND-GENERATION MULTIPLEXING

All trucks today use multiplexing. Some truck manufacturers use it much more than others. On every current truck, the chassis data bus is used to network all of the major system controllers (computers) used on the chassis. However, multiplexing is being increasingly used by a couple of original equipment manufacturers (OEMs) to do more than just get system controllers interchanging information. This new generation of trucks networks both the electronic controllers and many of the sensors and status switches used in the circuit. For instance, even the simplest electromechanical toggle switch requires two wires to signal *on* or *off* status, and those wires must run from switch to relay and from relay to control device. Multiplexed smart switches function differently, not by turning current flow on or off, but by broadcasting a message to the data bus. Once broadcast, this message can be sent through the data bus neural network and picked up by any controller that wants to use it.

Digital Communications

Communications by digital signals rather than switched electrical circuits eliminates miles of hardwiring, reduces the number of I/O (in-out) pins on modules, and optimizes vehicle operation by giving electronic subsystems an "accountability" that extends beyond the hardware they control. Many highway/city bus technicians might already have a more advanced understanding of multiplexing because they have progressed to a higher level of sophistication in bus chassis, at least at this moment in time. An example of how the volume of hard wire can be reduced by multiplexing is demonstrated by the Navistar Diamond Logic system, which has decreased the number of wires to the instrument gauge cluster from 67 to just 7.

Application of Multiplexing

So, what do you really have to know about multiplexing today? If you have ever used a six-pin or nine-pin **data link connector (DLC)** (also known as a **diagnostic link connector [DLC]** or a **data connector [DC]**, depending on the manufacturer) to connect an electronic service tool (EST) to a truck, you already have some experience with accessing a truck data bus. As every year passes, the extent to which a truck technician must be familiar with working with truck data bus systems increases. Within this chapter we reference Freightliner M-Series (multiplexing) and Navistar Diamond Logic systems for examples on how multiplexing functions. Up to now, the fully multiplexed chassis has not been embraced by all the chassis OEMs, with some opting to use it for just powertrain operations. However, both Freightliner and Navistar have used full chassis multiplexing on medium-duty trucks since 2003, and from 2007 have used it on their full lineup of trucks and school buses.

MULTIPLEXING, CLIENTS, AND SERVERS

We have already said that *multiplexing* refers to transactions between a series of networked computers. In the professional world, if you consult an accountant or lawyer, you become their customer and are known as their **client**. In the computer world, anyone or anything that wants something is referred to as a *client*. For a transaction to take place, there must be someone or something that fulfills that need. The fulfilling of a client need is done by a **server**. The data backbone serves as a path for connecting clients with servers. The messages used to make these connections are known as **packets**. There are rules about packets and how they are constructed—think of the difficulty and expense of sending an odd-shaped package by courier.

SPEED AND VOLUME

The roads used by telecommunications systems can be wires, fiber-optic cables, light beams, or radio waves. The speed limit on the highway is rated in miles per hour. The speed limit on a telecommunications channel is measured in baud and K-baud. More K-baud is better and faster. An interstate with more lanes is generally considered to be better, and the number of lanes on a road can be likened to the telecommunications term **bandwidth**. They both represent volumetric capacity of the road or transmission medium. One refers to the number of cars and trucks that can travel simultaneously, the other to the number of packets or data volume that can be pumped down a channel. On the highway, because there are other cars on the road, each filled with other people with their own objectives, you can closely compare the dynamics of road travel with data multiplexing: multiple packets traveling a highway heading from one place to another, using common transmission mediums, moving at pretty much the same rate.

MULTIPLEXING RULES

Multiplexing modernizes electronic communications by making electronic circuits a lot more like our highway system. In doing so, miles of unnecessary hard wire and replicated components can be eliminated. Multiplexing uses electrons modulated by some strict **protocols** (rules and regulations) to simplify subsystem-to-subsystem electronic transactions. Analog inputs are converted to digital signals by a controller with an address on the data bus. These signals can then be relayed digitally to any other controller with an address on the bus before being changed back to analog format to effect actions.

MULTIPLEXING BASICS

As mentioned before, if you have worked on trucks manufactured in the year 1990 and later, you already have some experience with multiplexing, even though it may have been unknowingly. Beginning in 2002, a new generation of truck chassis was introduced, launching a second generation of truck multiplexing. This replicated technology that has been used in city and highway buses since the late 1990s. From model year (MY) 2013 onward, generation-three multiplexing is required to permit high-speed communications between the powertrain and emission control management electronics; in addition, it is used to manage almost all chassis systems. Today, every vehicle technician must have an understanding of multiplexing.

TRANSIT BUSES

City and highway buses were the first to adopt multiplexing for non-powertrain systems, for the simple reason that the driver sits in the front of the vehicle and the engine, transmission, and most of the chassis electronics are located in the rear. To hardwire-connect the driver with these complex electronic systems located in the back of the bus required miles of wire that had to travel the length of the chassis. A data bus consisting of a twisted wire pair provided a simple solution. The driver generates commands from her position at the front of the bus, and these are sent as messages over the communications backbone. These messages can then be read by any modules connected (networked) to the data bus. The modules process the messages and generate whatever outcomes are desired.

INFORMATION SHARING

Our initial definition of *multiplexing* was to describe it as chassis information sharing between the different onboard computer control systems to optimize vehicle performance. For instance, some of the key input sensor signals are required by more than one of the chassis control modules. The throttle position sensor (TPS) is a good example of such a signal. The TPS signal is a required input for engine management, transmission management, dash display module, and antilock brake system (ABS)/automatic traction control (ATC) and collision warning systems. The TPS signal is hardwire-delivered to one module (usually the engine ECM), then broadcast over the data bus so that any other networked modules that require this signal can pick it up. Some electronic systems that are commonly multiplexed include the following:

- Engine control module
- Fuel injection control module
- Transmission control module
- Bulkhead control module
- Dash display module
- Chassis or body control module
- ABS
- ATC system
- Electronic immobilizer
- Collision warning/mitigation systems

In the preceding list, we have used generic names for the controllers, but you should note that each OEM has its own distinct preferences for naming its modules. **Figure 37–1** shows where some of these modules might be located on a typical truck chassis. The controllers shown in Figure 37–1 are usually networked to the vehicle powertrain bus.

Modules with an address on the powertrain bus are assigned a specific numeric address. On the current J1939 data bus, this is known as the **source address (SA)**. On the older J1587 bus (still in use by some OEMs), this address is known as the **message identifier (MID)**. The SAE acronym MID is also known as a *module identifier*. For instance, the engine controller or ECM is assigned:

- SA 00 on J1939
- MID 128 on J1587

In applications in which a truck chassis is equipped with two engines (such as a mobile crane), the second engine is assigned an SA 01 address on the J1939 data bus.

SAs and MIDs

As we get further into the material in this chapter, we will make frequent references to the J1939 and J1587/1708 powertrain buses and the modules that have addresses on them. SAs and MIDs are controllers. They may be known by such terms as

ECMs, ECUs, and dozens of others. SAs and MIDs have processing capacity and can receive and broadcast messages on the bus. A list of SAs and MIDs appears later in this chapter. The numeric value assigned to an SA cannot be changed by an OEM. For example, the engine controller or ECM is assigned SA 00 on J1939 regardless of the actual engine used or the chassis OEM.

CONVENTIONAL VERSUS DIGITAL TRANSMISSION

Conventional data transmission in a vehicle required that every input and output signal be allocated an individual conductor (dedicated wire and terminals), because binary signals can only be transmitted using the states "1" or "0" (binary code). On/off ratios can be used to transmit continually changing parameters such as the status of an accelerator pedal-travel sensor. However, the increase in data exchange volume between vehicle electronic systems has reached such dimensions that a single serial bus cannot handle the traffic. For this reason, most truck OEMs have added other buses to the core powertrain bus on the vehicle. These buses are known as **proprietary buses**, and because they do not adhere to powertrain bus protocols, OEM software is required to communicate with them.

FIGURE 37–1 Location of modules on a typical medium-duty truck data bus.

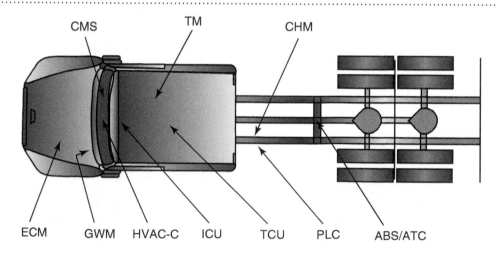

ECM = engine controller
GWM = gateway module
HVAC-C = climate control module
CMS = collision mitigation system,
          Wingman radar module
ICU = instrument cluster unit

CHM = chassis module
TCU = transmission control unit
PLC = pulse line controller (trailer)
ABS/ATC = antilock braking controller,
              automatic traction control
TM = telematics module

POWER LINE CARRIER

A more primitive method of multiplexing, known as **power line carrier (PLC)**, has been in use in trucks since 1985. Power line carrier enables communication transactions to take place on a nondedicated communication wire. PLC communications were introduced when ABS became an option on highway trailers, but its use became mandatory in 2001, three years after the introduction of mandatory ABS.

Trailer ABS requires that a warning light be illuminated in the dash of the truck in the event of a trailer ABS malfunction. Because all the wires on a standard SAE J560, seven-pin connector between truck and trailer were already dedicated, PLC technology was used to convert a digital communication signal to an analog radio frequency (RF) signal and then superimpose it over the 12-volt auxiliary power wire. A transducer converts the RF signal back to a digital signal that can be broadcast over the tractor data bus. Until 2010, these signals used the original **J1587/J1708** data bus hardware and protocols and were diagnosed accordingly.

TYPES OF LOGIC

Most current engine management systems use largely open-loop (fuzzy) processing as opposed to closed-loop logic, so inputs from any onboard electronic circuit can influence how the engine is being managed at a given moment. This adds to the volume of data exchanged among the various control modules managing a chassis. To illustrate the difference between closed-loop and fuzzy logic, we use an example you should be familiar with if you have worked on or driven a truck using cruise control.

Open versus Closed Loop

The older hard cruise required that the driver set a road speed of, say, 60 mph (100 kph). After the road speed has been selected, the road speed sensor drives the management of the powertrain to maintain the desired road speed regardless of conditions. This type of closed-loop operation puts the road speed sensor in command of the powertrain—and that can be a disadvantage. For instance, if the vehicle were traveling through a terrain consisting of rolling hills, attempting to maintain the input road speed at exactly 60 mph (100 kph) would waste fuel. Why not allow the vehicle to exceed 60 mph (100 kph) by a small amount going downhill and drop below set speed

while traveling up the next one? This is known as *road speed droop*. From a fuel economy point of view, it makes sense to do this. The processing cycle uses an algorithm to "learn" from the terrain and in doing so uses a variety of inputs to plot an actual road speed.

Hard cruise is an example of closed-loop operation, while soft or smart cruise is an example of fuzzy logic. Most trucks today use **soft** or **smart cruise**. When the driver inputs a road speed cruise control command into a soft cruise system, the circuit "thinks" for itself. It uses multiple inputs and programmed instructions to manage fueling. Smart cruise can be even further enhanced by allowing input from other modules with addresses on the data bus, giving them a say in what goes on. For instance, accident avoidance electronics can message modules on the bus to effect braking (engine and pneumatic) if it detects that the proximity and velocity of a vehicle in the intended travel path is insufficient.

> **TECH TIP:**
>
> **Algorithm** is a software term used by most OEMs that describes a programmed sequence of operating events: the rules and conditions for producing a processing outcome from a chassis control module. This is also less commonly known as *mapping*. The term is fully explained in Chapter 34.

SERIAL DATA TRANSMISSION

So, you can see now that many of the problems of data transfer volume using conventional interfaces (hard wire) can be simplified by using **bus systems** or data highways. The basis of serial data transmission is use of a single wire or pair of wires that deliver "instructions" rather than electrical signals to the controller modules. The common on-vehicle example is **controller area network (CAN)** technology, a data bus system developed by Robert Bosch and Intel for vehicle applications. CAN is a serial data transmission network used for the following applications in a vehicle:

- ECM networking
- Comfort and convenience electronics
- Mobile onboard and external communications

CAN 2.0 is the basis for SAE J1939, the high-speed powertrain network in standard use on trucks and buses in North America. J1939

FIGURE 37–2 Bus topology of J1939 showing nodes.

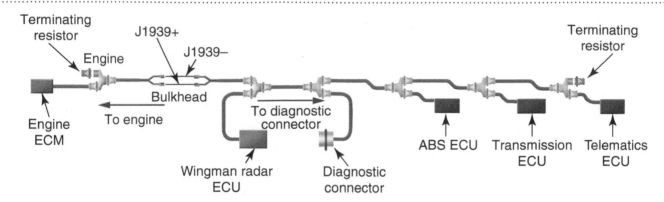

functions from 125 kilobits per second (kb/s) up to 1M b/s (500 kb/s is typical), making it a Class C bus; Class A and B buses use much slower speeds. In comparative terms, J1939 is about 25 to 50 times faster than the J1587/1708 (the original) data backbone. Transfer rates must be high to ensure that the required real-time responses are fast enough to enable technologies such as collision mitigation electronics.

Multiplexing Clock Speeds

Microprocessor clock speeds of at least 16 MHz are required for J1939 transactions. A clock speed of 16 MHz translates to an ability to make up to 16 million binary "decisions" per second: Millions of these binary decisions are required to process a simple output command. Most current truck engine and transmission management processors have clock speeds of at least 16 MHz and are designed to broadcast on both the J1587/1708 and J1939 buses.

Cluster Heartbeat

The **cluster heartbeat** refers to engine-to-cluster communications. It is a **state of health (SOH)** confirmation that all systems are working properly. Typically, the cluster heartbeat is set to check every second and logs a fault code if a malfunction is detected.

ECM Networking

CAN uses serial data transmission architecture. *Serial* means single track as opposed to multiple track, which is known as *parallel* transmission. Several system management modules, such as the engine, fuel system, ABS/ATC, electronic transmission, dash display, and collision warning modules, are networked on the serial data bus. Each ECM is assigned equal priority

and connected using a linear bus structure, as shown in **Figure 37–2**.

One advantage of this structure is the fact that should one of the stations (subscribers) fail, the remaining stations continue to have full access to the network. The probability of total failure is therefore much lower than with other logical arrangements, such as the loop or star (hub) structures that are sometimes used to connect multiple buses. With loop or star structures such as that shown in **Figure 37–3**, failure of a single station or the central or command controller necessarily results in a broader range of system failure.

ISO 9141 and ISO 15765

Control module interconnectivity and data protocols fall under the International Standards Organization's **ISO 9141** and **ISO 15765**. Because American-engineered and -built equipment is marketed throughout the world, it makes sense that both the hardware and communication protocols are internationally common. Most OEMs manufacturing equipment on the J1939 multiplexing platform ensure that it is ISO 9141/15765 compliant. ISO 9141/15765 specifies the requirements for the interchange of information between the various electronic/engine control units (ECUs) on vehicles to facilitate readout, diagnosis, adjustments, and data exchange. It does not apply to system-specific equipment or dedicated (proprietary) CAN connections.

Bus Topology

The word *topology* means an organized structural system that is unaffected by being subject to a sequence of events. The term **bus topology** is used in J1939 multiplexing to indicate that no single controller networked to the bus has

FIGURE 37–3 Star bus topology: This shows the proprietary buses used on a Freightliner Cascadia in which the **starpoint** is common to several networks. The central gateway module is used to permit Cascadia proprietary electronics to network with J1939 and J1587.

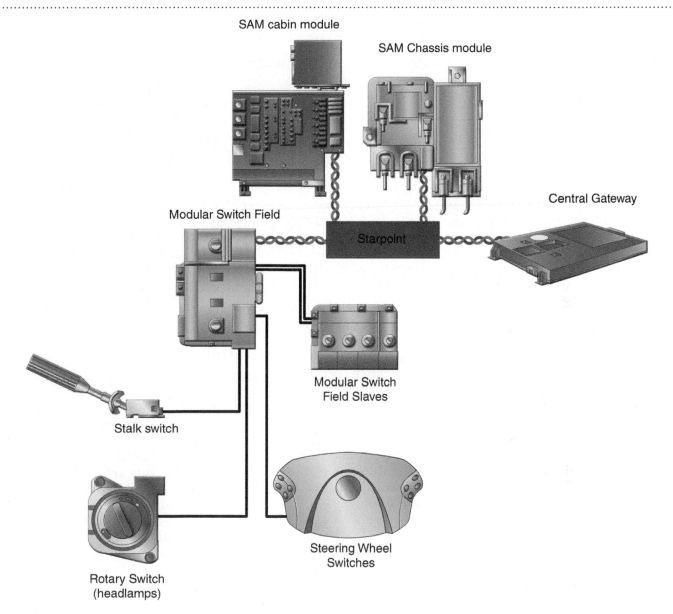

more priority or status than another. Unlike the network shown in Figure 37–3, no ECM/ECU is "in charge," although certain bus activities such as wakeup may fall under one module's responsibility. For instance, if a J1939 data bus were to be cut in half, theoretically all of the controllers on each side of the break should be able to communicate with each other, though not with the controllers on the other side of the break. **Figure 37–4** shows the bus topology used in a Freightliner Cascadia truck data backbone, to allow its proprietary electronics to communicate with the J1939 and J1587 powertrain buses.

Content-Based Addressing

CAN transactions are simplified. Instead of addressing individual stations in the network, an identifier label is assigned to every message pumped out onto the data highway. Each message is coded with a unique 11- or 29-bit identifier that identifies the message contents. For instance, engine speed data is of significance to

FIGURE 37-4 Freightliner Cascadia bus topology: The proprietary buses are networked with the powertrain buses. Note how the gateway module becomes the "star" between the powertrain and proprietary buses along with providing the means to access the vehicle network.

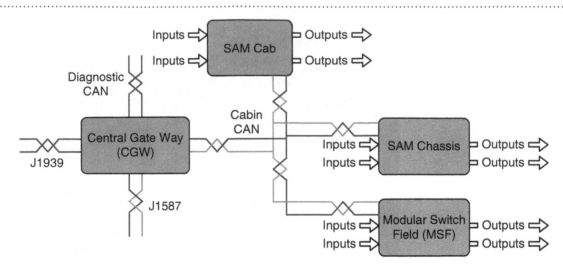

the engine, transmission, and collision warning systems, but probably has no importance to the climate control module. Each station is designed to process only those messages whose identifiers are stored in its acceptance list. This means that all other messages are simply ignored.

Content-based addressing means that a signal is broadcast to multiple stations. However, a sensor only has to send its signal directly to the bus network, where it can then be distributed accordingly and appropriately. Also, because it is easy to add further stations to an existing CAN bus system, a large number of equipment variations are possible.

Assigning Priorities

In a multiplex system, message identifiers can be labeled for data content and/or the priority of any message sent. In a vehicle management network, some signals are necessarily prioritized over others. An example of a high-priority signal would be the accelerator pedal angle or TPS signal. Any change in the TPS signal value must be responded to at high speed and is therefore allocated a higher priority than a signal that changes relatively slowly, such as that from the coolant temperature sensor. A brake request signal would have the highest priority status, and a critical signal such as this can effectively shut down the data bus for a nanosecond (one-billionth of a second) or so. Its high priority is due to its importance to critical vehicle safety

and ability to impact on rig rollover and vehicle directional stability.

Bus Arbitration

Handling traffic on the data highway requires rules and regulations. Just as every driver on an interstate is taught to cede to emergency vehicles, so must there be rules to handle data traffic. When the bus is free, any station can transmit a message. However, if several stations start to transmit simultaneously, bus arbitration awards first access to the message with the highest priority with no loss of either time or data bits. Lower-priority messages are shuffled by pecking order to automatically switch to receive and repeat their transmission attempt the moment the bus is freed up.

Message Tagging

In a busy airport with insufficient runways like Chicago's O'Hare, there is an orderly lineup at the beginning of each runway for takeoff. The protocol (rule) on the airport runway is usually to sequence takeoffs in line-up order. The protocol in the truck data bus is necessarily different. Each message is assigned a tag, a **data frame** of around 100–150 bits for transmission to the bus. The tag codes a message for sequencing transmission to the data bus and also limits the time it consumes on the bus. Tagging messages by priority and currency ensures that queue time is kept to a minimum until the next (possibly urgent!) data transmission.

FIGURE 37-5 Message bit encoding of a J1939 data packet.

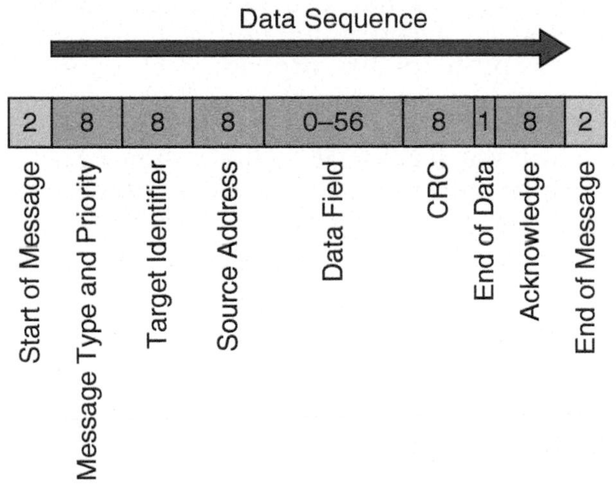

Data Sequence

| 2 | 8 | 8 | 8 | 0–56 | 8 | 1 | 8 | 2 |

Start of Message
Message Type and Priority
Target Identifier
Source Address
Data Field
CRC
End of Data
Acknowledge
End of Message

Each message or packet can be called a *data frame*. A data frame packet is made up of consecutive fields as indicated in **Figure 37-5**, which shows how a typical packet is constructed.

START OF FRAME Start of frame announces the start of a message and synchronizes all stations on the data bus.

ARBITRATION FIELD This contains the message identifier and an additional control bit. When this field is broadcast, the transmitter tags the transmission of each bit with a check to ensure that no higher-priority station is also transmitting. The control bit functions to classify the message as a data frame or remote frame.

CONTROL FIELD The control field simply indicates the number of data bytes in the data field.

DATA FIELD The data field is sized between 0 and 8 bytes. A message with data length 0 can be used for synchronizing distributed processes.

CYCLIC REDUNDANCY CHECK (CRC) FIELD The CRC proofreads a message to identify possible transmission interference.

ACK FIELD The ack or acknowledgment field contains acknowledgment signals by which the receiver stations on the bus indicate that they have received a noncorrupted message.

END OF FRAME FIELD The end of frame (EOF) indicates the end of a message.

Message Bit Encoding

Figure 37-5 shows the number of bits dedicated to each segment of a data packet. Remember that there are 8 bits to a byte.

Integrated Diagnostics

A vehicle multiplexing bus system must be provided with monitoring capability so that transmission, transaction, and reception errors can be detected. This would include the check signal in the data frame and monitoring components in a transmission. It is a feature of a multiplex bus that each transmitter receives its own transmitted message again and by file comparison can detect any deviation or corruption. If a station identifies an error, it sends out an error flag that halts the current transmission. This prevents other addresses networked to the bus from receiving a faulty message.

In the event of a major station defect, it is possible that all messages, both good and bad, would be terminated with an error flag. To protect against this, a multiplex bus system has a built-in function that enables it to distinguish between intermittent and permanent errors. Furthermore, this feature can sometimes localize station failures and route the data network to an appropriate failure strategy. The process of localizing a station-type failure is based on statistical evaluation of error factors, so it is not entirely foolproof.

Multiplexing Standardization

Multiplexing standardization for vehicles has been orchestrated by the ISO internationally and by the Society of Automotive Engineers (SAE) in North America. In North America, SAE standards **CAN-C** (light-duty vehicles) and **J1939** (heavy-duty on- and off-highway vehicles) define the hardware and software protocols of multiplexed components and data transfer.

ISO CAN 2.0

The ISO CAN 2.0 (ISO 15765) is the platform on which current CAN-C and J1939 standards are used worldwide. In heavy-duty equipment, the J1939 bus was combined with the earlier J1587/1708 hardware and software protocols so that until 2010 truck networks tended to be both J1939 and J1587/1708 compatible. From 2010 onward, some engine manufacturers have ceased to support J1587. Because J1587/1708 is still used, OEMs using it must use a gateway module to enable inter-bus communications to take place. Hardware and software engineered in compliance with J1939 means that they can connect into the vehicle data bus without the translator/transducer modules that were required in some of the older J1587/1708 systems. It can be compared to plug-and-play on your home computer.

Gateways

Data buses use a common communication language that works just fine as long as communication is confined on the data bus. However, current trucks are equipped with a minimum of two data buses—and may have more, as does the Freightliner Cascadia example shown in **Figure 37–6**. Where multiple network buses are required to communicate, **gateway modules** are used. Gateway modules link the buses by acting as protocol interpreters.

SAM Modules

Of all of the truck OEMs, Freightliner has led the implementation of multiplexing technology in its vehicles, so its system will be referenced

FIGURE 37–6 Cascadia network topology.

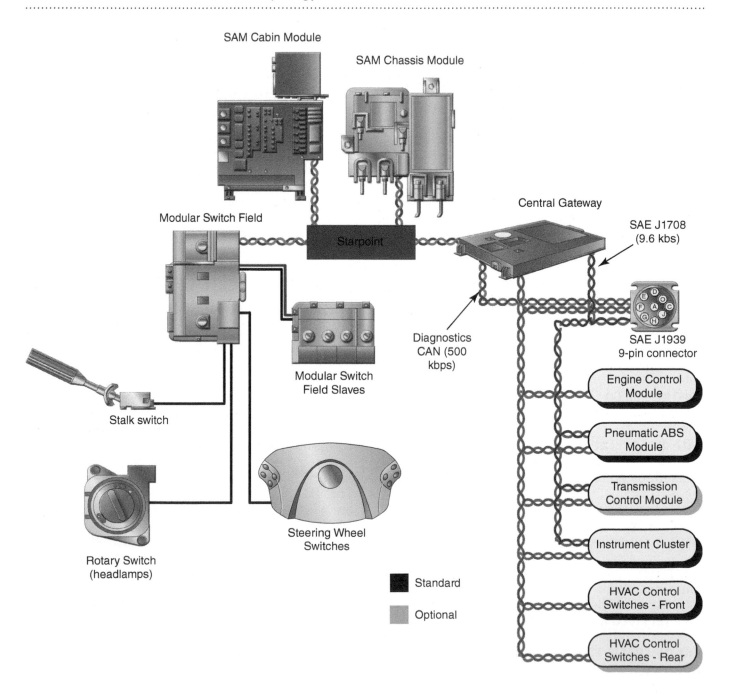

throughout this chapter. For reasons known only to Freightliner, it has recently renamed its body controller and chassis management controllers, calling them SAMs. A **system-detect and actuation module (SAM)** is no more than another way of saying ECU. The two SAMs we will reference in this chapter, and their SAs, are:

- SAM cab SA 33 body controller
- SAM chassis SA 71 chassis management controller

A list of SAs and their MID equivalents appears later in this chapter.

TECH TIP:

Truck OEMs today often ignore the SAE recommended terms and acronyms, preferring to invent their own. If you are confused about the function of any module with an address on J1939, check its SA: This will describe the controller function using the universal term.

Body and Chassis Controllers

The extensive chassis networking requirements of today's trucks means that the powertrain J1939 bus has insufficient bandwidth to handle the traffic. Inputs from several modules may be required before a crank-engine command can be broadcast from the ignition key. This has led OEMs such as Freightliner to add proprietary buses to handle much of the traffic that is not directly related to the powertrain. This is done by "bussing" the J1939 network to a proprietary network by means of a gateway. There are a couple of SAMs (a body controller and a chassis controller) on any fully multiplexed Freightliner chassis and because this OEM is the current market leader, you have no choice but to get used to the terms.

SAM Functions

The SAMs used on current Freightliner chassis have all of the characteristics of other ECUs, but we will take a look at some of the differences here. SAMs incorporate a **modular switch field (MSF)**. The MSF is a system of multiplexed switches consisting of a master control module and one or more slave modules and sub-bus switches.

The **master control module** continuously monitors switch status. The switches on the steering wheel, stalk switch, and headlight switch are hardwired (as opposed to multiplexed) to the master control module. The master control module has a cabin CAN network connection. The cabin CAN is a proprietary network that

connects the **central gateway**, the MSF, the SAM Cab (body controller), and the SAM chassis (chassis controller). The function of the central gateway is to enable communication between those modules with addresses on J1939 and those on Freightliner's proprietary buses.

Sub-Buses

Switches located within the slave module communicate with, and connect to, the master control module using a proprietary sub-bus. The slave module is a passive device that can house up to four individual sub-bus switches. There are two types of sub-bus switches that connect to the master control module or slave module:

- Multiplex (signal/message driven)
- Hard wire (load interrupting)

The Freightliner star point junction block acts as a router that provides an electrical termination point to the cabin CAN.

SAM Circuit Protection

Polyswitches are **positive temperature coefficient (PTC)** circuit protection devices that are built into some SAM chassis modules to handle certain kinds of intermittent faults. The objective is to provide circuit-breaker-like protection on trailer circuits that can affect the tractor chassis electrical circuits. Polyswitches are auto-resetting, meaning that they can be classified as SAE #1 circuit protection devices. The operating principles of polyswitches are covered in Chapter 34. SAMs also provide other forms of circuit monitoring and protection in the form of virtual and hard wire fuses.

THE J1939 BACKBONE

A multiplexing data bus must be stable and be protected against unwanted radiation interference that could corrupt the data signals. The data bus or backbone used in a J1939 multiplexed chassis is a pair of twisted wires, color-coded yellow and green. The reason for using a **twisted wire pair** is to minimize the surface area on which outside low-level radiation or **electromagnetic interference (EMI)** can act on the bus. The idea is to prevent the data backbone from acting like a radio antenna. Reducing EMI (electromagnetism, radar, microwave) susceptibility is critical to protecting data from transmission corruption.

Bus Hardware

The SAE standard for the J1939 data bus requires that the data bus wires twist through a full cycle once per centimeter—that is, $2\frac{1}{2}$ times per inch. At either end of the data bus, a **terminating resistor** is used. The function of the terminating resistors is to prevent the twisted pair from attracting signal interference by acting like a giant antenna. Terminating resistors test at 120 ohms; their function is explained in a little more detail later in this section. Also, there cannot be any open T-connector cavities. At points where the backbone has to be spliced, special Deutsch T-connectors with gold-plated contacts are used. Gold plating minimizes resistance because the nominal voltage on the data bus is low, usually around 3.5 volts or lower. **Figure 37–7** shows how to test a J1939 data bus for the presence of terminating resistors.

The J1939 data backbone uses stubs to make the physical connection between the backbone and each controller networked to it. The maximum length of a J1939 data backbone is 130 feet, and each stub should be no longer than 40 inches. Exceeding these dimensions can cause problems with data transmission accuracy.

High Bus/Low Bus

High (sometimes Hi) bus and low (Lo) bus are physically and functionally different. A high bus twisted wire pair is wrapped with bare copper wire and foil shielded; it should not be repaired. The copper wire is known as the *drain*: The drain is required to be grounded at a single point on the chassis. A high bus twisted wire pair transacts at the highest speeds (theoretically up to 1 Mb/s, but actually around 500 kb/s) and is used for real-time data signaling such as would be required by accelerator pedal and electronically

controlled transmission system initiated input/output transactions.

A low bus twisted wire pair has no foil shielding. Low bus signaling in older systems included such things as audio system transactions (for instance, a message requesting an increase in audio volume as road/engine speed increases). However, the use of low bus systems is increasing on late-model vehicles, especially in proprietary OEM buses.

The high speed and volume of data pumped through a truck chassis data bus requires wiring that is a little more complex. There are two reasons for twisting the two data wires used in the bus:

- To provide immunity to magnetic fields. The voltage induced into any conductor by a magnetic field depends on distance, so by twisting the data wires, induced voltage effect will be about equal on both wires. In digital signaling using binary pulses, signal transceivers (any modules networked to the bus) are designed to look at the difference between CAN H (or CAN +) and CAN L (or CAN –), not voltage levels referenced to ground.
- To provide consistent capacitance values. The distance between the two conductors on the bus alters the capacitance between them, with capacitance decreasing as the wires become further apart. The insulation material the conductor wires are wrapped in also affects capacitance because it acts like the dielectric discussed in Chapter 32. On the data bus, the dielectric properties of insulation should be constant: Substituting ordinary wire for J1939 cable can corrupt communications on the bus by altering the impedance.

TECH TIP:

CAN H (high) and CAN L (low) on a J1939 are not referenced to ground but to each other. CAN H and CAN L are referred to by some OEMs as CAN + and CAN –. Do not confuse CAN L with chassis ground: It must have a voltage value. The voltage differential is typically 2 V.

Impedance

If, like many persons growing up today, your first experience of electronic systems was setting up audio and visual equipment, you will know that high-frequency cables are specified in ohms. For instance, coaxial TV cable has a center conductor wrapped in Teflon with the other

FIGURE 37–7 Testing a J1939 bus for the presence of terminating resistors.

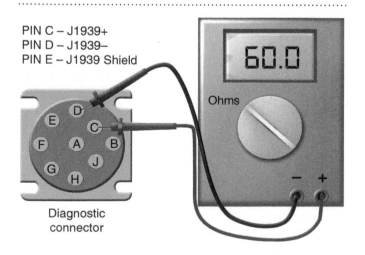

PIN C – J1939+
PIN D – J1939–
PIN E – J1939 Shield

60.0

Ohms

– +

Diagnostic connector

conductor braided around it. This type of cable has what is known as a *characteristic impedance* of around 75 ohms. You cannot test characteristic impedance with an ohmmeter; it is just a measure of how the conductor appears (regardless of length) to a high-frequency signal.

A truck J1939 data bus has a characteristic impedance of 120 ohms. This is achieved by maintaining the dielectric constant (wire insulation) and keeping the physical spacing between the two conductor wires constant by having a consistent twist pattern. Once again, because this is characteristic impedance, you cannot measure it with an ohmmeter. Do not confuse the 120-ohm characteristic impedance with the 120-ohm terminating resistors used at the end of a data backbone: The latter can be measured with an ohmmeter.

Terminating Resistors

Terminating resistors absorb signal energy, leaving no energy for reflections or echoes that result in electronic noise. Electronic noise causes scrambling of signals. It is a little like listening to an outdoor public address system where audio input is being received from several different speakers different distances away.

Besides minimizing electronic noise, terminating resistors also provide a low-resistance path for current to flow between CAN H and CAN L. This permits capacitance to discharge and cancel rapidly. The length of time for a capacitor to discharge is proportional to the resistance of the conductor it is discharging through. If system capacitance cannot rapidly discharge when a device is trying to transmit at a low level, then the voltage differential between CAN H and CAN L remains high, which can shut down the data bus.

Missing Terminating Resistors

If only one terminating resistor is missing from a J1939 data backbone, the backbone will likely function problem-free, though if you scoped the waveform, it could be noticed due to longer capacitive discharge times and increased signal reflections. However, if both terminating resistors are missing, no communication can take place. When this happens, the length of time required for each signal pulse pumped down the bus to neutralize increases and the resulting signal reflections scramble the data bus so that no transactions are possible. **Figure 37–8**

FIGURE 37–8 Comparison of J1939 scope patterns with and without 120-ohm terminating resistors.

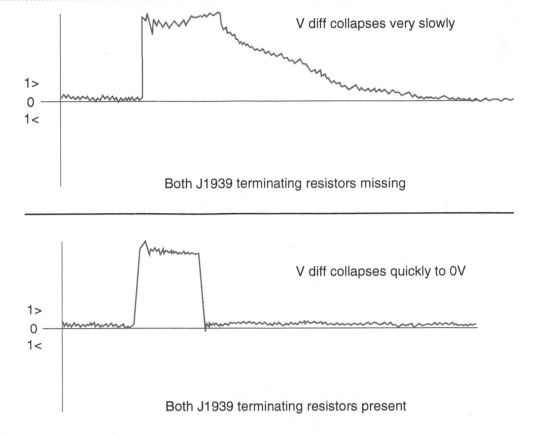

V diff collapses very slowly

Both J1939 terminating resistors missing

V diff collapses quickly to 0V

Both J1939 terminating resistors present

compares a pulsed scope signal on a J1939 data bus equipped with both terminating resistors with one that has had both terminating resistors removed. Some controller modules are supplied with an integral terminating resistor that has the effect of lowering resistance; this may muddle message packets and will create false readings during testing. **Figure 37–9** shows some examples of terminating resistors used on a J1939 bus.

Loss of J1939

In most trucks, if the J1939 connection is lost, the driver will be alerted by dash display and often a chassis signal such as flashing the hazard lights. Low bus wires are unshielded and may be repaired under some circumstances. Strictly observe the OEM instructions when repairing twisted wire pairs: This will include maintaining the existing twisting cycles and gauge size, and using the correct solder.

> **TECH TIP:**
>
> When repairing low bus twisted wires, avoid twisting the wires together prior to soldering. Lay the wires you wish to solder contacting each other, then apply tin solder. Twisting the wires together and applying a large blob of solder can create unacceptably high circuit resistance because of the low potential of message packets.

> **CAUTION:**
>
> It can be generally regarded as not good practice to attempt to repair physical damage to a data bus. Replace according to OEM guidelines.

Limitations of J1939

As truck chassis management electronics become increasingly dependent on the data bus, the consequences resulting from a data bus malfunction increase in severity. Physical damage to any data bus described as high bus (shielded) warrants replacement, not repair. High bus lines are shielded. A J1939 high bus consists of the twisted wire pair (communication wires) already discussed, a shield wire, and often a couple of filler wires that function to keep the communication wires separate. The harness is usually wrapped with tinfoil-like shielding.

J1939 has limitations. Some applications, such as the Cummins/Peterbilt Supertruck (fully multiplexed chassis) initiative, are already experiencing bandwidth challenges, so any of the following outcomes to vehicle communications architecture will take place in the near future:

- J1939 will be replaced with a bus protocol offering superior baud rate/bandwidth).
- J1939 is being joined by an increasing number of complementary buses to handle non-powertrain-related traffic.

SUMMARY OF MULTIPLEXING BASICS

Although the definition of multiplexing is fairly specific when applied to vehicle electronics, if we broaden the definition somewhat, it is easy to see how it can be effective. In organizational theory, a company president tends not to do very much of the actual work himself. He delegates those responsibilities to those who report to him. Communications within the company

FIGURE 37–9 Examples of terminating resistors on a J1939 bus.

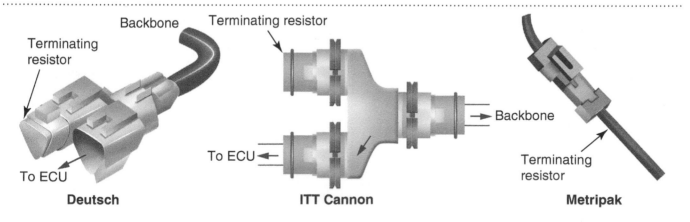

Deutsch   ITT Cannon   Metripak

flow through a chain of command. In an effective company, reports also flow back up the chain of command. Sure, there are going to be occasional problems in the two-way flow of information, but in a good company checks and balances are built into communication systems that quickly identify problems and rectify them. Using the example of a truck electrical system, rather than control a 20-amp blower motor directly through a switch that could overheat, we use a low-potential current through the control switch, which acts to control a relay that carries the high current load.

Programmable Logic Controllers

In computer technology, for many years electronics have been used to simulate relays in devices known as **programmable logic controllers (PLCs)**. These small computers can simulate thousands of relays in a fraction of the space, using elaborate stacking of transistors and **silicon-controlled rectifiers (SCRs)**. Now some of the principles used in PLCs are moving beyond the ECM housing. A key factor that has moved us into current generations of multiplexing is this "smart" switching technology, which we will take a closer look at in the next section of this chapter.

TECH TIP:

After the 2010 Environmental Protection Agency (EPA) model year (MY), Cummins and DDC stopped supporting J1587, meaning that their engines could only "talk" to modules with an address on J1939. A gateway module is required if these engines are installed on OEM chassis that use J1587.

Standard Switches

Every truck on the road today is equipped with many different switches, and multiplexed trucks will not reduce this to any great extent. Some examples of typical standard switches are cruise control on/off, cruise control set/resume, hazard warning switch, and ignition switch. We use the term *standard* to describe an electromechanical switch. Even where a standard switch is used, its status may be broadcast over the network bus.

Smart Switches

The term **smart switches** is used to describe two distinct types of switch used in multiplex circuits. A smart switch may have some processing capability and use that to broadcast switch

status onto the data bus. Alternatively, the term *smart switch* can be used to describe a **ladder switch**, so named because it contains a ladder of resistors, usually five per switch, known as a *ladder bridge*. The processor that receives data from the ladder switches has a library of resistor values that enables it to identify switch status and its commands. Freightliner's multiplexed chassis makes use of ladder bridge–type smart switches in the dash whenever possible, and also has the capability of monitoring the switch status that can be broadcast on the data bus. Each smart switch has a light-emitting diode (LED) designed to indicate (to the driver) that a switch request has actually been effected. Sometimes the LED will flash while a particular action is in the process of being effected and stay on when completed. Smart switches can be toggle (two-position on/off), multiposition, or spring-loaded, momentary operation.

The module responsible for monitoring data bus negotiations is designed to self-check smart switch operation and signal a fault if one is detected. It does this by analysis of the ladder bridge resistances. If a wire loosens or a terminal corrodes (high resistance), the system will not only know it, it can probably locate it. Ladder switches are simple in construction, with little to go wrong and eliminate the processing capability found in other types of OEM multiplex circuit switches.

TECH TIP:

When troubleshooting, if you disconnect a smart switch, a code will be logged immediately. Always use the system self-diagnostics to locate problems.

Field Effect Transistors

It is time to take a look at what is happening at the other end of the processing circuit. First, we should examine the role of field effect transistors (FETs). These are becoming commonplace in truck chassis electronics because they are inexpensive to manufacture and function reliably. An FET is an electronic relay switch that can also act as a circuit breaker. **Figure 37–10** demonstrates how an FET can be used as a relay.

FET OPERATION In their simplest formats, there are two types of FETs: N channel and P channel. The channel behaves as a resistor that can conduct current from the source side to the drain side. The gate controls the resistance, and

FIGURE 37–10 FET acting as a relay.

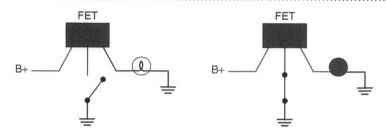

therefore the operation of the semiconductor device, by saying whether or how much current flows through the device. So, depending on the gate voltage, the FET can be used either as a straightforward relay switch (most current truck applications) or as an amplifier. As a relay, the FET has some great advantages, in that gate-channel resistance is so high that, first, there is almost no current flow in the gate-current circuit; and second, there is almost no effect on extern al components connected to the device. **Figure 37–11** shows a schematic of an FET.

Wakeup

In the same way that the electronics in your automobile "wake up" (usually on door open/dome light), the multiplexing electronics in a truck are designed to reactivate following a period of inactivity. Wakeup signals can be sourced from the door locks, microwave anti-theft circuit, ignition switch, dome light, brake lights, and headlights, depending on how advanced the chassis electronics are.

Simple Multiplexing Transaction

To show how a simple multiplexing transaction takes place, we take a look at a simple switch operation from switch to signal to outcome. The suspension dump smart switch is used to illustrate the execution of a data bus-enabled command. The mechanical objective (the desired "outcome") of this operation is to exhaust air from the chassis air suspension. The operator actuates the suspension dump ladder switch. This causes the dash suspension dump switch to start flashing and alters the resistance status on the ladder bridge so a packet is broadcast to the data bus. The data on this packet means nothing to any of the modules on the data bus until it is delivered to the module with the algorithm designed to process this input.

Using the example of a Freightliner multiplexed chassis, this would be the SAM chassis module. SAM chassis then broadcasts a command signal over the J1939 data bus to another module with some switching capability: the modular switch field (MSF). The MSF in turn generates a low-potential output signal to the FET that acts as a relay to actuate the suspension dump solenoid. The signal puts the FET in forward bias, completing the solenoid ground circuit and energizing the coil.

Source power for the solenoid is the power distribution module. At the point the action is completed—that is, when the suspension dump has been effected, and air drains from the suspension air bags—the dash LED on the suspension dump switch ceases to flash and remains on. This is a simple data bus transaction. FETs have become common in truck electrical circuits. The bus topology used in current Cascadia models is shown in Figure 37–11.

FIGURE 37–11 An FET uses a positive charge to the gate, which creates a capacitive field to permit electron flow. It acts like a relay with no moving parts.

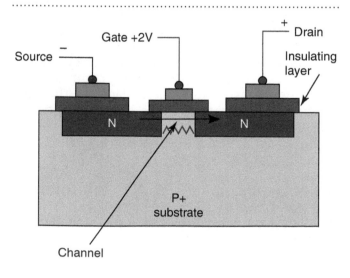

SHOP TALK

When adding loads to a multiplexed truck chassis, *always* consult the OEM service literature. Randomly splicing into circuits can create electrical problems that become very difficult to troubleshoot.

CAUTION:

Never splice into existing fuses in chassis power distribution modules to source a V-Bat (battery voltage) requirement. In dealerships today, it is not uncommon to hear horror stories about the results when a truck driver spliced into a "hot" wire to power up a personal electrical device. Most OEMs provide nondedicated terminals in their power distribution module that can be used for auxiliary electrical requirements. Use the OEM service literature and wiring schematics when connecting auxiliary electrical equipment.

POWER DISTRIBUTION MODULE

A **power distribution module (PDM)** is used on all current truck chassis. The primary function of a PDM is to manage the requirements of the chassis electrical system. The functions of a truck PDM can be categorized as follows:

- Supply electrical power to the powertrain PDM.
- Supply dedicated electrical power to the aftertreatment control module (ACM).
- Supply electrical power to proprietary buses such as the SAMs.
- Power-up keep-alive circuits such as the clock and security circuits.
- Supply electrical power to auxiliary circuits such as telematics, shore power electrics, and body builder PDM.
- Provide an optional disconnect; isolate chassis from batteries.

Figure 37–12 is a schematic showing the PDM functions on a current Freightliner Cascadia.

Remote Air Solenoid Module

Air modules are a means of controlling air-operated accessories such as differential locks, suspensions, or transaxles off the data bus. A system air supply is routed to one input on the air module. Modular air solenoids are supplied by this single air source. The on/off status of the solenoids is controlled by the chassis controller using the data bus.

VIRTUAL FUSING

FETs can be designed to feed back the current values they conduct to the controller that actuates them. This allows a microprocessor to shut off an FET if it is conducting more current than that for which it is specified. For instance, if too many lights were installed on a circuit, causing an excess current draw, the controller could shut down that circuit. FETs can also be designed to block current flow when it exceeds a specified threshold value.

Virtual fusing can also be engineered into an electrical power circuit; when it is, it is designed to have performance characteristics identical to those of circuit breakers. The difference is that processor logic is used to determine the manner in which virtual circuit breakers cycle, so we classify them into type 1 (cycling) and type 2 (noncycling).

Type 1 Virtual Fusing

This is used on headlamp and wiper circuits, which may use FET switching. In a current overload condition on the circuit, the system controller first turns the circuit off, then after half a second it retries the circuit. If the current overload no longer exists, the circuit functions normally. However, if the overload condition continues, the controller doubles the length of time between each retry: 1 second, 2 seconds, 4 seconds, ... up to 512 seconds. If the 512 recycle is achieved, the controller may shut down the circuit until the ignition key is cycled.

Type 2 Virtual Fusing

Type 2 virtual circuit breaking logic is on a majority of FET and chassis electrical circuits. Should a circuit be subject to a current overload, the controller shuts off the circuit, then retries after half a second. However, using type 2 virtual breaker logic, if the short or overload still exists after the initial retry, the controller shuts down the FET or circuit and does not initiate a retry until the ignition key is cycled. If three successive key cycles take place with an overloaded circuit in memory, the controller is usually programmed to only briefly (100 ms) permit the FET or circuit to be switched on after each key cycle, just to test the overload condition.

BENEFITS OF NETWORKING

There are four primary benefits of networking a truck electronic system:

FIGURE 37–12 Proprietary and powertrain bus topology in a current Freightliner Cascadia.

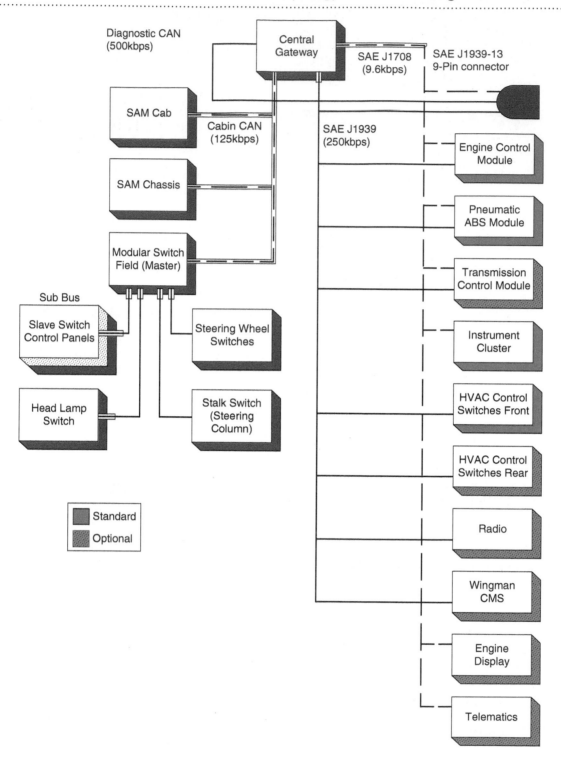

1. Greatly decreased hard wire requirement, reducing the size of the wiring harnesses. This impacts cost, weight, reliability, and serviceability.
2. Sensor data such as vehicle speed, engine temperature, and throttle position is shared, eliminating the need for redundant sensors.
3. Networking allows greater vehicle content flexibility because functions can be added by making simple software changes. Existing systems would require additional modules and additional I/O pins for each function added.
4. Many additional features can be added at little or no additional cost. For instance,

driver preference data once installed in memory can be routed on the data bus to multiple processors to share such diverse information as seat preference, mirror positions, radio station presets, and engine governor type (LS or VS); see Chapter 20.

ACCESSING THE DATA BUS

Truck technicians are required to access the chassis data bus to read, troubleshoot, and reprogram the systems networked to it. A number of different generic and proprietary tools may be used to make the connection, but today a handheld EST, laptop, or portable computer system with OEM software is required to do anything more than the most basic scanning of the bus. However, the pending introduction of HD-OBD may change this.

The connection procedure is outlined in detail in Chapter 35 and demonstrated in videos number 50 and 51 on the video DVD that accompanies this textbook. Whatever kind of computer is used, it must be loaded with either generic reader or OEM read/diagnose/reprogram software. To connect with a chassis data bus, a data link connector (DLC) is required. Today, several types of DLC are required, depending on the generation of the equipment used. It is important to note that any EST connecting to a post-2014 J1939 data bus must be **auto-baud detect capable (ABDC)**: Connecting an EST that is not ABDC compliant can take down the bus.

J1587/1708 DLC

A J1587 data bus was the original truck data backbone: It is accessed using a six-pin **Deutsch connector**. J1587 is an SAE standard that governs the communications protocols used for data transactions. J1708 governs all the hardware standards used on a J1587 data bus, so the six-pin Deutsch connector is correctly known as a J1708 DLC. The cavity pin assignments used on a J1708 DLC are identified and explained in Chapter 35.

J1939 Connector

The current J1939 data bus covers both hardware and software standards. Because most truck chassis equipped with a J1939 data bus are also equipped with the older J1587/1708 data bus, the DLC used has some extra pins. On all MY 2013 trucks and earlier, the J1939 connector is a nine-pin connector with the cavity pin assignments shown in **Figure 37–13**. High bus connections within the data bus backbone are made on a three-pin connector (also known as a *stub*) with cavity pin assignments as shown in Figure 37–13, while low bus connections use a two-pin connector.

J1939 DLCs

For years after its introduction, the truck DLC was the black nine-pin Deutsch connector. However, from EPA MY 2014, this changed. Today a J1939 data bus can be accessed using the following, depending on MY and OEM:

- Black nine-pin Deutsch DLC (J1939 MY 2013 and earlier)
- Green nine-pin Deutsch DLC (backward compatible)
- J1962 16-pin DLC (same as light-duty ALDL) for Volvo-Mack

Figure 37–14 shows the cavity pin assignments of a J1939 DLC and those on a three-pin inter-bus connector.

A black J1939 DLC cannot access a chassis data bus with a green receptacle (post-2013) because the F cavity is of a reduced size. There is a reason for this: ESTs designed to access post-2013 J1939 must be auto-baud detect capable: attempting to connect with older ESTs can take down the bus. **Figure 37–15** shows some 2014 green DLCs and receptacles. Rather than adopt the green standard agreed to by its competing OEMs, Volvo-Mack decided to go with the light-duty J1962 DLC. **Table 37–1** shows the cavity pin assignments used on the J1962 DLC adopted by Volvo-Mack.

CAUTION:
Ensure that any EST connected to a post-2014 data bus is ABDC compliant; failure to do this can take down the bus, necessitating costly repairs.

RP 1210 CAs

When connecting a PC-platform computer to a truck data bus, a communications adapter (CA) is required. The CA is a serial link adapter that identifies the bus protocol (J1587 or J1939), usually by illuminating LEDs. Although most CAs claim to be RP1210 compatible (some Paccar versions do not), this is not necessarily the case. OEM-supplied CAs are usually only tested on that manufacturer's product and often will not execute a connection to other OEM products. For this reason, generic CAs such as those

FIGURE 37–13 Power distribution schematic.

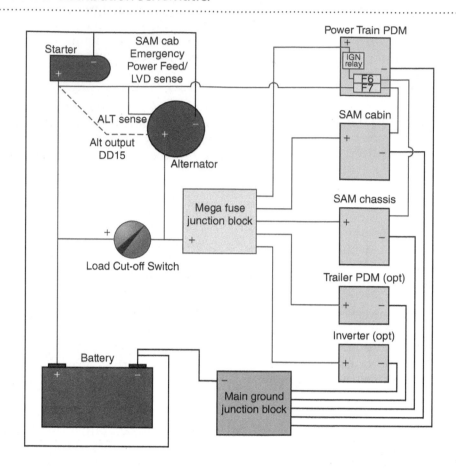

FIGURE 37–14 J1939 connector cavity pin assignments: Three-pin Deutsch for high bus connections within the bus backbone, and nine-pin Deutsch to connect an EST to the data bus.

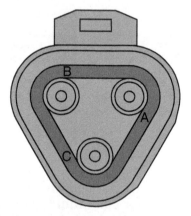

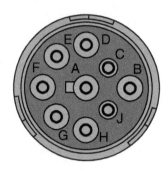

3-Pin J1939 Connector
A. CAN busline, dominant high (+)
B. CAN busline, dominant low (−)
C. CAN ground

9-Pin J1939 Connector
A. Battery negative
B. Battery positive
C. J1939 CAN busline, dominant high (+)
D. J1939 CAN busline, dominant low (−)
E. CAN shield
F. J1587 busline, dominant high (+)
G. J1587 busline, dominant low (−)

FIGURE 37–15 Face-on view of green 2014 J1939 DLCs.

TABLE 37–1 Recommended Cutting Fluid Processes

1	2	3	4	5	**6**	7	8
9	10	11	12	13	**14**	15	16

1. OEM discretion	9. OEM discretion
2. Bus positive + J1708	10. Bus negative − J1708
3. DLC +	11. DLC −
4. Chassis ground	12. OEM discretion
5. Signal ground	13. OEM discretion
6. **J1939 + high**	14. **J1939 − low**
7. K-line of ISO 9141	15. L-line of ISO 9141
8. OEM discretion	16. V-Bat

manufactured by Nexiq, Dearborn Group, and Noregon are recommended.

MAKING THE CONNECTION

You will need an EST loaded with the OEM software plus the appropriate connectors and cabling. Most transactions can be undertaken without network access. Examples of ESTs are:

- HH-EST with generic heavy-duty reader software
- HH-EST with OEM-specific software
- Laptop PC loaded with generic heavy-duty reader software
- Laptop/notebook PC loaded with OEM software
- PC station loaded with OEM software

Most current ESTs also require an online connection. Photo Sequence 4 demonstrates how to connect to a chassis data bus.

Identify SA or MID

After connecting the data connector, you may be required to identify the SA or MID you want to communicate with, unless you are using software that is designed to work exclusively with one controller. The following are some examples of common SAs and MIDs used on a truck data bus:

- Engine controller SA 00 or MID 128
- Transmission controller SA 03 or MID 130

- Body controller SA 33 or MID 249
- Chassis controller SA 71 or MID 142
- Engine retarder SA 15 or MID 173
- Central gateway SA 37 or MID 206
- Tractor ABS and traction control SA 11 or MID 136
- Instrument cluster controller SA 23 or MID 140
- Vehicle navigation controller SA 28 or MID 162
- Satellite communications controller SA 75 or MID 181
- Collision warning/mitigation controller SA 42 or MID 219

SAs and MIDs connected to the chassis data will be displayed as menu options on the EST you are using to read the system. If you wish to access the engine electronics, you will scroll to the SA 00/MID 128 option and select it. Once you have entered the engine electronics, everything displayed on the EST display screen will only relate to that engine. Menu choices will route you through the **subsystems identifiers (SIDs)** and parameter groups (PGs) **parameter identifiers (PIDs)** specific to the engine. **Figure 37–16** shows a screen capture from Daimler Trucks ServicePro software, which is used to communicate with Freightliner Cascadia multiplexed circuits and Detroit Diesel engine electronics. **Figure 37–17** shows the location of the bulkhead module (BHM), and **Figure 37–18** shows a firewall-mounted body controller module on a school bus chassis.

Parameter Groups

In J1939, a **parameter group (PG)** is a set of parameters belonging to the same topic within a controller; they also share the same transmission rate. Each PG has a message length that varies between 8 bytes (minimum) and 1,785 bytes (maximum). Each PG is assigned a unique **parameter group number (PGN)**, which can be identified in J1939 message code. When PGNs are broadcast on the bus, the message can be directed to all of the controllers (SAs) with addresses on the bus, in which case it is described as a **global PGN**.

Alternatively, PGNs can be targeted to a single SA on the bus, in which case it is described as a **specific PGN**. For purposes of troubleshooting, a **suspect parameter group (SPG)** is assigned to either a value/status condition or a component when an abnormal controller condition is identified. The source (SRC) is also identified in a message that broadcasts a **suspect parameter number (SPN)**. The function of an SPN is to:

- Translate PGNs
- Identify the DTC and related SIDs and FMIs

FIGURE 37-16 Screen capture from ServicePro used to communicate with Cascadia multiplex circuits and Detroit Diesel electronics.

FIGURE 37-17 Location of a Freightliner bulkhead module (BHM) on the firewall of a school bus. The BHM coordinates bus activities.

FIGURE 37-18 Location of a typical chassis controller module on the vehicle underbody.

It is important to understand what these terms represent when undertaking more advanced-level J1939 diagnostics.

Hexadecimal Code

Some of the more challenging problems that can arise when troubleshooting data bus problems may require the technician to interpret **hexadecimal message code**. The hexadecimal system is useful because it can represent each byte as a pair of hexadecimal digits, making it easier to read than binary numbers. Sixteen numeric digits are required: Digits 0 to 9 are represented by their decimal numeric equivalents, while the digits 10 to 15 are represented by the alpha

Photo Sequence 4

ACCESSING A TRUCK DATA BUS WITH AN EST

PS4–1 Locate and identify the chassis bus connector. The TMC recommends that this be located on the left side of the steering column, but this can be difficult to find, as on this older truck that uses a J1708 six-pin connector.

PS4–2 This 2013 Navistar Eagle positions a J1939 connector next to the ignition key, making it easy to locate, and where it stays protected from dirt and corrosion.

PS4–3 The green J1939 nine-pin connector shown in this image is a 2014 data bus connector. It is backward-compatible with earlier J1939 nine-pin connectors, but the socket is designed to block pre-2014 black connectors.

PS4–4 To connect to this 2013 Navistar Eagle chassis data bus, a black J1939 connector is required. Make sure to orient the connector pins to the dash-mounted socket.

Data Sequence →

2	8	8	8	0–56	8	1	8	2
Start of Message	Message Type and Priority	Target Identifier	Source Address	Data Field	CRC	End of Data	Acknowledge	End of Message

PS5–5 Insert the connector into the dash connector socket and lock it with a clockwise twist.

PS5–6 Most HH-ESTs, such as this Snap-On iQ, do not require a communications adapter (CA). So, to start working with the chassis data bus, switch on the EST and switch on the vehicle ignition circuit. The EST onscreen menu will then take over with prompts and options.

PS5–7 If the EST is a PC with proprietary software, a CA is required to make the connection. LEDs on the CA will indicate the connection protocol (J1708 or J1939) and the communication status.

PS–9 Entry page to a typical OEM service information system and diagnostic software. Almost all recent systems require the technician to be online before the full capacity software suite is made available.

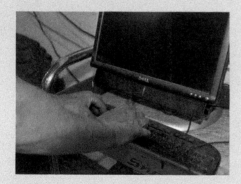

PS5–8 Shop computers can be laptops or dedicated desktops mounted on a shop cart, such as the unit shown in this image.

letters A through F. To translate hexadecimal to binary, convert each hexadecimal digit into its 4-bit binary equivalent.

CODE BASICS We become familiar with the basics of decimal numeric code in early childhood and interpret it without thinking. This makes adjusting to a different code system difficult at first. There are 10 single numeric digits in the decimal system (0 through 9): these ten digits form the basis of the system. The hexadecimal system uses a 16-digit code: therefore, the decimal numbers 10 to 15 are represented sequentially as A, B, C, D, E, F. To compare how we would express some numbers between 10 to 20 in the decimal and hexadecimal systems, take a look at the following table:

Hexadecimal	Decimal
9	9
A	10
B	11
E	14
F	15
10	16
11	17

It is important to identify the numeric system being referred to, so in any case where it is not obvious, $_{subscript}$ is used. Thus, 100_{10} (base 10) = 100 ... whereas 100_{16} (base 16) = 4096. Using the decimal system, most of us know that 10^2 (10 × 10) is equivalent to 100, while 10^3 (10 × 10 × 10) equals 1000. In the hexadecimal code system, the place values are based on powers of 16 instead of 10. So, the following hexadecimal expressions convert into decimal equivalents as follows:

$16^0 = 1$

$16^1 = 16$

$16^2 = 16 \times 16 = 256$

$16^3 = 16 \times 16 \times 16 = 4096$

$16^4 = 16 \times 16 \times 16 \times 16 = 65,536$

Converting from decimal to hexadecimal bases is good practice. Based on what we have said so far, we can say the following:

$C_{16} = 12_{10}$

$F_{16} = 15_{10}$

Get the idea?

You might ask yourself why we do this. We know that computers think in binary digits (voltage on/voltage off), but using the binary code system makes for some extended digit values when this can be made so much easier. For instance, the number 543 in the decimal system would be expressed like this in the binary system: 1000011111 ... and like this using the hexadecimal system: 21F, using just three digits. It is calculated like this:

Hexadecimal 21F converts to: Decimal $= 2 \times 16^2 + 1 \times 16^1 + 15 \times 16^0 = 543$

Consequently, using hexadecimal code is conducive to computers and much abbreviated when compared to binary coding. It is the primary coding system used in J1939. If you have studied some code in high school, you have probably picked up on what we have done so far. At the moment of writing, the ability to decipher J1939 hexadecimal code is only required by bodybuilders who must integrate electronic subsystems in the bus, and by advanced levels of troubleshooting beyond the scope of this textbook—but this is likely to change as the technology progresses. Currently, when a troubleshooting sequence requires the technician to interpret code, it is necessary to contact the OEM service operations hotline, but for students who might want to prepare for the not-so-distant future, a blank J1939 decoder sheet is provided in Appendix B of this book. Use the following University of Tulsa link for a user-friendly guide to interpreting J1939 code: http://tucrrc.utulsa.edu/J1939Database.html Download some hexadecimal J1939 code off a bus or off the web and see how you make out.

Identify FMIs

If you were troubleshooting a fault in the engine, having entered the SA 00/MID 128 address, you would then be routed through the appropriate PGNs/PIDs and SIDs to locate the FMI that had triggered the fault code. There are a limited number of malfunction categories that are assigned as FMIs, and these are listed in Chapter 35 of this book. It is important to note that those FMIs with numeric values from 13 to 20 were added after MY 2007; these are designed to denote pending or imminent failures. They are used for prognostic data reports with the intention of reducing over-the-road failures.

DIAGNOSING BUS FAULTS

Before beginning to diagnose any type of bus fault, it is necessary to consult the manufacturer service literature and identify the type of bus

FIGURE 37–19 A Pico Scopemeter that consists of a CA and Windows environment software. The PicoTech software that interacts with the CA is downloaded from the Web.

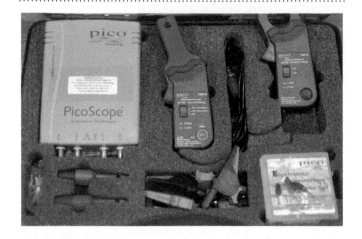

you are working with. Manufacturer software is designed to diagnose data bus problems, but the truth is that some do it a lot better than others. A scopemeter such as the PicoTech kit shown in **Figure 37–19** can be a useful tool in locating bus communication problems.

Using a Scopemeter to Verify CAN Activity

Make sure you read the information provided by the scopemeter manufacturer. The scopemeter may be equipped with accessories such as J1962, J1708, and J1939 DLCs, which allow a handheld scopemeter to be directly coupled into the chassis data bus. The same would apply to a scopemeter that uses a CA and PC software. We will assume here that you want to connect to a J1939 data bus. This means that you will have to identify the pin cavities for CAN high and CAN low (see Figure 37–14).

TROUBLESHOOTING BUS MALFUNCTIONS

Because two-line bus multiplexing can be regarded as a current technology, for the troubleshooting sequence that follows we will assume that PC-based software and a CA are being used, although scan tools will work with some systems. J1939 is a voltage differential bus, meaning that the digital bit logic is messaged by a high bit voltage not exceeding 4.0 V-DC (usually 3.5 volts) and a low bit voltage that does not

FIGURE 37–20 Scope pattern of a properly functioning J1939 CAN bus, showing approximately a 2-volt differential spread. The two 3-volt differentials between CAN high and CAN low indicate message stop bits.

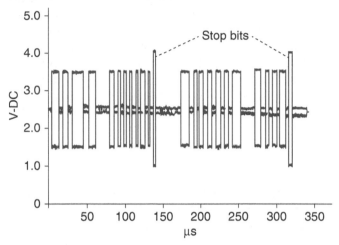

drop below 1.0 V-DC (usually 1.5 volts). The low voltage line is the dominant bit.

On a properly functioning bus (see **Figure 37–20**), the voltage differential is typically 2.0 volts, the exception being a 3.0 V-DC differential to punctuate an end-of-message signal known as a *stop bit*. In addition, a 12.0 V-DC "wake-up" pulse is used to activate all of the modules on the bus. Bus activity initiation is quarterbacked by one module on the bus (i.e., Freightliner SAM) by broadcasting a wake-up signal. It should be noted that a major advantage of the J1939 CAN bus is its ability to tolerate interference.

J1939 FAULT MODES

Seven general types of problems can occur in a CAN two-wire bus line:

1. Short to power side of circuit. Shuts down bus communications between all the modules with an address on the bus because no binary logic exchange can take place.
2. Short to ground side of circuit. Shuts down bus communications between all the modules with an address on the bus because no binary logic exchange can take place.
3. Short between CAN high and CAN low. Caused by pinching the two wires together during repair procedures or a collision.

4. Open. Result of an open varies with the type of bus. In a star network, this prevents data exchange between modules on the opposite side of the fault. When a single open occurs in a loop topography bus (used in some transit buses), there may not be any communications problems, due to multiple paths for message packets to travel through.

5. Interference. May be troublesome because message packets can become scrambled as binary high and low logic is pushed outside of range. Check with a scopemeter as described earlier in this chapter. Causes can be inappropriate repairs, physical rerouting/repositioning of bus lines, and missing terminating resistors.

6. High resistance. When severe enough, the effect can be similar to that of an open. Not a common problem, due to the high impedance of module internal circuitry, so it has to be pretty severe before messaging is adversely affected.

7. Baud irregularity. ESTs accessing post-2014 J1939 buses must have auto-baud detect capability. Baud irregularity can shutdown a data bus.

CAN DIAGNOSTIC ROUTINES

Begin by establishing communication between the PC, the CA (hereafter referred to as the EST), and the diagnostic link connector (DLC). When a failure-to-communicate condition occurs, begin by checking the EST, its connectors and cables. Use another vehicle if necessary to corroborate EST functionality. For purposes of outlining the following diagnostic routines, it will be assumed that the malfunction has occurred on a J1939 bus. Other chassis buses may require a different approach, especially if you are working on mass transit vehicles.

No Handshake with Any Module

When the EST fails to communicate with any module on the bus, identify the cavity pin assignments in Figure 37–14 and use the following routine:

1. Disconnect the EST from the DLC.
2. Use a digital multimeter (DMM) to verify a good ground at J1939 at cavity sockets B and E.
3. Attach the DMM positive probe to J1939 CAN high cavity pin C and the DMM negative lead to CAN low.

4. Set the DMM to the min-max mode on V-DC setting to measure voltage differential.
5. Trigger some activity on the bus, such as by turning the ignition key fob.
6. The minimum voltage should be close to zero and the maximum close to 2.0 volts. Remember that this is the *differential voltage* reading between CAN high and CAN low if you have the DMM set properly.

If the correct readings are displayed, the problem could be in the EST. If the readings are outside of specification, run the following diagnostic routine:

1. Connect the positive DMM probe to CAN high (pin C on a nine-pin Deutsch) and the negative DMM probe to chassis ground (pin A on a nine-pin Deutsch). The specification should read a maximum of 3.5 volts and a minimum of 2.5 volts.
2. Connect the positive DMM probe to CAN low (pin D on a nine-pin Deutsch) and the negative DMM probe to chassis ground. The specification should read a maximum of 2.5 volts and a minimum of 1.5 volts.

Based on what you have measured during the preceding sequence, you should be able to pinpoint the cause and come to one of the following conclusions:

- If the minimum and maximum of both the circuits are above their normal values by the same amount, either a module or its ground integrity is at fault.
- If both CAN high and CAN low show a maximum of 2.5 volts, the circuits are shorted together.
- If either circuit reads a maximum and minimum of close to zero volts, the circuit is shorted to ground. An exception to this would be in the event of an open between the DLC and the remainder of the network. Should this be the case, the vehicle will start and run normally, but there could be no communication with your EST.

- If either CAN high or CAN low displays a minimum and maximum above the specified pulse value, the circuit is shorted to power.

No Communication with One CAN Module

If communication is lost between the EST and one module on a data bus:

1. Disconnect the affected module.
2. Check the power and ground circuit connections at the connection stub.
3. Create some bus activity to check for signals reaching the bus stub at the module. If these three check OK, the module is likely defective.

Replacing a CAN Module

A CAN module should not be replaced before verifying the loaded resistance of both the power and ground circuits connected to the module. This can be done by connecting an electrical load equivalent to the current draw of the module in question (from the power to the ground at the module connector stub). The voltage reading should be no more than 0.5 V-DC less than the system voltage of 12.6 V-DC. If, for instance, the voltage reading was 11.6 V-DC (a 1.0 V-DC differential), high resistance at the power or ground circuits is likely. If high resistance is indicated during this test, it should be repaired and the failed module diagnosis reevaluated.

SUMMARY

- *Multiplexing* is the term used to describe the serial networking of system controllers connected to a truck (or heavy equipment) data bus.
- Multiplexing can eliminate miles of chassis harness wiring and duplication of hardware devices such as TPS by giving electronic subsystems a common communication language that allows data signals over a two-wire twisted pair to take the place of hard wire in the electronic input and output circuits.
- The data bus acts as the "information highway" in a multiplexed electronic truck chassis.
- A "smart" ladder switch contains a ladder of resistors. The processor that receives signals from the switch can interpret switch status data by comparing ladder resistances with a programmed library of resistance values that identify the switch, its status, and circuit integrity.
- The fields that usually make up a data frame on a truck data bus transaction are the start of frame field, arbitration field, control field, data field, cyclic redundancy check field, ack field, and end of frame field.
- Access to a truck data bus is gained by using one of four types of DLC. A six-pin Deutsch DLC is used to access the J1587/1708 data bus. A nine-pin, black Deutsch connector is used to access a pre-2014 J1939 data bus. For post-2014 data buses for all OEMs except for Volvo-Mack, a green nine-pin DLC must be used. For post-2014 Volvo-Mack, a 16-pin J1962 DLC must be used.
- Current trucks equipped with a J1939 data backbone are also fitted with a J1587/1708 bus. Beginning in 2010, some engine OEMs ceased to support J1587.
- When accessing a specific ECM/ECU on a truck data bus with multiple electronic systems, you may be required to select the correct SA or MID, if using generic EST software.
- All current trucks and buses, and most off-highway heavy equipment, use the CAN 2.0 J1939 data bus. This is a serial bus capable of high-speed transactions.
- Some truck chassis OEMs make use of the data bus for functions such as smart switches.
- Bus activity can be verified using a scopemeter to determine whether communications are taking place, producing the correct voltages, and producing appropriate voltage differential spreads.
- A process of elimination may be used to troubleshoot communication problems with individual nodes on the data bus. Some OEM troubleshooting software is designed to pinpoint bus communication problems.
- Advanced-level troubleshooting of the J1939 bus may require some knowledge of hexadecimal code.

REVIEW QUESTIONS

1. What is used to rate the speed of transmission on a data bus?
   a. Bandwidth
   b. K-baud
   c. Protocol
   d. CAN

2. Which of the following terms is used to rate the data volume that can be transmitted on a data bus?
   a. Bandwidth
   b. K-baud
   c. Frequency
   d. Bus arbitration

3. How many fields are typically used in a data packet in a J1939 data transaction?
   a. One
   b. One or two
   c. Five
   d. Seven

4. Which of the fields in a data packet contains the message identifier?
   a. Start of frame
   b. Arbitration
   c. Control
   d. Cyclic redundancy

5. Which field in a data packet is used by receiver stations to indicate that they have received an uncorrupted message?
   a. Arbitration
   b. Control
   c. Cyclic redundancy
   d. Ack

6. What is used to indicate the end of a data packet message?
   a. CRC field
   b. Ack field
   c. EOI
   d. EOF field

7. What current SAE J standard is used as the backbone of a multiplex data bus in current medium- and heavy-duty highway trucks?
   a. CAN-C
   b. J1939
   c. J1930
   d. J1667

8. Which of the following best describes the role of an FET in a smart switch transaction?
   a. Transformer
   b. Electronic noise suppression
   c. Relay or amplifier
   d. Signal filter

9. What will likely result if a smart switch is disconnected at the connector?
   a. The vehicle will stop.
   b. The data bus will shut down.
   c. Operation is in default mode.
   d. A fault code will be logged.

10. How many cavity pins are in a green J1939 Deutsch connector used to connect an electronic service tool (EST) to a truck data bus?
    a. One
    b. Four
    c. Six
    d. Nine

11. Technician A states that after connecting a generic EST to the chassis data connector, you must first identify the SA you want to work with. Technician B states that FMIs are used to categorize the different types of component failure. Who is correct?
    a. Technician A only
    b. Technician B only
    c. Both A and B
    d. Neither A nor B

12. Technician A states that a J1708 DLC uses nine-pin assignments. Technician B states that a current J1939 Deutsch DLC usually incorporates J1587/1708 data backbone access. Who is correct?
    a. Technician A only
    b. Technician B only
    c. Both A and B
    d. Neither A nor B

13. How many resistors are contained in a typical ladder switch?
    a. One
    b. Two
    c. Four
    d. Five

14. Which of the following would best describe the means used to identify a twisted wire pair on an electrical schematic?
    a. Circle
    b. Triangle
    c. Figure eight
    d. Trapezoid

15. Technician A states that voltage differential values on data bus message packets are usually 2.5 volts or lower. Technician B states that the twist frequency on a J1939 data bus is one complete cycle per 1 centimeter of length. Who is correct?
    a. Technician A only
    b. Technician B only
    c. Both A and B
    d. Neither A nor B

16. When using a DMM set at min-max, to read *voltage differential* between CAN high and CAN low on J1939, what should most of the packet read at if it is functioning normally?
    a. V-Ref
    b. V-Bat
    c. 5.0 volts
    d. 2.0 volts

17. When you observe a 3-volt differential between CAN high and CAN low on J1939, at the end of a packet message, which of the following is likely?
    a. CAN high is shorted to power.
    b. CAN low is shorted to ground.
    c. CAN high and CAN low are dead shorted.
    d. It is the end-of-message stop bit indicator.

18. What letter code is used for the CAN low pin cavity on a J1939 data connector?
    a. A
    b. B
    c. C
    d. D

19. Which of the following decimal numeric values would be associated with the hexadecimal code letter F?
    a. 16
    b. 15
    c. 8
    d. 2

20. Technician A says that a green J1939 DLC is backward compatible with any black J1939 receptacle. Technician B says that a J1962 DLC is required to connect to a post-2014 Volvo-Mack data bus. Who is correct?
    a. Technician A only
    b. Technician B only
    c. Both A and B
    d. Neither A nor B

38

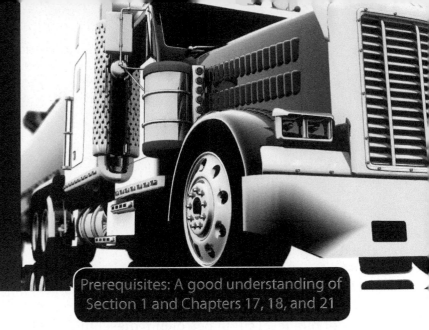

Prerequisites: A good understanding of Section 1 and Chapters 17, 18, and 21

NATURAL GAS, PROPANE, AND BIODIESEL FUELS

OBJECTIVES

After studying this chapter, you should be able to:

- Identify some alternatives to diesel fuel that may be viable in commercial vehicle engines.
- Describe the characteristics of biodiesel fuels.
- Outline the properties of B100 and biodiesel cuts from B20 to B2.
- Identify some of the advantages and disadvantages of gaseous fuels in medium- and heavy-duty commercial vehicle applications.
- Differentiate between methane-based fuels by source, fuel system requirements, storage, and handling.
- Outline the operating principles of a natural gas (NG) fuel system.
- Identify some pre-2010 and current NG-fueled engines.
- Describe the key management and fuel system components used in post-2015, Cummins Westport NG-fueled engines.
- Describe the operating principles of the coil-on-plug ignition system used on the current generation of Cummins Westport NG fueled engines.
- Identify the types of injectors used in current Westport NG fuel systems.
- Explain how Westport uses piezo-actuated injectors to deliver a diesel fuel pilot pulse to ignite an NG fuel charge.
- Outline the service requirements and maintenance intervals of Cummins Westport NG-fueled engines.
- List the reasons why hydrogen may become the fuel of the future.
- Identify the advantages and disadvantages of alcohol-based fuels used in medium- and heavy-duty commercial vehicle applications.

KEY TERMS

air-fuel ratio (AFR)

alcohol

biocide

biodiesel

biomethane

B20

B100

California Air Resources Board (CARB)

capacitive discharge ignition (CDI)

coil-on-plug ignition (CPI) system	direct-fire ignition (DFI)	greenhouse gases (GHGs)	methanol
coil-pack	drayage truck	high-pressure direct injectors (HPDIs)	natural gas (NG)
compressed natural gas (CNG)	ethanol		propane
compressed natural gas direct injection (CNG-DI)	FMVSS 304	hydrogen (H_2)	spark ignition (SI)
cryogenic	gasoline-equivalent-gallon (GEG)	liquefied natural gas (LNG)	stoichiometric
diesel gallon equivalent (DGE)		liquefied petroleum gas (LPG)	waste-spark system
dimethyl ether (DME)	global warming potential (GWP)	methane	Westport Innovations
			Westport MonoInjector

INTRODUCTION

The use of biodiesel cut in petroleum diesel fuel has become common today and mandatory in some jurisdictions. Because some jurisdictions require that diesel fuel include biodiesel cuts, its use has become commonplace and generally produces few problems. The biggest problem is that the "shelf life" of petroleum-source diesel mixed with biodiesel is reduced.

During the past decade, the abundance of low-cost, domestically sourced methane-base fuels has resulted in industry acceptance of **natural gas (NG)** as an engine fuel. Inner-city transit buses, especially those based on the West Coast, were the first to adopt NG as an alternative to diesel fuel, but this acceptance has spread to some segments of the trucking industry. As the use of NG has grown, so has the fueling infrastructure. In addition, propane has been used in pickup and delivery commercial vehicles for two generations; like natural gas, propane is also primarily methane, though it is sourced from petroleum refining processes and is not as "clean."

Although there are no alternate fuel technologies that could compete with the versatility of diesel fuel in the immediate future, NG has made significant gains recently. This progress has been due primarily to **Westport Innovations** and its engine partner, Cummins. Industry-wide competition has been significantly reduced since 2010 due to the difficulty in meeting NO_x emissions standards, leaving Cummins Westport dominant as the commercial NG option to diesel fuel.

CUMMINS WESTPORT

Essentially, what Westport does is take an existing diesel engine and convert it to a NG fuel system. In most cases, the engine OEM management controller is retained, but a Westport module is added to manage fueling and ignition. Today, Cummins Westport engines are used in a variety of inner-city applications, including transit buses, delivery vehicles, garbage packers, and (increasingly) in longhaul, heavy-duty, linehaul trucks. As a result, we will take a close look at the Cummins Westport NG engines in this chapter. **Figure 38–1** shows a 2015 Cummins Westport ISX 12G engine that has become the market leader in truck applications. This is a modified Cummins ISX 12 (11.9 liter displacement) that shares many components with its diesel engine sibling.

CALIFORNIA

NG technology arrived in California some time ago. The **California Air Resources Board (CARB)** has aggressively driven the use of alternates to diesel fuel. NG has been favored for a number of years in West Coast inner-city transit vehicles and **drayage truck** applications. Drayage trucks haul port loads from dock to linehaul terminals. The city of Los Angeles retired the last diesel-powered bus to be running on its roads nearly 10 years ago. Today, buses in Los Angeles rely on NG power, as they do in most other

FIGURE 38–1 A sign of times to come. A Freightliner equipped with a Cummins Westport ISL NG powerplant.

larger West Coast cities. The ports of Long Beach and Los Angeles, two of the largest ports in the country, have a long history of playing hardball on emissions enforcement, and they have been especially intolerant of the grandfathering of legacy emissions technology. This has promoted the use of NG-fueled drayage trucks because current CARB standards dictate that only vehicles compliant with post-2007 emissions standards will be permitted access to California ports after 2013.

WHY ALTERNATE FUEL TECHNOLOGY HAS BEEN SLOW TO TAKE OFF

At this time, not one medium- or heavy-duty truck engine has been specifically engineered for any type of fuel other than diesel. Engines that use any kind of alternate fuel technology have been re-engineered diesels, and most of those released into the market until around the year 2000 performed poorly.

In engines fueled by **alcohol**-based fuels or **methane**-based fuels, the fuel charge will not auto-ignite at diesel compression temperatures, so a means of ignition must be provided. The result is that either a spark ignition system has to be incorporated or a small shot of diesel fuel has to be injected as an ignition pilot. When an alcohol-based fuel is used in pumping hardware designed for diesel fuel, the low lubricity of the alcohol necessitates frequent overhauls of costly fuel pumping and injection apparatus, so alcohol fuels are seldom used today.

BIODIESEL

Biodiesel has a track record of success as a diesel fuel, largely because it combusts in the diesel engine without changing any hardware. This keeps up-front costs down. That said, pure biodiesel, known as **B100**, has real limitations because it is best suited to operation in warm climates, but it burns cleaner than petroleum-based fuels. However, when B100 is mixed with standard diesel fuel, at concentrations ranging from B20 (20% biodiesel/80% petroleum diesel) down to B2 (2% biodiesel/98% petroleum diesel), it improves its temperature-operating range while somewhat lowering harmful emissions, depending on the mixture cut (proportions).

One of the factors that has increased biodiesel usage in the recent past has been the introduction of B5 and B2 fuel. While cynics might argue that this is more about optics than substance, a response might be that if every fleet changed to B2 fuel, this would represent at least a 2% reduction in the dependence on imported petroleum products—with the additional bonus of at least a small decrease in noxious emissions.

Operators who use B2 or B5 fuel get to place a sticker on the truck advertising how environmentally conscientious they are. This factor, when added to the tax breaks that some jurisdictions throw in, has led most major consumers of diesel fuel to at least consider using B fuels. Using low-concentration cuts of biodiesel, such as B2 and B5, avoids many of the performance problems experienced by users of higher percentage biodiesel cuts.

WHAT IS BIODIESEL?

In the past, biodiesel conjured images of hippies concocting fuels from McDonald's waste cooking fat—an operation that could take place in a barn or perhaps a kitchen. The definition of *biodiesel* is a little hazy because the term can be applied to a number of homemade fuels as well as those refined under more stringent guidelines. However, we will say here that any biodiesel that finds its way into a truck fuel system should conform to American Society for Testing and Materials (ASTM) Standard D6751.

ASTM Definition

ASTM defines *biodiesel* as a domestic, renewable fuel for diesel engines derived from natural oils such as soybean and other vegetable oils. It is *not* raw vegetable oil: A biodiesel must be refined (processed) so that all natural glycerin is removed from the oil. The term *biodiesel* can refer to 100% vegetable-based fuel oil known as B100, or a range of blends (known as *cuts*) of biodiesel and petroleum fuel oil. For instance, B20 is petroleum-based diesel fuel blended with 20% ASTM D6751 biodiesel. Despite reports to the contrary, using spent frying oil from fast-food outlets will not likely be a large-scale source of biodiesel, due to the variables (read "contamination") of the base oil and the cost of refining this to a reliably performing highway fuel. In describing biodiesel in this chapter, we use ASTM Standard D6751 and the U.S. Department of Energy (DOE) research rather than referencing some of the cruder do-it-yourself technologies.

Biodiesel Chemistry

The chemical composition of biodiesel is given in **Table 38–1**. In the table, biodiesel manufactured

TABLE 38-1 Biodiesel Compared with Highway Diesel Fuel

Fuel Property	Diesel (ASTM Average 2D)	Biodiesel (B-100)
Specific gravity	0.85	0.88
Caloric value (heat energy)	140,000 Btu/gal	118,000 Btu/gal
Density (lb per gal at 15°C)	7.079	7.328
Water percentage of volume	0.05	0.05
Carbon (by weight)	87%	77%
Hydrogen (by weight)	13%	12%
Oxygen (by weight)	0%	13%
Sulfur (by weight)	0.05%	0 to 0.0025%
Flash point	60–80°C	100–170°C
Cetane number	40 to 55	48 to 60
Pour point	−35 to −15°C	−15 to 16°C

Source: Data from U.S. DOE, February 2002.

to ASTM D6751 is compared with a highway diesel fuel ASTM 975 manufactured to 2002 standards.

Biodiesel Characteristics

The advantage of biodiesel over petroleum-based diesel fuel is its biodegradability. However, this biodegradability is also the major disadvantage of the fuel, because it results in rapid degradation for two reasons:

- Hygroscopic: Biodiesels readily attract water from the atmosphere, giving it a much shorter "shelf life" than petroleum-based diesel.
- Vulnerability to microbial contamination: The problems that petroleum-based diesel fuels are subject to (see Chapter 18) can be multiplied by 10 times.

A chemist would describe biodiesel as a straight chain fatty acid, and as such it is a culinary delicacy for microorganisms. Given that biodiesel is also hygroscopic, it provides an ideal environment for microbes that tend to reside in the water and consume the hydrocarbon fractions of the fuel. We can summarize the features of B100 as follows:

- No aromatics or nitrogen (these can form toxins during combustion)
- Nontoxic and biodegradable
- Zero sulfur content (if ASTM D6751 standard)
- 10% less heat energy than ASTM #2 diesel fuel

- Fractionally less heat energy than ASTM #1 diesel fuel

Combusting Biodiesel

Biodiesel burns more cleanly than petroleum-based diesel fuel. Most of the harmful emissions produced by combusting petroleum diesel fuel are significantly reduced, with the exception of oxides of nitrogen (NO_x). NO_x emission is slightly increased over diesel fuel because biodiesel is an oxygenate fuel; that is, like alcohol, there is an oxygen component in the fuel.

Perhaps the biggest disadvantage of biodiesel is its inability to flow at colder temperatures. This means that as a pure fuel, its primary markets are going to be in warmer climates. When biodiesel is cut by petroleum diesel, it becomes a more viable fuel in cooler climates. There have been some government initiatives to popularize **B20**. Biodiesel B20 is able to retain some of the advantages of biodiesel B100 (100% vegetable base) and is probably more practical as a future commercial vehicle fuel. B20 and B100 are compared in **Table 38-2**.

Costs and Availability

Because reduced-cut biodiesels such as B5 and B2 have recently been introduced, their use has increased. This increased usage has been aided by steep increases in the cost of petroleum. Combine this effort with EPA efforts to make highway fuel cleaner (therefore more expensive!), reducing the cost differential, and the future for biodiesel may be bright. Currently, the DOE suggests that it is best to avoid any biodiesel that does not meet the ASTM D6751 standard.

Color and Odor

Biodiesel and biodiesel cuts can meet ASTM D6751 and D975 while having a variety of colors and odors. Examples of some acceptable colors are orange, red, yellow, brown, and green. These fuels can also have a range of odors, so fuels

TABLE 38-2 Biodiesel Emissions Compared with EPA-Certified Diesel Fuel

Emission	B100	B20
Carbon monoxide	−43%	−12%
Hydrocarbons	−56%	−11%
Nitrogen oxides	+6%	+1.2%
Air toxics	−80 to −90%	−20%

Source: Data from U.S. DOE, February 2002.

can seldom be condemned on the basis of odor alone. However, a distinct "septic tank" odor is a common indicator of bacterially degraded fuel. Running such a fuel through a truck engine fuel system is asking for trouble.

Biocides

Biocides can be added to biodiesel to kill bacteria in the same way antibiotics seek out and destroy bacteria in the human body, so you might ask why biocides are not added to all biodiesel fuel stocks. This is not done for the same reason that antibiotics are not routinely taken by humans: Bacteria have an uncanny way of developing a resistance to any substances humans develop to kill them. When a biodiesel fuel comes under attack by bacteria, shocking the system by dosing the fuel with biocides may rescue the fuel before it becomes chemically depleted to the point that it can no longer be used.

Power and Fuel Economy

Using B100 in place of #2 (ASTM Standard 975) diesel fuel will reduce power by about 10%. Put simply, there is less heat energy in biodiesel; therefore, more of it has to be used to accomplish the work equivalent to a similar volume of petroleum fuel. For every gallon of diesel fuel consumed, approximately 1.1 gallons of B100 will have to be consumed; it is rated in the trucking industry with a **diesel gallon equivalent (DGE)** of 1.1. The difference is obviously much less noticeable when B20 and lower concentration cuts are used.

WARNING:

B100 gels in anything but midsummer conditions. Unless blended with cloud and gel point suppressants, it should not usually be considered a year-round fuel for diesel engines except perhaps in the warmest climates.

CAUTION:

Some original equipment manufacturers (OEMs) do not approve of biodiesel use in their fuel systems, so check with the manufacturer. Most OEMs will approve the use of B5, and some even are using B5 cuts when establishing performance test profiles. Several approve the use of B20 in at least some engine lines. However, because of the fact that even low-concentration cuts degrade rapidly, engine OEMs will tend not to consider biodiesel-related fuel system failures in warranty claims.

Low-Temperature Operability

Even when biodiesels meet the ASTM 6751 standard, they have documented unreliability when it comes to defining the cloud point of the fuel. In Chapter 18 we described the *cloud point* of a fuel, which is the temperature at which it begins to form wax crystals large enough to start plugging a fuel filter. This unreliability has given biodiesel some bad press in colder parts of North America. Other factors that affect low-temperature operability are:

- Filter location on chassis
- Low-porosity (high-efficiency) filters
- Absence of a block heater
- Prolonged shutdown periods

Biodiesel Problems

Use of B100 and even low-level B2 and B5 biodiesel cuts has presented operating problems in diesel fuel systems. The problems tend to be more prevalent during cold weather operation, but in addition, storage life can be very limited in extreme heat.

Among the problems experienced are:

- Susceptibility to bacterial attack. Biodiesel is more susceptible to bacterial growth than petroleum fuel, and the metabolic waste of bacteria creates slime formation that can plug filters and restrict fuel subsystems. In addition, bacterial attacks chemically degrade the fuel and unbalance the fractions. This condition is more likely to occur in hot weather.
- Cold weather degradation. Biodiesel, even in low-level cuts, has presented problems with waxing and gelling during midwinter operation. These problems have proven to be difficult or impossible to remedy with additives.
- Lack of blender/refiner accountability. Despite ASTM D6751 (B100), there is still no current standard for B-cuts, meaning that fuel problems resulting from using biodiesels are usually paid for by the end user alone.

Biodiesel Conclusions

The use of biodiesel will increase because there are enough reasons to justify its use. Not the least of these reasons is an EPA requirement that the equivalent of 7.5 billion gallons of agricultural-source fuels must be blended into vehicle fuel sold in the United States. Three billion gallons will be pure biodiesel (prior to cutting with petroleum-base diesel), with the remainder being ethanol cut into gasoline).

One major challenge is that the ASTM has structured standards for B100 (ASTM 6751) and ASTM #1 and #2 petroleum diesel fuels (ASTM D975), but has not set a standard for any of the reduced-concentration cuts. It should be emphasized that any biodiesel cut (B20, B5, B2) is only as good as the B100 stock that it was sourced from. When experiencing problems with biodiesel blends, there is currently no standard that the fuel supplier can be held accountable to: This makes it almost impossible to attribute blame for a bad fuel. In most cases, when a biodiesel cut fails to perform, the fuel becomes useless and should be recycled. Attempting to rectify the problem by adding kerosene may sometimes work, but this practice results in a nonapproved fuel that can damage emission control systems.

METHANE FUELS

Natural gas (NG), propane, and **biomethane** are the results of organic waste decomposition and consist primarily of methane. As indicated previously, methane does not auto-ignite, so when it is used as fuel in an automotive engine, an ignition system is required. The ignition source may be a timed spark or a pilot charge of a fuel (such as diesel) that does auto-ignite.

Today, fuels are rated by their **global warming potential (GWP)**. All fossil fuels (from which NG is sourced) contribute to GWP because they emit **greenhouse gases (GHGs)** into the atmosphere. GHGs include carbon dioxide, nitrous oxide, water vapor, methane, and ozone. Because biomethanes are produced by the decomposition of vegetable matter and contain harmful methane, when they are contained and combusted, they are converted into much less harmful CO_2 and water vapor (both GHGs).

BIOMETHANE

Biomethane can be sourced from any type of decomposing vegetation or sewage. Most European countries have recognized and exploited this for decades. Biomethane has a negative GHG rating (which is good!), because it provides household and agricultural waste with an environmentally safer option to allowing the resulting methane to evaporate into the atmosphere. The Scandinavians have led the world in biomethane production, and it is a no-brainer to take a serious look at biomethane recapture in the United States and Canada, which have between them the most primitive garbage-handling infrastructure in the Western world. Recapture of biomethane comes with the double promise of lessening reliance on imported petroleum and reducing landfill mass. Production is on a relatively small scale at present because the infrastructure is in its infancy, and progress in expanding it will depend on investment by all levels of government, because it competes head-on with the interests of multinational oil companies.

Dimethyl Ether

Dimethyl ether (DME) is biomass-sourced gaseous fuel that is therefore composed primarily of methane. It is a clean-burning, nontoxic, potentially renewable fuel that Volvo-Mack is optioning as a fuel system. DME possesses high cetane value and produces quiet combustion. It is a relatively inexpensive diesel alternative for which a truck can retooled in much the same manner as a propane-fueled engine with low-cost equipment.

DME has been used for decades as an energy source in Asia and Scandinavia. The fuel can be produced domestically from a variety of feedstocks, including biogas and natural gas. It can be produced by biomass degradation (garbage), which adds to its *green* appeal. Regardless of source, its production is not dependent upon the availability or price of crude oil.

DME is a gas under ambient conditions, with properties similar to those of propane. It can be stored as a liquid under moderate pressure, eliminating the need for the high-pressure containers used for CNG or cryogenic storage of LNG. At this time, it is not widely used in North America and the absence of a fueling infrastructure limits expansion of its use. When a biomass fuel is used in place of petro-sourced NG, CO_2 emission is cut by 70%, so this represents a powerful incentive to increase use of DME.

COMPRESSED AND LIQUID NG

Compressed natural gas (CNG) and **liquefied natural gas (LNG)** are sourced from crude petroleum boil-off, obtained either from oil refineries or from underground fracking. It is inexpensive and plentiful; although the distribution infrastructure is currently limited, it is improving. CNG is stored on the vehicle as a gas in high-pressure tanks at pressures in the 3,000 to 4,500 psi (200 to 310 bar) range, but 3,600 psi (248 bar) is standard. **Figure 38–2** shows a CNG storage tank on a Class 8 linehaul truck.

FIGURE 38–2 The CNG operator interface module on the fuel tank of a Class 8 highway truck.

FIGURE 38–3 An LNG fuel station, an increasingly common sight at truck stops.

LNG is NG stored on the vehicle in liquid form at around 230 psi (16 bar). LNG is a low-pressure storage system and the liquid has to be vaporized prior to injection to the engine cylinders. The LNG is drawn from its storage tank and heated in a vaporizer just before injection. NG fuel systems require the fuel to be delivered to the fuel injection apparatus in a gaseous state and make no distinctions as to how the fuel is stored on the vehicle. **Figure 38–3** shows an LNG fuel station, an increasingly common sight at truck stops today.

COMPOSITION OF NG

Natural gas (NG) is a simple fuel that consists primarily of methane and is drawn from gas wells (fracking) or from petroleum vapors boiled off during refining processes. Although its chemistry is relatively consistent, when delivered through pipeline networks it also contains small quantities of hydrocarbons such as ethane and propane, along with impurities such as helium, sulfur compounds, and water vapor. Because it is almost odorless, odorants are usually added to NG, for reasons of safety and to facilitate leak detection. A major advantage of NG is that when at atmospheric pressure it is lighter than air and quickly disperses in the event of leakage. This provides it with a significant safety advantage over gasoline or LPG. **Figure 38–4** shows a comparison of the chemistry of methane with that of a typical diesel fuel.

FIGURE 38–4 A comparison of a methane molecule with that of a typical diesel fuel fraction; the simplicity of methane makes it easier to manage post-combustion emissions.

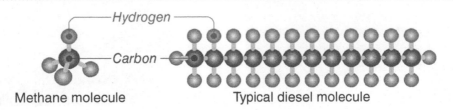

Methane molecule   Typical diesel molecule

CHALLENGES OF NG FUEL

Part of the problem with using NG as a fuel for commercial engines is that no engines have been designed specifically for NG. That said, Westport has specialized in re-engineering diesel engines for NG fueling. Prior to 2010, other OEMs including Volvo-Mack and Navistar offered in-house NG engines, but these could not meet EPA model year (MY) NO_x emissions, leaving the Cummins Westport engines as the dominant supplier of NG engines in North America. The fact that NG does not auto-ignite means that either a spark ignition (SI) system, glow plug, or diesel pilot must be used to fire the fuel charge. Today, Cummins Westport options are either spark ignition or diesel pilot ignition. Sometimes these engines are known as *dual-fuel engines*, but they are really NG-fueled engines that only use a diesel pilot charge for purposes of ignition. **Figure 38–5** shows a left side view of a 2015 Cummins Westport ISX 12G spark-ignited, CNG-fueled engine.

Advantages of NG Fuel

Nontoxic

Abundant, with good inner-city distribution infrastructure

Dense; sufficient quantity can be carried for linehaul

Lighter than air; disperses rapidly if leaked

Technology already exists for use as a vehicle fuel

High octane (permits a high compression ratio)

Relatively clean burning; lower HC, CO, PM, and NO_x tailpipe emissions

Disadvantages of NG Fuel

Low calorific value compared with diesel fuel

Bulky storage tanks of large volume (see **Figure 38–6**)

Reduced peak power performance

Refueling can be a problem, especially with CNG (very slow)

Range limitations

Electronic or diesel pilot ignition system required

NG as Drayage Truck and Transit Bus Fuel

Drayage trucks operating in West Coast ports make substantial use of NG fueling. Drayage trucks operate within port compounds and

FIGURE 38–6 A CNG vertical fuel tank-mounted module that is the user interface for refueling; note the clearly marked fuel shutoff valve.

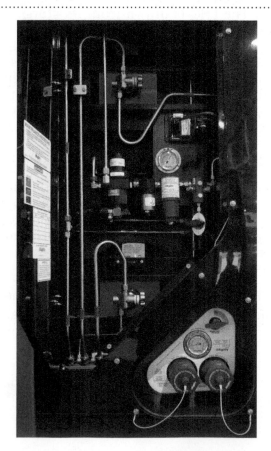

FIGURE 38–5 A left side view of a Cummins Westport ISX 12G CNG-fueled engine.

transfer loads to linehaul terminals. Transit buses operate in congested downtown traffic. The stop-start operation and repeated acceleration cycles of this type of bus and truck use make them heavy emitters of HC, NO_x, and CO_2. Carbon dioxide was defined as a pollutant by the Supreme Court in 2007 (see Chapter 47) even though it is not chemically toxic. Using NG reduces the emissions of all three.

Economics of NG

NG produces lower fuel economy and requires high levels of maintenance than equivalent diesel engines. Some research undertaken by CARB in 2005, using a broad range of CNG and LNG engines of different OEMs and generations, produced a mean average of 4.1 mpg for CNG versus 6.9 mpg for equivalent diesel power. This means that for NG fueling to compete with diesel power on the basis of fuel economy, there must be a significant cost advantage over diesel fuel pricing along with the lower emissions. Because NG engines require the use of special engine lubricants and higher levels of maintenance monitoring and intervention than equivalent diesel-fueled engines, using them has to be justified by reduced emissions and lower fuel costs.

OEM NG ENGINES

Commercial medium- and heavy-duty engines produced by OEMs in North America after the year 2001 using NG fueling include the following:

- Detroit Diesel Series 50G (8.5 liter) and Series 60G (12.7 liter). These engines use lean burn combustion technology. Early versions did not make use of O_2 feedback, but later versions adopted resistance-type exhaust density feedback sensors (older ZO_2 sensors will not function in a lean burn environment; see Chapter 34 for an explanation). Used primarily in transit bus applications.
- John Deere 6068 (6.8 liter) and 6081 (8.1 liter). These engines use lean burn technology and a closed-loop feedback system based on a resistance-type O_2 sensor.
- Mack Trucks E7 (12 liter). These engines were used primarily in inner-city, vocational applications such as garbage packers. This engine uses lean burn technology and a closed-loop feedback system based on a resistance-type O_2 feedback sensor. Mack Trucks did not offer this engine after 2010,

choosing to option the Cummins Westport ISL 8.9G engine in its place.
- Caterpillar dual-fuel C-7, C-10, and C-12. These engines make use of the usual direct injection diesel fuel injection system, introducing just enough diesel fuel into the engine cylinder to ignite the gas charge. The NG is injected using automotive-type injectors.
- Navistar MaxxForce 13: This uses a Westport NG management system and was available in ProStar Class 8 chassis with sufficient tank volume to undertake linehaul trips. Navistar ceased production of its MaxxForce 13G in 2013.
- Cummins Westport ISB-G (5.9 liter), ISC-G (8.1 liter), ISL-G (8.9 liter), ISX 12G (11.9 liter), and ISX 15G (15 liter). Cummins Westport has been producing NG-fueled engines for a generation, beginning with the moderate success of the Cummins L10G engine in the 1990s, which it consolidated with its versions of the ISB and ISC engines. Since 2010, it has emerged as the market leader NG engine supplier with its ISB-G, ISC-G, ISL-G, ISX 12G, and ISX 15G engines.

NG FUEL SYSTEM COMPONENTS

A typical NG fuel system will consist of the following components:

- Fuel tank(s)
- High-pressure stainless steel lines
- Tank interface module
- Manual shutoff valve
- Electronic shutoff valve
- Regulator (controls flow to fuel module)
- Fuel filter(s)
- Low-pressure indicator lamp
- Ignition module (in SI applications)
- Fuel management module (including injector drivers)
- Engine management module

SPARK IGNITION THEORY

Because NG does not auto-ignite, some means of igniting the fuel is required, either by using a diesel fuel pilot or providing a hot point or spark. For this reason, it is necessary to understand the basics of **spark ignition (SI)** theory. Because this description is primarily aimed at diesel technicians, it is assumed that the reader has a good understanding of basic electricity and how coils and transformers function, subject matter that is reviewed in Chapter 32.

IGNITION BASICS

The overall function of an SI system is to trigger ignition at a precise point toward the end of the compression stroke, using an accurately timed spark. Triggering must be phased so that the ignition coil is sufficiently charged before actual ignition is required. This necessitates a time period known as *coil saturation time* or *dwell*.

The electrical energy that is discharged as a spark is usually stored in a coil as electromagnetic energy in conventional SI systems. In other systems, the electrical energy can be stored in a capacitor as an electrostatic charge in what is known as a **capacitive discharge ignition (CDI)**. In a CDI system, the role of the coil becomes that of an energy transfer device (transformer). The high-voltage pulse results from initially charging the primary section, then by rapidly disconnecting the primary inductor from the power supply: This results in a high-voltage (primary) pulse. Then, through the process of induction, the now higher (approximately 600 volts) primary circuit is induced to the secondary windings, resulting in a high-voltage spark (to around 50,000 volts). This ionizing (jumping) of the precisely timed spark plug gap is used to ignite the compressed air-fuel mixture in the engine cylinder. Should ignition not occur, for whatever reasons, the occurrence is known as a *misfire*.

Ignition Coil

The ignition coil can be regarded as the heart of an SI system. An ignition coil can be divided into:

1. A primary winding
2. A soft iron core
3. A secondary winding

Current supply to the primary winding is switched on and off by the ignition module. Current flow through the primary winding is defined by the following factors:

1. Battery voltage during cranking
2. System voltage when running

At the precise moment an ignition spark is required, power to the primary winding is interrupted by an ignition module control circuit signal. This produces a much higher primary electrical energy pulse (approximately 600 volts). Then, the primary voltage (small number of wire turns) is induced to the secondary winding. The secondary winding has a much larger number of coils (ampere turns), which results in stepped-up voltage with reduced current. The function of the coil is that of the step-up

transformers described in Chapter 32. The secondary winding of the coil is now set to discharge its high voltage as a pulse-timed spark to ignite the cylinder air/fuel charge.

Ignition Circuit Components

After building the high voltage (often referred to as *high tension*) within the secondary section of the ignition coil(s), the voltage has to be delivered to the spark plugs by means of high-tension wire(s). With the coil-over-plug system described a little later, a coil located directly above each spark plug. Current designs of high-tension wires use spiral core or latex-impregnated graphite wires, which provide longevity, high spike suppression (reduced RFI), and specified electrical resistance.

CAPACITIVE DISCHARGE IGNITION

In a CDI ignition system, electrical energy is stored in a capacitor. The storage capacitor can be charged using a constant current or with pulses. Charging the coil is achieved by a small transformer that steps up the voltage to a value of around 400 volts. At the ignition point, a thyristor is switched, allowing the capacitor to discharge its accumulated energy to the ignition coil. This type of ignition provides increased power advantages as the ignition coil "rise time" or saturation time of the primary section of the coil is reduced, providing a consistent high-voltage supply for the timed spark to occur.

Advantages of CDI systems include:

- Provides a high voltage capable of igniting wet/fouled spark plugs.
- Provides a high enough voltage to ignite lean air-fuel mixtures.
- Recovers rapidly following a high voltage discharge.

Because a CDI system has specific design and component characteristics (circuits, resistance, diodes), only coils specific to that application should be used. Using nonapproved replacement components can result in serious electrical component failures. Note that using nonresistance, solid core wires will produce high levels of electrical interference (RFI spikes) that can damage the ignition and other sensitive vehicle electrical systems.

COIL-ON-PLUG IGNITION

In a **coil-on-plug ignition (CPI) system**, also known as **direct-fire ignition (DFI)**, such as the system that is used currently with SI Cummins

Westport engines, one ignition coil is used per engine cylinder. Westport refers to this as high-energy ignition (HEI). In the description that follows, the term CDI will be used.

CDI Construction and Operation

The coil-pack assembly connects directly onto the spark plug, eliminating the use of spark plug wires. This means that there is an individual ignition coil per cylinder, allowing each coil to develop its own high-voltage potential, without having to share saturation (build) time with the other cylinders.

The advantage of incorporating multiple ignition coils is that all the coils in the engine can be charged simultaneously, which increases dwell or saturation time. The result is that maximum potential spark energy is available at all engine speeds. Unlike single-coil CDI systems, which are capable of discharging only a single, short spark because it has to be shared with all the spark plugs, CPI can output a high-energy, multi-sparks (long burn) pulse at the highest engine speeds and load conditions.

Triggering

Triggering is typically accomplished by a signal from the engine camshaft position sensor to the ECM. By using this signal, the ignition module computes engine speed and factors it with input from other critical sensors (vehicle speed, turbo boost, TPS, etc.) to calculate the extent of spark advance or delay. This ensures that the plugs are fired at the optimum timing angle. The charging and output of the individual coils is measured dynamically, so changes in rpm, battery voltage, and temperature variables can be precisely measured to ensure maximum spark energy, fuel economy, and emission compliance.

A defective coil-pack can result in misfire, a dead cylinder, increased fuel consumption, and excessive emission output. All these conditions will result in reduced engine power. **Figure 38-7** shows the top of the coil-packs

FIGURE 38-8 Location of the ignition module immediately above the ECM on a Cummins Westport CNG-fueled engine.

on a Cummins Westport ISX 12G engine, and **Figure 38-8** shows the location of the Westport ignition module on the same engine.

In some CPI systems, the coils are contained within a single molded block unit and use multiple high-tension (spark plug) terminals and high-tension wires to conduct the spark to remote-located spark plugs. These are commonly referred to as **coil-packs**.

FIGURE 38-7 The top of the coil-packs on a Cummins Westport CNG engine.

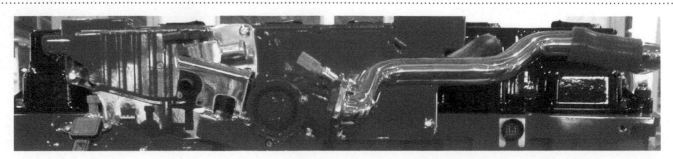

Other systems use coils that have two secondary (spark plug) terminals per coil. This is known as a **waste-spark system**. The purpose is to fire both spark plugs at the same time. Because cylinders are usually paired on a crankshaft, two pistons will reach the top of the cylinder bore at the same time: one will be on its compression stroke and the other on its exhaust stroke. The cylinder on its compression stroke will receive a spark, igniting the compressed air-fuel mixture, while the other (on its exhaust stroke) will also receive a spark. This is referred to as a *waste-spark system* because the cylinder completing its exhaust stroke also receives a spark. This waste spark is used to ignite any uncombusted fuel that remains in the cylinder on the exhaust stroke. This helps in reducing hydrocarbon emissions.

Electronic Management System

All current Cummins Westport NG systems are electronically managed. The current Cummins Westport lineup of engines uses the Cummins Interact System (IS) (see Chapter 42) ECM bussed to Westport ignition and fuel modules. The Westport electronics manage gaseous fuel mixing, fuel injection, EGR blending, and SI in systems that require it.

To troubleshoot engine problems, it is necessary to use Cummins InSite diagnostic software. However, Westport diagnostic software is required to troubleshoot fuel system problems. Diagnosing NG fuel system problems requires both specialized training and certification.

Exhaust Gas Aftertreatment

There is significantly less exhaust gas aftertreatment hardware on the Cummins Westport engines than would be found on comparable diesel-fueled equivalents. Post-2010 engines use a dual-stage (oxidation and reduction), three-way catalytic converter that is entirely passive in operation. **Figure 38-9** shows the fuel module on a Cummins Westport ISX 12G CNG-fueled engine.

DIESEL PILOT INJECTION

From the onset, Westport combustion technology was based on managing a **stoichiometric** AFR (see Chapters 34 and 47) with closed-loop feedback to the engine management modules (ECMs). **Air-fuel ratio (AFR)** and stoichiometric fueling are explained in Chapters 17 and 37 of this book. Over the years, Westport's engine fuel systems may be

FIGURE 38-9 The fuel module on a Cummins Westport ISX 12G CNG-fueled engine.

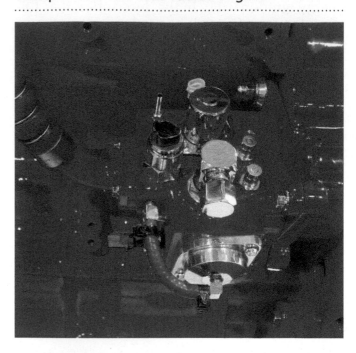

spark, glow plug, or diesel pilot ignited, but in this section we will study diesel pilot ignition. Diesel pilot ignition is more often used with LPG systems, but can also be used for CNG systems. When LNG is used, it is liquefied and stored in tanks (see **Figure 38-10**) at −220° Fahrenheit (−140°C): This can provide a Class 8 truck carrying an 80,000-lb (36,300-kg) load with a range of 300 miles (500 km). Volvo states that if biomass fuel is used in place of petro-sourced NG, CO_2 emission is cut by 70%. **Figure 38-11** shows a schematic of a Cummins Westport ISX 15G LNG fuel management system that uses a diesel fuel pilot pulse to ignite a main pulse of NG.

FIGURE 38-10 The cryogenic fuel tank used in an LNG fuel system.

FIGURE 38–11 A Westport HD15 engine with an LNG fuel system using high-pressure direct injection (HPDI).

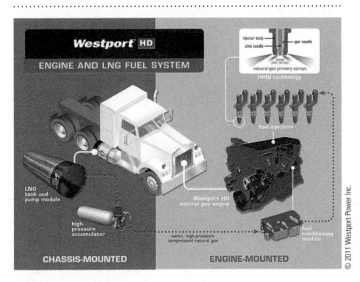

© 2011 Westport Power Inc.

LNG Fuel System Layout

The critical fuel system components are shown in **Figure 38–12**. The Westport LNG fuel system uses a **cryogenic** (extreme low temperature) fuel tank and pump to store and deliver liquefied gaseous fuel (stored in cryogenic tanks at –220° Fahrenheit [–140°C]) to the fuel delivery system. In current applications, the cryogenic tanks are of sufficient size to provide a Class 8 truck carrying an 80,000-lb (36,300-kg) load with a range of 300 miles (500 km).

FIGURE 38–12 Westport HD fuel system components, showing external and internal engine components.

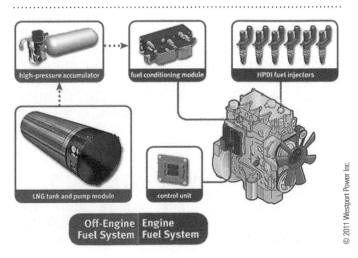

© 2011 Westport Power Inc.

FIGURE 38–13 The LNG cryogenic fuel tank fill port.

© 2011 Westport Power Inc.

Westport's designs for compact cryogenic pumps and storage vessels are well suited to high-vibration applications, but, because of cryogenic structure, weight is a consideration. The LNG pump is located inside the cryogenic tank to minimize heat leakage and limit external exposure of cryogenic components. **Figure 38–13** shows a truck chassis cryogenic tank, and **Figure 38–14** shows the fueling nozzle being inserted into the tank in preparation for refilling. **Figure 38–15** shows the operator interface of an LNG fueling station; note that some training is required before one attempts to refill NG tanks.

FIGURE 38–14 Fill nozzle being inserted into a LNG cryogenic fuel tank.

FIGURE 38–15 The operator interface of an LNG fueling station. Note that some training is required before a person attempts to refuel CNG and LNG tanks.

FIGURE 38–16 The Westport HPDI. This dual-fuel injector uses a piezo actuator and delivers a short shot of diesel fuel to ignite a main charge of gaseous fuel.

© 2011 Westport Power Inc.

HPDI

The injectors used in the direct-injection system are designed to provide a small diesel pilot shot, accompanied by a much larger gas spray. The diesel fuel percentage averages around 5% of the total energy input: It is simply used to initiate a flame field to pilot-ignite the NG gas charge. Westport calls these injectors **high-pressure direct injectors (HPDIs)**. They are best described as dual-fuel, common rail, piezo-actuated, and electronically controlled. **Figure 38–16** shows an HPDI.

The Westport proprietary HPDIs can be incorporated into most diesel platform engines with minimal or no modifications to the cylinder head. No special pistons, cams,

gas mixers, or port injectors are needed. Late-cycle, high-pressure direct injection ensures diffusion type combustion, retaining the high cylinder pressure, torque, and efficiency of a diesel engine. The most recent examples use piezo actuators and are capable of multipulse injection events.

CNG-DI

What Westport describes as **compressed natural gas direct injection (CNG-DI)** injectors use only gaseous fuels (usually natural gas or hydrogen). For this reason, ignition must be initiated in the cylinder with either a spark or a hot surface (usually a continuously energized glow plug). For this reason, CNG-DI fueled engines have to be engineered in close collaboration with the engine OEM. CNG-DI injectors can also be classified as common rail and capable of the same rate-shaping capability of HPDIs. **Figure 38–17** shows a Westport CNG-DI injector known as a **Westport MonoInjector**, and **Figure 38–18** shows the mixing module used on a Cummins Westport engine.

NG ENGINE SERVICE INTERVALS

Most NG-fueled engines require more frequent service intervention than equivalent diesel engines. In addition, the consequences of

FIGURE 38–17 A Westport MonoInjector, using compressed natural gas direct injection (CNG-DI). The injector can also be adapted for fueling hydrogen.

© 2011 Westport Power Inc.

FIGURE 38–18 The electronic modules and fuel management components used on a Cummins Westport ISX 12G engine.

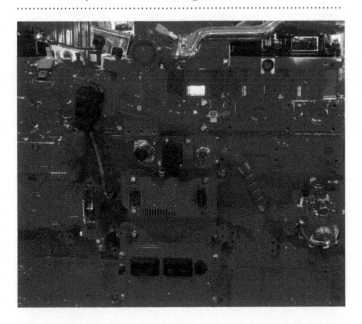

prolonging service intervals tend to be more costly. Note that most NG-fueled engines require the use of a specialty lubrication oil; using general-purpose diesel engine lubes can shorten

TABLE 38–3 Service Intervals: NG Medium-Duty Trucks

Service Item	Interval mi	Interval km	Engine hrs
Oil and filter change (lube oil: CES20074)	15,000	24,000	300
Fuel filter	30,000	48,000	600
Change spark plugs	45,000	72,000	900
Coolant filter	15,000	24,000	300
Valve adjustment and coolant change	60,000	96,000	1,200

TABLE 38–4 Service Intervals: City Transit Buses

Service Item	Interval mi	Interval km	Engine hrs
Oil and filter change (lube oil: CES20074)	7,500	12,000	150
Fuel filter	15,000	24,000	300
Change spark plugs	22,500	36,000	450
Coolant filter	7,500	12,000	150
Valve adjustment and coolant change	30,000	48,000	600

engine life. In the case of the Cummins Westport ISL 8.9G engine, the recommended engine lube is CES20074. **Table 38–3** shows the recommended service intervals for the Cummins Westport ISL 8.9G when powering a medium-duty truck, and **Table 38–4** does the same for the same engine in a city transit bus application. Intervals for spark plug change-outs are provided, but many of these engines do not use spark plugs.

ISX-G Service Intervals

The service intervals for 2015 Cummins Westport ISX-G engines that are designated as line-haul are longer, as can be seen in **Table 38–5**.

NG Power and Torque Output

Because of the lower energy density of NG compared with diesel fuel, NG engines often produced torque inferior to that of equivalent-sized diesel-fueled engines. However, this has changed in more recent NG engines, as can be seen in **Figure 38–19**, which shows the torque output of various HP ratings of Cummins Westport ISX

FIGURE 38–19 Cummins Westport ISX 12G torque output for a range of HP ratings. Note the relatively flat torque profile in the lower power output engines.

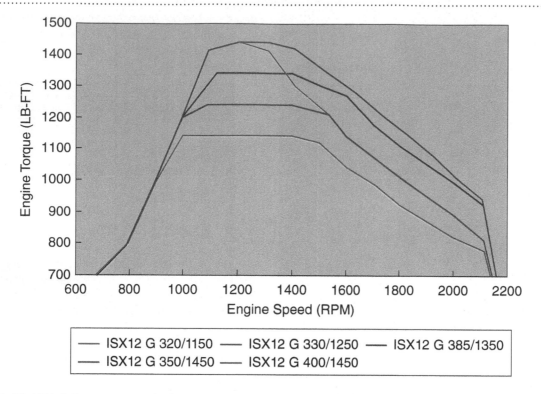

—— ISX12 G 320/1150	—— ISX12 G 330/1250	—— ISX12 G 385/1350
—— ISX12 G 350/1450	—— ISX12 G 400/1450	

TABLE 38–5 ISX-G Recommended Service Intervals—Normal Duty

Maintenance Item	Mileage	Hours	Months
Oil and filter	18,000 miles 30,000 km	400	6
Coolant filter	67,500 miles 108,000 km	1,500	12
Spin-on fuel filter	45,000 miles 72,300 km	1,000	12
Spark plugs	67,500 miles 108,500 km	1,500	12
Overhead (valve) adjustment	67,500 miles 108,500 km	1,500	12
Engine brake adjustment	270,000 miles 435,000 km	6,000	24
Coolant change standard EG	270,000 miles 435,000 km	6,000	24

Source: Air Cleaner Element: this varies with the type and location: check OEM service literature.

12G engines. **Figure 38–20** shows the critical fuel management and electronic components on the left side of the Cummins Westport ISL-G engine.

FMVSS 304 PRECAUTIONS

FMVSS 304 covers compressed natural gas (CNG) container integrity; some of the key points are included here because of the extreme storage pressures involved. Because of the increased use of NG as a vehicle fuel, it is important that technicians have some awareness of combustible gas safety, whether they actually work on the equipment or

FIGURE 38–20 View of the left side of a Cummins Westport ISL-G showing the key fuel management and mixing modules.

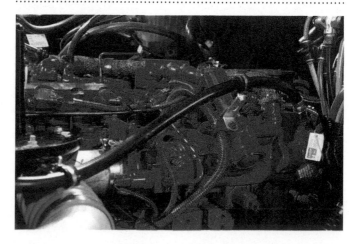

not. The regulations for LNG are similar to those for CNG outlined here, but note that propane handling regulations are different. Propane is heavier than air, and consequently has distinct handling and refueling regulations. Under FMVSS 304, a visual inspection of the on-vehicle fuel installation must be undertaken by a qualified individual every 3 years or 36,000 miles, whichever comes first. A detailed inspection will include:

- Complete high-pressure fuel installation
- Pressure release device (PRD)
- CNG storage cylinder

Cylinder inspection is considered a priority. The shields should be removed and the cylinder exterior cleaned, so a high-intensity light and mirror can be used to check for any visible damage. If damage is evident, the cause should be determined (heat, impact, corrosion. abrasion, chemical attack, etc.) and cataloged. Any damage must be measured, photographed, and recorded on the inspection data sheet, then assessed a damage level as follows:

- Level 1 damage. Damage that is acceptable and requires no repair; the cylinder can be returned to service.
- Level 2 damage. Requires repair and more thorough evaluation, testing, or destruction. The cylinder manufacturer's guidelines will determine the outcome.
- Level 3 damage. Damage that condemns the cylinder.

TECH TIP:

Technicians working on, or around, NG-fueled vehicles should be aware that CNG is odorized and LNG is non-odorized. Suspected leaks should be responded to immediately.

SERVICING CNG-FUELED VEHICLES

When parking a CNG-powered vehicle in a garage not designed for servicing NG-fueled vehicles during normal operating hours, the following precautions must be observed:

- 50% of the roll-up doors must be raised a minimum of 12 inches (305 mm).
- The shop exhaust extraction and ventilation system must turned on and be capable of transferring five times the volume of the shop per hour.
- All open flame heaters must be turned off and space heaters with a skin temperature exceeding 750 degrees must be shut down.

- The CNG fuel system must be checked for leaks before the vehicle is moved inside the building.
- When the vehicle is parked inside, the gas fuel cylinder storage valve must be turned off.
- After shutdown, the vehicle must be checked for CNG odor.
- At the end of normal operating hours, the CNG vehicle must be removed from the building and parked outside. The bay door must be closed.

RULES FOR DEFUELING

Consume as much fuel as possible before the defueling operation and notify all nearby personnel that a CNG vehicle is to be defueled. The vehicle should be outdoors and the technician should be wearing personal protective equipment (PPE). Ground (earth) the vehicle and the fuel system. The technician and anyone nearby should be familiar with evacuation routes.

There are three common defueling options:

1. Atmospheric venting. First, check to see if this is legal. The local authority should be consulted; typically this is the fire marshal, who may or may not be aware of FMVSS 304. A vent stack should be fitted.
2. Compressor inlet method. This requires special equipment installed at the refueling station. The vehicle should be connected through the defueling nozzle to the defueling panel; the compressor at the fueling station then extracts the gas from the vehicle tanks.
3. Vent to gas main. This is the least common method, and it also requires specialized equipment. The local gas supplier installs specialty valving and piping that enables the gas to be drawn back into the mains.

Two types of valves are used on CNG cylinders:

1. Mechanical—a manual valve ensures that the technician knows whether it is open or closed.
2. Electromechanical—when energized or de-energized, the valve opens or closes an orifice valve. These are designed to close when the ignition key is turned off. Although ANSI test procedures require that they fail in the closed position, this does not always happen. In the event of an electromechanical valve failure, or if the valve has to be removed, the technician must use an mechanical override to open the valve to defuel the cylinder.

WARNING:

When disconnecting a component that may be pressurized, the technician has no way of checking the integrity of the vessel or determining whether the threads are intact. Applying torque to the component to be removed physically stresses the cylinder shell, meaning that it could fail catastrophically without warning, so the following safety guidelines must be observed:

- Observe the OEM guidelines
- When replacing solenoid valves, adhere to the OEM procedure
- Ensure that the valve specified by the cylinder manufacturer is used
- Exercise caution working around CNG equipment that is 15 years old or older
- Inspect the valve and the threaded interface between it and the tank
- Check the valve bore pilot orifice; this can be plugged by dirt or ice
- Use the correct venting tools when exhausting cylinders equipped with solenoid valves
- Handle cylinders as if they are under full pressure
- Physically hold your body away from the direction of travel of a possible failed component

COALESCING FILTERS

Oil present in the fuel system of an NG-powered vehicle can result in:

- Hard starting
- Rough idle
- Hesitation under acceleration
- Stalling

The source of oil in a vehicle CNG fuel system is usually the compressor at the fueling station, despite the fact that a well-maintained station should have filters to prevent this. A typical NG-fueled vehicle should use two or more coalescing filters, a high-pressure filter located upstream of the high-pressure regulator, and a low-pressure filter located downstream from the regulator. A typical arrangement is shown in **Figure 38–21**.

The coalescing efficiency of the filters (liquid and aerosol removal) is determined by:

- Gas velocity
- The grade of the filter element

Gas velocity is governed by both the fuel requirement at any given moment of operation, and the actual pressure of the gas in the system. In high-pressure gas, the molecules are packed close together, and when fuel demand is at its highest (full accelerator travel), flow rate through the circuit is at its highest. This means that the high-pressure coalescer has to produce its highest efficiencies when fuel demand is at maximum. If it fails to do this, evidence of oil can often be found in the low-pressure coalescer but not in the high-pressure coalescer. For this reason, the coalescing efficiency on the high-pressure side of the regulator is critical if the chance of allowing oil to be transferred into the fuel system is to be minimized.

Filters are rated by coalescing and entrapment grades, but as filtration efficiency increases, a small system pressure drop results. This means that before using a higher-efficiency coalescer, the OEM should be consulted. Coalescing filters are graded in **Table 38–6**.

Table 38–6 Coalescing Filter Grades

Finite Grade	Coalescing Efficiency	Entrapment Efficiency
10	95%	1.0μ
8	98.5%	0.7μ
6	99.97%	0.3μ
4	99.995%	0.2μ

FIGURE 38–21 High- and low-pressure coalescing filters used in a CNG fuel system.

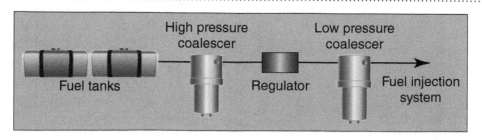

DISPENSING NG

The state of California has recently ruled on how CNG and LNG must be retailed when dispensed for highway use. It is thought that the California ruling (AB 1907) is likely to be adopted by other states. Effective January 1, 2015, CNG retail sales must be measured in **gasoline-equivalent-gallons (GEG)** and LNG in DGEs. A GEG of CNG is 126.67 cubic feet or 5.66 pounds. A DEG of LNG is rated at a weight of 6.06 pounds. The measure is likely to be adopted nationwide with some urgency because fuel taxation depends on it.

LIQUEFIED PETROLEUM GAS

Propane-fueled vehicles have been used for generations: It is not uncommon to see propane-fueled pickup and delivery vans and light trucks in our cities. Propane is known by the term *autogas* in Europe and is correctly known as **liquefied petroleum gas (LPG)**. It is perceived as being a "clean" fuel, so operators often like to broadcast the power source on the side of the vehicle, as you may have noticed on UPS vans.

Propane does not auto-ignite when subject to cylinder pressure and the resulting heat, so it requires an ignition source. In most cases, a propane charge is ignited using a spark ignition system identical to that required by the NG systems described earlier in this chapter. Because propane tends to be used in light-duty applications, the systems are not described in detail here, but the reality is that they differ little from NG systems. Like NG, propane is odorless, but usually has an odorant added to it so that system leakage can be identified before it becomes dangerous.

> ## WARNING:
> Unlike NG, propane is denser and heavier than air. This means that it will descend into the lowest space when leaked from a system, giving it a significant safety disadvantage.

Liquefied petroleum gas (LPG) consists mainly of petroleum vapors, including propane, propylene, butane, and butylene in various mixtures, but it is mostly what we call methane. It is produced as a by-product of natural gas processing and petroleum refining. The components of LPG are gases at normal temperatures and pressures. One challenge with LPG is that it can vary widely in chemical composition, leading to variable engine performance and cold-starting performance. At normal temperatures and pressures, LPG evaporates. Because of this, LPG is stored in pressurized steel cylinders.

Unlike NG, LPG is heavier than air, so it flows along floors and settles in low spots, such as unventilated service bay pits. Accumulations of LPG are a serious explosion hazard. Many jurisdictions prohibit LPG-fueled vehicles from indoor parking and warehouses.

LPG-FUELED ENGINES

LPG fueling is less common than NG fueling in commercial highway vehicles because of some of the dangers associated with the fuel; in its liquid state it weighs 20% more. It possesses inferior fuel economy to diesel fuel but is superior to NG. Another factor is that its pricing fluctuates with petroleum pricing.

As with NG, there are numerous existing designs, but none of them have prevailed beyond some limited (usually intracity) light-duty, commercial vehicle designs. Cummins Westport manufactured an ISB-LPG engine up until 2010, but did not update the engine to pass EPA 2010 emissions standards. LPG is more likely to remain the fuel of taxicabs, pickup and delivery, and forklift trucks than to become a viable commercial vehicle fuel.

PROS AND CONS OF LPG

LPG is not currently thought of as providing much of a long-term solution to America's energy challenges because it is petroleum derived and—though less costly than gasoline or diesel—its pricing fluctuates in correlation with other petroleum products. When combusted, it produces lower emissions than equivalent diesel- or gasoline-fueled engines. However, propane fueling is disadvantaged by the fact that there are no commercial vehicle engines engineered for propane fuel; they are adapted from existing diesel (Cummins Westport) or gasoline (Ford) powerplants.

Advantages of LPG

Equals fuel weight-to-mileage range of gasoline

Technology already exists for use as a vehicle fuel

High octane

Relatively lean burning—emits less HC, CO, and NO_x

Disadvantages of LPG

Heavier than diesel fuel by 20%

Must be stored at −260°F (−162°C) or less to remain liquid

Lower heating value than diesel fuel

Reduced peak power performance

Existing engine aftertreatment hardware for diesel does not work with LPG

Electronic or diesel pilot ignition system required

ALCOHOL-BASED FUELS (METHANOL/ETHANOL)

Alcohols are biofuels. Although alcohol-based fuels have enjoyed some success as an automotive fuel, usually cut with gasoline, this has not been replicated with medium- and heavy-duty engines. Alcohol fuels such as methanol and ethanol have less than half the energy density of diesel fuel, and they are also an oxygenate fuel, meaning that an oxygen atom is bonded onto the hydrocarbon molecule. Oxygenate fuels deteriorate more rapidly due to oxidization of the hydrocarbon component.

It has become common to blend alcohol-based fuels into commercially sold gasoline, and if you purchase fuel for chainsaws, snowmobiles, and ATVs, you are probably aware of the advisory to purchase high-test fuels that tend to have lower percentages of alcohol (ethanol)—this varies according to geographic region. Because ethanol and methanol are oxygenates, they oxidize more rapidly, meaning the fuel has a shorter shelf life. Regular grade gasoline is almost always sold cut with up to 10% ethanol in North America. What you may not be aware of is that some auto manufacturers retain the right to void fuel-related warranties if gasoline is cut with more than 5% ethanol. Some engines are designed to operate on E85, a fuel composed of 85% ethanol and 15% petroleum-sourced gasoline. E85 has become popular in geographic regions that use excess agricultural products for processing into liquid biofuels.

ETHANOL

Ethanol is a biofuel. It is also the form of alcohol you may elect to drink if you are partial to a shot of Jack Daniels. It is a volatile, flammable, colorless liquid. We know it as drinking alcohol, denatured alcohol, or pure alcohol, and it can be classified as a potent psychoactive drug, capable of causing brain damage in high concentrations. It is also great for dissolving dirt and the human liver. It can be manufactured by fermenting most types of biomass grains, including barley, corn, sugar cane, and oats.

Recently, agricultural overproduction in North America has been routed to ethanol production rather than aid to the starving in the third world. This introduces an ethical factor in the use of ethanol as fuel, because when push comes to shove, the first world has way more money to pay for fuel than the third world possesses to purchase food. The real danger occurs when a third-world country whose agricultural production may be owned by multinational corporations redesignates its food-source agricultural areas to grow fuel for the first world.

METHANOL

Methanol is the simplest alcohol. Its molecule consists of one carbon, one oxygen, and four hydrogen atoms. We know it as wood alcohol, methyl alcohol, or carbinol. It is poisonous, flammable, and relatively volatile. It has little taste and no color, but it does possess a slight odor. It is poisonous to all animals. Methanol is often refined from wood by-products and its best known usage is as the fuel for all Indy car (CART) racing. Unfortunately, the methanol used in Indy car racing is usually synthesized from petroleum fossil fuels. Methanol can be easily mixed with gasoline to be used as a cut fuel, but it is highly toxic. It has better energy density than ethanol and there are some who consider it a fuel of the future. At present, though, producing it is costly.

CURRENT USAGE

A generation ago, when it became popular to ban the use of diesel fuel within some city limits, there were a few alcohol-fueled engines used in commercial vehicles, mostly intracity buses. Engine longevity can be drastically reduced when alcohol fuels are used in diesel engines adapted for alcohol fueling, because of the low lubricity and corrosiveness of alcohol. Its use in commercial vehicles has been confined to short-haul operations within cities where local jurisdictions have banned or discouraged the use of diesel fuel. At this time, we can probably say there are superior technologies available to respond to a ban on the use of diesel fuel.

ADVANTAGES AND DISADVANTAGES OF ALCOHOL-BASED FUELS

The big advantage of alcohol-based fuels is that they are domestically produced. During the one generation we have been using biomass overproduction as fuel, both domestic and world food prices have risen significantly, because agricultural overproduction is no longer relegated to compost or foreign aid.

Advantages of Alcohol-Based Fuels

Produced from natural gas, coal, petroleum, or vegetation (garbage)

Adapts readily to current liquid fuel delivery technologies

High octane rating—up to 110

Reduced HC emissions

Technology exists for use in diesel engines with few modifications

Disadvantages of Alcohol-Based Fuels

Half the calorific value of diesel fuel

Low lubricity (a disadvantage for use in current diesel engines)

Low cetane number (CN)—requires spark or piloted ignition

Poor cold weather performance (does not readily vaporize)

Higher acidity promotes corrosion and lube oil breakdown

FUEL ALTERNATIVES FOR ENGINES

Generally, where engines and fueling apparatus have been successfully adapted for fueling with any of the alternatives to diesel fuel, their use is confined to short-haul and intracity transit applications. The thrust toward maximizing engine efficiency and finding alternatives to diesel fuel and gasoline has taken a different path in North America than in Japan and Western Europe. The objective of lower reliance on imported fossil fuels has driven development in Japan and Western Europe, due to the much higher cost of fossil fuels in those geographic areas. It should be stated that a large portion of this high cost is a result of government addiction to taxation of fuels.

TABLE 38–7 Comparisons of Heat Energy in Different Fuels

Fuel	Typical BTUs Per U.S. Gallon
ASTM diesel fuel average	140,000 Btus
Average pump gasoline	125,000 Btus
CNG	75,000 Btus
Alcohol (methanol M-100)	76,000 Btus
Propane	93,000 Btus

Development of low-emissions engines has been the primary objective of North American OEMs, which are driven by clean air legislation. We now look at the characteristics of some of the possible alternatives to the gasoline and diesel fuel we use today. **Table 38–7** shows the energy density of some automotive fuels: Note that heat energy by volume in diesel fuel exceeds that in the alternatives by a considerable margin.

HYDROGEN

Hydrogen could be the fuel of the future. It is the most abundant element in the universe, and it oxidizes (combusts) producing no harmful emissions. There are no current commercial vehicle engine designs in production, but most of the major manufacturers have experimented with using hydrogen as a fuel. The uses of hydrogen are not limited to burning it; it can also be used to produce electricity using fuel cells, which are addressed in Chapter 39.

A rocket engine runs on hydrogen fuel, which reacts with oxygen. When you observe a rocket launch, the clouds of white smoke you see emitted are composed of vaporized water or steam. Combusted hydrogen combines with oxygen to form water (H_2O), so if the oxygen in the reaction is pure, the result is a zero-toxic emissions engine. However, if hydrogen is reacted with the oxygen in air, then NO_x can result from the combustion reaction.

Because of its explosiveness and difficulty in the storage/refueling process, hydrogen is unlikely to be combusted in mobile engines in the near future. For instance, a hydrogen tank similar in size to one 100-gallon truck diesel fuel tank would provide the truck with only enough fuel for a single 100-mile trip.

If hydrogen is ever to be adopted as commercial vehicle fuel, it will more likely be to fuel advanced versions of the fuel cells described in Chapter 39.

Uses of Hydrogen

Hydrogen or H_2 gas is highly flammable and will burn at concentrations as low as 4% H_2 in air. For automotive applications, hydrogen is generally used in two forms:

- Internal combustion
- Fuel cell conversion

In combustion, it is essentially burned as conventional gaseous fuels are, whereas a fuel cell uses the hydrogen to generate electricity that in turn is used to power electric motors on the vehicle. Hydrogen gas must be produced and is therefore is an energy storage medium, not an energy source. The energy used to produce it usually comes from a more conventional source. Hydrogen holds the promise of very low or no vehicle emissions and flexible energy storage; however, many believe the technical challenges required to realize these benefits may delay hydrogen's widespread implementation for several decades.

Hydrogen can be obtained through various thermochemical methods utilizing methane (natural gas), coal, liquefied petroleum gas, or biomass (biomass gasification), from electrolysis of water, or by a process called *thermolysis*. Each of these methods poses its own challenges.

Products of Hydrogen Combustion

Hydrogen has the simplest atomic structure of any element. It consists of one proton and a single electron. When hydrogen is oxidized or combusted, two hydrogen atoms bond with an oxygen atom to form H_2O, or water. The water formed from reacting hydrogen with oxygen is so pure that astronauts on space shuttles drink the "waste" from the liquid hydrogen fuel that powers their rocket engines.

Sources of Hydrogen

Despite its abundance, hydrogen atoms only exist naturally in combination with other elements on Earth. That means that it has to be stripped away from whatever other atoms it is combined with—and that takes energy. In most cases, the energy required is electricity (if water is the source), and lots of it is needed. Producing hydrogen by electrolysis occurs when a lead acid battery is overcharged.

Advantages of Hydrogen

High heating value, three times that of diesel fuel

Clean burning—oxidizes to H_2O (water)

Lightweight

Abundant

Disadvantages of Hydrogen

Expensive to produce

Low boiling point –423°F (–252°C)

Difficult to store safely on a vehicle

Highly explosive

WARNING:

Hydrogen is highly explosive. Special training is required when working with hydrogen-fueled vehicles. Leaks may result in life-threatening situations.

Current Uses of Hydrogen-Fueled Engines

Some experimentation has been undertaken by auto OEMs using hydrogen to fuel adapted versions of their gasoline-fueled vehicles. In the commercial vehicle arena, the Ford Motor Company began supplying hydrogen-fueled V-10 engines in shuttle buses in experimental trials. These trials are ongoing, the hold-backs being the high cost of producing hydrogen and the tanks required to store it in. The Cummins Westport fuel system can be adapted to accommodate hydrogen injection, but the hydrogen option is seldom used.

Hydrogen Storage

While hydrogen is in some ways an ideal fuel, one of the biggest challenges is storing it on a vehicle. A combination of high pressure and low temperature (boils at –252°C) is required to contain hydrogen, meaning that a steel tank would be required to have 3-inch (750-mm) thick walls. The United States Department of Energy's position on vehicle hydrogen storage is that 6% of the tank weight must be hydrogen in order to make the vehicle mileage per tank equivalent to current petroleum-fueled vehicles. This factor in current vehicles is closer to 1%, so it will be some time before hydrogen fuels anything other than experimental commercial vehicles.

SUMMARY

- Biodiesel, hydrogen, propane, natural gas, and alcohol-based fuels provide alternatives to diesel fuel. Although some of these are currently used, only NG is used to any great extent in medium- and heavy-duty trucks.
- Biodiesel fuels are refined from vegetable oils and waste cooking grease. They are currently used nationwide, and when cut with petroleum diesel have been proved to perform to a satisfactory standard in some areas.
- Biodiesel marketed as B100 is a pure vegetable oil–based stock, and B20 is a fuel composed of 80% petroleum-based diesel and 20% biodiesel.
- Gaseous fuels have the advantage of producing lower emissions when combusted in an engine, but generally have lower energy density and present storage challenges onboard a vehicle. This limits range because the refueling infrastructure is generally inadequate, though currently being developed on major interstate routes.
- NG and LPG fuels do not auto-ignite at compression temperatures: This means they must be pilot-ignited by diesel fuel or glow plug/spark-ignition.
- The popularity of NG-fueled engines grew during the first decade of the 2000s and most OEMs offered at least one NG engine option up to 2010.
- Since 2010, Cummins Westport has become the dominant supplier of NG-fueled commercial engines.
- Westport fuel systems are available for CNG, LNG, and hydrogen fueling, using spark or diesel pilot ignition.
- The Westport SI system uses coil-on-plug ignition.
- The Westport diesel pilot ignition system uses piezo-actuated dual-fuel injectors known as high-pressure direct injectors (HPDIs).
- The Westport LNG system consists of a cryogenic tank, in-tank cryogenic pump, and ECM-controlled fuel injectors.
- Westport provides either HPDIs in which a short shot of diesel fuel is used to ignite a main gaseous fuel charge, or a gaseous fuel–only injector which must be supported by glow plugs or a spark-ignition system. Both types function on a common rail.
- Westport HPDIs use piezo actuators and are capable of multipulse injections. Diesel fuel is used for pilot-ignition only; the main fuel pulse is NG only.
- The ratio of NG to diesel fuel in the Westport HPDI fuel system is typically 95:5 (19:1) when in most operational modes.
- NG-fueled engines produce generally lower emissions. The current lineup of Cummins Westport engines is fueled stoichiometrically and aftertreatment consists of a three-way catalytic converter.
- When used in diesel engines, alcohol-based fuels produce lower emissions, but because of the low lubricity of alcohol, they tend to wear out the fuel delivery distribution systems when existing diesel engine fuel injection systems are adapted for alcohol delivery.

REVIEW QUESTIONS

1. Which of the following is a correct description of a B5 fuel?
   a. 95% biodiesel cut with 5% petroleum-based diesel
   b. 95% petroleum-based diesel cut with 5% biodiesel
   c. Biodiesel rated with a CN of 50
   d. Petroleum-based diesel with an ignition temperature of 500°C

2. What would a B100 fuel be composed of?
   a. 100% petroleum-based diesel fuel
   b. 100% alcohol-based stock
   c. Even mixture of petroleum- and vegetable-based stock
   d. 100% vegetable-based stock

3. Which of the following makes pure biodiesel (B100) less suitable for use in cooler geographic locations?
   a. Pour point
   b. Cetane number
   c. Sulfur content
   d. Particulate emissions

4. Which of the following noxious emissions tends to increase when the combustion of pure biodiesel (B100) is compared with the combustion of petroleum-based diesel fuel?
   a. Sulfur oxides
   b. Particulate matter
   c. Hydrocarbons
   d. Nitrogen oxides

5. Technician A states that NG fuels will not auto-ignite at the compression temperatures achieved in a diesel engine. Technician B states that LPG fuels will not auto-ignite at cylinder compression temperatures. Who is correct?
   a. Technician A only
   b. Technician B only
   c. Both A and B
   d. Neither A nor B

6. Which of the following has the most amount of heat energy by mass (weight)?
   a. Propane
   b. Natural gas
   c. Hydrogen
   d. Diesel fuel

7. When propane or natural gas is used as the only fuel in an internal combustion engine designed for diesel fuel, what must also be provided?
   a. Particulate trap
   b. Means of igniting the fuel
   c. Cooled EGR
   d. Distributor

8. Technician A states that a disadvantage of alcohol as an internal combustion engine fuel is its low octane rating. Technician B states that an advantage of LPG over gasoline as an internal combustion engine fuel is its high calorific value. Who is correct?
   a. Technician A only
   b. Technician B only
   c. Both A and B
   d. Neither A nor B

9. Which of the following fuels has the most heat energy (calorific value/Btus by mass)?
   a. Alcohol
   b. Natural gas
   c. Propane
   d. Diesel fuel

10. What is natural gas (NG) mainly composed of?
    a. Hydrogen
    b. Oxygen
    c. Methane
    d. Carbon dioxide

11. Which of the following fuels is often a byproduct of crude petroleum?
    a. Biodiesel
    b. Propane
    c. Alcohol
    d. Hydrogen

12. Which of the following is true of the post-2010 Westport HPDI LNG fuel system?
    a. It uses a cryogenic fuel tank.
    b. The injectors use piezo actuators.
    c. The injectors deliver both NG and diesel fuel.
    d. All of the above.

13. Which of the following best describes the term *cryogenic*?
    a. Extreme heat
    b. Extreme cold
    c. Explosive
    d. Unreactive

14. Which of the following is true of a Westport HPDI injector?
    a. It injects diesel fuel.
    b. It injects natural gas.
    c. It uses piezo-actuator technology.
    d. All of the above.

15. Technician A says that a Westport MonoInjector requires a continuously operating glow plug to ignite the gas charge after injection to the engine cylinder. Technician B says that a Westport HPDI injector is supplied by a common rail. Who is correct?
    a. Technician A only
    b. Technician B only
    c. Both A and B
    d. Neither A nor B

16. How many ignition coils are used on a Cummins Westport ISX 12G engine with SI?
   a. One
   b. Two
   c. Six
   d. Twelve

17. Which of the following fuels is heavier than air?
   a. Propane
   b. NG
   c. Hydrogen
   d. DME

18. Which of the following fuels is commonly commercially produced by decomposing biomass materials (garbage)?
   a. Propane
   b. NG
   c. Hydrogen
   d. DME

19. Technician A says that CDI is currently used in Westport SI because it provides higher spark energy at all engine speeds. Technician B says that coil-on-plug SI is used on ISX 12G engines requiring spark ignition. Who is correct?
   a. Technician A only
   b. Technician B only
   c. Both A and B
   d. Neither A nor B

20. Technician A says that Cummins InSite software is required to diagnose ISX 12G engine problems. Technician B says that Westport diagnostic software is required to troubleshoot ISX 12G fuel system problems. Who is correct?
   a. Technician A only
   b. Technician B only
   c. Both A and B
   d. Neither A nor B

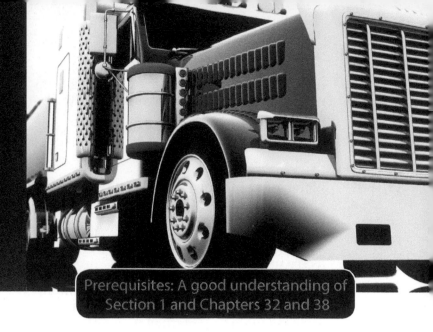

ELECTRIC, ELECTRIC HYBRID, AND HYDRAULIC HYBRID DRIVES

OBJECTIVES

After studying this chapter, you should be able to:

- Outline how batteries have developed over the past decade and describe how lithium-ion batteries have emerged as the current electric and hybrid electric battery of choice.
- Outline the operating principles of ultracapacitors and describe how they can be used to complement batteries in electric-powered vehicles.
- Describe how diesel electric, parallel hybrid drivetrains are used in city transit bus applications.
- Identify the drivetrain components used in hybrid electric vehicles.
- Describe how a blended torque transmission can accept input torque from more than one source and output continuously variable torque and speed ratios.
- Outline the operating principles of parallel and series hydraulic hybrid drive systems used in military, shuttle bus, and courier vans.
- Identify some types of fuel cells currently used and being considered for use in city transit and highway vehicles.
- Outline the operating principles of a proton exchange membrane (PEM) fuel cell.
- Identify the powerflow equation in a fuel cell powered transit bus.

KEY TERMS

auxiliary power unit (APU)

blended torque transmission

cassette architecture

electric-only vehicle (EV)

grid electrification (GE)

hybrid electric vehicle (HEV)

hydraulic hybrid, advanced materials and multifuel engine research (HAMMER)

hydraulic hybrid vehicle (HHV)

hydraulic launch assist (HLA)

hydrogen

lithium-ion (Li-ion) [battery]

nickel metal hydride (NiMH) battery

parallel hybrid (PH)

parallel hydraulic hybrid (PHH)

proton exchange membrane (PEM) fuel cells

regenerative braking

series hydraulic hybrid (SHH)

Shorepower Truck Electrification Project (STEP)

sodium metal hydride (NaNiCl2) battery

supercapacitor (SC)

ultracapacitor (UC)

INTRODUCTION

There is a commitment by the federal government to reduce U.S. carbon dioxide emissions (CO_2) produced by commercial vehicles by a full 20% by the year 2020. Some of the cutback will come from improving the fuel efficiency of the diesel and alternate fuel commercial fleet, but all original equipment manufacturers (OEMs) are seriously looking at and developing various types of electric and hybrid drive systems. In this chapter, we will take a look at some of these "emerging" technologies, some of which can be said to have emerged already.

CASSETTE ARCHITECTURE

Energy storage is a key to making electric and hybrid systems work effectively. The storage systems for both electric and hydraulic technologies are known as **cassette architecture**. This term refers to the way groups of battery cells, ultracapacitor (UC) cassettes, and hydraulic accumulator cassettes are arranged and contained in formats that are suitable for mobile vehicles. Weight and safety are foremost considerations.

APPLICATIONS

Most of the electric and hybrid technology used in contemporary commercial vehicles is found in stop-start, inner-city vehicles in applications such as:

- Transit buses
- Airport shuttles
- Courier pickup and drop-off
- Garbage packers
- School buses

Electric power off a dedicated grid has been used for more than a hundred years in streetcar, subway, and railway applications, but more recent electric commercial vehicles have emerged that use the grid to charge onboard batteries. **Electric-only vehicles (EVs)** are obviously limited in their range of travel by battery storage capacity, but most of the chassis original equipment manufacturers (OEMs) are currently assessing their potential.

Most of the current generation of hybrid commercial vehicles use the diesel engine as the primary power source. Diesel engines powering hybrid vehicles can be rated at lower power than in a nonhybrid application, and run at optimum speeds to produce the best fuel economy.

Because of the pivotal role of diesel power, we are likely to see continued efforts led by the Environmental Protection Agency (EPA) and California Air Resources Board (CARB) to improve the chemical characteristics of diesel fuel in an effort to reduce or eliminate its more toxic combustion by-products.

FUEL CELLS

We will also examine fuel cells, because they continue to generate plenty of talk, and they are finding their way into some intracity transit buses. The city of Vancouver has 20 fuel cell powered buses, San Francisco has 10, and they are undergoing trials in other cities. If a way can be found to get the costs down, they may eventually become a viable propulsion system for city transit buses. In addition, they can be used in a limited way on trucks, say, as an **auxiliary power unit (APU)**.

Despite these successes, it is unlikely that the fuel cell will ever be a viable technology to replace the diesel engines in our commercial trucks. Even in transit buses, the challenge is cost. The Vancouver buses price out at $2 million per unit, compared with the $500,000 per unit cost of a diesel-powered transit bus. However, we will take a close look at fuel cell powered vehicles at the end of this chapter.

AUXILIARY POWER UNITS

An APU is used on a truck to provide heating, cooling, and electrical power when the engine is not running. Most current APUs are fueled using diesel fuel: This is contentious in itself. While some might argue that a diesel-fueled APU is preferable to running the main vehicle engine, others—including CARB— would object that it is just another source of harmful environmental emissions. APUs are required on longhaul vehicles today because of increasingly aggressive anti-idling legislation. Also, technologies to manage more environmentally friendly APUs represent much less challenge than those presented by the motive powerplant of the truck chassis.

GRID ELECTRIFICATION

By 2013, along five interstate routes, truck stops will provide electrical grids in an initiative known as the **Shorepower Truck Electrification Project (STEP)**. **Grid electrification (GE)** refers to the offboard supply of electrical power to trucks for hotel loads when parked. Although some are quick to argue that the sources of grid electricity are not so green (coal, oil, nuclear), there is no arguing with the fact that the average North American truck spends 1,500 hours a year idling, and linehaul, long distance rigs spend much more. There has been a suggestion that shorepower stations use hydroelectric-, wind-, or solar-sourced electricity, but that is unlikely to be viable. *Shorepower* normally refers to a 120-volt, 60-cycle, 20-amp supply.

Anti-Idling Legislation

As of 2011, anti-idling legislation existed in 31 states and 47 jurisdictions, numbers that are expected to grow in the coming decade. The Energy Independence Act of 2007 is administered through the National Highway Transportation Safety Association (NHTSA), which reports that longhaul sleeper-equipped trucks typically idle during 10 layover hours a day. If that truck is operated for 320 days of the year, the cost exceeds $28,000 (2010 fuel price).

GE Infrastructure Requirements

Grid electrification requires trucks to be equipped with 120 V-AC appliances in trucks. It also requires dependable routes and infrastructure. Initially, the STEP-GE project will evaluate major corridors for longhaul truck loads and equip 50 truck stops with 25 connections each. The launch project was to report its findings in 2014 before proceeding. STEP-directed funds will provide money as an incentive to convert trucks to mains voltage: heating, ventilation, and air-conditioning (HVAC) systems will be the primary target, but the program is intended to cover the full range of cab comforts, including wireless Internet and comprehensive TV.

GE Cost Savings

The anticipated connection charges (using 2011 data) of a GE connection will be a $1 startup fee, plus $1 per hour, making the cost of a 10-hour layover $11. The cost of idling the same truck for 10 hours with fuel priced at $3.50 a gallon would range from $28 to $36. It is expected that STEP will be rapidly expanded due to significant environmental benefits in fuel emissions and reduction of greenhouse gases (GHGs).

SCOPE OF THIS CHAPTER

We will begin by looking at battery and ultracapacitor technology before studying EVs, hybrid electric vehicles (HEVs), and hydraulic hybrid vehicles (HHVs).

BATTERIES AND ULTRACAPACITORS

Mass, space, and longevity have hindered the development of commercial EVs. The first generation of hybrid electric transit buses produced continual problems mostly related to the batteries. For the past couple of decades, the challenge to industry has been to develop batteries of much larger storage capacity combined with lower weights. Cars, vans, buses, and light trucks powered by **nickel metal hydride (NiMH) battery** packs manufactured in the early years of the millennium produced mixed results. During the late 1990s, the state of California promoted the electric vehicle concept, but poor technology and performance pushed the idea to the wayside. Now it has re-emerged. The key to making this work today compared to a generation ago is improved electrical energy storage systems. Some cities are experimenting with all-electric transit buses, but to this point they have produced poor results due to a high incidence of on-the-road breakdowns.

LITHIUM-ION

Recent developments in NiMH, **lithium-ion (Li-ion)**, lithium polymer (Li-Po), and lithium metal polymer (LiMePo) battery technology have made battery power commonplace in certain types of commercial vehicles. Unlike many of the first generation of hybrid-power batteries, lithium battery technology provides moderate energy and high power density. In addition, these batteries can sustain deep cycling while producing good longevity.

In recent years, the lithium family of batteries has generally replaced lead acid and NiMH batteries as the battery of choice in all-electric and electric hybrid powered vehicles. The lithium-ion family of batteries includes:

- Manganese Li-ion
- Phosphate Li-ion
- Cobalt Li-ion

Although Li-ion batteries are considered slightly unstable due to overheating and explosion potential, they are currently used in commercial transit operations in conjunction with air or liquid cooling technology. Cobalt Li-ion has the highest energy density of the lithium family of batteries and shows the most promise

FIGURE 39–1 A typical lithium-ion cylindrical battery. The steel case forms the negative electrode and has to be tough enough to contain an explosion. The PTC switch opens the vent to prevent explosion should pressure rise.

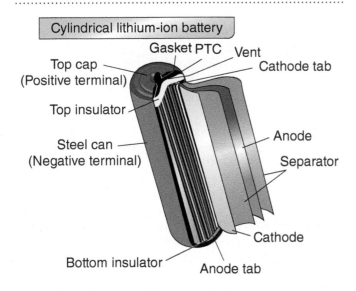

for the future. **Figure 39–1** shows a single-cell, cylindrical Li-on battery. The steel case doubles as the negative electrode and must be tough enough to withstand internal pressure. A positive temperature coefficient (PTC) switch trips a vent if internal pressure becomes excessive.

If there is a downside to the Li-on family of batteries, it is that their energy storage capacity limits travel range. This means that although they provide lots of power for acceleration, the distance they can get a vehicle to travel can be a problem. When Li-on batteries are used in combination with sodium metal hydride batteries, which have higher energy storage capacity, the range of travel can be extended.

SODIUM METAL HYDRIDE BATTERIES

The **sodium metal hydride (NaNiCl$_2$) battery** has the best energy density of currently known batteries, but lower power potential than equivalent Li-on batteries. In simple terms, the power of a Li-on battery is good for acceleration and climbing hills, but it comes at the expense of energy storage capability. Sodium metal hydride batteries are not good at supplying a fast surge of power, but they have better storage capacity than Li-on batteries. GE's Durathon batteries are used in conjunction with Li-on battery banks in all-electric and

hybrid electric transit buses: Power management computers are used to manage the contribution of each set of batteries during operation.

A sodium metal hydride battery consists of a sodium-metal halide cathode and liquid sodium anode into which the anode is immersed. A current collector connects to the positive cell terminal. Individual cell voltage is around 2.5 V-DC. GE states that the Durathon battery can have an operational life of up to 20 years.

ULTRACAPACITORS AND SUPERCAPACITORS

Recent developments in **ultracapacitors (UCs)** and **supercapacitors** (the terms are synonymous) suggest that in the near future they will be used for more than just short-term storage of electrical potential. They are currently used in conjunction with battery storage systems in some electrically powered vehicles, but their use is expected to expand. UCs function by physically separating the positive and negative charges, holding the charge in a manner that can be compared to static electrical buildup. The major advantage of UCs is their super-fast rate of charge and discharge. Another advantage is that they do not chemically and physically degrade as do batteries. On the downside, they have lower energy density than most batteries.

UC versus Battery Discharge Rates

In current applications, UCs are used in conjunction with batteries where they can be charged during regenerative braking and rapidly discharged as the vehicle needs to accelerate. However, the way a battery can pump out electrons is severely limited compared to a UC. A good comparison is the bathtub drain analogy: If a tub is filled with water, it drains when the plug is pulled; this can be compared to how a battery discharges electrons. However, the rate at which a UC discharges an equivalent quantity of electrons can be likened to the spill rate that would result if a basketball-sized hole were punched into the same tub. UCs can be used in parallel to batteries with the objective of prolonging battery life; this is already being done in stop-start applications such as hybrid electric transit buses and straddle carriers used in ports.

UC Operation

An ultracapacitor functions by polarizing an electrolytic solution to store charge energy electrostatically. Although it is an electrochemical

FIGURE 39–2 Operating principle of an ultracapacitor.

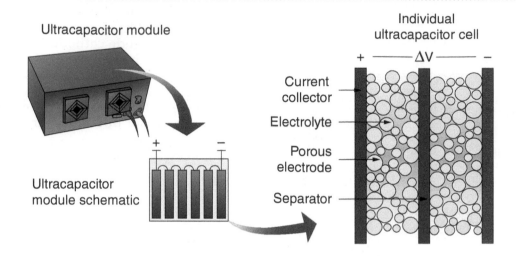

device, no chemical reactions take place. The charge accumulation is highly reversible, and ultracapacitors are said to be capable of up to 1,000,000 charge/discharge cycles.

After a UC is loaded with a charge, a load (such as an electric vehicle's motor) can use this energy. The amount of energy stored is much greater than an equivalent standard capacitor, because the charge storage surface area is much larger. A UC can be charged in as little as 1 second with electrical storage volume that would take an equivalent lithium battery 1 hour and a lead acid battery 10 hours. In addition, a lead acid battery is capable of around 3,000 load cycles versus more than 1,000,000 load cycles for the UC. Modern UCs have low leakage rates, typically 1 farad per 24 hours for a 3,000-farad battery.

UC Construction

The basic material of an ultracapacitor is carbon sourced from coconut shells. The coconut shells are ground into a dust and then the activated carbon is rolled into shape by kneading. The double-sided, plate-type cassette is the most common. A UC the size of a 12-ounce soda can be rated at 3,000 farads.

UC Operating Principle

A UC uses a pair of nonreactive porous plates, or *collectors*, that are suspended within electrolyte. In each UC, the applied voltage on its positive electrode attracts negative ions in the electrolyte, while the potential on the negative electrode attracts the positive ions. A dielectric separator between the two electrodes prevents the charge from moving between the two electrodes.

UCs actually store their electrical charge on an electrode. Devices such as batteries use the electrode to create (by chemical reaction) an electrical charge at the electrodes. This means that a battery's ability to store or create electrical charge is a function of the surface area of the electrode. UCs have vastly greater electrode surface area, to increase both the capacitance and energy storage capacity.

As a storage device, a UC depends on the microscopic charge separation at an electrochemical interface to store electrical energy. Because UC capacitance is proportional to the active electrode area, increasing that surface area increases capacitance. The electrode surface area in UCs uses activated carbon or sintered metal powder coatings. **Figure 39–2** shows the operating principle of a UC.

UC Cranking Assist

Recently operators have realized the advantage of using 12-VDC ultracapacitor cassettes for purpose of cranking engines. The "bathtub drain" effect of a UC cassette can significantly reduce cranking duration. **Figure 39–3** shows a typical UC cassette, and **Figure 39–4** is a cutaway of the same cartridge.

ELECTRICITY

Most of the automobile and a few commercial vehicle OEMs either have an EV in production or are planning to produce one. As we said in the introduction, electric motors have powered vehicles such as subway trains and streetcars

FIGURE 39–3 An ultracapacitor cassette cartridge commonly used to crank commercial truck engines.

FIGURE 39–4 A cutaway of an ultracapacitor cassette cartridge.

since the early years of the last century—an easy thing to do given a dedicated grid and 100% consistent route. When electricity can directly power drive motors on vehicles, they are capable of thermal efficiencies of up to 60%. However, in the absence of an electrified rail or other conduit to provide a source of direct electrical energy to a vehicle, cassette architecture in the form of batteries and capacitors is required to store electrical energy on the vehicle. While this eliminates the problem of a fixed route, a significant limiting factor is vehicle range, which becomes defined by the battery capacity in the vehicle.

ALL-ELECTRIC COMMERCIAL VEHICLES

Freightliner CCC, in partnership with Morgan Olson, a specialty pickup and delivery van manufacturer based in Sturgis, Michigan, developed a walk-in van based on a Sprinter chassis for release during 2011. City-use delivery vans with low payloads tend to be the initial target for commercial EVs, and other initiatives are being driven by Smith Electric Vehicles and Navistar-Modec. These vehicles commonly locate banks of Li-on batteries underneath the cargo body of the van. Drive is by an electric motor located at the axle assembly.

The betting is that all-electric commercial vehicles are unlikely to sell well until further advances in battery and UC technology have taken place. However, the optics and public relations value of pasting an "all-electric power" sticker on the vehicle are attractive, as is the fact that they do produce zero emissions within the zone in which they are operated. Although the electricity they consume may have been produced by coal or combusting bunker C oil, in the mind of the observer they truly are emissions free.

A fleet of 50 EV buses was used in Beijing during the 2008 Olympics. The buses were used all day with air conditioning on and reportedly experienced few mechanical problems. However, at the end of each day, all of the Li-on batteries used to power the units were removed and placed into a 24-hour charge cycle before being returned to service. The math of this arrangement suggests that 3 sets of batteries for each bus were required to keep it running for a 12-hour workday.

HYBRID ELECTRIC VEHICLES

If you live in one of the larger cities in North America, chances are you have already been transported in a **hybrid electric vehicle (HEV)** bus. Transit bus operations are the ideal application for HEVs—especially with the emergence of reliable battery technology (Li-on) backed up by cassettes of UCs. **Figure 39–5** shows an increasingly common sight on the streets of New York City: an HEV bus.

ELECTRIC MOTOR, GAS TURBINE DRIVEN

The thrust toward higher-efficiency powerplants has been driven by the Europeans, who have the

FIGURE 39–5 An HEV transit bus in New York City.

FIGURE 39–6 A simple PH, diesel electric drive system. On the West Coast, city transit corporations have entirely diesel engines with NG-fueled engines.

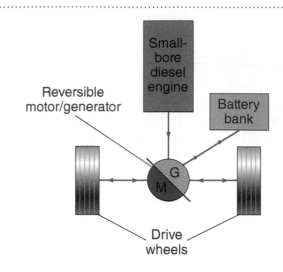

best motivation for increasing fuel efficiency: namely, astronomically high fuel prices. They are engineering and manufacturing long-range, light vehicles that use a super-efficient gas turbine fueled with kerosene to drive an electric motor. Combusting kerosene has a tendency to produce high NO_x, so the key to expanding this technology is in using small, highly efficient turbines. Until Euro V (fully effective in 2013), the European standards of NO_x emission were not as tough as our EPA 2010, so there may be significant challenges in getting turbines to meet NO_x standards.

The Metropolitan Transportation Authority (MTA) in New York City and Chicago Transportation Authority (CTA) in Chicago have both conducted trials using turbine-powered, hybrid electric drive buses. The objective of the trials was to evaluate the buses in the real world of city driving conditions, but as yet, no results have been published.

PARALLEL HYBRID, DIESEL ELECTRIC

Dual powerplant or **parallel hybrid (PH)** vehicles overcome some of the disadvantages, and exploit the advantages, of the electric motor as a vehicle engine. This is achieved by using a traditional internal combustion engine as a generator to power an electric motor; the simplest possible PH drive arrangement is shown in **Figure 39–6**. We usually describe these as hybrid electric vehicles (HEVs).

HEVs AS INNER-CITY BUSES

Several design variations of HEVs are available in the marketplace, and some large cities have invested heavily in parallel hybrid city buses. A decade ago, this was led by New York City's Metropolitan Transportation Authority (NYC-MTA) and the Toronto Transit Corporation (TTC). Although there were initial problems, the initiative is now regarded as successful and has spread to most other large cities, including Houston, Chicago, Los Angeles, San Francisco, San Diego, and Seattle. Our focus in this section is on this particular HEV system, because it already has a successful track record. In addition, both Freightliner and Navistar are manufacturing HEV school buses, another application for which a PH diesel-electric powertrain is well suited.

HEV TRUCKS

If you make a habit of attending truck shows, it is easy to see that all of the major OEMs have either production or preproduction HEVs on display. However, unlike their transit bus counterparts, medium-duty truck HEVs are not as yet making much impact in the marketplace. The odds favor light-duty truck and inner-city vans doing a little better. Of these, the Toyota Hino 155h (class 4 truck) and 195h (class 5) are probably best poised to make some initial sales, because of the more than decade-long reputation of Toyota electric hybrids in the automotive market ... and the fact that their commercial vehicle hybrid technology has already sold well outside the North American continent. In addition, the Freightliner Sprinter is now available with a PH electric drive, and because of the track record of success of this vehicle, it is likely to notch up some sales. Caterpillar has plans to release a heavy-duty PH electric truck in the near future using a blended torque version of its CX transmission.

How It Works

A parallel hybrid drive system uses two sources of power to move a vehicle. In the case of commercial vehicles, the two power sources are a diesel- or natural gas (NG)-fueled engine and a battery bank. The diesel engine/generator/ motor unit in an HEV is coupled to provide two outputs, as indicated in Figure 39–6:

- Generate electrical energy to maintain charge to the batteries
- Deliver continuously variable drive to the drive axle wheels

The objective is to allow the diesel engine to run at optimum efficiency for as much time as possible. In practice, as an HEV bus accelerates from a standstill, the batteries power a high-torque electric drive motor off the line. As the bus accelerates to its cruise speed, drive is provided by a blending of mechanical and electric motor sourced torque. Once at the cruise speed, the light-duty diesel engine may take over as the drive source, but also continues to generate charge to the batteries. In other words, there are three power delivery paths:

- Pure electrical path: batteries power electric motor(s)
- Torque blending: diesel engine and electric motor blended torque input
- Pure mechanical path: diesel engine direct drive

HEV Powertrain

At the moment of writing, most HEV buses use a powertrain consisting of a Cummins ISB or ISL diesel or NG engine, typically rated at 275 BHP, to provide mechanical drive or generate electrical power supplied to three-phase AC electric motors. On its own, the Cummins ISB 275 engine (shown in **Figure 39–7**) would have insufficient power and torque to drive a full-size city bus, but in a PH arrangement it becomes an ideal power source. The key to making the HEV powertrain work as a package is the **blended torque transmission**.

FIGURE 39–7 Cummins ISB 6.7 liter engine, a powerplant commonly used in HEV drivetrains.

BLENDED TORQUE TRANSMISSION In describing HEV transmissions, we are going to assume that the reader fully understands the operation of a planetary gearset (see Chapter 18 of *Heavy Duty Truck Systems*, 6E). The HEV transmission uses a two-mode, split compound principle that provides continuously variable torque (CVT) and speed. In appearance, it is not unlike a typical heavy-duty automatic transmission. To understand the blended torque feature of the HEV transmission, we first have to change some notions we have about the "laws of planetary gearsets": namely, that to produce an output, you have to hold one of the three members (sun, carrier, or ring gears) and deliver input torque to another member, so that the third can become the output. Hybrid drive requires two input sources to the planetaries, and one of those "inputs"—namely, the electric motor/generator—can also double in the role of an "output." **Figure 39–8** shows the arrangement of powertrain components of a transit bus PH drive system along with the mechanical and electrical powerflows.

Blended torque takes this concept one stage further. Instead of holding one of the three planetary members, why not "partially" hold it? Doing this permits the gearset to produce an output from two input sources, each contributing at different levels of torque. It is this feature that provides the infinitely variable torque output that we know as *blended torque*. Blended torque transmissions used in North America are manufactured by Allison, Caterpillar CX, and

FIGURE 39–8 Mechanical and electrical powerflows in a transit bus PH drivetrain.

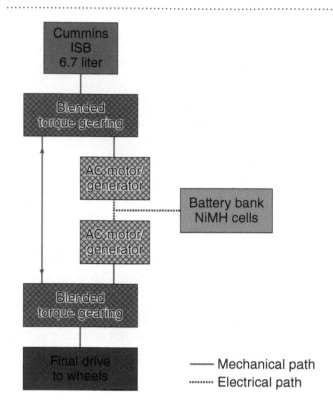

— Mechanical path
······· Electrical path

Aisin. We can summarize the blended torque output principle in the following way:

- The two input devices rotate at different shaft speeds and generate a complementary output based on the at-the-moment input torque of each.

HEV PERFORMANCE Bus drivers will tell you that HEV buses produce better off-the-line acceleration than any conventional diesel-powered bus they have driven. This makes them ideal people movers on busy city streets with a high frequency of stop-start events. The puff of black smoke and engine roar at each takeoff is eliminated, providing benefits to those not riding the bus in addition to a much smoother ride for the driver and passengers. The Cummins ISB and ISL diesel engines used in current applications are equipped with a diesel particulate filter and two-stage catalytic converter. Some cities, such as San Diego and Los Angeles, have opted for an NG power unit. Testing with the MTA in New York City has shown a 50% reduction in NO_x, 98% less CO, and better than 200% improved fuel economy over equivalent diesel-only powered buses. The two keys that enable this fuel economy are:

- Engine drives a genset: This allows the engine to be run in the sweet spot of its fuel economy performance curve—constantly.
- Regenerative braking: Described a little later in this section, but essentially this "recovers" retarding energy that would otherwise be wasted.

HEV Batteries

The first generation of commercial HEVs tended to use the nickel metal hydride or NiMH battery. This has given way to the lithium-ion batteries described earlier in this chapter. Li-on batteries still have some challenges to overcome, the main one being their volatility. They are disadvantaged by having a high self-discharge rate, but this is generally not a problem in a transit vehicle that is used daily, and this problem can be lessened by using sodium metal hydride ($NaNiCl_2$) banks to increase range. The high power density and reliability of the Li-on compared with most other current battery technologies have been assets. **Figure 39–9** shows the location of all of the mechanical and electrical powertrain components on a typical HEV transit bus.

Regenerative Braking

A bonus of a diesel electric hybrid drive is achieved with **regenerative braking**. When the drive electric motor magnetic field is reversed, it applies retarding torque and generates electricity used to charge the batteries and load capacitors. Regenerative braking significantly contributes to the energy equation in a city bus application featuring constant stop-starts, because somewhere around 40% of the power required to accelerate a bus to a cruise speed comes from the energy "recovered" from stopping it.

Blended Torque Transmission

To maximize the benefit of the HEV drivetrain, a blended torque transmission is required. A blended torque transmission is designed to receive input drive from:

- The diesel or NG engine
- The chassis-drive electric motor
- Both at the same time

Figure 39–10 shows a cutaway of a typical blended torque transmission. Full coverage of the transmissions used in hybrid drive technology is located in *Heavy-Duty Truck Systems, 6th Edition*.

FIGURE 39-9 Location of HEV powertrain components on a transit bus.

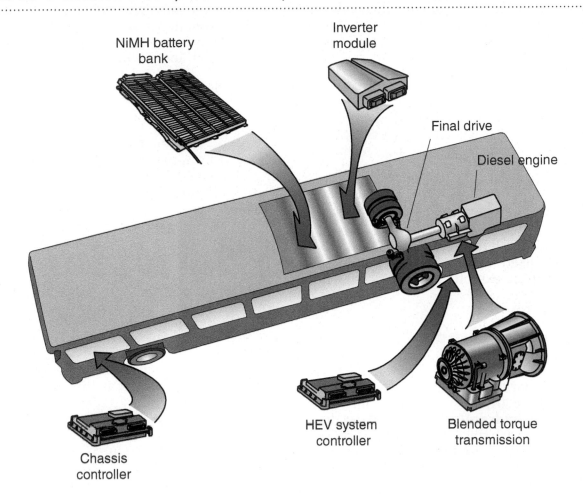

FIGURE 39-10 Blended torque transmission used in an HEV powertrain.

Drive Motor/Generators

The drive motors used are synchronous alternating current (AC) electric motors that must

be precisely phased. The drivetrain powerflow when operating under electric drive alone is engine-to-generator-to-battery-to-electric motor. Because batteries are direct current (DC) storage devices and the motors used are AC motor/generators, the electrical characteristics to drive or effect regenerative braking must undergo cycles of rectification and inversion. These are managed by the system controller.

INVERTERS The inverters used in HEV buses tend to be their most vulnerable component because they produce large amounts of heat, which has to be dissipated or the unit will fail. A typical inverter module is a bulky, heavy unit weighing up to 165 lb (75 kg). They are rated at a nominal 600 V-DC with 150-kW continuous three-phase AC output. The units are oil cooled.

SYSTEM CONTROLLER The system controller used on commercial HEVs is networked to the

J1939 data bus (see Chapter 37) and masters the operation of all system hardware. Operation of system controllers is the subject of Chapter 34.

HEV Summary

Diesel electric drive is not new. It has been used for many decades on railway locomotives. The HEV system we have discussed here simply takes this one stage further to exploit the best features of the diesel engine mechanical and electric motor drive options. Many experts believe that this will become the drive system of choice for city transit over the next decade. Geography will dictate whether the main engine is diesel or NG fueled. HEV drive provides plenty of potential for certain types of vocational truck used in stop-start applications: Whether it will be exploited or not depends on the marketplace.

HYDRAULIC HYBRIDS

Hydraulic hybrid vehicles (HHVs) can be divided into parallel drive (dual-drive input) and series drive (hydrostatic drive-only) systems. **Parallel hydraulic hybrid (PHH)** drive systems began with an Eaton Corporation collaboration with the United States Army aimed at reducing fuel consumption in military ground vehicles: The program was known as **hydraulic hybrid, advanced materials and multifuel engine research (HAMMER)**. With the military trials in progress, Eaton developed a version for nonmilitary purposes known as **hydraulic launch assist (HLA)**, intended to power small intracity vehicles such as courier vans and shuttle buses. In addition, a **series hydraulic hybrid (SHH)** drive, which is a hydraulic vehicle propulsion system, is being used in similar applications.

- PHH: Hydraulic circuit "assists" a conventional drivetrain.
- SHH: Hydraulic circuit replaces the conventional drivetrain.

HLA OPERATING PRINCIPLES

The Eaton HLA is a PHH drive system. It functions by using a conventional diesel-driven powertrain assisted by a hydraulic system. Equivalent systems are manufactured by Bosch Rexroth and Freightliner Parker. The hydraulic system consists of the following:

- Reversible hydraulic piston pump/motor
- Hydraulic pump/motor clutch coupling to the conventional drivetrain
- High-pressure accumulator
- Reservoir and circuit plumbing

In the first available commercial version of HLA, a Ford (Navistar) 6-liter PowerStroke engine rated at 235 horsepower is used to master the powertrain, but this has been joined by a Chrysler van. Much lower fuel consumption is achieved by regenerative braking and an accumulator, and by managing the powertrain so that the engine shuts down, eliminating idling. When the vehicle brake pedal is actuated, deceleration energy converts the pump/motor into its "pump" role, so that it charges hydraulic fluid from the reservoir into a high-pressure accumulator. This "potential energy" is then stored in the nitrogen gas–loaded high-pressure accumulator. A powertrain similar to this in a Ford 150 pickup truck produced a reported 60 mpg, a 400% improvement over its gasoline-fueled sibling.

During acceleration, the role of the pump/motor is reversed so that the stored energy in the high-pressure accumulator is used as the driving force of the hydraulic motor. This allows the pump/motor to apply torque to the drivetrain by means of the HLA clutch. The nitrogen gas–loaded accumulator has a capacity of 2.6 gallons (10 liters) and is capable of storing hydraulic pressures of up to 5,000 psi (345 bar). Current hydraulic accumulators are manufactured using a composite shell weighing one-fifth the weight of steel. Unlike steel, the shell is resistant to corrosion, with better fatigue life than most metals. **Figure 39–11** is a schematic that shows the powerflow arrangement used in a PHH system equipped with an accumulator.

A major advantage of the Eaton HLA, Bosch Rexroth, and Parker drive systems is the greatly improved power density enabled by the hydraulic accumulator. In the Eaton HLA system, a Navistar 6.0 PowerStroke diesel that typically produces 235 BHP and around 440 lb-ft. of torque is capable of boosting the conventional drivetrain output to around 300 BHP and nearly 1,000 lb-ft. of torque. Mack Trucks is using the Bosch Rexroth system in garbage packers. Inner-city refuse haulers are known to be especially tough on brakes, and the hydrostatic regenerative braking system used on the Mack Granite trucks enables close to 100% hydrostatic braking: Apart from fuel savings, this greatly extends brake service intervals.

FIGURE 39–11 Parallel hydraulic hybrid (PHH) system capable of mechanical or hydraulic similarly configured drive assist and regenerative braking.

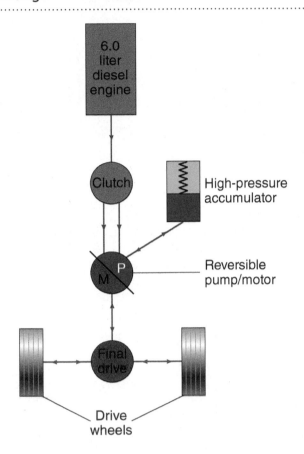

Drive wheels

FIGURE 39–12 Series hydraulic hybrid (SHH) drive featuring hydraulic propulsion and regenerative braking.

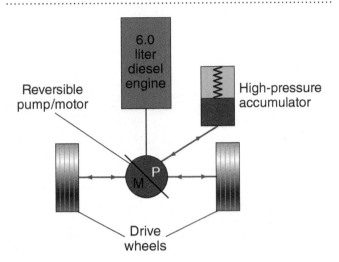

Drive wheels

SHH OPERATING PRINCIPLES

In the SHH drive system, hydraulics are used as the vehicle propulsion system. In both the United States Army and commercial vehicle versions of SHH, the original engine was a Navistar 6.0-liter PowerStroke (see Chapter 27). However, in SHH the conventional drivetrain consisting of a transmission, driveshaft, and final drive carrier is dispensed with. The diesel engine transfers drive torque to a reversible pump/motor that can both power the vehicle and recycle regenerative braking effort using an accumulator. SHH is said to yield up to a 70% improvement in fuel economy. This can be achieved because:

- The diesel engine powerplant can be run at a constant, optimum speed during all phases of operation.
- Regenerative braking energy is unloaded into an accumulator where it can be stored until required.

A stated disadvantage of the SHH system over a PHH system is that it lacks redundancy. However, so does any other type of series drive system; therefore, this is really not that significant, especially in view of the potential advantages of the technology. Series hydraulic propulsion has been used by the off-highway equipment segment for decades. SHH promises:

- Significantly greater engine longevity
- Reduced maintenance costs due to savings in brake servicing and powertrain components
- 60% to 70% lower fuel costs
- Lower emissions, including 40% reduction in carbon dioxide
- Quieter vehicle noise and reduced operator fatigue

Figure 39–12 shows an SHH drive system that features hydraulic propulsion and regenerative braking. **Figure 39–13** shows the powertrain arrangement of the Freightliner Parker PHH system.

FUEL CELLS

A *fuel cell* is an electrochemical device in which the energy of a chemical reaction is converted into electricity. It does nothing more than produce electricity. If a vehicle is to be powered by a fuel cell, the fuel cell simply produces electricity, and electric motors are used to drive the vehicle. Fuel cells are not new, having been invented by Sir William Grove in 1839. After

FIGURE 39–13 The powertrain arrangement of the Freightliner Parker PHH system.

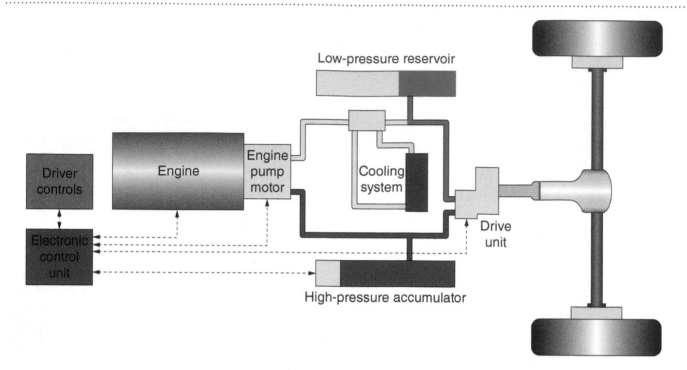

their invention, not a whole lot was done with fuel cells until the National Aeronautics and Space Administration (NASA) used them to provide some of the electrical requirements of its spacecraft in the 1960s.

As far as fuel cell powered commercial vehicles are concerned, Ballard Power Systems of Burnaby, British Columbia, has led the way. Ballard fuel cells were used to power 20 New Flyer buses in the Whistler and Vancouver area during the 2010 Winter Olympics. The reported cost of each bus was $2 million, about 4 times the cost of a standard diesel-powered city bus, so to some degree this was a publicity stunt. However, the 20 buses remain in service with few reported problems.

Fuel cells are not "free" energy, as some have described them; they need **hydrogen** to function, which creates problems. Commercial hydrogen is usually produced electrolytically from water, which is a process that requires large amounts of electricity. Further, safe storage of highly explosive hydrogen on a vehicle is not so easy: it requires the use of high-pressure vessel-rated tanks.

REFORMING HYDROGEN

The option is to use *fuel reforming* to extract the hydrogen from hydrocarbon (HC) fuels such as gasoline, natural gas, or alcohols (usually methyl hydrate). Some experimental buses in a Georgetown University project used methyl hydrate reforming to source the hydrogen. Some would say that this is a better option than storing compressed hydrogen onboard a passenger vehicle; others might argue that reforming HC fuel just contributes more CO_2 dump into our atmosphere.

The fuel cells themselves do not discharge like a battery; they will run so long as they are supplied with hydrogen fuel. The claim that fuel cells are zero-emission energy producers is only true when the fuel provided is pure hydrogen and the hydrogen source is electrolytic using hydroelectricity. A major plus is that fuel cells can produce thermal efficiencies of up to 50%. **Figure 39–14** shows the power equation of a fuel cell.

REFORMING PROCESS

Most current fuel cells used in small vehicles require an HC fuel such as gasoline as the hydrogen source, using a reforming process. *Reforming* is the separating of H_2 from the HC fraction molecule in the gasoline, methanol, or other HC fuel. When a fuel cell is fueled with reformed hydrogen, the results are not as environmentally friendly as some might claim because the carbon by-product of the process has to be considered.

FIGURE 39–14 Fuel cell power equation.

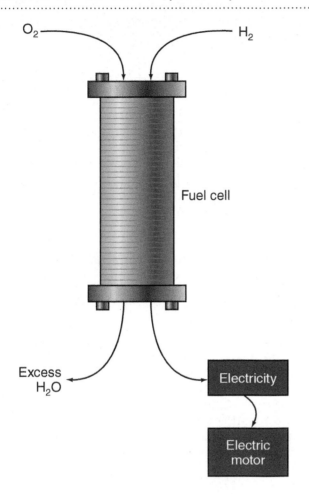

So, although hydrogen is the most abundant element in the known universe, producing it on Earth either takes lots of electricity (the production of which often causes noxious emissions) or involves reformation from a fossil fuel, the greater percentage of which is carbon. These factors are likely to make the fuel cell a very limited mobile technology in the immediate future. Only when the hydrogen is produced electrolytically using hydroelectric power can it be considered a truly *green* fuel resource. **Figure 39–15** is a schematic showing a fuel cell powered by hydrogen reformed (sourced) from methanol.

HOW A FUEL CELL WORKS

A fuel cell functions on the principle of the thermodynamic reversibility of the electrolysis of water. For many years we have produced hydrogen and oxygen by the electrolysis of water, and, as mentioned before, it does take a lot of electricity to do this. When supplying hydrogen and oxygen to the two electrodes of an electrolytic cell, a potential difference is created, and electric current begins to flow. Join several cells together and you create a multicell fuel cell. The electrochemical reaction is:

$$2H_2 + O_2 \text{ produces } 2H_2O + \text{electricity}$$

FIGURE 39–15 Fuel cell power equation when the hydrogen is sourced from methanol. The electricity produced powers electric traction motors.

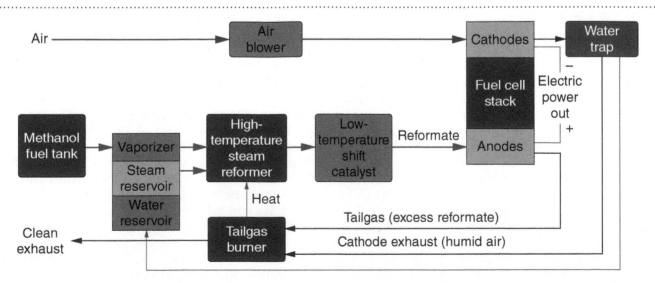

FIGURE 39–16 Fuel cell chemical reaction.

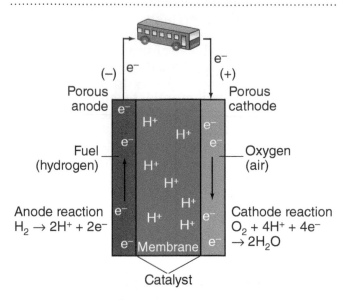

Overall electrochemical reaction
$2H_2 + O_2 \rightarrow 2H_2O$ + electricity

Figure 39–16 demonstrates the operating principle of a fuel cell: Hydrogen and oxygen are electrochemically reacted to produce water and electricity.

TYPES OF FUEL CELLS

There are a number of different types of fuel cells. We look briefly at some of them and in more detail at one currently being tested in city buses that may perhaps have a future as a short-range, small truck powerplant. Each type of fuel cell is distinguished by the electrolyte material used.

Alkaline Fuel Cells

Alkaline fuel cells have been used by NASA in the Apollo and space shuttle programs. To function, they must be provided with pure hydrogen and pure oxygen, substances that are stored and readily available on a spacecraft, but difficult to store on a truck or automobile.

Phosphoric Acid Fuel Cells

Phosphoric acid fuel cells are suitable only in stationary power generation applications due to the corrosive nature of the liquid electrolyte and high operating temperatures, usually in the range of 392°F (200°C). The British Aerospace Electronics (BAE) fuel cell technology used in some transit buses (including the Georgetown University models) uses a phosphoric acid fuel cell. In addition, these cells have been used as electrical generators in large buildings, such as hospitals and hotels, that need a power source independent from the grid.

Solid Oxide Fuel Cells

Solid oxide fuel cells operate at the highest temperatures, between 1,292°F (700°C) and 1,832°F (1,000°C), but because of this, they will tolerate relatively impure fuels such as the HC gas obtained from the gasification of coal. These fuel cells have a relatively simple design and are thought to be most suitable for large stationary power generators. It is unlikely that there would be any mobile vehicle application in the near future.

Proton Exchange Membrane Fuel Cells

Proton exchange membrane (PEM) fuel cells have created some excitement in the automotive industry because they are the most viable mobile fuel cell technology. The PEM fuel cell has been used as a primary power source in some vehicles, and Freightliner chose this technology for its optional APU unit. A PEM fuel cell uses a solid polymer membrane (a thin plastic film) as the electrolyte. If the fuel cell can be supplied with pure hydrogen (as opposed to reforming it from a fossil fuel), then the only emissions that have to be considered are those used to produce the pure hydrogen. The Ballard fuel cell being used to power city buses uses a PEM principle. **Figure 39–17** shows how a PEM functions.

Ballard Power Systems has led the way in developing fuel cells for automotive use and has partnership liaisons with several OEMs. The Ballard Mark 900 fuel cell is being used in both trial and operational applications in city buses in Chicago, San Francisco, Vancouver, and Palm Springs. Ballard is also supplying fuel cells to Daimler-Benz for use in European trials taking place in a number of cities, including Paris, Barcelona, Reykjavik, and Hamburg.

All these trial programs are in a process of long-term, continuing evaluation and indication are that PEM could become a viable technology for the next generation of city buses. The performance results have been reported to be satisfactory; the real drawback has been the high cost, at the moment around four times the cost of a diesel-powered bus. The good news is that the costs will go down. If enough consumers buy into fuel cell technology, the costs of producing it will go down significantly. **Figure 39–18** shows the layout of key fuel cell powertrain components in a city transit bus.

FIGURE 39–17 PEM fuel cell principle.

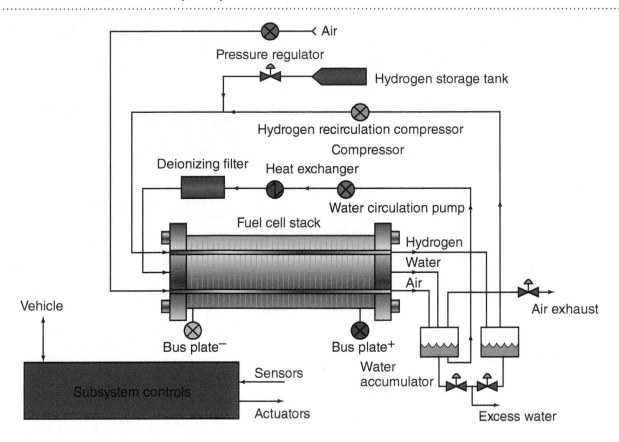

FIGURE 39–18 Layout of key fuel cell powertrain components in city transit bus.

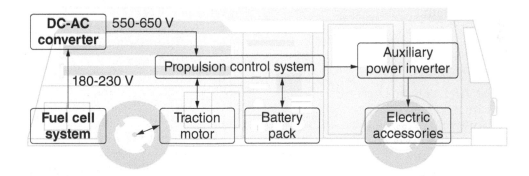

SUMMARY

- Electrical power both in the form of fuel cells and hybrid drive powerplants offers some possible alternatives to the diesel engine.
- Direct electricity is used to power heavy-duty highway commercial vehicles in limited applications. It is used through an overhead or rail-based grid to power transit light rail and trolley buses. This type of application is obviously limited by the range of the electrical grid.
- Diesel electric hybrid drive engines known as parallel hybrid (PH) drive or hybrid electric vehicles (HEVs) have become commonplace in city transit bus applications. This technology uses a small-bore diesel or NG-fueled engine to drive a motor/generator.

- PH drive systems make use of a blended torque transmission to provide all-electric or all-mechanical, or combinations of both, torque to the final drive unit.
- Blended torque transmissions use planetary gearsets to receive drive torque from two sources and provide continuously variable output torque and speed ratios.
- Ultracapacitors are used to complement battery banks in hybrid electric vehicles.
- Ultracapacitors have better power density than batteries. They assist acceleration drivability by being able to unload large current loads into traction motors without sustaining damage.
- Parallel hydraulic hybrid (PHH) and series hydraulic hybrid (SHH) propulsion systems have progressed beyond the research and development phase and are now being used on inner-city delivery trucks and shuttle buses.

- The fuel cell is currently undergoing extensive trials as the primary powerplant in transit buses both on- and offshore. Currently, cost is a limiting factor, but that has not stopped a number of cities from using it, including San Francisco and Vancouver.
- The fuel cell used in most current fuel cell powered commercial vehicles is the proton exchange membrane (PEM) fuel cell, but other technologies are being trialed.
- The operating principles of a PEM fuel cell are simple: Hydrogen and oxygen are reacted to produce electricity and water. The procedure is the reverse of electrolysis.
- Fuel cells require hydrogen to operate. Either compressed hydrogen must be stored onboard, or hydrogen must be reformed from an HC fuel such as gasoline or methanol.

REVIEW QUESTIONS

1. What is the fuel required by a fuel cell?
   a. Nitrogen only
   b. Hydrogen and oxygen
   c. Hydrogen only
   d. Water

2. What results from the electrochemical reaction in a fuel cell?
   a. Electricity only
   b. Water only
   c. Hydrogen and oxygen
   d. Electricity and water

3. Which type of fuel cell is currently being used in trials in city buses?
   a. Proton membrane exchange
   b. Alkaline
   c. Solid oxide
   d. Phosphoric acid

4. When a regenerative braking cycle is engaged in an HEV (diesel electric) hybrid drive system, which of the following should be true?
   a. The diesel engine turns in reverse.
   b. The diesel engine compression retarder is actuated.
   c. The AC motor-generator reverses.
   d. The DC motor magnetic field is reversed.

5. Technician A states that an advantage of a parallel hydraulic hybrid (PHH) drive system is that a small diesel engine can be used in place of a larger one. Technician B states that a PHH system can only impart hydraulic drive torque, so that in the event of a leak, the vehicle would be crippled. Who is correct?
   a. Technician A only
   b. Technician B only
   c. Both A and B
   d. Neither A nor B

6. Which type of batteries tends to be used in the most recent generation of HEV transit buses?
   a. Lead acid
   b. Nickel cadmium (Ni-cad)
   c. Alkaline
   d. Lithium-ion (Li-on)

7. When a blended torque transmission is used on an HEV transit bus, which of the following features are possible?
   a. Input torque from more than one source
   b. Continuously variable output ratios
   c. Infinitely variable output speeds
   d. All of the above

8. Which of the following is true of a motor/generator used in an HEV transit bus?
   a. It produces three-phase AC power.
   b. It requires the use of an inverter.
   c. Output must be rectified to DC to charge battery banks.
   d. All of the above.

9. What type of hydraulic accumulator is used in an Eaton PHH and an SHH drive system?
   a. Mechanically loaded with a maxi-spring rated at 3,000 psi (207 bar)
   b. Nitrogen gas loaded at 5,000 psi (345 bar)
   c. Hydraulically loaded at 29,000 psi (2,000 bar)
   d. Any of the above, depending on application

10. Technician A says that UCs will sustain up to a million charge and discharge cycles. Technician B says that UCs can hold large amounts of electrical energy but discharge it more slowly than most types of batteries. Who is correct?
    a. Technician A only
    b. Technician B only
    c. Both A and B
    d. Neither A nor B

11. Which of the following cities has entirely eliminated diesel engines from its transit bus fleet?
    a. Chicago
    b. New York City
    c. Houston
    d. Los Angeles

12. Technician A says that HEV buses can use NG-fueled engines. Technician B says that blended torque transmissions are used in most HEV city buses. Who is correct?
    a. Technician A only
    b. Technician B only
    c. Both A and B
    d. Neither A nor B

40

Prerequisites: Chapters 19, 21, 22, 24, 25, 28, 30, 31, 34, and 37

BOSCH EDC SYSTEMS

OBJECTIVES

After studying this chapter, you should be able to:

- Outline the scope of Bosch diesel technology in fuel, engine management, and emission control systems.
- Describe how Bosch integrates its control technology into OEM management systems.
- Define the term *proprietary bus*.
- Explain why multiple-module engine, fuel, and emissions management modules are sometimes used.
- Describe the electronic management circuit components used in a typical EDC engine, fuel, and emissions management system.

INTRODUCTION

For nearly a century, Bosch has been at the forefront of diesel technology innovation, and this track record continues in the electronic era. In the early 1990s, Bosch partial authority fuel management systems were adopted by original equipment manufacturers (OEMs) such as Mack Trucks and Volvo. Because of the recent emergence of diesel common rail (CR) fuel injection, along with the requirement for exhaust aftertreatment, Bosch hardware and software are found on more than half the medium- and heavy-duty diesel engines sold in North America. One of the reasons for Bosch's dominance is that it works closely with OEMs when technology is in its earliest development phase, to ensure that its supplied components and electronics dovetail into the OEM's requirement.

This chapter looks at the way Bosch's electronics interface with OEM electronics and powertrain data buses. In doing this, we will use the terms and acronyms that Bosch uses, rather than those used by its partner OEMs. Because Bosch components are used by so many OEMs, often the same component can be called something different by each of five OEMs.

BOSCH DIESEL SYSTEMS

Bosch has become the single most important supplier of leading-edge technology and components to North American diesel engine OEMs. It engineers and supplies components for the following:

- Fuel injection systems
- Engine management systems
- Emission control systems

The company is a major player in every aspect of North American diesel technology, and more than half of the fuel systems covered in Section 2 of this textbook use Bosch systems and components in big ways and small. In addition, Bosch partnered with Intel Corporation in engineering **CAN 2.0** architecture, which has become the basis for all light-duty and heavy-duty mobile equipment powertrain **multiplexing**. In the truck arena, we know powertrain multiplexing as **J1939**, and in light duty it is currently known as **CAN-C**.

In this chapter we will briefly examine the management systems used by Bosch to electronically control the following systems:

- Inline port-helix pump-line-nozzle (PLN; partial authority)
- Rotary distributor, sleeve metering (partial authority)
- **Unit injection systems (UISs)** (full authority)
- **Unit pump systems (UPSs)** (full authority)
- Common rail systems (CRSs)

ENGINE CONTROLLER ACRONYM

Because Bosch electronics are used by the smallest to the largest diesel engines in service, some confusion may arise over what exactly constitutes an engine controller. The confusion is increased because OEMs like to choose their own distinct names for the engine controller. For our purposes, the engine controller module will generally be known as the **engine control module (ECM)** and occupy the SA 00/MID 128 address on the data bus. This means that many engines with Bosch management systems may use a Bosch controller that has a proprietary bus connection to an OEM module that occupies the SA 00 address on the bus.

The terms used to describe management modules that require more than a single physical module are *two-box system* or *master and slave* modules. In some contemporary systems, four separate modules may be arranged in three distinct ways to manage engine outcomes, as follows:

- Fuel injection control (FIC) (used on the first-generation J1578/1708 bus with a MID 143 address), ECM (SA 00/MID 128), aftertreatment module also known as a dosing control module (DCM) (SA61/MID 223), and chassis controller (SA 71/MID 142), each with an address on the powertrain data bus (J1939 or J1587). This arrangement permits open bus access to all four modules.
- Chassis controller (SA 71/MID 142) with an address on J1939 and proprietary bus connections to ECM and DCM. This means that all access to the slave modules must be via the chassis controller. It can facilitate some kinds of troubleshooting (using OEM software), but hinder others.

And anything in between. When OEMs use proprietary bus connections, they usually direct communications access through the module with an address on the powertrain data bus. This works pretty well when submodule faults fall into the OEM failure identification maps, but not so well if they do not. It can lead to submodules being falsely condemned.

A current example is the Detroit Diesel (DD) management system for its post-2007 engines in which a DDEC ECM, known as a common

FIGURE 40–1 Arrangement of the DDEC CPC and MCM used to manage DD-Series engines.

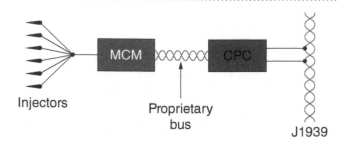

platform controller (CPC), is bussed to a motor control module (MCM) that can be programmed to drive three entirely different fuel systems:

- EUI system on Series 60
- EUP system on MB 4000
- ACRS on DD-Series

This is an example of how a Bosch management system has been engineered into an OEM interface. **Figure 40–1** is a schematic representing the DDC and Bosch arrangement. The engine electronics are accessed by networking an electronic service tool to the DDEC platform in the CPC.

Some of the other terms and acronyms used by Bosch and its OEM partners to describe an ECM are as follows:

- **Electronic control unit (ECU)**
- **Motor control module (MCM)** (DDEC term)
- Powertrain control module (PCM) (light duty)
- PLD (German acronym) (used by Mercedes-Benz [MB] until 2007)

Figure 40–2 is a schematic showing a multiple module arrangement used in some first-generation partial authority engine management

systems: The Bosch **Electronic Diesel Control (EDC)** drove the fuel injection system while the ECM managed engine logic. The technician accessed the engine electronics via the chassis module. EST access was through the chassis management module. In this generation of engine management system, the engine only, or engine and brakes, were the only computer-controlled chassis components.

Modern systems tend to rely more on the powertrain data bus (J1939) than on proprietary buses, some of which continue to use J1587/1708 protocols. **Figure 40–3** is a schematic showing a Bosch ECM with its own address on the data bus. The ECM and DCM must exchange significant data volume, but rely on the powertrain data bus to do so.

For the sake of consistency, the SAE-recommended acronym ECM will be used in this textbook when referring to engine system controllers, except when making reference to a

FIGURE 40–3 Example of how EDC is used as the engine controller and is provided with the SA 00 address on the data bus.

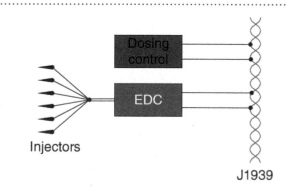

FIGURE 40–2 An arrangement used on some first-generation partial authority engine management systems in which a Bosch FIC (EDC) was connected by a proprietary bus to an OEM ECM, itself connected to a chassis management module. Technician access to the engine electronics was through the chassis management module.

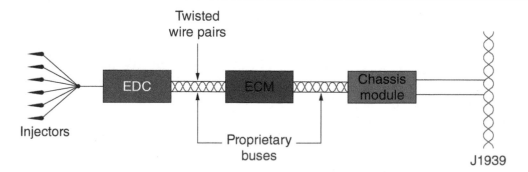

FIGURE 40–4 A Bosch ECM.

specific OEM that prefers one of the other terms. In addition, you may see one of the alternative terms used in some of the figures and schematics in this and other chapters in the book. **Figure 40–4** shows a Bosch ECM.

EDC MANAGEMENT LOGIC

Because Bosch supplies its systems to the OEMs, it tends to use whatever terms the OEM chooses to describe its system. Bosch's own terms have changed very little over the years, although the technology managed has changed from crude partial authority fuel systems to today's advanced CR fuel systems and aftertreatment systems. The details of input circuit components, the processing cycle, and output drivers are covered in Chapter 34. The output systems that Bosch electronics manage are covered in Section 2 of this textbook.

INPUT CIRCUIT

The sensor circuit inputs data to the EDC microprocessor by means of protective circuitry and, where necessary, via signal transducers and amplifiers. Both analog and digital signals are input to the ECM processing cycle. Typical data signaled to the ECM includes:

- Manifold air quantity or mass
- Engine fluid temperatures
- Intake air temperatures
- Shaft speed data (i.e., crankshaft, etc.)
- Shaft position data (i.e., camshaft)
- Engine fluid pressure values, including oil and boost
- Coolant level and (sometimes) pressure

- Accelerator pedal status
- Battery voltage
- Message data off powertrain data bus
- Message data off aftertreatment controller
- Hard wire switch status
- Smart-switch status

Data input may be analog, digital, or optical. At the time of writing, it is mostly analog in a typical system.

SIGNAL CONDITIONING

In order to suppress interference pulses and other electronic noise, pulse-shaped input signals from inductive sensors, which carry information on such things as shaft speed and position, are conditioned by a special circuit in the ECM and converted to square-wave form. Signal conditioning essentially cleans up electronic noise prior to processing.

Depending on the level of integration, some signal conditioning can take place either completely or partially in the sensor. Protective circuitry is used to limit the incoming signals to a maximum voltage level. Inputted signals are freed of superimposed interference signals by filtering and then amplified to match them to the ECM working voltage.

As smart sensors begin to replace simple signaling sensors, the need to condition signals broadcast to the ECM is eliminated. Smart sensors are equipped with processing capability and can message the data bus, thereby speeding up processing responses.

PROCESSING CYCLE

Because of the range of fuel system types and engine applications of EDC, the programming and switching apparatus within the ECM varies considerably. Engine-specific curves and engine management maps are also written to ECM memory banks and include such data as immobilizer strategies, calibration, and manufacturing data. Current ECMs also have a write-to-self capability that will log fault codes and audit trails to electronically erasable, programmable read-only memory (EEPROM).

FUELING ALGORITHM

In Section 2 of this textbook, we looked at how the fuel system electronics balance what is *actually* happening in the engine at any given moment of operation with what the engine electronics computes *should be* happening. The key processing transaction that concerns engine fueling is the "closed"-loop cycle between *desired* engine fueling versus the *actual* fueling. This can be summarized as follows:

- Desired engine fueling—Computed by the ECM based on sensor inputs (this includes accelerator position), emissions monitoring, and stored instructions in memory.
- Actual engine fueling—Signaled to the ECM by sensors such as rack position and common rail pressure.

Because *desired* and *actual* values are always known in a properly running engine, the function of the ECM is to keep the two sets of values as close as possible. Should there be problems with the input actual values, fault codes are logged; then, depending on their severity, the management system may adopt failure strategies which can run the engine in a corrective cycle, run it in a default mode, or shut it down completely.

Data Programming

The extent to which EDC accepts customer data programming depends largely on the engine OEM. That said, most current fuel injection devices are specified with fuel flow code ratings. These are usually expressed as numeric codes that must be programmed to EDC whenever changed out. These fuel flow codes tell EDC how specific injectors flow fuel in operation so that cylinder fueling can be balanced.

OUTPUT CIRCUITS

With its output signals, EDC translates the results of the processing cycle into actions. When output commands are triggered within the ECM, the signals produced are usually powerful enough for direct connection to the actuators. Output drivers (usually located within the ECM) are responsible for the entire output circuit. Depending on the system, these drivers perform the following functions:

- Switch the fuel injection control actuators
- Switch devices such as injection timing actuators
- Modulate V-Ref output
- Broadcast messages to the powertrain data bus

Injector and Pump Drivers

A primary function of the EDC ECM in most current systems is to control the injector drivers. The term *injector drivers* is a loose one used

to describe the fueling functions. For instance, the fueling functions in a Paccar MX smart **electronic pump (EUP)** system that uses Bosch UPS fueling include:

- Switching EUP actuators to control effective stroke
- Switching the smart EHIs to manage injection pulses

Similarly, in a Bosch **common rail system (CRS)**, the critical fueling functions are:

- Controlling the rail pressure management valve
- Switching the EHI actuators

Most switching output uses pulse width modulated (PWM) signals, explained in Chapters 32 and 34. Switching voltages for the various types of injectors used in Bosch fuel systems range between 48 V-DC to values in excess of 100 V-DC. There has been a recent trend toward lower injection actuation voltage, and most piezo actuators tend to be switched with lower voltage values. **Figure 40–5** shows a Bosch CR injector and **Figure 40–6** shows the calibration flow rate as a quick response (QR) code on the same injector.

FIGURE 40–5 A Bosch CR injector.

FIGURE 40–6 The QR Code on a Bosch CR injector.

EDC AFTERTREATMENT MANAGEMENT

EDC can manage Bosch aftertreatment hardware by two methods:

- Direct connection by proprietary bus to the aftertreatment module
- Data bus negotiation via J1939

The terms used to describe Bosch aftertreatment systems are:

- Departronic: DPF fuel dosing management
- Denoxtronic SCR: DEF dosing management

Each system is qualified by generation: for example, the first version of **Departronic** was known as Departronic 1.0 and the current version of **Denoxtronic** is known as Denoxtronic 2.0. As the names suggest, Departronic manages diesel particulate filter (DPF) monitoring and dosing, while Denoxtronic manages selective catalytic reduction (SCR) dosing and reduction modes. **Figure 40–7** shows a block schematic of the Denoxtronic 2.0 SCR management system.

BLOCK DIAGRAMS

Finally, an example of an EDC block diagram is shown to demonstrate how the EDC interfaces with a specific OEM system. **Figure 40–8** shows the engine electronic circuit of a DD-Series engine. Familiarize yourself with the circuit that drives injectors, engine breaks, dosing valve, and EGR actuator; attempt to identify the input circuit to the MCM.

Figure 40–9 shows a block schematic of a much older partial authority EDC block diagram.

MAKING THE CONNECTION

Because Bosch EDC is engineered to interface with the OEM electronics, the rules of troubleshooting and networking with the system are whatever the specific OEM decides. Both heavy-duty and light-duty data buses are used to work the system.

FIGURE 40–7 Bosch Denoxtronic 2.0 aftertreatment management circuit.

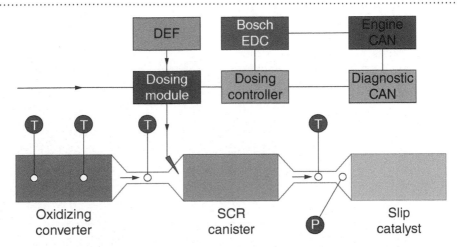

T = temperature sensors
P = pressure differential sensor

FIGURE 40–8 Block diagram of the engine electronics showing the DD-MCM output circuits.

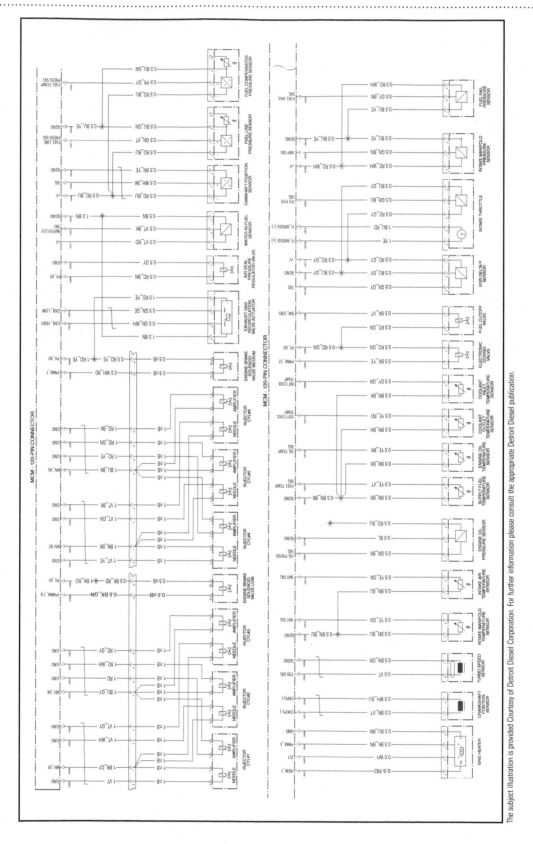

FIGURE 40–9 Block diagram of a partial authority EDC-managed engine.

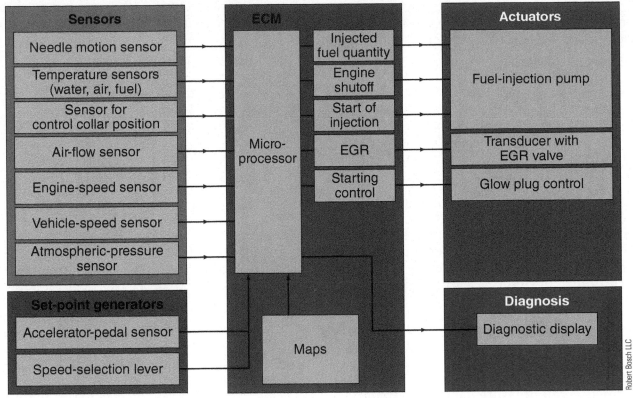

Robert Bosch LLC

EST HANDSHAKE

Depending on the OEM and the generation of EDC, a connection may be made using any of the following means, which are fully described in Chapter 35:

- J1962 connector (light-duty ALDL)
- J1708 connector (for heavy-duty J1587)
- J1939 connector
- Wireless to J1939 and CAN-C (where OEM supported)

The means required to make a connection may depend on the chassis OEM. For instance, a Cummins ISB in a Dodge chassis is accessed using a J1962 connector. The same engine in a Freightliner FL60 is accessed using a J1939 connector. **Figure 40–10** shows a Tier 4 compliant, 4-cylinder Cummins ISB 4.5 liter engine that uses a Bosch CR system.

SIS

Although Bosch publishes excellent general information and service literature, both hard

FIGURE 40–10 Bosch CR system on the Tier 4 compliant, 4-cylinder Cummins ISB 4.5 liter engine.

copy and electronic, it does not host an online service information system (SIS), leaving that function to the engine and chassis OEMs. The SIS used therefore depends on the OEM engine builder software. Some examples:

- Cummins ISB: QSOL
- Detroit Diesel DD-Series: PSL
- Navistar MaxxForce: ISIS
- Paccar: DAVIE

DIAGNOSTIC SOFTWARE

Again, the diagnostic software used to trouble-shoot EDC depends on that used by the OEM engine builder. Some examples:

- Detroit Diesel DD-Series: DDDL
- Navistar MaxxForce: ServiceMaxx
- Paccar: Rapido
- Cummins ISB: InSite

SUMMARY

- Bosch EDC has been used in some form or other by almost every engine OEM to manage its fuel systems, engines, and engine emissions controls.
- Because Bosch supplies and engineers for the OEMs, EDC may entirely manage the engine electronics or interface with OEM management electronics.
- A EDC system consists of an input circuit, processing hardware, and actuator circuit.
- A critical processing action of EDC is to compute *desired* rail pressure based on inputs and fuel map data monitoring. By monitoring *actual* rail pressure data, EDC attempts to match desired and actual rail pressures.

- The actuators in most fuel injection components are PWM switched by EDC drivers.
- Most current fuel injection devices are specified with fuel flow code ratings. These are usually expressed as numeric codes that must be programmed to EDC whenever they are changed out.
- EDC interfaces with aftertreatment electronics either by proprietary bus line or by network connection to the powertrain bus (J1939).
- Bosch Departronic manages DPF fuel dosing and monitoring.
- Bosch Denoxtronic manages SCR dosing and monitoring.

REVIEW QUESTIONS

1. Technician A states that Bosch online service information is required to work with the Bosch CR system used on ISB engines. Technician B states that Rapido diagnostic software is required to troubleshoot Paccar MX engines. Who is correct?
   a. Technician A only
   b. Technician B only
   c. Both A and B
   d. Neither A nor B

2. Which company partnered with Bosch to develop CAN 2.0 architecture?
   a. Microsoft
   b. Google
   c. Motorola
   d. Intel

3. What is the Bosch proprietary name for its DPF management system?
   a. EDC
   b. PLD
   c. Departronic
   d. Denoxtronic

4. What is the Bosch proprietary name for its SCR management system?
   a. EDC
   b. PLD
   c. Departronic
   d. Denoxtronic

5. Technician A says that to access ISB engine electronics, a J1962 connector may be required. Technician B says that to access ISB electronics, a J1939 connector may be required. Who is correct?
   a. Technician A only
   b. Technician B only
   c. Both A and B
   d. Neither A nor B

Prerequisites: Chapters 19, 21, 25, 26, 30, and 35

CATERPILLAR ENGINE MANAGEMENT SYSTEMS

OBJECTIVES

After studying this chapter, you should be able to:

- Define the acronyms *ADEM* and *ACERT*.
- Identify Caterpillar engines that use electronic controls.
- Identify Caterpillar online service information and diagnostic software.
- Identify some of the features of ACERT engine management used in current Caterpillar engines.
- Perform some basic troubleshooting on ADEM-managed engines.
- Describe how <SMART> programming has replaced hard limits with soft parameters to optimize system operation.
- Identify the ESTs required to read ADEM electronic systems.
- Perform some basic troubleshooting using Caterpillar's Electronic Technician (ET).
- Use Caterpillar's service information system (SIS).
- Describe flash memory and programming.
- Access the data recording features used by ADEM.

KEY TERMS

advanced combustion and emissions reduction technology (ACERT)

advanced diesel engine management (ADEM)

Caterpillar Fleet Information Software (FIS)

Caterpillar information display (Cat ID)

Cat Messenger

clean gas induction (CGI)

direct-operated check (DOC)

Electronic Technician (ET)

electronic unit injector (EUI)

E-Trim

flash programming

four-terminal MEUIs

Highway Master

injector drivers

mechanically actuated, electronically controlled unit injector (MEUI)

MEUI-C injector

personality module

programmable electronic engine control (PEEC)

Service Information System (SIS)

SoftCruise

spill valve solenoid (SVS)

telematics

variable valve timing (VVT)

INTRODUCTION

Up until Environmental Protection Agency (EPA) model year (MY) 2007, Caterpillar engines were the market leader in class 4 to class 8 truck engine sales. In 2007, Caterpillar announced that from EPA MY 2010, it would no longer be supplying engines to the on-highway market. Overnight, this fractioned Caterpillar sales to the truck transportation industry. That said, there continues to be a significant number of Cat engines on the road today. It remains to be seen whether the company will once again get seriously back into the business of supplying trucks to on-highway markets: The recent launch of a Caterpillar vocational truck suggests that this may happen sooner rather than later, but although the current vehicle is powered by a Cat C15 short block, it is currently badged as a Navistar engine. This will change in 2016 when the Caterpillar vocational truck will be manufactured entirely in-house; it is not yet known what engine will be used to power this proposed initiative.

CAT HISTORY OF ELECTRONIC ENGINES

Caterpillar's first electronically managed diesel engine used in truck applications was the 3176, launched in 1989. This was a full authority, **electronic unit injector (EUI)**-fueled engine. Caterpillar calls its EUIs a **mechanically actuated, electronically controlled unit injector (MEUI)** system. The operating principles of MEUIs were covered in Chapter 25. Since 2007, Caterpillar has used twin-actuator MEUIs, which it calls MEUI-Cs: These were studied in detail in Chapter 26. Because of the rapid emergence of the electronic age in truck diesels, driven by EPA emissions legislation, Caterpillar introduced its **programmable electronic engine control (PEEC)** system shortly after 1991 emission laws were passed. PEEC was a partial authority electronic management system that adapted the port-helix metering injection pump on Cat's popular 3406 engine to computer controls. PEEC was used on highway diesel engines up until EPA MY 1997, by which time almost all EPA highway-compliant engines required full authority engine controls.

KEY SYSTEM DATA

The following is a quick reference guide to some of the Caterpillar-specific system terminology and acronyms used in this chapter.

Management Systems

- Programmable electronic engine controls (PEEC). PEEC is the management system used to adapt Caterpillar port-helix metering injection pumps to electronic controls. Introduced in 1989.
- **Advanced diesel engine management (ADEM)** system. Cat uses a numeric suffix to indicate the software generation used (e.g., ADEM 4). The term has been used since the early 1990s to describe the management system on all Caterpillar engines, beginning with off-highway versions.
- Advanced combustion and emissions reduction technology (ACERT). Term used for the various different means Cat uses to describe its emission controls since 2004.

System Software Tools

- Service information system (SIS). This is the name for Cat's subscription online service information system. It is accessed through the Caterpillar data hub and has entirely replaced all hard-copy service literature, including that on engines that preceded the electronic era. But do not recycle your old paper service manuals yet! Many of the older service manuals have been scanned into SIS at low resolution and are difficult to interpret.
- Electronic Technician (ET). ET is the Cat diagnostic software designed to run in conjunction with its SIS. This is the software required to diagnose and reprogram on- and off-highway Caterpillar engine malfunctions.

CAT ELECTRONIC ENGINES

The following are some examples of Caterpillar electronically managed engines used since the beginning of the electronic era. Most are EPA highway-compliant for the year they were introduced, but it should be noted that their off-highway versions may use a different setup. The year indicated in the following list indicates the EPA compliance year and not the year of release; for instance, the C7 and C9 hydraulically actuated electronic unit injector (HEUI) engines were not available until 2005. Post-2010 versions of C13 and C15 ACERT engines are available in Caterpillar trucks supplied to Australian and other offshore markets.

3176 MEUI	1989	10.3-liter displacement
3406B PEEC	1989	14.6-liter displacement
3196 MEUI	1991	12.4-liter displacement
3406E MEUI	1991	14.6-liter displacement
3126 HEUI	1994	6.6-liter displacement
C-10 MEUI	1996	10.2-liter displacement
C-12 MEUI	1996	11.4-liter displacement
C-15 MEUI	1998	14.6-liter displacement
C-16 MEUI	1998	15.8-liter displacement
C7 HEUI	2004	7.2-liter displacement
C9 HEUI	2004	8.8-liter displacement
C11 MEUI	2004	11.1-liter displacement
C13 MEUI	2004	12.5-liter displacement
C15 MEUI	2004	15.2-liter displacement
C18 MEUI	2004	18.1-liter displacement
C7 CR	2007	7.2-liter displacement
C9 CR	2007	8.8-liter displacement
C13 MEUI-C	2007	12.5-liter displacement
C15 MEUI-C	2007	15.2-liter displacement
C13 MEUI-C OH	2010	12.5-liter displacement
C15 MEUI-C OH	2010	15.2-liter displacement
C18 MEUI-C OH	2010	18.1-liter displacement

Note:

The absence of a hyphen between the C and a number indicates an ACERT engine. The acronym OH denotes *off-highway only*

Figure 41–1 shows the torque and power curves of a C7 engine.

ACERT

Caterpillar **advanced combustion and emissions reduction technology**, or **ACERT**, engines were introduced for the engine model year 2004 for the entire range of Caterpillar highway engines and many of its off-highway products. This includes its Perkins range of engines. There are six primary features of ACERT, although they may not all be used on all of the Cat family of engines. ACERT is briefly described in this chapter, because it is required to understand some of the features of the management system.

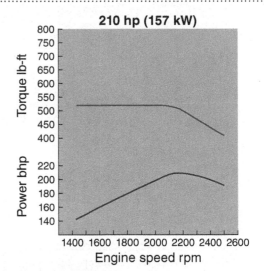

FIGURE 41–1 Torque and power curves of a C7 engine.

Performance data

Operating range (rpm)	1440–2500
Governed speed—(rpm)	**2500**
Advertised hp (kW)	210 (157)
Max hp (kW)	210 (157)
Peak torque—lb-ft. (N·m)	**520 (705)**
Peak torque—rpm	1440
Torque rise (%)	28
Altitude capability—ft (m)	10,000 (3048)

The technology of the components is studied in greater detail in Chapters 47 and 48 addressing emissions controls. **Figure 41–2** shows a block diagram of the ADEM-ACERT system as used on C13 and C15 engines.

ACERT SYSTEMS

1. Series turbocharging. Not used in all ACERT engines. Twin, in-series turbochargers—one with electronic control module (ECM)-managed variable geometry (wastegate), the other constant geometry—provide ECM management of manifold boost over the widest possible engine load and rpm range. This feature maximizes the rejected heat "recycling" and provides precision control over combustion.

2. Electronically controlled **variable valve timing (VVT)**. Not used in all ACERT engines. The VVT feature provides a *soft* intake valve closure feature. Providing the ECM with the ability to delay the closing of the intake valves results in better control of the

FIGURE 41–2 Block diagram of the electronic components used on an ACERT C13 or C15 engine.

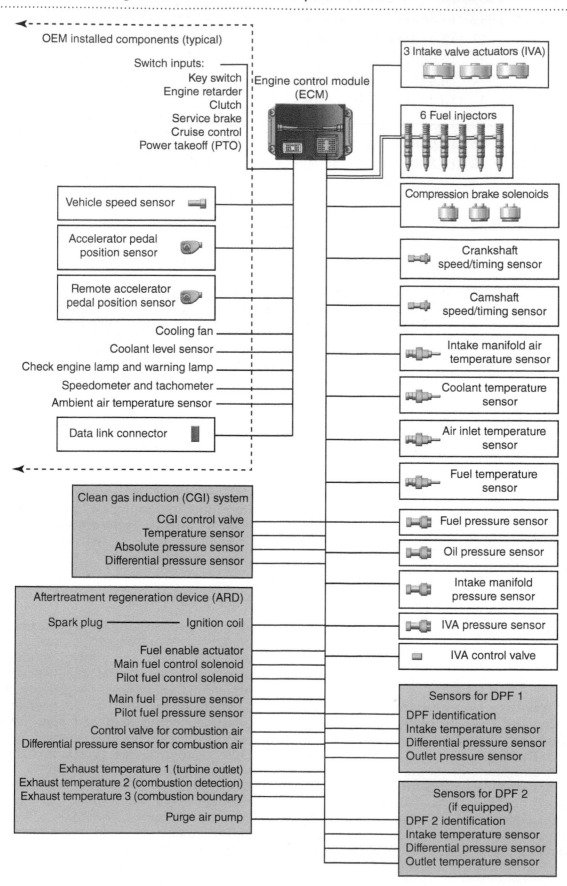

amount of air (read *oxygen*) in the cylinder before combustion. VVT is actuated when the engine is operated in the middle range of its power and torque bands, a running condition in which typically fuel efficiency is at its best and NO$_x$ output tends to rise. Cylinder breathing becomes engine computer managed rather than being confined to the hard limits of camshaft management.

3. Twin-actuator MEUI introduced in C13 and C15 engines in 2007 and Caterpillar CR introduced on C7 and C9 engines, also in 2007. Twin-actuator MEUIs (see chapter 26) are also commonly described as **four-terminal MEUIs**, but Caterpillar identifies them as **MEUI-C injectors**. They incorporate an electrohydraulic nozzle assembly in place of the hydraulic nozzle assembly used in the pre-2007 product. Cat CR was introduced on post-2007 C7 and C9 engines.

4. Multipulse injection. MEUIs and CR injectors are capable of ECM-driven multiple pulses. Breaking up an injection pulse into multiple events provides the MEUI with features associated with CR systems.

5. Exhaust gas aftertreatment. ACERT technology uses a combination oxidation catalyst and diesel particulate filter (DPF) integrated into a single canister to help manage engine emissions. The DPF is capable of both passive and active regeneration cycles. Active regeneration cycles are managed by dosing fuel into the aftertreatment canister along with coil-induced spark ignition. DPF operation and management are studied in some detail in Chapters 47 and 48.

6. **Clean gas induction (CGI)**. CGI is a variation on exhaust gas recirculation (EGR) used on Caterpillar's post-2007 ACERT family of engines. It differs from EGR in that it sources its "dead" exhaust gas downstream from the DPF. Cat refers to its CGI system as "clean EGR." CGI is monitored by a mass airflow sensor (MAF) and just like its competitors' EGRs, the system objective is to keep combustion temperatures lower to reduce NO$_x$ emissions under certain running conditions. It is easy to identify a Cat CGI engine because the CGI pipe can be seen to leave the muffler/converter/DPF assembly close to its exit. This pipe routes the theoretically clean dead gas back to the intake circuit via the low-pressure turbocharger compressor.

Caterpillar indicates that the core of ACERT emissions management is the ability to manage in-cylinder combustion more effectively than its competitors, enabling it to meet tough emissions standards without compromising engine power, fuel economy, and engine longevity.

ADEM ELECTRONICS

The Caterpillar ADEM system is known as one of the more comprehensive engine management packages found on current diesel engines, both for its programmability and its diagnostics. It has rapidly evolved from its first introduction in the middle 1990s. The current version is networked to the J1587 and J1939 CAN buses and drives the electronics required to manage the emissions controls. Electronic service tool (EST) access is by means of a data connector, either six- or nine-pin Deutsch socket, connected to the chassis data bus. All engine and emissions controls are driven from a single ECM at the SA 00 address on the chassis data bus.

SINGLE-MODULE SYSTEM

Caterpillar's ADEM has been a single-module system for a number of years now. In the early 1990s, Caterpillar used a bolt-on **personality module** on which the PROM and EEPROM data retention hardware were embedded. The personality module was loaded by external flash programming and ECM-driven write-to-self capability. The personality module is integrated into the ECM housing in its current product and is simply flash-programmed at factory initialization—and thereafter on an as-required basis. The processing hardware and all of the output switching apparatus are contained within the ECM housing.

INPUT CIRCUIT

Command and monitoring sensors and switches in Caterpillar applications are consistent with other comparable full authority management systems with the exception of the throttle position sensor (TPS). The Caterpillar TPS is dealt with later in this section. Most of the remaining input circuit components are generic in terms of operating principles. The operating principles of input circuit components are described in detail in Chapter 34. **Figure 41–3** shows a left-side view of a C13 engine. The ADEM ECM and many of the input circuit components are located on the left side of the engine.

FIGURE 41–3 ECM, sensor, and connector locations viewed from the left side of a C13 engine.

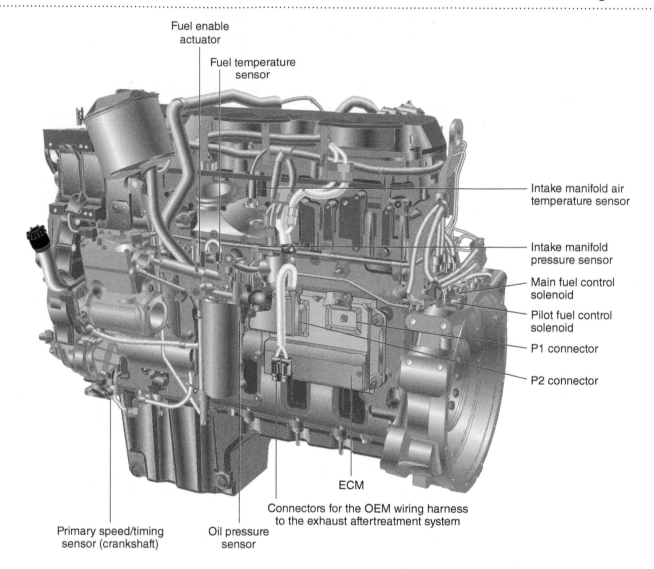

CATERPILLAR TPS

Caterpillar ADEM ECMs require a pulse width modulated (PWM) signal to be delivered by the TPS used on its engine. This PWM signal is generated in three ways in current systems, depending on when the engine was manufactured.

Cat Can-Style TPS

The first type of TPS used by Caterpillar was a floor-mounted, variable capacitance device designed to output a constant frequency PWM signal; it had the appearance of a can. Caterpillar states that this digital PWM signal overcomes errors that can be produced by analog signals due to pin-to-pin leakage or contamination in either the connectors or harnesses. These and other signal variables are an important factor in any drive-by-wire system. If the PWM signal is invalidated for whatever reason, the engine defaults to run at the programmed low-idle speed. Mechanically, the sensor is designed to have 30 degrees of active travel, with an additional 5 degrees of under-travel and 10 degrees of over-travel for linkage tolerance. The can-type TPS operates on a variable capacitance principle. The TPS is powered by 8 volts (not the Caterpillar V-Ref, which is always 5 volts), and internal digital circuitry converts the capacitive signal to a PWM value, which is returned to the ECM. The upper half of **Figure 41–4** shows a Caterpillar floor-mounted TPS.

FIGURE 41–4 The floor- and pedal-mounted throttle position sensors used exclusively on Caterpillar engines.

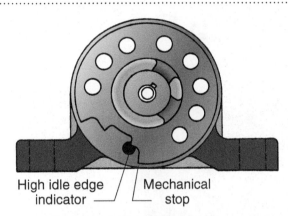

Floor-Mounted Throttle Sensor

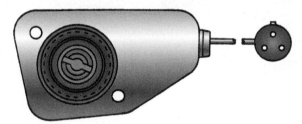

Pedal-Mounted Throttle Sensor

Cat Pedal-Mounted TPS

Caterpillar replaced the can-style TPS midway through the 1990s with a pedal-mounted unit. This unit functions on a potentiometer electrical principle, but that is all it has in common with other original equipment manufacturer (OEM) TPSs. Like the can type, the Cat pedal-mounted TPS must be powered by 8 volts. This TPS has built-in digital circuitry that converts the analog signal produced by the potentiometer to a PWM signal. The can-type TPS and the pedal-type TPS cannot be regarded as interchangeable. Later-version TPS units can automatically recalibrate themselves. They are a Caterpillar-supplied component and must not be replaced with a generic TPS. The lower half of Figure 41–4 shows a pedal-mounted Caterpillar TPS.

Cat Pedal-Mounted Hall-Effect TPS

More recent Caterpillar engines option a pedal-mounted TPS that use a Hall-effect operating principle. This unit is powered-up using an 8 V-DC input and outputs a 500 Hz PWM signal based on pedal angle. This means that in terms

of output functionality it does not differ from the earlier pedal-type TPS. However, in dispensing with the contact-style potentiometer used in earlier versions, the noncontact Hall-effect TPS produces greater accuracy and longer service life.

ECM

The ECMs used on ADEM-managed engines are microprocessor-driven management and switching devices that are usually mounted on the left side of the engine cylinder block. The ECM is responsible for engine governing, fuel management algorithm, self-diagnostics, and system monitoring, creating data audit trails and controlling all the exhaust aftertreatment devices. The ECMs are programmable with customer and proprietary data. While there may have been some problems with the first generation of Caterpillar electronic systems, today's ECMs are resistant to radio frequency, electromagnetic interference, and other low-level radiation. **Figure 41–5** is a right-side view of a post-2007 ACERT engine featuring twin turbochargers.

ECM DRIVERS

Caterpillar ECMs incorporate all of the required system drivers within the ECM housing. The various drivers are responsible for outputting system reference voltages (a 5-volt circuit), powering-up sensors (on the 8-volt circuit), switching the injectors, and operating all the emissions control hardware. While the input circuit receives data from engine monitoring sensors and those broadcast on the data bus, it can also broadcast itself onto both the J1587 and J1939 powertrain data backbones. Although ECM computing power, speed, and memory capability have increased exponentially, the physical size has generally decreased over the years.

PROCESSING ALGORITHM

As with most electronically controlled engine management systems, the control algorithm requires hundreds of rules and thousands of values. The values are received into the processing cycle by the input circuit, from memory, and off the chassis data bus. The rules are retained in the ECM memory components we know as read-only memory (ROM),

FIGURE 41–5 Location of ACERT components on a post-2007 C13 engine.

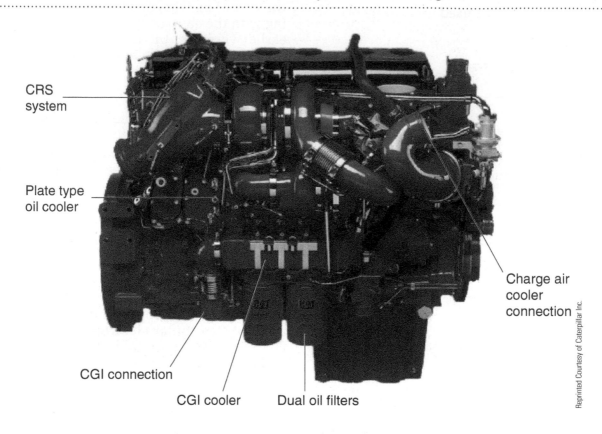

CRS system

Plate type oil cooler

Charge air cooler connection

CGI connection

CGI cooler

Dual oil filters

Reprinted Courtesy of Caterpillar Inc.

programmable read-only memory (PROM), and electronically erasable, programmable read-only memory (EEPROM). The computer manipulates this data in main memory or random access memory (RAM) and computes an outcome. **Figure 41–6** is a schematic representation of a Caterpillar processing cycle.

The control algorithm contains a comprehensive fuel map. The ECM analyzes the data input from the command and monitoring sensors, and after referencing the instructions programmed to its data retention media, plots a fueling profile. Startup fueling strategy, failure modes, and all the system default values are programmed into the ECM software. Some Caterpillar engines have software that enables the cycling of cylinders during certain conditions, such as warm idling, with the objective of saving fuel and minimizing engine wear. The ECM is also programmed to run diagnostic tests on input and output circuits and identify specific component and circuit faults using blink codes, reader programmers, or personal computers (PCs). Most troubleshooting can be performed using the appropriate EST and a digital multimeter (DMM).

CATERPILLAR PERSONALITY MODULE

The Caterpillar personality module combines the memory components we have called PROM and EEPROM in other systems. A full description of the PROM and EEPROM functions within an ECM is provided in Chapter 34 but in essence, this type of memory contains:

- Engine-specific data
- Customer-specific data
- The reprogram and write-to-self capability of the system

The personality module was bolted to older-version ECMs so it could be removed and replaced if necessary. Also attached to the older-version ECMs was a transducer module. It was responsible for transducing (that is, translating) all system pressure values to electrical signals so they could be sent to the ECM.

Current version ECMs are integral units. When these are reprogrammed with data, the term used is **flash programming**. The flash memory chip in the personality module contains

FIGURE 41–6 Control algorithm schematic used in a Caterpillar ECM processing cycle.

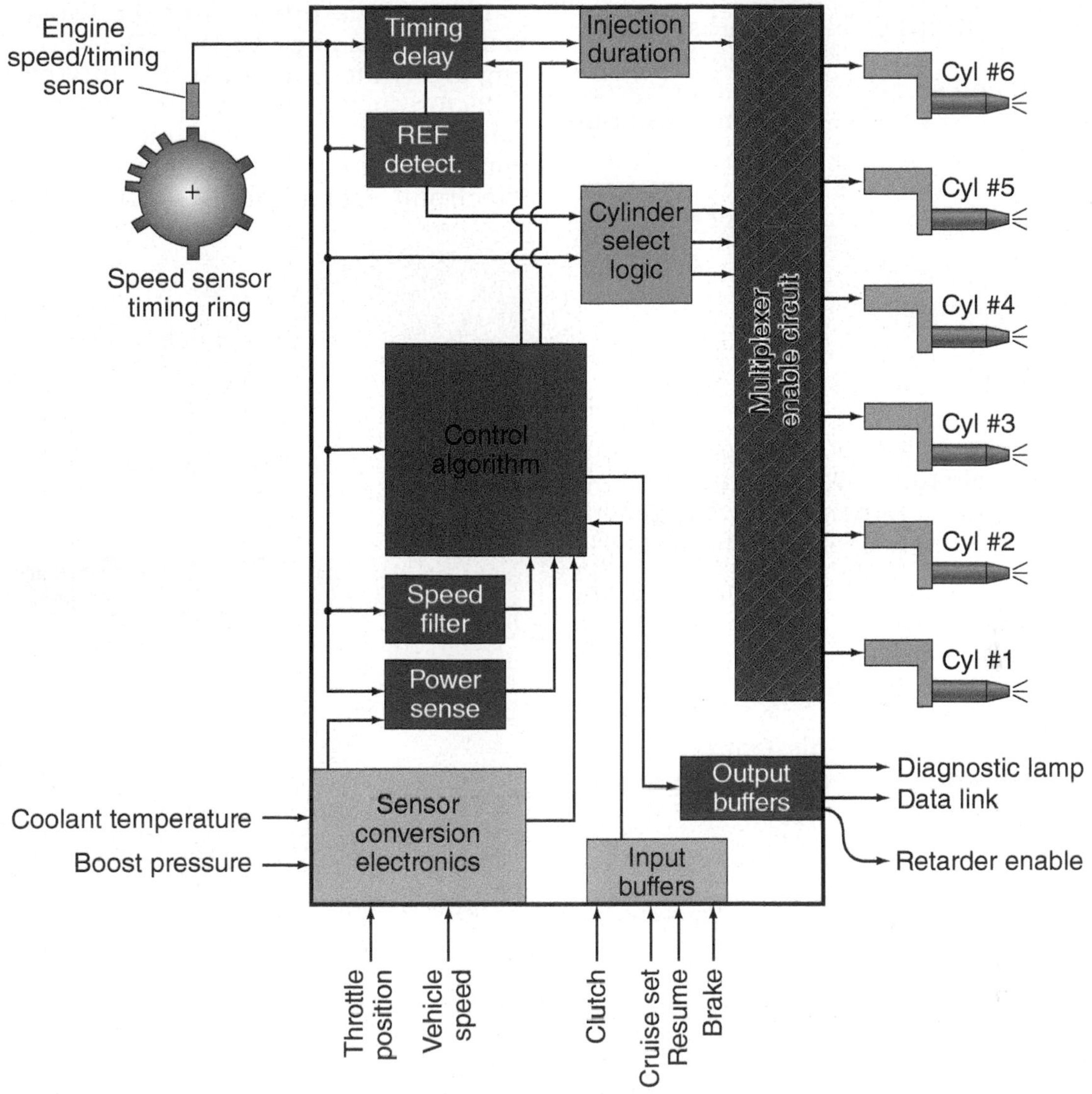

engine series-specific control software. Caterpillar ECMs have a nonvolatile RAM (NV-RAM) component for storing certain customer data and audit trails. This is backed up by an internal ECM battery. If the vehicle batteries are disconnected or have failed, it should not result in the loss of NV-RAM data.

CAT ECM INJECTOR DRIVERS

Caterpillar **injector drivers** are integral with the ECM. They produce a spiked control signal to energize injectors at a nominal voltage value of around 108 V-DC (expect to see between 90 and 120 V-DC when scoped), which is obtained by using induction coils. The voltage spike is

initial and the circuit holds at 12 volts: The inductive kick produced by the coil when the injector control solenoid circuit is opened and its magnetic field collapses is suppressed to prevent back-feed spikes. In cases of the MEUI-C (twin-actuator EUI), both **spill valve solenoid (SVS)** and **direct-operated check (DOC)** actuators (see Chapter 26) are triggered at the nominal 108 V-DC. The same voltage is used to trigger Caterpillar EHIs. Injector open-close cycles are measured in milliseconds.

OUTPUT CIRCUIT

Caterpillar output circuit devices put the results of the computer processing cycle into action.

In a post-2007 MEUI-C fuel management system, the ECM outputs include:

- The injectors (MEUI-Cs and CR-EHIs)
- Engine controls such as fan hub, compression brake, and so on
- The conditioned V-Ref (5-VDC) and power-up (8-VDC) circuits
- Dash display data
- Broadcast drivers to the chassis data backbone
- EGR system controls
- DPF system controls

E-TRIM

Caterpillar **E-Trim** is a bench-test specification that precisely evaluates how each injector flows fuel during operation. Depending on the generation of engine, E-Trim is one of the following:

- A four-digit number printed on either the solenoid or the upper face of the injector tappet flange. This must be manually programmed to the ECM using ET and an appropriate EST.
- A downloadable engine file from SIS which must be flashed to the engine ECM using ET and an appropriate EST.

Figure 41-7 is a graphic representation of the fuel flow differential that would be found in a set of injectors when subjected to factory bench flow testing. After the bench test, each injector is assigned either a numeric E-Trim code or a calibration flash file. After the E-Trim code has been programmed to the ADEM ECM, the fueling algorithm can adjust the duty cycle of each injector so that it can compensate for fueling variables. The E-Trim value for each injector must be programmed to the engine ECM using Electronic Technician (ET) software.

TECH TIP:

Whenever an injector has to be replaced, ensure that the new E-Trim value is programmed to the ECM using ET. If this step is overlooked, the ADEM ECM will use the E-Trim values of the old injector, which can result in engine fueling balance problems.

CAUTION:

Always observe original equipment manufacturer (OEM) instructions for draining the fuel charging rail when removing injectors from an engine cylinder head. When a cylindrical MEUI is removed, the contents of the fuel charging rail end up in the engine cylinder if the cylinder head fuel gallery is not first drained. CR-EHIs rails should also be drained into a catch vessel prior to quill and line removal, if for no other reason than to avoid creating a mess.

FIGURE 41-7 E-Trim balancing of MEUI fuel flow rates.

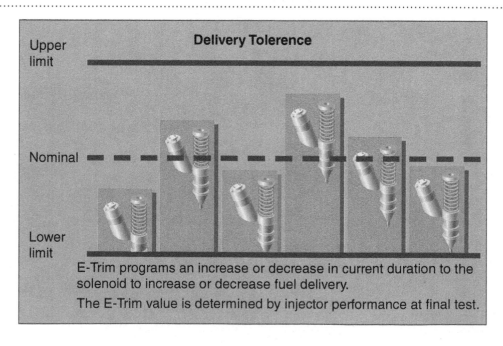

SYSTEM DIAGNOSTICS AND COMMUNICATIONS

Caterpillar electronic system self-diagnostics are consistent with those of its competitor OEM systems. The self-diagnostic capabilities of the system may be accessed by a range of means, beginning with simple flash codes and extending through a number of PC-based software, data management, and analysis programs. In the event of electronic system or component failure, the operator is alerted by the dash-mounted check engine light (CEL). The code may be read on the CEL using the cruise control switches on vehicles equipped with cruise control or with one of the ESTs listed previously.

DIAGNOSTIC RECORDER

Current Caterpillar electronic management systems have a built-in diagnostic recorder. This diagnostic recorder is a sort of constant snapshot mode that is triggered whenever a fault code is logged or by the driver toggling the cruise switches. The data recorded can be accessed with an EST and used to diagnose a set of conditions that may have contributed to the failure. A snapshot test is commonly used to diagnose intermittent problems in electronic management systems. The test is triggered by an event such as a trouble code and records data frames at the instant of, before, and after the event. These data frames display all the critical system parameters for analysis: The data immediately prior to the event can be critical in determining the cause of the code.

While the technician troubleshooting an electronically managed engine must not overlook the fact that an engine does have systems that are not electronic, in most of the current generation of electronically managed engines, the correct troubleshooting strategy is usually driven electronically. For this reason, whenever diagnosing any problem on an engine, the manufacturer's sequential troubleshooting sequence must be observed.

ESTs AND SOFTWARE

The recommended EST for accessing Caterpillar on-board electronics is a PC loaded with Caterpillar proprietary software. Various different generic handheld ESTs loaded with Cat-specific software are available, but their functionality is

FIGURE 41-8 ET screen display following a cylinder cutout test.

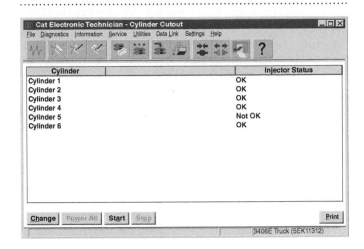

limited, especially as engine electronics become more advanced. Caterpillar marine and industrial engines since 2013 have featured built-in monitoring-diagnostics such as Engine Vision Display (EVD).

Caterpillar had its own EST in the early days of its electronic systems, known as the Electronic Control Analyzer Programmer (ECAP), and some of these survive and can interact with older engines. For current systems, a PC with proprietary Windows-environment software called **Electronic Technician (ET)** and **SIS** (Caterpillar's **Service Information System**) are required. Cat ET is a user-friendly software package that enables system diagnosis, customer and proprietary (Caterpillar) data reprogramming, and access to fuel/mileage information. All troubleshooting of Caterpillar engines should be driven by ET. You can see an example of the ET graphical user interface (GUI) or display screen in **Figure 41-8**, which shows the results of an injector cutout test. Using ET requires a minimal knowledge of Windows software. The read, diagnostic, and programming protocols are similar to those used on other electronically managed engines.

DATA LINK

ESTs connect to the Caterpillar ADEM ECM by first accessing the chassis data bus using the appropriate data connector, or directly to the engine electronics using the dedicated Cat data connector. Alternatively, a J1708 six-pin or J1939 nine-pin DLC can access the engine electronics via the chassis data bus. The DLC connectors and their cavity pin assignments are shown in Chapter 35.

CAT ID

Caterpillar information display (Cat ID) is a driver display option located on the truck dash that can either be integrated or added on to the engine electronics. Caterpillar ID accesses data from the ADEM ECM and displays it to the driver. Data displayed includes:

- Fuel usage
- Feedback on engine operating conditions
- Fault codes
- First-level diagnostics

The driver is able to navigate through the displayed data using a four-button keypad. Cat ID displays critical fault codes as they occur with both the code number and an alpha description of the fault. Flash codes are provided for drivers who prefer operating the vehicle without a dash display. Cat ID has a built-in theft deterrent option: When activated, a four-digit password must be entered on engine shutdown and reentered before the engine will restart.

Cat Messenger

Cat Messenger is an enhancement of the Cat ID driver display unit. It provides real-time feedback on engine-operating conditions (fuel usage, miles per gallon [mpg], fluid temperatures, and so on), maintenance scheduling, diagnostic reporting, and theft deterrence. Drivers are required to enter a four-digit access code before the ignition circuit can be closed when the theft deterrence feature is enabled. A driver or owner can also set personal fuel economy goals and base oil change intervals on fuel consumed rather than mileage.

HIGHWAY MASTER

Remote programming technology can be used to reprogram engine parameters for a single truck or an entire fleet from an office location. This **telematics** wireless technology is available through Caterpillar's **Highway Master**, working in conjunction with Qualcomm. Highway Master can also handshake with other chassis OEM telematics as well as proprietary wireless telecommunications providers. The type of data that can be broadcast by Highway Master includes fuel economy, mileage, and trip run/idle times. Highway Master can create fuel economy histograms (chart consisting of rectangular columns to show data on a graphed comparative scale), engine events, maintenance reports, and customer data programming.

CAT FIS

Caterpillar Fleet Information Software (FIS) permits data to be tracked and stored in the ADEM software. Once enabled, this data can be downloaded to:

- Handheld Nexiq or equivalent EST with hard-wire connection
- Handheld Argo mobile data terminal that allows a PC to extract data from up to 200 engine ECMs in less than 10 seconds per unit
- Caterpillar communications adapter routed to a PC loaded with ET and SIS

FIS provides the ability to analyze driver and engine performance data by unit and can compare the data from any number of units in a fleet.

PROGRAMMING OPTIONS

Caterpillar offers a wide range of programming options. These options expand with each successive generation of software. Some of the Caterpillar programming options are briefly described here.

<SMART> Options

Smart parameters or functions are those that will bend a hard-programmed limit or value when it makes sense to do so. Most current engine management electronics feature some <SMART> programming options. Some examples are:

VEHICLE SPEED LIMIT (VSL) The hard-programmed vehicle speed limit (VSL) used in early versions of ADEM can be optionally reprogrammed with soft-limit VSL technology. Soft-limit programming permits a cushion on either side of a hard limit value. Soft VSL modulates engine fueling when the truck is running over rolling terrain, permitting some latitude on either side of the programmed vehicle speed to maximize fuel economy. Vehicle maximum speed can be programmed at a value under peak cruise speed. This feature encourages the driver to use the **SoftCruise** option: It works on the idea that the chassis electronics have better odds of achieving good fuel economy than the human driver.

VSL can be programmed as a soft parameter that actually "learns" from the running conditions of the vehicle. For instance, when running through undulating hills, a run profile is created. The result means that instead of an abrupt fuel cutoff each time the vehicle achieves the programmed VSL on a down grade, the engine is fueled to keep the manifold boost up and gain some speed advantage as it approaches upcoming hills. Soft VSL improves fuel economy and driver comfort. It works in conjunction with SoftCruise logic.

SOFTCRUISE SoftCruise is a <SMART> cruise control option that essentially "learns" running and terrain conditions, then modulates engine fueling to eliminate the abrupt cutoffs in fueling and engine braking actuations that are characteristic of hard cruise programming. SoftCruise can manage the engine retarder if programmed to do so: Automatic brake activation reduces driver fatigue while also increasing the vehicle fuel economy.

PROGRAMMABLE EXTENDED DROOP Governor droop can be programmed to extend up to 150 rpm above the top engine limit (TEL) or rated speed value. This reduces driver shifting frequency when the engine is coupled to mechanically shifted transmissions.

ADEM MULTITORQUE ADEM MultiTorque is an option that, when enabled, senses when the truck is in the top gear ratios by:

- Analysis of engine rpm and vehicle speed ratio (mechanical transmissions)
- Data bus monitoring (electronically managed transmissions)

MultiTorque provides extra torque when running conditions require it. Extra torque would typically be provided when negotiating hills. This option results in reduced driver fatigue because the driver is shifting less often, and it has evidently been proven to reduce driveline component wear, presumably as a result of fewer shifts.

COOLING FAN CONTROL The ECM constantly receives input from the temperature sensors monitoring the engine coolant, oil temperature, intake manifold temperature, compression brake cycles, and air conditioning (A/C) refrigerant system pressure to determine whether the cooling fan should be actuated. An ECM output switches and manages (cycles on and off) the engine cooling fan, eliminating the requirement for such devices as fanstats. Additionally, the ECM may engage the fan when engine retarder high mode is selected to increase retarding effort: The effectiveness of this depends on the type of cooling fan used. Some heavy-duty, rigid steel blade cooling fans can "leach" up to 18 hp

(13 kW) of engine power when engaged: During braking, this translates into 18 hp (13 kW) of additional retarding effort.

POWER TAKEOFF (PTO) RAMP RATE PTO ramp rate can reduce the PTO work cycle time by enabling programming of the PTO rotational speed. This means that engine speed is, therefore, close-loop factored by PTO speed. This works well in applications where the PTO is driving a compressor used to charge a tanker for load transfer—or a generator in which the electrical load varies but the rpm should not. The cab TPS is disabled when the PTO ramp rate option is selected, to eliminate the possibility of PTO overspeed.

GEAR DOWN PROTECTION The programmable gear down feature prevents engine overspeed conditions by limiting engine rpm in the higher gear ratios, with the objective of ensuring that cruising speed can only be attained in the top gear. It is an effective programmable option in fleet-type operations.

PROGRESSIVE SHIFTING Progressive shifting can assist less-experienced truck drivers by providing engine speed prompts to the driver during operation-limit rpm below the upper shift limit. Progressive shifting narrows the engine operating range, which can be a driver irritant because with a mechanically shifted transmission it increases the number of shift events. However, when this is programmed in conjunction with the electronics on automated or automatic transmissions, shifting is optimized to produce the best vehicle fuel economy.

OPTIMIZED IDLE Optimized idle is a programmable strategy used to reduce fuel consumption and emissions during even short periods of engine idling. Providing the engine fluid sensors indicate to the ECM that the engine is at operating temperature, during phases of engine idling (even of short duration, such as waiting for a traffic light to change) the ECM can run the engine on three cylinders. This condition is audible and may produce a small amount of vibration, but it is a normal operation.

IDLE SHUTDOWN TIMER In common with most other truck electronic management systems, Caterpillar offers an idle shutdown timer programmable from 1 minute to 24 hours. Because of anti-idle legislation in many jurisdictions, this is essential on today's trucks. The idle shutdown timer programming can be defeated by a driver-activated override feature.

TRIP DATA LOG This standard feature permits monitoring and recording of the engine parameters by three methods:

1. Lifetime totals
2. Trip totals
3. Instantaneous readings

The following parameters are monitored:

- Engine running hours/ECM hours
- Machine miles
- Idle mode miles
- PTO mode hours
- Total fuel consumed
- Idle fuel consumed
- PTO fuel consumed
- Average engine load factor

SUMMARY

- Caterpillar engine management electronics are known as ADEM.
- Caterpillar's emissions management technology used in post-2004 engines is known as ACERT.
- Caterpillar's engine diagnostic software is Electronic Technician.
- Caterpillar's online service information system is known as SIS. A subscription is required to access it.
- The current Caterpillar ADEM ECM is a single module incorporating both the processing capability and output drivers required by the engine and emissions control system.
- All Caterpillar throttle position sensors (TPSs) are powered-up at 8 V-DC and output a PWM digital signal to the ECM.
- Caterpillar locates the injector drivers within the ECM housing and uses induction coils to spike the MEUI actuation voltage to nominal values of 108 V-DC.
- First-generation Caterpillar ECMs used a bolt-on personality module that was flash-programmed with PROM and EEPROM data. The personality module logs proprietary data, customer programmed options, write-to-self, and data audit trails.
- A Caterpillar ECM has a nonvolatile electronic memory component (NV-RAM) and an integral battery to sustain it should battery power be interrupted for any reason.

- Caterpillar injectors are assigned calibration flow values when factory bench-tested that are known as E-Trim codes.
- When a Caterpillar injector is changed out, new injector E-Trim codes must be programmed to the ECM. Depending on the generation of engine, this is either done manually by entering a four-digit E-Trim code, or by downloading and flashing the ECM with a new calibration file. In both cases, ET must be used to access the engine electronics.
- Caterpillar electronics support a wide range of <SMART> programming options that "soften" hard-limit programming such as vehicle road speed and programmed cruise settings with flexible limits to optimize fuel economy and driver state of mind.
- Programming options in current systems include a data log that records critical engine and vehicle running parameters in three formats: lifetime totals, trip totals, and instantaneous readout. Caterpillar's engine electronics telematics provide vehicle-to-base wireless communications using Highway Master software.
- Microsoft Windows, ET, and SIS software are required to troubleshoot Caterpillar engine management systems.

REVIEW QUESTIONS

1. What is the Caterpillar online service information system known as?
   a. ET
   b. SIS
   c. ISIS
   d. QSOL

2. What is Caterpillar diagnostic software known as?
   a. Master Diagnostics (MD)
   b. InSite
   c. Caterpillar Diagnostic Link (CDL)
   d. Electronic Technician (ET)

3. What engine management system was used to manage port-helix metering injection pumps on 3406 engines?
   a. PEEC
   b. ACERT
   c. ADEM
   d. HEUI

4. What type of signal does a Caterpillar throttle position sensor send back to the ECM?
   a. V-Ref
   b. Analog DC
   c. Analog AC
   d. PWM

5. What is the emissions management technology on post-2004 Caterpillar engines known as?
   a. ADEM
   b. PEEC
   c. ACERT
   d. MEUI-C

6. Which of the following is an ACERT engine?
   a. 3406E
   b. 3176
   c. C-15
   d. C13

7. Where are Cat ADEM injector drivers located?
   a. Integral with the ECM
   b. On the firewall bulkhead
   c. Under the dash
   d. Integral with each MEUI

8. What voltage is sent to a Caterpillar TPS?
   a. V-Ref
   b. 8 V-DC
   c. V-Bat
   d. 108 V-DC

9. Caterpillar injectors are switched by the ECM drivers at:
   a. 5 V-DC.
   b. 12 V-DC.
   c. 24 V-DC.
   d. 108 V-DC.

10. Caterpillar's electronic theft deterrent option is a feature of which of the following options?
    a. Cat SIS
    b. Cat LED
    c. ET
    d. Cat ID

11. Which of the following systems uses wireless technology to download vehicle performance data such as fuel economy?
    a. Highway Master
    b. Global positioning satellite (GPS) unit
    c. ET
    d. Cat ID

12. Which of the following is the Caterpillar ADEM driver digital display?
    a. Highway Master
    b. Qualcomm
    c. ET
    d. Cat ID

13. Technician A states that Cat ADEM electronics permit the programming of the cruise control speed limit at a higher value than maximum vehicle speed limit. Technician B states that VSL is always a hard-value parameter that cannot be exceeded. Who is correct?
    a. Technician A only
    b. Technician B only
    c. Both A and B
    d. Neither A nor B

14. Technician A states that ET is required to program injector E-Trim codes to an ADEM ECM. Technician B says that failure to correctly program an E-Trim code to the ECM on injector change-out can result in unbalanced engine fueling. Who is correct?
    a. Technician A only
    b. Technician B only
    c. Both A and B
    d. Neither A nor B

15. Technician A says that all Caterpillar C9 engines use a CR fuel system. Technician B says that a post-2007 C15 uses MEUI-C dual-actuator EUIs. Who is correct?
    a. Technician A only
    b. Technician B only
    c. Both A and B
    d. Neither A nor B

42

Prerequisites: Chapters 21, 25, 29, 30, and 34

CUMMINS MANAGEMENT SYSTEMS

OBJECTIVES

After studying this chapter, you should be able to:

- Define the acronyms *CELECT* and *IS*.
- Identify Cummins engines that use electronic controls.
- Identify Cummins online service information and diagnostic software.
- Identify some of the features of the IS engine management used in current Cummins engines.
- Perform some basic troubleshooting on IS-managed engines.
- Identify the primary inputs to the IS ECM.
- Describe the different fuel systems managed by CELECT and IS engine management electronics.
- Describe some of the governing options programmable into IS.
- Identify customer and Cummins data programming options for IS.
- Outline the procedure required to troubleshoot and diagnose electronic problems on Cummins electronic engines.

KEY TERMS

ADEPT

common rail (CR)

Compulink

Cummins electronic engine control (CELECT)

Echeck

electronic control module (ECM)

electronic smart power (ESP)

engine position sensor (EPS)

extreme pressure injection (XPI)

high-pressure injection-time pressure (HPI-TP)

INSITE

integrated fuel system module (IFSM)

Interact System (IS)

Interbrake

PACE/PACER

Quantum System (QS)

QuickServe OnLine (QSOL)

RoadRelay

road speed governing (RSG)

throttle position sensor (TPS)

vehicle speed sensor (VSS)

INTRODUCTION

Since 2007, Cummins has been the leader in medium- and heavy-duty truck engine sales in North America. In addition, it has expanded its off-highway and international engine sales. Cummins electronics have managed the following fuel systems:

- Pressure-time (PT) (partial authority)
- CELECT EUI systems
- **High-pressure injection-time pressure (HPI-TP)**
- Cummins Accumulator Pump system (CAPs)
- Bosch Common Rail (CR)
- Cummins XPI CR

CUMMINS HISTORY OF ELECTRONIC ENGINES

Cummins's first engine management system was the partial authority **PACE/PACER** introduced on its pressure-time (PT) fueled N-Series engines in the late 1980s. This was little more than an engine and road speed governing system. Because it became obsolete a generation ago, you will have to reference earlier editions of this textbook to research the PACE/PACER system.

Cummins followed with its **Cummins electronic engine control (CELECT)** system, its first full authority electronic management system, in 1991 on L10 and N14 engines, and later on its M11 engine family when it was introduced in 1994. A second-generation CELECT Plus was introduced in the marketplace in 1996 and was used to manage M11 and N14 Plus engines. The N14 engine ceased production in 2000 and the M11 was adapted to be managed by Interact System electronics in 2001. ISM ceased production in 2009.

Interact System (IS) is a common platform engine controller designed to manage all Cummins Environmental Protection Agency (EPA) highway-compliant engines. **Quantum System (QS)** is the off-highway and industrial engine equivalent of IS. Both IS and QS can be programmed to run any of the Cummins family of engines.

KEY SYSTEM DATA

The following is a quick reference guide to some of the Cummins-specific system terminology and acronyms used in this chapter.

Management Systems

- **CELECT**. An acronym for Cummins electronics introduced in 1994 to manage Cummins electronic unit injector (EUI)-fueled engines.
- **CELECT Plus**. Second-generation CELECT introduced in 1997 and used to manage Cummins EUI-fueled engines.
- **Interact System (IS) controls**. Introduced in 1998 to manage ISX 15-liter engines (with the HPI-TP fuel system) and adapted to run all Cummins EPA highway-compliant engines regardless of fuel system.
- **Quantum System (QS) controls**. Introduced in 1999 to manage QSX 15-liter engines and adapted to run all Cummins industrial and off-highway engines regardless of fuel system.
- **ADEPT technology**. Set for phased introduction in ISX engines from 2015 through 2017, this will incorporate some hardware changes such as improved variable-geometry turbocharging (VGT) controls and Cummins's Ecoboost exhaust aftertreatment system (see Chapter 48), a lightweight single canister that combines diesel oxidation catalyst (DOC), selective catalytic reduction (SCR), and diesel particulate filter (DPF) functions. However, the more significant changes are in the software, which will adjust engine fueling to continuously variable operating factors such as grade and actual load. **ADEPT** (not an acronym) is designed to work with automated manual transmissions. ADEPT's SmartCoast feature disconnects the engine from the drivetrain during downhill runs and SmartCoast eliminates unnecessary downshifts: both are fuel-saving strategies.

System Software Tools

- **QuickServe OnLine (QSOL)**. Cummins's subscription online service information system. QSOL is accessed through the Cummins data hub and has replaced its hard-copy service literature.
- **INSITE**. INSITE is the Cummins diagnostic software designed to run in conjunction with QSOL. This is the software required to diagnose and reprogram on- and off-highway Cummins engine malfunctions.

Electronic Service Tools

For a number of years, a subscription to QSOL and INSITE software has been required to effectively diagnose and program Cummins engines. QSOL and INSITE are driven off a Windows environment and QSOL requires an active Web connection to be fully functional. As with many original equipment manufacturers (OEMs) in the past, Cummins also had two in-house electronic service tools (ESTs):

- **Compulink**
- **Echeck**

Compulink and Echeck were superseded by faster, more powerful PC-based software. In addition, some limited access to CELECT and IS electronics by generic ESTs, both from a Windows environment or integral handheld, is possible. This access will be enhanced with the implementation of heavy-duty on-board diagnostics (HD-OBD).

CUMMINS ELECTRONIC ENGINES

The following are some examples of Cummins electronically managed engines used since the beginning of the electronic era. Only the EPA highway-compliant engines are listed here, but most have an off-highway sibling. It should be noted that the engines underwent radical changes over the years and used different fuel systems. For instance, since its initial introduction the Cummins B-Series engine has used Lucas DPA, Bosch VE, Bosch 7100 inline port-helix, Bosch VP-44, and Bosch CR fuel systems. Post-2010 versions of the ISX 15, ISX 11.9, and ISL 9 use the Cummins XPI CR fuel system. Some examples of on-highway Cummins electronic engines are:

NTC 855 PT PACE	1986	14-liter displacement
L10 CELECT	1994	10-liter displacement
N14 CELECT	1994	14-liter displacement
M11 CELECT Plus	1995	10.8-liter displacement
ISX–HPI-TP	1998	15-liter displacement
ISB Bosch CR	1998	3.9-liter displacement
ISB Bosch CR	1998	5.9-liter displacement
ISC CAPs	1998	8.3-liter displacement
ISM–CELECT Plus	2001	10.8-liter displacement
ISC–Bosch CR	2003	8.3-liter displacement
ISL–Bosch CR	2003	8.9-liter displacement
ISB Bosch CR	2007	6.7-liter displacement
ISL–XPI CR	2010	8.9-liter displacement
ISX12–XPI CR	2013	11.9-liter displacement
ISX15–XPI CR	2010	15-liter displacement

In addition to Cummins badged engines, the company supplies engines to Paccar and manufactures NG-fueled versions of its engines in conjunction with Westport. The post-2010 PX8 uses the ISC 8.3-liter engine and the PX6 is essentially the ISB 6.7-liter engine.

SYSTEM OVERVIEW

Take a glance at the 1998 version of the ISX HPI-TP engine at its inauguration in 1998 and another at its final version in 2007: These two engines tell the story of how progressive emissions controls have changed the diesel engine in a period of less than 10 years. The clean lines of the 1998 version have been cluttered by a wide range of external emission control apparatus by 2007, while the fuel system and most of the guts of the engine underwent few notable changes.

For 2010, the ISX engine was re-engineered and came out in two displacements. The twin overhead camshafts (OHCs) were replaced by a single OHC and an in-house Cummins CR system known as **extreme pressure injection (XPI)** replaced the HPI-TP fuel system. Currently, there are two versions of the ISX-XPI engine, a 15 liter and an 11.9 liter. The post-2010 ISL shares the Cummins XPI fuel system. XPI is functionally the same as a standard CR fuel system as described in Chapter 30.

EMISSION CONTROLS

Emission controls have become a feature of all current diesel engines. Cummins IS manages the external apparatus including post-combustion exhaust gas recirculation (EGR), diesel particulate filter (DPF), and selective catalytic reduction (SCR), along with precisely controlling combustion aided by multipulse injection.

POST-2010 FUEL SYSTEMS

All Cummins EPA post-2010 highway-compliant diesel fuel systems use **common rail (CR)** fuel systems. Bosch CR continues to be used on the small-bore ISB, whereas Cummins CR is used on ISL and both versions of ISX. Cummins in conjunction with Westport Innovations also manufactures natural gas (NG) versions of their ISC, ISL, and ISX 12 engines that are widely used in transit bus, and more recently, truck applications, especially on the West Coast. NG-fueling using Westport management is discussed in Chapter 38.

INPUT CIRCUIT

Cummins input circuit subsystems components are usually connected to the ECM by a single wiring harness, integrating the separate sensor and actuator harnesses. The electrical principles on which they are based are explained in Chapter 34. Cummins engines are designed to receive a throttle position sensor (TPS) signal from either a potentiometer (contact-type) or Hall-effect (noncontact-type) TPS.

ENGINE MONITORING SENSORS

The operating principles of sensors are covered in Chapter 34, but some of the specific sensors used on Cummins electronically controlled diesel engines are covered here using Cummins terminology.

- **Ambient pressure sensor (APS).** Piezoelectric type, for altitude fuel deration.
- **Oil pressure sensor (OPS).** Piezoelectric type, located in the main oil rifle in the block.
- **Engine position sensor (EPS).** Magnetic pulse generator-type sensor. Usually a camshaft gear-located pulse wheel with 24 evenly spaced recesses to feed back rotational speed data and a small dowel to locate top dead center (TDC) #1 cylinder for engine position data.

- **Oil temperature sensor (OTS).** Thermistor, located in the main oil rifle in the block.
- **Intake manifold temperature (IMT) sensor.** Thermistor, located centrally on the intake manifold.
- **Boost pressure sensor (BPS).** Piezoresistive type, located in the intake manifold.
- **Coolant temperature sensor (CTS).** Thermistor, located in the thermostat housing.
- **Coolant level sensor (CLS).** Switch-type sensor that grounds through the engine coolant with dual probes to indicate normal or low coolant levels.

Figure 42–1 shows the CELECT monitoring sensor harness.

COMMAND SENSORS AND SWITCHES

- **Throttle pedal assembly.** OEM-supplied accelerator pedal that incorporates a 5 V-DC TPS that uses a potentiometer or Hall-effect principle. Some versions are equipped with an idle validation switch circuit (open-close circuit). An accelerator interlock is optional.
- **Interbrake.** A Cummins-designed engine compression brake managed by the IS electronics. Depending on the specific engine and the year it was produced, engine retarding

FIGURE 42–1 The CELECT sensor harness.

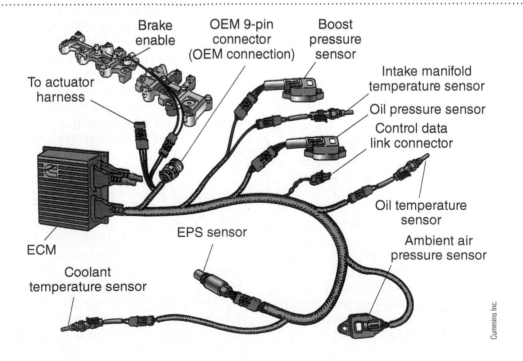

Cummins Inc.

down to 900 rpm is possible, actuated in multiple stages. IS electronics can automatically actuate engine braking in SmartCruise mode. Interbrake is discussed in more detail in Chapter 13.

- **Cruise control**. Managed by IS electronics with some advanced features: (a) governor tailoring (see Chapter 20); (b) cruise auto-resume after gear shift; (c) OEM cruise switch configuring; (d) automatic engine braking in cruise mode. The maximum cruise control speed limits the top vehicle speed while in cruise control mode, and this cannot exceed the maximum vehicle speed setting.
- **Power takeoff (PTO) control**. This feature controls engine rpm at a constant speed selected by the operator. Either a cab or a remote switch can be used, and PTO mode can be selected up to 6 mph (10 km/h) vehicle speed.

ELECTRONIC CONTROL MODULE (ECM)

The **electronic control module (ECM)** receives and processes information from the various engine and chassis sensors and switches, plots fueling and timing commands, and outputs signals to the injector driver circuitry (switching apparatus). It has an SA of 00 on the J1939 bus. A more detailed description of ECM functions appears elsewhere in this text.

Cummins was the first OEM to introduce vented ECMs. Moisture ingression into ECM housings results in premature failure, so most OEMs waterproofed their modules using seals. The problem is that like all computers, ECMs generate heat: High internal temperatures produced outward stress on the seals, and when the unit was turned off, lowering the internal temperature, the seal was subject to high inboard stress. Hot-cold cycles eventually caused seal failure, with the result that the ECM drew in moisture-laden air.

Until the introduction of vented ECMs, the number-one reason for ECM internal failures was moisture corrosion following a seal failure. Cummins ECMs solved this problem by venting the ECM to atmosphere using a Gore-Tex™ seal. This alleviated stress on the housing seal by allowing the module to breathe to atmosphere. Today most ECMs are manufactured using a similar moisture-exclusion principle.

ECM DRIVERS

The IS ECM injector driver unit uses coils to spike the actuator voltage to whatever voltage is required by the system. The injector actuators are one of the primary outputs of the IS ECM, along with reference voltage (V-Ref), rail pressure control, and the ability to broadcast on J1587 (until 2004) and J1939 data buses.

Cummins ISX engines from 1998 to 2009 with HPI-TP fueling used mechanically actuated time-pressure (TP) injectors. However, fuel control into and out of TP injectors was managed externally by IS electronics. TP injectors are equipped with two separate fuel circuits controlled by rail-located actuator valves. A pair of timing actuators was used to manage fuel into the TP injector timing circuit to set injection timing each cycle. Another pair of metering actuators was used to define injection fuel quantity. The four actuators were pulse width modulated (PWM) and located on the **integrated fuel system module (IFSM)**. In addition to the actuators, the IFSM was fitted with sensors. A full explanation of the HPI-TP fuel system appears in Chapter 29. **Figure 42-2** is a Cummins representation of how its processing cycle operates.

OUTPUT CIRCUIT

IS electronics control a range of actuators depending on the specific engine. Among the actuators are: electronically switched, mechanically actuated injectors (such as those in CR or CELECT engines), and the actuators used in pre-2010 ISX engines. In ISX engines prior to 2010, the fuel control outputs are the rail-located timing and metering actuators described in Chapter 29. In addition, the engine retarder (Interbrake or Jacobs C-brake), PTO apparatus, and all ECM broadcasts to the data bus can also be described as being part of the output circuit. **Figure 42-3** shows the XPI CR high-pressure pump used on post-2010 ISX 15 engines.

ENGINE PROTECTION SYSTEM

CELECT Plus and IS electronics monitor critical engine sensors and log fault codes when an out-of-normal condition is determined. If an out-of-range condition is detected in a critical sensor, an engine derate action may be initiated if the system is programmed for this feature. When this occurs, the operator will be alerted by a broadcast on the digital dash display, the

FIGURE 42–2 Cummins processing cycle graphics.

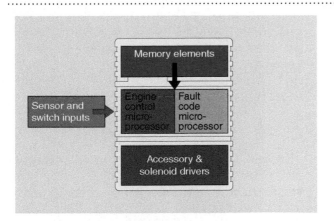

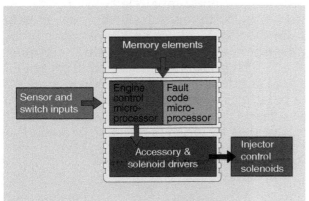

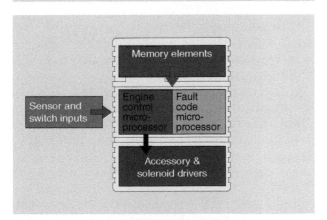

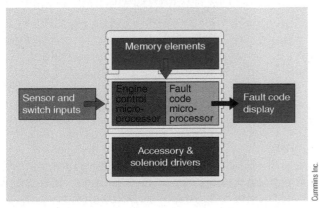

FIGURE 42–3 Current ISX 15 XPI-CR fuel pump.

flashing of appropriate dash lights, or both. Typically, the engine protection system monitors:

- Coolant temperature
- Oil temperature
- Intake manifold temperature
- Oil pressure
- Coolant level
- Engine overspeed
- EGR management
- DPF temperatures
- DPF efficiency
- SCR efficiency
- SCR dosing

At engine derate, the operator is alerted by the flashing light, and engine power and speed deration will occur incrementally depending on the severity of the condition. The engine will not actually shut down unless the ECM is programmed with the engine shutdown option. The engine protection shutdown option automatically shuts down the engine when a fluid pressure or temperature out-of-normal range problem occurs that could lead to catastrophic damage. Should this occur, the dash engine protection lamp will flash for 30 seconds before the shutdown. Key-off is required to restart the engine, but if the shutdown trigger persists, the engine will be shut off once again after 30 seconds.

PROGRAMMABLE FEATURES

CELECT Plus and IS offer a full range of programmable features consistent with other full authority management systems, including:

- Cruise control
- Automatic engine brake in cruise control

- PTO governing
- Gear-down protection
- Progressive shifting
- Limiting speed/variable speed governing
- Disable air conditioner
- Low-idle adjustment
- Idle shutdown option
- Engine protection shutdown
- Vehicle speed monitoring
- Disable engine fan
- Chassis data bus priorities
- Maintenance monitor options
- DPF active regeneration

Depending on the generation of the engine, these features and their options are programmable as customer data using Compulink, Echeck, or INSITE ESTs.

BUS COMMUNICATIONS

For EPA model year (MY) 2010, Cummins engine electronics ceased to support the J1587 bus, meaning that a gateway is required on any chassis using the older bus. Depending on the generation of the engine electronics, it may be possible to access the engine electronics via the J1939 three-pin connector. More recently, this connector has not been built into the engine harness. It can be "homemade" using the wiring schematic, but this is not recommended because it requires physical intrusion into the bus line. In addition, it may not work: For instance, Cummins ISB engines in Dodge chassis after 2004 will only communicate with Dodge electronics, not INSITE.

ROAD SPEED GOVERNING TAILORING

Road speed governing or **RSG** adjusts or moderates the upper and lower droop values. *Droop* is governed speed deviation from a given set speed. Moderating droop can tailor the torque curve (by managing injected fuel quantity) to optimize engine fuel economy as road and speed conditions vary. Upper droop will tailor the torque curve upward (by providing extra fuel) before maximum vehicle speed is reached under conditions of high engine load.

Lower droop tailors the torque curve upward in a downhill or light load condition, permitting increased road speed before cutting off fueling. This allows a vehicle to accelerate above the governed road speed, permitting an increase in momentum before going up the next hill. RSG upper and lower droop can be set between

0 and 3 mph (0 and 5 km/h). For instance, if road speed droop were set at zero, this would represent a hard value. However, if it were programmed at 3 mph (5 km/h), this would be a *soft* value because it would permit 3 mph (5 km/h) of latitude around the set cruise speed. Using increased droop settings enables the ECM to strategize fueling to road conditions and engine load to optimize fuel economy.

ELECTRONIC SMART POWER

Electronic smart power (ESP) engine ratings improve drivability and fuel economy in hilly terrain. In these conditions ESP results in more consistent road speed, faster trip times, and less shifting. It is essentially a cruise option that "learns" terrain and manages vehicle speed using soft limits. On level or near-level terrain, ESP engines operate at a base power rating determined by the ESP calibration programmed into the ECM. The ECM continually monitors the average speed the operator is attempting to maintain and logs this as "learned speed." The engine then automatically switches to the high-torque ESP mode if all ESP operating conditions have been met.

ESP Operating Conditions

1. Engine must be operating in cruise control or between 90% and 100% throttle (a momentary throttle position change such as required by a gear shift sequence will not disable ESP).
2. The transmission must be in a drive ratio of 2.62:1 or higher.
3. Vehicle speed must not exceed the ECM programmed maximum cruise control speed.
4. Using the foot brake to reduce vehicle speed will not activate ESP mode, but momentary use will not disable it.
5. Any active fault codes that relate to the **throttle position sensor (TPS)**, **vehicle speed sensor (VSS)**, or **engine position sensor (EPS)** will lock out ESP operation.

The foregoing conditions being met, the ECM switches to the ESP high-torque mode any time the vehicle speed drops more than a calculated value (3 mph or 5 km/h) below "learned speed." Once "learned speed" has been regained and the load reduced, the engine rating will return to the base power mode.

RoadRelay

RoadRelay is a dash-mounted driver data display option that keeps the operator informed of conditions on board. All RoadRelay data is recorded and may be downloaded to a PC database for analysis. The system will track the following data:

- Trip length and average mpg
- Trip running time and fuel consumed
- Idle fuel consumed
- Cruise control time
- Top road speed

SYSTEM TROUBLESHOOTING AND ENGINE TESTING

Troubleshooting the CELECT Plus and IS engines requires the use of INSITE and QSOL. Both systems cover legacy electronic and mechanical engines, so hard-copy service manuals should not be necessary. Troubleshooting is guided and sequential, requiring that the stepped procedures be undertaken precisely. As with most troubleshooting electronics, skipping a step usually invalidates subsequent steps.

CONNECTING TO THE DATA BUS

In this example, we are going to access the chassis data bus on a post-2010 Freightliner school bus powered by an ISB engine. Freightliner's ServicePro is umbrella software and when it is launched in Windows it will produce a screen like that shown in **Figure 42–4**. This shows the modules with addresses on J1939. Clicking on the engine field accesses the Cummins data hub

FIGURE 42–4 Freightliner ServicePro launch screen. This is a school bus with Cummins ISB power. When the engine field is selected, Cummins software and data hub access will be launched.

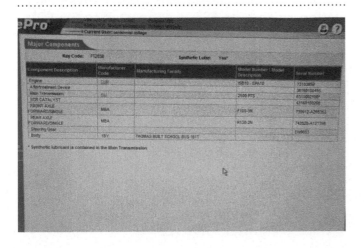

FIGURE 42–5 QSOL entry screen.

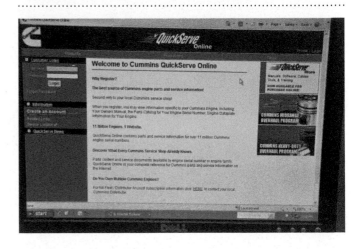

and produces the QSOL launch screen shown in **Figure 42–5**.

Cummins electronics are designed to execute self-diagnostic procedures during operation. Some of these are briefly outlined in the remainder of this section, with an emphasis on tests and procedures that have least in common with other OEM tests.

SETUP FOR DYNAMOMETER TEST

This test mode enables some advance diagnostic tests to run, which are structured by IS and CELECT electronics. In chassis dyno mode, the maximum engine speed without VSS, maximum vehicle speed in top gear ratio, and the maximum vehicle speed in lower gear are all set to their maximum values. Progressive shift programming and idle shutdown are also disabled for the duration of the dynamometer test run. To properly enable the "setup for dynamometer test," some chassis electronic subsystems may have to be disabled for the duration of the test, depending on the OEM. Some OEMs, on their newer chassis, provide a vehicle dynamometer test mode option. When selected, this automatically defeats systems such as automatic traction control, air conditioning, accident avoidance, and yaw-correction electronics that might interfere with the test results. Dynamometer testing is covered in detail in Chapter 16.

AUTOMATED CYLINDER PERFORMANCE TEST

The objective of a cylinder performance test is to evaluate cylinder load contribution in percentage terms. This test can be performed

FIGURE 42–6 CELECT Plus injector.

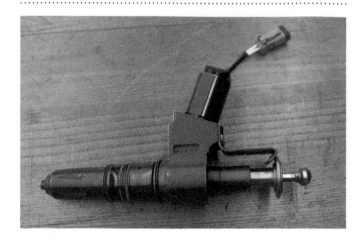

on most generations of Cummins injectors that are computer controlled, including those using the CELECT Plus injectors shown in **Figure 42–6** and those using the XPI-CR injectors shown in **Figure 42–7**. The driver software for the test is contained in INSITE, which must be connected.

FIGURE 42–7 XPI CR injector.

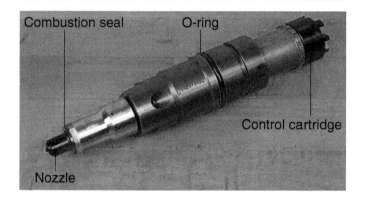

Combustion seal   O-ring
Control cartridge
Nozzle

The following requirements must be met to run this test:

1. Ensure that the area around the engine and fan is clear and the exhaust is properly vented.
2. Ensure that the engine oil temperature is at a minimum of 170°F (77°C).
3. Shut down the engine.
4. Lock the fan clutch to the engaged position; disable the air conditioning (A/C) system and any other auxiliary devices that could represent a parasitic load on the engine.
5. With the vehicle stationary, start the engine and allow it to idle.
6. Engage the PTO (the test cannot be performed unless the PTO feature is programmed to the ECM).

The test profile instructions should be run according to Cummins INSITE service literature. The test produces a *pass/fail* message for each engine cylinder.

In the event of cylinder performance outside the specification window, the percent contribution value will be displayed with the *fail* message. When the test is complete, the following sequence should be run:

1. Shut down the engine.
2. Return the fan clutch, A/C system, and all other disabled devices to normal operation.

CYLINDER CUTOUT TEST

The cylinder cutout test can be performed on Cummins electronic engines with electrically switched injectors. The test routine removes individual injectors from the cylinder firing cycle and monitors engine parameters while a selected cylinder is electronically disabled. INSITE displays the percent load and engine rpm value while the cylinder cutout test is being run. Again, the test is performed while the vehicle is stationary and the EST is connected to the ECM.

SUMMARY

- The Cummins Engine Company is the current market leader in supplying diesel engines to the truck sector, selling a wide range of power options from small bore to large bore.
- Cummins engines have used three generations of electronic management systems on engines operating on-highway: the partial authority PACE/PACER system, CELECT, and Interact System (IS) controls.
- The Cummins electronic engine management system used on industrial and off-highway diesel engines is Quantum System (QS) controls.
- Cummins Westport natural gas (NG) engines also use IS controls.
- The Cummins online service information system is known as QuickServe OnLine (QSOL).
- Cummins diagnostic and programming software is known as INSITE.

- Cummins electrically triggered injectors are switched using a coil-spiked actuation signal. The actual actuator voltage spike depends on the specific fuel system and the generation of the engine.
- The fueling control outputs in ISX engine electronics from 1998 to 2010 are the metering and timing actuators.
- All Cummins electronically controlled engines have self-diagnostic capability and are programmable with customer and Cummins data.

- IS electronics have a wide range of programmability. They are also designed to interact with other nodes with an address on J1939 to optimize vehicle performance.
- CELECT- and IS-managed engines have "smart" capability, including RSG tailoring and ESP.
- Cummins RoadRelay is a dash-mounted driver data display option that keeps the driver updated with trip data such as mpg and service intervals. RoadRelay data can be downloaded to a PC for subsequent analysis.

REVIEW QUESTIONS

1. What is the Cummins online service information system known as?
   a. QSOL
   b. ISX
   c. INSITE
   d. SIS

2. What is Cummins diagnostic software known as?
   a. Master Diagnostics (MD)
   b. INSITE
   c. QSOL
   d. Electronic Technician (ET)

3. What was the partial authority engine management system used on Cummins PT-fueled engines known as?
   a. PACE
   b. IS
   c. QS
   d. NTC

4. What electronic management system is used to manage current industrial and off-highway Cummins diesel engines?
   a. PACE
   b. IS
   c. QS
   d. CELECT

5. What electronic management system is used to manage post-2010 EPA highway-compliant diesel engines?
   a. PACE
   b. IS
   c. QS
   d. CELECT

6. Which of the following describes how an IS ECM prevents moisture from entering the housing?
   a. Vacuum sealed
   b. WeatherPac sealed
   c. Vented with a Gore-Tex seal
   d. WeatherProof II technology

7. Which of the following Cummins IS input sensors could be categorized as a "command" input?
   a. Ambient pressure
   b. Oil pressure
   c. Coolant level
   d. Throttle position

8. The Cummins IS boost pressure sensors would be described electrically as:
   a. piezoresistive.
   b. potentiometer.
   c. variable capacitance.
   d. thermistor.

9. At what electrical pressure are Cummins electrically actuated injectors switched?
   a. 5 V
   b. 12 V
   c. 78 V
   d. 100 V

10. The "smart" road speed governing option used by Cummins electronics is called:
    a. Echeck.
    b. ESP.
    c. INSITE.
    d. RSG tailoring.

11. Which of the following will prevent ESP operation?
    a. Any logged fault code
    b. Any active fault code
    c. TPS, VSS, or EPS active code
    d. 1:1 transmission drive ratio

12. Technician A states that IS engine position sensors use a magnetic pulse generator principle. Technician B states that the IS engine position sensors are located on the engine crankshaft. Who is correct?
    a. Technician A only
    b. Technician B only
    c. Both A and B
    d. Neither A nor B

13. Technician A states that IS engine position sensor signals are sourced from the engine camshaft. Technician B states that a typical Cummins engine position sensor is fitted with 24 evenly spaced recesses with a dowel indicating the #1 piston, TDC position. Who is correct?
    a. Technician A only
    b. Technician B only
    c. Both A and B
    d. Neither A nor B

14. What on-highway engine management system is used by current Cummins Westport natural gas–fueled engines?
    a. CELECT Plus
    b. PACE
    c. INSITE
    d. IS

15. Technician A says that all Cummins EPA highway-compliant post-2010 diesel engines use CR fueling. Technician B says that there is almost no difference between a 2009 ISX and a post-2010 version. Who is correct?
    a. Technician A only
    b. Technician B only
    c. Both A and B
    d. Neither A nor B

Prerequisites: Chapters 19, 21, 25, 26 and 31

DETROIT DIESEL ELECTRONIC CONTROLS (DDEC)

OBJECTIVES

After studying this chapter, you should be able to:

- Describe how DDEC electronics have evolved since their introduction through DDEC 10 and beyond.
- Identify the Detroit Diesel and Mercedes-Benz engine families using DDEC.
- Describe the main subsystems and components in the DDEC electronic management system.
- Understand the principles of operation of a DDEC ECM and its output drivers.
- List the primary inputs to the DDEC ECM and categorize them as command and monitoring sensors.
- Identify the different generations of DDEC EUIs, including N2, N3, and E3 injectors.
- Describe the importance of programming EUI calibration data to the ECM.
- Explain injector response time (IRT).
- Describe the governing options that may be programmed to DDEC-managed engines.
- Outline the basics of DDEC system diagnosis and troubleshooting.
- Explain the application of DD Virtual Technician, ProDriver, Visibility Package, and ProManager.
- List the parameters that require calibration reprogramming to DDEC electronics.

KEY TERMS

AdBlue

audit trails

beginning of energizing (BOE)

beginning of injection (BOI)

BlueTec

breakout boxes

check engine light (CEL)

common powertrain controller (CPC)

communications adapter (CA)

critical flow venturi (CFV)

data link connector (DLC)

Detroit Diesel (DD)

Detroit Diesel Data Summaries (DDDS)

Detroit Diesel Diagnostic Link (DDDL)

Detroit Diesel Electronic Controls (DDEC)

Detroit Diesel Reprogramming Station (DDRS)

digital diagnostic reader (DDR)

duty cycle

electronic distributor unit (EDU)

electronic foot-pedal assembly (EFPA)

electronic unit injector (EUI)

ending of energizing (EOE)

ending of injection (EOI)

fuel pressure sensor (FPS)

idle speed balance (ISB) test

idle speed compensation (ISC)

injector driver

injector quantity compensation coding (IQCC)

injector response time (IRT)

mass airflow (MAF) sensor

motor control module (MCM)

pilot injection

Power Service Literature (PSL)

pulse width (PW)

rail pressure sensor (RPS)

remote data interface (RDI)

Series 50

Series 60

Series 92

split-shot injection

stop engine light (SEL)

stop engine override (STEO)

synchronous reference sensor (SRS)

tattletale

telematics

throttle position sensor (TPS)

timing reference sensor (TRS)

turbo-boost sensor (TBS)

valve closing pressure (VCP)

Virtual Technician (VT)

Visibility Package (VP)

INTRODUCTION

Detroit Diesel (DD) was the first diesel engine manufacturer to offer an electronically managed diesel engine in the North American truck and bus markets. DD electronics are described by the acronym **DDEC**, which stands for **Detroit Diesel Electronic Controls**. DDEC I was introduced in 1985 and made generally available in 1987 on two-stroke cycle, **Series 92** engines (displacement of 92 cubic inches per cylinder). DDEC I was a full authority management system with mechanically actuated (camshaft) **electronic unit injectors (EUIs)** that were computer-controlled by a dash-located engine control module (ECM) and an engine-mounted, **injector driver** unit called an **electronic distributor unit (EDU)**. The injector drivers are the ECM actuators responsible for effecting ECM-plotted fueling commands by switching the EUI duty cycle. **Figure 43–1** shows a typical block diagram of the DDEC system when used to manage an EUI-fueled engine such as the Series 60.

DD SERIES 60 AND 50

Shortly after the introduction of the full authority EUI system on the Series 92 engine, Detroit Diesel launched what was to become the most successful diesel engine of the 1990s: the Series 60. The **Series 60** engine is an inline, six-cylinder, four-stroke cycle engine fueled by EUIs and managed by full authority electronics. The engine was the first truck diesel engine to be sold in North America that was designed specifically for computer controls. Electronic management was by DDEC II electronics. DDEC II combined the EDU and ECM assemblies into a single, engine-mounted module. Initially, the Series 60 engine was available in 11.1- and 12.7-liter displacements. DD added a 14-liter displacement version in 2002.

The 14-liter displacement Series 60 engine was not available from 2004 through 2007, but became the only Series 60 option for 2007 to 2010 engines. The **Series 50** engine was a four-cylinder version of Series 60, which shared a high degree of component commonality with the six-cylinder version and most of its operating principles. Series 50 was basically a Series 60 with two cylinders chopped off, and it became a popular transit bus engine. The Series 50 ceased production in 2007.

CORPORATE CHANGES

DD was purchased by the DaimlerChrysler Corporation in 2001 and became allied with Daimler Mercedes-Benz and Freightliner trucks. This move meant that Detroit Diesel lost its "independent" identity, and overnight Freightliner's competitors no longer considered spec'ing DD engines in their trucks, significantly reducing their market potential. In addition, DD announced that it would cease to supply engines to bus OEMs other than those owned by Daimler after 2007. More recently, Daimler Trucks North America (DTNA) announced that Detroit Diesel Corporation would be known as Detroit Diesel. DD now manufacture transmission and final drive units.

FIGURE 43–1 DDEC management system schematic of a typical pre-2007 Series showing input and output circuits.

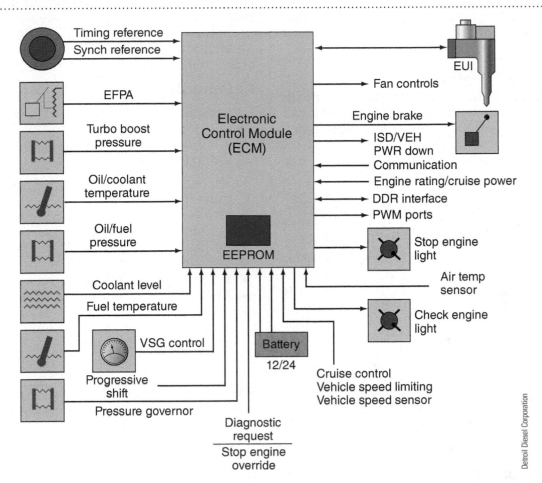

KEY SYSTEM DATA

The following is a quick reference guide to some of the Detroit Diesel–specific system terminology and acronyms used in this chapter.

Management Systems

- DDEC is an acronym for Detroit Diesel Electronic Controls. Versions one (introduced in 1987) through six (released in 2007) used Roman numerals to designate the generation.
- DDEC I was a two-module system consisting of an ECM housing and a separate injector driver module known as an electronic distributor unit (EDU).
- DDEC II to DDEC V used a single-module ECM which incorporated the EDU. These versions of DDEC managed DD-badged engines only.
- DDEC VI was introduced in 2007 to manage DD common platform engines that used three different fuel systems: EUI Series 60, the Mercedes-Benz MB-4000, and the DD Series engine. DDEC VI used a two-module

system consisting of a **common powertrain controller (CPC)** that connected by proprietary bus to a **motor control module (MCM)**.
- DDEC 10 was introduced for Environmental Protection Agency (EPA) model year 2010. DD ceased production of on-highway Series 60, Series 50, and MB-4000 at the end of 2009, so DDEC 10, similar in layout to DDEC VI, is used to manage only DD Series engines with an amplified common rail system (ACRS).

System Software Tools

- **Power Service Literature (PSL)** is Detroit Diesel's subscription online service information system. Can be accessed through the Freightliner ServicePro portal.
- **Detroit Diesel Diagnostic Link (DDDL)** is the DDEC diagnostic software designed to run in conjunction with PSL.
- **Detroit Diesel Reprogramming Station (DDRS)** is the DDEC10 software required to reprogram the engine electronics with customer

and proprietary data and perform the functions of DDDL on earlier generations of engine.

- **Virtual Technician**. DD and Freightliner telematics: remote diagnostics and data mining capable, described in some detail in the section that follows.

Virtual Technician

The DD Virtual Technician™ onboard diagnostic system is factory-installed on DD Series engines. When a check engine light (CEL) illuminates, data is collected immediately. This provides a technical snapshot of engine status before, during, and after a fault code event.

The information collected is immediately sent to both the owner and the Detroit Customer Support Center (CSC). When DTC data is analyzed by Detroit's CSC, a service strategy is recommended, including information on the nearest location where service and parts are available. Using the vehicle telematics, CSC can instruct the driver to pull over and stop the vehicle to prevent damage.

Virtual Technician (VT) has optional fleet management software known as **Visibility Package (VP)**, which is an upgrade to the Pro-Manager software. VP in conjunction with the DD Ground Traffic Control website provides operational and tracking data that includes:

- Vehicle stops and real-time speeds
- Routes and mileage traveled by region
- Excessive idling and fuel consumption
- Driver management of the vehicle powertrain

DDEC Operator Enhancements

DDEC has been enhanced in Detroit's current DD Series engines to assist drivers to learn smart engine and powertrain management techniques. The objective is to improve fuel economy, engine performance, and driving efficiency, and reduce maintenance needs, in order to optimize idle efficiency, increase available power for passing, and reward drivers who achieve fuel economy targets with performance increases. In addition, dash display prompts help operators control idling better, improve shifting techniques, and effectively manage the engine aftertreatment system.

Electronic Service Tools

For a number of years, Detroit Diesel supported generic handheld EST manufacturers such as Pro-Link and Nexiq with software better than most of their competitors. The **digital diagnostic reader (DDR)** driven from a ProLink HH-EST platform was the recommended EST, and this could execute most DDEC system maintenance

and diagnostic requirements as well as act as a serial link for DD data hub downloads. However, DD currently requires a PSL subscription and DDDL/DDRS software to effectively diagnose and program DD engines. DDDL and PSL are driven off a Windows environment, and PSL requires an active Web connection to be fully functional.

Communications Adapter

Detroit currently recommend using the Detroit-specific **communications adapter (CA)** manufactured by Nexiq (part number 124032). This CA features:

- Higher-baud communication processor and more integral memory
- Mobile vehicle grade USB connector with latching mechanism
- 26-pin ISO 22900 MVCI-compliant vehicle connector
- Bluetooth vehicle-to-PC wireless connectivity
- RP1210 (A, B, and C) plus J2534 compliant
- CAN/J1939/ISO 15765 250K, 500K, and 1M bits per second (b/s) with auto-baud detection (3 channels)
- ISO 9141/KWP 2000 (ISO 14230) K/L line

DD Electronic Engines

The following are some examples of DD electronically managed engines used since the beginning of the electronic era, and the MB engine managed by DDEC. The successful Series 60 engines underwent few changes from introduction to final production. One of the reasons for the success of this line was its simplicity and ease of service and rebuild procedure. Some examples of on-highway DDEC electronic engines are shown in **Table 43–1**.

TABLE 43–1 Examples of DDEC Engines by Model Year

Series 92 6V EUI	1987	9-liter displacement
Series 92 8V EUI	1989	12-liter displacement
Series 60 EUI	1989	12.7-liter displacement
Series 50 EUI	1993	8.5-liter displacement
Series 60 EUI	1993	11.1-liter displacement
Series 55 EUP	1996	12-liter displacement
Series 60 EUI	2001	14-liter displacement
MB-4000 EUP	2007	12.8-liter displacement
DD15 ACRS	2008	14.8-liter displacement
DD13 ACRS	2009	12.8-liter displacement
DD16 ACRS	2011	15.6-liter displacement

DDEC ELECTRONICS

DDEC electronics were upgraded through the years, but until 2007 basically had to manage just their EUI fuel system, other than a brief 1-year period in 1996 when the Series 55 EUP engine was sold. This changed in EPA model year 2007 when the DDEC VI was released. DDEC VI was required to manage Series 60 EUI, MB-4000 EUP, and DD Series ACRS. The result was that DDEC adopted a twin-controller (two-module) management system. Although Detroit Diesel only manufactures the DD Series today (Series 60 and MB-4000 ceased production at the end of 2009), the twin-controller system continues to be used.

DDEC10 was introduced for DD engines engineered for EPA model year 2010 and beyond. Because DD ceased to manufacture EUI and EUP engines after 2010, DDEC10 is only required to manage its DD Series ACRS-fueled engines. There are few real functional differences between current versions of the DDEC and the earlier DDEC VI in the ways pre- and post-2010 DD Series engines are managed, but the latter are equipped with the ability to manage selective catalytic reduction (SCR) technology.

DDEC TWIN CONTROLLERS

DDEC VI and DDEC10 use a two-module management system, as shown in **Figure 43–2**. The module with an SA 00 address on the data bus is known as the *common powertrain controller (CPC)*. The CPC uses a proprietary bus connection to the second controller, which is known as the *motor control module (MCM)*. **Figure 43–3**

FIGURE 43–2 Schematic showing the role played by DDEC CPC (SA 00) electronics used on post-2007 Series 60 and all DD Series engines.

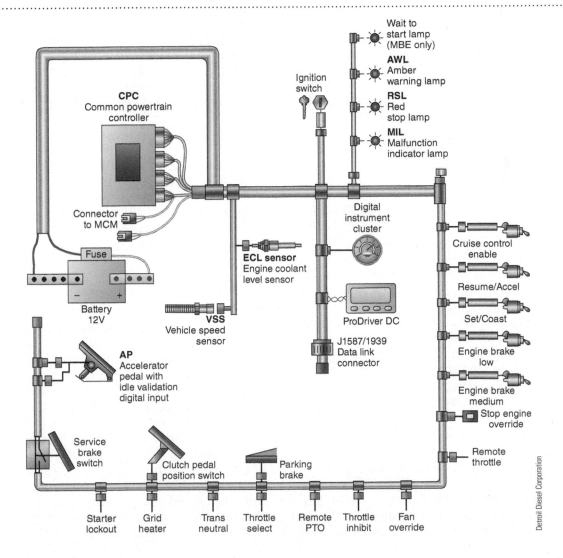

FIGURE 43–3 Simplified networking schematic showing the relationship between the DDEC MCM, CPC, and the two chassis data buses. Note that after 2010, DDEC ceased to support J1708/1587 bus communications.

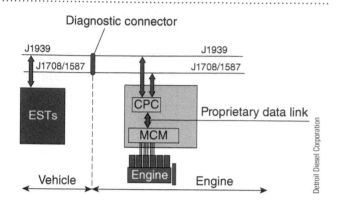

shows the networking relationship between the CPC, MCM, and the chassis data buses.

Common Powertrain Controller

The common powertrain controller (CPC) is mounted on the chassis. It uses the SA 00 address and "quarterbacks" engine management. The CPC connects to the MCM by means of proprietary bus connections, as shown in **Figure 43–4**. Access to the MCM must be via the CPC. The CPC is multiplexed to the other electronic modules on the chassis. **Figure 43–5** shows the DDEC VI CPC module and its connector ports.

Motor Control Module

The motor control module (MCM) is engine mounted. The MCM puts into effect directives from the CPC and directly controls the fuel system components. The DD Series injector and rail pressure control drivers are located within the MCM. Because the CPC receives most of the sensor data, MCM logic is limited to effecting CPC commands and managing the emission control devices. The overall functions of the two-module system are not dissimilar to those of the single-module system, so in most cases it is not necessary to distinguish between the two. **Figure 43–6** is a more detailed schematic of the bus topology between the MCM, the CPC, and the Freightliner proprietary buses.

EMISSIONS MANAGEMENT

DDEC-managed engines have used C-EGR since the EPA 2004 model year (introduced in October 2002), and for 2007 adopted a multiple-stage exhaust gas aftertreatment system with a diesel particulate filter (DPF). For 2010, DD incorporated SCR into the exhaust aftertreatment circuit and a dosing module to inject diesel exhaust fluid (DEF).

DD calls its SCR system **BlueTec**, the same term used by German auto manufacturers VW, Audi, and Mercedes-Benz for their diesel SCR technology. Perhaps reflecting its current German ownership, DD refers to DEF by the European name **AdBlue**, but it is the identical aqueous urea mixture known as DEF here. For this reason, DEF purchased at the pump functions identically to the AdBlue sold in Freightliner and DD dealerships.

With the adoption of SCR, DD engines improved their fuel economy and saw reduced EGR-related failures. In DDEC10, emissions strategy is managed by the CPC while the MCM directly controls the hardware.

ECM FUNCTIONS

Whether single or dual module, the controllers house the microprocessor and output actuators. DDEC electronics are responsible for engine governing, fuel timing logic, self-diagnostics, comprehensive system monitoring, **audit trails** (data tracking), **tattletales** (covert writing of electronically monitored events or conditions to EEPROM), and customer and DD data programming.

INJECTOR DRIVERS AND DUTY CYCLE

The results of ECM arithmetic, logic, and fetch-and-carry computations in the processing cycle are converted to actuator or control signals that switch the EUIs, EUPs, or EHIs. Injector command pulses can be referred to as **duty cycle** or **pulse width (PW)** and are measured in milliseconds; DDEC electronics can optionally display duty cycle in crank angle degrees.

Duty cycle or PW is the time period in which fuel is actually being injected. With the EUI or EUP fuel systems, it must occur within the cam-actuated downstroke. In CR fuel systems, the available PW window is not limited by cam geometry.

PW is calculated and controlled by the ECM. It is switched by the injector driver unit located either in the ECM (pre-2007 systems) or in the MCM in 2007 and later systems. In both cases, it is the EDU that energizes the EUI actuators.

DD ACRS electrohydraulic injectors (EHIs) are capable of multiple injection events during a single cycle, so duty cycle consists of the total EHI energized time. This, in conjunction with the rail pressure, determines the actual volume of fuel injected into the engine cylinder.

FIGURE 43–4 CAN networking schematic showing the relationship between the DDEC MCM, CPC, and other powertrain controllers.

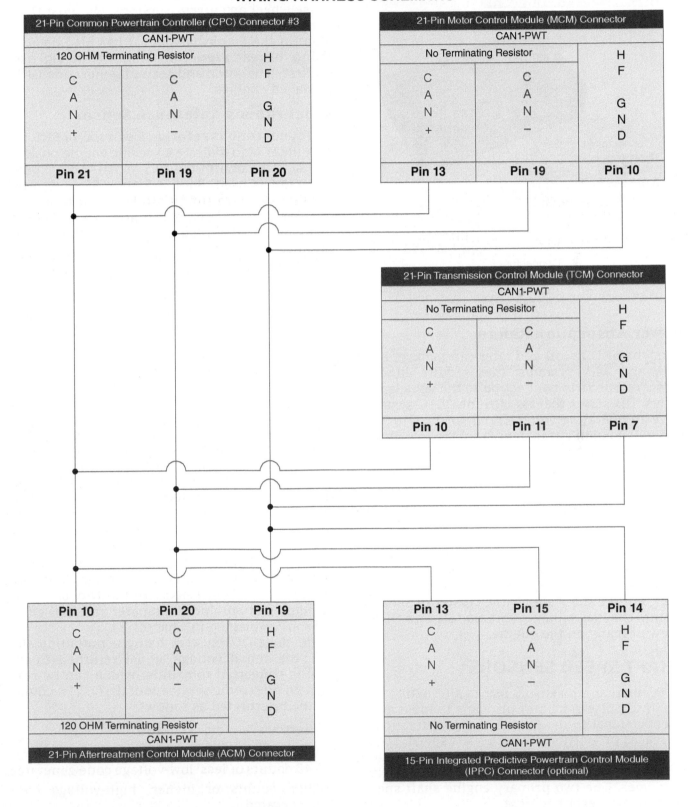

GHG14 POWERTRAIN CONTROLLER AREA NETWORK
WIRING HARNESS SCHEMATIC

FIGURE 43–5 A DDEC common powertrain control (CPC) module.

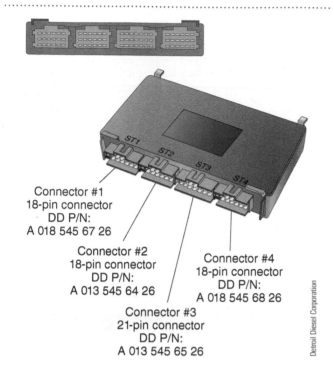

Connector #1
18-pin connector
DD P/N:
A 018 545 67 26

Connector #2
18-pin connector
DD P/N:
A 013 545 64 26

Connector #4
18-pin connector
DD P/N:
A 018 545 68 26

Connector #3
21-pin connector
DD P/N:
A 013 545 65 26

Detroil Diesel Corporation

Power Absorption Range

Versions of DDEC III and later can manage both 12-V and 24-V systems; they require either a direct or bus strip connection to the vehicle batteries. DD states that its current DDEC systems have an operating voltage range of 11 V to 32 V and will sustain a transient cranking low of 9 V.

INPUT CIRCUIT

As DDEC has evolved, the sensor circuit has become more comprehensive. The following is a description of some current DDEC sensors without detailing of the electrical operating principles, which are covered in Chapter 34. Only the sensors specific to DDEC are covered. **Figure 43–7** shows the cluster of sensors around the fuel management module on a DD15, a few of many on the engine.

SHAFT SPEED SENSORS

DDEC shaft speed sensors use an alternating current (AC) pulse generator principle to input a frequency signal to the ECM. The signal frequency increases proportionally with shaft speed. Speed sensing, whether turbo speed or transmission tailshaft speed, is critical for factoring engine outcomes. The two primary engine shaft speed sensors are described next.

Timing Reference Sensor

The **timing reference sensor**, or **TRS**, signals crank position to the ECM. An AC pulse generator is used. A 6-tooth pulse wheel (reluctor) is used on DDEC II, and this was upgraded to a 36-tooth pulse wheel on current versions. On most DDEC generations, the pulse wheel is fitted to the front of the crankshaft, but it has also been fitted to the rear. **Figure 43–8** shows the TRS used on first-generation and second-generation DDEC managed engines.

Synchronous Reference Sensor

The **synchronous reference sensor**, or **SRS**, signals the ECM to indicate a specific engine position and acts to confirm the TRS signal. An AC pulse generator is used. Both TRS and SRS must work for the engine to run; if either is not functional in DDEC II, a code is logged after 10 seconds of cranking; in later versions of DDEC, this code is produced immediately. The SRS consists of a single dowel that acts as a reluctor tooth located on either the cam or the bull gear and a stationary magnetic pickup: the location depends on the generation of DDEC. Figure 43–8 shows comparisons between the SRS units used on the first and more recent generations of DDEC managed engines.

ELECTRONIC FOOT-PEDAL ASSEMBLY

Current DDEC can be enabled for either a potentiometer or Hall-effect–type accelerator pedal. The critical sensor in the potentiometer-type **electronic foot-pedal assembly (EFPA)** is the **throttle position sensor (TPS)**. A potentiometer-type TPS receives a 5-V reference voltage (V-Ref) and returns a portion of it proportional to pedal mechanical travel. Alternatively, a non-contact Hall-effect TPS can be used to signal accelerator pedal angle. An EFPA also contains an idle validation sensor (IVS). The electrical principles of both potentiometer and Hall-effect TPSs are explained in Chapter 34.

In the DDEC system using a potentiometer TPS, the actual voltage signal returned to the ECM is converted to counts, which can be read with an electronic service tool (EST). TPS counts can be interpreted as follows:

Zero travel, idle: 100–130 TPS counts

Full travel: 920–950 TPS counts

48 counts or less: low-voltage code generated

968 counts or higher: high-voltage code generated

FIGURE 43-6 DD15 to Freightliner bus topology showing the CAN network relationship with the J1939 and J1587. Identify the CPC, MCM, the Gateway module, AMT controller, and starpoint in the schematic.

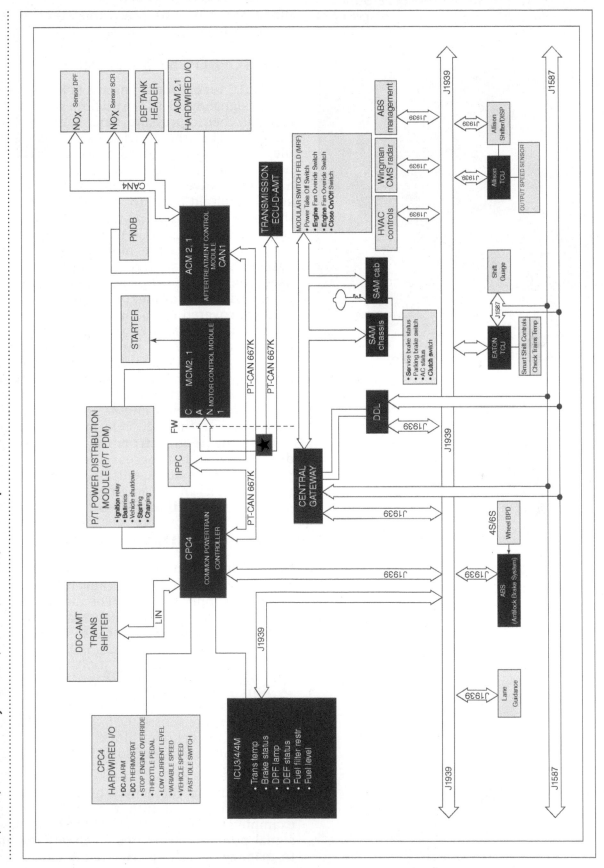

FIGURE 43-7 The cluster of sensors around the fuel management module on a 2015 DD15 module.

FIGURE 43-8 DDEC SRS and TRS sensors on early and later versions of DDEC engines.

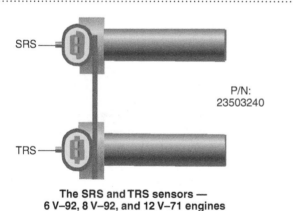

SRS

P/N:
23503240

TRS

The SRS and TRS sensors —
6 V–92, 8 V–92, and 12 V–71 engines

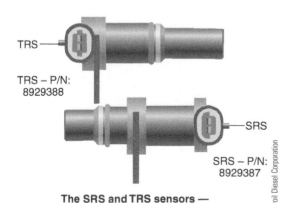

TRS

TRS – P/N:
8929388

SRS

SRS – P/N:
8929387

The SRS and TRS sensors —
Series 50 and Series 60 engines

Detroit Diesel Corporation

The EFPA is supplied by the chassis manufacturer, but must be consistent with DD specifications.

TURBO-BOOST SENSOR

The DDEC **turbo-boost sensor (TBS)** is responsible for signaling the ECM with both manifold boost and barometric pressure data. Early versions of the DDEC TBS used a variable capacitance principle. Pressures from 0 to 45 psi (3 bar/304 kPa) can be measured. Later generations of DDEC adopted a piezoresistive (Wheatstone bridge) sensor to signal manifold boost to the ECM. This sensor is the same as that used by General Motors (GM) on some of its Gen III and IV managed engines.

These sensors are more accurate and less susceptible to tampering. Whichever type is used, the TBS is a DD-provided sensor. The electronic principles of piezoresistive pressure sensors are covered in Chapter 34.

TBS data is required by the ECM to plot air-fuel ratio (AFR). By monitoring atmospheric pressure, oxygen density is known, so ECM fuel quantity programming is automatically derated at altitude. Turbo-boost pressure monitoring indicates actual engine load and prevents transient overfueling. This means that a sudden full-fuel request from the accelerator pedal does not result in excess fuel being injected before there is sufficient air (supplied by the turbocharger) in the engine cylinders to completely burn it. **Figure 43-9B** shows a DD TBS.

FLUID PRESSURE SENSORS

Most of the fluid pressure sensors on DDEC-managed engines use a variable capacitance principle. They are supplied by DD. The electronic principles of this category of sensors are discussed in Chapter 34. Fluid pressure sensors include:

- **Fuel pressure sensor (FPS)**. Location: charge side of the transfer pump
- **Rail pressure sensor (RPS)**. Location: on common rail
- Oil pressure sensor (OPS). Location: lube gallery in the cylinder block
- Coolant pressure sensor (CPS). Location: water manifold

In addition, there may be special function sensors integrated into the input circuit. An example is a fire truck pressure sensor used to signal pumping pressures to enable the engine to manage them. **Figure 43-9A** shows a typical FPS; most DDEC FPSs share the same part

FIGURE 43–9 A. Oil, fuel, and coolant pressure sensors; **B.** Turbo-boost sensor.

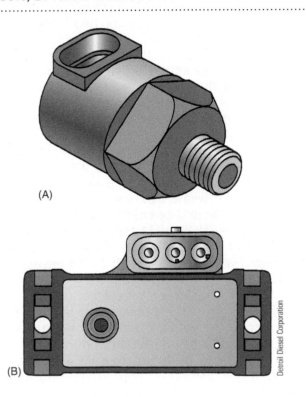

(A)

(B)

Detroit Diesel Corporation

number and are identical. **Figure 43–10** shows a DD15 rail pressure sensor.

TEMPERATURE SENSORS

The fluid temperature sensors used on DD engines (except those used on exhaust gas after-treatment devices) use a thermistor operating

FIGURE 43–10 Rail pressure sensor on a 2015 DD15 engine.

principle, fully described in Chapter 34. Thermistors are supplied with system V-Ref at 5 V-DC. The thermistor characteristic used is negative temperature coefficient (NTC). In an NTC thermistor, resistance decreases as temperature increases. In operation, the voltage signal returned to the ECM increases proportionally with temperature rise. All the temperature sensors are DD supplied. Examples of thermistor temperature sensors are:

- Fuel temperature sensor (FTS)
- Coolant temperature sensor (CTS)
- Air (ambient) temperature sensor (ATS)
- Intake (boost side) temperature sensor (ITS)
- Oil temperature sensor (OTS)

MASS AIRFLOW SENSORS

DDEC uses a pressure differential-type **mass airflow (MAF) sensor** in its post-2004 EGR engines. The DDEC MAF sensor uses a **critical flow venturi (CFV)** with variable capacitance sensors positioned upstream and downstream from the venturi. The operating principle is based on the relationship between inlet pressure and flow rate through a venturi. When the pressure is known both at the entry point to the venturi and at its exit point, the differential pressures can be used by the ECM to calculate the mass of the airflow. Differential airflow-type MAF sensors are described in more detail in Chapter 34.

COOLANT LEVEL SENSORS

A coolant level sensor (CLS) is a switch-type sensor consisting of an integrated resistor that grounds through the engine coolant and is located in the top radiator tank. If the ground is interrupted, engine protection strategy is initiated after a prescribed time period (if so programmed). The CLS is original equipment manufacturer (OEM)-supplied.

DDEC PROGRAMMING AND DIAGNOSTICS

DD currently requires a PSL subscription and DDDL/DDRS software to effectively diagnose and program DD engines. DDDL and PSL are driven off a Windows environment, and PSL requires an active Web connection to be fully functional. The previous DDR EST with a DDEC card or cartridge could perform many of the DDEC system maintenance, troubleshooting, and programming requirements, but as the electronic systems became more complex, PC-driven software became a requirement. Handheld ESTs can still read DDEC, and their portability makes them useful for diagnosing problems for which a road test is required. In this section, we will look at some DDEC-specific procedures and programming options.

Calibration Codes

DDEC injectors are graded with a calibration code. These codes are a precise bench-test reckoning of how an injector flows fuel. Any time an injector is changed out, the new calibration code must be reprogrammed to the ECM/MCM using the appropriate EST and software. Calibration codes are known as **injector quantity compensation coding (IQCC)** on the EHIs used on the DD ACRS family of engines. The actual code depends on the DDEC generation and the fuel system used. Some examples include:

- DDEC first generation. Single-entry alpha code: A, B, or C
- DDEC EUI on Series 60/50. Two-digit numeric: range from 00 to 99
- DDEC on ACRS. Six-digit numeric, code located on EHI

Programming IQCC data to the ECM (CPC/MCM) allows the fueling logic to precisely balance fueling to each engine cylinder. The programming of calibration codes is achieved in the customer data programming field. The injector cylinder number has to be selected first, after which the digital calibration code is input. In systems using alpha calibration codes—flow codes A, B, or C—A denotes the least fuel flow and C the most fuel flow. Where the codes are numeric, an increase in number indicates an increase in fuel flow. This critical procedure helps the ECM balance cylinder fueling.

> ### TECH TIP:
> Whenever an EUI or EHI is replaced, the fuel flow code(s) or IQCC *must* be reprogrammed. Failure to perform this critical step will result in unbalanced engine fueling.

INJECTOR RESPONSE TIME

DDEC EUIs were switched at 12 V, unlike most other EUI systems that spiked the application voltage to values around 100 V. This meant that the time lag between **beginning of energizing (BOE)**, or the instant that the EDU initiates current flow to the EUI solenoid, and **beginning of injection (BOI)** was to some extent variable.

DDEC electronics managing EUI fuel systems were programmed to measure the response time between BOE and BOI by studying the actuation voltage wave of the previous two actuations of each EUI on a continual basis. **Injector response time (IRT)** is essentially the time lag between the output of the actuating signal at the EDU and the moment the EUI poppet control valve actually closes. It is measured in milliseconds and is displayed on a DDR. Because IRT is monitored, DDEC is capable of adjusting to minor electrical circuit resistance variations within a certain window to maintain balanced fueling and timing.

It should also be noted that there is a fractional lag between EUI control valve closure (BOI) and the actual opening of the EUI hydraulic nozzle valve (NOP) that truly begins injection. Similarly, at the completion of the switched duty cycle or PW known as **ending of energizing (EOE)**, there is not an immediate cessation of injected fuel because some fraction of time is required to drop the pressure in the EUI pump chamber to the **valve closing pressure (VCP)** value at which point the injection pulse truly ceases—**ending of injection (EOI)**. DD claims that this collapse phase is of shorter duration in N3 injectors than in N2s.

IRT and Impact on Fuel Delivery

In Chapter 25, we took a closer look at IRT and the effect it can have on the injection pulse if it is not monitored and compensated. An IRT abnormality permits a certain amount of timing compensation to balance fueling providing that amount falls within a certain window. When it exceeds DDEC's ability to compensate for the EUI pulse width, a fault code is logged. IRT should be monitored on the EST data parameters when performing any type of engine diagnostics. **Figure 43–11** shows how IRT can impact cylinder fueling if not compensated for by the engine electronics.

FIGURE 43–11 Response time effect on the injection cycle.

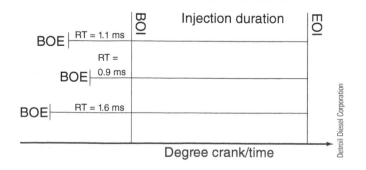

MULTIPULSE INJECTION DDEC electronics, in conjunction with N2 and N3 single-actuator EUIs, could manage **pilot injection**, which DD commonly referred to as **split-shot injection**. This technology was a forerunner of the multipulse capability of current EUIs. Initially, it was an ECM cold-start strategy designed to eliminate diesel knock and minimize startup smoke emission. Pilot injection essentially breaks up the fueling pulse by switching the EUI nozzle to open and close at high speeds. Using split-shot injection under cold-start conditions means delivering a short pulse of fuel to the engine cylinder, allowing the ECM to calculate the moment of ignition, and at that moment resuming the EUI fueling pulse.

Diesel knock is a cold-start detonation condition caused by delayed ignition and excess fuel in the cylinder at the point of ignition. When pilot injection is controlled by the ECM, it can be used to help manage the combustion process. Besides cold-start fueling, it is also used at low-speed, high-load lug. In addition to reducing engine wear, pilot injection also greatly lowers cold-start emissions.

GOVERNOR OPTIONS

All versions of DDEC engine management offer both limiting speed governing (LSG) and variable speed governing (VSG). Although managed electronically, both LSG and VSG are designed to function similarly to mechanical governors from the driver/operator perspective. See Chapter 20 for a full explanation of LSG and VSG.

The ECM (DDEC versions before 2007) or CPC (DDEC 2007 and later) are programmed with a detailed fuel map that manages engine fueling through both normal and transient abnormal conditions. Smoke control and cold-start fueling are managed by the ECM, which calculates optimum injection timing and injected fuel quantity based on such factors as ambient temperature, barometric pressure, manifold boost, and throttle demand. Cold-start strategy on DDEC-managed engines may produce an automatic increase in engine idle speed and advanced injection timing to minimize cold-start operation white smoke emission; this returns to normal as the engine approaches operating temperatures.

CRUISE CONTROL

Cruise control can be operated in any gear when engine speed is above 1,100 rpm, providing the road speed is above 20 mph (32 km/h). Cruise control can be programmed to master engine brake operation so that if the vehicle accelerates above set cruise speed on a downgrade, the engine brake will automatically actuate.

PROGRESSIVE SHIFTING

Progressive shifting is an engine governing feature designed to achieve better fuel economy on vehicles equipped with manual shift transmissions by encouraging the driver to upshift before the engine reaches governed speed. When the speed of the engine is limited, the driver remains in the higher torque range of torque rise (that is, the lower rpm range) longer, where the engine operates at better fuel efficiency.

ENGINE PROTECTION

DDEC electronics monitor a range of vehicle and chassis functions and are programmed with an engine protection strategy that may derate or shut down the engine when a running condition could result in catastrophic failure. The operator is alerted to system problems by illumination of dash lights: the **check engine light (CEL)**, and the **stop engine light (SEL)**. When a system fault is logged, the CEL is illuminated to alert the operator that DDEC fault codes have been generated. The SEL is illuminated when the ECM detects a problem that could result in a more serious failure.

ENGINE PROTECTION STRATEGY

Engine protection strategy can be programmed to three levels of protection in most versions of DDEC. The levels begin at a low level of protection, essentially a driver alert, and progress to a complete shutdown of the engine. The level of protection is selected by the vehicle owner and programmed to DDEC as a customer option. Because it is a customer option, the failure strategy can be changed at any time by a technician equipped with the access password and an EST with the DDEC software. The parameters monitored are:

- Low coolant level
- Low coolant pressure
- High coolant temperature
- Low oil pressure
- High oil temperature
- EGR system
- DPF system
- SCR system
- DEF level

When DDEC detects a fault that may result in catastrophic engine damage, it can be programmed to react to the problem in three ways:

1. *Warning only*. In this mode the CEL and SEL will illuminate, but it is left up to the operator to take action to avoid potential engine damage. No power or speed reduction will occur. Engine protection is therefore left entirely to the discretion of the operator. This low level of protection should only be programmed to emergency vehicles such as fire trucks.

2. *Ramp down*. The CEL and SEL will illuminate when a fault is detected, and the ECM will reduce power (fuel quantity injected) over a 30-second period after the SEL illuminates. The maximum power value (fuel quantity) for this initial reduction is set by the fuel rate just before the logging of the fault condition. A diagnostic request/stop engine override switch is required when this engine protection option is selected.

3. *Shutdown*. Both the CEL and SEL will illuminate and the engine will shut down 30 seconds afterward. Once again, a diagnostic request/stop engine override switch is required if this option is selected. DD recommends this maximum level of protection.

Stop Engine Override Options

Three types of **stop engine overrides (STEOs)** are available:

1. *Momentary override*. This resets the 30-second shutdown timer, restoring engine power to the value at the moment the SEL was illuminated. To obtain subsequent overrides, the switch must be recycled after 5 seconds. DDEC will record the number of overrides actuated after the initial fault occurrence.

2. *Continuous override, option 1*. This stop engine override option is used when a vehicle needs full power during a shutdown sequence. Full power capability is maintained for as long as the override switch is pressed. It is intended for coach applications only.

3. *Continuous override, option 2*. This stop engine override option is used primarily for industrial and construction applications. It essentially disables the engine protection system until the ignition key is cycled.

DIAGNOSTIC TOOLS

Faults that occur are stored in ECM memory and may be recalled by any of the following means.

BLINK CODES

The CEL and SEL will flash codes when the diagnostic request switch is toggled. The CEL flashes inactive codes, and the SEL flashes active codes.

DETROIT DIESEL DIAGNOSTIC LINK

Detroit Diesel Diagnostic Link (DDDL) and Detroit Diesel Reprogramming Station (DDRS) are the troubleshooting software programs required to communicate with DDEC. All troubleshooting and even routine servicing should be routed through DDDL. It functions similarly to other OEM interactive diagnostic and analytical software with full-function online service information capability.

Chassis OEMs can program engines on their assembly lines using a DD software package called *Vehicle Engine Programming Station (VEPS)* and a PC with a Windows environment or DDRS. A PC interface (serial link adapter) is required to translate the datalink signal of the ECM to the VEPS or DDRS software. Either software package can be used to rewrite some of the parameters programmed to the DDEC electronics.

DIAGNOSTIC DATA READER (DDR)

DD recommends that a PC with DDDL/DDRS software and online access be used to diagnose, read, and reprogram DDEC-managed engines. In addition, DDEC can be accessed using a digital diagnostic reader (DDR) using DD software or HD-general reader software. DD has traditionally supported ProLink/Nexiq with the software required to make their ESTs effective tools.

The DDR connects to the chassis data bus by means of an J1708 six-pin or a J1939 nine-pin Deutsch data connector in the same way that a serial link adapter for a PC connects. This provides two-way communications for reading system parameters, calibration data, diagnostics, and data programming; recalling faults; and tracing audit trails. Chapter 35 provides detailed information on using ESTs and service information systems (SISs).

DIAGNOSTIC ROUTINES

The correct approach to diagnosing DDEC problems is to use DDDL and DDRS. DDEC troubleshooting requires a basic knowledge of electrical circuits and schematics, DDEC operating fundamentals, and the DD *DDEC Diagnostic and Troubleshooting Guide*. The latter is available online through DDDL or DDRS. The *DDEC Diagnostic and Troubleshooting Guide* covers the following areas:

- Reading diagnostic codes
- Clearing codes
- Calibration/IQCC reprogramming
- Connector checkout
- Using a digital multimeter (DMM)
- System testing
- Sequential troubleshooting
- Reprogramming engine parameters
- DDEC schematics

Troubleshooting DDEC requires the use of ESTs such as the DDR (not recommended for DDEC VI versions and higher), PC-based hardware with DDDL and DDRS software, DMMs, plus the appropriate **breakout boxes** and Ts, and the DDEC service literature. A DD15-specific breakout box is shown in the final chapter of this book as Figure 50–3.

Idle Speed Compensation

Detroit Diesel **idle speed compensation (ISC)** is integrated into the MCM architecture that drives all DD Series engines. The ISC software algorithm monitors crankshaft speed per segment of rotational travel and then compensates EHI fueling on a per-cylinder basis to ensure that the engine runs as smoothly as possible. When the engine is run at idle speeds, the compensation values are recorded to EEPROM.

In addition, ISC monitoring can be a powerful diagnostic tool that can identify an injector that is getting close to either its maximum or minimum limit. **Figure 43–12** shows an **idle speed balance (ISB) test** run on a DD15 with DDEC10. Testing the EHIs assigns each a numeric positive or negative limit value. The Figure 43–12 screen image shows the assigned EHI performance value on each cylinder on an engine that has a potential problem. The screen display can be interpreted as follows:

- High *positive* value: injector compensating for *low* injection rate
- High *negative* value: injector compensating for a *high* injection rate

HIGH POSITIVE On an ACRS, a high positive value can be the result of an EHI fueling issue caused by:

- Actuator malfunction
- Lack of amplification
- Restricted nozzle
- Restricted high-pressure supply to one EHI

HIGH NEGATIVE A high negative suggests that there is little wrong with the EHI (i.e., it is flowing fuel properly), but indicates that there could be a problem with cylinder pressure. High negative reporting from one engine cylinder will cause the ISC algorithm to increase the PW to the EHI in an effort to smooth out the rotational speed of the engine.

FIGURE 43–12 Screen capture showing a DD Series ISB test indicating that two cylinders have exceeded their compensation limits.

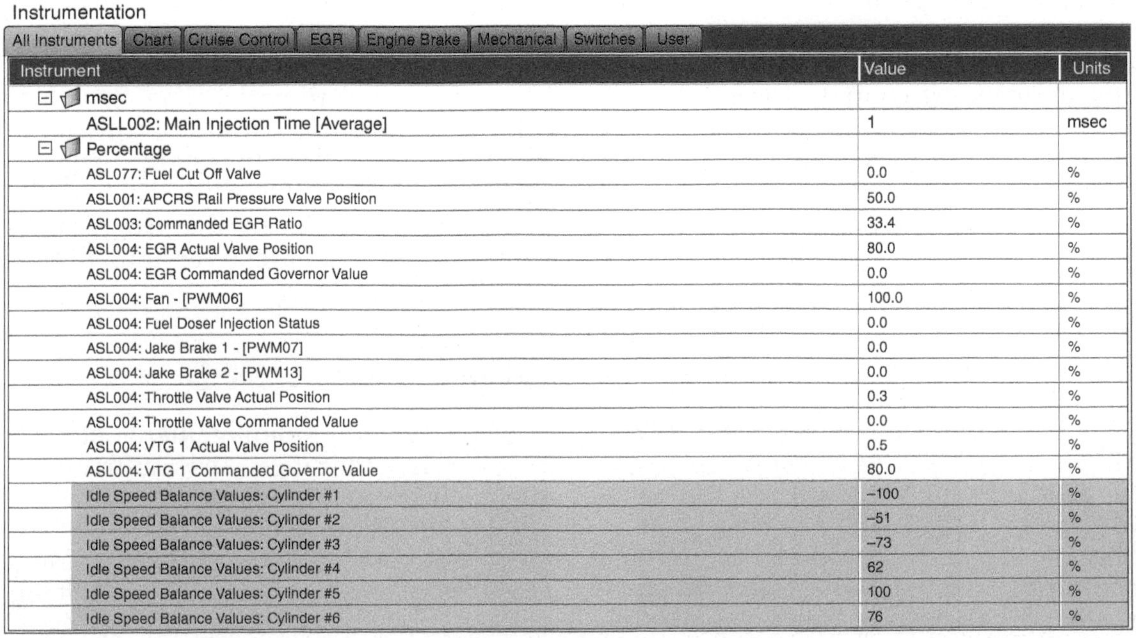
Instrumentation

All Instruments | Chart | Cruise Control | EGR | Engine Brake | Mechanical | Switches | User

Instrument	Value	Units
msec		
ASLL002: Main Injection Time [Average]	1	msec
Percentage		
ASL077: Fuel Cut Off Valve	0.0	%
ASL001: APCRS Rail Pressure Valve Position	50.0	%
ASL003: Commanded EGR Ratio	33.4	%
ASL004: EGR Actual Valve Position	80.0	%
ASL004: EGR Commanded Governor Value	0.0	%
ASL004: Fan - [PWM06]	100.0	%
ASL004: Fuel Doser Injection Status	0.0	%
ASL004: Jake Brake 1 - [PWM07]	0.0	%
ASL004: Jake Brake 2 - [PWM13]	0.0	%
ASL004: Throttle Valve Actual Position	0.3	%
ASL004: Throttle Valve Commanded Value	0.0	%
ASL004: VTG 1 Actual Valve Position	0.5	%
ASL004: VTG 1 Commanded Governor Value	80.0	%
Idle Speed Balance Values: Cylinder #1	–100	%
Idle Speed Balance Values: Cylinder #2	–51	%
Idle Speed Balance Values: Cylinder #3	–73	%
Idle Speed Balance Values: Cylinder #4	62	%
Idle Speed Balance Values: Cylinder #5	100	%
Idle Speed Balance Values: Cylinder #6	76	%

ISC COMPENSATION WINDOW The ISC compensation window extends from +100 to −100. Outside of this window, ISB cannot compensate. If values of 100 are displayed, a problem is indicated and the cause will have to be determined. In Figure 43–8, the EHI on #1 cylinder is displaying a negative 100 reading and that on #5 shows a positive 100 reading: both these cylinders should be checked.

NORMAL ISB When the ISB values are displayed at zero, no ISC compensation is required. DD states that values of +40 and −40 are not uncommon for a new fuel system. When ISB readings of +70 and −70 are displayed, injection compensation values are getting close to their limit and should be noted. At 100 either side of zero, no ISB compensation can occur and further troubleshooting is required.

CALIBRATION REPROGRAMMING

Depending on the software version, a DDR or PC with DDDL or DDRS can be used to make the following calibration changes:

- Rewrite DDR calibration configuration password
- Add/delete 5-minute idle shutdown
- Change droop (governor speed deviation from set speed)
- Set PTO droop (isochronous if required)
- Enable/disable cruise control
- Add/delete a VSS
- Change vehicle speed limit
- Change cruise control speed limit
- Add/delete engine shutdown
- Set PTO maximum speed
- Switch between available engine ratings
- Enter injector calibration values
- Set progressive shift configuration

PRODRIVER

DDEC III versions and later (up to the present day) feature as an option ProDriver, a dash-mounted data display that can provide the operator with immediate feedback on idle time, fuel economy, and other performance factors. Depending on the generation, ProDriver has a graphical user interface and user-friendly, five-key controls and will write to a data card, or can be integrated into the Freightliner or Nova digital dash display electronics. The display provides instant data feedback to the driver and has been proved to produce an almost immediate performance improvement. It can be regarded as low-cost

FIGURE 43–13 ProDriver display screen.

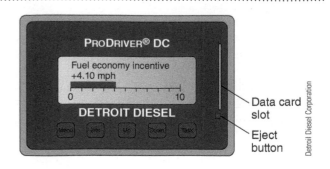

(compared to a human driver trainer) driver training. **Figure 43–13** shows the display screen used by the ProDriver digital dash display.

DDDS, VISIBILITY PACKAGE AND PROMANAGER

ProManager, **Detroit Diesel Data Summaries (DDDS)**, and the more recent Visibility Package (VP) are PC software programs that permit data to be downloaded from the DDEC ECM for analysis. Fleets interested in improving vehicle and operator performance have found DDDS, VP, and ProManager to be useful tools. The latest DDEC versions are driven from MS Windows software, and remote data interface (RDI) technology (see next section) is used.

REMOTE DATA INTERFACE

The **remote data interface**, or **RDI**, is a communications device that enables data exchange among the vehicle-based electronics, data hub products, and a fleet's computer network. System operation is automatic. The driver parks the vehicle adjacent to the RDI and connects the extraction cable to the **data link connector (DLC)** on the vehicle. RDI includes status lights to update the driver on the progress of the communications. The latest versions of RDI transfer are wireless-capable.

DDEC FEATURES

Because vehicle management electronics are continually upgraded, it is difficult to identify the significant changes that mark a numeric graduation from one generation of electronics to the next. This section outlines some of the features that DDEC provides, extending through the most recent versions.

FUEL ECONOMY DRIVER INCENTIVE

The vehicle owner can set a fuel economy goal and program a maximum vehicle speed. If the driver fails to meet the goal, nothing changes. However, for each 0.10 mpg increase over the fleet economy target, the maximum vehicle speed is increased by a speed value programmed by the owner. DD claims that analysis of driver electronic logs suggests this feature can produce significant cost savings along with increased driver satisfaction.

LOW GEAR TORQUE LIMITING

This permits the use of smaller transmissions by limiting torque in the lower ratios and allowing higher engine torque output in the higher gears.

INTERNAL COMPRESSION BRAKE

DDEC engine internal engine compression brakes usually permit three levels of braking. DD engine brakes continue to be engineered and supplied by Jacobs. Engine braking is controlled electronically and may be optioned into cruise control strategy using the DDEC platform or with collision warning systems (CWSs), vehicle stability control (VSC), and accident avoidance electronics, using the chassis data bus.

OPTIMIZED IDLE

Versions DDEC IV and later can be programmed to an Optimized Idle mode that operates like a home heating thermostat when the vehicle is parked (in jurisdictions where this is legal). The objective is to automatically stop and start the engine to:

- Maintain a comfortable cab/bunk temperature.
- Keep the vehicle batteries charged.
- Keep the engine warm.

CAUTION:

It is a legal requirement in some jurisdictions to have optimized idle programming disabled. Anti-idling legislation is aggressively enforced in some areas.

DATA ANALYSIS

As the computing power of vehicle ECMs increases, more parameters are monitored and the data recorded can be used for progressive analysis of operating conditions (as, for instance, in the driver fuel economy incentive). The extent to which the data can be analyzed can be greatly

FIGURE 43-14 ServicePro entry screen required to access and launch DDDL.

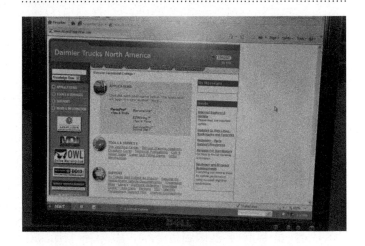

increased by **telematics** and subsequent download to a PC-based system programmed with software designed to study every performance detail of the vehicle. Data-mining technology, usually driven by telematics, is becoming increasingly popular both with large fleets and with OEMs such as DD, who use the data to develop condition-based maintenance profiles (see Chapter 33). **Figure 43-14** shows the entry access screen used in ServicePro to access DDDL.

Data analysis is useful to the service technician. First-generation electronic systems identified what was malfunctioning in a system, but offered few clues as to why the problem was occurring. Current troubleshooting packages can produce precise performance profiles that tell the diagnostic technician exactly how the vehicle has been driven and handled and the conditions at the exact moment a fault code was logged. Data-mining analysis can also provide predictive profiles on potential imminent failures.

ProDriver (described earlier in this section) data can be downloaded by DD's ProManager software for analysis and produce a profile showing exactly how a driver operates a piece of equipment. ProDriver data may be accessed with ProDriver Reports software (requires Windows software) or the RDI system. RDI is weatherproofed, so it can be mounted in a convenient location such as a fuel island for hardwire downloads. ProDriver can now also be programmed for wireless extraction of data from the vehicle electronic system.

DDEC SCHEMATICS

Figure 43-15 shows a DDEC-managed DD15 engine harness schematic.

FIGURE 43–15 MY 2013 DD15 vehicle interface to CPC wiring schematic.

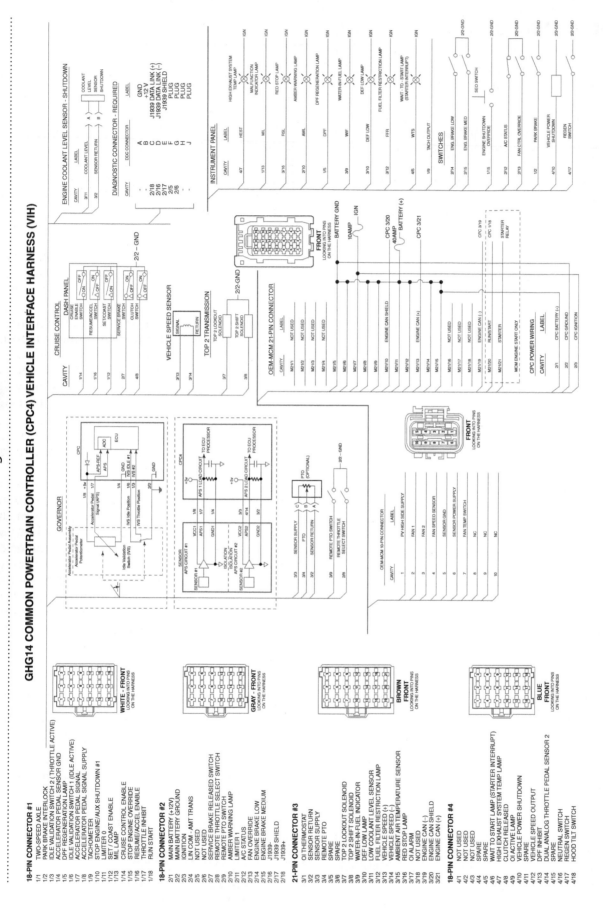

SUMMARY

- DD was the first OEM to offer an electronically managed truck diesel engine to the North American market.
- As the DDEC generation version number increases, so does the processing speed, software detail, programming scope, and self-monitoring capability.
- The DDEC ECMs have used both single- and dual-module systems through their history. The most recent versions of DDEC use a two-module system.
- The EDU is the DDEC injector driver unit responsible for switching the injectors.
- DDEC ECMs have an electrical operating range of 11 V to 32 V and will sustain a transient cranking low of 9 V.
- The more recent versions of DDEC are DDEC VI (2007) and DDEC10 (2010), but the fundamental software does not change significantly by generation.
- After 2007, DDEC adopted a two-module system. The module using the SA 00 address is the CPC that masters engine operation. The CPS is connected by a proprietary data bus to the MCM. The MCM contains processing capability and manages the injector drivers.
- DDEC may be programmed with customer and DD data electronically loaded into EEPROM.
- Multipulse injection in DDEC has varying capability depending on the generation. Mid-generation DDECs using N2 EUIs were pilot-injection capable. The E3 injectors used in DD Series 60 engines up until 2010 were fully multipulse capable.
- The current DD Series ACRS EHIs are fully multipulse capable.

- Injector calibration codes known as IQCC must be programmed to the DDEC ECM/CPC when injectors are changed out, to enable DDEC to balance engine fueling.
- DDEC governing can be programmed for either LS or VS governing.
- DDEC systems may be read for troubleshooting purposes at different levels, using flash codes, the DDR, and PC-based software with online enhancement. The latter with DDDL or DDRS software is recommended for more recent versions of DDEC.
- ISC is a DDEC algorithm used on DD Series engines that compensates for EHI fuel flow variability by monitoring crankshaft speed through sectors of rotation.
- ISC can be analyzed during an ISB test run on DDRS software to identify problem or potentially problematic EHIs.
- DDEC may be programmed to protect the engine when threshold values are exceeded at three different levels: driver alert, ramp down to default, and shutdown.
- DDEC supports Virtual Technician, ProDriver, a driver data display, ProManager, and Visibility Package.
- Virtual Technician (VT) is a factory-installed onboard diagnostic system on DD Series engines. When a CEL illuminates, data is collected in snapshot format for analysis of conditions before, during, and after a fault code event.
- ProManager and VP are software programs that enable vehicle data and driver behavior to be hard wire, or wirelessly, downloaded from the ECM for analysis.

REVIEW QUESTIONS

1. What is the Detroit Diesel online service information system known as?
   a. DDEC
   b. SIS
   c. ISIS
   d. PSL

2. What is Detroit Diesel's latest reprogramming and diagnostic software known as?
   a. MD
   b. DDRS
   c. DDEC
   d. ET

3. What version of DDEC would have to be used with a DD Series, SCR-equipped engine?
   a. DDEC I
   b. DDEC IV
   c. DDEC VI
   d. DDEC10

4. Which of the following versions of DDEC uses a two-module system?
   a. DDEC10
   b. DDEC V
   c. DDEC IV
   d. DDEC III

5. What is the primary function of the SRS?
   a. Signal engine position data
   b. Signal engine rpm data
   c. Signal vehicle road speed data
   d. Signal ambient temperature

6. How many teeth does the TRS pulse wheel have on a typical DDEC system?
   a. 6
   b. 12
   c. 24
   d. 36

7. Which dash diagnostic light is used to flash active DDEC fault codes in systems without ProDriver?
   a. Oil pressure warning
   b. SEL
   c. Electronic malfunction
   d. CEL

8. What is the primary objective when the progressive shifting option is selected?
   a. To extend the service life of the transmission
   b. To improve fuel economy
   c. To frustrate the driver
   d. To ensure that engine oil temperature remains stable

9. When a DDEC engine programmed for *ramp down* as a failure strategy detects a low oil pressure condition, which dash light(s) will illuminate?
   a. CEL
   b. SEL
   c. CEL and SEL
   d. Ignition

10. The reason for programming DDEC ECMs with IQCC is to:
    a. enable the ECM to balance cylinder fueling.
    b. maintain charging pressure values.
    c. synchronize EUI solenoid valve closure.
    d. maintain the same IRT for each injector solenoid.

11. Technician A states that one of the reasons DDEC VI electronics uses a two-module system is that the electronic management system is used on three engines with different fuel systems. Technician B states that in DDEC10, the injector drivers are located in the MCM. Who is correct?
    a. Technician A only
    b. Technician B only
    c. Both A and B
    d. Neither A nor B

12. In the DDEC10 management system, which module uses the SA 00 address on the chassis data bus?
    a. ECM
    b. CPC
    c. MCM
    d. EDU

13. Technician A states that during an injector speed balance (ISB) test, an EHI displaying a positive value of plus 100 is likely to be defective. Technician B states that an EHI displaying a negative value of minus 100 has no problems with fuel flow. Who is correct?
    a. Technician A only
    b. Technician B only
    c. Both A and B
    d. Neither A nor B

14. Where is the EDU located on a 2004 Series 60 engine?
    a. Within the DDEC ECM
    b. On the firewall
    c. On the dash
    d. Within the CPC

15. What do DDEC electronics use as the basis for determining the rate of EHI fuel flow compensation required as a result of idle speed compensation (ISC) analysis?
    a. Voltage wave produced by EHIs
    b. Crankshaft sector speed variations
    c. Cylinder pressure values
    d. Injector response time (IRT)

Prerequisites: Chapters 19, 27, 30, 34, and 35

NAVISTAR DIAMOND LOGIC

OBJECTIVES

After studying this chapter, you should be able to:

- Define the acronyms *ISIS* and *DL*.
- Identify online service information and diagnostic software.
- Identify the Navistar engines that use electronic controls.
- Explain how Diamond Logic multiplexing simplifies vehicle electrical circuits.
- Describe some typical Navistar engine controller modules.
- Describe the role of the consolidated engine controller.
- Identify Navistar engines using HEUI fueling.
- Identify Navistar engines using CR fueling.
- List the Navistar MY 2013 engine line-up.
- Perform basic electronic troubleshooting on Navistar-managed engines.
- Perform a Navistar self-test.
- Perform a Navistar injector cutout test.

KEY TERMS

calibration parameters

camshaft position sensor (CPS)

consolidated engine controller (CEC)

Diamond Logic

engine family rating code (EFRC)

exhaust gas recirculation (EGR)

EZ-Tech

fuel demand command signal (FDCS)

hydraulically actuated electronic unit injector (HEUI)

injector driver module (IDM)

International Service Information System (ISIS)

keep-alive memory (KAM)

Master Diagnostics (MD)

Navistar Service Information (NSI)

OnCommand

reference voltage (V-Ref)

self-test input (STI)

service information system (SIS)

ServiceMaxx (SM)

Tech Central

vehicle personality module (VPM)

INTRODUCTION

Navistar released its first electronically controlled engines in Environmental Protection Agency (EPA) model year (MY) 1994 with a pair of **hydraulically actuated electronic unit injector (HEUI)** fueled engines, the DT466E and T444. Both these engines were evolutions of earlier pump-line-nozzle (PLN) fueled engines. The 466 already had a reputation as a workhorse engine used in many of Navistar's medium-duty trucks, and a version of this engine is still available today, badged as a MaxxForce DT.

Navistar International was the first truck chassis original equipment manufacturer (OEM) to make extensive use of multiplexing in its trucks. The company builds bumper-to-bumper trucks, including some of its own engines, and it has used the term *Diamond Logic (DL)* since 2001 to describe its multiplexing, chassis, and engine electronics. It is only since 2007 that Navistar has manufactured electronic engines larger than 10 liters in displacement; until then, the company relied on specialty engine OEMs to power its class 7 and 8 trucks.

The generation of Navistar MaxxForce engines was the only post-2010 diesel engines that did not use selective catalytic reduction (SCR) to meet emissions standards, relying instead on high-cut volume **exhaust gas recirculation (EGR)**. This lasted until 2013, when the company re-engineered its engine line-up and adopted SCR exhaust gas treatment on its engines. Navistar is currently defending an EPA lawsuit which alleges that its 2010–2013 engines did not meet MY 2010 emissions standards. **Figure 44-1** shows a right-side view of a MaxxForce 13 with its twin turbochargers and EGR circuit.

KEY SYSTEM DATA

The following is a quick reference guide to some of the Navistar-specific system terminology and acronyms used in this chapter.

Management System

- Diamond Logic. An umbrella term Navistar has used since 2001 to describe its multiplexed electronic and electrical chassis system.

System Software Tools

- **International Service Information System (ISIS).** The Navistar subscription online **service information system (SIS)**, accessed through the Navistar International data hub. Contains fields for fleet vehicle data management and technician training. ISIS has replaced Navistar's hard-copy service literature, although elements of the program are available on DVD.
- **Navistar Service Information (NSI).** Recent upgrade to ISIS for dealership use.
- **OnCommand.** Recent upgrade to ISIS for fleet use. Contains comprehensive capability for fleet vehicle data management and technical training.
- **Master Diagnostics (MD).** The Navistar diagnostic software required to troubleshoot and reprogram engines up to EPA model year 2007.
- **ServiceMaxx (SM).** The Navistar diagnostic software required to troubleshoot and reprogram the MaxxForce generation of Navistar engines. SM is backward compatible with earlier generations of Navistar electronic engines.
- **Tech Central.** The Navistar central data hub that hosts its subscription software and databases.

Electronic Service Tools

For a number of years, a subscription to ISIS/NSI and MD/SM software has been required to effectively diagnose and program Navistar engines at the dealership level. Both sets of software are driven off a Windows environment, and ISIS/NSI requires an active Web connection to be fully functional. OnCommand is a fleet version

FIGURE 44-1 Right-side view of a post-2010 MaxxForce 13 highlighting the twin turbo and EGR apparatus.

of ISIS/NSI with enhanced features designed for fleet vehicle management. EZ-Tech Windows-environment software incorporates Navistar packaging of its SIS and diagnostic software. Navistar recommends that this be installed on a laptop PC dedicated solely to Navistar software, to minimize the chances of file clashes. The laptop should be connected to the chassis data bus by means of a Navistar communications adapter (CA) known as:

- NavCom
- NavLink

In addition, some limited access to the Diamond Logic data bus electronics is possible by generic ESTs, both from a Windows environment or integral handheld. Some of the available generic systems are addressed in Chapter 35. Generic EST access will be enhanced with the implementation of HD-OBD.

NAVISTAR ELECTRONIC ENGINES

Although Navistar International has a long history of manufacturing trucks up to class 8 in payload capability, its engine technology was confined to small- and medium-bore truck engines until recently. In fact, its engines relied heavily on the HEUI fuel system developed in conjunction with Caterpillar.

Navistar HEUI-fueled engines sold well in truck and school bus applications and, in addition, were badged as Ford PowerStrokes. Navistar supplied engines to the Ford Motor Company until 2011, when Ford released its own diesel engine, a 6.7-liter PowerStroke.

Some years ago, Navistar began joint engineering projects with the MAN Diesel and Turbo Group in Germany. The impact of this shared venture became evident in 2007 when a couple of engines that were fundamentally MAN in origin were badged as MaxxForce engines. For the first time, Navistar was supplying its own company brand engines capable of powering class 7 and class 8 trucks.

In 2010, Navistar and Caterpillar joined forces to produce the Caterpillar vocational truck, and this joint engineering endeavor resulted in shared engine and chassis technology until MY 2016. The truck chassis was built by Navistar, and the engine was a re-engineered Caterpillar C15. In 2015, Caterpillar announced that the joint initiative with Navistar would end, and from 2016 forward, the Caterpillar truck would be built in house. At the time of

TABLE 44–1 Examples of Navistar Electronic Engines

DT 466E HEUI	1994	7.6-liter displacement I-6
T444E HEUI	1994	7.3-liter displacement V-8
DT 530 HEUI	1997	8.7-liter displacement I-6
VT 275 HEUI	2003	4.5-liter displacement V-6
VT 365 HEUI	2003	6-liter displacement V-8
DT 570 HEUI	2004	9.3-liter displacement I-6
MaxxForce 7 CR	2007	6-liter displacement V-8
MaxxForce DT HEUI	2007	7.6-liter displacement I-6
MaxxForce 9 HEUI	2007	8.3-liter displacement I-6
MaxxForce 10 HEUI	2007	8.3-liter displacement I-6
MaxxForce 11 CR	2007	10.5-liter displacement I-6
MaxxForce 13 CR	2007	12.4-liter displacement I-6
MaxxForce 15 CR	2011	15.2-liter displacement I-6

writing, it was not known what engine would be used in the new truck. **Table 44–1** shows some examples of Navistar electronically managed engines used since the beginning of the electronic era.

NAVISTAR FUEL SYSTEMS

Until the EPA 2007 model year, all Navistar brand engines used a HEUI fuel system. Up until 2004, the HEUI system injectors were Caterpillar-manufactured and known by Navistar as G1. In 2004, all Navistar HEUI-fueled engines began using Siemens-manufactured HEUIs known as G2. Refer to Chapter 27 for comprehensive coverage of the HEUI fuel system.

In 2007, Navistar began what was planned to be a phased introduction of its CR-fueled MaxxForce engines. These additions to the MaxxForce family of engines were jointly engineered by Navistar and MAN. In addition, Navistar and Caterpillar joined forces to develop the MaxxForce 15, which was released as a MY 2010 engine. This engine used a substantial amount of Caterpillar C15 hardware, but was re-engineered for CR fueling and Navistar EGR-based emissions management. It was dropped for MY 2013 and replaced by the Cummins ISX. The pre-2013 Navistar 11-, 13-, and 15-liter engines using CR fueling and relying on solely on EGR exhaust gas aftertreatment were all discontinued in 2013.

Navistar N13

For MY 2013 and beyond, Navistar manufactured just one engine with greater displacement than 10 liters, the Navistar N13. The N13 displaces 12.4 liters and uses twin turbochargers, CR-fueling, and a Cummins-supplied SCR aftertreatment system. In addition to the N13, Navistar also options Cummins diesel engines in its class 7 and 8 trucks.

DIAMOND LOGIC CONTROLS

Both the HEUI and CR fuel systems are full authority electronic management systems with comprehensive monitoring, customer programmability, and self-diagnostic capabilities. In early Navistar HEUI systems, the logging of fault codes was the responsibility of nonvolatile RAM (NV-RAM), which is described as **KAM** or **keep-alive memory**. The circuit that provides continuous power (in other words, it is not dependent on the ignition circuit) to maintain KAM data is known as KAMPWR.

Depending on the specific engine and the construction date, the Navistar management ECM, vehicle personality module, and the switching apparatus may be housed separately (three modules, as shown in **Figure 44–2**), in two modules, or in a single controller module known as a **consolidated engine controller (CEC)**. The CEC, as its name suggests, consolidated the microprocessing and switching functions of the ECM, the personality module, and

the **injector driver module (IDM)** (switching unit with limited processing capacity).

ECM FUNCTIONS

According to Navistar service literature, ECM functions can be divided as follows (**Figure 44–3**):

1. Reference voltage regulator
2. Input conditioning
3. Microcomputer
4. Outputs

Reference Voltage

Reference voltage (V-Ref) is delivered to system sensors that return a percentage of it as a signal to the ECM. Thermistors (temperature sensors) and potentiometers (TPS) are examples of sensors requiring reference voltage. Reference voltage values used are at 5 V-DC pressure, and the flow is limited by a current-limiting resistor to safeguard against a dead short to ground. Reference voltage is also used to power-up the circuitry in Hall-effect sensors used in the system, such as the **camshaft position sensor (CPS)**. There is a full explanation of the electrical principles of input circuit components in Chapter 34.

Input Conditioning

Signal conditioning consists of converting analog signals to digital signals, squaring up sine wave signals, and amplifying low-intensity signals for processing. Part of this process includes cleaning up electronic noise induced in the circuit wiring.

FIGURE 44–2 HEUI system layout using three-module (box) management.

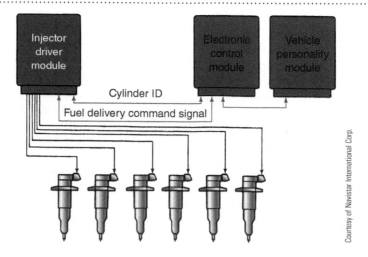

Courtesy of Navistar International Corp.

FIGURE 44–3 ECM processing cycle.

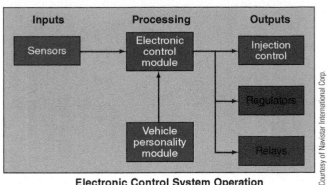

Electronic Control System Operation

Courtesy of Navistar International Corp.

Microcomputer

Diamond Logic microprocessors function similarly to other vehicle system management computers. They store operating instructions, control strategies, and tables of values, which are **calibration parameters**. They compare sensor monitoring and command inputs with the logged control strategies and calibration parameters and then compute the appropriate operating strategy for any given set of conditions. The more recent ECMs used by Navistar are equipped with 32-bit processor technology, but older Navistar and Ford multiple module units used 16- and 8-bit processors. In multiple-module units, a proprietary data bus connects the ECM to the personality and injector driver modules. **Figure 44–4** shows the ECM used to manage a post-2010 MaxxForce 13 engine.

FIGURE 44–4 MaxxForce 13 ECM.

Personality Module

Navistar Diamond Logic electronics describe its combined programmable read-only memory (PROM) and electronically erasable, programmable read-only memory (EEPROM) banks as a **vehicle personality module (VPM)**. The VPM is customer and proprietary data programmable. The function of the VPM is to trim engine management to a specific chassis application and customer requirements. The **engine family rating code (EFRC)** is located in the VPM calibration list and can be read with an EST; this identifies the engine power and emissions calibration of the engine.

BOXES

Navistar's **Diamond Logic** system is a comprehensive chassis management system used to drive all data bus networking. Navistar Diamond Logic is the chassis data bus. The engine ECM is networked into Diamond Logic and uses the SA 00/MID 128 bus address. As indicated earlier in this chapter, Navistar has used different module arrangements to manage its electronic engines and schematics. Most Navistar techs refer to the modules as *boxes*.

- **Three-box system**: Three modules incorporating an ECM, IDM, and VPM.
- **Two-box system**: Two modules, one combining the ECM and VPM, the other the IDM.
- **One-box system**: A single module incorporating the ECM, IDM, and PM and known as a CEC.

INJECTION DRIVER MODULE

The injector driver module (IDM) is responsible for switching the injectors. In Navistar HEUI systems the IDM may be integral with the ECM, or it may use a separate module. The IDM is housed separately in some Navistar HEUI-managed engines. When a single engine controller module is used by Navistar, the IDM is integrated into the CEC. The IDM has four functions:

1. Electronic distributor for the HEUIs
2. HEUI power-up
3. Output driver for the HEUIs
4. IDM and HEUI diagnostics

Electronic Distributor for the Injectors

The ECM calculates engine position from the CMP sensor located at the engine front cover. The ECM uses this signal to determine cylinder firing sequence and then delivers this command data to the IDM by means of a **fuel demand command signal (FDCS)**. The FDCS contains injection timing and fuel quantity data. Note how the FDCS and cylinder ID signals are communicated between the IDM and ECM. These communications are transacted on a proprietary bus.

Injector Power-Up

The IDM supplies the voltage required to switch the HEUI or CR injector actuators. Depending on the generation of the engine, the power-up voltages are:

- A constant 115 + V-DC supply
- A constant 48 + V-DC supply

The actuation voltage is created in the IDM by making and breaking a 12 V-DC source potential across a coil using the same principles employed by the ignition coil in a spark-ignited (SI) engine. The resultant voltage induced by the coil is stored in capacitors until discharged to the injector actuators. **Figure 44–5** is a graphic showing how the IDM functions to switch a HEUI system equipped with the pre-2004 Caterpillar units, and **Figure 44–6** shows how a more recent Siemens HEUI is managed.

FIGURE 44–5 Injector driver module operation: Output driver operation.

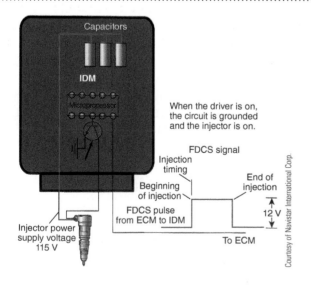

FIGURE 44–6 ECM switching of spool valve in a Siemens HEUI.

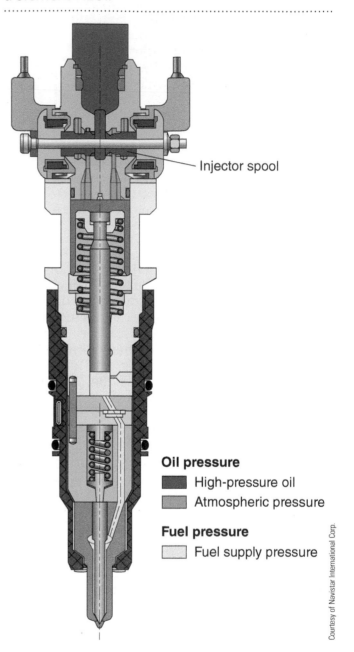

INJECTION CONTROL LOGIC

The ECM is responsible for maintaining the correct injection pressures whether an HEUI or CR system fuels the engine. This means monitoring and continually adjusting the critical system pressures that result in fuel injection:

- HEUI: the high-pressure oil circuit responsible for actuating HEUI fueling
- CR: the common rail fuel pressure

The engine controller logic does this by comparing *actual* pressure in the circuit with the ECM-calculated *desired* pressure in the circuit. As with all current management systems, keeping actual and desired circuit pressures as close to each other as possible is a requirement.

Actual circuit pressure in both CR and HEUI systems is measured by a variable capacitance pressure sensor and signaled to the ECM. Desired circuit pressure is based on the fueling algorithm (computed by ECM) effective at any given moment of operation. In the processing loop, the ECM will evaluate any differential between actual and desired actuation pressures and will modulate an output signal to the injection actuation control solenoid valve to keep the values close.

ECM DIAGNOSTICS

Early versions of Navistar HEUI were accessed using ProLink and a dedicated cartridge or its Ford equivalent. More recent versions require the use of Navistar's MD/SM and ISIS/NSI. The Navistar ECM is designed to interact with the **EZ-Tech** EST, which coordinates Master Diagnostics (MD)/ServiceMaxx (SM) and the online International Service Information System (ISIS)/NSI software.

In common with other engine ECM-driven systems, the software is capable of identifying faults within its electronic circuitry and can determine whether an HEUI solenoid or its wiring circuit is drawing too much (or too little) current. In the event of such an electronic malfunction, a fault code is logged. The self-diagnostics can also set an ECM code indicating a module failure.

DIAGNOSTIC SOFTWARE

MD and SM are the software platforms required to read, program, and troubleshoot HEUI systems. Navistar states that MD and SM software is best run on a dedicated EZ-Tech notebook computer. To access the ECM, the appropriate CA must be used. MD and SM are designed to do the following tests on their respective systems:

- Test injector actuators
- Test system pressure sensors
- Perform cylinder cutout tests
- Identify active faults
- Identify logged faults
- Identify logged events
- Display engine configuration data
- Rewrite customer-programmable parameters
- Flash new software
- Print configuration and test results

Injector Cutout Test

MD/SM can perform injector cutout tests on HEUI-managed engines. Cylinder cutout testing on HEUI-fueled engines is not unlike that used on other fuel systems with electrical actuators. MD/SM can perform multiple cylinder cutout and produce a more comprehensive cylinder balance analysis. The test sequence should be performed with the engine at operating temperature and with intermittent parasitic loads such as the A/C disconnected. The test sequence for single cylinder cutout is described here:

1. Governor maintains programmed idle speed.
2. The diagnostic software turns off one injector at a time: This means the five functioning HEUIs must increase their duty cycle if the specified engine rpm is to be maintained.
3. The diagnostic software measures the average duty cycle of the five functioning injectors at each stage of the cutout test.
4. A test value is assigned for each injector tested.
5. The cutout test cycle is then repeated.

Navistar Self-Test

Navistar's electronics are capable of performing self-test procedures. When the dash-mounted **self-test input (STI)** button is depressed and the ignition circuit is key-on, engine-off (KOEO), the ECM begins the self-test cycle. When complete, the oil/water and warn engine dash lights are used to signal fault codes. All Navistar in-house (as opposed to SAE) fault codes are three digits. The following is the sequence:

1. Oil/water light flashes once, indicating the beginning of the active faults display.
2. Warn engine light flashes each digit of the active fault code, pausing between each. The oil/water light will flash once between each active code readout when multiple codes are logged. Code 111 indicates no active fault codes.
3. Oil/water light flashes twice to indicate that inactive fault codes will be displayed.

Inactive fault codes are then blinked out in the same manner as active fault codes.

4. When all codes have been displayed, the oil/water light will flash three times.

5. Test sequence can be repeated by retracing the preceding steps, but all active faults should be repaired before progressing to later tests.

Troubleshooting Navistar electronics is made easier by using a Hickok breakout box and breakout Ts. Both diagnostic circuit tools enable a DMM to test active electronic circuits. **Figure 44–7** shows the location of a dash STI and a DMM used with a breakout box; **Figure 44–8** shows the torque and power profiles of a 2015 N10 engine.

FIGURE 44–7 Navistar self-test button location and troubleshooting with a breakout box that permits DMM testing of active electronic circuits.

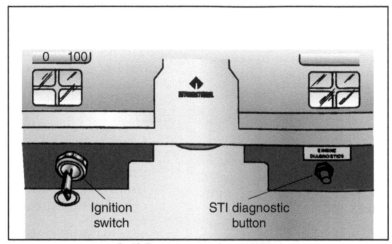

Self-Test Button Location

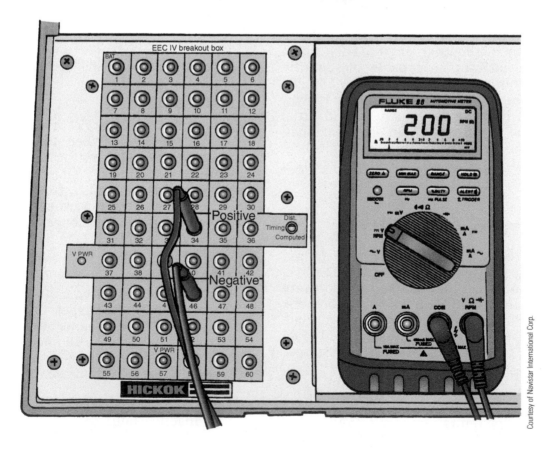

FIGURE 44–8 Torque and power bands on a 2015 Navistar N10 engine.

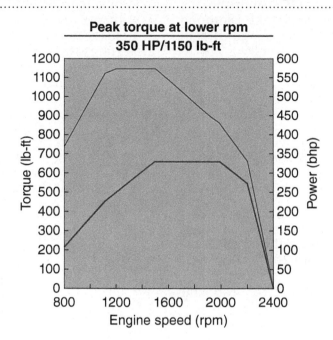

SUMMARY

- The Navistar chassis multiplexing system is known as Diamond Logic.
- Master Diagnostics (MD) software is used to diagnose and program Navistar engines prior to 2007.
- ServiceMaxx (SM) replaces MD for post-2007 Navistar engines.
- ISIS (before 2007) and NSI (post-2007) are the Navistar online service information systems (SISs) used at the dealership level.
- OnCommand is the Navistar online SIS especially tailored for truck fleet requirements.
- Navistar ECMs may use three-, two-, or single-module architecture to run the engines.
- A three-module system consists of an ECM, IDM, and a personality module. A two-module system combines the ECM and personality module in one housing and uses a separate IDM. A single-module system combines the three "boxes" used in the three-module system and calls it a consolidated engine controller (CEC).
- The MY 2010 MaxxForce 11 and 13 engines used CR fueling and EGR aftertreatment and were developed in cooperation with the MAN engine company. These engine lines were dropped for MY 2013.
- The MaxxForce 15 engine was designed on a Caterpillar C15 platform and used CR fueling and EGR aftertreatment. This engine was discontinued in 2013.
- For MY 2013 and later, Navistar manufactures just one engine with larger than 10 liters displacement, the N13. The Navistar N13 uses Bosch CR fueling and a Cummins-supplied SCR exhaust gas aftertreatment system.

REVIEW QUESTIONS

1. What is the online SIS used for Navistar engines manufactured before 2007 known as?
   a. SIS
   b. ISIS
   c. NSI
   d. Oracle

2. What is the dealership-level, online SIS used for working on Navistar engines manufactured after 2007 known as?
   a. SIS
   b. ISIS
   c. NSI
   d. HEUI

3. Technician A says that Diamond Plus is a Navistar term for its chassis multiplexing system. Technician B says that Diamond Plus electronics are used to manage current Navistar engines. Who is correct?
   a. Technician A only
   b. Technician B only
   c. Both A and B
   d. Neither A nor B

4. What is the Navistar online SIS especially designed for fleet applications known as?
   a. SIS
   b. ISIS
   c. NSI
   d. OnCommand

5. What is Master Diagnostics software used for?
   a. Troubleshooting pre-2007 Navistar engines
   b. Troubleshooting post-2010 Navistar engines
   c. Training diesel technicians
   d. Training parts personnel

6. If you had to troubleshoot a problem on a Navistar N13 engine, which of the following software packages would be the most help?
   a. MD
   b. SM
   c. ISIS
   d. ICR

7. Which engine manufacturer has a connection with the development of the MY 2010 MaxxForce 11 engine?
   a. MAN
   b. Caterpillar
   c. Ford
   d. Detroit Diesel

8. Siemens-manufactured HEUIs are switched at:
   a. 12 V-DC.
   b. 48 V-DC.
   c. 90 V-AC.
   d. 115 V-AC.

9. Navistar fault codes may be read from the vehicle dash when the STI button is depressed using which lights?
   a. Check engine and stop engine
   b. Warn engine and oil/water
   c. Electronic malfunction and shutdown engine

10. Technician A states that in a Navistar two-box engine controller, the ECM and IDM are incorporated into one module, and the personality module in the other. Technician B states that a Navistar single-box system can be known as a CEC system. Who is correct?
    a. Technician A only
    b. Technician B only
    c. Both A and B
    d. Neither A nor B

11. Technician A states that the 2010 MaxxForce 15 engine was based on a Caterpillar C15 engine platform. Technician B states that a MaxxForce 15 engine uses the Caterpillar ACERT system and SCR. Who is correct?
    a. Technician A only
    b. Technician B only
    c. Both A and B
    d. Neither A nor B

12. Technician A states that processing logic *desired* pressure relates to the ECM calculated rail pressure in a CR fuel system. Technician B states that *actual* pressures in an HEUI or CR system are always values signaled to the engine controller by means of sensors. Who is correct?
    a. Technician A only
    b. Technician B only
    c. Both A and B
    d. Neither A nor B

13. Technician A states that the 2010 MaxxForce 11 used an HEUI fuel system. Technician B states that the Navistar N13 uses a CR fuel system. Who is correct?
    a. Technician A only
    b. Technician B only
    c. Both A and B
    d. Neither A nor B

14. What is the post-2010 version of the Navistar 466 engine known as?
    a. MaxxForce 10
    b. MaxxForce DT
    c. DT 466E
    d. VT 466 E

15. What engine configuration is used in a MaxxForce 7 engine?
    a. V-8
    b. V-6
    c. I-6
    d. I-4

Prerequisites: Chapters 19, 21, 28, and 30

PACCAR ENGINE MANAGEMENT SYSTEMS

OBJECTIVES

After studying this chapter, you should be able to:

- Define the acronym DAVIE.
- Identify the Paccar engines that use electronic controls.
- Explain the differences between the PX, MX-EUP, and MX-CR fuel systems.
- Describe the Delphi F2R CR fuel system used on post-2013 MX-Series engines.
- Identify Paccar online service information and diagnostic software.
- Identify some of the key features of Paccar families of electronic engines.
- Identify the ESTs required to access Paccar engine electronics and data hub.
- Outline the suite of emissions management hardware devices used on MX-Series engines.
- Describe the procedure used to regenerate a DPF.
- Interpret DEF warning light signals.

KEY TERMS

common rail (CR)

communications adapter (CA)

DAF vehicle information electronics (DAVIE)

electrohydraulic injector (EHI)

electronic unit pump (EUP)

high-pressure heavy-duty diesel common rail (HPHDDCR)

MX-Series

PX-Series

Rapido

ServiceNet (SN)

SMART [injector]

ultra high-pressure heavy-duty common rail fuel injection (UPCRI)

vehicle communication interface (VCI)

web ECAT

INTRODUCTION

Paccar Trucks took control over Dutch truck builder DAF in 1996 and the company acquired the British Leyland Trucks in 1998. In overall worldwide sales, Paccar DAF is the third-largest truck builder following Daimler (Freightliner here) and Volvo. Paccar's two U.S.-based units, Kenworth and Peterbilt, built their reputation with prestige broker class 8 trucks, but in more recent years the companies have expanded to offer a full range of fleet, highway, and vocational trucks. In 2012, Peterbilt and Kenworth combined had around a 28% share of the North American market.

Until 2007, Paccar did not supply engines in its truck chassis, relying mainly on Caterpillar and Cummins power. However, the Dutch division DAF had a previous history of engine manufacturing, and for the Environmental Protection Agency (EPA) model year (MY) 2007, Kenworth and Peterbilt offered Paccar engine options with their **PX-Series** line for light- and medium-duty trucks. In 2010, Paccar engine options were expanded to include high horsepower power units for its class 7 and class 8 trucks with the addition of the **MX-Series** line. **Figure 45–1** shows a left-side view of a MY 2010 Paccar MX-Series engine configured with typical post-2010 auxiliary hardware.

PX-SERIES

There are two PX series offerings from Paccar. Both engines are DAF adaptations of Cummins-engineered engines, the ISB 6.7 liter and ISC

8.3 liter. As with the Cummins original versions, both PX series engines use a Bosch **common rail (CR)** fuel system. The management electronics on these engines were developed by Paccar, but in other respects they differ little from the equivalent displacement Cummins engines, so they will not be addressed in any detail in this chapter.

PRE-2013 MX-13 SERIES

The first generation of MX-Series engines was DAF engineered and used an **electronic unit pump (EUP)** fuel system with **SMART** electro-hydraulic injectors (EHIs). This makes the fuel system similar to that used by Mack Trucks until 2007, and almost identical to the version used on Mercedes-Benz MB-4000 from 2007 until 2010. This first generation of Paccar engines was introduced in 2010 and replaced in 2013 by a common rail fueled engine described in the next section of this chapter.

Both the pre- and post-2013 MX engines are built on a 12.9-liter platform. The numeral in the suffix of the engine series designation refers to the power rating in kilowatts. For instance, the top power and torque rating of a Paccar MX-375 engine produces 500 BHP—not bad for a 13-liter engine.

EUP FUEL SYSTEM

The first generation of Paccar MX series engines featured an EUP fuel system used in conjunction with **electrohydraulic injectors (EHIs)** known as SMART injectors because the engine control module (ECM) controlled nozzle opening and closing. The SMART injectors were multipulse capable. **Figure 45–2** shows a cutaway view of the EUP fuel system as it appears on one of the six engine cylinders. Note that the ECM controls both the EUP effective stroke and the SMART injector.

POST-2013 MX-SERIES

Paccar re-engineered the fuel system on the MX-13 engine for EPA MY 2013, upgrading it to a Delphi common rail (CR) fuel system. This engine became the default power unit in Class 8 Kenworth and Peterbilt chassis, although Paccar also optioned the popular Cummins ISX engines. The MY 2013 MX-13 did not differ significantly in appearance from the earlier

FIGURE 45–1 Left-side view of a Paccar 2010–2013 MX-Series, EUP-fueled engine.

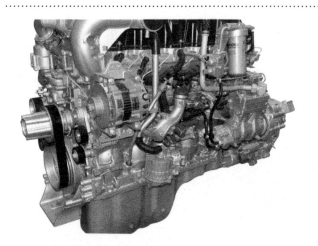

FIGURE 45–2 EUP and SMART injector arrangement. Note that the EUP actuator and the SMART EHI are both controlled by the ECM.

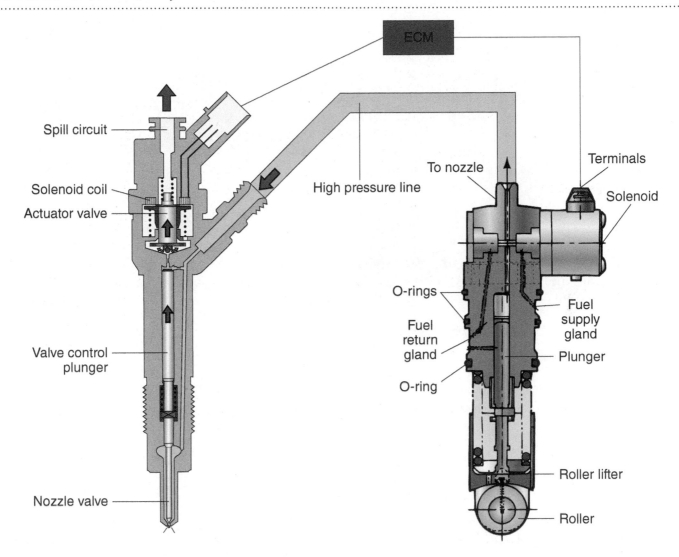

version, but its CR fuel system significantly enhanced the ability of the engine control electronics to manage combustion. **Figure 45–3** shows a MY 2013 (2015 version) of a Paccar MX-13 engine.

MY 2015 MX-11

Paccar introduced its MX-11 engine into DAF-badged vehicles in Europe in MY 2013, and this is scheduled for a North American introduction in the fall of 2015. The MX-11 is a 10.8-liter, 6-cylinder, in-line engine with power ratings that will range between 280 hp and 430 hp and torque output of up to 1,550 lb.-ft. The engine features a double overhead camshaft and a compact graphite iron (CGI) cylinder block for lighter weight. It is intended as a fleet powerplant with an emphasis on fuel

FIGURE 45–3 Left-side view of a post-2013 Paccar MX-13 engine featuring the key components of the Delphi CR system.

FIGURE 45–4 Cutaway view of the MY 2015 Paccar MX-11 engine.

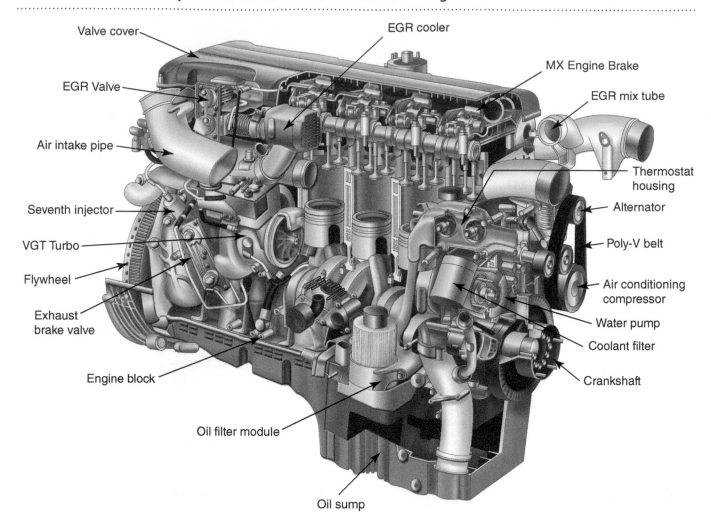

economy. **Figure 45–4** shows a cutaway view of the Paccar MX-11.

DELPHI CR

The Paccar post-2013 MX-11 and MX-13 share a common fuel system. This Delphi CR system is known by Paccar as **ultra high-pressure heavy-duty common rail fuel injection (UPCRI)** and by Delphi as its F2R **high-pressure heavy-duty diesel common rail (HPHDDCR)** system. It should be noted that the fundamental operating principles of the Delphi CR do not differ from other CRs—but the fuel system components do readily lend themselves to an engine that was originally designed for EUP fueling, because rail pressure pumps are camshaft-actuated EUPs.

In the Delphi F2R CR system, the EUPs are integrated into the cylinder block: this pair of high-pressure pumps feeds the common rail.

Because the main engine camshafts are no longer required to sustain the stresses of driving the high-pressure unit pumps used in the pre-2013 MX-engine, a hollow camshaft design is used to reduce weight. **Figure 45–5** highlights the key components of the Paccar MX-Series fuel system.

The UPCRI system runs at rail pressures of potentially up to 43,500 psi (3000 bar), but in 2015 applications DAF states that this typically runs at a maximum of 36,000 psi (2500 bar). The electrohydraulic injectors (EHIs) used are multipulse capable, and can provide pre- and post-injection pulses in addition to a main pulse.

Because there is no separate common rail pump on the outside of the engine, the exterior of the engine has a relatively uncluttered appearance compared to other CR-fueled engines. In addition, the air intake manifold is integrated into the cylinder head architecture.

FIGURE 45–5 Cutaway highlighting the key components of the Delphi F2R common rail fuel system.

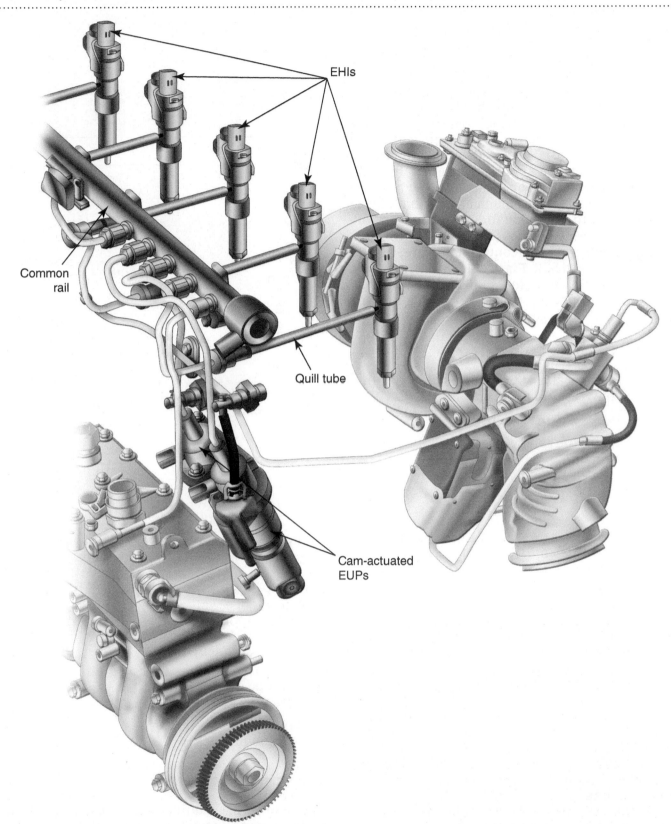

EHIs

Common
rail

Quill tube

Cam-actuated
EUPs

MX-SERIES FEATURES

The MX-series engines have an integral internal engine brake, and when it is applied, only one camshaft is actuated to choke off the exhaust gas flow. The MX-11 can deliver up to 429 hp (320 kW) of braking power, and is 70% effective when engine speed drops to 1500 rpm. Paccar claim that the diesel particulate filter (DPF) can produce cleaning intervals that can be extended up to 300,000 miles (490,000 km).

The cooling system water pump features a two-speed electromagnetic coupling to permit the ECM to manage cooling efficiency. In addition, the air compressor is managed by the ECM so that it is operated as much as possible during deceleration to minimize fuel consumption.

The MX-Series engines use a full suite of typical post-2010 emission control hardware, including EGR, DPF, and SCR. **Figure 45–6** is a right-side view of an MX-13 engine showing the variable-geometry turbocharger and intake gas routing from the turbocharger to the EGR controls.

MY 2013 POWER RATINGS

Both the MX-11 and MX-13 are available with a range of power and torque specifications.

MX-11 Power and Torque

The MX-11 engine can be spec'd with torque trim to 2100 N·m and five power ratings:

- 282 hp (210 kW)
- 322 hp (240 kW)

FIGURE 45–6 Right-side view of a post-2013 Paccar MX-13 engine featuring the VGT, EGR routing controls, and EGR cooler.

FIGURE 45–7 Paccar MX-11 power and torque graphs.

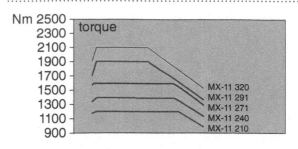

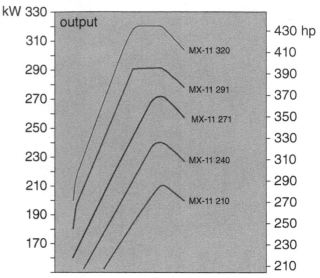

- 363 hp (271 kW)
- 390 hp (291 kW)
- 429 hp (320 kW)

Figure 45–7 is a graph showing the power and torque profiles of a MY 2015 MX-11.

MX-13 Power and Torque

The MX-13 engine can be spec'd with torque trim to up to 2500 N·m and four power ratings:

- 360 hp (265 kW)
- 408 hp (300 kW)
- 462 hp (340 kW)
- 510 hp (375 kW)

Figure 45–8 is a graph showing the power and torque profiles of the MY 2015 MX-13.

KEY SYSTEM DATA

The following is a quick reference guide to some of the Paccar-specific system terminology and acronyms used in this chapter.

FIGURE 45-8 Paccar MX-13 power and torque graphs.

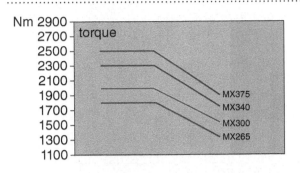

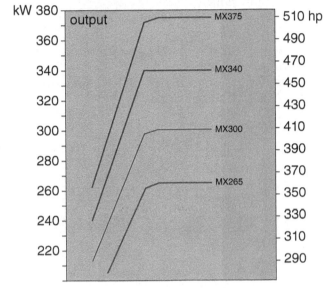

FIGURE 45-9 The Paccar VCI required to connect to the first generation of Paccar MX engine electronics.

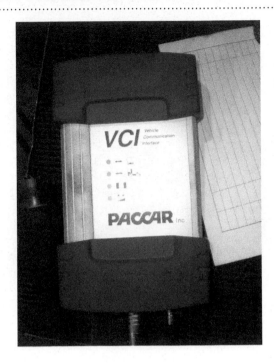

System Software Tools

- Paccar **ServiceNet (SN)**. Paccar's subscription online service information system. Accessed through the Paccar **web ECAT** (electronic catalog) dealer data hub. For Paccar MX-engines, the SIS sector is known as **DAF vehicle information electronics (DAVIE)**. This is almost always referred to as DAVIE.
- **RAPIDO** is the Paccar diagnostic software designed to run in conjunction with its ServiceNet DAVIE. RAPIDO is accessed through the DAVIE portal. The software is required to diagnose and reprogram on- and off-highway Paccar engine malfunctions.

PACCAR ELECTRONICS

The Paccar ECM is bused into J1939, but technicians used to working on other original equipment manufacturer (OEM) American-built engines are going to find these a little different.

Online and software access to DAVIE and RAPIDO are by subscription. Some may find that navigating Paccar electronic system is less than intuitive. The first hitch is that for the first generation of Paccar MX-13 electronics (2010 to 2013), the **communications adapter (CA)** was not RP1210-compliant, meaning that generic aftermarket CAs could not connect with the engine electronics. A Paccar-supplied **vehicle communication interface (VCI)** must be used. From MY 2013, this changed and Paccar data buses could be accessed using a generic RP1210-compliant CA. **Figure 45-9** shows the Paccar VCI.

INPUT CIRCUIT

Command and monitoring sensors and switches in Paccar engine management systems are consistent with other comparable full authority management systems. The operating principles of input circuit components are described in detail in Chapter 34. The Paccar ECM is located on the lower left side of the engine, along with many of the input circuit components, which are also located on the left side of the engine. Paccar electronics will accommodate either a potentiometer or a noncontact Hall-effect throttle position sensor (TPS).

FIGURE 45–10 The ECM used on a Paccar MX-Series engine: The engine harness (top) is connected and the chassis harness disconnected.

ECM

The ECMs on the MX-Series engines use 32-bit technology. **Figure 45–10** shows the ECM used on an MX-Series engine. The ECM is responsible for engine governing, fuel management algorithm, self-diagnostics, and system monitoring. It also manages the exhaust aftertreatment devices. Paccar electronics log proprietary data, customer programmed options, write-to-self, and data audit trails.

ECM Drivers

Paccar ECMs incorporate all of the required system drivers within the ECM housing. The various drivers are responsible for outputting system reference voltages, switching the EUP actuators, switching the EHIs, and running all the emissions control hardware. While the input circuit receives data from engine monitoring sensors and those broadcast on the data bus, it can also broadcast itself onto both the J1587 and J1939 data backbones.

OUTPUT CIRCUIT

Paccar output circuit devices put the results of the computer processing cycle into action. The ECM outputs for MY 2010 to 2013 engines include:

- The EUPs (six, one for each cylinder)
- The EHIs (six, one over each cylinder)
- Engine controls such as fan hub, compression brake, and so on
- The conditioned V-Ref (5V-DC) and power-up (8V-DC) circuits
- Dash display data
- Broadcast drivers to the chassis data backbone
- EGR, SCR, and DPF system controls

The ECM outputs for MY 2013 MX13 (and later) engines and MY 2015 MX11 engines include:

- EUPs (two used to charge the high-pressure common rail)
- Rail pressure management actuators
- EHIs (six, one over each cylinder)
- Engine controls such as fan hub, compression brake, and so on
- The conditioned V-Ref (5V-DC) and power-up (8V-DC) circuits
- Dash display data
- Broadcast drivers to the chassis data backbone
- EGR, SCR, and DPF system controls

SYSTEM DIAGNOSTICS AND COMMUNICATIONS

Paccar electronic system self-diagnostics are consistent with its competitor OEM systems. However, unlike its competitors, Paccar engine electronics can (at the moment of writing) only be accessed using Paccar proprietary EST software and a CA. In the event of electronic system or component failure, the operator is alerted by the dash-mounted check engine light (CEL). The code may be read on the CEL using the cruise control switches on vehicles equipped with cruise control, or with one of the ESTs listed previously. **Figure 45–11** shows a shop-based laptop station with a VCI set up for accessing a Paccar data bus.

CONNECTING TO THE BUS

Paccar ESTs connect to the chassis electronics by means of a J1939 nine-pin Deutsch connector. The vehicle communications interface (VCI) used must be a Paccar unit, as shown in Figure 45–9, in pre-MY 2013 chassis. In post-MY 2103, an RP1210 CA can be used. After physically connecting the laptop to the data bus, DAVIE should be launched. **Figure 45–12** shows the DAVIE entry screen. RAPIDO is located within the DAVIE portal.

FIGURE 45–11 A shop-based laptop workstation equipped with DAVIE software and a Paccar VCI.

FIGURE 45–12 DAVIE entry screen.

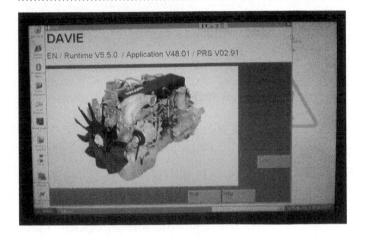

PACCAR EXHAUST AFTERTREATMENT

Paccar PX-, pre-MY 2013 MX-, and post-MY 2103 MX-Series engines use a full suite of aftertreatment hardware devices that includes cooled-exhaust gas recirculation (C-EGR), diesel oxidation catalyst (DOC), selective catalytic reduction (SCR), and diesel particulate filter (DPF). **Figure 45–13** is a Paccar representation of its aftertreatment circuit devices.

DPF REGENERATION

Paccar DPF regeneration cycles are initiated using a dash-mounted, three-position regeneration switch shown in **Figure 45–14**. The three positions are:

Start position. Moving the button in the *start* direction for between 4 to 8 seconds initiates a parked regeneration event.

Center position. The *center* position is the normal switch position. The only time it should be moved out of this position is when manually initiating a parked regeneration event or intentionally stopping a regeneration cycle. When the switch is in the center position, automatic regenerations are enabled, providing the vehicle operating conditions permit.

Stop position. When *stop* is pressed, the DPF will not regenerate under any circumstances. It is important not to leave the switch in the stop position when operating the vehicle because it will ultimately result in the DPF plugging with soot and engine deration.

FIGURE 45–13 Paccar MX-Series aftertreatment schematic.

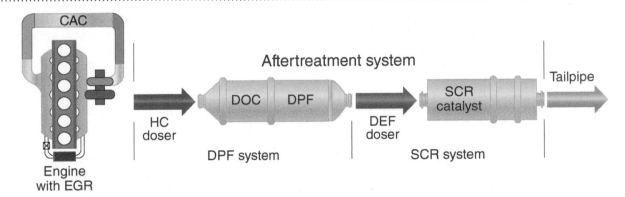

FIGURE 45–14 Paccar DPF three-position switch.

FIGURE 45–15 Paccar DEF fluid level and warning light display gauge.

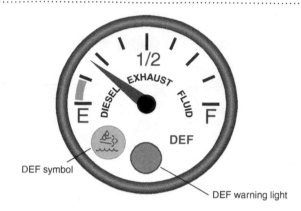

DEF symbol

DEF warning light

DPF Warning Lamps

ATS-specific warning lamps and indicator symbols are located on the main gauge cluster. The following are used:

- DPF warning lamp symbol
- High exhaust system temperature (HEST) warning lamp symbol

SCR SYSTEM

The operating principles of SCR are covered in some detail in Chapter 47, and the approach here is to outline the Paccar version of the system. SCR requires routine replenishing of the urea solution known as *diesel exhaust fluid (DEF)*. Because DEF is consumable and the SCR circuit has a major influence on the engine's ability to manage NO_x output, fluid levels are electronically monitored. Consequently, a DEF dash warning light is used to alert the operator. When the DEF lamp located on the dash DEF level gauge (see **Figure 45–15**) illuminates, it does so for three reasons:

1. **DEF level**. There are four stages to a DEF level warning. The first stage, represented by the lamp illuminating and staying on, means that the level has dropped to about 10%. The second stage is initiated when the DEF warning light begins to flash, indicating that the level has dropped to around 5%. The third stage is launched when the DEF tank is almost empty; in addition to the flashing DEF warning light, the check engine light is illuminated, and engine power is derated at this point. The fourth stage means that the tank is empty; in addition to the CEL lamp being illuminated, the stop engine light (SEL) illuminates, and both engine power and road speed are derated.

2. **DEF quality**. There are three stages to a DEF quality warning. The first stage is represented by the DEF lamp illuminating along with the malfunction indicator lamp (MIL). Stage two is initiated after operating the vehicle for one hour after the first-stage warning: At this point the engine derates. After three hours of operation following the first alert, the warning lights continue to illuminate along with illumination of the SEL and deration of engine and road speed.

3. **SCR system tampering**. If the electronic management system detects tampering with the SCR system, there are three progressive stages to the warning sequence. The first stage is represented by the DEF lamp illuminating along with the malfunction indicator lamp (MIL). Stage two is initiated after operating the vehicle for one hour after the first-stage warning: At this point the engine derates. After five hours of operation following the first alert, the warning lights continue to illuminate along with the illumination of the SEL and deration of engine and road speed.

SUMMARY

- Paccar's engine diagnostic software is RAPIDO.
- Paccar's data hub is known as ServiceNet and its online service information system is known as DAVIE. A subscription is required to access it.
- Paccar engine management uses a single-module ECM incorporating both the processing capability and output drivers required by the engine and emissions control system.
- Paccar PX engines were introduced in 2007 and, like their sibling Cummins engines of the same displacement, use a Bosch common rail fuel system. Two engine displacements are available: 6.7 liters and 8.3 liters.
- The first generation of Paccar MX engines was introduced in 2010 and used a Bosch EUP system in combination with SMART injectors. SMART injectors are EHIs. The EHIs connect to the unit pumps by means of a short high-pressure pipe. Production of the first-generation MX engines was discontinued in MY 2013.
- Second-generation MX engines were introduced for MY 2013. The MY 2013 MX13 uses a Delphi CR fuel system. In 2015, Paccar introduced its MX11, a fleet version of the larger-bore MX13 that also uses CR fueling.
- Paccar locates the EUP actuator drivers within a single module ECM housing.
- Paccar electronics log proprietary data, customer programmed options, write-to-self, and data audit trails.
- A Windows environment and online access are required to launch and use Paccar web ECAT, ServiceNet, DAVIE, and RAPIDO diagnostics.

REVIEW QUESTIONS

1. What is the Paccar online service information system known as?
   a. ET
   b. DAVIE
   c. RAPIDO
   d. PacNet

2. What is Paccar diagnostic software known as?
   a. ET
   b. DAVIE
   c. RAPIDO
   d. Electronic Technician (ET)

3. Which of the following Paccar chassis engines uses an EUP fuel system?
   a. Cummins ISX
   b. Paccar PX-Series
   c. Post-2013 Paccar MX-Series
   d. Pre-2013 Paccar MX-Series

4. Where is the Paccar ECM located on an MX-Series engine?
   a. Left side
   b. Right side
   c. Under the bell housing
   d. Above the rocker covers

5. Where are the Paccar EUP drivers located?
   a. Integral with the ECM
   b. On the firewall bulkhead
   c. Under the dash
   d. Integral with each EUP

6. Technician A states that to access post-2013 Paccar MX-Series engine electronics, an RP1210 CA must be used. Technician B states that MY 2013 MX-Series engines use a two-module ECM system. Who is correct?
   a. Technician A only
   b. Technician B only
   c. Both A and B
   d. Neither A nor B

7. Technician A says Paccar DAVIE is a free Web download. Technician B states that Paccar RAPIDO diagnostics are required to troubleshoot MX engines. Who is correct?
   a. Technician A only
   b. Technician B only
   c. Both A and B
   d. Neither A nor B

8. Technician A says that all pre-2013 Paccar engines use an EUP fuel system. Technician B says that accessing Paccar MY 2013 and later chassis data buses can only be achieved using a Paccar-supplied VCI. Who is correct?
   a. Technician A only.
   b. Technician B only
   c. Both A and B
   d. Neither A nor B

9. Which of the following is the Paccar catalog system?
   a. web ECAT
   b. RAPIDO
   c. DAVIE
   d. MX

10. Technician A says that a pre-2013 Paccar MX engine uses six EUPs. Technician B says that a post-2013 Paccar MX engine uses two EUPs to supply the high-pressure common rail. Who is correct?
   a. Technician A only
   b. Technician B only
   c. Both A and B
   d. Neither A nor B

11. Who manufactures the CR fuel system used on the Paccar MX-11 engine?
   a. Bosch
   b. Cummins
   c. Paccar
   d. Delphi

12. What is used to produce the required rail pressures on post-2013 Paccar MX-Series engines?
   a. Swashplate pump
   b. A single-element piston pump
   c. A cam-actuated EUP
   d. A pair of cam-actuated EUPs

46

Prerequisites: Chapters 18, 29, 32, and 35

VOLVO AND MACK ENGINE MANAGEMENT

OBJECTIVES

After studying this chapter, you should be able to:

- Define the acronyms VECTRO and V-MAC.
- Identify the Volvo and Mack electronic engine families.
- Identify the online SIS used by Volvo and Mack.
- Define the role of input circuit components.
- Describe how the EECU and VCU manage EUI duty cycle to control engine fueling.
- Outline some of the factors that govern the engine fueling and engine management algorithm.
- Identify the J1939 source addresses (SAs) used by the engine and chassis management controllers.
- Perform some basic troubleshooting using Volvo and Mack diagnostic software on VECTRO and V-MAC managed engines.
- Identify the ESTs required to read VECTRO and V-MAC.
- Describe how EUI calibration code programming is effected.
- Access the data recording features used by VECTRO and V-MAC.
- Navigate through DID software menu options.

KEY TERMS

common platform

driver information display (DID)

Electrical Information System (EIS)

electronic engine control unit (EECU)

engine management system (EMS)

IMPACT

partial authority

Premium Tech Tool (PTT)

Tech Tool (TT)

VECTRO

vehicle control unit (VCU)

vehicle management and control (V-MAC)

vehicle computer-assisted diagnostics (VCADs) [Volvo]

Volvo electronic controls (VECTRO)

INTRODUCTION

Mack has iconic status in our language, embedded in phrases such as "built like a Mack Truck," but in actual fact its ownership has been European for more than a generation. In 1990, Mack Trucks became a wholly owned subsidiary of Renault (France), and in 2001, the truck division of Renault was assimilated by Volvo (Sweden). While under Renault management, the technology of Mack products did not undergo significant changes, but this changed when Volvo assumed ownership. Although Volvo and Mack present separate corporate identities to the world, this is more about marketing than substance. Today, there is little difference between a Volvo- or Mack-badged engine other than paint color.

MACK HISTORY

Mack Trucks first sold an electronically controlled fuel system in 1989. This was a **partial authority** fuel management system using an inline port-helix metering fuel system. Mack used these computer-controlled, pump-line-nozzle (PLN) systems until 1998, when they could no longer meet Environmental Protection Agency (EPA) emissions standards. Mack Trucks engine and chassis management electronics are known as **V-MAC (vehicle management and control)**. **Figure 46–1** shows a block diagram

FIGURE 46–1 Block diagram showing the inputs and outputs to a V-MAC II PLN engine management system.

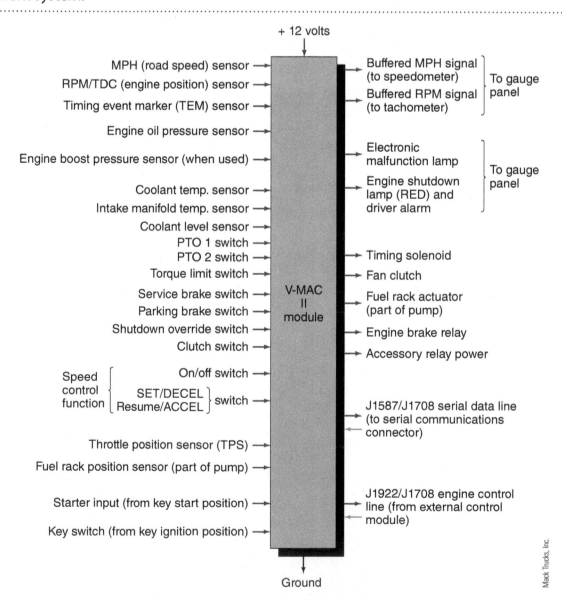

Mack Trucks, Inc.

of a V-MAC II PLN fuel system. Partial authority PLN fueling was replaced in 1998 by a full authority electronic unit pump (EUP) fuel system (see Chapter 28) that was used until EPA model year 2007. In 2007, Volvo and Mack introduced their common platform engines, differentiated by little more than paint color. This family of engines used a fuel system based around twin-actuator, Delphi E3 injectors, described in Chapter 26.

VOLVO HISTORY

Volvo launched its first electronically controlled, mechanically actuated, unit-injected engine with the introduction of the first generation of electronically controlled VDE-12 engines in the mid-1990s. This family of engines was fueled by single-actuator electronic unit injectors (EUIs) (see Chapter 25). Following the amalgamation of Volvo and Mack Trucks, a new generation of **common platform** engines was introduced beginning in the 2007 model year. Volvo has a long history of using Delphi EUIs to fuel its VDE-12 engines since their introduction to North America, and this relationship continued when the company launched the common platform engines. In this chapter we reference the earlier generations of Volvo **VECTRO (Volvo electronic controls)**, along with the various generations of V-MAC (vehicle management and control).

Pre-2007 Engines

The post-2007 version is known as VECTRO III or **engine management system (EMS)** to describe its chassis electronics. The Mack Trucks engine and chassis management system is known as V-MAC, an acronym for vehicle management and control. The current version is known as V-MAC IV, but generational numbers on chassis software versions tend not to be that important when learning the operating principles of management electronics. While VECTRO III shares a high degree of commonality with its previous versions, it is important to remember that V-MAC IV has less in common with previous versions of V-MAC, because of significant changes in engine architecture and fuel systems.

For whatever reasons, Volvo and Mack Trucks have attempted to maintain some degree of corporate identity when describing each original equipment manufacturer (OEM) badged set of engines. This may be effective from a marketing viewpoint, but it makes it a little confusing for technicians learning the technology. It means that separate terminology and acronyms are required to describe exactly the same components depending on whether the engine is called a Volvo or a Mack. We can begin by stating that Volvo-badged engines have their usual forest green paint job. However, if the engine is Mack Trucks badged, the engine gets a brand new scarlet paint job. Engine color is the easy part. In dealing with this subject matter in this book, there is little option but to use both the Mack and Volvo terms and hope that it does not create confusion.

KEY SYSTEM DATA

The following is a quick reference guide to some of the Volvo- and Mack-specific system terminology and acronyms used in this chapter.

System Software Tools

- Electrical Information System (EIS). Mack Trucks subscription online service information system.
- IMPACT. Volvo's subscription online service information system.
- Premium Tech Tool (PTT). Mack Trucks diagnostic software designed to run in a Windows environment, handshake into EIS, and reference a DVD platform database. The software required to diagnose and reprogram on- and off-highway Mack Trucks engine malfunctions.
- Tech Tool (TT). Volvo's diagnostic software designed to run in a Windows environment, handshake into IMPACT, and reference a DVD platform database. The software required to diagnose and reprogram on- and off-highway Volvo trucks and equipment.
- DataMax. Mack onboard data recorder.
- InfoMax. Windows-environment software used to analyze DataMax.

GENERATIONS OF MANAGEMENT ELECTRONICS

While Volvo's VECTRO has always managed an EUI fuel system on its North American engines, V-MAC has been through four generations, three of which manage distinct fuel systems.

- V-MAC I: Partial authority PLN on E-7 engine using two modules
- V-MAC II: Partial authority PLN on E-7 engine using single module
- V-MAC III: Full authority EUP on E-Tech engine
- V-MAC IV: Full authority EUI on common platform lineup

VOLVO AND MACK ELECTRONIC ENGINES

The following lists some of the Volvo and Mack Trucks lineup of electronic engines. The fuel system is listed in the first column and the displacement in the far right column.

Mack V-MAC I PLN	1989	12-liter displacement
Mack V-MAC II PLN	1992	12-liter displacement
Mack V-MAC III EUP	1997	12-liter displacement
Volvo VE D12 EUI	1995	12-liter displacement
Volvo V-Pulse D-12 EUI	2004	12-liter displacement (EGR)
Volvo D-16 EUI	2004	16-liter displacement (EGR)

EPA 2007 and 2010 Common Platform

The following lists 2007 and later common platform engines, all of which currently use twin-actuator EUI fueling:

Volvo VE D11 (11-liter)	Mack Trucks MP7 (700 cu. in.)
Volvo VE D13 (13-liter)	Mack Trucks MP8 (800 cu. in.)
Volvo VE D16 (16.1-liter)	Mack Trucks MP10 (1000 cu. in.)

Other than the addition of selective catalytic reduction (SCR) and a separate module to manage exhaust emissions, the Volvo-Mack common platform of engines underwent few other changes between the 2007 and 2010 EPA model years.

Family Codes

The numeric values used in Volvo engine family codes can be interpreted as the engine displacement in liters. The VE-D11 code can be interpreted as follows:

V = Volvo

E = electronic

D = diesel

11 = engine displacement in liters

The numeric values used in Mack Trucks engine family codes can be interpreted as the engine displacement to the nearest 100 cubic inches displacement. The MP-10 code can be interpreted as follows:

M = Mack

P = power

10 = engine displacement in 100s of cubic inches

So the 10 is equivalent to 1,000 cubic inches, which is close to the 16.1 liters the engine displaces.

V-MAC AND VECTRO ELECTRONICS

Current V-MAC and VECTRO management electronics offer full authority engine controls and are bussed into J1939. Most of the emphasis in this chapter will be on the current versions of V-MAC and VECTRO:

- V-MAC IV (introduced in 2007, continued through 2015 and beyond)
- VECTRO III (introduced in 2007, continued through 2015 and beyond)

INPUT CIRCUIT

Command and monitoring sensors and switches in the Volvo and Mack Trucks applications are consistent with other comparable full authority management systems. Both VECTRO and V-MAC can accommodate either a potentiometer or a noncontact, Hall-effect throttle position sensor (TPS) (explained in Chapter 34). The input circuit components used by Volvo and Mack Trucks electronics are similar and mostly generic. **Figure 46–2** shows the location of some of the input circuit sensors on a Mack Trucks MP-10 engine, and **Figure 46–3** shows the engine harness from a Volvo VE-D16 showing the location of engine sensors and actuators.

MANAGEMENT ELECTRONICS

The architecture and organization of the chassis data bus and functions of the controllers networked to it in both Volvo and Mack Trucks chassis are nearly identical. Both Mack and Volvo use a chassis controller module known as a **vehicle control unit (VCU)** (SA 71/MID 144) to "master" powertrain operations on the data bus and a separate **electronic engine control unit (EECU)** (SA 00/MID 128). Sharing of input data takes place

FIGURE 46-2 Location of input sensors on a Mack Trucks MP-10 engine.

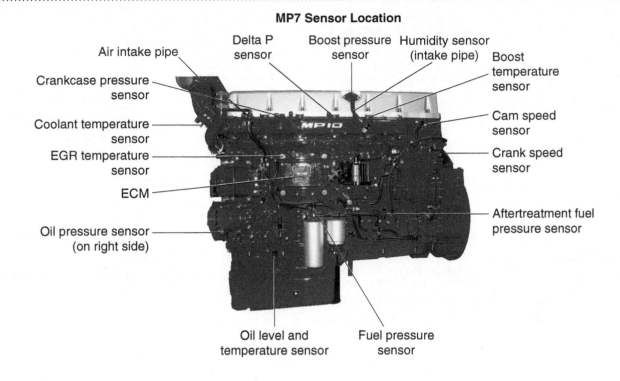

MP7 Sensor Location

Air intake pipe

Crankcase pressure sensor

Coolant temperature sensor

EGR temperature sensor

ECM

Oil pressure sensor (on right side)

Delta P sensor

Boost pressure sensor

Humidity sensor (intake pipe)

Boost temperature sensor

Cam speed sensor

Crank speed sensor

Aftertreatment fuel pressure sensor

Oil level and temperature sensor

Fuel pressure sensor

FIGURE 46-3 Engine wiring harness from a Volvo VE-D16 engine.

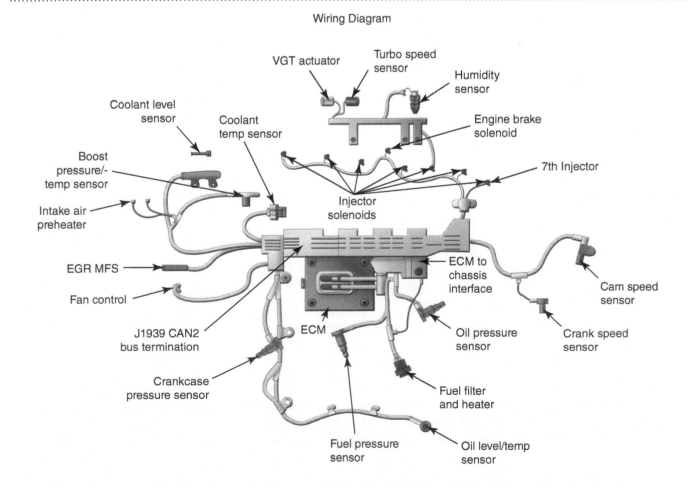

Wiring Diagram

VGT actuator

Turbo speed sensor

Humidity sensor

Coolant level sensor

Coolant temp sensor

Engine brake solenoid

Boost pressure/-temp sensor

7th Injector

Intake air preheater

Injector solenoids

EGR MFS

ECM to chassis interface

Cam speed sensor

Fan control

J1939 CAN2 bus termination

ECM

Oil pressure sensor

Crank speed sensor

Crankcase pressure sensor

Fuel filter and heater

Fuel pressure sensor

Oil level/temp sensor

over the chassis data bus. Some post-2007 Mack chassis equipped with noncatalyzed diesel particulate filters (DPFs) use a separate processor mounted on the exhaust stanchion: This processes and manages DPF active cycles, the operation of which is explained in Chapters 47 and 48. All post-2010 Volvo and Mack electronics use a separate emissions controller to manage DPF and SCR dosing controls. Volvo-Mack use a mixture of J1587 and J1939 terms when teaching their electronics: the acronyms used in this chapter are those that the company uses in their courses.

HOW SA 00 AND SA 71 SHARE DATA

The operating principles of chassis computers are explained in Chapter 34, and there is nothing especially different in the Volvo or Mack Trucks units. Here we take a brief look at how the input circuit routes signals to the EECU and the VCU, and identify the PGN/PID or SID (see Chapter 35 for the explanations of PGN/PIDs and SIDs). The lists shown in **Table 46-1** and **Table 46-2** are not comprehensive; they are just a sample to give you an idea how the "responsibilities" of each ECU are shared.

EECU AND VCU PROGRAMMING

Both the engine and vehicle management ECUs are programmable with customer and proprietary (Volvo or Mack Trucks) data. The same processors are used regardless of whether badged

TABLE 46-1 Inputs to EECU (SA 00/MID 128)

PID 26	Fan speed %
PID 27	EGR position 1
PID 84	Vehicle speed
PID 91	Accelerator position
PID 94	Fuel supply pressure
PID 97	WIF sensor
PID 100	Engine oil pressure
PID 105	Boost pressure
PID 158	Battery voltage
PID 171	Ambient temperature
SIDs 1–6	SIDs 1–6, EUIs 1–6
SID 22	Engine rpm, flywheel sensor
SID 211	V-Ref
SID 230	Idle validation switch
SID 231	J1939 control link

TABLE 46-2 Inputs to VCU (SA 71/MID 144)

PID 84	Vehicle speed
PID 91	Accelerator position, percentage position
PID 150	PTO output
PID 191	Output shaft speed (tailshaft of transmission)
PPID 61	Retarder switches, Volvo engines only
PPID 69	Idle validation switch, Volvo engines only
PPID 71	Cruise control and engine brake supply voltage
PPID 74	VECU power supply
SID 230	Idle validation switch circuit
SID 231	SAE J1939 control data link
SID 240	Program memory
SID 243	Cruise control set switch
SID 250	Data exchange link to J1587/1708
PSID 4	Engine brake stalk for six-stage Cummins ISX
PSID 200	Engine timeout

as Volvo or Mack Trucks. Current ECUs are resistant to radio frequency (RF), electromagnetic interference, and other low-level radiation experienced during normal driving. The EECU is additionally responsible for outputting system reference voltages and receiving inputs both directly from engine monitoring sensors and those broadcast on the J1587 and J1939 data backbones. Their output capability includes the ability to broadcast on the data buses and control engine and chassis actuators. Communication between the two ECUs is on J1939, with the slower J1587 providing system redundancy. The EECU also incorporates the injector driver units within the housing. The computing power and memory capacity of the ECUs have greatly increased with each successive generation, while their physical size has generally decreased.

PROCESSING TRANSACTIONS

The control algorithm contains a comprehensive fuel map. The EECU analyzes data input from the command and monitoring sensors, and plots a fueling profile referencing the instructions programmed to its data retention media. Startup fueling strategy, failure modes, and all the system default values are programmed into the ECU software. The EECU is programmed to run self-diagnostic tests on input and output circuits and identify specific component and circuit faults. Mack Trucks and Volvo troubleshooting software is known as Premium Tech Tool (PTT), or just Tech

Tool (TT), which runs on an Microsoft-Windows environment and can perform interactive and guided diagnostics. Some PTT functions require the use of specialty breakout boxes.

EECU INJECTOR DRIVERS

Volvo and Mack Trucks state that the trigger pulses delivered to their EUI control cartridges are driven at 100 V. The 100 V is induced by coils and the EUIs draw about 10 amps current during the initiation spike. Once the control solenoid has closed to put the EUI into effective delivery stroke, current draw by the cartridge drops to around 4 amps. The inductive kick produced on magnetic field collapse in the solenoid is suppressed by a capacitor. Though not required for any kind of troubleshooting, you can use training or test engines to observe the pulse width modulated (PWM) voltage profile by connecting a lab scope to the actuator terminals, then run the engine. If you plan to do this, actuation frequency should be set for a maximum of 5 msec and voltage peaks set for a maximum of 130 V-DC.

OUTPUT CIRCUIT

The Volvo and Mack Trucks output circuit devices put the results of the computer processing cycle into action. In pre-2007 Volvo trucks, single-actuator EUIs were used in the 12- and

FIGURE 46–4 Delphi single-actuator EUI used in Volvo pre-2007 products.

FIGURE 46–5 Delphi E3 twin-actuator EUI used in post-2007 Volvo and Mack engines.

16-liter engines. **Figure 46–4** is an image of a single-actuator Delphi EUI, and a detail study of the fuel system appears in Chapter 25. Mack Trucks used an EUP fuel system in its pre-2007 products, and this fuel system is examined in details in Chapter 28.

Volvo and Mack engines manufactured since 2007 use a common platform. These engines use Delphi E3 twin-actuator EUIs. In a twin-actuator EUI fuel system, the primary engine outputs are the EUIs and exhaust aftertreatment devices or bus broadcasts to the emissions management module. Other outputs are V-Ref and (other) information broadcast to the data backbone, such as instrument cluster displays and powertrain management. **Figure 46–5** shows a Delphi E3 twin-actuator injector.

Fuel Calibration Codes

In common with equivalent EUIs, Volvo and Mack Trucks twin-actuator EUIs have a fuel flow code printed on side of the unit. The code numeric value is established when an EUI is factory bench-tested and a precise determination is made of how the injector flows fuel. This data is required by the EECU to ensure that the fueling to each engine cylinder is balanced by compensating for minor hydraulic differences between injectors. A new fuel calibration code for an EUI must be programmed to the EECU when the EUI is changed out.

CAUTION:

Failure to reprogram fuel calibration codes when EUIs are replaced will result in the EECU defaulting to the previous fuel flow data programming, which can result in engine fueling balance problems.

CAUTION:

Always observe OEM instructions for draining the fuel manifold when removing EUIs from an engine cylinder head. When an EUI is removed, the contents of the fuel charging rail end up in the engine cylinder if the cylinder head fuel gallery is not first drained.

DRIVER INFORMATION DISPLAY

The digital information displayed by the **driver information display (DID)** is for the benefit of both the driver and the technician. The display data is read off the chassis data bus and can be used to read all the SAs/MIDs networked to it. This means that fault routing through PGNs/PIDs and SIDs to the identification of the specific fault mode indicator (FMI), including the frequency of occurrence, can be achieved using the dash display electronics. In common with most manufacturers, the first indications of a failure are the warning lamps, buzzer, and driver digital information display (if the vehicle is so equipped).

WARNING LAMPS AND BUZZER ALERTS

In the Volvo and Mack Trucks chassis electronics systems, driver alerts can be classified as follows:

- Yellow lamp. Illumination of the yellow lamp indicates that an engine fault of a nature not likely to result in engine damage has been detected. The cause should be diagnosed as soon as possible because it could limit certain engine functions and affect vehicle drivability. It is equivalent to the *Check Engine* lamp used by other OEMs.
- Red lamp. Illumination of the red lamp indicates that an engine fault of a serious nature has been detected. Depending on the specific fault detected, engine power output may be

derated and may result in engine shutdown. It is equivalent to the *Stop Engine* lamp used by other OEMs.
- Buzzer. This sounds when the red dash lamp is illuminated.

DID NAVIGATION

The DID can be used as a first-level diagnostic tool, but it also provides the operator with comprehensive chassis management analytical tools. Some of its features include:

- Fuel economy analytical data
- Trip information
- Message in/out functions using wireless/satellite to base communications
- Driver ID and theft deterrence
- Display of DPF cycles and status
- Diagnostics of any SAs/MIDs on the data bus

Figure 46–6 shows a routing map of the menu options used on a Mack Trucks DID. It should be noted that some of the features, such as those appearing under Road Connect, require enabling by subscription to satellite or WiFi providers.

Using DID to Identify an Active Fault

If you take a look at **Figure 46–6**, you should be able to identify the path to display a fault code. From the main menu, select the option, then scroll through to select the suboption. This will display any active faults and the SA/MID within which it occurred. **Figure 46–7** shows how a DID displays an active code. Use the information on SAs/MIDs, PGNs/PIDs, SIDs, and FMIs (discussed in Chapter 33) to identify the problem.

ACCESSING THE BUS

To access Volvo and Mack Trucks data buses, the following electronic service tools are required:

- J1587 bus: a J1708 six-pin Deutsch DLC
- Pre-2014 J1939 bus: black nine-pin Deutsch DLC
- Post-2014 J1939 bus: a 16-pin J1962 DLC

Volvo-Mack made a decision to use the J1962 DLC for all of their products beginning in 2014. Refer to Chapter 35 for information on the J1708 and black J1939 DLCs. The terminal pin assignments for the J1962 connector appear in **Table 46–3**; note that this is the same DLC known as an assembly line data link (ALDL) in light-duty automotive applications.

FIGURE 46–6 Mack Trucks DID menu map.

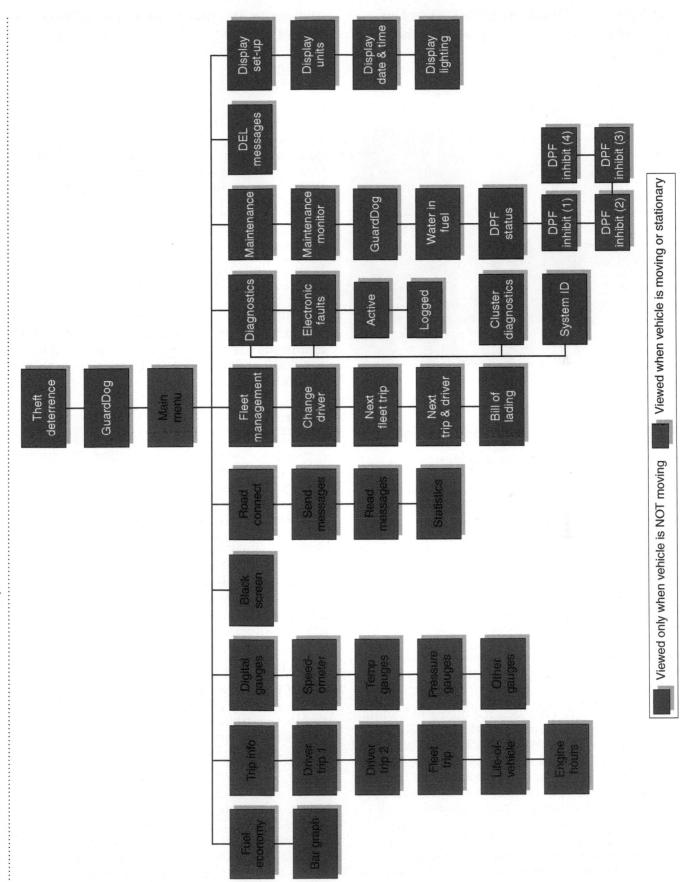

FIGURE 46–7 Mack Trucks DID view of an active fault reported and displayed by the engine MID.

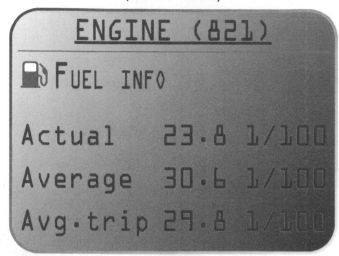

MACK Fault Codes Display
(Active Faults)

ENGINE (821)

⛽ FUEL INFO

Actual   23.8 1/100

Average   30.6 1/100

Avg.trip 29.8 1/100

TABLE 46–3 J1962 Cavity Pin Assignments

1	2	3	4	5	6	7	8
9	10	11	12	13	14	15	16

1. OEM discretion	9. OEM discretion
2. Bus positive + J1708	10. Bus negative − J1708
3. DLC +	11. DLC −
4. Chassis ground	12. OEM discretion
5. Signal ground	13. OEM discretion
6. J1939 + high	**14. J1939 − low**
7. K-line of ISO 9141	15. L-line of ISO 9141
8. OEM discretion	16. V-Bat

TECH TOOL

Tech Tool (TT) replaces the pre-2007 vehicle computer-assisted diagnostics (VCADs) software for Volvo and Mack Trucks. It is backward compatible. In a Mack Trucks application, this software is known as **Premium Tech Tool (PTT)**. Loaded onto a Mack or Volvo laptop, it is designed for wireless interface with both the truck database and the Volvo or Mack data hub via the Internet. We reference the PTT software for purposes of our description here. PTT is best defined as an "umbrella" software package that

"quarterbacks" applications (apps) from three root categories:

- PC-installed apps
- Online apps
- Disc media apps

> **TECH TIP:**
>
> Using a wireless TT/PTT connection to the truck data bus is not recommended for purposes of programming EECUs/VCUs. A lost connection or corrupted signal can render the vehicle immobile.

PC-Installed Apps

PC-installed apps include **vehicle computer-assisted diagnostics (VCADs)** and Guided Diagnostics, both of which can still be used on pre-2007 chassis. Volvo and Mack suggest that the functionality of the full-service PTT is limited in the pre-2007 chassis. They also state that pre-2007 software will not function with post-2007 chassis.

Online Apps

For TT/PTT to function properly, the PC driving the software must be online. To properly manage the guided interactive diagnostics of the system, the PC software must connect to the Volvo or Mack data hub. The online facets required by PTT/TT are the key **IMPACT** (Volvo electronic information) and (Mack) **Electrical Information System (EIS)** programs hosted at the data hub. IMPACT and EIS have entirely replaced troubleshooting service manuals for Volvo and Mack products and although versions of both are available on DVD, service updates are embedded into the online version.

Disc Media Apps

TT/PTT also can default to DVD database versions of IMPACT and EIS when no online connection is available. These can be used on pre-2007 products and perform limited interactions with post-2007 products.

PTT LogOn and Navigation

TT is designed to be launched in a Windows environment. The TT icon should be selected. This takes the user to a log-on screen in which the user ID and password must be entered. Once these are entered, connectivity to both

Central Systems (the Volvo and Mack data hub) and the truck chassis data bus (via the J1939 data connector or wireless) should be established. From this point onward, navigation should be straightforward to anyone familiar with the Windows graphical user interface (GUI) environment. Each routine is anchored by vehicle ID, and drop-down menus option the diagnostic path.

GUIDED DIAGNOSTICS

To use the full potential of TT, an accurate digital multimeter (DMM) is required plus an assortment of breakout adapters and boxes, Tees, and harnesses. **Figure 46–8** shows some of the breakout tools required for the guided diagnostic features of the TT.

FIGURE 46–8 Tech Tool breakout tools.

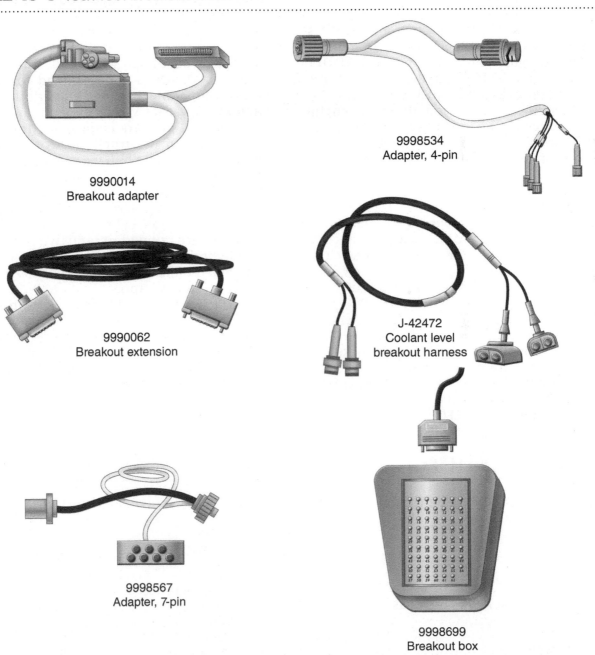

9990014
Breakout adapter

9990062
Breakout extension

9998567
Adapter, 7-pin

9998534
Adapter, 4-pin

J-42472
Coolant level
breakout harness

9998699
Breakout box

SUMMARY

- From 2007 onward, Volvo and Mack Trucks engines have been designed and constructed on a common platform. Therefore, Volvo and Mack engines are essentially the same with different badging and paint jobs.
- VECTRO is used to manage Volvo engines.
- V-MAC is used to manage Mack engines.
- TT is Volvo diagnostic software.
- PTT is Mack Trucks diagnostic software.
- Mack Trucks SIS is known as EIS.
- Volvo SIS is known as IMPACT.
- Volvo and Mack Truck twin-actuator EUI fuel systems are used in all of their post-2007 and 2010 EUI-fueled engines, including the Volvo VE-D11, VE-D13, and VE-D16, and their Mack Trucks relatives known as MP-7, MP-8, and MP-10.
- The numeric values used in Volvo engine family codes can be interpreted as the engine displacement in liters. The VE-D11 code can be interpreted as follows: V = Volvo, E = electronic, D = diesel, 11 = engine displacement in liters.
- The numeric values used in Mack Trucks engine family codes can be interpreted as the engine displacement to the nearest 100 cubic inches displacement. The MP-10 code can be interpreted as follows: M = Mack, P = power, 10 = engine displacement in 100s of cubic inches. So, the 10 is equivalent to 1,000 cubic inches, which is close to the 16.1 liters the engine displaces.
- ECM functions in Volvo and Mack Trucks EUI-fueled engines are divided between two modules. A VCU (SA 71/MID 144) interacts with the EECU (SA 00/MID 128) to produce engine powertrain outcomes. The EECU incorporates both the processing capability and output switching apparatus required to manage fueling and emissions controls in post-2007 engines.
- Volvo and Mack post-2010 engines use an emissions control module bussed to the EECU. The emissions control module manages DPF cycles and SCR dosing.
- The EECU houses the injector drivers and uses induction coils to spike the EUI actuation voltage to values around 100 V in post-2007 engines.
- TT (Volvo) and PTT (Mack) software is used to diagnose system problems on all post-2007 and post-2010 products: This software replaces VCADs. TT is designed to be backward compatible, but the compatibility is limited to the earlier VCADs functionality.
- TT and PTT software is designed for wireless interface with the truck electronics and the Volvo or Mack data hub via the Internet. Using a wireless connection is not recommended when programming engine maps.
- TT and PTT can perform typical diagnostic routines such as cylinder cutout tests, but also feature guided interactive diagnostics and hyperlinks into the Volvo Mack SIS.
- The Volvo online SIS is known as IMPACT. It is an integrated TT app.
- The Mack Trucks online SIS is known as Electrical Information System (EIS). It is an integrated PTT app.
- DID is the digital information display that can be used to read system parameters and perform first-level diagnostics.

REVIEW QUESTIONS

1. What is the Volvo engine management system known as?
   a. V-CADs
   b. VECTRO
   c. V-MAC
   d. Virtual Volvo

2. What is the Mack SIS known as?
   a. EIS
   b. MSIS
   c. IMPACT
   d. EMS

3. What is the Volvo SIS known as?
   a. EIS
   b. VSIS
   c. IMPACT
   d. EMS

4. What generation of V-MAC was used to manage Mack E-Tech, EUP-fueled engines used until 2007?
   a. V-MAC I
   b. V-MAC II
   c. V-MAC III
   d. V-MAC IV

5. What version of Volvo VECTRO is used to manage post-2010 twin-actuator EUI-fueled Volvo engines?
   a. VECTRO I
   b. VECTRO II
   c. VECTRO III
   d. VECTRO IV

6. Which of the following metric values would be closest to the engine displacement of a Mack MP-7 engine?
   a. 7 liters
   b. 10 liters
   c. 11 liters
   d. 13 liters

7. What color lamp is used on Volvo and Mack chassis to perform the functions of the check engine lamp (CEL) used by other OEMs?
   a. Blue
   b. Yellow
   c. Clear
   d. Red

8. Which module on a current Volvo or Mack truck receives the TPS signal (PID 91)?
   a. Fuel module
   b. EECU only
   c. VCU only
   d. Both b and c

9. Where is the humidity sensor located on a Mack Trucks MP-7 engine?
   a. Exhaust manifold
   b. Turbocharger
   c. EGR manifold
   d. Intake pipe

10. Volvo and Mack twin-actuator EUIs are switched by the injector drivers at:
    a. 5 V.
    b. 12 V.
    c. 24 V.
    d. 100 V.

11. What is required to diagnose system problems on any post-2007 Mack Trucks engine?
    a. Mack service manual
    b. VCADs
    c. Premium Tech Tool (PTT)
    d. Mack CoPilot

12. If a driver wanted to inhibit a DPF regeneration using DID, which of the following menu headers would he or she have to route through?
    a. Maintenance
    b. Diagnostics
    c. Road connect
    d. Electronic faults

13. Technician A states that twin-actuator EUI calibration codes must be reprogrammed to the EECU whenever an EUI is changed out. Technician B states that the twin-actuator EUI uses a four-digit code. Who is correct?
    a. Technician A only
    b. Technician B only
    c. Both A and B
    d. Neither A nor B

14. Technician A states that when the dash warning yellow lamp illuminates on a 2015 Mack Trucks chassis, the driver should immediately pull over to the side of the road. Technician B says that when the dash warning red light illuminates, a buzzer is usually activated. Who is correct?
    a. Technician A only
    b. Technician B only
    c. Both A and B
    d. Neither A nor B

15. Technician A states that current Mack Trucks EECUs are mounted on the right side of the engine. Technician B states that current Volvo Trucks EECUs are bus connected to a VCU. Who is correct?
    a. Technician A only
    b. Technician B only
    c. Both A and B
    d. Neither A nor B

47

EMISSIONS MANAGEMENT

OBJECTIVES

After studying this chapter, you should be able to:

- Define the origin of the word *smog*.
- Define *photochemical smog* and describe the conditions required to create it.
- Describe the role that vehicle emissions play in the formation of smog.
- Describe how ozone is formed at ground level.
- Identify the compounds exhausted in engine end gases and identify those that are classified as noxious.
- Identify how greenhouse gases are produced by engines and outline what is required to reduce them.
- Explain how tailpipe emissions are affected by fueling, timing, temperature, and combustion factors.
- Outline the operating principles of C-EGR, oxidation catalytic converters, reduction catalytic converters, diesel particulate filters, and selective catalytic reduction systems.
- Identify the fuel and urea dosing systems used on current diesels.
- Define the term *new technology diesel exhaust (NTDE)*.
- Outline the key features that are used on a *freight-efficient* truck rig.

KEY TERMS

active regeneration

AdBlue

adsorption

aneroid

aqueous urea

auxiliary power
unit (APU)

California Air Resources
Board (CARB)

carbon dioxide (CO_2)

carbon monoxide (CO)

catalyst

catalytic converter

clean gas induction (CGI)

closed crankcase
ventilation (CCV)

constant volume
sampling (CVS)

cooled exhaust gas
recirculation (C-EGR)

diesel exhaust
fluid (DEF)

diesel particulate
filter (DPF)

dosing

dosing control
module (DCM)

electrostatic oil
separator (EOS)

end gas

Environmental Protection
Agency (EPA)

freight efficiency

fueling algorithm

gas analyzers

greenhouse gases (GHGs)

Health Effects
Institute (HEI)

Highway Diesel Rule

hydrocarbons (HC)

inert

infrared

internal exhaust gas recirculation (I-EGR)

low-temperature filter (LTF)

new technology diesel exhaust (NTDE)

nitrogen dioxide (NO_2)

NO_x adsorber catalyst (NAC)

noxious emissions

opacity meter

oxides of nitrogen (NO_x)

ozone

palladium

passive regeneration

photochemical reaction

photochemical smog

platinum

positive crankcase ventilation (PCV)

regeneration cycle

regeneration system (RS)

rhodium

selective catalytic reduction (SCR)

self-regeneration

seventh injector

smart dosing actuator

smog

substrate

sulfur dioxide (SO_2)

ultraviolet (UV) radiation

urea

volatile organic compounds (VOCs)

INTRODUCTION

Until the late 1990s, the **Environmental Protection Agency (EPA)** focus on the noxious emissions from diesel engines was primarily on the engine manufacturer and testing of new engines prior to certification. By definition, **noxious emissions** refers to any harmful gases exhausted from the tailpipe of a vehicle, regardless of chemical composition. The state of California has traditionally led the way for the rest of the jurisdictions in North America when it comes to defining vehicle emissions standards and enforcing them. The California agency responsible for emissions legislation and enforcement is the **California Air Resources Board**, or **CARB**. Any new engines introduced to the marketplace require testing to ensure that they meet EPA and CARB standards prior to certification.

FUEL ECONOMY

Part of the emissions equation is fuel economy itself. The American Trucking Association (ATA) has been proactive in lobbying for better fuel efficiency: This lobbying has included a move to increase vehicle payload ratings and trailer length. A decade ago, if an organization lobbied in favor of increasing truck over-axle weights and total rig length, the argument tended to be dismissed by public sentiment that could attribute it to motives of operator profitability; that is, greed. Not so today. When every load carried on our roads is correlated to the amount of fuel required to haul it, this presents an argument both for the environment and for less dependence on imported petroleum. Today we tend to use the term **freight efficiency** in preference to *fuel economy*: freight efficiency is fuel consumed per ton hauled. The EPA and United States government are currently in the process of mandating fuel efficiency standards for trucks, using a phasing-in process beginning in 2014. The standards will extend to new emissions standards (there is more information on this later in this chapter).

IMPORTANCE OF CARB

For many years CARB (http://www.arb.ca.gov/) was important to engine original equipment manufacturers (OEMs) because, to market engines in the most populous U.S. state with the most powerful economy, CARB certification was required. Until a recent ruling by the EPA, 17 other states adopted the CARB standard. The list of so-called "green" states includes Connecticut, Maine, Maryland, Massachusetts, New Jersey, New York, Oregon, Pennsylvania, Rhode Island, Vermont, and Washington, representing more than half of the United States economy. However, the EPA has ruled that states other than California are not permitted to set their own standards; this has promoted a lawsuit against the EPA by the 17 "green" states, which are contending that if California can have clean air, why can't they? It is not clear what the outcome of this lawsuit will be because of the number of issues involved.

You might ask why California is permitted to set its own standards while other states under federal jurisdiction are not, at least according to the EPA. The answer is that CARB was established before the federal EPA came into existence, so it legally has precedential legitimacy.

ENFORCING EMISSIONS STANDARDS

Emissions standards have to be adhered to by engine OEMs before they can get an engine certified, and the standards in North America are the toughest in the world. However, field testing of emissions is not so rigorous. Most jurisdictions continue to use opacity testing to an outdated SAE standard known as J1667. Although J1667 has been moderately toughened up since its introduction, the truth is that it does not begin to examine the type of emissions system shortcomings of modern, computer-controlled truck engines. The J1667 testing procedure is detailed in Chapter 48.

ROLE OF GOVERNMENT

Anybody who believes that industry would regulate itself when it comes to vehicle emissions should take a walk around any large city in the third world. The EPA-2010-compliant engine purchased in the United States can also be purchased in markets worldwide, but outside of North America and Europe, the engine has the appearance of one sold here back in 1997. Although these U.S.- and European-engineered engines are being supplied to operators in the most polluted regions of the world, few emission control devices remain on the engine. Until our corporations are legislated into understanding that tailpipe emissions are a worldwide problem, which will not be remedied by emissions controls that affect less than a fifth of the world's population, there will be escalating global problems.

SCOPE OF THIS CHAPTER

This chapter begins by providing the technician with a basic understanding of the causes of smog, how diesel engine exhaust gases contribute to fouling the environment, and a description of operating principles of the components used to help reduce noxious emissions. During the past few years, the number of service repair orders relating directly or indirectly to exhaust aftertreatment hardware has risen exponentially. We will focus on servicing and testing vehicle exhaust aftertreatment systems in Chapter 48; this chapter deals only with the operating principles.

POLLUTANTS

In a Supreme Court ruling in 2007, the term *pollutant* was redefined, and though scientific opinion may differ, what is regarded as a noxious combustion emission has changed. We will take a look at how that impacts the way vehicle emissions are classified later in this section.

SMOG

The word **smog** comes from the words "fog" and "smoke." Throughout the world there are two main types of smog. The first type is **sulfur dioxide (SO_2)** smog produced by the burning of sulfurous fuels such as coal and heavy oils. Sulfurous smog conditions are aggravated by humidity and, therefore, fog. It is produced mostly by industry, especially in those countries that have lax standards for combusting industrial coals and heavy oils. The extent to which the burning of modern vehicle fuels contributes to this problem in our markets is minimal, due to the adoption of ultra-low sulfur fuels.

Photochemical Reaction

A **photochemical reaction** is any type of chemical process initiated by exposure to visible **ultraviolet (UV) radiation** or **infrared** radiation. For example, photosynthesis, the process by which green plants transform light energy into chemical energy and gaseous oxygen, is a photochemical reaction. To say that a photochemical reaction has occurred, light energy has to be absorbed by a substance. Another natural example of a photochemical process is the production of **ozone** in the earth's upper atmosphere. Ozone (O_3) is responsible for filtering out most of the sun's harmful UV radiation. It is produced when sunlight breaks the bonds of some oxygen molecules (O_2) to form atomic oxygen (O), which then combines with O_2 to form O_3.

Photochemical Smog

The second type of smog is **photochemical smog** (also known as *photosynthetic* and *photoelectric smog*), which requires neither smoke nor fog for its formation. It is produced mainly by the gases emitted from vehicle exhaust systems. Photochemical smog is characterized by a yellowish/light brownish haze. The effects of photochemical smog are as serious as those produced by sulfurous smog: Plant damage, eye irritation, and respiratory failure in animals (including humans) are characteristic. Photochemical smog is produced in two stages. First, **hydrocarbons (HCs)** and nitrogen oxides (emitted mostly by vehicles) react with exposure to sunlight to produce O_3. The O_3 then reacts with gaseous HCs to produce smog. O_3 by itself is highly toxic in low concentrations, and the smog that results from exposure to light is a major problem in America today.

GEOGRAPHICAL FACTORS Most large cities have experienced problems with photochemical smog, especially during the summer months. The location most noted for the problem is Los Angeles, California. Conditions in Los Angeles are ideal for producing photochemical smog. It is the second largest population center in the United States, per capita automobile ownership is the highest in the world, the area experiences a high ratio of sunny days, and the San Gabriel mountains act as a wall that helps entrap air masses that tend to move from the west to the east. Many years of exercising the toughest emissions standards in the world have contained, but by no means eliminated, the photochemical smog problem in Southern California. In fact, throughout North America, photochemical smog problems have worsened slightly since the first emissions control legislation several decades ago, due to increased per capita ownership of vehicles and greatly increased yearly distances traveled.

ECONOMIC FACTORS Doing something about this problem is not simple. Money is the issue. There is a cost attached to developing low-emissions engines, and fueling them with friendlier fuels can be more costly and sometimes less fuel efficient. Environmentalists counter this argument by saying that the "hidden" costs of polluting the environment are borne by health care and the generations that follow ours. One thing is for sure: Addressing the problem in North America and Europe alone is going to have little global effect, especially as industrial globalization has spurred enormous growth outside these two continents.

GREENHOUSE GASES **Greenhouse gases (GHGs)** include water vapor, CO_2, methane, NO_x, and ozone (O_3). While methane, NO_x, and ozone are obviously pollutants, the issue associated with global warming is carbon dioxide emission from combusting HC fuels. **Carbon dioxide (CO_2)** used to be classified as a greenhouse gas but *not* as a noxious emission. This changed in 2007, when the Supreme Court ruled (5–4) in *Massachusetts v. EPA* that GHGs were pollutants.

The Supreme Court ruling is having a major influence on how we develop engine technology and generate electricity. Combusting fossil fuels produces vast quantities of CO_2 (see Chapter 17). In 2011, the Obama administration set a goal of 17% nationwide reduction in CO_2 emissions for phased implementation from 2014 to 2018. This requirement will be accompanied by a mandatory 15% improvement in fuel economy; as usual, the legislation will have provisions for corporate averaging.

Reducing CO_2 emissions will mean taking a serious look at the chemical composition of the fuels we burn, specifically reducing or eliminating the carbon content. This is a tough proposition. Because gasoline and diesel fuel are composed of approximately 85% carbon, some major changes in fuel formulations are probable in the coming years. For the immediate future, the emphasis will be on increasing fuel efficiency.

WHO PRODUCES CO_2? Back in Chapter 17 we answered the tricky question of how burning 1 gallon (3.79 liters) of diesel fuel can produce more than 22 pounds of CO_2. Here we take a brief look at what and who is producing CO_2. The average human in America directly and indirectly produces 20 tons of the gas in a 1-year period, whereas one cow directly contributes 6 tons. Gasoline usually has a slightly lower percentage of carbon than diesel fuel, so burning 1 gallon of gasoline produces around 20 pounds of CO_2. In North America, we greatly exceed the CO_2 output of other industrialized nations: The combined population of the United States and Canada represents 5% of the world's population, but we currently account for around 25% of global CO_2 emissions.

LAW OF UNINTENDED CONSEQUENCES A major challenge for both government and industry is the pursuit of emissions strategies that really work because, often, confronting one problem head-on results in creating another problem as or more serious. This is known as the *law of unintended consequences,* and it has been a recurring problem as emission controls have developed. For instance, jurisdictions that effected tough anti-idling legislation over the past decade forced **auxiliary power units (APUs)** to be installed on trucks. The unintended consequence was that the considerable weight of the APU now has to be hauled when the unit is working on the highway, resulting in more fuel being burned than was saved by not running at idle. More fuel burned means higher emissions and higher GHGs.

Ingredients of Smog

Knowing a little basic chemistry helps in understanding the nature of smog. Combustion is a chemical reaction. Under optimum conditions, when an HC fuel is combusted using the oxygen available in ground-level air as the reactant, the HC fuel is oxidized to form H_2O (water) and CO_2. The term *perfect combustion* was usually applied to this type of combustion reaction. Although H_2O vapor is a GHG, it is not produced in large quantities by burning HCs. However, the Supreme Court's reclassification of CO_2 as a pollutant will probably mean that we no longer use the term *perfect* to describe any kind of combustion. More problems arise when the combustion of the HC is not "perfect" or the nitrogen that makes up 80% of air at ground level becomes involved in the combustion process.

When a hydrocarbon fuel is not completely oxidized, gaseous HC, particulate HC, and **carbon monoxide (CO)** result. When emitted from the tailpipe of a vehicle, these chemicals are all classified as noxious emissions. Nitrogen can participate in the combustion process under certain conditions. Within the combustion temperature window of a typical internal combustion engine, this tends to be when temperatures are higher. When nitrogen is oxidized, it forms a number of different compounds known collectively as **oxides of nitrogen** or **NO_x**; of these, **nitrogen dioxide (NO_2)** presents the most problems. NO_2 is a key to the formation of ozone and acid rain. The EPA classifies all NO_x emissions as noxious emissions.

SULFUR In recent years, the maximum sulfur content of diesel fuels has been dramatically reduced. The current maximum permitted sulfur content in an ASTM 1D or 2D fuel is 0.0015% (15 ppm). This standard was introduced in October 2006 and from 2010, applies to 100% of the total fuel dispensed at the pumps in North America. This standard has come close to eliminating the tendency of diesel fuel to contribute to sulfurous combustion emissions.

When sulfur is oxidized in the combustion process, it forms SO_2, an ingredient of sulfurous, but not photochemical, smog. Sulfur is acidic, toxic, and an ingredient of acid rain. Although sulfur-compound emissions from the combustion process are serious, highway trucks are no longer a major contributor. Sulfur emissions produce an unpleasant, acidic odor. Because of the acidity, high sulfur emissions from a diesel engine will usually produce tattletales such as rust-out of exhaust piping.

HYDROCARBONS The HCs emitted in the combustion process of an internal combustion engine

burning liquid or gaseous petroleum product may be in gaseous, liquid, or solid (particulate) states. They are observable only in liquid or solid states, when they may be seen as white smoke (liquid emission) or black smoke (particulate emission). A more detailed analysis of diesel engine smoke emission appears in Chapter 50. In the days before rigid emissions standards, a truck diesel engine commonly emitted HC in liquid state (that is, condensing in the exhaust gas) at cold startup and in particulate state under conditions of overfueling, acceleration, or air starvation.

PARTICULATE MATTER Anything in the exhaust gas that is in the solid state can be classified as particulate matter (PM). Carbon soot and dust form PM. Incomplete combustion is the main culprit in the formation of PM. These minute particulate compounds can cause respiratory problems in both humans and animals. The EPA classifies particulates into two general categories:

1. Inhalable particulates that range between 2.5 and 10 microns in diameter
2. Respirable particulates that tend to be 2.5 microns or less in diameter

Respirable particulates are not entrapped by nasal filters and are small enough to get deep into the lungs, causing wheezing, coughing, and shortness of breath. PM emission is always visible from a diesel engine and is easily detected with smoke density–measuring equipment such as opacity meters. The objective of diesel particulate filters (DPFs), studied later in this chapter, is to minimize PM. Trucks and transit buses account for approximately 25% of the PM emitted in North America.

VOLATILE ORGANIC COMPOUNDS **Volatile organic compounds** or **VOCs** are HCs in the gaseous state that boil off fuels during production, distribution, and pumping. Diesel-fueled vehicles contribute VOCs in a small way: Fuel tanks exposed to the high heat of a summer's day vaporize the more volatile fuel fractions to the extent that the cetane number (CN) rating can degrade. The transportation sector accounts for approximately 30% of the VOCs found around population centers. VOCs are more likely to be an atmospheric problem in hot weather conditions when the most volatile fractions of fuels more readily boil off. VOCs react with sunlight to produce ground-level O_3.

CARBON MONOXIDE CO is a colorless, odorless, tasteless, and highly poisonous gas. It is a result of the incomplete combustion of an HC fuel. CO can be combusted to form harmless CO_2. Approximately two-thirds of the atmospheric levels of CO in North America can be attributed to vehicle emissions. Exposure to CO can impair brain function, cause fatigue, and be fatal in high concentrations.

OZONE Atmospheric oxygen is diatomic, that is, it combines to form molecules consisting of two oxygen atoms (O_2). O_3 is triatomic, that is, three oxygen atoms covalently bond to form a molecule of O_3. It occurs naturally in small quantities in the earth's stratosphere, where it absorbs solar UV radiation, but when it is emitted in vehicle exhaust, it is a GHG. O_3 can be produced by passing a high-voltage electrical discharge (arc) through air; you can sometimes smell it during a thunderstorm. It is manufactured commercially using an electric arc process. As a pollutant, O_3 results from the photochemical reaction between NO_x and various HCs (especially those categorized as VOCs). Ozone is known to irritate the eyes and mucous membranes. Exposure to O_3 at low-level concentrations can be a health threat.

OXIDES OF NITROGEN Despite the fact that nitrogen under usual atmospheric conditions and temperatures is **inert** (unlikely to participate in chemical reactions), when subjected to certain conditions in an engine cylinder, it reacts. That is, it can be oxidized. It forms nitrous oxide (N_2O), nitric oxide (NO), and NO_2 when oxidized. All NO_x produced in the combustion process of internal combustion engines are known collectively simply as NO_x. NO_2 is the most reactive of the NO_x compounds emitted from vehicle tailpipes. In North America, on- and off-highway vehicle engines are the source of about 60% of the NO_x in our atmosphere. NO_x directly affects persons with respiratory problems, and medical opinion states that children's lungs are susceptible to concentrations of 0.1 ppm (parts per million). This is why the EPA has so aggressively attacked NO_x emissions from diesel engines in its certification requirements. Trucks and transit buses account for approximately 30% of NO_x emissions in North America.

AIR QUALITY INDEX Most jurisdictions today monitor air quality and use the monitoring results to alert the public on days when pollution rises above acceptable standards. If you suffer from asthma or other respiratory problems, you probably notice that each year that passes usually has more smog alert days when you are advised to avoid the outdoors. **Table 47–1** is an air quality index (AQI) used by one jurisdiction.

SMOG SUMMARY

We can summarize the consequences of vehicle emissions as follows:

$$NO_x + VOCs + Sunlight = Ozone$$

$$Ozone + Particulate matter = Smog$$

$$CO_2 = Polluting GHG$$

Water vapor is also officially classified as a GHG. However, hydrogen typically makes up less than 20% of an HC fuel, so the amount of water vapor emitted by combustion is relatively insignificant.

EPA CERTIFICATION TESTING

It is not really necessary for a truck technician to know much about the precertification testing used by the EPA, although you should recognize that it is highly exacting and goes well beyond the basic opacity or smoke density field testing used by most jurisdictions. Gaseous emission of toxic combustion by-products cannot be measured using an **opacity meter** because gaseous emissions do not show as smoke when discharged from the vehicle tailpipe. Before EPA certification, diesel engine OEMs must conduct gaseous exhaust analysis and what is known as **constant volume sampling (CVS)** testing. CVS is a process that involves diluting exhaust gas with purified ambient air and subsequently routing the air through three tests:

1. Filtration. The gas is forced through filters which are then weighed. The increase in mass indicates particulate emission.
2. Flame ionization detection (FID). This test indicates HC concentration.
3. Exhaust sample bags. These measure CO, CO_2, and NO_x.

Noxious gas emissions can also be tested by sampling and analyzing raw exhaust gas using **gas analyzers** not unlike those used for spark-ignited (SI) engine testing (described later in this chapter).

TABLE 47–1 Air Quality Index and Environmental Effects

Air Quality Index and Environmental Effects	Category	Carbon Monoxide (CO)	Nitrogen Dioxide (NO_2)	Ozone (O_3)	Sulfur Dioxide (SO_2)	Suspended Particles (SP)	SO_2 + SP	Total Reduced Sulfur (TRS)
100 and over	Very poor	Increasing cardiovascular symptoms in nonsmokers with heart disease. Some visual impairment.	Increasing sensitivity of patients with asthma and bronchitis.	Light exercise produces respiratory effects in patients with chronic pulmonary disease.	Increasing sensitivity in patients with asthma and bronchitis.	Increasing sensitivity in patients with asthma and bronchitis.	Significant respiratory effects in patients with asthma and bronchitis.	Sensitive individuals may suffer nausea and headache due to severe odor.
50–99	Poor	Increased cardiovascular symptoms in smokers with heart disease.	Odor and discoloration. Some increase in bronchial reactivity and asthma attacks.	Decreasing performance by athletes exercising heavily.	Odorous. Increasing vegetation damage.	Visibility decreased. Soiling evident.	Increased symptoms in patients with chronic respiratory disease.	Extremely odorous.
32–49	Moderate	Blood chemistry changes but no detectable impairment.	Odorous.	Injurious to many vegetation species (e.g., white beans, tomatoes).	Injurious to some species of vegetation.	Some decrease in visibility.	Injurious to vegetation due to sulfur dioxide.	Odorous.
16–31	Good	No effects.	Slight odor.	Injurious to some vegetation species in combination with SO_2.	Injurious to some vegetation species in combination with ozone.	No effects.	No effects.	Slight odors.
0–15	Very good	No effects.	No effects.	No effects.	No effects.	No effects.	No effects.	No effects.

ACTUAL EPA EMISSIONS REQUIREMENTS BY YEAR

Given the fact that emissions from highway truck diesel engines were unregulated until 1970, what has been accomplished since is nothing short of astounding. In 1970, a typical diesel engine emitted 16 grams per HP/h of NO_x and 10 grams of PM per HP/h. The NO_x emission standard required for 2010 and later is 0.2 gram per HP/h—an 8,000% reduction. Similarly, the PM standard required for 2007 was reduced to 0.01 gram per HP/h, a 10,000% reduction. **Table 47-2** outlines the progress of heavy-duty highway truck EPA emissions standards from 1990 to 2010.

Summary of Today's EPA Standards

To summarize Table 47-2, here is a bottom-line summary of the last two generations of EPA emissions standards. Truck engines manufactured prior to 2007 are considered legacy trucks and may be prohibited from operating in some jurisdictions. The EPA model year (MY) 2010 standards for both NO_x and PM emissions are not expected to change before the year 2020.

EPA 2007

- 1.1 grams per BHP hour (g/BHP-hr) of NO_x
- 0.01 g/BHP hr of PM

EPA 2010

- 0.20 grams per BHP hour (g/BHP-hr) of NO_x
- 0.01 g/BHP hr of PM (no change from 2007) (EURO V is 0.02 g/BHP hr)

TABLE 47-2 EPA Emissions Requirements by Year

Year	HC (Grams BPH/h)*	PM (Grams BPH/h)	NO_x (Grams BPH/h)
1990	1.3	0.60	6.0
1991	1.3	0.25	5.0
1994	1.3	0.25	5.0
1996	1.3	0.25	5.0
1998	1.3	0.25	4.0
2004	0.5	0.25	2.5
2007	0.28	0.01	1.2
2010	0.14	0.01	0.2
*BPH/h = brake horsepower per hour			

DIESEL ENGINE EMISSIONS CONTROLS

In the early years of legislated emissions controls designed for diesel engines, the primary emission control device on the engine was the computer that managed it. This meant that from the late 1980s, full authority computer-controlled systems were introduced in truck engines well ahead of their automobile counterparts, which tended to rely on external controls. The external devices used on automobiles beginning in the 1970s included catalytic converters, air pump units, exhaust gas recirculation (EGR) systems, and positive crankcase ventilation (PCV) systems.

This has changed. Now the diesel engine relies on a full range of external emission control devices that include oxidation catalysts, reduction catalysts, particulate filters, and urea injection systems. Most of the emission control additions to diesel engines are required to operate with now-standard ultra-low sulfur (ULS) diesel fuel (see Chapter 18). In this next section, we take a look at the operating principles of the devices used on today's diesel engines to limit pollutants.

ENGINE CONTROL MODULE

Those of you who have studied automobile technology will be familiar with the term *closed-loop fueling*. That is the term used to describe running an SI, gasoline-fueled engine using the exhaust gas sensor signal to manage a stoichiometric air-fuel mixture. In the lean burn technology of the highway diesel engine, things are a little more complex, in that the input of a single sensor is never used to drive the **fueling algorithm** written to the electronic/engine control module (ECM) software. The fueling algorithm is the set of ECM-programmed rules and procedures designed to produce the desired performance and emissions from the engine at any given moment of operation. It is based on monitored sensor data, operator commands, and programmed instruction in memory. It is also known as *mapping*. In today's engines, the fueling algorithm is required to manage the engine to meet emissions standards in all operating phases.

Temperature Factors

Managing fuel injection quantity, timing, and features such as multipulse injection in diesel engines while meeting emissions standards requires high-speed processing capability. In most cases, combustion temperatures have to be managed within a narrow temperature window. HC emissions tend to increase when combustion temperatures are in the lower range and the air-fuel ratio (AFR) is richer. In contrast, NO_x emissions tend to increase when AFR leans out and the combustion temperatures are in the higher range.

Timing Factors

It is also important to note that injection timing—or, more specifically, ignition timing—affects noxious emission characteristics. Retarded timing tends to reduce NO_x emission, but over-retarded timing can greatly increase HC emission. Timing deviations of as little as 1 degree crank angle can increase NO_x or HC content in the **end gas** by as much as 10%. This timing sensitivity has made computer management of CI engines essential in attempting to meet emissions requirements.

In general terms, advancing the engine timing will increase engine temperatures and therefore tend to increase NO_x emission, while retarding timing can lead to incomplete combustion of the fuel and therefore an increase in HC emission. In general, tampering with injection timing today requires defeating the base fuel maps programmed by the OEM: This practice is illegal and is more common on light-duty than heavy-duty diesel engines. For those who do not cheat, injection timing precision and combustion management have been greatly enhanced with the multipulse injection capability used on most current diesel engines, which optimizes emissions, power, and fuel economy.

EXTERNAL EMISSION CONTROLS

If you looked at any truck diesel engine series manufactured in the year 2001 and compared it with its series equivalent today, you would have difficulty in identifying them as being the same engine family. Today's diesel engines use an extensive array of external emission control hardware. In this section we take a close look at some of these devices.

COOLED EGR

Until 2004, diesel engine manufacturers had been able to meet NO_x emissions requirements without the use of EGR systems. In EPA MY 2004 (initiated in October 2002), almost all highway diesels incorporated some form of EGR. The objective of EGR is to dilute the intake charge with "dead" gas; that is, the spent gas that will make a percentage of the cylinder volume unreactive. The idea is to reduce NO_x emission by lowering combustion heat, but because this occurs at the expense of engine power and fuel efficiency (along with the introduction of end gas contaminants routed back into the cylinders), it has never been popular with engine OEMs. It was even less popular with truck owners who had to pay for the EGR-related repairs on their equipment.

With the introduction of selective catalytic reduction (SCR) in EPA MY 2010, most engine OEMs have either eliminated or kept the EGR cut percentages to a minimum. When rerouting engine exhaust gas back into the engine cylinders, it makes sense to cool it as much as possible. For this reason, most engine OEMs use **cooled exhaust gas recirculation**, usually known by its acronym of **C-EGR**. **Figure 47–1** shows the exhaust gas treatment systems used on a typical EPA MY 2010 truck engine; note how C-EGR is integrated into the circuit.

C-EGR Components

A typical C-EGR system on a diesel engine has to be controlled by the ECM because the mixture percentage (commonly known as *cut-percentage*) varies according to how the engine is being operated. This ranges between 0% and 50% depending on the manufacturer and year of production. Typically, a C-EGR system consists of:

- A heat exchanger (engine coolant is used)
- ECM-controlled mixing chamber (mixes boosted air [from the turbo] with exhaust gas to set cut-percentage)
- Mass airflow sensor
- Plumbing to route engine coolant through the heat exchanger
- Piping to route exhaust gas to the mixing chamber

Next we take a look at a couple of variations on diesel engine EGR systems, including Caterpillar's "clean" version of EGR. When an EGR system is used on any engine, C-EGR makes sense because it lowers the initial heat of the intake charge that can in itself produce more NO_x. One OEM uses an **internal exhaust gas recirculation (I-EGR)** on some of its medium-bore, vocational engines. I-EGR eliminates the need for a heat exchanger. At valve overlap, the engine is designed to reroute some of the end gas back

FIGURE 47–1 Typical EPA MY 2010 and later exhaust gas aftertreatment system featuring C-EGR, DOC, DPF, and SCR systems

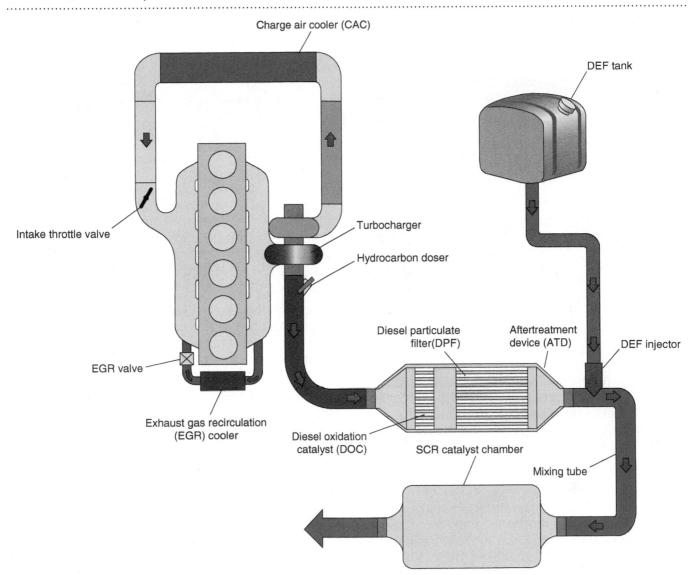

into the cylinder for the next cycle. Figure 47–1 shows a schematic of a typical C-EGR system.

CLEAN GAS INDUCTION (CGI)

Caterpillar was able to meet the EPA 2004 highway diesel engine emissions standards without resorting to EGR. However, Caterpillar opted to use a modification of EGR to meet the 2007 EPA standards and beyond. Earlier, we defined the objective of an EGR system as diluting the intake charge with "dead" gas. *Dead gas* is unreactive gas: It enters the engine cylinder, but the objective is for it to do nothing but take up volumetric space. It is sort of like reducing the engine displacement during certain modes

of operation. The objective is to reduce engine temperatures and therefore NO_x output. It has the effect of making a large-displacement engine behave like a smaller-displacement engine. To make the EGR principle function properly, you need a source of dead gas. The fact of the matter is that there is no better source of dead gas than the engine exhaust system because it is produced any time the engine is running.

Clean gas induction (CGI) is a variation on EGR used exclusively on Caterpillar's post-2007 ACERT family of engines. It differs from EGR in that it sources its "dead" exhaust gas downstream from the DPF. Cat likes to call its system "clean EGR." CGI is monitored by a mass airflow sensor (MAF) and, just like its competitors' EGR,

FIGURE 47–2 Caterpillar schematic of a CGI system.

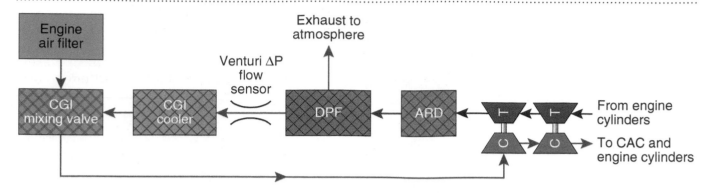

the system objective is to keep combustion temperatures lower to reduce NO_x emissions under certain running conditions. It is easy to identify a Cat CGI engine because the CGI pipe can be seen by the muffler/converter/DPF assembly close to its exit. This pipe routes the theoretically clean dead gas back to the intake circuit via the low-pressure turbocharger. **Figure 47–2** is a schematic of the Caterpillar CGI system.

In terms of managing CGI cycles, the CGI gate is spring-loaded to default to no-recirculation. Gas from the clean side of the DPF is admitted up to a 15% mixture concentricity (with EGR systems, this can be as high as 50%). CGI is ECM managed, so it does not occur during DPF regeneration cycles.

CGI Sensors

A CGI system uses three sensors. Two of these are pressure sensors, an absolute pressure sensor and a pressure differential measurement sensor (these are explained in Chapter 34); the third is a temperature sensor. Gas exiting the CGI venturi passes into a bundle-type, coolant-cooled heat exchanger. In common with EGR engines, there is an advantage to cooling recycled exhaust gas. Cat's heavy-duty family of engines also uses a precooler. The CGI pressure sensor is a delta (three-terminal), variable capacitance-type sensor. The CGI gate is controlled by a pulse width modulated (PWM) actuator; in other words, a linear proportioning solenoid, energized by V-Bat voltages.

CATALYTIC CONVERTERS

Some truck and bus diesel engines used **catalytic converters** before 2002, but all diesel engines today require the use of oxidation converters; some use both oxidation and reduction converters. By definition, a **catalyst** is

a substance that enables a chemical reaction without itself undergoing any change. For many years, automobile catalytic converters have been two-stage, three-way converters, but it is only since 2007 that truck diesels have incorporated two-stage devices. The two stages are:

- Oxidation stage—Attempts to oxidize HC and CO not oxidized in the engine cylinder.
- Reduction stage—Attempts to reduce NO_x back to elemental nitrogen and oxygen when NO_x compounds have been formed during combustion.

Oxidation Stage

When cylinder end gas contains HC and CO, the oxidizing stage of the catalytic converter attempts to oxidize (combust/burn) these to less harmful H_2O and CO_2. **Platinum** and **palladium** are both oxidation catalysts. They are expensive. Oxidizing catalysts enable what can be termed *catalytic afterburning,* sometimes assisted by the introduction of fresh air into the reaction; peak temperatures run in the range of 1,472°F to 1,832°F (800°C to 1,000°C). Because of the high operating temperatures, it is not unusual for an oxidation converter to glow red during nighttime operation, especially when engines are under load.

Reduction Stage

Where oxidized nitrogen compounds (known collectively as NO_x) are present in the exhaust gas, a reduction stage attempts to reduce these back to elemental nitrogen and oxygen. **Rhodium** is the usual reduction catalyst and has been used by automobile manufacturers since the 1970s. It has the capability to break up NO_x compounds into their original oxygen and nitrogen states. However, rhodium can only function as a reduction catalyst when the cylinder burn is managed close to stoichiometric ratios. This means that to use a rhodium catalytic converter in a lean burn diesel engine, the AFR mixture concentricity in the converter has to be close to stoichiometric. OEMs that use rhodium-based catalytic converters achieve this by **dosing**, that is, injecting excess fuel into the cylinder late in the combustion cycle or into exhaust upstream from the converter, to produce a temporary rich burn state. Today, reduction catalysts tend to be found on small-bore engines not equipped with SCR.

Dosing

Dosing may be achieved in two distinct ways:

1. In-cylinder dosing—This is achieved in common rail (CR) fuel systems by injecting a pulse of fuel into the engine cylinder so late into the combustion phase that it cannot be fully combusted in the cylinder.
2. Aftertreatment dosing—This requires the use of a dedicated injector that directs fuel into the exhaust gas somewhere upstream from the reduction catalyst.

The term *dosing* is also used to describe the injection of fuel into the exhaust aftertreatment circuit for purposes of regenerating DPFs and to urea injection, so take care to avoid confusion.

Dosing Management

Dosing of the aftertreatment circuit may be managed in three ways:

- By the engine ECM directly
- By a **dosing control module (DCM)** networked to the ECM by a proprietary bus
- By a dosing control or aftertreatment module with an address on the J1939 bus

Dosing management means that dosing fuel is introduced to the exhaust gas stream only when it is required.

Smart Dosing Actuators

Smart dosing actuators function by directly sensing exhaust gas emission, processing the data, and dosing accordingly. They are connected to the data bus but do not rely on a remote ECM or dosing module broadcast to function. They will be used increasingly as OEMs attempt to meet 2016 and 2020 emissions and GHG reduction standards.

NO$_x$ ADSORBER CATALYSTS

As mentioned earlier, rhodium-based reduction catalysts have been used on gasoline-fueled automobile engines for many years. These used a rhodium catalyst to "reduce" NO$_x$ compounds back to elemental nitrogen and oxygen. Because rhodium only functions as a reduction catalyst when the air-fuel ratio is at stoichiometric or richer, it could not be used on lean burn diesels that continuously unload excess (unreacted) oxygen into the exhaust. With the introduction of the **NO$_x$ adsorber catalyst (NAC)**, diesel engine designers found a way around this problem.

Adsorption is a chemical term that is best defined as *adhesion*: When a substance is adsorbed, it does not undergo any significant chemical change—do not get this confused with the term *absorb*. NO$_x$ adsorber catalysts (NACs) use base metal oxides to initially "store" NO$_x$ compounds, then use a rhodium reduction catalyst to reduce them back to N$_2$ and O$_2$ during an ECM-managed reduction phase.

In the storage phase, NO$_x$ is adsorbed onto a metal (barium) oxide substrate. When the available NO$_x$ storage sites within the device are occupied, the engine ECM temporarily simulates a "rich" (reduced-oxygen) running condition or injects fuel directly into the exhaust system. Operation in this simulated "rich" mode releases the NO$_x$ from its base metal storage locations and allows a rhodium catalyst to convert it to nitrogen gas (N$_2$), oxygen (O$_2$), and water vapor (H$_2$O). In other words, an NAC functions in two stages:

- NO$_x$ storage—NO$_x$ is adsorbed to the base metal oxide substrate during the normal lean burn operation of the diesel engine.
- NO$_x$ reduction—The engine ECM temporarily operates the engine in a rich AFR mode or injects fuel into the exhaust system to simulate a rich AFR, allowing a rhodium catalyst to reduce the NO$_x$ to elemental nitrogen (N$_2$), elemental oxygen (O$_2$), and water vapor (H$_2$O).

NAC Regeneration Cycle

The key to enabling an NAC to function in its regeneration cycle is temporary elimination of excess oxygen from the exhaust. NACs require the use of ULS fuel. Sulfur at any level can be damaging to NACs and some systems require occasional de-sulfation regenerative modes even when only the appropriate ULS fuel has been used. A de-sulfation regenerative cycle requires temporarily raising the exhaust temperatures using fuel injected directly into the exhaust system.

Cat Converter Construction

The noble metal catalysts are thinly coated on aluminum oxide or granulate monolith **substrate** (catalytically inert material onto which active catalysts are coated), providing optimum use of catalyst surface area combined with minimal flow resistance. Catalytic converters only operate efficiently when at operating temperatures, and do little to limit emissions during startup/warmup; computer-controlled variable timing and minimal fueling attempt to achieve this.

Prolonged cold-temperature engine operation (that is, engine loading is light or idle), especially where ambient temperatures are low, can cause the oxidation stage of catalytic converters to plug. When this occurs, a full load run on a dynamometer for 30 minutes may burn off the deposits that restrict the converter. In some cases, the catalytic converter will have to be replaced.

DIESEL PARTICULATE FILTERS (DPFs)

Diesel particulate filters (DPFs) have been around in the industry for a number of years, usually in special applications such as a garbage packer required to operate inside for long periods of time. On this type of application they used to be known as *particulate traps*. Things have changed. A DPF is now a requirement on every on-highway diesel engine meeting 2007 emissions and beyond. In the state of California, they are now required even on small-bore diesel engines such as those required to power trailer refrigeration and auxiliary power units.

By definition, a DPF is an exhaust aftertreatment device designed to eliminate diesel particulate matter (PM), or soot, produced by the engine cylinder combustion process. The DPF substrate is an extruded material, typically cordierite or silicon carbide, that is housed in a muffler body. DPF substrates typically capture more than 95% of the diesel PM, but they will plug up unless they are cleaned or regenerated.

REGENERATION METHODS

There are two main regeneration approaches: passive and active. Passive DPFs are coated with precious metal catalysts, such as platinum and palladium. These enable a flameless burning or oxidizing of the diesel PM. The function of the catalysts is to reduce the oxidation temperature of diesel PM to 570°F (300°C) (compared to 1200°F [650°C] in air). These temperatures fall within the normal operating exhaust temperature range of typical diesel engines. However, to ensure effective filter regeneration, the exhaust temperature should be monitored to make sure the low threshold temperature for passive regeneration is met.

Active regeneration events do not rely on catalysts, but instead use alternately developed heat to regenerate the DPF substrate. Active system approaches currently employed by engine OEMs include fuel injection and fuel burners. Electric systems are also used in retrofit or aftermarket applications. Fuel injection systems inject diesel fuel across a diesel oxidation catalyst, which ignites releasing heat. One OEM uses the term **seventh injector** to describe a diesel fuel injector dedicated to fueling the DPF. Another way to supply fuel for DPF regeneration is by in-cylinder post-combustion injection. Controlled fuel injection (dosing) is designed to raise the temperatures to 1200°F (650°C). At this temperature, the DPF will burn off collected soot.

Regen Chemistry

HC matter such as diesel PM converts to CO_2 and H_2O during the oxidation process. Inorganic materials, like lube oil additives, may produce CO_2 and H_2O, but they also create a residue or ash. Ash builds up in the filter over time, gradually creating a restriction and increasing exhaust backpressure. This eventually degrades engine performance; thus, active DPF regeneration and cleaning are required at intervals.

Types of DPF

In this section, our objective is to focus primarily on the mandatory post-2007 DPFs. Determining what type of DPF is used on a particular diesel engine depends largely on average exhaust temperatures. There are three general types of DPF in use:

- Catalyzed. This more common type of DPF is integrated into a canister that also contains multistage catalytic converters and what used to be known as the muffler. It is probably best described as a comprehensive aftertreatment device. Catalyzed DPFs will be found on most highway trucks and are capable of both passive and active regeneration cycles. They are suited for applications in which *average* exhaust temperatures exceed 437°F (225°C).

- Noncatalyzed. This type of DPF is required in diesel-powered, vocational vehicles that spend prolonged periods in low engine load operation. Typical applications are cement trucks, fire trucks, and garbage packers. Noncatalyzed DPFs are only capable of active regeneration cycles, and manage them with a control module that is independent of the engine ECM. The noncatalyzed DPF control module is assigned an address on the J1939 data backbone and communicates with the engine ECM via the data bus. The aftertreatment module may also manage the SCR system on post-2010 engines.

- **Low-temperature filter (LTF)**. The LTF is designed to remove entrapped diesel particulate emissions from applications that run at low loads. LTFs use oxidation catalysts. Cleaning cycles tend to be more frequent, and collected ash also has to be removed periodically. LTFs are designed for applications in which *average* exhaust temperatures are less than 437°F (225°C) but generally exceed 392°F (200°C).

DPF Operating Principles

The idea behind a DPF is that engine-emitted soot first collects on the walls of the device. Engine manufacturers design DPFs to function primarily in self-regeneration mode. This means that when soot collection reaches a threshold level, it is burned off in what is known as a **regeneration cycle**. In most cases, the regeneration cycle will occur when exhaust temperatures are sufficiently high during normal operation. When this regeneration takes place unassisted by additional fuel or air injection to the exhaust gas, it is known as **self-regeneration**. Self-regeneration can also be known as **passive regeneration**; the terminology varies by engine OEM.

Operating temperatures of the combined oxidation converter and DPF can exceed 1,112°F (600°C), so most of these devices incorporate heat shielding. Depending on the engine and its power rating, both single- and dual-canister versions are used. Typically, single and dual canisters are specified by horsepower rating as follows:

- Single canister: Up to 600 BHP (447 kW)
- Dual canister: 600 BHP (447 kW) and higher

When the operating environment is not conducive to a self-regeneration cycle, regeneration can also occur assisted by injection of some fuel (diesel), sometimes assisted by spark ignition. This mode of regeneration is known as **active regeneration**. Fuel for an active regeneration cycle is usually sourced from the fuel subsystem and delivered at the specified charging pressure. For instance, on a Caterpillar ACERT C15, this would be at 250 psi (17 bar) delivered by an electromechanical injector.

Most diesel engine OEMs are using similar DPF devices, but they are managed in different ways. The key difference among OEMs using catalyzed DPFs is whether an active regeneration cycle requires the assistance of a spark plug. **Figure 47-3** shows a cutaway core view of a Detroit Diesel DPF—a unit that regenerates without the assistance of spark ignition.

Regen Frequency

Regeneration cycles are designed to occur at set intervals. These set intervals may be as often as once every hour or as infrequent as once every 8 hours of operation, depending on the engine, its power ratings, how the engine is being operated, and the type of DPF. Truck drivers should be informed about the expected intervals of the regeneration cycles of the equipment they operate. During both passive and active regeneration,

FIGURE 47-3 Cutaway view of a Detroit Diesel DPF core showing gas flow.

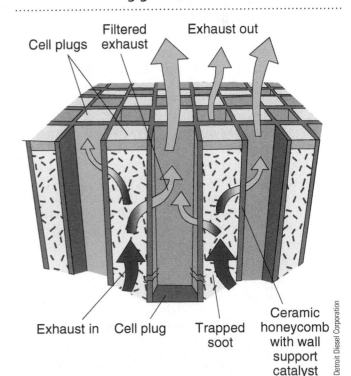

Cell plugs — Filtered exhaust — Exhaust out — Exhaust in — Cell plug — Trapped soot — Ceramic honeycomb with wall support catalyst

Detroit Diesel Corporation

there will be an increase in exhaust gas temperatures, so in all cases the driver can inhibit the regen.

Regeneration Cycles

We are going to use as reference one engine manufacturer's DPF to outline regeneration cycles. This OEM uses spark assist for active regens, but is otherwise generally consistent with what is used industry-wide:

1. Passive: This occurs when exhaust temperatures are high enough for regeneration to occur without the assist of a flame burn-off cycle. This is intended to be the primary means of DPF regeneration, and it should usually occur when the vehicle is running down the highway with the engine under load. In this regen mode, engine-out NO_x and exhaust heat are used to oxidize (burn) DPF soot, resulting in nitrogen, CO_2, and ash residues. Typically, the normal passive cycle of regeneration is designed to occur as infrequently every 8 hours or so. During this normal passive cycle, DPF temperatures can exceed 1,112°F (600°C).
2. Passive plus: This is designed to occur after a prolonged period of idling, as soot buildup reaches 125% and the DPF is becoming restricted. This mode of passive regeneration occurs at a much lower temperature than the normal passive regeneration cycle. A small quantity of fuel (much less than during active transient mode) and spark ignition are used. The objective is to burn off a little soot every 2 hours or so to maintain the status quo. During passive plus regeneration, DPF outlet temperatures do not exceed 752°F (400°C).
3. Active transient: This is set to occur when soot levels are at 100% and the DPF is becoming restricted. The vehicle must be traveling at a speed exceeding 20 mph (32 km/h) for an active transient burn cycle to take place.
4. Active steady state: This is commanded by the engine diagnostic software or by using a dash button. The vehicle must be at 0 mph (km/h) and in park mode. Fuel is injected and a spark ignites the fuel.

Transient regeneration events will *not* occur when:

1. Ambient temperatures are less than 68°F (20°C)
2. Turbo-out temperature exceeds 1,022°F (550°C) (because passive regeneration is possible)
3. Coolant temperature is below 150°F (65°C)

Regeneration system (RS) alerts (broadcast on data bus by engine ECM) occur:

When soot level exceeds 100%:	RS light illuminates
When soot level exceeds 125%:	RS light blinks
When soot level exceeds 150%:	engine derates by 25%
When soot level exceeds 175%:	engine derates by 75%
When soot level exceeds 200%:	engine shuts down

> **NOTE:**
>
> On DPFs that use no spark assist during active regeneration events, the heat required to achieve the soot burn-off is sourced from the exhaust gas discharged from the engine cylinders. An afterburn pulse of injected fuel may also be used.

Regeneration System Hardware

The RS hardware consists of an RS head incorporating:

- A fuel injector
- A swirler plate
- A spark plug
- Cooling system ports

The fuel injector nozzle can be compared to the low-pressure injectors used in gasoline fuel injection: The fuel injector is supplied by the diesel fuel subsystem at its specified charging pressure, and this is the reason some OEMs have significantly raised fuel subsystem charging pressures in their post-2007 products. A defective fuel injector is usually not serviceable and often the whole RS head must be replaced. **Figure 47–4** is a schematic showing the layout of the Caterpillar regeneration system (CRS), and **Figure 47–5** shows the detail of a CRS head.

The CRS spark plug consists of an electrode only (it does not self-ground). Instead, it is designed to ground to a swirler plate located directly below it. Spark plug cycles are driven by the ECM. The gasket should be replaced any time the head is removed because it functions as an insulator.

DPF Cleaning Frequency

Regeneration leaves some ash residues. These ashes originate primarily from the additive

FIGURE 47–4 Schematic layout of the Caterpillar CRS.

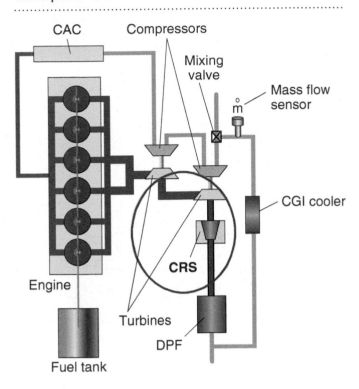

package in the engine lube that is burned in the cylinder during normal combustion. Ash residues have to be removed manually. Federal law requires that this cleaning process occur no more frequently than once a year or 150,000 miles (240,000 km), whichever comes first. Having said that, some manufacturers are aiming to have RS service intervals that exceed 300,000 highway miles (480,000 km).

Because RS spark plugs are fired routinely (that is, outside RS cycles) to limit carbon buildup, an RS can be deactivated using the OEM software to prevent activation on the shop floor. The DPFs used by most engine OEMs should usually regenerate under *any* conditions: Some manufacturers are using DPFs with extended in-operation cycles, but the disadvantage is that they must pull off the road to regenerate.

Temperature monitoring is by dual and single thermocouples (pyrometers) or by PRT/RTDs (see Chapter 34). The operating principles of pyrometers are discussed in Chapter 32, and it is important to note that these thermocouple devices must be replaced as a complete unit when diagnosed as having failed. The DPF is a complex assembly within which the regeneration

FIGURE 47–5 Detail of the CRS head.

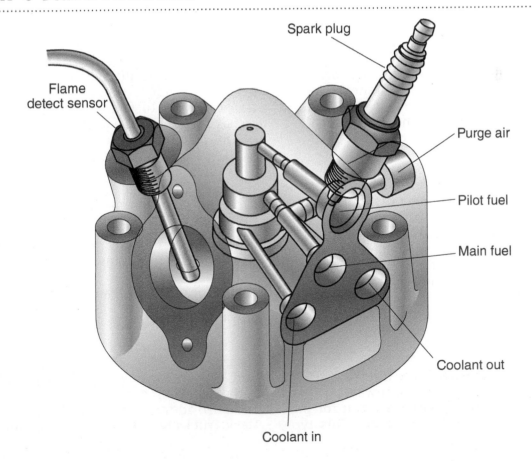

FIGURE 47-6 Comprehensive schematic of the Caterpillar CRS showing the location of the key components and sensors.

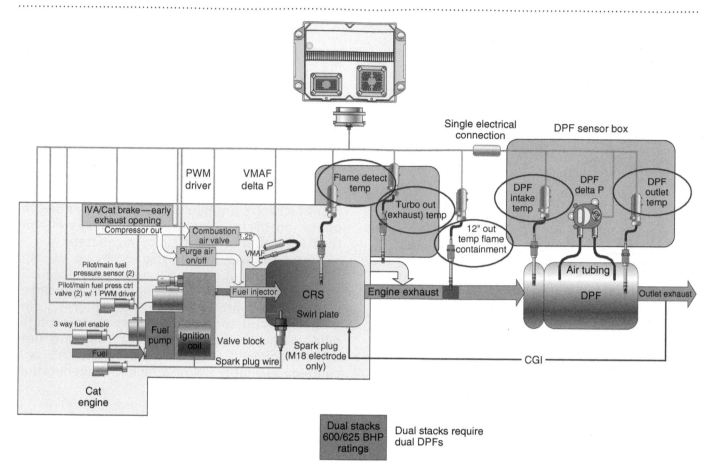

cycles and temperatures have to be precisely managed. **Figure 47-6** is a comprehensive electronic schematic of the CRS showing the location of the key components and sensors. **Figure 47-7** identifies the hardware in the circuit.

DPF Monitoring

The monitoring of DPF operation on a vehicle is comprehensive, with many inbuilt safety mechanisms to prevent unwanted thermal events (i.e., fire). **Figure 47-8** shows the dosing and monitoring controls used on a catalyzed DPF. **Figure 47-9** is a photographic image of the same DPF. The servicing and maintenance requirements of DPFs are covered in Chapter 48.

NONCATALYZED DPFs

Noncatalyzed diesel particulate filters (NC-DPFs) are required to be used in highway-certified, vocational diesel engines that are run for prolonged periods at low engine load. This type

of application is distinct in that exhaust temperatures seldom rise high enough for oxidation catalysts to function properly or for DPF passive regeneration cycles. The unit described in this section is a typical Mack Trucks unit used in a garbage packer. Because of the lower exhaust temperatures characteristic of this type of vocational vehicle, all regeneration cycles are active and may be initiated in the following ways:

- System initiated or automatic. Requires that the vehicle be moving faster than 10 mph (16 km/h).
- Driver or EST software initiated.

NC-DPF Controls

NC-DPFs are managed by a dedicated electronic control unit (ECU) known as a thermal control unit (TCU). Although there is provision for a dedicated source address (SA)/message identifier (MID) address on the J1939 data bus, the first Mack Trucks NC-DPF was managed by the engine

FIGURE 47–7 Schematic of the Caterpillar post-2007 ACERT.

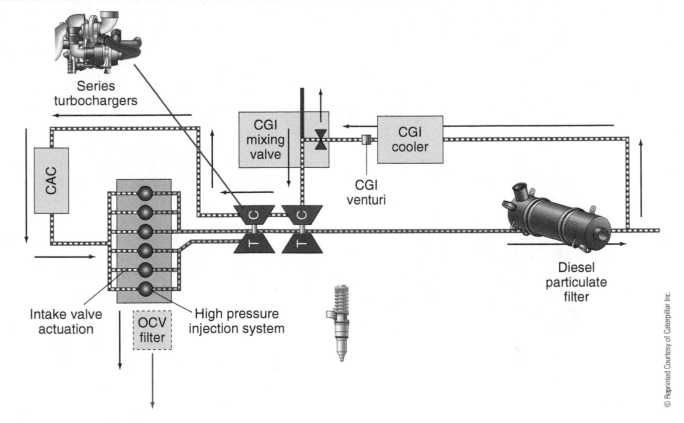

FIGURE 47–8 Schematic of a Mack catalyzed DPF.

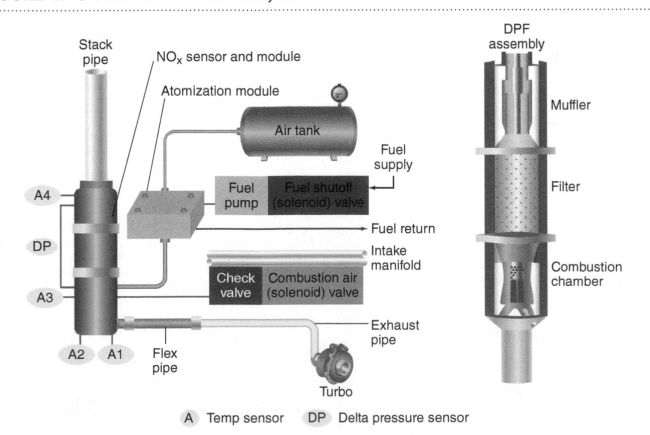

FIGURE 47–9 Mack catalyzed DPF.

Vertical Back of Cab Catalyzed DPF

Mack Trucks Inc.

ECM using a proprietary bus connection. Some post-2010 versions use an aftertreatment module networked to J1939 with an SA 61 address. The input and output circuits of a typical NC-DPF are shown in **Figure 47–10**.

NC-DPF Components

An NC-DPF aftertreatment canister is usually mounted vertically to a stanchion behind the vehicle cab and can be subdivided into three sections as follows:

1. Combustion chamber section. Engine exhaust downstream from the turbocharger is piped into the base of the combustion chamber. The key components in or mounted close to the combustion chamber section of the NC-DPF are:

   - Combustion air valve (ported from intake manifold) and check valve
   - Supplementary air valve (ported from the pneumatic system; supplies atomization module)
   - Fuel pump, fuel shutoff valve, and atomization module

- Ignition module and coil
- Ignitors (pair of spark plugs)
- Fuel injection nozzle
- Inlet air temperature probe (A1: exhaust temperature pyrometer)
- Flame temperature probe (A2: flame temperature pyrometer)
- Delta pressure sensor (upstream probe)

2. DPF section. This is the center section of the aftertreatment canister and contains the particulate filter. Exhaust gas from the combustion chamber is routed through it to be discharged to the muffler section of the canister. The key components in or mounted close to the DPF section are:

   - DPF filter core
   - Supplementary air valve (ported from the pneumatic system; supplies atomization module)
   - DPF
   - A3 temperature sensor (DPF upstream pyrometer)

3. Muffler section. Exhaust gas exiting the DPF section of the aftertreatment canister is routed through the muffler section. The key components in or mounted close to the muffler section of the NC-DPF are:

   - Resonator-type muffler
   - A4 temperature sensor (pyrometer monitors temperatures downstream from the DPF prior to exiting the stack)
   - Downstream probe of the delta pressure sensor (reports the differential pressure to signal pressure drop across the DPF section)
   - NO_x sensor (data is broadcast to the engine ECM via a proprietary bus [pre-2010] or the J1939 data bus)

NC-DPF Operating Principle

The NC-DPF acts as a particulate trap when not regenerating. When entrapped soot begins to restrict the DPF, active regeneration is required. An active regeneration cycle may be automatic or may be driver- or EST-initiated. If the regeneration is to be automatic, usually certain criteria (such as a minimum road speed, minimum engine temperature, and so on) must be met. Once the regeneration has been initiated, the TCU, usually mounted on the exhaust stack stanchion, manages the process. Air from the intake manifold is admitted to the combustion chamber section while diesel fuel (from the fuel

FIGURE 47–10 Noncatalyzed DPF electronic schematic.

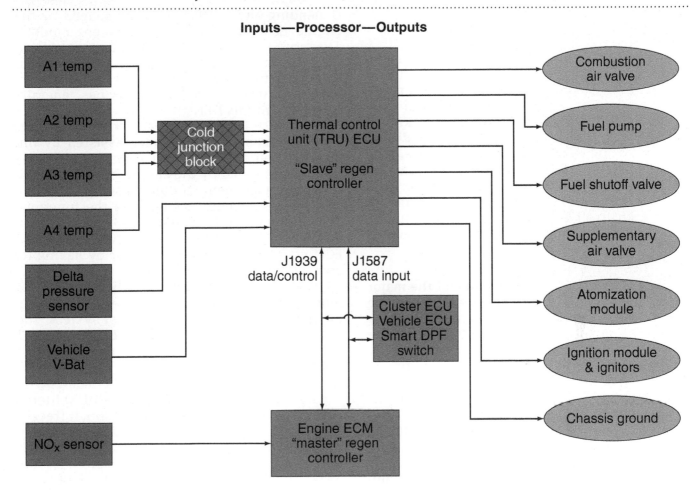

subsystem) is atomized, which is helped by system air pressure and injected across a pair of ignitors (spark plugs). This produces a flame of sufficient intensity to oxidize soot particles entrapped in the DPF.

SELECTIVE CATALYTIC REDUCTION (SCR)

Like DPFs, **selective catalytic reduction (SCR)** is also an exhaust gas aftertreatment process. Whereas the DPF addresses particulate HCs, an SCR system attempts to "reduce" NO_x back to nitrogen and oxygen. Although SCR has been used in Europe and Australia for more than a decade, the EPA did not approve SCR use until 2007. The reason for the EPA's reluctance to approve SCR systems is that to function, this type of system depends on using a "consumable," specifically urea, which has to be routinely replenished, just like fuel. This fact meant that

the EPA approval for 2010 required some compliance conditions. Very briefly, we will take a look at the simple chemistry that enables SCR operation.

SCR CHEMISTRY

NO_x is formed when conditions in the combustion chamber have caused the normally inert nitrogen (N_2) component of air to oxidize to compounds of oxygen and nitrogen. SCRs attempt to "reduce" these compounds back to the harmless elemental oxygen (O_2) and nitrogen (N_2) that are the constituents of the air we breathe.

Gasoline-fueled auto engines have used NO_x reduction catalytic converters (rhodium is the catalyst) for more than 30 years, but these have the disadvantage of being able to function only when the AFR is at stoichiometric or richer. They do not function as stand-alone devices in lean burn diesel engines and, when used, are incorporated into a more complex device known as a

NO_x adsorber catalyst, which is described earlier in this chapter.

Aqueous Urea

SCRs use consumable **urea** to achieve what the rhodium catalyst does in the gasoline-fueled engine. Urea is composed of crystallized nitrogen compounds sourced from natural gas. The urea is in a solution with water, known as **aqueous urea** and marketed as **diesel exhaust fluid (DEF)** in North America. The DEF is injected into the exhaust gas stream by a computer-controlled injection or doser system. After injection, the urea reduces to ammonia, which itself reacts with NO_x compounds, reducing them back to oxygen and nitrogen.

SCR Advantage

The adoption of SCR by all but one of the major truck OEMs in 2010 has been the number one reason for the improvement in fuel economy of current engines compared to 2007, the year in which DPFs became mandatory. SCR greatly reduces the need to retard fuel injection timing in order to minimize NO_x dump. This allows the ECM to manage injection timing closer to the optimum fuel efficiency window—and in addition, complete the combustion phase earlier in the cycle, lowering PM dump and thereby giving the DPF less work. In addition, it can eliminate or reduce EGR cut-percentages, which significantly reduces engine fouling.

SCR Management

Depending on the OEM, SCR is managed by the engine ECM or by an aftertreatment module. The urea is contained in aqueous/water form (32.5%) in a replenishable vessel. One manufacturer uses the European name for aqueous urea, **AdBlue**, but the trucking industry has generally opted to call this DEF.

DEF is injected upstream from the aftertreatment canister, sometimes assisted by on-chassis compressed air. DEF injection has to be precisely metered by the engine ECM or its dedicated aftertreatment module. In some cases, the aftertreatment module combines the functions of a dosing control module (DCM) and SCR management. This module may network with the ECM via a proprietary data bus or by having its own address on the J1939 bus.

DEF injection must be precisely managed and monitored. Too much urea can result in ammonia discharge through the exhaust system. Too little results in NO_x emission. **Figure 47–11** shows a schematic of SCR components and operation.

DEF is carried onboard the truck in tanks with capacities of 20 to 50 gallons (75 to 190 liters). Because it is an aqueous urea solution, it freezes at 12°F (–8°C), requiring it to be freeze-protected during winter operation. DEF is consumed at a rate that varies between approximately 1% and 5% of the fuel used, the variability depending on how the engine is being operated, that is,

FIGURE 47–11 Schematic of SCR components and operation.

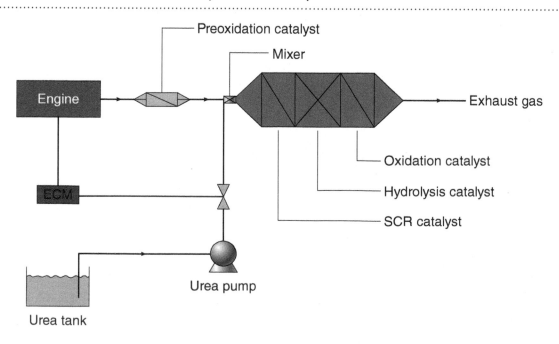

how much NO_x has to be reduced. For instance, no DEF is injected during engine cranking and startup.

SCR Injector Cooling and System Purge

The SCR injector is usually cooled by engine coolant because it lacks the high flow volume of fluid that engine fuel injectors have to achieve their required cooling. Sensors monitor SCR efficiency at all times when the engine is running. At engine shutdown, the DEF supply pump reverses and draws the fluid out of the lines, returning it to the DEF tank. This process typically takes around 60 seconds. Whenever the engine is running, the DEF lines are monitored by thermostats and electrically heated if required to prevent freezing.

EPA SCR COMPLIANCE GUIDELINES

According to the EPA, an SCR management strategy must incorporate:

- Driver warning system—Alerts when the DEF reservoir is low
- Driver inducement—Limited number of restarts, fuel lock-out system, or engine derate until the reducing agent is replenished
- Monitoring system for aqueous urea quality to prevent dilution or substitutes
- Supply infrastructure—Ensures aqueous urea availability
- System reliability and durability—A warranty precondition of 435,000 miles (700,000 km) and minimum service interval of at least 150,000 miles (240,000 km) for heavy-duty highway diesels
- Tamper-resistant protection and deactivation protection

Since SCR became an aftertreatment requirement in all but Navistar- and Caterpillar-manufactured engines in 2010, a supply infrastructure has emerged, making DEF available at truck stops, OEM dealerships, fueling stations, and repair/service operations. All DEF sold in North America is chemically identical regardless of branding. There is no difference between DEF and the AdBlue that one OEM names its product. Navistar marketed engines that did not meet 2010 EPA NO_x emissions until 2013. It did this, first, using an accumulation of emissions credits earned on its engine families over the past decade; thereafter, it paid EPA fines per engine sold. Since EPA MY 2013, Navistar has adopted the use of SCR systems.

FIGURE 47–12 Multicanister DPF and SCR assembly with aftertreatment control module.

When using SCR to meet NOx standards, the EPA requires last-resort persuasive alerts to the operator to be incorporated to minimize the chances of the system being operated without DEF. Compliance requires the system to be able to immediately detect either incorrect or excessively diluted DEF.

In the United States, the 32.5% aqueous urea solution known as DEF was priced at around $3 a gallon in 2015. This means that there is some negative cost of operation impact. However, DEF pricing should remain somewhat more stable than that of fuel because it is entirely home-produced and not dependent on worldwide market price fluctuations. **Figure 47–12** shows a current multicanister approach to SCR and DPF management: The aftertreatment module is mounted on the side of the vertical DPF canister.

Is DEF Toxic?

In 2010, when Navistar made its original decision not to incorporate SCR on its engines, it stated that DEF was potentially harmful. This is not true, but it has unfortunately promoted the myth that it can be toxic. *DEF is not considered toxic under any conditions.* It should be stored at a temperature of 80°F (27°C) or less to maximize shelf life. When DEF is heated to temperatures above 120°F (49°C), it begins to hydrolyze to form small amounts of ammonia in solution, but even under these circumstances it would have to be stored for more than 2 years to reach the level of household ammonia. Household ammonia is not classified as toxic. All Navistar engines manufactured after EPA MY 2013 use SCR with DEF dosing.

CLOSED CRANKCASE VENTILATION

To meet 2007 emissions standards, highway diesel engines were required to incorporate a **closed crankcase ventilation (CCV)** system, which is a diesel engine equivalent of the automotive **positive crankcase ventilation (PCV)** system. In some 2010 engines, crankcase gas emission is eliminated using static electricity. Current DD-Series engines use an **electrostatic oil separator (EOS)**, which first charges liquid droplets in the crankcase gas, then separates them. The objective of a CCV system is to prevent venting to atmosphere of crankcase gases. Crankcase gases consist of:

- Blow-by gas from engine cylinders
- Boil-off gases from lubricant

Crankcase Gas Composition

The actual composition of gases in a diesel engine crankcase is a complex mix of raw fuel, partially combusted fuel, combustion by-products, and the boil-off residues of engine lube. There is agreement that it is toxic, but it is not produced in large quantities. The chemical action in the crankcase is made even more complex because of the presence of moisture-laden air and heat combined with plenty of sloshing and churning activity. However, as technicians we classify crankcase gas simply as HC emission.

CCV and EOS Operation

Diesel CCV and EOS systems can be directly compared with PCV circuits used on automobiles. The CCV system is plumbed upstream from the turbocharger impeller housing so that some pull is exerted on the crankcase. The CCV piping is routed through a filter assembly, which in the case of the 2007 Cummins ISC engine shown in **Figure 47–13** is located on top of the rocker housing cover. OEM recommendations for CCV service intervals should be observed.

EOS functions by imparting an electrical charge to suspended oil droplets in crankcase gas, then electrostatically separating them for reabsorption into the sump oil. EOS reduces internal engine fouling along with cleaning the crankcase gas.

EMISSIONS CIRCUIT LAYOUT

A post-2010, highway-compliant diesel engine has an extensive emission control circuit that clutters the external appearance of the engine. DPF and SCR are almost universally used on

FIGURE 47–13 Overhead view of a Cummins 2007 ISC engine. Note the location of the CCV filter on top of the rocker housing cover.

current highway diesels. The consequence of not using SCR is to have to rely heavily on high percentage EGR cuts, which can foul the internal engine components. **Figure 47–14** is a schematic showing the typical components used to control emissions on a modern diesel engine.

AUXILIARY DEVICES

In an effort to meet ever more stringent emissions standards, the diesel engine has changed over the years. Here are some of the changes that have taken place and how they have helped reduce emissions. Most of them are still used or have an equivalent in the most recent versions of diesel engines.

VCO Injectors

Valve closes orifice (VCO) injectors were introduced in Chapter 21. Elimination or reduction of nozzle sac volume in hydraulic injection injectors reduces the cylinder boil/dribble of sac fuel at the completion of injection. This nozzle design principle is used in all injectors today.

Charge Air Cooling

Effective cooling of intake air lowers combustion temperatures, making it less likely that the nitrogen in the air mixture will be oxidized to form NO_x. Air-to-air charge air coolers cool air more effectively than those that rely on engine coolant. Note that anything that compromises the charge

FIGURE 47–14 Layout of the exhaust aftertreatment circuit on a truck equipped with a DPF and SCR assembly.

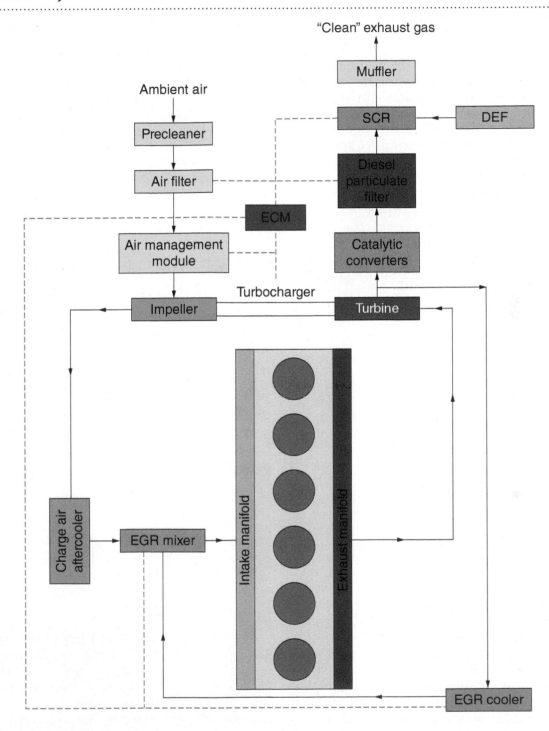

air cooler's ability to cool will result in higher NO_x emissions. This is why codes are logged when charge air heat exchangers become plugged.

Variable Geometry Turbochargers

Variable-geometry turbochargers (VGTs) that perform effectively over a much wider load and rpm range can make a significant difference to both HC and NO_x emissions, especially when ECM controlled, by providing the ability to manage boost on the basis of the fueling and emissions algorithms. VGTs are used rather than constant geometry turbos in most highway-compliant diesel engines. When a constant geometry turbocharger is used today, it is usually as one of the pair used in series turbocharged engines.

Low Headland Pistons

Low headland volume pistons raise the upper compression ring close to the leading edge of the piston crown. This keeps the headland gas volume close to minimum. Headland gas volume tends to be unreactive and can increase HC emissions. The requirement for low headland volume pistons by engine designers has resulted in some radical design changes in diesel engine pistons within a short period of time. Most diesel engine manufacturers today favor trunk-type steel pistons such as the Mahle Monotherm™, which features low headland volumes.

Aneroids

Although most types of manifold boost measuring devices have been covered elsewhere in different chapters of this book, some of the more common methods of smoke control used on older hydromechanical engines are briefly examined here for ease of reference. By definition, **aneroids** are low-pressure measuring devices. Basically, they measure manifold boost and delay engine fueling until there is enough air in the cylinder to actually burn the fuel metered by the injector. Aneroid operation differs by OEM, but aneroids do have some importance today because the test fields used by the SAE J1667 were developed based on how aneroids function. In other words, compliance to J1667 opacity (smoke emission) standards is based on a field test that is 30 years out of date. The various types of aneroid and smoke control devices used on these older engines are looked at in Chapter 48.

2014 GHGs AND EMISSIONS

The Obama administration recently confirmed the commercial vehicle emissions rules scheduled for phased implementation from 2014 to 2018. This set of rules is based on per gallon, per mile, and per chassis application; it is beyond the scope of this textbook to outline in them in detail. Put simply, diesel-powered highway trucks will be required to reduce EPA 2010 levels of emissions by 6% to 9% by 2018; reduce GHGs by 17% (expressed as CO_2 per ton-mile); and improve fuel economy (expressed as per ton-mile hauled) by 15%. The bottom line for technicians is that the percentage of shop work associated with emissions control devices

is likely going to increase rather than decrease over the coming decade.

HEALTH EFFECTS INSTITUTE STUDY

While it is not suggested that anyone breathe tailpipe gases, a recent study by the **Health Effects Institute (HEI)** on EPA post-2010 diesels indicated that laboratory rats suffered no lung illnesses during a lengthy exposure. The HEI term used to refer to EPA post-2010 diesel engines is **new technology diesel exhaust (NTDE)**. The results of the HEI testing can be interpreted to mean that people's lungs are also not harmed by NTDE exhaust gas, because animal and human organs operate in similar fashion.

END OF THE HYDROMECHANICAL ERA?

EPA over-the-road regulations generally apply only to engines above 70 horsepower. **Figure 47–15** shows a 2015 reefer diesel engine

FIGURE 47–15 EPA- and CARB-compliant diesel engine with 100% hydromechanical controls.

FIGURE 47–16 The freight efficient rig. Many of these features are already becoming a common sight on our highways.

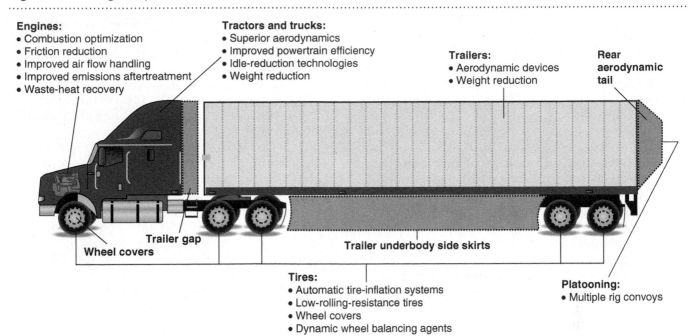

Engines:
- Combustion optimization
- Friction reduction
- Improved air flow handling
- Improved emissions aftertreatment
- Waste-heat recovery

Tractors and trucks:
- Superior aerodynamics
- Improved powertrain efficiency
- Idle-reduction technologies
- Weight reduction

Trailers:
- Aerodynamic devices
- Weight reduction

Rear aerodynamic tail

Trailer gap

Wheel covers

Trailer underbody side skirts

Tires:
- Automatic tire-inflation systems
- Low-rolling-resistance tires
- Wheel covers
- Dynamic wheel balancing agents

Platooning:
- Multiple rig convoys

used in a Carrier refrigeration unit. This engine is fully compliant and uses no electronic control; the same engine can be made CARB compliant by adding a DPF.

MEETING CHASSIS GHG REDUCTION STANDARDS

Until EPA MY 2010, the diesel engine was the primary focus for mandated changes in technology. However, the NTDE engines of today have changed the playing field and shifted the focus onto the tractor and trailer as a unit, as the industry replaces the term *fuel economy* with the now-preferred *freight efficiency*. Yes, there will continue to be advances in engine technology,

most notably in the area of waste heat recovery, but nothing dramatic is expected to occur in the immediate future.

FREIGHT EFFICIENT RIGS

Due to the next implementation phase of the EPA **Highway Diesel Rule**, the freight efficient commercial highway transport will look something like the rig shown in **Figure 47–16**. Many of the features shown on this vehicle have already become common on our highways, and they will become even more common as the industry attempts to achieve the fuel efficiency and GHG-reduction strategies mandated for phased implementation from 2017 to 2020. A more comprehensive look at the Highway Diesel Rule appears in Chapter 48.

SUMMARY

- Emissions standards that engine OEMs must meet are set nationwide by the EPA. The influence of CARB has greatly increased in recent years because the California standards have been adopted by nearly 20 other states, representing well over half of the U.S. economy. The states that have adopted the CARB standards are known as *green* states.

- The EPA has determined the green state initiative to be illegal. The green states are currently suing the EPA, asserting that they have as much right to clean air as California. The outcome of the litigation is being monitored by a number of other states that were planning to join the green state movement.

- A Supreme Court ruling defined CO_2 as a pollutant. Although it was always known to be a GHG, it can now also be regulated as a noxious emission. This initiated a federal initiative to significantly cut back on CO_2 emissions by 2018.
- Cutting back on CO_2 discharge means looking for non-HC fuels or greatly improving fuel economy.
- The word *smog* is derived from the words *smoke* and *fog*.
- Photochemical smog is formed by gaseous and particulate hydrocarbons (HCs) combining with ozone and oxides of nitrogen (NO_x), followed by a period of exposure to sunlight.
- Because creating photochemical smog requires a period of exposure to sunlight, a relatively still air mass is required for its formation.
- Vehicle emissions are the largest single contributor to photochemical smog formation in most geographic areas of North America.
- Conditions in southern California are ideal for the formation of photochemical smog. These include a high percentage of per capita vehicle ownership, plenty of sun, and a natural wall formed by the San Gabriel mountains to the east that acts to trap air mass movement.
- VOCs are hydrocarbon fractions that have evaporated from fuels during production, transportation, storage, and production. VOCs are a more severe problem in high-temperature climatic conditions.
- Ozone is known to be toxic in concentrations of 80 parts per billion, but some experts believe that any exposure to ozone can cause health problems.
- Diesel engines today rely on exhaust gas recirculation (EGR), NO_x adsorber catalysts, oxidation and reduction catalytic converters, diesel particulate filters (DPFs), and selective catalytic reduction (SCR), along with computer control of combustion, to meet emissions compliance standards.

- The DPF entraps soot particles. The entrapped soot is then combusted in what is known as a *regeneration process.*
- DPF regeneration can be passive (occurs during normal vehicle operation) or active (requires dosing fuel and sometimes spark ignition).
- Dosing of fuel into the exhaust aftertreatment circuit may be required for certain types of reduction catalyst and to manage some modes of DPF regeneration cycles.
- NO_x is formed when combustion temperatures become high enough to oxidize the nitrogen that is a component of the air we breathe.
- Diesel engines require NO_x reduction systems to meet current emissions standards. NO_x reduction strategies include combustion temperature management, EGR, and SCR.
- SCR-equipped engines use metered DEF that is delivered to the exhaust aftertreatment circuit. SCR is an effective NO_x reduction system that reduces or eliminates EGR.
- All EPA MY 2010 emissions compliant diesel engines other than those manufactured by Navistar and Caterpillar were equipped with an SCR system.
- From EPA MY 2013, all truck diesel engines sold in North America were SCR-equipped and used metered DEF delivered to the exhaust aftertreatment circuit.
- The EPA requires stringent warning, engine deration, and shutdown strategies to avoid SCR engines being operated with diluted, contaminated, or no DEF.
- A recent HEI study showed that EPA post-2010 NTDE diesel engine emissions showed no significant potential threat to animal life.
- The freight efficient truck rig of the immediate future will focus less on engine technology and more on such things as the aerodynamics and rolling resistance of the tractor-trailer combination.

REVIEW QUESTIONS

1. Which of the following compounds is classified by the EPA as a pollutant?
   a. Oxides of nitrogen
   b. Hydrocarbons
   c. Carbon dioxide
   d. All are pollutants

2. Which of the following are GHGs?
   a. CO_2
   b. Methane
   c. NO_x
   d. All are GHGs

3. Which exhaust gas emission does an NO_x adsorber catalyst attempt to reduce?
   a. Particulate matter (PM)
   b. Oxides of nitrogen
   c. Hydrocarbons
   d. All of the above

4. Which of the following engine OEMs was the last to adopt SCR NO_x reduction on its diesel engines?
   a. DDC
   b. Cummins
   c. Navistar
   d. Volvo

5. Which of the following would properly describe atmospheric oxygen at ground level?
   a. O
   b. O_2
   c. O_3
   d. O_4

6. Which two compounds would result from theoretically "perfect" combustion of an HC fuel reacted with oxygen?
   a. Carbon monoxide and carbon dioxide
   b. Carbon dioxide and nitrogen dioxide
   c. Nitrogen dioxide and water
   d. Carbon dioxide and water

7. When a diesel engine is operated at lower-than-normal combustion temperatures, which of the following categories of noxious exhaust emissions is likely to increase?
   a. Hydrocarbons
   b. Oxides of nitrogen
   c. Carbon dioxide
   d. Ozone

8. Which of the following best describes what happens in an oxidation-type catalytic converter?
   a. Nitrogen in NO_x is combusted.
   b. CO and HCs are combusted.
   c. HCs are entrapped on substrate.
   d. Particulate matter is filtered out.

9. Technician A states that DPFs can run up to 8 hours in a linehaul diesel engine before regeneration. Technician B states that some DPFs must be removed from the vehicle for cleaning on a weekly basis. Who is correct?
   a. Technician A only
   b. Technician B only
   c. Both A and B
   d. Neither A nor B

10. Technician A states that photochemical smog formation requires both HC and NO_x plus a period of exposure to sunlight. Technician B states that the presence of ozone is a requirement for creating photochemical smog. Who is correct?
    a. Technician A only
    b. Technician B only
    c. Both A and B
    d. Neither A nor B

11. What is the 2018 target percentage reduction for GHGs emitted by highway diesel-powered trucks over 2010 standards?
    a. 6%
    b. 9%
    c. 17%
    d. 50%

12. If the federal government's target for fuel economy for commercial trucks in 2018 is met, fuel consumption per ton-mile hauled should decrease by:
    a. 6%.
    b. 9%.
    c. 15%.
    d. 40%.

13. What is the function of a seventh injector?
    a. Provide a fuel boost for fast acceleration
    b. Dose DEF into an SCR module
    c. Dose diesel fuel for DPF regeneration
    d. Provide fuel for the EGR circuit

14. Technician A says that all EPA MY 2013 highway compliant diesel engines use SCR. Technician B says that an SCR system relies on replenishing DEF on a regular basis. Who is correct?
    a. Technician A only
    b. Technician B only
    c. Both A and B
    d. Neither A nor B

15. Which of the following is likely to be used on a freight efficient rig?
    a. Automatic tire inflation systems
    b. Wheel covers
    c. Aerodynamic fairings
    d. All of the above

48

Prerequisite: Chapter 47

SERVICING AND MAINTENANCE OF EXHAUST AFTERTREATMENT SYSTEMS

OBJECTIVES

After studying this chapter, you should be able to:

• Explain the effect that fuel injection timing can have on diesel engine end gas.

• Describe the smoke control devices used on legacy engines.

• Outline the service, maintenance, and troubleshooting procedures for exhaust gas recirculation (EGR) circuits.

• Outline the service, maintenance, and troubleshooting procedures for selective catalytic reduction (SCR) systems.

• Outline the service, maintenance, and troubleshooting procedures for diesel particulate filter (DPF) systems.

• Understand what constitutes emission control tampering and the fines for which a technician or service facility can be liable.

• Describe the SAE J1667 test procedure.

• Perform a J1667 opacity smoke test.

• Analyze diesel engine visible smoke emission.

• Remove and replace a typical DPF canister for servicing.

• Remove and replace a typical SCR canister for servicing.

• Outline the advantages of single-canister exhaust aftertreatment devices.

KEY TERMS

active regeneration

AdBlue

aftertreatment module

aneroid

cooled exhaust gas recirculation (C-EGR)

diesel exhaust fluid (DEF)

diesel particulate filter (DPF)

dosing

DPF delete

Ecoboost

EURO VI

Highway Diesel Rule

J1667

low-temperature filter (LTF)

opacity meter

passive regeneration	regeneration cycle	resistance temperature detector (RTD)	selective catalytic reduction (SCR)
platinum resistance thermometer (PRT)	regeneration system (RS)		urea

INTRODUCTION

An extensive array of diesel emissions control apparatus has been mandatory on highway trucks since 2004; because this equipment requires servicing, truck service shops have experienced a surge in emissions-related repairs. Chapter 47 dealt with the operating principles of exhaust aftertreatment hardware, and this chapter looks at some of the challenges in maintaining this equipment.

It is assumed that the reader has a good understanding of the operating principles of emissions control devices, including the following:

- Exhaust gas recirculation (EGR)
- Clean gas induction (CGI)
- Oxidation catalytic converters
- Reduction catalytic converters
- NO_x adsorber catalysts (NACs)
- Diesel particulate filters (DPFs)
- Selective catalytic reduction (SCR)

CO-DEPENDENCE OF ALL ENGINE SYSTEMS

A modern diesel engine is a complex set of systems that are all co-dependent. Tampering with one system can impact engine performance and significantly affect emissions. For instance, most truckers and truck technicians are aware that advancing fuel injection timing can both increase engine horsepower and improve fuel economy. What they may not be aware of is that it also sends NO_x output off the charts (perhaps they may not care too much about this) and drastically decreases engine longevity (they may care a lot about this if they happen to own the truck). Technicians should always be aware of the ways in which emissions and smoke control devices can be tampered with, because it is technicians who ultimately have to diagnose and repair abuses.

HIGHWAY DIESEL RULE

The EPA Highway Diesel Rule is a single comprehensive national program that regulates commercial vehicles and the fuels they use through a single system. The Highway Rule initiative was launched in 2001 with phased implementation dates that began in 2006 and currently extend to 2020. The first phase of the program concerned the chemistry of diesel fuel, specifically the introduction of ultra-low sulfur (ULS) in 2006, and an aggressive reduction of on-highway diesel engine emissions in 2007 and 2010. By 2010, the EPA emissions standards for diesel engines and those for NG and gasoline engines were brought in line, as can be seen by the data in **Table 48–1**.

The standards in Table 48–1 apply to commercial vehicles that weigh more than 14,000 lb (6350 kg). Those that apply to vehicles under that weight are less stringent and can be checked by referencing the EPA website. Because the focus of the Highway Diesel Rule is on the emissions performance of the entire rig, anything that affects fuel consumption is covered by the mandate. Specifically, this applies to greenhouse gases (GHGs), especially CO_2 output, so factors such as rig aerodynamics and vehicle rolling resistance are becoming increasingly important (as can be seen in Figure 47–16 in the previous chapter).

> **WARNING:**
>
> All post-2007 diesel engines with DPFs must use CJ-4 or CK-4 engine oils with less than 1% ash, or risk damage to the DPF. This includes small-bore CARB-certified engines equipped with DPFs such as those used in trailer reefers. Post-2017 diesel engines should use FA-4 engine lubricant.

TABLE 48–1 EPA Maximum Emissions for EPA MY 2010

Engine/Fuel Type	Pollutant	Maximum Output
Diesel, NG, gasoline	NO_x	0.200 grams/ BHP-hr
Diesel, NG, gasoline	NMHC (non-methane hydrocarbons)	0.140 grams/ BHP-hr
Diesel, NG, gasoline	HCHO (formaldehyde)	0.016 grams/ BHP-hr
Diesel, NG, gasoline	PM (particulate matter)	0.010 grams/ BHP-hr

IMPORTANCE OF COMBUSTION TEMPERATURE

Computers are used to manage today's engines because they are required to operate within a very narrow window to meet the emissions standards for which they have been certified. Overlooking small maintenance procedures, such as ensuring that engine compartment heat exchangers are not clogged with dirt and debris, can produce performance problems: Higher than specified combustion temperatures result in increased NO_x emission. Operating an engine without a thermostat(s) can result in lower operating temperatures and higher hydrocarbon (HC) and particulate emissions; this can rapidly overload the aftertreatment devices on the engine.

FUEL

All diesel fuel used on our highways since 2010 must be classified as ultra-low sulfur (ULS), with a maximum sulfur content no greater than 0.0015% or 15 parts per million (ppm). Use of a fuel on a highway diesel engine that fails to meet the ULS standard is not only illegal, it can also damage modern exhaust aftertreatment systems. It appears that the older LS fuel is still obtainable in some regions, so technicians troubleshooting problems with aftertreatment systems should consider fuel quality. When the odor of fuel is suspect (combusting pre-2007 LS fuel produced a more sulfurous smell), have it checked by a fuel supplier.

Most of the world outside North America adheres to EURO standards of fuel chemistry and engine emissions. The **EURO VI** diesel fuel sulfur maximum is actually lower (10 ppm/0.0010%) than that specified by the EPA, but in Europe there are so many phase-in loopholes that most diesel fuel continues to be sold with higher sulfur content.

FUEL INJECTION TIMING

It was easy to tamper with fuel injection timing on older hydromechanical engines. Although it is more difficult to do this on modern highway diesel engines, it is still done. Advancing injection timing by as little as 1 degree crank angle can improve fuel economy and power. The downside is increased NO_x emission, which may not trouble some, and drastically shortened engine longevity, which may trouble the owner. Fuel timing in today's engines is variable and critical in meeting emissions standards. Similarly, retarding injection timing can increase HC emission because it leaves insufficient time to complete combustion.

LEGACY ENGINES

We begin by looking at some of the controls used on legacy engines. *Legacy engines* are those manufactured before 1997; there are still many of them around, the ones that fail roadside opacity tests. Because these engines have more primitive smoke control devices, technicians involved in smoke opacity testing—and the repairs required when engines fail these tests—should know something about the ways diesel exhaust smoke was controlled a generation ago.

VISIBLE SMOKE EMISSION: LEGACY ENGINES

Because J1667 tests visible smoke emissions, the primary system being tested was that used to sense manifold boost and limit maximum fueling until turbo-boost pressure reached a specified pressure value. Turbo-boost sensing devices are known as **aneroids**. An aneroid is a low-pressure measuring device. The aneroid devices used in hydromechanical truck engines were known by names such as turbo-boost sensor, manifold boost sensor, puff limiter, or air-fuel ratio control, and most of them could be disabled by a person with minimal mechanical knowledge. They were disabled because drivers believed that they were being cheated of low-end power by these aneroid devices. A disabled aneroid produced a telltale puff of smoke from the exhaust stack at every upshift, and it was often difficult to explain to a driver that if fuel exited the exhaust pipe in the form of smoke, then it was probably being wasted. The good news is that a J1667 opacity will identify any of these engines of a generation ago that have been tampered with. The bad news is that it can be difficult to determine exactly *how* a smoke control device has been tampered with, often leading to costly repairs.

SMOKE CONTROL DEVICES

We took a brief look at the operating principles of aneroid devices in Chapter 47, and here we will look at them a little more closely. Although aneroids are not used on any current engines, they were a feature of most highway spec'd, hydromechanical, and early-generation electronically controlled engines. In addition, they were used in off-road diesel engines until 2008. In the SAE J1667 opacity test we are going study in this chapter, most of the tests were based on the functionality of one type of smoke control device, usually an aneroid, or another. It is also important to bear in mind that when these older engines have difficulty in passing a J1667 compliance test, it is commonly due to the smoke control device having been disabled or otherwise tampered with. For this reason, technicians should understand how each type functions. The following are the different types of smoke limiting devices used in the hydromechanical age of truck diesel engines:

- Caterpillar AFRC (air-fuel ratio control). An aneroid device that is not effective until after the first boost application. This feature permits the engine to be full fueled for cold engine startup, but not after the AFRC has been activated.
- Cummins AFC (air-fuel control). An aneroid built into the pressure-time (PT) pump. Manifold boost is ported directly to the AFC diaphragm, which can then modulate fueling based on actual boost values.
- Mack Trucks puff limiter. Used on many Mack engines of the 1980s, the puff limiter used an aneroid device located on the intake manifold to sense manifold boost and system air pressure to signal a plunger-type bimba valve located on the fuel injection pump and designed to block rack travel to full fuel. It functioned by cutting system air pressure to the bimba valve when boost pressure was sufficient; this allowed devices such as air brake status and transmission gear ratio to be used to limit unnecessary full fueling.
- Robert Bosch LDA. LDA is a German acronym meaning "aneroid"; it became known by many Mack Truck technicians as a "lazy dog adjuster" because of its connection with complaints about lack of power. The device is a direct-acting aneroid which requires that manifold boost be ported to it. Like the puff limiter, this type of aneroid is on/off and rated with a preset trigger pressure.

Throttle Delay Cylinder

Perhaps the most primitive of smoke control devices, the Detroit Diesel throttle delay cylinder was used on its two-stroke cycle, mechanical unit injector (MUI) engines. It does not measure manifold boost; it is simply a crude device whose function was to create a hydraulic lag between a full fuel request (from the accelerator pedal) and the act of moving the rack control tube to full fuel. It consists of a throttle delay cylinder and piston that reciprocates within it. The piston is attached by means of a yoked lever clamped to, and actuated by, the control rack. Engine oil is drizzled into the throttle delay cylinder so that when the control tube attempts to move from a low or idle fuel position, oil has to be displaced from the throttle delay cylinder first by means of a restriction port. You should know something about how throttle delay cylinders function if you are performing opacity-compliance testing. These devices were defeated by drilling to oversize the cylinder spill port or by loosening the rack yoke.

EXHAUST GAS RECIRCULATION (EGR) SYSTEMS

The operating principles of exhaust gas recirculation (EGR) systems are covered in detail in Chapter 47. EGR has been problematic to truck engines, from when it was introduced in EPA model year (MY) 2004, to 2010 when SCR became common. The problems increase when heavy EGR cut-percentages are used.

Since EPA 2010, most original equipment manufacturers (OEMs) have been able to depend much less on EGR to manage NO_x emissions. Today, only Navistar relies exclusively on EGR to meet NO_x emission standards, and it achieves

FIGURE 48–1 A right-side view of a Navistar 13-liter engine featuring the EGR circuit.

this by using heavy EGR cut-percentages during some modes of operation. **Figure 48–1** shows a right-side view of a MaxxForce 13 engine with series turbocharging and EGR.

The overall function of a diesel EGR is to route dead exhaust gas back into the engine cylinders to dilute the intake charge. Because diesel end gas is hot, EGR systems use heat exchangers or coolers to reduce the temperature. For this reason, we often describe a diesel EGR circuit as **cooled exhaust gas recirculation (C-EGR)**.

An EGR cooler is a pressurized heat exchanger whose cooling medium is usually engine coolant. The exhaust gas being recirculated moves through an isolated gas circuit in the heat exchanger and should never come into direct contact with the engine coolant (providing it is not defective).

The function of the EGR heat exchanger is to use lower-temperature engine coolant to draw heat from higher-temperature exhaust gas before delivering it back to the engine cylinders. A typical EGR cooler is shown in **Figure 48–2**, which indicates the gas and coolant flow routing.

C-EGR COOLER MAINTENANCE

Because heat is transferred from the exhaust gas into the engine coolant by means of an EGR heat exchanger, a significant additional heat load is placed on the engine coolant circuit. One obvious result is that local coolant temperatures within the EGR cooler become higher than the mean (average) coolant temperature in the cooling system. In EGR-equipped engines, it becomes critically important to maintain the cooling system in the best possible condition, paying special attention to:

- Radiator pressure caps
- Coolant quality
- Coolant level
- Belts and belt tensioners
- Charge air cooler (CAC) and radiator fins
- Fan clutches, fan blades, and radiator shrouds

EGR COOLER PLUGGING

Although EGR heat exchanger plugging is not common with well-maintained diesel engines that are not allowed to idle for prolonged periods, it can be a problem in vocational applications. It should be noted that some carbon and soot coating of the gas (exhaust) circuit is normal and nothing to worry about. Plugging of

FIGURE 48–2 Typical EGR heat exchanger showing the gas and coolant flow routing.

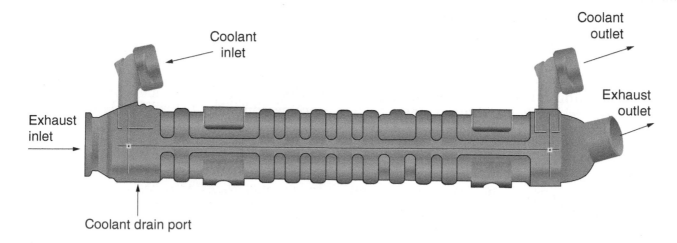

EGR coolers usually occurs when the exhaust gas mixes with:

- Engine coolant
- Engine oil
- Raw fuel
- Blow-by gas

Symptoms of a Plugged EGR Circuit

The common complaint that accompanies a plugged EGR circuit is loss of engine power. This is usually first noticed by a lag in accelerator response and is followed by lower than usual power when attempting high-load, uphill hauls. In most cases, the lower power is accompanied by decreased fuel economy. As the condition worsens, check engine alerts and fault codes are logged.

In pre-2007 EGR-equipped engines, clogged EGR coolers are likely to produce black smoke emission. In post-2007 EGR-equipped engines, the operator is likely to complain that the **diesel particulate filter (DPF)** is frequently regenerating. In these more current engines, it should be noted that a clogged EGR heat exchanger can damage exhaust aftertreatment components if allowed to persist.

Causes of Cooler Plugging

When troubleshooting a plugged EGR cooler, odor may be a tattletale. Scorched engine oil, heated antifreeze mixtures, and blow-by vapors all have a characteristic smell that can help as a first step to diagnosing the problem. Look for the following contributing causes:

- EGR valve failure
- Increased coolant consumption
- Increased oil consumption
- Incorrect fuel, especially use of high-sulfur fuels (higher than 500 ppm sulfur content)
- Excessive engine blow-by
- Sensor failures

EGR SYSTEM DIAGNOSTICS

When beginning the diagnostic procedure, it makes sense to look at the vehicle repair and service logs to determine if there is a history of EGR problems. If oil analysis is done during engine servicing, check for the following tattletales, especially if there is a rising trend in a sequence of analyses:

- Increased soot loads
- Coolant leak indicators or potassium/sodium levels rising

Inspect the engine breathing circuit for leaks. This means checking every joint in the intake and exhaust systems and paying special attention to sensor ports, hose clamps, and band clamps. If the EGR cooler has external fins, check these for damage or clogging, then check the gas circuit for indications of wetness.

If a coolant leak is suspected and its source is not obvious, add a fluorescent dye to the coolant and run the engine until it is at operating temperature to enable the dye to properly mix. Then use a ultraviolet (UV) (black) light to trace the leakage point.

EST-EGR Diagnostic Routines

In most cases, to do anything but the most basic EGR diagnostic routines, the OEM diagnostic software rather than a generic EST will be required. This may change with the introduction of HD-OBD. Run diagnostic tests on the following:

- VG turbocharger calibration
- EGR valve function
- EGR flow sensor(s)
- All EGR circuit sensors

Leak-Testing an EGR Cooler

Testing an EGR cooler for leaks is not that different from testing other vehicle heat exchangers. Having gotten to this stage, the EGR cooler first has to be removed from the engine. The following tests are bench tests.

COOLANT SIDE PRESSURE DROP-OFF Plug off the coolant in and out ports and fit a supply fitting and pressure gauge into the coolant side of the heat exchanger. Apply regulated air pressure to the cooler liquid circuit. Check the OEM specifications for the recommended pressure; for purposes of this explanation, we will use 10 psi (65 kPa). After supplying the regulated air to the cooler, isolate the circuit and watch for pressure drop-off.

INTERNAL LEAK LOCATION TESTING This is a bubble test that can help identify the location of a leak. Plug, pressurize, and hold the air supply to the EGR cooler as in the previous test. Now immerse the heat exchanger in water and check for bubbles by looking in through each gas port connection.

EXTERNAL LEAK LOCATION TESTING Plug, pressurize, and hold the air supply to the EGR cooler as in the previous tests. Then plug the gas in and gas out ports. Submerge the heat exchanger and look for bubbles.

FIGURE 48–3 A suspended C-EGR cooler being hosed down with high-pressure steam. This can be done following an ultrasonic or mineral spirit cleaning process, or as a preventive measure during engine servicing.

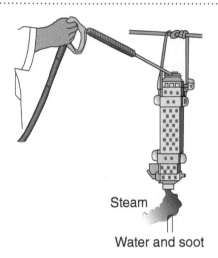

Steam

Water and soot

Vertical cleaning: begin at the inlet.

EGR Cleaning Methods

Although some OEMs recommend mineral spirits and dip tanks to clean EGR coolers, ultrasonic cleaning is the generally preferred method. Usually no more than 1 hour in an ultrasonic bath is sufficient to loosen most contaminants. The ultrasonic bath can be followed by hosing down with a high-temperature steam cleaner. This method, shown in **Figure 48–3**, can also be used as a preventive measure during preventive maintenance, but check to see if it is endorsed by the OEM; some high-pressure washers may damage the heat exchanger core. **Table 48–2** shows the effectiveness of hot water versus ultrasonic cleaning of DPFs.

TABLE 48–2 EGR Cleaning Methods

Cooler Type	Recommended Cleaning Method	
	High-Pressure Hot Water	Ultrasonic
Straight core with straight diffuser pipes	Yes	Yes
Straight core with angled diffuser pipes	No	Yes
Multipass core with box section coolers	No	Yes

Ultrasonic Cleaning

Ultrasonic cleaning of EGR coolers should be undertaken in an ultrasonic bath. The ultrasonic fluid in the bath is an alkaline solution with properties designed to attach to diesel exhaust residues. A combination of sound waves and mechanical agitation is used in the cleaning process. A maximum of 1 hour is all that is required in the ultrasonic bath. At the conclusion of the cleaning process, the cooler must be thoroughly hosed down with hot water and leak-tested prior to reinstallation onto the engine.

Mineral Spirits Cleaning

Mineral spirits are an alternative to ultrasonic cleaning for C-EGR coolers. There are a couple of aftermarket mineral spirit–based cleaning systems. This requires a period of soaking the heat exchanger element followed by steaming. Because of the volume of clogged EGR coolers, it is not unusual for larger truck service facilities to have either EGR cleaning equipment on site. **Figure 48–4** shows a graph produced by a manufacturer of C-EGR ultrasonic baths indicating the superiority of its system over competing mineral spirit methods.

DIESEL PARTICULATE FILTERS (DPFs)

To understand this section, the reader should be completely familiar with the operating principles of DPFs (see Chapter 47) and understand what is involved in the different types of DPF **active regeneration** and **passive regeneration** cycles. When PM accumulates in the ceramic walls of a DPF, the filter begins to restrict flow. To prevent the DPF from plugging, periodic **regeneration cycles**, usually accompanied by **dosing**, are required to combust the accumulated soot, reducing it to ash. The burning of soot produces CO_2 and small quantities of ash. The CO_2 is discharged through the exhaust system while the ash remains in the DPF. Ash accumulation in a DPF reduces its soot holding capability, forcing more frequent regeneration cycles.

WHAT IS ASH?

After DPF regeneration, all that remains of carbon-based PM is ash. However, technicians are advised to heed OEM warnings about exposure to DPF ash when handling these components

FIGURE 48–4 Graph comparing the results of ultrasonic and mineral spirits cleaning of C-EGR heat exchangers.

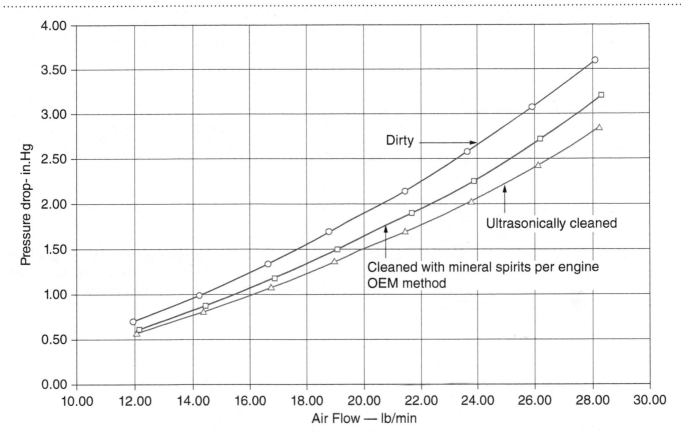

during servicing. First, it needs to be said that fuel has almost no potential to contribute to DPF ash, because it is close to 100% carbon-based and highly filtered by the fuel subsystem before it gets to the injection circuit. This means that after regeneration and the burning-off of all of the PM (carbon), the ash that remains in the DPF is composed of what cannot be combusted. Its primary constituents are:

- Remnants of lube oil additives
- Engine wear metals

For this reason, DPF ash should be handled with care and it should always be a primary consideration when handling diesel engine aftertreatment devices. It is also a major reason why the specified CJ-4 or CK-4 engine oil (see Chapter 10) should always be used.

WARNING:

DPF ash is known to be hazardous to health. Avoid direct contact with bare hands and wear a good-quality particulate breathing mask when handling aftertreatment hardware.

REGENERATION SYSTEMS: CLEANING FREQUENCY

Ash residues from the vehicle **regeneration system (RS)** have to be removed manually. Federal law requires that this cleaning process occur no more frequently than once a year or 150,000 miles (240,000 km), whichever comes first. Having said that, some manufacturers state that their RS service intervals should exceed 300,000 highway miles (480,000 km). The service interval is also specified in engine hours for vocational engines; it should be noted that certain types of vocational operation can be especially demanding of the DPF system.

Spark Plug Safety

When working on RS, it is important to know that those systems that use spark plugs fire them routinely outside RS regen cycles to limit carbon buildup. When working on exhaust systems, spark-fired RS should be deactivated using the OEM software to prevent activation on the shop floor. The DPFs used by most engine OEMs should usually regenerate under *any* conditions: Some manufacturers are using DPFs with extended in-operation cycles, but the disadvantage is that trucks with this equipment must pull off the road to regenerate.

DPF MONITORING

DPF performance can be evaluated by measuring total exhaust system backpressure. Each engine OEM produces its own backpressure specifications, but there is not too much variance between them. During a full load dyno test, typical specified backpressures (measured at the DPF outlet) are in the region of 15 to 20 in. H_2O (380 to 508 mm H_2O). Most engine OEMs will provide a maximum backpressure specification; if this is exceeded, the DPF requires shop cleaning. The vehicle operator is usually notified by dash lights and a display on the digital dash display unit. Another factor that will cause the DPF monitoring system to broadcast alerts is soaking of the DPF substrate by fluids caused by an upstream engine failure.

In addition, DPF operational temperatures must be accurately monitored. To monitor high DPF temperatures, pyrometers and resistance thermometers must be used. Pyrometers and resistance thermometers are discussed in Chapter 32. Resistance thermometers can replace thermocouple-type pyrometers where temperatures do not exceed 1,100°F (600°C) and because this is on the threshold of the highest DPF temperatures, some OEMs use these in place of pyrometers. **Resistance temperature detectors (RTDs)** or **platinum resistance thermometers (PRTs)** are the terms used to describe these devices.

Interpreting DPF Dash Lights

Any driver-training program today must include clear-cut instructions on how to interpret DPF dash warning lights. Failure to respond to dash light prompts can result in costly repairs and downtime. **Figure 48–5** shows the DPF warning light prompts on a chassis using a current DD15 engine.

DPF-Related Codes

DPF performance is monitored by either the engine ECM (SA 00) or an **aftertreatment module** (this is more common on post-2010 and off-highway engines) with an SA 61 address on the J1939 data bus. Typically, there are three types of failures that can trigger codes:

- High restriction
- Failure to ignite
- Failure to combust

DPF SHOP CLEANING

There are three possible reasons for a DPF to require removal for shop cleaning:

1. Ash removal: Normal service required between 200,000 and 500,000 miles (322,000 and 800,000 km)

FIGURE 48–5 Interpreting DPF dash warning light prompts.

EXHAUST AFTERTREATMENT SYSTEM INFORMATION					
INDICATOR LAMP(S)	(Solid) Level 1	(Flashing) Level 2	CHECK (Flashing) Level 3	CHECK STOP (Flashing) Level 4	⚠ WARNING
Indicator Lamp Message(s)	Filter Regeneration Recommended	Filter Regeneration required	Parked Regeneration Required – Engine Derate	Parked Regeneration Required – Engine Shut Down	HEST (High Exhaust System Temperature)
DPF Condition	Filter is requires regeneration	Filter is approaching maximum capacity.	Filter has reached maximum capacity.	Filter has exceeded maximum capacity.	**Flashing** A regeneration is in progress.
Action required	Bring vehicle to highway speeds to enable an Automatic Regeneration or perform a Parked Regeneration.	To avoid engine derate bring vehicle up to highway speed to enable an Automatic Regeneration or perform a Parked Regeneration as soon as possible.	Vehicle must be parked and a Parked Regeneration performed – engine will begin derate.	Vehicle must be parked and a Parked Regeneration or Service Regeneration must be performed. Check engine service literature for details –engine will shut down.	**Solid** Exhaust Components and exhaust gas operate at high temperatures. When stationary, be aware of people, flammable materials, vapors, and structures.
For a driver performed Parked Regeneration, vehicle must be equipped with a dash mounted Regeneration Switch.					
See OEM service literature for complete Regeneration Instructions.					

FIGURE 48–6 Exploded view of an oxidation catalyst and DPF assembly.

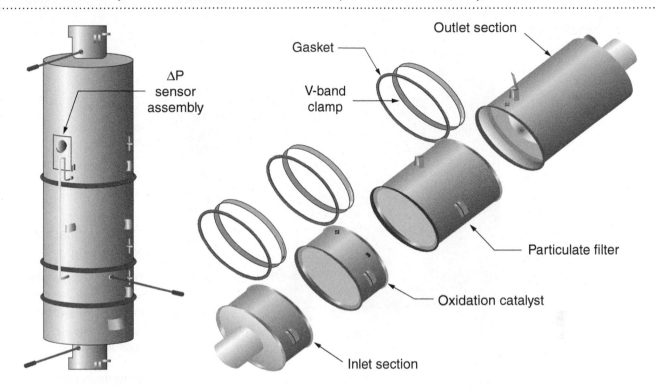

2. Excessive soot buildup (excess can melt substrate)
3. DPF soaked with liquid (oil, coolant, or fuel)

DPF shop cleaning requires the use of special apparatus provided by the OEM or an aftermarket supplier. Attempting to clean DPFs without using the specified tooling and method can result in damage. Depending on the type of DPF, the canister assembly that contains it will usually have to be disassembled. **Figure 48–6** shows an exploded view of one type of DPF assembly.

DPF Cleaning Station

Most engine OEMs state that their DPFs require routine in-shop cleaning using special equipment in the form of a DPF cleaning station. DPF shop cleaning stations are either OEM- or aftermarket-supplied. Most DPF cleaning requires that the aftertreatment canister be removed from the chassis for the cleaning procedure. Some OEMs (DDC, for example) state that DPFs must not be cleaned in the field: They supply rebuilt-exchange units that take around 30 minutes of shop time to replace. When a shop cleaning process is used, it is considered to be about 85% effective. **Figure 48–7** shows a Donaldson generic DPF cleaning station.

Cleaning Procedure

A typical DPF cleaning station is a two-stage device capable of:

- Backpressure pulsing the DPF filter
- Thermally regenerating (in an oven) the filter

A typical DPF cleaning procedure would only require the pulse cleaning stage of the process. After the first stage is complete, the filter is tested for restriction. If the restriction measured falls below specification, the filter is thermally regenerated (baked), followed by a second round of pulse cleaning. Figure 48–6 shows the principles behind a Donaldson generic DPF cleaning station. It should be noted that any DPF cleaning station will only function on certain designated DPFs and that OEM service literature must be referenced before connecting a cleaning station to a DPF.

CAUTION:

An appropriate respirator (not just a particulate mask) should be worn when servicing DPF components. Submicron ash particulate is known to cause respiratory problems.

FIGURE 48–7 Donaldson generic DPF cleaning cart.

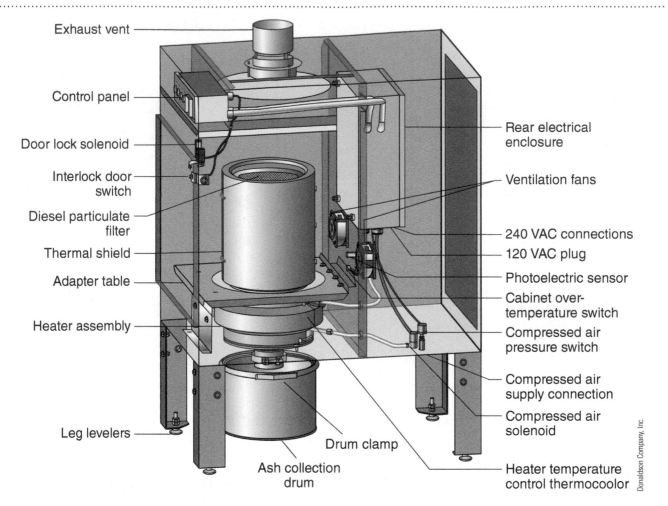

Exhaust vent
Control panel
Door lock solenoid
Interlock door switch
Diesel particulate filter
Thermal shield
Adapter table
Heater assembly
Leg levelers
Ash collection drum
Drum clamp
Rear electrical enclosure
Ventilation fans
240 VAC connections
120 VAC plug
Photoelectric sensor
Cabinet over-temperature switch
Compressed air pressure switch
Compressed air supply connection
Compressed air solenoid
Heater temperature control thermocoolor

Donaldson Company, Inc.

Three-Step Cleaning Process

The following step-by-step cleaning and evaluation process is used by one OEM when servicing DPFs once they have been removed from the chassis.

1. Visual inspection:

   Pass > Go to step 2.
   Fail > Scrap filter.

2. Pneumatic cleaning:

   Flow test and crack inspection.
   Acceptable filter > Final process and seal in package.
   Fail > Proceed to step 3.

3. High-temperature oven:

   High-temperature baking.
   Second pneumatic cleaning.
   Second flow test/crack inspection.
   Acceptable filter > Final process and seal in package.
   Fail > Scrap filter.

The OEM from which this procedure was sourced states that almost 75% of DPFs are only routed through the first two stages of the reconditioning procedure. They also state that 10% fail outright and 15% require the stage-three baking process to return them to serviceability.

Reasons for Scrapping DPFs

The melting point of the DPF ceramic filter substrate is 2,550°F (1,400°C). Melting the ceramic produces ash column voids that render the DPF ineffective. DPF filters should be scrapped if:

- Soot is observed on the outlet header (see **Figure 48–8**).
- There are visible cracks in the ceramic.
- Ceramic protrudes from can (high thermals).
- Channels appear rounded.
- Swirl pattern appears on inlet.

FIGURE 48–8 Soot on outlet header of a DPF substrate.

CAUTION:

Some OEMs (DDC for instance) oppose any type of field attempts to clean DPFs. They require DPF cores to be sent in and replaced with factory-reconditioned units. A change-out of a DDC DPF requires only 30 minutes downtime.

TECH TIP:

Following DPF replacement or cleaning, the DPF maintenance algorithm must be reset by accessing customer data programming fields in the controller that manages DPF cycles. This may be the ECM or an aftertreatment module, depending on the OEM.

DPF Service Routines

When troubleshooting DPF-related problems, make a habit of using the OEM diagnostic software linked to the OEM's SIS. In this way, you will ensure that you have the most up-to-date information available. **Figure 48–9** shows the DDDL screen display for a DPF set to receive a parked regen command.

Low-Temperature Filters

Low-temperature filters (LTFs) are aftermarket devices fitted to equipment that predates mandatory DPFs. Most are designed for passive regeneration and when used on equipment that runs at low loads, they tend to restrict easily. They are often installed onto pre-2007 school buses because this tends to be a politically

FIGURE 48–9 The DDDL diagnostic routines screen enabled for a DPF parked regeneration.

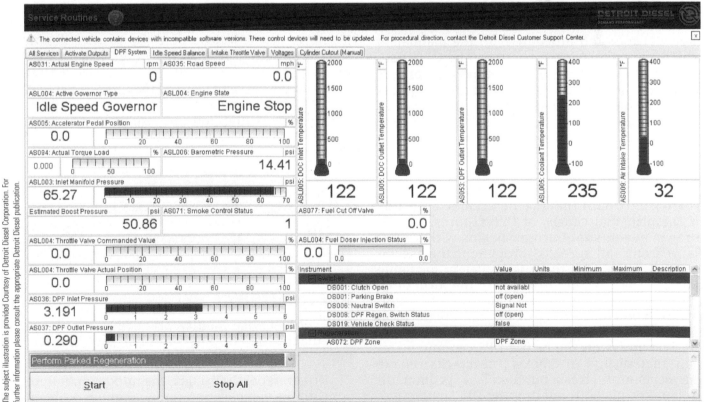

FIGURE 48–10 DPF used on a John Deere Tier 4 compliant engine.

sensitive application when it comes to emission controls. In many jurisdictions, operators may be eligible for grants to assist with the cost of retrofit LTFs. Some LTFs are of questionable effectiveness, but they are usually better than using nothing. They should be serviced in accordance with the manufacturer's requirements: Usually they are cleaned using a DPF cleaning station. **Figure 48–10** shows the DPF used on a John Deere Tier 4 compliant diesel engine.

DPF FAILURES

Since their introduction in MY 2007, DPF failures have caused much debate in the trucking industry. An outright DPF failure is costly and OEMs will do their best to deflect blame from their product and attribute it to the manner in which the engine was operated. The OEM usually has the final say on whether it approves a warranty claim; contesting a denial requires some knowledge of the operating principles of (see Chapter 47) and the thermal stresses that the DPF substrate is subjected to.

REGEN FAILURES

There is no doubt that regeneration itself is one of the principal causes of DPF failures. During a regen event, soot burn-off begins with a local flame front and spreads throughout the assembly, providing that there is sufficient available oxygen: The oxygen present is in the form of O_2 (diesels use lean burn combustion) and NO_x molecules. The combusting of PM can create local high temperature spikes, resulting in extreme thermal stress on the brittle DPF ceramic materials that results in cracks. The cracks relieve the mechanical stress, but high leakage immediately takes place, rendering the DPF ineffective.

The filter may not fragment until later, but the DPF becomes useless at the point it is cracked.

PARTIAL REGENERATIONS

Partial regenerations also contribute to DPF damage. Following a partial regen event, soot remaining in the DPF substrate may not be evenly distributed in the channels: Plugged channels, when subjected to high thermals, can result in radial stresses causing cracking. DPFs can also fail while being cleaned of ash. Cleaning of a DPF substrate requires baking it in an oven to remove anything that will burn, then pulsing pressured air to blow out the ash that remains. However, the baking process can also create high thermal stresses resulting in minute cracks that can later develop into fractures.

VIBRATION FAILURES

Another reason for DPF failure is excessive vibration. The DPF ceramic substrate is usually located close to the diesel engine (to take advantage of exhaust heat for regeneration), meaning that it is subject to both engine and chassis vibration. This can result in cracks to the brittle porous ceramic substrate.

OPERATIONAL ABUSE

DPFs also fail due to the way in which they are operated in a vehicle. A common reason for a DPF failure is that it has become too restricted with soot to be able to regenerate. In too many cases, the assumption is made that the DPF itself is at fault and the decision is made to replace it without properly diagnosing the root cause of the failure. This type of assumption can result in the replacement DPF failing within a short period of operation.

> **TECH TIP:**
> Make it your business to understand how DPFs are constructed and operate. This is the first step in understanding how they fail. To contest a DPF denied-warranty claim, you should understand what caused the failure.

PRELIMINARY CHECKS

It is good service facility practice to develop a DPF diagnostic checklist; the list should incorporate the following:

- Driver report. Discuss the mode of failure with the vehicle operator. A common problem is a vehicle that has been operated in a low-load, stop-start operation in which the temperature has not been able to reach the levels required for a regeneration event. A similar problem can occur if the vehicle is operated on the highway with a light load. It goes without saying that prolonged idling will also produce this problem.

- DPF warning light. DPF problems can result when a vehicle operator ignores the dash warning lights advising that a regeneration is required or overrides automatic regeneration cycles. When a DPF is approaching around a 50% soot load, the ECM begins to modify fuel injection timing with the objective of increasing exhaust temperatures to burn off entrapped particulates. If this process is interrupted or overridden, a dash warning light will be illuminated indicating a partial DPF restriction. At this point, it usually possible to clear the warning by reverting to a normal drive cycle.
- Prolonged warning light alerts. Continuing to ignore a DPF warning light alert will result in increased entrapped soot in the DPF and exhaust restriction. Depending on the specific model and the engine programming, when regeneration is postponed to the point where the DPF is 75% plugged, an automatic regeneration is usually not possible, and the regen event will have to be performed in a service facility using OEM software.
- Restriction at 95%. When DPF soot reaches around 95% restriction, the ECM will usually put the vehicle into derate or limp mode. This is required to protect the engine from damage due to the increased exhaust backpressure. In most cases this condition is caused by abusive operation of a vehicle, and the outcome usually requires DPF replacement.
- Check service records. If the vehicle has been recently serviced, check that the correct engine oil was used. The correct engine oil in vehicle MYs 2007 and beyond is SAE CJ-4, which is defined as low ash (less than 1%).

DIAGNOSTIC ROUTINES

Diagnostic checks should be undertaken using an EST loaded with the appropriate software. If the engine is not HD-OBD compliant, the only software that will enable diagnostic routines may be the OEM service diagnostic package,

but check with the manufacturer. Check for any engine DTCs, because a wide range of engine problems can create problems in the exhaust aftertreatment circuit. After checking for DTCs, visually inspect the components according to the following checklist.

1. Oil level: High oil levels can be caused by fuel contamination. Fuel contamination can result from repeated failed regeneration attempts. Odor is a good indicator of fuel-contaminated engine oil; ensure that the oil is changed if it is contaminated with fuel.
2. Oil specification: Ensure that the specified engine oil was used in the previous oil change. The only oils approved for MY 2007 DPF-equipped engines and later is SAE CJ-4 or CK-4. Both these oils are backward-compatible. MY 2017 and later diesel engines should use FA-4 engine lubricant.
3. DPF sensors: Check to ensure that these are functioning properly. In most cases, a defective sensor will log a code.
4. Inspect DPF pressure pipes: These should be free from visible external damage.
5. Check EGR circuit: This should be checked for visible external damage and by looking for logged codes.
6. General engine condition: Check for engine and turbocharger wear, leaking injectors, and all intake and exhaust system sensors.

SELECTIVE CATALYTIC REDUCTION (SCR)

All but Navistar and Caterpillar post-2010 highway diesel engines and most post-2011 off-highway diesels with more than 70 horsepower (52kW) are equipped with a **selective catalytic reduction (SCR)** system. From EPA MY 2013 onward, all domestic commercial diesel engines of greater than 70 BHP (52 kW) use SCR.

SCR uses aqueous **urea** (see Chapter 47) as a reduction agent; aqueous urea is known as **diesel exhaust fluid (DEF)** in North America and as **AdBlue** in Europe. The SCR system automatically injects DEF into the exhaust system, but it is essential to ensure that the DEF tank is sufficiently full. The layout of the SCR in the Bosch Denoxtronic system (outlined earlier in the discussion of the Bosch engine management system) is shown in Figure 40–5.

DEF LEVEL

For the SCR system to operate properly, the DEF level must be maintained. In light-duty diesel applications, the DEF tank is large enough that it only has to be refilled at each oil change service, but this is not usually possible in heavy-duty commercial trucks. DEF is consumed by diesel engines at variable rates influenced by such things as driving style, the weight of the load being hauled, vocational or off-highway operation, and a heavy accelerator foot. DEF temperature and level are monitored using sensors contained in a manifold assembly in which a pump and supply circuit is integrated. **Figure 48–11** shows a typical onboard DEF tank: The fill cap is always color-coded in blue.

Low DEF

The ECM monitors the fluid level in the DEF tank. Running a system check in the driver digital display electronics indicates to the driver whether the DEF level is OK or if it is less than half full. A message automatically displays when the DEF level is low and requires refilling. When this message appears, the DEF tank should be refilled.

DEF Trimback Strategy

When the vehicle is operated with the DEF level either low or contaminated, it defaults to a trimback mode in which road speed is limited. A typical trimback limits vehicle speed to 55 mph (89 km/h), dropping to 50 mph (80 km/h) with continued operation. Under low-DEF trimback operation, the truck should be driven with caution and the DEF replenished as soon as possible. Should the DEF tank become completely

FIGURE 48–11 A typical vehicle DEF tank with blue fill cap and sensor/pull-circuit manifold.

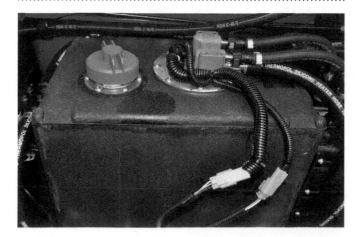

empty (or contaminated), the vehicle speed will be limited to idle speed once stopped.

The driver display unit is designed to display a sequence of messages regarding the amount of DEF available in the tank. A typical OEM systems check displays messages indicating the DEF available in the following sequence:

- OK
- Under 1/2 full
- Warning message displaying the mileage (kilometers) remaining as the fluid in the DEF tank nears empty with a predicted 800-mile (1,287-km) range. Vehicle drives normally.
- Warning message and audio alert as DEF projected driving distance drops below 300 miles (483 km), along with road speed trimback accompanied by a message posted to the driver display unit (DDU).
- Continued operation without refilling the DEF tank will result in the engine being limited to idle-only operation after refueling. At this point, it is required that a minimum of 1 gallon (3.8 L) of DEF be added to the tank to exit the idle-only mode, but the vehicle will still be in speed-limiting mode until the tank is refilled.
- To exit the vehicle speed-limiting or idle-only condition, refill the DEF tank; normal vehicle operation will resume only after the DEF tank is refilled.

DEF Consumption

DEF consumption is monitored. Time is managed in drive cycles usually of 4-hour duration if run continuously, or by key-on to key-off events that are less than 4 hours. For this reason, there could be a rapid progression from a safe operating condition to a trimback alert in the event of a problems such as a severe leak.

> **TECH TIP:**
>
> When refilling the DEF tank from empty, there may be a short delay before the ECM or emissions module detects the increased level of DEF. This has to occur before the trimback mode is exited and normal engine power resumes.

Filling the DEF Tank from a Container

Trucks with SCR are equipped with a DEF tank with a blue-capped fill port (see **Figure 48–12**), usually located next to the diesel fuel fill inlet. The tank can be filled using a nozzle at a DEF filling station (similar to fuel fill) or using a portable DEF container with a spout.

FIGURE 48–12 The DEF fill cap is always blue. Because this tank is on a Freightliner chassis, the cap is inscribed AdBlue; this is simply this OEM's way of saying DEF.

WARNING:

Do not put DEF in the fuel tank. This can result in damage and void the warranty.

TECH TIP:

Immediately wipe away any DEF that has spilled on painted surfaces with water and a damp cloth, to prevent damage to the paint.

DEF can be purchased at most OEM dealerships, truck service facilities, and all highway truck stops. Only DEF certified by the American Petroleum Institute (API) meeting ISO 22241 should be used in the DEF tank, so look for the API certification trademark on dispensers and containers. **Figure 48–13** shows a DEF filter that can help eliminate contaminants during DEF refilling operations.

WARNING:

Refill DEF in a well-ventilated area. When opening the cap on the DEF container, ammonia vapors may escape. Ammonia can mildly irritate skin, eyes, and mucous membranes. Inhaling ammonia vapors may cause burning to the eyes, throat, and nose and cause coughing and watery eyes.

FIGURE 48–13 A DEF filter can help ensure that the urea solution remains uncontaminated.

Use the following step-by-step procedure to refill the DEF tank using a portable container:

1. Remove the cap from the DEF container. Remove the spout from the bottle and insert the straw end into the bottle. Ensure that the arrow above the nut is aligned with the bottle handle and the small tube end extends into the far corner of the bottle. Twist the spout nut on the container until it is tight.
2. Open the DEF filler port on the vehicle by twisting open the blue cap counterclockwise.
3. Lift and hold the DEF container, without tipping, and insert the spout into the DEF filler port until the small black seal on the spout is fully seated into the DEF filler port.
4. While pouring the DEF into the tank, the fluid level in the container will be seen to drop.
5. When the vehicle DEF tank is full, the fluid level in the bottle will cease to drop. This indicates that the fluid is no longer flowing.

6. When the level in the DEF container has ceased to drop, return the container to a vertical position slightly below the DEF filler port and allow any DEF to drain from the spout. Do not attempt to continue to add DEF to the tank by shaking or repositioning the container to induce flow, because this can result in spillage and overfilling.

7. Once the spout has drained, remove it from the DEF filler port and reinstall the blue cap on the DEF filler port. Remove the spout from the DEF container and install the cap back on the bottle.

8. If the container has been emptied, recycle it and the spout. If some DEF remains in the container, retain it and the spout for later use. Ensure that the spout stays clean.

9. Use water and a damp cloth to wipe away any DEF that has spilled on painted surfaces.

DEF Refill from a Fuel Station Nozzle

Filling the DEF tank using a nozzle is similar to a normal fuel fill. The nozzle is designed to shut off automatically when the tank is full. Do not continue to fill the tank after shutoff, as this may cause spilling and overfill the tank, which can cause damage.

TECH TIP:

Some filling station nozzles may hinder the filling of a DEF tank due to a magnetic mechanism in the nozzle. This is not a problem with most North American–built 2010 and later vehicles. Where this is a problem, another refueling station or portable container will have to be used to fill the tank.

Filling DEF in Winter Conditions

DEF freezes at 12°F (–11°C) but that said, vehicles designed for operation in North America are equipped with an automatic preheating system. This allows the DEF system to function below 12°F (–11°C). When a DEF-equipped vehicle is not in operation for an extended period of time when temperatures are at or below 12°F (–11°C), the DEF tank may freeze. If the tank is overfilled and it freezes, it could be damaged. DO NOT OVERFILL.

DEF Storage

DEF should be stored away from direct sunlight and in temperatures between 23°F (–5°C) and 68°F (20°C). Always ensure that the DEF is protected from being exposed to temperatures below 12°F (–11°C). DEF containers should not be stored in the vehicle because, in the event of a leak, it can damage interior components and release an ammonia odor inside the vehicle. DEF should never be diluted with water or any other liquid. It is normal to smell an ammonia odor when removing the container or tank caps.

TECH TIP:

DEF is a nonflammable, nontoxic, colorless, and water-soluble liquid. However, DEF refills should always be undertaken in a well-ventilated area.

SINGLE-CANISTER DPF/DEF

One of the problems with most current aftertreatment device hardware is that it adds significant weight, bulk, and complexity to diesel exhaust systems. Cummins's recent introduction of its single-canister DPF/DEF **Ecoboost** module takes a big step toward addressing these problems. Weight and bulk reduction in the Ecoboost is 50% improved over twin-canister devices and because of this, helps the drive toward meeting EPA 2017 fuel efficiency and GHG reduction requirements. Ecoboost will be used on the ISX engines, but Cummins supplies aftertreatment solutions to at least two of its competitors.

The Ecoboost device uses single-pass gas flow, which minimizes exhaust backpressure. Because Cummins currently supplies aftertreatment hardware to several of its engine-building competitors, the Ecoboost and other single-canister aftertreatment modules are likely to become more common as manufacturers aim to reduce weight for EPA MY 2017.

EMISSIONS TAMPERING

Emissions tampering is commonly practiced today; every technician should be aware of the risks involved, because pleading innocence has not had much success when cases get to court. The definition of *emissions tampering*, as set by law in 1990, is: "to remove or render inoperative any device or element of design installed on or in a motor vehicle or motor vehicle engine in compliance with regulations." A better way of saying this is to describe *emissions tampering* as the act of doing anything that takes a vehicle out of its EPA/CARB certified state.

EPA 2007 TO 2018

The 2007 rule required North American OEMs to reduce NO$_x$ and PM emissions by more than 90% over 2001 levels. The EPA stated that the 2007 rule would eliminate 2.6 million tons of oxides of nitrogen (NO$_x$) emissions and 110,000 tons of PM released into the atmosphere each year by commercial vehicles. EPA 2007 was fine-tuned by EPA 2010, and additional regulations created by the Highway Diesel Rule set GHG and fuel efficiency standards for 2011, 2014, 2017, and 2020.

To meet these standards, OEMs introduced DPFs, SCR, EGR, and a full suite of computerized engine management controls. Along with the hardware and software required to manage emissions systems came the myth that anything that minimized emissions must do so at the expense of fuel efficiency. The bottom line is that even minor modifications to today's sophisticated, computer-controlled engines affect reliability and longevity, inevitably creating costs that far exceed any modest fuel savings that might be realized.

DPF DELETE

One of the more common tampering procedures in the heavy-duty market today is the removal of a DPF. **DPF delete** is illegal, but despite this, an Internet search will showcase many different ways of doing it: The procedure usually consists of a software package and instructions on how to physically remove the DPF. The physical removal of a DPF has little effect on the engine combustion dynamics, but eliminating the DPF sensors can result in engines running at higher than specified temperatures, greatly increasing the thermal stress on all engine components and significantly reducing engine longevity. In addition, the minuscule fuel savings that can be achieved by a DPF delete relate to the fuel required to effect a DPF regeneration cycle. Given that the fine for removing a DPF currently is set at $37,500, there is little to justify the risks involved.

INDUSTRY MISCONCEPTIONS

Perhaps the greatest misconception about emissions tampering is that it increases engine performance and fuel economy. The opposite is almost universally true. The bottom line is that today's engines with OEM calibrations achieve better fuel efficiency and better power than older designs, despite what any old-timers might say. Manipulating OEM calibrations, software, and hardware results in negative performance, reduced longevity, and fractioned resale value. Modern diesel engines run head-to-head with those of 20 years ago not only outperform the oldsters by a considerable margin, but also, in terms of highway mileage, last nearly twice as long.

> **TECH TIP:**
> Tampering with emission control devices and programming not only voids OEM warranty but also nullifies most vehicle insurance contracts.

WHO PAYS?

When a truck with tampered emission controls is discovered by authorities, the vehicle owner isn't the only one on the hook for a fine. Enforcement agencies can levy fines on service providers who perform tampering and also on those who identify tampering infringements during emission system maintenance and fail to bring the vehicle into compliance.

The bottom line is that a service facility can be busted without actually having tampered with the emission controls on a truck. A service provider that ignores an obvious violation is fined as if it had actually performed the tampering, and at $37,500 per incident, this can be costly.

ALTERATIONS

The EPA language on tampering states that alterations made to an engine and emission system post-tampering, whether legal or illegal, that do not bring the unit back into compliance are violations. An attempt to repair a vehicle emission control system that fails to bring it back into compliance can result in a fine if not reported to the vehicle owner and EPA. It is essential that any service provider know this, because a well-meant attempt to correct tampering that fails can result in a fine. Bottom line: Never attempt to partially repair a tampered system unless it can be tested to meet the original EPA standard.

TECH TIP:

Service providers are currently not liable for tampering penalties when performing nonemission-related service on a vehicle that is later discovered to exhibit tampering—but if the provider touches anything on the engine or emission control system, then the noncompliant conditions must be either repaired or reported. Ignoring an illuminated check engine light is considered sufficient to make a service provider liable.

CAUTION:

There is no statute of limitations when it comes to a truck's emission systems. Illegal alterations to a 1989 tractor are punished with the same fines as are changes to a 2015 tractor.

SHOP POLICY FOR EMISSIONS TAMPERING

It makes sense for shops to have a clearly stated shop procedure that should kick in when tampering is evident on a truck. When tampering is discovered while work is being done on an engine, service technicians should immediately notify the customer that the emissions system has been tampered with and that the shop has a legal requirement to bring the vehicle back into compliance. With ever more advanced emission systems being introduced every year, the EPA advises that education is critical in every area of the industry. Tampering with emission systems will never be eradicated, but the objective is limit fines to those who have knowingly broken the law rather than those who have accidentally infringed it.

FIELD TESTING OF SMOKE DENSITY

Field testing for emissions refers to any testing performed after an engine series has been EPA certified. Although precertification exhaust emissions standards on diesel engines are ever more demanding, the standards that field-tested diesel engines currently are required to meet are much less stringent than those required of gasoline-fueled, spark-ignited engines. This is because most field testing currently used

in North America is based on an outdated SAE standard known as **J1667**. Published in 1991, the SAE J1667 standard was based on a trucking world that used mostly hydromechanical diesel engines. Very few of these engines remain on our roads today, but J1667 remains very much alive.

J1667 TESTING

J1667 test requirements address only visible smoke emissions, and the test procedures are entirely based on the highway diesel engines commonly used in the 1980s. You might ask why this is so. Although the EPA plays hardball with the diesel engine manufacturers prior to certification, field enforcement of highway diesel engine emissions is left to state and municipal jurisdictions. Their enforcement agencies are caught in a squeeze between the voting public, who are demanding tougher standards, and the hard fact that aggressive enforcement and tough penalties can hurt them economically. J1667 exhaust emissions measurement is based on a smoke opacity test. The tool used to measure smoke opacity is an opacity meter.

OPACITY METERS

Opacity meters are simple to use and usually require that the unit's sensor head probe be fitted to the outlet of the exhaust pipe. Two different types are used: partial flow and full flow. In the partial flow type, during the test procedure, a portion of the exhaust gas flow is diverted to a sensing chamber in which the opacity of the smoke can be read by the light sensor in the head assembly. A partial flow opacity meter is shown in **Figure 48–14**. The full flow type is more commonly used and makes the opacity measurement directly at the stack outlet. **Figure 48–15** shows the operating principle of a full flow opacity test meter.

Light Extinction

Partial and full flow opacity meters are classified as light extinction test instruments: A beam of light from a light-emitting diode (LED) is directed at a photo diode sensor through the exhaust gas stream. The amount of light blocked from the photo diode sensor is determined by the particulate density in the engine exhaust. The higher the particulate density, the less light is capable of penetrating it to be read by the sensor. Smoke density is expressed as a percentage reading by

FIGURE 48–14 Partial flow opacity meter.

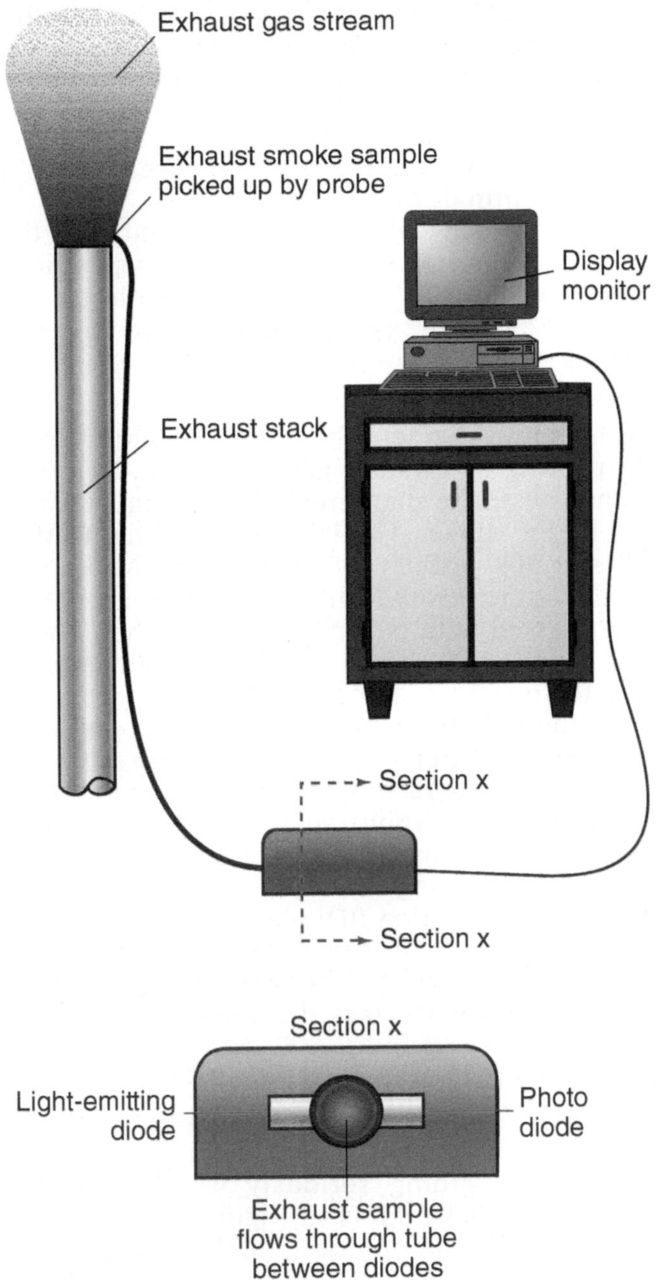

Exhaust gas stream

Exhaust smoke sample picked up by probe

Display monitor

Exhaust stack

Section x

Section x

Section x

Light-emitting diode

Photo diode

Exhaust sample flows through tube between diodes

FIGURE 48–15 Full flow opacity meter.

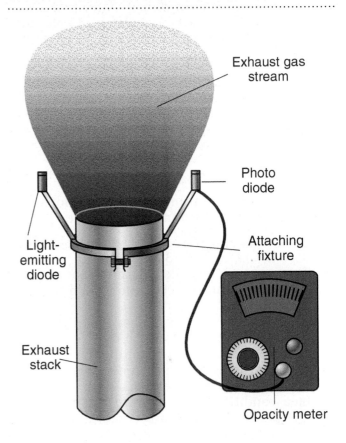

Exhaust gas stream

Photo diode

Light-emitting diode

Attaching fixture

Exhaust stack

Opacity meter

the opacity meter. In most cases, the opacity meter is equipped with an extension handle for the sensor head, so the device can be placed at the exhaust stack outlet by a technician working at ground level.

Opacity meter readings are displayed in percentage readings, and the actual readings must always be factored with engine power output and the exhaust system outlet pipe diameter. Most should produce accurate results regardless of weather conditions, and many will log

the data electronically. The data logged into the opacity meter can be hard-copy printed or transferred to personal computer (PC) or Web-based systems for analysis. Manufacturers of opacity meters claim accuracy factors within 2% and programmed response times within 1 second. Any opacity meter can be used to evaluate smoke density in diesel smoke. However, those used for official testing and to enforce compliance must be approved and have PC-managed and logged test sequences.

PERFORMING J1667 TESTING

In 1997, the EPA recommended that all jurisdictions adopt the SAE J1667 procedure for the testing of heavy-duty diesel vehicles, perhaps because it would promote some consistency in test standards between different jurisdictions. The test routine outlined here adheres closely to that performed by compliance enforcement agencies. Although the emissions standards do vary by jurisdiction and year of manufacture of the truck, there is some consistency nationwide, and recently the maximum opacity standards have been reduced in many jurisdictions.

Ambient environmental conditions can have some impact on smoke density, and changes in air density influence the operation of any internal combustion engine. Air density is influenced by ambient temperature: generally, high air density will result in higher air-fuel ratios, which will tend to produce lower smoke opacity readings. For this reason, SAE J1667 imposes restrictions on the environmental conditions during the administration of an "official" snap acceleration test.

Environmental Conditions

The following environmental conditions are required when performing a J1667 test:

- Temperature in the test area must be between 35°F (2°C) and 86°F (30°C).
- Testing must not take place outdoors when there is visible precipitation such as rain, snow, or fog.
- Testing must not take place when the temperature is at or below the dew point, such as during fog or high-humidity conditions.
- Vehicles using downward-directed exhaust systems should be tested over ground surface conditions that are not dusty, so that dirt particulates are not combined with the exhaust gas being measured.

Snap Test

Each J1667 throttle snap consists of a three-phase cycle that must be precisely executed by the test administrator:

1. Accelerator is snapped to high idle and held for 1 to 4 seconds or until prompted by the opacity meter to release.
2. Engine rpm must be allowed to drop to the specified low idle speed.
3. Engine must run at the specified low idle for a minimum of 5 seconds and a maximum of 45 seconds before initiating the next snap as prompted by the opacity meter.

SAE J1667 Test Cycle

The SAE J1667 test cycle consists of four phases and, again, must be precisely executed by the test administrator:

1. Preliminary snaps. Three full snaps are required to clear the exhaust system of loose particles and precondition the vehicle.
2. Official snaps. Three official snaps should be undertaken as prompted by test instrument software.

3. Validation. The difference between the highest and the lowest maximum opacity readings of the three official test snaps should be within five opacity percentage points. If the difference is less than 5%, the meter software will compute the average. If the difference is greater than 5%, additional official snaps must be undertaken, up to a maximum of nine.
4. Drift factor. Validation is required that the drift between three official test cycles does not exceed 2% opacity. A variation greater than ±2% will result in an invalid test.

Stack Dimensions

Exhaust pipe diameter has an effect on the opacity reading of exhaust gas. Before undertaking a snap test, the diameter of the exhaust stack has to be known. For instance, an engine that tests at 30% opacity when tested with a 3-inch exhaust stack would only measure 20% opacity when tested with a 5-inch tailpipe. This is why you have to input the stack diameter dimension into the opacity meter software.

Although there are exceptions, because horsepower rating usually determines the stack diameter, it is recommended that the horsepower rating be inputted into the opacity test instrument before the exhaust pipe diameter. Horsepower rating is often specified on the engine identification (ID) plate (aka *option plate* or *data plate*) or in the electronic service tool (EST) accessible read-only data. **Table 48–3** correlates power with stack diameter.

Evaluating J1667 Test Results

If a truck fails a J1667 snap test, a quick glance at the emitted exhaust smoke will suggest that there is something seriously wrong with the engine, especially if it is an engine manufactured after 1991. If the engine is hydromechanically

TABLE 48–3 Horsepower and Recommended Exhaust Pipe Diameter

Rated Engine Power (BHP)	Rated Engine Power (kW)	Exhaust Pipe Diameter (Inches)	Exhaust Pipe Diameter (Millimeters)
Less than 101	Less than 75	2	51
101 to 200	75 to 149	3	76
201 to 300	150 to 224	4	102
301 or more	225 or more	5	127

managed and manufactured before 1991, the cause is frequently in the boost management system, which is a circuit often managed by an aneroid device.

Current Throttle Snap Cutpoints

There is some variance on the throttle snap cutpoint, because J1667 is used by state, provincial, or municipal enforcement agencies—or not used. Those jurisdictions enforcing J1667 will generally use only the throttle snap test, because it is easy and can be done with the vehicle parked so long as the engine is running and at operating temperature. The most common opacity cutpoints used for compliance citations at present are:

- Engine model years before 1991: maximum throttle snap opacity: 55%
- Engine model years after 1991: maximum throttle snap opacity: 40%

Table 48–4 shows the original 1991 J1667 specifications. Most jurisdictions using J1667 have made them slightly tougher since ... but only by a little.

Opacity Readings

Because J1667 is used for compliance testing of diesel engine emissions, the compliance test profiles have to be simple and not vulnerable in court if offenders decide to fight fines. That is why the snap test is used. However, if you have an opacity meter, you can also look at some of the other criteria that were components of J1667. Smoke opacity readings of 5% or less are not easily observed. When using an opacity meter, it is important to meticulously

observe the test procedures if any credence is to be given to the results. There are a number of manufacturers of J1667 opacity test equipment, but the procedure for undertaking the tests must adhere to J1667. **Figure 48–16** shows the sequence required to perform a J1667 test using a Wager 6500 unit.

Gas Analysis

Exhaust gas analysis is performed only in major OEM dealerships because of the cost of the test equipment and the requirement to have the OEM diagnostic software to undertake repairs. **Figure 48–17** shows a multi-gas analyzer and **Figure 48–18** the sensor head used to draw test samples of exhaust smoke for analysis.

SMOKE ANALYSIS

Any truck diesel engine that fails an opacity snap test has a *severe* smoking problem, one that could not pass unnoticed under any circumstances. Many sick engines emitting large amounts of visible smoke can still pass the opacity standards defined in J1667 testing. Chapter 50 on troubleshooting explains in some detail how to evaluate smoke emission from diesel engines, but in this section we quickly outline some examples. The appearance of exhaust smoke to the observer's eye depends on the *state* of the emission. Physical matter has three states: vapor or gaseous, liquid, and solid.

- Gaseous emission. To the observer's eye, this is "clean" exhaust smoke. And it may be clean—or contaminated with noxious pollutant in a vapor state. Because light is not affected by passing through a gas, we see nothing when we look at exhaust in a 100% gas state exiting the stack(s).
- Liquid emission. To the observer's eye, liquid condensing in the exhaust gas stream appears white. When light attempts to pass through condensing liquid droplets in the exhaust, it either *reflects* or *refracts,* making it appear white to the observer.
- Solid emission. To the observer's eye, solids (we call these *particulates*) contained in the exhaust gas stream appear black. When light attempts to pass through particulate suspended in the exhaust gas, it is blocked, making it appear black to the observer.

TABLE 48–4 Original (1991) J1667 Specifications

Engine Operating Mode	Maximum Opacity (Smoke Density)
Idle speed	10%
High-idle speed	15%
Rated speed and low (peak power)	20% (requires chassis dynamometer)
Engine lug	25% (requires chassis dynamometer)
Maximum puff on throttle snap	50% (transient response to throttle snap)
Full acceleration	30% (requires chassis dynamometer)
Cold start at 0°F (−17°C)	Specific to OEM in original J1667

Note: Current compliance specs vary by jurisdiction.

Refer to the section titled "Smoke Analysis" in Chapter 50 for a more detailed look at the causes of diesel engine smoking.

FIGURE 48–16 J1667 test procedure using a Wager 6500 opacity meter.

SNAP ACCELERATION TEST

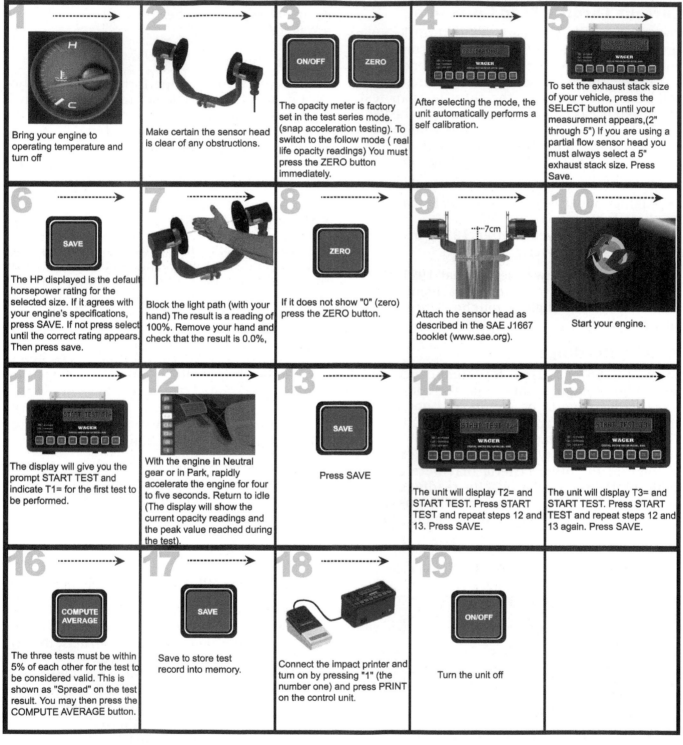

1. Bring your engine to operating temperature and turn off

2. Make certain the sensor head is clear of any obstructions.

3. The opacity meter is factory set in the test series mode. (snap acceleration testing). To switch to the follow mode (real life opacity readings) You must press the ZERO button immediately.

4. After selecting the mode, the unit automatically performs a self calibration.

5. To set the exhaust stack size of your vehicle, press the SELECT button until your measurement appears,(2" through 5") If you are using a partial flow sensor head you must always select a 5" exhaust stack size. Press Save.

6. The HP displayed is the default horsepower rating for the selected size. If it agrees with your engine's specifications, press SAVE. If not press select until the correct rating appears. Then press save.

7. Block the light path (with your hand) The result is a reading of 100%. Remove your hand and check that the result is 0.0%,

8. If it does not show "0" (zero) press the ZERO button.

9. Attach the sensor head as described in the SAE J1667 booklet (www.sae.org). 7cm

10. Start your engine.

11. The display will give you the prompt START TEST and indicate T1= for the first test to be performed.

12. With the engine in Neutral gear or in Park, rapidly accelerate the engine for four to five seconds. Return to idle (The display will show the current opacity readings and the peak value reached during the test).

13. Press SAVE

14. The unit will display T2= and START TEST. Press START TEST and repeat steps 12 and 13. Press SAVE.

15. The unit will display T3= and START TEST. Press START TEST and repeat steps 12 and 13 again. Press SAVE.

16. The three tests must be within 5% of each other for the test to be considered valid. This is shown as "Spread" on the test result. You may then press the COMPUTE AVERAGE button.

17. Save to store test record into memory.

18. Connect the impact printer and turn on by pressing "1" (the number one) and press PRINT on the control unit.

19. Turn the unit off

Wager Company

FIGURE 48–17 A multi-gas exhaust emissions analyzer.

FIGURE 48–18 The sensor head used with a multi-gas analyzer.

AFTERTREATMENT DEVICE REMOVAL AND REPLACEMENT

This procedure primarily references Cummins EPA MY 2010 and later aftertreatment device removal and replacement (R&R) on a Freightliner chassis. The procedure for other OEMs' engines and chassis will be similar. The method is outlined here so that it can be understood by technicians. It is not intended to replace OEM service literature, which should always be referenced when working on emission control devices.

WARNING:

Exhaust aftertreatment device (ATD) internal temperatures can remain dangerously hot for hours after the engine is shut down. This can cause serious injury and ignite combustible materials. Technicians must wear the appropriate PPE.

Precautions:

- Allow the ATD to cool before handling it; be especially careful when opening a canister to expose the DPF.
- Do not place the ATD close to flammable gases or combustible materials that may come into contact with hot interior parts.
- Component alignment is critical. Using a paint pen, mark every component's position before disassembly. Failure to do this will result in improper assembly and may result in leaks or damage.

DPF REMOVAL

Refer to **Figure 48–19** to follow this procedure.

1. Shut down the engine and chock the tires.
2. Ensure that the DPF is cool enough to work on; verify this by using an infrared temperature gun.
3. Make alignment marks on all of the components to be removed.
4. Disconnect the wiring harness to the DPF control module.
5. Remove the spherical clamp and gasket that connect the inlet pipe to the DPF. Discard the clamp and gasket.
6. Remove the spherical clamp and gasket that connect the DPF to the mix tube. Discard the clamp and gasket.

FIGURE 48–19 ATD (DPF) component identification for purposes of removal and installation.

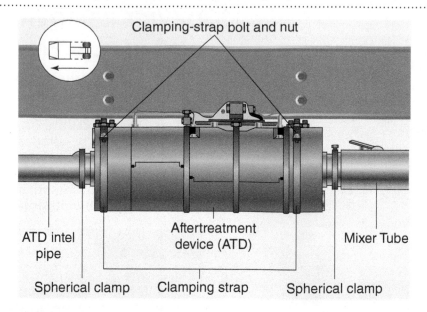

Clamping-strap bolt and nut

ATD intel pipe

Aftertreatment device (ATD)

Mixer Tube

Spherical clamp   Clamping strap   Spherical clamp

7. Position a jack under the DPF assembly; secure it with straps.
8. Remove the fasteners from the clamp straps.
9. Lower the DPF assembly on the jack.
10. Perform a thorough visual inspection and make a list of any fasteners, clamps, and gaskets that will require replacement.

DPF INSTALLATION

1. Position the DPF assembly onto the jack and secure it with straps. This is important because it must be precisely aligned for reinstallation, a task that will be made more difficult if the DPF assembly shifts around.
2. Move the jack under the truck or vehicle and raise it into position.
3. Install the new clamp straps and align and position the assembly in the straps. Install the clamp fasteners but do not tighten them at this time.
4. Connect the DPF to its inlet pipe and install a new spherical clamp and gasket; do not tighten at this time.
5. Connect the DPF outlet to the mix tube and install a new spherical clamp and gasket; do not tighten at this time.
6. Carefully check the alignment of all components. Adjust the clamp straps as necessary, then incrementally torque them to the OEM specification.
7. Next, tighten the spherical clamps at the connections to the DPF inlet pipe and torque them to the OEM specification.

8. Connect the wiring harnesses to the DPF control module.
9. Remove the straps to the jack.

SCR REMOVAL

Refer to **Figure 48–20** to follow this procedure.

1. Shut down the engine and chock the wheels. Ensure that the SCR assembly is cool enough to work on; verify this using an infrared temperature gun.
2. Make alignment marks on all of the components to be removed.
3. Disconnect the wiring harness to the NO_x sensor.
4. Remove the NO_x sensor module from the frame rail bracket and secure it to the SCR catalyst. Refer to **Figure 48–21**.
5. Disconnect the wiring harness to the control module on the SCR catalyst.
6. Remove the marmon clamp that connects the SCR catalyst to the mixer tube. Discard the clamp.
7. Remove the wide-band clamp that connects the SCR catalyst to the exhaust pipe. Discard the clamp.
8. Position a jack under the assembly and secure the SCR assembly with straps.
9. Remove the fasteners from the four clamp straps.
10. Remove and discard the clamping straps and hardware.
11. Lower the unit onto the floor.

FIGURE 48–20 SCR catalyst component identification for purposes of removal and installation.

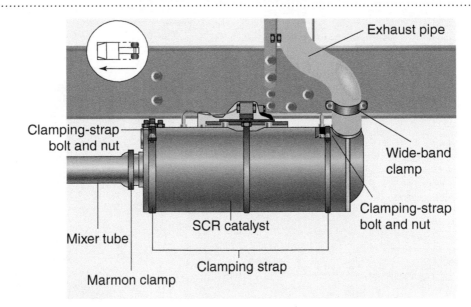

FIGURE 48–21 NO$_x$ sensor module identification for purposes of removal and installation.

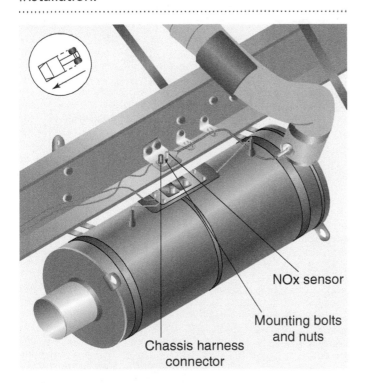

SCR INSTALLATION

1. Position the assembly onto the jack and secure it with straps.
2. Install new clamp straps onto the SCR assembly.
3. Slide the jack under the truck and raise the SCR assembly into position.
4. Move the assembly in the clamp straps, and install the fasteners, leaving them loose.
5. Connect the SCR catalyst to the mixer tube and install a new marmon clamp and gasket. Do not tighten at this time.
6. Connect the SCR catalyst to the exhaust pipe. Install a new wide-band clamp, leaving it loose at this time.
7. Check the alignment of all components. Make any adjustments required to the clamp straps and then incrementally torque to the OEM specification.
8. Torque the marmon clamp at the connection of the SCR catalyst and the mixer tube and torque to the OEM specification.
9. Install the NO$_x$ sensor module on the frame rail, then connect it to the chassis electrical harness.
10. Connect the wiring harness to the control box on the SCR catalyst.
11. Unstrap the SCR assembly and remove the jack.
12. Start the engine and check for leaks.

AFTERTREATMENT SYSTEM ELECTRONICS

The aftertreatment hardware on all post-2010 diesel engines is electronically managed, so any technician working on such systems must know how to navigate electronic wiring schematics. The wiring circuit for a DD-Series engine is shown in **Figure 48–22**.

FIGURE 48–22 Wiring schematic for a DD15 exhaust gas aftertreatment circuit.

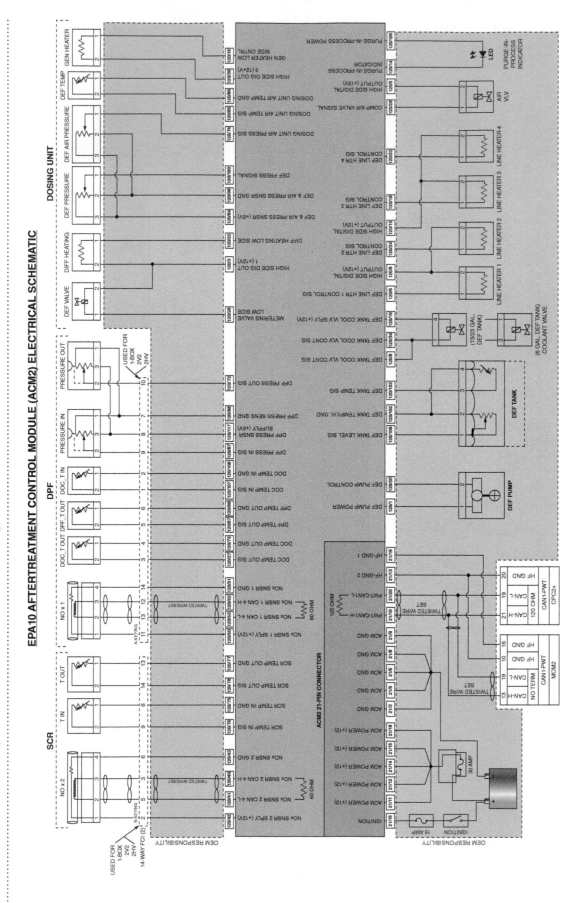

SUMMARY

- Most diesel engine subsystems are interconnected, so that a small malfunction in one circuit can result in increased emissions.
- To meet emissions compliance standards, diesel engines today rely on exhaust gas recirculation (EGR), NO_x adsorber catalysts, oxidation and reduction catalytic converters, diesel particulate filters (DPFs), and selective catalytic reduction (SCR), along with computer control of combustion.
- EGR system malfunctions have accounted for more than their share of work orders since their introduction in EPA 2004. EGR circuits should be regularly inspected and EGR coolers serviced.
- EGR cooler cores may be cleaned using steam, mineral spirits, or ultrasonic baths. Ultrasonic baths tend to produce better results.
- When fluids such as fuel, oil, and coolant get into the EGR circuit, the EGR heat exchanger can become restricted.
- The DPF entraps soot particles. The entrapped soot is then combusted in what is known as a regeneration process. DPF systems are also known by the term *regeneration systems*.
- DPF regeneration can be passive (occurs during normal vehicle operation) or active (requires dosing with fuel and sometimes spark ignition).
- In addition to regeneration, DPFs have to be removed periodically for cleaning and ash removal. Ash residues are what remains after combustion of soot.
- DPFs are cleaned in a specialized cleaning station.
- All post-2010 highway trucks except for those manufactured by Navistar use an SCR system to reduce NO_x emissions back to elemental nitrogen and oxygen.
- SCR doses the exhaust with aqueous urea known as diesel exhaust fluid (DEF).

- An SCR system relies on DEF to function, so a number of mandatory failsafe mechanisms are incorporated into the circuit. When the DEF level becomes low, the SCR system initiates progressive trimbacks that ultimately can limit engine operation to idle speed only.
- J1667 exhaust opacity field testing is required in many jurisdictions. It tests for visible smoke only. Compliance is mandatory regardless of vehicle age.
- Opacity meters use a light extinction method of measuring exhaust gas density; this consists of directing a light beam through the exhaust gas and using a sensor that measures the amount of light that succeeds in penetrating it.
- Opacity meters produce readings indicated as percentage density: The higher the percentage reading, the higher the smoke density.
- Some opacity meter tests require the use of a dynamometer, but SAE J1667 throttle snap testing is a field test that can be performed with no load on the engine. Throttle snap tests are commonly used by roadside enforcement officers because it can be performed at no load.
- Actual opacity compliance standards have been modified slightly by state and provincial jurisdictions over the years, but do not come close to meeting EPA new engine certification standards.
- The EPA can levy a fine of up to $37,500 per incident for tampering with engine emissions control devices. The same fine can be levied on a person for failure to report such an incident; this can be something as innocent as ignoring a check engine light.
- When removing and replacing exhaust gas aftertreatment system hardware, it is important to check and follow the procedures in the OEM service literature. It may also be necessary to update ECM or aftertreatment module files.

REVIEW QUESTIONS

1. Which of the following exhaust gas test instruments uses a light extinction principle to measure smoke density?
   a. CVA sampler
   b. Seven-gas analyzer
   c. Two-gas analyzer
   d. Opacity meter

2. When a diesel engine is operated without a thermostat(s), which of the following categories of noxious exhaust emissions is likely to increase?
   a. Oxides of nitrogen
   b. Carbon dioxide
   c. Ozone
   d. Hydrocarbons

3. Which method of EGR cooler cleaning tends to produce the best results?
   a. Ultrasonic bath
   b. Power washing
   c. Steam cleaning
   d. Mineral spirits soaking

4. Which SAE standard defines the guidelines for testing diesel engine exhaust opacity emissions?
   a. J1587
   b. J1667
   c. J1708
   d. J1939

5. Technician A states that advancing the static timing of a fuel injection pump by 1 crank degree can increase NO_x emission. Technician B states that retarding static timing could produce higher HC emissions. Who is correct?
   a. Technician A only
   b. Technician B only
   c. Both A and B
   d. Neither A nor B

6. Technician A states that the maximum puff test when using an opacity meter can be performed with the vehicle stationary and zero load on the engine. Technician B states that the full acceleration test when using an opacity meter is a throttle snap test that can be performed with the vehicle stationary. Who is correct?
   a. Technician A only
   b. Technician B only
   c. Both A and B
   d. Neither A nor B

7. Technician A states that DPFs can run up to 8 hours in a linehaul diesel engine before regeneration is required. Technician B states that some DPFs must be removed from the vehicle for cleaning on a weekly basis. Who is correct?
   a. Technician A only
   b. Technician B only
   c. Both A and B
   d. Neither A nor B

8. Technician A states that most DPF regeneration in highway diesel engines should occur as passive regeneration. Technician B states that DPF active regeneration cycles usually require the injection of fuel upstream from the DPF. Who is correct?
   a. Technician A only
   b. Technician B only
   c. Both A and B
   d. Neither A nor B

9. How many official throttle snaps are required when performing a J1667 opacity test?
   a. One
   b. Two
   c. Three
   d. Four

10. An (older) hydromechanically managed, diesel-powered truck is road tested and produces a puff of smoke at each upshift. Which of the following devices should be checked out first?
    a. Shift tower air signal
    b. Aneroid
    c. Turbocharger wastegate
    d. Governor torque trim spring

11. Which of the following smoke control devices is *not* an aneroid?
    a. DDC throttle delay cylinder
    b. Caterpillar AFRC
    c. Mack Trucks puff limiter
    d. Cummins AFC

12. Which of the following would be the most likely cause of too-frequent DPF regeneration cycles?
    a. Engine running too hot
    b. Ash buildup in the DPF
    c. Long uphill full-power hauls
    d. Prolonged use of cruise control

13. What color is the cap on a DEF tank?
    a. Pink
    b. Amber
    c. Clear
    d. Blue

14. What is the maximum fine that can be levied if you work on a vehicle engine and fail to report suspected emissions system tampering?
    a. $100
    b. $1,000
    c. $10,000
    d. $37,500

15. What can result if a shop attempts to repair a truck diesel engine emission control system malfunction and fails to bring it back into compliance?
    a. A $37,500 fine
    b. A fired technician
    c. An unpaid bill
    d. All of the above

16. What is the J1939 source address of an exhaust gas aftertreatment module?
    a. SA 03
    b. SA 37
    c. SA 61
    d. SA 128

49

FAILURE ANALYSIS

OBJECTIVES

After studying this chapter, you should be able to:

- Organize the evidence produced by an engine failure.
- Identify the facts associated with an engine failure.
- Analyze the facts to produce findings.
- Distinguish consequential damage from root cause(s).
- Organize the findings to define the root cause of the failure.
- Communicate findings to a work order.
- Develop a repair strategy that prevents a recurrence.
- Interpret B-life and identify how the terms *B10*, *B50*, and *Bx* are used by engine OEMs.
- Analyze failures on some failed engine components, including pistons, rings, rod and main friction bearings, cylinder sleeves/liners, crankshafts, valvetrains, turbochargers, and injectors.

KEY TERMS

abrasive wear	coincidental damage	ferrous metals	scuffing
adhesive wear	collateral damage	fretting	spalling
alloy	contact stress fatigue	glazing	steel
arcing	corrosion	gumming	stress raiser
B-life	creep	lacquering	thermal failure
beach marks	ductile	metallurgy	torched piston
brittle	erosion	pitting	
cavitation	etching	root cause	

INTRODUCTION

Failure analysis is all about problem sourcing and solving. It is about getting to the root cause of a failure and ensuring that it does not repeat itself. For instance, if an 18-gauge electrical wire is overloaded with current due to a short circuit, we know that it will likely overheat, tripping a circuit breaker and possibly melting the insulation on the wire. If the repair plan was simply to replace the damaged wire with a thicker 12-gauge wire, it would be just a matter of time before the failure recurred, because the source of the original problem was not repaired. The job of the technician is to determine the **root cause** of any failure. The root cause is the source of a failure in our example, which is a short circuit. The technician's task should be to source the cause of the high current draw, not simply replace the most evident failed component in hopes that the failure will not recur. The molten insulation on the wire in this example is known as **coincidental damage**: It is also referred to as **collateral damage**.

Failure analysis training requires learning a structured approach to problem solving. Technicians must learn to distinguish between causes and results. They must learn how to analyze evidence. To develop skillful failure analysis techniques, technicians must learn how to:

- Find and focus on facts
- Eliminate collateral effects of the root cause
- Analyze the facts to produce findings
- Communicate the findings to a report (work order)
- Develop a repair strategy that prevents a recurrence

Failure analysis in itself is a process and should take place in five steps:

1. Observe and organize the evidence of the failure.
2. Identify the facts that have contributed to the failure.
3. Determine the causes of the failure.
4. Analyze the facts and causes of the failure.
5. Communicate the root causes of the failure.

Caterpillar defines the term *failure analysis* as "a thoughtful review of product and environmental facts which leads to identification of root causes of product problems." Its definition emphasizes *facts* and *root causes*. Both are keys to developing an effective failure analysis process.

The root cause of a failure is the specific condition that initiated a failure. Root cause has to be the focal point of failure analysis. The challenge for the technician is to eliminate collateral damage evidence while zeroing in to identify the root cause of a failure.

FAILURE ANALYSIS TRAINING

Developing failure analysis skills is not something learned overnight, because experience and exposure to failed systems and components are required. However, while experience is a component of developing failure analysis skills, so is training. Technicians should also be aware of the fact that advanced failure analysis can often require lab analysis and equipment not normally available in the typical service facility. Broadly speaking, failure analysis training falls into two areas:

- The technician must first gain an elementary understanding of some of the basic principles of metallurgy, fracture, wear, and visual examination of failed components.
- Next, the technician must learn structured methods for conducting failure analysis procedures and learn to eliminate collateral damage factors. Poor failure analysis results in a repair strategy that focuses on collateral damage because the root cause has not been identified, leading to a recurrence.

TECH TIP:

A diesel engine powering a highway truck and achieving a relatively commonplace 1,000,000 miles (1,600,000 km) will have produced as many power strokes in each of its engine cylinders as the human heart beats during five life spans. Unlike the human heart, the diesel engine can be rebuilt to reproduce that longevity once again. However, the success of an engine rebuild procedure depends on the skill of the technician in determining the cause of a failure and quality of replaced components.

STRUCTURED FAILURE ANALYSIS

The technician who has had many years experience of diesel engine technology has also probably developed an inventory of failure analysis profiles that make identifying root causes of a problem easy. With such a person, all it may take is a quick glance at a failed component to classify a failure. For those who do not have years of hands-on knowledge, it is a safer bet to use a more structured approach. A structured method for conducting failure analysis can be organized into eight steps.

1. State the problem clearly.
2. Check repair history and service records.
3. Observe and record the facts.
4. Eliminate collateral damage.
5. Analyze the facts.
6. Identify possible and probable root cause(s).
7. Communicate the conclusions (work order/ warranty/ customer).
8. Perform the repairs required.

Skipping a step, or performing steps out of sequence, is likely to result in a failure to identify the root cause of a problem. This means that the resulting repair strategy will be flawed because collateral damage will be repaired while the root cause is overlooked. This results in comebacks, unnecessarily high invoices, policy adjustments to work orders, downtime, and dissatisfied customers.

Failure analysis is necessarily a process that relies on facts to determine events and zero in on the root cause of system and component failures. Facts have to be located in the material evidence observed on failed components. The technician is then tasked with interpreting the facts to identify the events that produced the facts, and this must include an examination of the vehicle repair history. Finally, all this data should be organized in a logical sequence so that the root cause can be identified.

PRINCIPLES OF FAILURE ANALYSIS

As indicated a little earlier, in order to better understand how components fail on engines, the technician has to understand some basic principles. These basic principles can be divided into the following four areas:

- Metallurgy: The science of metals
- Wear: Identifying normal and abnormal wear conditions
- Fractures: Primary indicator of the manner and speed of a failure
- Visual examination: Ability to correlate visual evidence with a type of failure

METALLURGY

Metallurgy is the science of metals. It deals with properties, structure, and behavior of metals. A diesel or truck technician who aspires to develop failure analysis expertise must have a basic understanding of metallurgical principles. Vehicles are constructed from a range of alloys. An **alloy** is a mixture of two or more elements, at least one of which is a metal. In vehicle technology, we are primarily concerned with **ferrous metals**. To a lesser extent, we have to understand aluminum alloys. Ferrous metals are composed primarily of iron. For instance, **steel** is an alloy of iron and a small quantity of carbon. There are many different types of steel. Because there are many different elements that can mix with iron, many types of steel can be manufactured with characteristics that suit a variety of purposes.

Metal Structure

All metals are composed of grains. The grain is produced by crystals that form from molten metal as it solidifies. For instance, in cast irons and steel, the grain boundaries almost always contain some minor impurities such as refractory brick or trapped slag left over from the casting and production processes. Grain impurities are known as *inclusions* (just as we describe them when entrapped in a weld). Most inclusions that result from a manufacturing process are small enough not to significantly weaken the metal—but a larger inclusion in the wrong place, such as a high-stress focal point, could result in a failure. This is known as a *metallurgical defect*. In performing failure analysis, the technician should always keep in mind that the root causes of a small percentage of failures are metallurgical in origin. When warranty is a factor, a metallurgical sourced failure would be an original equipment manufacturer (OEM) responsibility.

Iron and Steel

Iron and steel are made into useful forms by casting and shaping processes. Casting requires that the base metal be reduced to a completely molten state, then set in a form. Both iron and steel can be cast. In vehicle technology, we use a variety of irons and steels. In production, steel can be cast or formed by one of more of the following shaping processes:

1. Rolling
2. Forging
3. Extruding
4. Drawing

Steel that is reshaped by one of the preceding processes is referred to as *wrought*. The term *wrought* means that something has been worked into a specific shape. Cast and wrought steels form two general categories of metal with quite different sets of properties.

ROLLING Rolling is the most common steel working process. Rolling steel produces wrought shapes such as plates, sheets, slabs, and bars. Rolling requires steel to be heated to about 2,200°F (1,200°C). Heating the steel to this temperature makes it plastic, that is, susceptible to yield when pressure is applied. When high pressure is applied to heated steel using large rollers, it can be formed or squeezed into a desired shape. Often rolling takes place in multiple stages. For instance, rolled steel slabs are often further reworked by extruding, forging, drawing, or a variety of other metal-forming processes.

When steel is subjected to rolling, the grains in the metal reform. This means that the grain boundaries take on a new shape without tearing apart. The new grain structure of rolled steel aligns in the rolling direction to form new grain flow lines. This has the desirable effect of making a steel stronger in the direction of the grain flow. This *grain flow* in production-formed metals causes different material properties in different directions. Grain flow also affects the appearance of a fracture surface, which you can see when observing fracture faces. Sometimes a fracture follows the grain flow; at other times it will run against it. Learning to identify grain flow in fracture faces can tell us a lot about the root cause of the fracture.

FORGING Forging is a common manufacturing process. A century ago, forging was something performed by a blacksmith: At its simplest, forging required heating a metal to a specific temperature, then shaping it using percussive force delivered by a hammer. Today, it is a manufacturing process that is more scientific. Metals are heated to precise temperatures and the force is applied hydraulically. Drop-forging is used to form components ranging from connecting rods to crankshafts.

EXTRUDING *Extruding* literally means squeezing. In metal forming, extrusion requires forcing a semimolten metal through a die. This process both shapes the metal and gives it some desirable surface characteristics.

DRAWING Drawing is another forming process in which heated steel is pulled through an aperture. This provides the steel with a specific shape and sectional area. Drawing is commonly used to produce individual strands of copper, aluminum, and steel wire.

Heat Treatment

Heat treatment is a common method used to redefine the structure and properties of a range of metals. The term *tempering* is used to describe a range of heat treatment processes. Heat treatment of metals predates accurately recorded history, and we know that it was used by the ancient Greeks 3,000 years ago. Heat treatment processes require controlled heating and cooling to alter the characteristics of a metal and produce the desired material properties. A metal can be heated in several ways, but in modern steel production, the most common method is to use a furnace. The manner in which heat is applied to a metal and the manner in which it is cooled are both important in determining the properties of a metal. For instance, rapid cooling of heated steel, known as *quenching*, produces the hardest characteristics, sometimes even making the material **brittle** (susceptible to fracture). Slower cooling of heated steel generally produces a less hard steel but provides higher plasticity.

In truck and engine technology, heat treatment processes are usually designed to make steels tougher and harder. But the opposite may be true. For instance, to anneal copper (make it softer), the metal is first heated, then rapidly cooled by quenching in water. Heat treatments change the structure of a metal, especially when the metal has been alloyed with carbon and other alloying elements such as nickel, chromium, titanium, and molybdenum. If metal that has been tempered in manufacture is subjected to temperatures that exceed the tempering temperature, the effects of the controlled tempering process can be entirely lost. This may result in a metal that is either much harder or much softer than desirable.

Stress Raisers

When vehicle components are designed it is necessary to calculate the applied loads, determine where loads will be applied to the component, and determine how the geometry (shape/section modulus) of the component will respond to applied loads. Components respond to applied loads by setting up internal stresses. A geometric change in a component caused by an applied load can result in a **stress raiser** located in the deformed area. A *stress raiser* is a feature in either the shape or composition of a component that causes a localized increase in stress. The greater the change in geometric shape, the more aggressive the stress raiser effect. This can initiate metallurgical failure and result in a crack.

Apertures (holes), keyways, threads, shoulders, and other irregular shapes can all be stress raisers. Where known stress raisers occur in a component, they can be compensated for by design, material selection, heat treatment, or forming techniques. Stress raisers due to metallurgical problems, manufacturing process abnormalities, or abuse can result in component failures when there is an insufficient safety factor built into the design.

EXAMPLES OF STRESS RAISERS There are many causes of potential stress raisers that designers must take into account. They can be generally divided into the following categories, with the first three relating to design and production defects:

Geometry

- Fillets: Should be radiused rather than sharp angled
- Holes: Chamfering at top and radiused at bottom reduces localized stresses
- Keyways: Should be chamfered at edges

Metallurgical Defects

- Inclusions: Usually a manufacturing (casting) or production (welding) defect
- Voids: Manufacturing defect
- Cracks: Can be embedded into castings while cooling from liquid to solid state in the manufacturing process

Production Defects

- Forging laps
- Quench cracks
- Weld crystallization
- Grinder cracks

Abuse

- Overloading
- Scratches
- Nicks
- Gouges

Root Causes of Failures

The root causes of most failures can usually be sourced to the application, operation, and maintenance areas. In other words, a large percentage of failures can be traced to the way in which equipment is operated and maintained. After this, the next most probable root cause area is installation. Installation malpractice is traceable to the technician and caused either by lack of training or carelessness. The least likely root cause sources are deficiencies in manufacturing and design. The good news is that failures due to design or manufacturing shortcomings tend to be the easiest to diagnose. Failures generated by the other root cause areas are often harder to diagnose because it is more difficult to establish the facts connected to the failure.

Collecting Evidence

When investigating an equipment failure, the first step should be to identify all of the systems affected, then collect and isolate the damaged components and fragments. This first step should include visually damaged components and those components that interact with them. Using the example of a connecting rod failure, the evidence should include the failed conn rod, plus the piston assembly, wrist pin and bushing, rod cap, friction bearings, rod fasteners, and crankshaft throw journal. This evidence should be laid out in a systematic manner so that the clues in sourcing the root cause of the failure can be identified.

Collecting Facts

Failure analysis facts come from four sources, the first three of which are the responsibility of the technician:

1. The operator's report
2. The failed component(s)
3. Vehicle and engine service history
4. OEM failure analysis lab

Having stated this, most failure analysis problems should be solved by properly undertaking steps 1 through 3. In a small number of cases, microstructure facts using source 4 are required to determine root causes: This requires the use of lab instruments and specialized expertise, so the problem exceeds the capabilities of the typical service facility. In reality, source 4 type problems are only investigated by the manufacturer of the failed component. It is in the interests of the manufacturer to do this to avoid costly recurrences that could damage product credibility and increase warranty claims.

Conducting an Examination

Because visual examination is such an important component of failure analysis, it is important that the technician optimizes the inspection environment. Good lighting is essential. Before cleaning, failed components should be visually inspected, and a record made of anything unusual. Use a magnifying glass when examining fractures. Next, carefully clean the components in a way that is guaranteed not to damage surfaces. The use of mild solvents, soft-bristle brushes, and air-drying will clean components without destroying evidence. Take special care when cleaning components with soft surfaces such as engine friction bearings. Gently rinse in solvent, then allow to air-dry. Key indicators of a failure can too easily be destroyed by aggressive cleaning, so the use of glass bead blasters, grit blasters, wire brushes, or grinders should be avoided.

Think *CSI*

During any failure analysis procedure, try to avoid resorting to preconceived notions about what might have caused the failure. For instance, if a truck driver complained that his engine produced a loud knocking noise before seizing, the diagnostic technician might easily conclude that low crankcase oil level producing insufficient lubrication could have been the cause. And it could have. But a thorough technician should treat every failure analysis as a challenge worthy of a *CSI: Crime Scene Investigation* TV show plot. Doing this will allow more facts to be gathered; these facts might suggest that the oil pump gears failed, shutting down the lube circuit—or any of half a dozen other conditions. Using preconceived ideas based on past experience of similar failures can often lead the technician in the wrong direction and result in coming to faulty conclusions. A good failure analysis technician has to have a little of Sherlock Holmes's blood.

As the facts of a failure are collected, the technician should carefully identify and sort through the evidence. This means regarding the wear and fracture facts of the failure as road signs along a highway that will lead to the root cause of the problem—and establish a means of avoiding a recurrence.

WEAR

Wear may occur over a period of time and often be regarded as expected. However, there are many different types of wear, and some can act as key tattletales in the search for a root cause of a failure. Specific environments cause different types of wear. Although all components age

in operation and produce wear, the interest of the failure analysis technician obviously goes into recognizing abnormal types of wear.

There are many types of wear, but whether the wear is normal or abnormal can usually be categorized into one of the following seven areas:

1. Abrasive wear
2. Adhesive wear
3. Corrosion
4. Erosion
5. Cavitation erosion
6. Contact stress fatigue
7. Fretting

Each type of wear has its own characteristics that stem from operation in a specific environment. Recognizing specific wear characteristics helps technicians to identify the environment that caused the wear. **Figure 49–1** shows various types of wear on engine friction bearings.

Abrasive Wear

Abrasive wear accounts for a majority of wear failures. It may occur in both lubricated and nonlubricated components. When particulate grit comes into contact with metal surfaces, it begins to wear the metal down: For instance, take a look at the dump box in any aggregate hauler. In lubricated components, any time hard particles larger than the lubricant film thickness get between two moving surfaces, wear will result. First, surface faces are scored; this then produces secondary debris that accelerates the condition. Hard surfaces such as bearings do not score easily when exposed to particulates, but more heat is generated, so wear rate depends on how effectively the lubricant acts as a coolant. Given adequate lubrication, the heat generated is held in check and can slow down the abrasive wear effect.

Adhesive Wear

Adhesive wear tends to produce accelerated failures. It occurs when two moving surfaces contact each other with insufficient lubrication. An example is when the hydrodynamic suspension of a rotating shaft in a friction bearing fails. The resulting contact produces friction and enough heat to approach melting point: This creates localized welding or an adhesive effect.

Adhesive wear in engines can usually be attributed to a lubrication problem. This type of wear failure is often initiated in extreme cold conditions, especially mid-winter cold start in applications where an inappropriate engine

FIGURE 49–1 Bearing failure analysis.

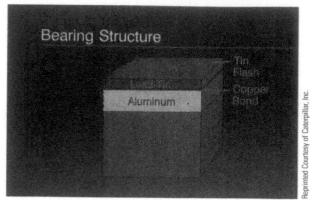

Bearing structure

High mileage wear: lead-tin bond
weakens in high load area

Sliding contact stress fatigue
caused by normal, high mileage
wear

High mileage, normal wear: wear in
high load areas with some cavitation

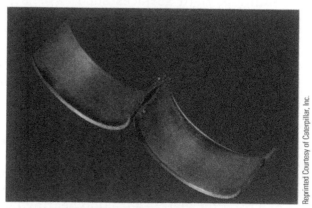

Misaligned loading: wear occurs on
opposite sides

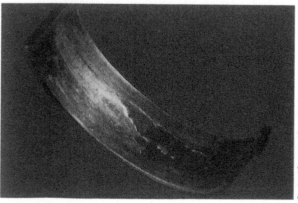

Thermal growth (overheating) of
aluminum layer causes bond
separation

lube is the culprit. Flow ability is an important characteristic for good lubrication. At low temperatures, viscosity increases significantly (see Chapter 10), and at −30°F (−35°C), the commonly used 15W-40 engine oil has the consistency of axle grease; that is, it has no flow ability. A single cold-start event under these conditions using this engine oil can destroy an engine.

Corrosion

Corrosion is chemical deterioration of a metal surface. Unrefined ore is oxidized metal. During metal processing, ores are refined to produce pure metals that tend to be less stable. Pure metals often revert back to the more stable oxidized states and will do so when exposed to electrolytic substances. An *electrolyte* is a liquid solution (like that in a lead acid battery) that enables electrolytic interactions on metals such as steel or aluminum.

Most corrosion on engine components is oxidation related, but nonoxidation corrosion can also occur when metals are exposed to acids and alkalines within engine fluids. A severe type of corrosion can result when engine coolant deteriorates and becomes acidic: The role of the engine coolant becomes that of electrolyte, and metal surfaces become electrodes, resulting in rapid failures.

Erosion

Erosion occurs when abrasive particles suspended in fast-moving fluids contact surrounding surfaces, resulting in fine impact and abrasive damage. An eroded surface usually has a rough, matte appearance. Erosive wear can occur anywhere in an engine where fluids move at some velocity, but it will be especially noticeable when dust enters the intake circuit. Observing filter change intervals is one of the best strategies for controlling erosive wear.

Cavitation

Cavitation erosion occurs when gas bubbles in liquids collapse against metal surfaces, creating a percussive effect. Under some circumstances liquids can suspend dissolved gases, which form bubbles in low-pressure areas. Also, the pulsing action of wet liners against the wall of coolant creates vapor bubbles as the liner pulses inward. Bubble implosion can generate forces exceeding 60,000 psi (414 MPa) that are capable of first pitting and ultimately eroding through a wet liner. Cavitation usually occurs on the outside of wet and wet/dry liners in line with the piston thrust faces. It results when the cavitation protection of an antifreeze mixture depletes or in high-pressure fuel pumping mechanisms when charging pressures fall below spec. The best remedy for repeated wet liner cavitation failures is to use waterless engine coolant (WEC); the reasons are explained in Chapter 11.

Contact Stress Fatigue

Contact stress fatigue occurs when two surfaces slide, roll, or are dragged against each other. This results in high stress, surface face removal, and fatigue cracks in one or both surfaces. Unintended contact surface movement can occur if applied stresses become excessive, or if a component is underspecified and cannot withstand intended working loads. Cyclic movement of a pair of surfaces exceeding design limits can result in cracks, surface pitting, and spalling: This condition is known as *contact stress fatigue*.

Fretting

Fretting corrosion occurs when two parts that fit tightly, usually under significant clamping force, are allowed to move slightly against each other. This can result in microwelding and producing patterned surface irregularities. Left unchecked, fretting can result in small pieces separating from each surface. Sometimes these small pieces corrode and form reddish-brown oxides on either or both clamped surfaces. When replacing worn components, their mating surfaces should be carefully checked for fretting, because the failure could recur.

Most tightly clamped components in an engine have to be provided some ability to move independently. For instance, a cylinder head has much less mass than a cylinder block, so as an engine heats up, the cylinder head will expand more quickly than the cylinder block. It will also contract more quickly when the engine is shut down and cools. The same would apply to many other mating surfaces represented by manifolds. This differential in expansion and contraction is known as **creep**. Therefore, a key function of a gasket is to permit thermal creep in mated components while effectively maintaining a seal.

> **TECH TIP:**
> Technicians who fail to observe the OEM-specified torque increments and sequence can cause fretting wear between clamped components.

LOADS

When components fail, each failure produces a pattern of tattletales that the failure analysis technician learns to identify. When we look at wear, we find that each type of wear correlates with a specific operating environment. In the same way, when components fracture, the type of fracture correlates with the specific way the load was applied to the failed component. In this section, we review some of the basics of fracture mechanics.

Components generally fracture either when they contain material defects or when they are subjected to excessive loads. Loads can be generally divided into three types:

- *Impact loads* are sudden and excessive.
- *Overloads* are also excessive, but are applied over a period of time.
- *Fatigue* or *cyclic loads* are loads that are applied repeatedly over a period of time; they usually involve much lower applied loads than impact or overloads.

The direction or plane on which a load is applied to a component will have an effect on the nature and direction of a fracture. Also significant are the metallurgical properties of the material under load. A brittle steel (one that cannot sustain any plastic deformation) will produce a fracture characteristic different from one that is **ductile** (flexible or malleable). If you understand some of the metallurgical basics of the component that fractured and you can correlate the appearance of the fracture characteristics to the type of load that caused it, you should then be able to make an accurate assessment of root cause.

Types of Load

Generally, loads can be divided into the following categories:

- Bending
- Compressional
- Tensional
- Torsional

BENDING LOADS   When a component is bent, it is deformed in such a way that one side can be said to be convex in shape and the other concave. *Bending* loads place the convex surface under tension (stretch) and the concave surface under compression (squeeze). A fracture initiates on the tension side and runs through toward the compression side of the component. The actual appearance of the fracture surface depends on the type of load (impact, overload, or cyclic) and the physical properties of the material. A bending failure of a crankshaft could take place in the event of a main bearing cap separation.

COMPRESSIONAL LOADS   When something is compressed, it is squeezed by opposing forces. *Compressional* loads produce compressive stress in the direction of the applied load and tensile loads perpendicular to the applied load. When compressive loads are applied to ductile materials, depending on the shape of the material, the result may be to cause a bulge or other plastic deformation. Any resulting deformation will usually be perpendicular to the applied load or, in the cases of thinner components, buckling.

Components manufactured from brittle materials are more likely to fracture in a direction parallel to the applied load when subjected to compressional loads, depending on the physical shape of the material. Fractures result because compression loading produces tensile stress in the direction perpendicular to the applied load. This often initiates with multiple minor cracks that eventually converge, resulting in shatter. A connecting rod could be subjected to a compressional overload in the event of hydraulic lock in an engine cylinder resulting from head gasket failure and coolant leakage into the cylinder.

TENSIONAL LOADS   *Tensional* loads are the result of stretching force applied to a component. Stretching force produces tensile stress in the direction of loading and compressive stress perpendicular to the direction of loading. Tensional loads cause materials to elongate in the direction of the applied load. In the case of ductile materials, the cross section perpendicular to the applied load may decrease in size. This characteristic can be seen in an overtorqued bolt that produces a characteristic known as "necking." More brittle materials, such as cast irons, may initially elongate (slightly) but then fracture perpendicularly. In most cases, brittle materials that fail due to tensional overloads produce little observable plastic deformation prior to fracture. Tensional failures of connecting rods may occur during an engine overspeed event.

TORSIONAL LOADS   Torsion is a twisting force. Failures resulting from *torsional* loading tend to be more complex. In a shaft that conducts torque, shear stresses are generated both across and through the length of the shaft. This results in tensile and compressive stresses at 45-degree angles along the shaft. Shear stresses tend to predominate in shafts that have a ductile characteristic, producing both transverse (across the shaft) and longitudinal fractures. When torsion is applied to shafts manufactured from more brittle materials, tensile stresses tend to predominate, so when a fracture occurs it is in a spiraling, 45-degree direction. Cyclic loads applied to either brittle or ductile shaft materials can produce fractures in any of the three directions, making them more difficult to diagnose. Torsional failures occur in shafts when they are subjected to more twisting force than they were engineered to sustain.

FRACTURES

When components fracture, the cause can usually be categorized as:

- Brittle fracture
- Ductile fracture
- Fatigue fracture

Brittle fractures are the result of a shock load or high force impact. Brittle fractures rapidly produce crystalline or grainy fracture face surfaces. In most cases, little or no plastic deformation occurs during the fracture event. Depending on the specific material fractured, there may or may not be chevrons on the fracture face surface. Fracture surfaces can range from bright and sparkly to dull in appearance, this depending once again on the material.

Ductile fractures are often the result of a component overload. Ductile fractures occur quickly, but not as fast as brittle fractures. In most cases, they produce rough, dark surfaces, with some evidence of plastic deformation (bending, twisting, or stretching) prior to the failure. The plastic deformation that may accompany ductile fractures often results in shear lips at the outside edge of the fracture.

Fatigue fractures are typically the result of cyclic overloading. Fatigue fractures are the result of much lower loads than those characteristic of brittle or ductile fractures. They are also less catastrophic, and because they occur much more slowly, they produce lighter, smoother fracture face surfaces. Fatigue fractures can often leave **beach marks** (ripples) as a tattletale.

COMPONENT FAILURES

Identifying the root cause of a component failure is always made much easier when the disassembly is organized and methodical. It helps to label and tag components on removal from the engine. Clean and inspect every component as it is removed from the engine. When inspected components are to be reused on reassembly, they should be sealed in polyplastic paper. Make a point of not beginning an engine reassembly until the exact cause of the failure has been determined. This section deals with some common failure modes of engine components, but it should be remembered that it is by no means comprehensive.

PISTONS

When disassembling an engine, numerically tag pistons for location on removal, even when the primary cause of the failure has been identified and you plan to replace the pistons. Most OEM warranty processing requires that pistons be tagged. You should have a basic knowledge of the operating principles of diesel engine piston assemblies, as outlined in Chapter 7. The pistons used in diesel engines have undergone some significant changes in recent years: For instance, Caterpillar's popular 3406/C15 engine has progressed through aluminum trunk, steel/aluminum articulating, and single-piece, forged steel trunk pistons within a period of a dozen years. Some typical piston failure conditions correlated with possible causes are identified in **Table 49-1**. In order to maximize piston life, the piston must be properly assembled and then properly installed. Once in operation, piston life depends both on how the engine is operated and the performance of the engine support circuits that remove combustion heat from the pistons:

- Air intake circuit
- Lube circuit
- Cooling system
- Exhaust circuit

Heat is the biggest enemy of pistons. This is what OEMs like to call **thermal failures**. A performance breakdown in any of the systems designed to take heat away from pistons can produce a failure. Some of the tattletales of piston thermal failures are:

- Piston crown carboning
- Ring carboning
- Discoloration of the underside of the piston crown
- Erosion of the wall around the toroidal crater of a Mexican hat crown

cause the crown to expand relatively more than the skirt. It is much less common in modern diesels using articulating or drop-forged steel pistons, so when you do see this type of failure, it will more likely be in aluminum trunk pistons. Some causes of piston crown scuffing are:

- Injector dribble
- Inadequate undercrown cooling
- Restricted exhaust system or other breathing circuit problem
- Overfueling
- High air intake temperatures
- Prolonged lug operation

Skirt scuffing occurs more commonly than crown scuffing and, once again, is more likely to occur in aluminum trunk-type pistons. When an aluminum trunk piston skirt is overheated, overexpansion usually occurs where the mass is highest: This means that the "corners" of the piston bosses expand relatively more, creating a "four-corner" vertical scuff profile. As the scuffing continues, so does the heat buildup, and the result may be engine seizure or disintegration of the piston. Skirt scuffing is caused by:

- Insufficient cooling
- Lack of lubrication
- Distorted or fractured cylinder liner

Cold Start

When diesel engines are cold-started, the pistons and rings are cold and ring end gaps are wider than at operating temperatures. In addition, only residual oil (boundary lubrication) is present to act as lube. The consequence is that rings have to sustain cylinder pressures while being supported by a lower sectional area until the ring land warms to its operating temperature. For this reason, on cold starts it is important to run a diesel engine under no load long enough to enable the pistons to warm to operating temperature. This is especially important on engines using aluminum trunk-type pistons.

Fast-Track Analysis of Piston Failures

The following is a summary of typical piston failures and some pointers toward their root causes. Always remember that every failure has a certain uniqueness to it, so there are no absolutes when it comes to accurate identification of root cause.

TORCHED PISTONS Torching of pistons occurs when either one piston or a set of pistons has been overheated to such an extent that meltdown has occurred. The condition was obviously more common in engines using aluminum trunk-type pistons. Diagnosing a torched piston in isolation from the engine from which it was removed may be a game of guesswork rather than sound failure analysis practice. However, the cause of the condition must be unmistakably diagnosed before the engine is reassembled, or a recurrence of the failure will result. If only one piston is affected, the diagnosis may be simpler, but it is always important to remember that piston torching may be related to lubrication, cooling system, or fuel injection causes.

SKIRT SCORING The usual causes of skirt scoring are overheating, overfueling, insufficient piston clearance, lack of lubrication, and fuel injector nozzle problems.

CRACKED SKIRT The causes of a cracked piston skirt are excessive use of ether, excessive piston-to-bore clearance, and foreign objects in the cylinder.

UNEVEN SKIRT WEAR The common causes of uneven skirt wear are contaminated lube oil (either with abrasives or fuel/coolant), abrasives in air charge (dusting), and too little piston-to-bore clearance. The latter can be caused by aftermarket pistons that may measure to specification when cold but expand to a greater extent when at operating temperature.

BROKEN RING LANDS Broken ring lands are caused by excessive use of ether, excessive piston-to-bore clearance, and foreign objects in the cylinder. Engines subjected to high cylinder pressures before warming to operating temperatures can also produce ring land fractures.

WORN PISTON PIN BOSSES The causes of worn piston (wrist) pin bosses are old age (normal wear), contaminated lube oil, and insufficient lubrication. When a pin boss is starved of lubrication, the root cause is in the lube delivery system, so be sure to check this out.

BURNED OR ERODED CENTER CROWN When the center of a piston crown is burned or eroded, the usual causes are plugged injector nozzles, injector dribble, cold loading of engine, retarded injection timing, and water/coolant leakage into the cylinder.

Piston Failures Related to Fuel Injection/Ignition Timing

With the almost universal adoption of computer controls on diesel engines today, most of the problems associated with fuel injection timing have disappeared. It is fair to say that a majority of fuel injection timing problems were the result of abuse, either intentional or due to a lack of training. Although there are ways of manipulating fuel injection timing in modern diesel engines, most OEM audit trails can pinpoint the time of any tampering abuse, so it is not common in commercial diesels.

ADVANCED INJECTION TIMING Advanced engine timing causes excessive combustion pressures and higher than specified temperatures. In severe cases, it may result in torching or blowing out the lower ring lands. In less severe cases, erosion and burning of the top ring land or headland area result, which are evidenced by pitting. The latter condition is more common and is often the result of abuse by technicians attempting to increase engine power and fuel economy. It often does increase, but at a heavy cost because of a significant reduction in engine longevity. Advancing injection timing also results in high NO_x output. Total failure resulting from advancing timing usually occurs in one cylinder, with evidence appearing in the remaining cylinders.

RETARDED INJECTION TIMING Retarded engine timing will cause excessive cylinder temperatures and burning/erosion damage through the central crown area of the piston. An indicator of retarded injection timing is piston crown scorching immediately under the injector nozzle. This is caused by droplets condensing on the piston crown before vaporizing and ignition. In the days when engine timing was a technician responsibility, this condition occurred much less frequently than advanced injection timing because it was seldom intentional. It was usually the result of technician error or component failure, though

it can result from actuating component wear. Examples of actuating component wear are cam profile and camshaft bearing degradation.

> ## TECH TIP:
> Number pistons by cylinder when disassembling an engine, even when it is known that they are to be replaced—it may help diagnose a failure.

PISTON RINGS

Piston rings provide plenty of tattletales when it comes to determining the root cause of an engine failure. Most engine overhauls are initiated due to normal wear of piston rings over the life of the engine. As piston rings wear, their ability to effectively manage the oil film on the cylinder wall and seal becomes reduced, as illustrated in **Figure 49–9**. Here are some of those tattletales.

Cold Stuck/Gummed Rings

Cold stuck rings are a condition in which the piston ring seizes in the ring groove when the engine is cold but frees and starts to seal the cylinder when the engine is at operating temperature. Cold stuck or gummed rings are caused by carbon/sludge buildup in the ring groove. The condition can be caused by a defective thermostat, operating for short periods in cold weather, and constant stop/start operation. It results in high crankcase pressure during engine warmup and fuel contaminated with engine lubricating oil.

Hot Stuck Rings

Hot stuck rings are caused by crystallized carbon buildup resulting from the use of contaminated or improper fuel or the failure of oil control rings. The ring is usually captured stationary in

FIGURE 49–9 How wear affects the ability of rings to effectively form a seal with the liner.

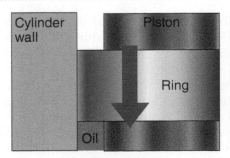

New ring and liner.

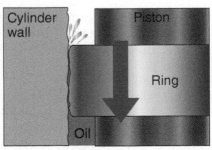

A worn ring and liner permit oil to pass through.

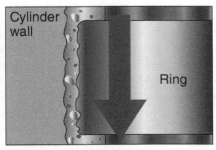

Debris in oil wears both the ring and liner.

TABLE 49–2 Piston Ring Failures

Condition	Causes/Results
Land failures	Excessive manifold boost, ether abuse, overfueling.
Sticking/stuck rings	Lacquering and gumming caused by high sulfur or contaminated fuel, overfueling, or prolonged lugging. May result in engines fueled with fuel cut with used engine oil.
Broken rings	Overfueling, ring erosion followed by fracture caused by dirt, improper installation (fracture 180 degrees from the end gap).
Cylinder scuffing	Insufficient ring end gap.
Seized rings	High-operating temperatures, overfueling, contaminated fuel.

the groove and the contact face blackened by cylinder blow-by gas.

Scuffed Rings

Scuffed rings are usually related to an improper ring-to-cylinder bore fit, such as would occur with an out-of-specification ring end gap, piston-to-bore clearance, or ring-to-groove side clearance. The condition may also be caused by cylinder wall lubrication failure. Because scuffing is a localized weld condition, created by frictional heat resulting from metal-to-metal contact, the result is often seizure of the piston in the liner bore.

Eroded/Glazed Rings

Eroded or glazed rings are usually a result of poorly filtered or unfiltered intake air to the engine cylinders. Diesel engines used in construction and aggregate hauling applications often ingest enough ultra-small particles of abrasive silica sand through a properly functioning air cleaner system to glaze and erode rings and liners and shorten engine life. However, whenever this condition is identified, always test the engine intake system for leaks.

Broken Rings

Broken rings are usually caused by improper installation or crystallized carbon buildup in a sector of the ring groove. Broken compression rings are not often observed in current engines because flexible centrifugally cast or special alloy steels are used. More brittle cast irons are still used as oil control rings, and these are vulnerable to fracture on installation if not handled correctly. A ring fracture that occurs 180 degrees from the end gap is a classic indicator of improper installation (overstretch).

Plugged Oil Control Rings

Plugging of oil control rings is often caused by low engine operating temperatures or broken-down,

sludged engine lubricant. The result of this condition is usually an engine that burns engine oil, because the oil applied to the liner walls by the piston and bearing throw-off is not controlled. The condition causes coincidental problems such as compression ring **gumming** or sticking.

Carefully remove the piston rings and tag them for location on the piston and on the engine in sequence as they are removed during disassembly of the engine. Some common causes of piston ring failures are shown in **Table 49–2**.

TECH TIP:

Always check that piston rings were originally installed correctly when removing them from piston assemblies. Place the rings with the pistons from which they were removed.

TECH TIP:

Prematurely worn rings, pistons, and liner bores are an indication that abrasives have entered the engine by means of the intake air system.

CYLINDER HEAD VALVES

You should understand the operating principles and construction of cylinder head valves to the extent they are examined in Chapter 8. Cylinder head valves may be of one-piece, two-piece, or multiple-piece construction, depending on engine manufacturer. For instance, some manufacturers will use a single-piece construction on their intake valves and two-piece construction on their exhaust valves: Because one way in which valves may fail is at the weld joints on multiple-piece construction valves, it helps to know something about how the valve was manufactured.

Valve Terminology

The technician should be familiar with cylinder head valve terminology so that the location of a failure can be identified. Cross-reference the following parts of a valve with Figure 8–16, which shows a typical, inertia-welded, two-piece construction valve:

- Stem
- Head
- Keeper grooves
- Inertial weld
- Fillet radius
- Hard surfacing

Valve Construction

Valves are required to sustain high temperatures (especially exhaust valves) and rapidly disperse heat. They must also be capable of flexing during closing while maintaining a positive seal. These required characteristics determine what materials are used in valve manufacture. One-piece valves tend to be manufactured from low alloy, medium carbon steels that are tempered to permit some flexing at the lower stem and fillet, and are either induction or hard surfaced at the keeper groove section of the stem and head. Two-piece valves use a low alloy, medium carbon steel stem that is joined by a friction weld to a heat resistant, high alloy steel head assembly. The head assembly is often so highly alloyed that it may not attract a magnet. In this type of cylinder valve, the two pieces are joined by an inertia weld in the stem, usually just above the fillet. In addition, some multiple-piece valves use a friction-welded, stellite head plate manufactured from a high alloy steel.

HARD SURFACING Hard surfacing of cylinder head valves is performed either chemically or by an arc welding procedure. In cases where an arc welding process is used, a high alloy (nickel, chrome, molybdenum) steel is applied to the seat circumference of the valve head.

FRICTION WELDING Friction welding, sometimes known as *inertial welding*, is used to join a low alloy valve stem to a high alloy valve head. The process requires that the stem be rotated by a spun-up turret (establishing a fixed amount of energy) that is then forced against a held-stationary valve head. The energy of the rotating stem is released as frictional heat, resulting in melting and the welding of the two sections. The location of a friction weld in a two-piece valve can

be easily identified because the low alloy upper stem attracts a magnet, and the high alloy lower stem and head either do not attract or barely attract a magnet. If a valve were to fail by separating at the friction weld, this would usually be considered a manufacturing defect. It is not a common failure, but it is also not unheard of.

Valve Loading

Cylinder head valves are subjected to three types of loads:

1. Spring forces
2. Valve closing forces
3. Cylinder pressures

SPRING FORCES When a cylinder valve is in its static closed position, it is subjected to a light tensile load between the valve seat and the keeper grooves. As a valve is opened, a compressive load is applied between the keeper grooves and the stem end. Neither of these normal light loads is sufficient to cause fatigue failures.

VALVE CLOSING FORCES As a valve closes, it slams back into its seat, coming to an abrupt halt, shock-loading the valve between the seat and keeper grooves. Valves are designed to yield (to a small extent) to accommodate this type of tensile shock loading. However, the tensile shock loading increases with engine rpm and can be further increased by valve maladjustment. Loose valve adjustments can result in higher valve closing speeds because seat contact occurs before the valvetrain has ridden the valve transition geometry of the actuating cam profile. Additionally, engine overspeed increases both the frequency and velocity of the valves as they seat, and this tensile overloading can result in valve failures. When an engine "drops a valve," in more cases than not this can be related to an engine overspeed event.

Stresses concentrate anywhere there is a physical irregularity. This means that cracks often initiate in valve fillet radii and the keeper grooves in the stem when subject to tensile overloads. A majority of catastrophic valve failures can be attributed to their being subjected to excessive closing forces.

CYLINDER PRESSURES During recent years, engine cylinder combustion pressures have greatly increased in diesel engines. Some engines produce peak cylinder pressures of 3,000 psi. Because the head of a cylinder valve is subject to cylinder pressure, the head of a cylinder valve is designed to flex. This flexing action places the underside of the valve head under compression and the top side under tension. When an engine is operated under abnormally high combustion pressures, fatigue cracks usually initiate on the top side of the valve head close to the fillet. Valve failures due to excessive cylinder pressures are comparatively rare.

Reusing Cylinder Valves

During an engine overhaul, cylinder valves can normally be reused. **Figure 49–10** shows valve

FIGURE 49–10 Cylinder valve failure analysis.

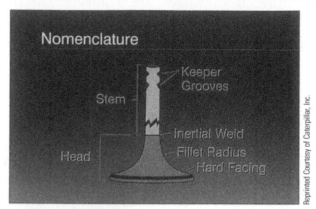

Valve terminology

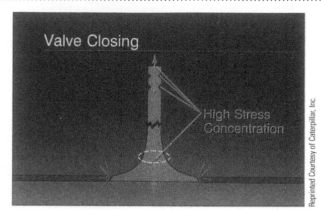

Valve closing stress points

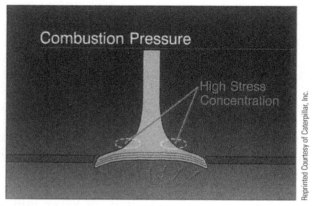

Stress during combustion

Thermal cracks caused by overheating

Cupping or dishing: usually caused by overheating

Effects of valve leakage caused by ash and carbon build-up on the valve face

nomenclature and some typical failure modes. Valves should be checked for:

- Fatigue cracks
- Thermal cracks
- Pitting
- Carbon coking
- Dishing distortion

Loose Valve Adjustment

Apart from producing a lack of power, loose valve adjustment results in cyclic overloading of cylinder head valves and the valvetrain. This occurs because the transition geometry on the camshaft lobe that governs how a valve is accelerated on opening and decelerated on closing is eliminated. This results in cyclic:

- Compressive overloads on the valve during opening
- Tensile overloads on the valve as it seats on closing between the valve seat and the keeper grooves
- Shear overloads on the keeper groove lands

Figure 49–11 illustrates the action of a properly set cylinder valve versus one set loosely: Excessive lash tends to increase the impact force as the valve seats on closing.

Tight Valve Adjustment

Valves cold set with too little lash, or set when hot to a cold engine specification, can also be damaged because when the engine is at operating temperature, the valve may not seat with the required amount of force. Valves, especially exhaust valves, depend on being properly seated to dissipate the heat they are subjected to. When cylinder head valves overheat, they thermally distort and fail rapidly.

> **TECH TIP:**
>
> Set valve lash to specification. Setting valves too tight results in as many failures as loosely set valves. Minimal drag on feeler gauges means exactly that: Use go/no-go feeler gauges if you have doubts as to how to interpret *minimal drag.*

CAMSHAFTS

There are two primary reasons for premature camshaft failure:

- Poor lube quality
- Excessive valvetrain lash

FIGURE 49–11 Closing forces of a properly set valve versus a loosely set valve.

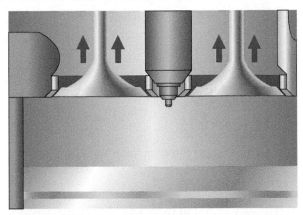

Valvetrain operation with valve lash properly adjusted.

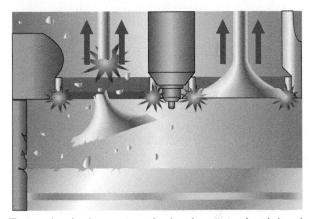

Excessive lash creates closing impact, shock load.

When poor lube quality is the cause of a camshaft failure, the cause may be high contaminant levels (soot load) or low viscosity. High soot loads suspended in lube oil results in abrasive wear to both cam lobes and the followers that ride the cam profile. Abrasive wear of camshafts is illustrated in **Figure 49–12**, and the consequences of low-viscosity oil providing poor boundary lubrication are shown in **Figure 49–13**.

Excessive valve lash results in a hammering effect on the cam profile. On actuation, the valvetrain is accelerated to the extent it loses contact with the valve lobe. Almost immediately, the valve spring drives the follower back down onto the cam profile, pounding out the subsurface of the cam profile below the hard surfacing. **Figure 49–14** shows the effect of excessive valvetrain lash on a camshaft.

LINERS

The inside diameter of most liners is surface hardened and honed to provide a horizontal

FIGURE 49-12 Clean lube oil versus oil with elevated soot levels on cam contact surfaces.

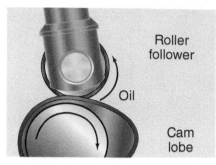
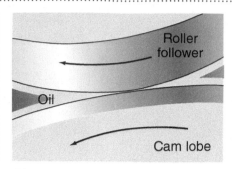
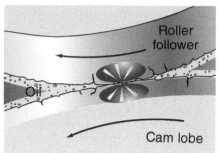

Clean oil around the cam lobe and roller follower.

Clean oil allows for smooth contact between the cam lobe and roller.

High soot levels in the oil result in abrasive wear.

FIGURE 49-13 Oil with low viscosity provides inadequate boundary lubrication.

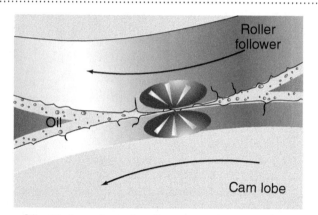

Oil with low viscosity allows metal-to-metal contact, which results in rapid wear and failure

crosshatch of 60 to 70 degrees. This provides a surface that can retain oil to lube and seal the ring contact faces while wearing well. Having the specified crosshatch is essential to prevent combustion gases from blowing by the rings while limiting oil consumption. Anything that compromises the liner contact surfaces will result in cylinder gas blow-by and oil burn-off during combustion.

When attempting to determine the root cause of an engine failure, ensure that the liners are removed, numbered by cylinder using a paint stick or crayon, and paired with their pistons. Do the same with the rings. Clean up the components using a noncorrosive solvent. The objective is not to remove any of the indicators that may have caused the failure, so never use bead or grit blasting, wire brushes, or aggressive cleaning solutions.

Scoring

A tight fit of a dry sleeve od to its cylinder bore can cause sleeve distortion. A modern dry sleeve is usually designed to expand into the cylinder block bore as it heats up, so if fitted with an interference fit it can cause buckling. A tight fit of the piston assembly to the sleeve id can also result in scoring.

FIGURE 49-14 Effect of excessive valve lash on cam profile.

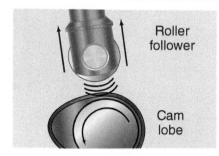
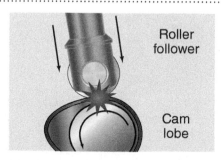
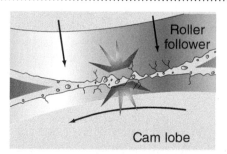

The roller follower accelerates upward at high velocity and briefly loses contact with the cam lobe.

The valve spring slams the follower back down onto the cam lobe.

High contact between the follower and cam lobe generates subsurface fatigue in the hardened surface.

Scuffing

Scuffing results when the sleeve-to-bore fit is too loose in dry liners, resulting in poor heat transfer. Sleeve temperatures are higher than usual and discoloration often results.

Etching

Etching has become a problem in some post-2004 exhaust gas recirculation (EGR) engines. Soot routed back into the intake from the EGR circuit can create etching at the top of the ring belt sweep. Soot, while in itself abrasive, also combines with moisture and fuel to form acidic residues that can etch a groove in the liner.

Running Cool

Running an engine at lower than specified operating temperature may result in condensing combustion end gases, and this can produce acids. Although most diesel engine oils specified by the engine OEM are designed to neutralize these acids, inferior oils or prolonged cold operation can deplete the additives, resulting in liner pitting or etching. When the duration of this type of corrosive attack is prolonged, graphite (carbon) flakes start to separate from the liner cast iron. The result is an engine that burns oil.

Prolonged Low-Load Operation

Despite the fact that idling a diesel engine is now illegal in most jurisdictions, truck drivers can be pretty inventive when it comes to defeating idle-shutdown programming, and not too many states aggressively enforce anti-idling regulations as yet. Diesel engine piston rings and liners are engineered to operate with high surface contact loads. Prolonged periods of idling create frictional heat that erodes the liner cross-hatch, producing a glazed finish. Once the liner ring belt surface area becomes glazed, cylinder blow-by increases and the engine begins to burn oil. Most OEMs agree that prolonged idling creates oil-burning diesel engines. The good news is that engine control module (ECM) audit trails can identify the incidence and duration of unnecessary idling, and this may be used by fleets to crack down on this type of abuse.

Exterior Scaling

Exterior scale on wet liners can be caused by using depleted coolant mixtures, improper coolants, or water in place of coolant mixtures. Any type of scale formation on a wet liner has a considerable insulating effect, resulting in higher cylinder temperatures. If a water-only coolant is used in a diesel engine, the result can be rapid formation of rust on the outside of the liner. The liner then overheats, causing heat discoloration and heat checks on the inside diameter of the liner. The quality and mineral load in water that is mixed with diesel engine antifreeze/coolants is also a factor in liner exterior wall scaling. You can avoid many problems by mixing antifreeze with pure distilled water—or better still, use long-life, premixed diesel engine coolants.

Liner Cavitation

Cavitation caused by vapor bubble implosion can shorten the life of wet liners, but this should not be a problem if the coolant chemistry is properly monitored. A full explanation of cavitation erosion is provided in Chapter 9. Wet liners, when subject to cylinder pressures, which in today's engines may be as high as 3,000 psi (24 MPa), expand outward into the wall of coolant that surrounds them and then contract, creating a vapor bubble. This "bubble" almost immediately collapses, causing the wall of coolant to collide onto the liner exterior wall. When this condition repeats itself at high frequency (17 times per second at 2,000 rpm), cyclic pressures of up to 60,000 psi (414 MPa) eat away at the liner wall. Bubble collapse erosion only occurs when diesel engine coolant is depleted or contaminated with high-mineral content in the water.

Wet liner cavitation can be identified by pitting/erosion that usually appears on the liner outside the thrust faces of the piston. If left, the erosion can actually perforate the liner.

When liners show evidence of cavitation erosion, the coolant quality and service frequency should be examined. The practice of reusing a cavitated liner by rotating it 90 degrees on reinstallation is probably not cost-effective. Persistent cavitation problems on wet liners can usually be cured by using premix extended life coolant (ELC) or waterless engine coolant (WEC).

Liner O-Ring Failure

Check seating areas thoroughly and also check that the correct sealing medium has been used. The sealing medium used on the O-ring during installation depends on the O-ring material. This can be dry (nothing), antifreeze (ethylene glycol [EG], propylene glycol [PG], etc.), soap solution, OEM sealants, and so forth. It is important to remember that what may be referred to as a *rubber* can actually be one of a number of different rubber, silicone, and petrochemical compounds; therefore, the OEM instructions should be observed. When performing failure analysis on failed O-rings, check for chemically degraded O-ring material caused by inappropriate sealing compounds.

Coolant in Combustion Chamber

This condition is evidenced by white smoke emission and the characteristic bittersweet odor of vaporized coolant; a cracked wet liner flange can leak coolant into the combustion chamber.

Wet liners should be installed by hand and subsequently checked with a plug gauge. This is machined to within 0.0015 inch (0.038 mm) of the liner id and ensures that it is not distorted. Liner flange protrusion of a set of liners clamped under one head should normally be within 0.001 inch (0.025 mm) of each other; check OEM specifications.

> ## TECH TIP:
> Always label cylinder liners numerically on removing them from the cylinder block, even when they are going to be replaced. You never know when failure analysis evidence may be required.

Installation Malpractice

Diesel engine dry sleeves and wet liners are routinely replaced at a scheduled engine overhaul without much inspection. Correct installation procedures should be observed to ensure maximum engine life. It is common practice to install current sleeves 0.0005 inch (0.0127 mm) to 0.0015 inch (0.038 mm) loose; this means that in some cases, the sleeve can be pressed into its cylinder bore entirely by hand. Interference-fit sleeves are seldom used in current diesel engines, and machining an interference can result in premature failure because the sleeve will buckle. Selective fitting of sleeves to bores should be practiced; this requires measuring the

od of each new sleeve and each bore id, then getting the largest sleeve to the largest bore, down to the smallest sleeve to the smallest bore.

Counterbore depth should be inside the specification window and usually within 0.001 inch of each other under one cylinder head. Recutting counterbores and shimming are common practices, but these procedures usually require special tools to properly perform them. When honing cylinder dry sleeve bores in the engine block, ensure that the machining residues of the procedure are completely removed. This is especially important when undertaking the procedure in chassis with the crankshaft in place.

> ## WARNING:
> Removal of a seized cylinder sleeve from an engine block should be performed in a manner that does not distort or damage the cylinder block bore—fracturing the sleeve in sections almost always results in damage to the block bore. If a sleeve cannot be removed using a hydraulic puller, try gently applying oxyacetylene heat on the lower portion of the ring belt sweep on the sleeve, cool with a small quantity of water, then attempt to pull out hydraulically again.

FRICTION BEARINGS

Despite some OEMs' opinions to the contrary, it does not make economic sense to reuse connecting rod and main bearings. When bearings are removed from an engine, whether at overhaul, bearing rollover, or for another engine problem, they should be numbered and examined with a view to determining the cause of failure. Many failures are related to lube oil, especially contaminated engine oil. When engine lube becomes contaminated, the bearings become especially vulnerable, as shown in **Figure 49–15**.

FIGURE 49–15 Consequences of contaminated engine lube on friction bearings.

New bearing.

Debris in oil separating the bearing from the journal.

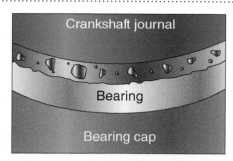

Worn bearing from debris in oil.

TABLE 49–3 Friction Bearing Failures

Condition	Causes/Results
Etching	Chemical contamination of lube—usually fuel, coolant, or sulfur.
Glazing	Broken-down lube or improper lube.
Lacquering	Orange/brown film on bearing face caused by poor quality lube or high sulfur content in lube.
Pitting	Particulate/abrasives in lube oil.
Spalling (localized welding)	High cylinder pressures caused by high manifold boost, overfueling, lugging, or detonation—less commonly a result of excessively high lube oil temperatures.
Arcing	Incorrect chassis welding practices.
Low oil pressure	Associated with bearing wear and may be grounds for a bearing rollover.
Bottom end failures	Spalling enlarges the bearing id and the resultant hammering increases tensional loading on the throw/conn rod assembly.
Insufficient bearing crush	Results in poor heat dissipation and a failure characterized by heat discoloration.

Improper installation practices can also shorten a bearing's life. An example of a color bearing failure analysis guide is shown in Figure 49–1. **Table 49–3** lists some friction bearing failures and identifies some causes and outcomes of those failures. **Figure 49–16** shows a broad range of typical engine bearing failures.

TECH TIP:

Obtain a color bearing failure analysis guide from the OEM whose product you are working on. This is an excellent way for rookie technicians to begin to perform accurate failure analyses and avoid recurrent failures.

B-Life

Projections of engine longevity often refer to **B-life** ratings. The term *B-life* actually originated from engineers' analyses of ball bearing life: It was a statistically based study of how long a given percentage of bearings would last in terms of operational hours. Today, we use B-life as a means of reckoning costs over the life of engines and other powertrain components. The *B* refers to "bearing" and the number that follows is a percentage. Most B-ratings in the trucking industry relate to linehaul miles (truck vocational and off-highway engines use engine hours).

Table 49–4 shows some Navistar data that relates to two of its older engine series. The B10 mileage indicates the specific mileage achieved before 10% of the engines in the model family failed. Similarly, the B50 rating indicates that 50% of the engines had failed at the next mileage

TABLE 49–4 B-Life Ratings of Two Engines

Engine Model	B10	B50
DT 466E	300,000 miles	450,000 miles
T 444E	200,000 miles	350,000 miles

value. This type of data today tends to be pretty accurate due to the audit trails recorded by engine ECMs and downloaded for OEM analysis.

The T 444E and DT 466 compared in Table 49–4 are small- to medium-bore engines used in applications such as school buses and pickup and delivery vehicles. Both these applications tend to be tough on diesel engines because they involve a lot of stop/start running. Most fleet managers will say that the B10 rating is the better predictor of how long an engine will reliably last. When an engine has achieved its B10 rating, it has arrived at the point where it is more vulnerable to breakdown and has become a liability, so some fleets sell off vehicles when the B10 life is achieved. The B50 life is more often used by OEM salespersons, especially in a well-rated engine family. Engines with high B10 and B50 ratings are easier to sell, for obvious reasons. B50 ratings are often used by engineers as the basis of making redesign changes in engines. We can summarize B ratings by saying:

- Bx life is a prediction of engine life before major repair.
- Average life to first overhaul is known as B50.
- B10 life is more important to fleets that like to keep downtime risks close to zero.

FIGURE 49-16 Engine bearing distress analysis.

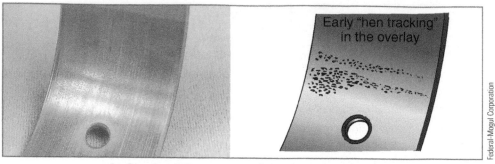

A. Overlay fatigue, normal wear: early stages

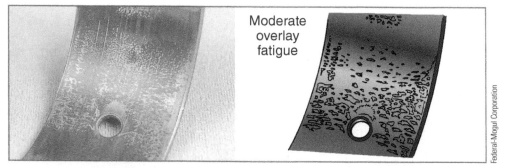

B. Overlay fatigue, normal wear: intermediate stage

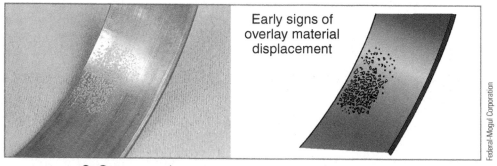

C. Orange peel appearance, normal wear: early stages

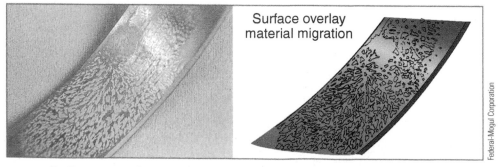

D. Orange peel appearance, normal wear, high mileage condition, intermediate stage

FIGURE 49–16 (*Continued*)

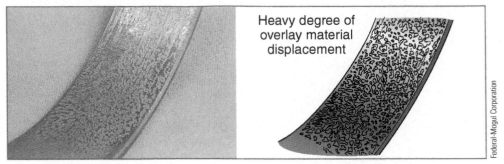

E. Orange peel appearance: advanced suction erosion condition caused by high mileage

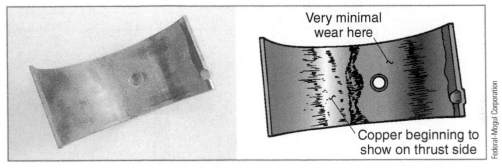

F. High mileage, normal wear

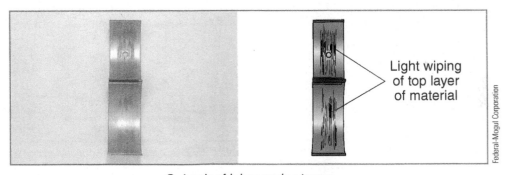

G. Lack of lube: early stages

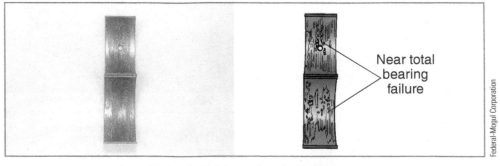

H. Lack of lube: advanced stage

(*Continued*)

FIGURE 49–16 (*Continued*)

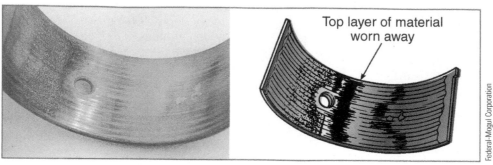

I. Coolant contaminated lube

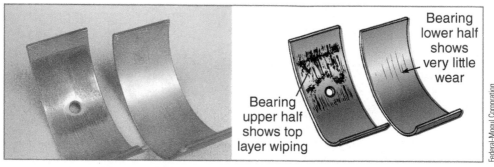

J. Fuel contaminated lube: early stages

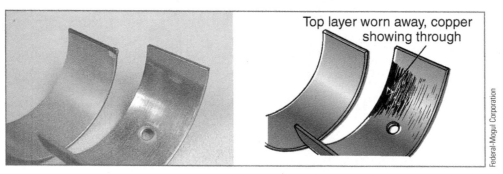

K. Fuel contaminated lube: advanced stage

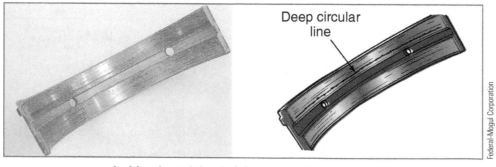

L. Metal particles in lube: early stages

FIGURE 49-16 (Continued)

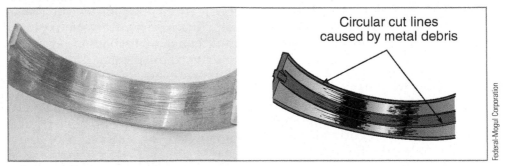

M. Metal particles in lube: advanced stage

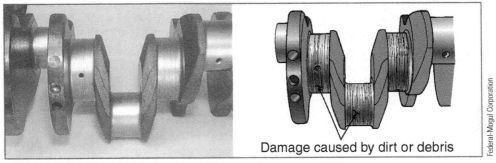

N. Crankshaft journals damaged by dirt or metal debris in lube

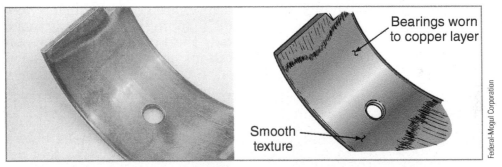

O. Airborne dirt in oil: abrasive action wear to a smooth texture

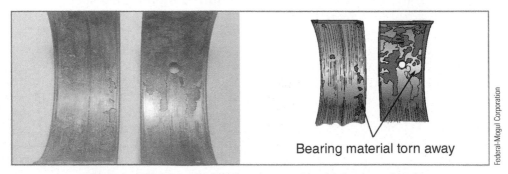

P. Hot short rod bearing failure caused by high shear loads
and extreme temperatures

CRANKSHAFTS

Modern crankshafts seldom fail. On a newly introduced engine series, they may fail according to a pattern. Always report crankshaft failures to the manufacturer, whether or not the equipment is under warranty. Metallurgical failures are infrequent. Subjected to abuse, crankshafts will fail, but more often the abuse will manifest itself with the failure of a subsidiary component. Crankshaft failures can be categorized by the type of loading that initiates the failure.

Torsional Failures

Torsional failures are usually caused by a loose or defective crank vibration damper or flywheel, out-of-balance engine-driven components, engine lugdown, or engine overspeed. Torsional failures of crankshafts are characterized by fractures that initiate at the journal oil holes or run circumferentially through the journal fillets.

Bending Failures

Crankshaft bending failures are caused by misaligned main bearing bores, main bearing failure, or broken/loose main bearing caps. This type of failure is characterized by cracks that initiate at the main journal fillet and extend at a 45-degree angle through the throw journal fillet.

> **TECH TIP:**
>
> Most OEMs suggest that the vibration damper be replaced at every engine overhaul; Chapter 7 outlines some of the reasons why. This should certainly be done following a crankshaft failure.

TURBOCHARGERS

When turbochargers fail, the cause of the failure can usually be related to one or more of the following:

- Lack of lubrication
- Contaminated lube oil
- Excessively high exhaust temperatures
- Foreign objects in the impeller or compressor housings

Lack of Lubrication

Turbochargers are pressure lubed directly by the engine lubrication circuit, in most cases by a dedicated feed hose and dedicated return pipe. Because the lube oil is responsible for both lubrication and cooling, the consequences of oil deprivation are often almost immediate. A common cause of turbocharger lubrication failures is driver abuse caused by hot shutdown. Other causes of lack of lubrication in a turbocharger may be low crankcase oil level, low oil pressure, inappropriate oil, or excessively high oil temperatures. When a turbocharger is not properly lubricated, one or more of the following may result:

- Tempering of metal surfaces indicated by coloration, usually blue
- Varnishing of lube oil onto bearing surfaces
- Failure of the turbine housing seal
- Contact of the turbine and/or compressor wheels with the housings
- Turbine or compressor wheel separation from the turbo shaft

INAPPROPRIATE LUBRICATION A turbo shaft is supported hydrodynamically by the engine lube, and because it can wind out revolutions as high as 140,000 rpm, turbochargers are sensitive to inappropriate, contaminated, or degraded lube oil. Inappropriate oil would include lube oil that falls short of meeting the manufacturer specifications or viscosity. For instance, a single cold-start event in an engine using 15W-40 lube oil in northern, mid-winter conditions can trigger a range of engine problems, including damage to the turbocharger. The use of low-cost bulk lube oils is widespread among fleets: Because these oils often lack additives that define the hydrodynamic and boundary throw-off properties required by the OEM specification, when turbine shafts are wound out at their highest speeds, centrifugal force throws oil from the turbine shaft, resulting in accelerated wear and bearing failures.

When oil becomes contaminated with abrasives or liquid contaminants such as fuel or coolant, the hydrodynamics of the turboshaft are compromised: The result can wear out the shaft and destroy seals and bearings. Another common cause of turbocharger lubrication failures is degraded lube oil. Not observing the OEM-recommended oil change intervals results in engine lube supporting a higher load of blow-by residues and reduction in the ability of the additives to function effectively to maintain the hydrodynamic and boundary lubrication requirements of the turbo.

HOT SHUTDOWN When an engine is shut down immediately after a high-load run, the oil feed to the turbocharger immediately ceases. Lubrication oil to the turbocharger supports the turbine shaft hydrodynamically, but also plays a major role in cooling. When a hot shutdown occurs, the turbine shaft is usually rotating, so initially lube oil is thrown off the shaft by centrifugal force. Next, high shaft temperatures boil off oil and bake residual oil to the shaft, causing varnishing. When the engine is next started, the turbo remains dry until lube oil reaches it from the lube circuit: This dry-start condition, accompanied by the abrasive effect of the varnished oil, scores the shaft and rapidly wears the softer bushings.

Because it is such a common cause of turbocharger failure, the tattletales associated with hot shutdown should be identified. Hot shutdowns often result in varnishing of the turbine side bearing: When the cooked varnishing is peeled away, abrasive scoring of the shaft is often evident. A key to identifying hot shutdown abuse are quench spots or rings on the turbine shaft close to the turbine housing: This is caused when drops of oil fall on a severely overheated shaft, causing quenching discoloration. The abrasive effect of hot shutdowns impacts on the bushings, wearing them rapidly to the point that both the turbine and compressor wheels contact their housings.

External Debris Failures

When considering "external" debris damage to a turbocharger, the gas flow through the assembly obviously has to be accounted for to source the material. Debris entering the impeller housing is sourced upstream from the compressor or "cold" side, while debris entering the turbine housing or "hot" side has been discharged through the engine cylinder or cylinder head. External debris entering a turbocharger impeller housing has usually bypassed the air intake system components upstream from the housing, meaning that the failure begins there. When intake ducting, hose clamps, or the engine air filter fail, in more cases than not, the damage that results is gradual rather than catastrophic in nature. *Dusting* of an engine occurs when an air filter develops a small puncture or tear, an intake air hose clamp loosens, or a small hole develops in ducting or hoses upstream from the impeller housing. The fine dust ingested by an engine in this location may be extremely abrasive. Its effect on the turbocharger impeller can be to wear its vanes or blades paper thin, resulting in loss of power and possible fracture.

When external debris enters a turbine housing, the turbocharger suffers collateral damage caused by an internal engine condition such as a dropped valve, separated valve seat, broken ring(s), or injector damage. Unlike most cold-side originated turbocharger failures, external debris originating from within the engine cylinder tends to cause immediate, catastrophic failures. When investigating external debris turbocharger failures, it is important to describe the appearance of debris so that it can be sourced and/or referenced to others for analysis:

- Size
- Shape: uniform, nonuniform
- Material: magnetic, nonmagnetic
- Color: may indicate temperature at which the failure occurred

Some typical indicators of foreign debris in a turbocharger are:

- Bent vanes
- Broken vanes
- Bent turbine shaft
- Wheel separation

Note that damage to the impeller wheel is more likely to occur at its inside diameter. Similarly, damage to the turbine wheel is more likely to occur at its outside diameter. This is common sense, really: it results from the gas flow through the turbocharger.

High Exhaust Temperatures

Turbocharger failures due to excessively high exhaust temperatures are less common today simply because with computer-controlled engines it has become more difficult to either overfuel or advance injection timing. High exhaust temperatures heat the turbine housing, and this heat can penetrate the turbo core. The result can be oxidation and distortion of the core components, including the seals and bearings. High engine exhaust temperatures cause:

- Carburized, degraded engine oil
- Oxidation, surface erosion
- Scaling and coking (carbon crystallization) on components
- Tempering of components (indicated by surface coloring blue/purple/yellow)
- Turbine seal failure
- Worn bearings
- Turbine and impeller wheel housing contact
- Wheel separation from the turbine shaft

EGR-RELATED PROBLEMS

EGR failures are commonly sourced to the EGR heat exchanger, the valve that controls EGR mixture concentricity, or the Delta pressure sensor circuit. Symptoms of EGR circuit failure relate to soot and sludge buildup in the venturi, the control gate, or the intake manifold. When there is evidence of excessive soot or sludge in the intake manifold, troubleshooting the EGR circuit should be undertaken, beginning with checking any logged codes. Most OEMs comprehensively monitor EGR circuit performance, so in almost all cases either fault codes or an audit trail should provide some clues as to the source of the problem. Investigating EGR failures should take into account EGR valve malfunctions and EGR heat exchanger internal failure. Some indicators for troubleshooting EGR problems are provided in Chapter 48, but this should always be undertaken guided by the OEM service literature when working on actual engines.

DIESEL PARTICULATE FILTER (DPF)-RELATED PROBLEMS

DPF failures are often characterized by black smoke emission, but when attempting to source the problem, you will be required to check out all the circuits upstream from the DPF. As in the case of the EGR circuit, all OEMs comprehensively monitor the DPF and its regeneration history, so you must begin any troubleshooting procedure by connecting to the chassis data bus. When checking the cause of black smoke emission from an EGR- and DPF-equipped diesel engine, you should use the OEM electronic service tool (EST) and service information system (SIS) to do the following:

- Check for any diagnostic trouble codes that relate to the engine breathing circuit.
- Inspect the DPF for external dents and cracks (impact damage).
- Remove the DPF and check for the presence of oil or fuel. If either is present, this should direct you to source the fuel or oil ingression into the circuit (e.g., fuel injection, turbocharger, etc). If not:
  - Check out the venturi for the EGR or clean gas induction (CGI) system. Check out the EGR or CGI control valve and the EGR or CGI heat exchanger.

INJECTOR-RELATED PROBLEMS

We are going to take a brief look at injector-related failure problems. To do this we are going to focus on electronic unit injector (EUI) and electro-hydraulic injector (EHI) assemblies. Before beginning, it should be pointed out that the self-diagnostic capability of most of today's electronically controlled diesel engines identifies a majority of injector failures. Most injector failures tend to produce no external evidence that is visible to the naked eye.

Internal Leakage

A major cause of injector failure is internal leakage. Internal leakage is caused by a failure of the control or poppet valves to seal. An EUI poppet valve has an angled seat that, when closed, traps fuel in the EUI pumping circuit. Similarly, EHI control valves alternately open and close a pilot circuit at injection pressures. Because these valves open and close with some force up to 19 times per second at rated engine speed, any abrasives in the fuel can create wear. When an EUI poppet valve fails to seal, the result is low power, sometimes accompanied by fueling imbalance, visible smoke emission, and more frequent DPF regen cycles. In most engines manufactured after 2004 (and some before), performing an engine cylinder balance test (or multicylinder cutout test) can identify internal leakage before it begins to seriously affect performance. Contaminated fuel is the usual cause of internal leakage in an EUI, but leakage may also be caused by cavitation erosion, which is described in the next section.

Fuel Supply Pressure

The fuel subsystem must charge injection pumping chambers (on EUIs, hydraulically actuated electronic unit injectors [HEUIs], electronic unit pumps [EUPs], and pump-line-nozzle [PLN] systems) at their specified pressure, or cavitation damage can result. After the completion of the effective stroke in all types of high-pressure injection pump, the pumping plunger is retracted by a powerful spring. As the plunger lifts to aspirate the pump chamber, supply fuel at charging pressure must flow into the pump chamber rapidly to avoid creating lower-than-atmospheric pressure. If fuel subsystem charging pressures are lower than specification due to restricted filters, vacuum bubbles may be formed: As system pressure recovers (almost instantly afterward), this fuel pressure acts on vacuum bubbles, causing them to implode. The result is what we know as *cavitation erosion*. Vacuum bubble implosion can eat away the surface material of the plunger and barrel and also damage sealing surfaces. Cavitation erosion usually requires replacement of the injector pumping mechanism. **Figure 49–17** shows how cavitation can damage an EUI.

Seized Injector Failure

Seized injectors are usually easy to identify because the follower usually binds well below the stop tram, as shown in **Figure 49–18**. The usual cause is fuel contamination, usually with water. If this occurs, check the fuel tanks for water and investigate to determine whether excessive methyl hydrate (alcohol) is being dumped into the vehicle fuel tanks. If an EUI seizes when it is nearly new, it may indicate an OEM quality control problem. In all cases, when an EUI seizes, change it: Do not attempt to unseize and reuse it.

Broken EUI Spring

When an injector retraction spring breaks, it may also damage the control cartridge. The breakage is usually the result of metal fatigue. The condition produces a pronounced top end rattle and sometimes rhythmic engine rpm roll at idle. **Figure 49–19** shows an EUI with

FIGURE 49–17 Low fuel subsystem charging pressure can result in injector cavitation damage due to delayed pump chamber fill.

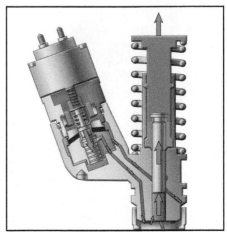

On most EUI injectors, the tappet and tappet spring lift the plunger and pull supply fuel into the pump chamber.

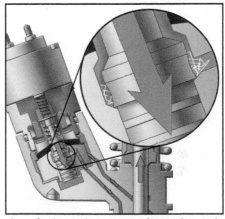

Low fuel supply pressure from plugged fuel filters can cause cavitation damage to injector poppet valve during injector fill.

a broken spring that has also damaged the control cartridge stator screw. When an EUI spring breaks, most OEMs require the EUI to be changed: Some permit just the spring to be replaced, but in cases where the stator has also been damaged, there is no choice but to change out the EUI.

Loose or Missing EUI Stop Plate Screw

EUI stop plate integrity should be checked when you have a fuel-in-oil complaint that has no other obvious cause. The stop plate should be checked for looseness along with the stop plate screws. The actual stop plate seal is an O-ring, so even in cases where the stop plate screw torque

FIGURE 49–18 Seized injector.

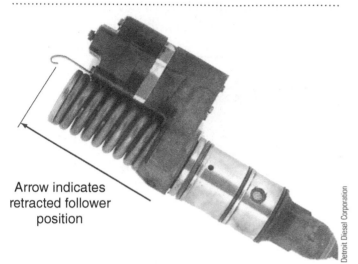

Arrow indicates
retracted follower
position

Detroit Diesel Corporation

FIGURE 49–19 Broken injector follower spring and damaged stator.

Detroit Diesel Corporation

FIGURE 49–20 Loose stop plate screw failure.

Detroit Diesel Corporation

FIGURE 49–21 Cracked injector body failure.

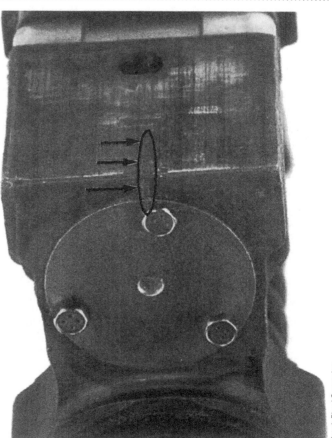

Detroit Diesel Corporation

appears OK, a rolled or pinched O-ring may be the cause. **Figure 49–20** shows the location of the stop plate and its three screws on a DDC EUI.

Cracked Injector Body

At minimum, a cracked injector body will result in a fuel-in-oil problem: It is usually accompanied by cylinder misfire. The cause is usually fatigue caused by prolonged high-load operation or plain old age. It is mostly commonly seen in EUIs that have been in service for a decade of operation. The crack may be difficult to identify with the naked eye. **Figure 49–21** shows an EUI with a cracked body.

Broken Injector Electrical Terminal

The usual cause of broken injector terminals is overtorquing during installation. It is a common problem that you get to know about quickly if you have caused it, because it usually produces a next-day "come back." Although one OEM permits control cartridge replacement, in most cases there is no choice but to replace the injector, this time observing the torque specification. **Figure 49–22** shows a sheared EUI terminal.

FIGURE 49–22 Solenoid terminal screw failure.

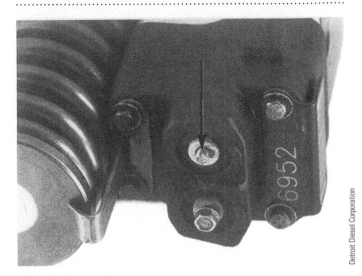

Detroit Diesel Corporation

Blown Nozzle Tip

The symptoms of a blown nozzle tip are misfire, low power, and engine smoking. The more common cause is water in fuel so when this occurs, check the tanks. To get water pumped through a modern fuel system as far as the injectors usually requires substantial abuse of methyl hydrate (alcohol); refer to Chapter 19 if you are not familiar with the consequences of methyl hydrate/fuel conditioner dosing in diesel fuel. The other cause of blown nozzle tips is physical damage caused by dropping the EUI prior to installation or a dropped cylinder valve. **Figure 49–23** and **Figure 49–24** are images of EUIs with their

FIGURE 49–23 Blown nozzle spray tip failure on a EUI injector.

Detroit Diesel Corporation

FIGURE 49–24 Blown nozzle spray tip failure on a DDEC EUI injector.

Detroit Diesel Corporation

nozzle tips blown away. **Figure 49–25** shows a HEUI injector with a fried solenoid.

TECH TIP:

When one injector fails, check the others in the engine, especially when the engine miles or hours are high. If you do not, you risk a failure recurrence in another engine cylinder. A good preventive maintenance (PM) program should identify the performance life of injectors, allowing scheduled replacements; this will help avoid costly on-the-road equipment breakdowns.

EHI Failures

EHIs are especially sensitive to any kind of fuel contamination, and a high percentage of failures are fuel related. This means that the frequency of EHI failures tends to be higher in geographical areas where fuel quality is suspect or fuel is stored for prolonged periods. Fuel-related problems are seldom caught before an injector fails, and this can lead to other subcomponent damage. Bosch supplies a large percentage of EHIs to commercial

FIGURE 49–25 HEUI injector with a scorched solenoid.

engine OEMs, and its most recent research classifying EHI failures produced the following data:

Valve seat failure	35%
Nozzle assembly failure	30%
High-pressure sealing failure	25%
Actuator assembly failure	5%
Armature set failure	3%
Body failure	2%

In addition, contaminants in fuel can block or restrict passages. This can disable an EHI, but not necessarily damage it: Cleaning and bench-testing may be all that is required before returning the injector to service.

COMMON ABUSES OF ENGINES AND FUEL SYSTEMS

The following are some common abuses of engines and fuel systems that the diagnostic technician should always keep in mind when performing failure analysis.

- Cold-startup procedure: Excessive use of ether, excessive engine speeds when oil temperatures are low, excessive engine loading when engine temperature is low.
- Excessive engine idling: This can glaze cylinder walls or break down engine lube (rings do not seal well when cylinder pressures are lower); prolonged idling at low temperatures may cause fuel contamination of engine lube.
- Overfueling: Causes high cylinder pressures (which can reduce engine life or cause outright mechanical failure), increases noxious emissions, reduces engine longevity, and costs money through wasted fuel.
- Use of inappropriate engine oil: Using 15W-40 engine oil during winter in northern United States, Canadian, and subarctic conditions damages engines and, on the way to doing that, can make cold-start cranking extremely difficult.

- Engine overspeed: Can cause valve float, which may result in dropping a valve, and increases tensional loading on connecting rods and crank throws, which may result in complete engine failure.
- Advancing fuel injection timing: A common abuse, the objective being to improve engine performance; the consequences of this practice vary from greatly reducing engine life (at best) to rapid mechanical engine failure.
- Fuel additive abuses: These include adding to fuel moth balls, gasoline, kerosene, alcohols, aftermarket fuel conditioners, engine oil, and automatic transmission fluid (ATF).
- Use of fuel heaters: Fuel heaters are not generally recommended by OEMs, as the fuel's lubricity is compromised by heating it. The preferred method of running an engine through arctic, subarctic, Canadian, and northern United States mid-winter conditions is to use #1D fuel, which is temperature conditioned by the refiner with cloud point depressants and glycol additives (arctic fuel).
- Hot shutdown: Can damage turbocharged engines especially. The turbine bearings are vulnerable because the turbine shaft is still rotating after the oil flow has ceased. Additionally, the heat from the hot turbine exhaust cooks the oil at the bearings, rendering them baked dry for the next startup.

TECH TIP:

When diagnosing engine performance complaints and component failures, keep an open mind and avoid making assumptions before developing a foundation for them. *Try not to* indulge in coffee-table diagnosis, that is, diagnosing a condition based on a nontechnical person's report. In most cases, a truck driver can be considered a nontechnical person. *Do* consult experienced technicians when in doubt, especially where the results of a troubleshooting sequence indicate that the next step is to begin the disassembly of a component.

SUMMARY

- Failure analysis, by definition, is the examination of failed components to attempt to determine the root cause of a failure.
- Diesel technicians should aim to develop sound failure analysis skills to prevent repeated failures.

- In seeking out the root cause of a failure, technicians must learn how to organize facts so that collateral damage is identified as such.
- Failure analysis is usually performed on completely disassembled components or subcomponents.

- The key to accurate failure analysis is to develop the skills to properly organize information.
- Abrasive wear accounts for a majority of wear failures, and may occur in both lubricated and nonlubricated components.
- Adhesive wear produces accelerated failures. It occurs when two moving surfaces contact each other with insufficient lubrication.
- Corrosion is chemical deterioration of a metal surface.
- Erosion occurs when abrasive particles suspended in fast-moving fluids contact surrounding surfaces, resulting in fine impact and abrasive damage.
- Cavitation erosion occurs when gas bubbles in liquids collapse against metal surfaces, creating a percussive effect.

- Contact stress fatigue occurs when two surfaces slide, roll, or are dragged against each other.
- Loads can be categorized as bending, compressional, tensional, or torsional. It follows that when a load becomes an overload, the failures that result can be categorized using the same terms.
- Brittle fractures result from a shock load or high force impact.
- Ductile fractures result from component overloads and occur quickly, but not as fast as brittle fractures.
- Fatigue fractures are typically the result of cyclic overloading.
- Contaminated fuel is a major cause of injector failures. In such cases, it makes sense to investigate the source of the fuel contamination to avoid repeat failures.

REVIEW QUESTIONS

1. An aluminum trunk-type piston has failed with a hole burned through the center of the crown. Technician A states that this might be due to a retarded timing condition. Technician B states that such a failure could occur caused by a dribbling injector nozzle. Who is correct?
   a. Technician A only
   b. Technician B only
   c. Both A and B
   d. Neither A nor B

2. Which of the following conditions could cause carbon buildup on pistons?
   a. Overfueling
   b. Injector nozzle failure
   c. Retarded injection timing
   d. All of the above

3. Which of the following conditions is the more likely result of advanced timing in a diesel engine?
   a. Erosion near the center of the piston crown
   b. Erosion pitting above the top compression ring land
   c. Overall piston scuffing
   d. Fractured rings

4. Which of the following operating modes would be most likely to result in a tensile conn rod failure?
   a. Overfueling
   b. Lugdown
   c. Ether abuse
   d. An overspeeding engine

5. Etched main bearings could be caused by all of the following conditions *except:*
   a. fuel in lube.
   b. coolant in lube.
   c. sulfur in lube.
   d. particulate in lube oil.

6. Evidence of cavitation erosion on a set of wet liners would most likely be caused by:
   a. high cylinder pressures.
   b. incorrect coolant chemistry.
   c. piston spalling.
   d. liner O-ring failure.

7. Which of the following might result in glazed cylinder sleeves?
   a. High cylinder pressures
   b. Prolonged engine idling
   c. Ether usage
   d. Engine lugging

8. When observing a disassembled engine, you see that the outer edges of all the pistons have evidence of melting and erosion. This would most likely be caused by:
   a. advanced timing.
   b. a dribbling injector.
   c. retarded timing.
   d. high sulfur content fuel.

9. When examining a set of pistons from a disassembled engine, you observe scuffing on the thrust sides of all of the pistons. Which of the following would be the more likely cause?
   a. High cylinder pressures
   b. Overheating
   c. Contaminated engine lube
   d. High sulfur content fuel

10. Which of the following components, when worn, may cause lower oil pressures?
   a. Main bearings
   b. Valve guides
   c. Oil control rings
   d. All of the above

11. What is the most common cause of EUI failure?
   a. Cavitation
   b. Internal leakage
   c. Metal fatigue
   d. Fried stator

12. You have determined that a set of EUIs has failed due to cavitation. Which of the following would be the more likely *root cause* of the failure?
   a. Restricted secondary filter
   b. Prolonged high-load operation
   c. Incorrect injector timing setting
   d. Double-gasketing the EUI seat

13. Technician A states that B-life is used as a means of reckoning costs over the life of an engine. Technician B states that the letter B in the term *B-life* references predicted bearing longevity. Who is correct?
   a. Technician A only
   b. Technician B only
   c. Both A and B
   d. Neither A nor B

14. Which of the following is the correct technical description of what we call *scuffing*?
   a. Scraping
   b. Adhesive failure
   c. Thermal failure
   d. Catastrophic

15. Technician A states that B10 life is used by some fleets to determine how long they should keep trucks before selling them. Technician B states that Bx life is a prediction of engine life before major repair. Who is correct?
   a. Technician A only
   b. Technician B only
   c. Both A and B
   d. Neither A nor B

16. What does Bosch research indicate to be the major cause of EHI failures?
   a. Valve seat failure
   b. Actuator failure
   c. Injector body cracks
   d. Control circuit plugging

17. When an EHI failure is attributed to contaminated fuel, which of the following is required to avoid a repeat failure?
   a. Replace all six injectors in the engine.
   b. Locate the source of the contaminated fuel.
   c. Drain the fuel tanks and refill.
   d. Add two cans of diesel fuel conditioner to the tanks.

18. Technician A says that hot shutdown of a diesel engine can destroy turbocharger bearings. Technician B says that when a diesel engine is run for prolonged periods at rated speed and load, turbocharger bearings can be destroyed. Who is correct?
   a. Technician A only
   b. Technician B only
   c. Both A and B
   d. Neither A nor B.

50

Prerequisites: Chapters 35 and 49, plus sound knowledge of all engine and fuel systems

TROUBLESHOOTING AND DIAGNOSIS

OBJECTIVES

After studying this chapter, you should be able to:

- Quarterback all engine troubleshooting using the OEM-recommended EST and online SIS.
- Adhere to software-driven sequential troubleshooting paths to diagnose engine faults.
- Interpret engine OEM expectations when diagnosing engine complaints.
- Understand when it is appropriate to think "outside the box."
- Use your technical and mechanical skills only when the OEM software fails to reveal the root cause of a failure.
- Analyze exhaust gas smoke emission by color.
- Relate some typical engine performance malfunctions to smoke color.
- Outline step-by-step sequential troubleshooting practices.
- Troubleshoot some typical engine and fuel system failures.
- Identify common operator and technician abuses of engine and fuel systems.
- Develop a checklist for tackling lack-of-power complaints specific to an engine or chassis system.
- Profile some of the most common engine malfunction symptoms and relate them to typical causes.
- Identify the role played by a DSM in providing product technical support.
- Navigate troubleshooting charts and trees to investigate typical engine problems.
- Understand the importance of connecting an EST to the chassis data bus as a first step in troubleshooting engine problems.

KEY TERMS

black smoke
blue smoke
cavitation
communications adapter (CA)
cylinder leakage test
dynamometer
electronic service tool (EST)
HD-OBD
master gauge
master pyrometer
sequential troubleshooting chart
service information system (SIS)
technical service bulletin (TSB)
troubleshooting
white smoke

INTRODUCTION

The term **troubleshooting** is generally used to describe noninvasive (meaning that as little of the engine is disassembled as possible) methods of determining the cause of an engine problem. These methods can vary from educated guesswork to highly structured procedures, such as are required when diagnosing electronic engine management systems. Manufacturers make troubleshooting guides available for purposes of diagnosing common engine complaints. This chapter should be used in conjunction with Chapter 35, which outlines how to use proprietary **service systems (SISs)** and **electronic service tools (ESTs)**. We use the acronym SIS generically to describe the various proprietary original equipment manufacturer (OEM) online diagnostic software programs.

According to Mack Trucks, before model year 2002 a single symptom typically had five potential causes. From model years 2002 to 2010, a single symptom could have up to 10 potential causes, due to the increase in emission controls and monitoring electronics. Because post-2010 engines have added an even more complex array of monitoring and actuator circuits, a single symptom can have up to 25 potential causes. This makes life challenging for a diagnostic technician, especially when the cause of the problem falls outside of the troubleshooting software's diagnostic routines. More than ever, truck technicians are required to fully understand engine systems and the ways in which they are interdependent on other chassis systems.

TROUBLESHOOTING TOOLS

The following tools are required to effectively troubleshoot diesel engines today:

- EST loaded with the OEM diagnostic software and SIS
- Serial link interface or **communications adapter (CA)**
- Wireless or wired Internet connection
- Breakout boxes, Tees, terminal spoons, and a digital multimeter (DMM)

THINKING INSIDE THE BOX

Troubleshooting today's diesel engines could not be more different than troubleshooting your dad's diesel engine. Troubleshooting today is driven by diagnostic software. In most cases, you are required to connect to the chassis data bus and access the engine source address (SA 00/MID 128) controller. The EST you are required to use is loaded with the OEM diagnostic software and has an active Internet connection. After connecting with the engine SA, you are required to follow a structured troubleshooting path, which is often interactive. In other words, the technician could be instructed to make a voltage measurement using a DMM, then input the value measured into the diagnostic software. The next step in the diagnostic sequence depends on the value input. Troubleshooting electronically managed engines uses this type of structured procedure based on software-guided **sequential troubleshooting charts** because it reduces the time required to identify the source of a problem. Failure to observe OEM diagnostic routines can result in:

- Voiding of warranty or denial of warranty claims
- Excessive amounts of wasted troubleshooting time
- Trial-and-error diagnostics (a common practice that makes the whole industry look bad)
- Engine damage incurred by the troubleshooting itself
- Costly comeback repairs

You might argue that thinking inside the box does not require you to think. That is correct in a way; although you navigate diagnostic software, you are really just obeying a sequence of instructions. The bottom line is that a high percentage of engine malfunctions can be quickly and accurately identified as to root cause using computer diagnostics. Another major advantage of online SIS is that a repair procedure can be tagged with all the relevant **technical service bulletins (TSBs)**. Technicians today have to learn to accept that their technical ability should be brought into play only when diagnosis of a problem falls outside the scope the software diagnostic maps.

> **TECH TIP:**
> Never skip a software-guided diagnostic routine. This happens all too often when a technician knows from experience what the "probable cause" of a complaint is. This practice can result in actually extending the time spent troubleshooting and denial of warranty.

THINKING OUTSIDE THE BOX

Because today's diesel engines are capable of some pretty exacting self-diagnosis, the most challenging troubleshooting problems tend to be those that fall just outside the scope of the troubleshooting paths embedded in the OEM software. This requires a troubleshooting technician who can think outside the box, when the limitations of the diagnostic software are exceeded. The trick is to methodically work with the software guided diagnostic routines as required by the OEM—and only when this fails to produce a result should the technician resort to that higher level of analytical skills that make the human brain a superior instrument to a computer. Thinking outside the box requires a toolbox of technical skills, some of which take some experience to develop:

- Thorough understanding of a diesel engine's mechanical systems
- Thorough understanding of the engine's computer control systems
- OEM-specific training on the engine the technician is working on
- Ability to navigate the online SIS using an EST and OEM software
- Ability to navigate OEM wiring schematics and virtual schematics

The general objective of this chapter is to help technicians to work methodically and not overlook an obvious possible cause of a problem. Although we cannot sufficiently stress the importance of online SISs, sometimes technicians forget that an engine is a fundamentally mechanical device and that some problems not only require knowledge of how those mechanical systems fail, but may not be identified by diagnostic software.

ONLINE SERVICE INFORMATION SYSTEMS

All truck diesel engine OEMs require that technicians use online SISs to quarterback troubleshooting routines. These are covered fully in Chapter 35, but must be also referenced here. As indicated earlier, the consequence of not using the OEM's SIS can result in excessive time spent in identifying the cause of a problem and possible denial of warranty. The advantage of using SISs is that technology changes so rapidly that hard-copy paper approaches to repair methods become dated as soon as they are published. Most OEMs update their online information daily.

An SIS connection is usually oriented by engine serial number and provides the technician with user-friendly website search engines that can even include parts data. Most truck chassis OEM SISs use an umbrella approach that permits the technician direct access to the SIS Web locations of the manufacturer of the chassis subsystems. For instance, if you log onto Navistar's NSI, among the options you can select will be a route into Cummins QSOL, because Cummins supplies engines as an option to Navistar chassis. There is a double message when it comes to using SISs. Yes, using online information systems is crucial ... but an expert technician also must have a good understanding of engine mechanics.

HD-OBD

Soon, heavy-duty onboard diagnostics **(HD-OBD)** will be mandatory on all trucks. HD-OBD, like its light-duty counterpart OBDII, will apply to all critical emissions-related faults. Once HD-OBD has been fully effected, third-party ESTs must be able to access all covered fault codes to a repair level. This is not to say that current generic ESTs cannot do this, but after the implementation, OEMs must ensure that HD-OBD covered codes can be interpreted to a final repair level. This includes any software reprogramming required by the repair procedure.

SMOKE ANALYSIS

An engine exhausts noxious gases, water, and carbon dioxide. Providing these emissions remain in the gaseous state, they will not be observed exiting the exhaust piping. For exhaust gas to be identified as smoke, the emission must be in a liquid or a solid state. When smoke appears to be black, the state of the emission is solid; specifically, particulate solids through which light will not pass at all, making it appear black to the observer's eye. The root causes of black smoke are associated with incompletely combusted fuel or engine oil.

When exhaust smoke is white, the emission is in the form of condensing liquid droplets from which light reflects or refracts, making it appear white to the observer's eye. The condensing liquid could be engine coolant, fuel, or (when cold enough) the water that is a normal product of combustion. When smoke is blue, it is normally associated with engine oil emission. This is usually classified as a condensing liquid emission from which light is mainly reflected rather than refracted, due to the usually dark color of engine oil.

There are three states of matter—solid, liquid, and vapor—and diesel end gas can be emitted in all three states. The technician analyzing the smoke emitted from a tailpipe is making an observation on the *state* of the emission. It is important to note that the absence of observable smoke does not mean that the engine is not producing noxious emissions. It means only that engine emissions are in a gaseous state. Gaseous emissions can only be analyzed using costly exhaust gas analysis equipment. Nevertheless, observable smoke emitted from an engine tells a story, and the technician should have some ability to interpret the causes of a smoking engine.

In summary, exhaust emission from the stack(s) of a diesel engine can appear in one of the following four ways:

1. Clear. The exhaust gas stream is in a gaseous state.
2. White. Some liquid (water, coolant, or fuel) is condensing in the exhaust gas stream.
3. Black. Some solid matter (particulate soot) is contained in the exhaust gas.
4. Blue. This usually indicates presence of engine oil (condensed and partial soot) in exhaust gas.

BLACK SMOKE

The term **black smoke** is used to describe anything from a grayish haze to heavily sooted exhaust gas emission. It is the result of the incomplete combustion of fuel and therefore has many causes, the most common of which are:

- Insufficient combustion air
- Restricted exhaust
- Exhaust gas recirculation (EGR) failure
- Diesel particulate filter (DPF) failure
- Excess or irregular fuel distribution
- Improper grade of fuel
- Degraded fuel: CN definers boiled off

TECH TIP:

When black smoke emission is caused by using fuel that has been stored for an excessive period (a problem in equipment used seasonally), addition of a cetane improver may help. Cetane improvers should not be used for more than one tank of fuel because fuel and emission systems damage can occur.

TECH TIP:

Frequent DPF regeneration cycles are usually an indication of an internal engine problem. Investigate the problem even when no DTCs are logged. By the time a DTC is logged, the DPF substrate may be damaged beyond repair.

Insufficient Combustion Air

The causes of insufficient combustion air are air starvation caused by any performance defect in the air intake system components, from the air filter, turbocharger, boost air/heat exchanger, plugged EGR or CGI heat exchanger, EGR or CGI control valve failure, through to intake valve problems; clogged cylinder sleeve ports (two-stroke cycle engines); restricted emergency stop gate; and so on.

In electronically managed engines, check first for a problem that can be read electronically. Test for intake air inlet restriction using a negative pressure gauge or manometer that reads in inches of H_2O (mm of H_2O). The specifications should always be checked with the OEM values, but typical maximum values will be close to:

15-inch H_2O (380-mm H_2O) vacuum—naturally aspirated engines

25-inch H_2O (635-mm H_2O) vacuum—boosted engines

Exhaust System Restriction

Exhaust system restriction problems can usually be related to turbocharger failure, collapsed exhaust system piping, internal failure of engine silencer or catalytic converter, a plugged-up DPF, or exhaust brake malfunction. Because of the emissions systems electronic monitoring found in most post-2004 and all post-2007 highway diesel engines, connect to the chassis data bus to troubleshoot even if a fault code has not been logged.

Excess Fuel/Irregular Fuel Distribution

Excess fuel (overfueling) or irregular fuel distribution can be caused by out-of-spec injection timing (intentional or accidental), injector nozzle failure, variable timing control device failure, unbalanced fuel rack settings, lugging engine (operation at high loads at speeds below peak torque rpm), incorrect governor settings, inoperative or tampered-with manifold boost management system, or defective barometric capsule (altitude compensator). When trouble-shooting electronically managed engines, make sure you connect to the chassis data bus, select the engine SA (see Chapter 35), and perform a cylinder cutout test: This can pinpoint unbalanced cylinder fueling and usually identify the cause.

Improper Fuel Grade

When fuel is stored for prolonged periods, the more volatile fractions evaporate, altering the fuel's chemical characteristics. Additionally, fuel suppliers seasonally adjust fuel to accommodate temperature extremes. The use of used engine lube/fuel mixers often produces smoking. Heavier residual oils may not vaporize, and if they do, there is insufficient time to properly combust them. This practice may cause high acidity in the exhaust gas (high sulfur), which may rust out exhaust systems unusually quickly. Ensure that the engine lube/fuel mixer permits the engine to meet the emissions standards for the year the engine was manufactured. Check the American Petroleum Institute (API) gravity using a hydrometer as outlined in Chapter 18.

TECH TIP:

It is essential to use the correct ultra-low sulfur (ULS) fuel with engines using DPFs. Though it is now rare, it appears that pre-2007 LS formulated fuel is still obtainable; this fuel can terminally destroy a DPF in as little time as 1 hour of operation. *Never* use lube/fuel mixers with engines equipped with DPFs.

WHITE SMOKE

White smoke is caused by condensing liquid in the exhaust gas stream. Temperature usually plays a role when white smoke is observed: both ambient temperature and the engine operating temperature. Remember that water is a natural product of the combustion of any hydrocarbon fuel, and in mid-winter conditions it is normal for some of this to condense in the exhaust gas. However, when white smoke is a problem, the following are some of the possible causes.

Cylinder Misfire

On electronically managed engines, first check for a problem that can be read electronically; perform an electronic cylinder cutout test using a personal computer (PC) or other EST if that option is in the software diagnostics. With nonelectronic

engines, disable each injector in sequence using a rocker claw/lever for mechanical unit injectors (MUIs) and pressure-time (PT) injectors, and by cracking (loosening the line nut) high-pressure pipes in hydromechanical pump-line-nozzle (PLN) systems.

CAUTION:

Never attempt to mechanically disable the injectors on electronically controlled diesel engines.

CAUTION:

When cracking high-pressure pipes on hydromechanical engines, ensure that suitable eye and hand protection is worn and that spilled fuel is not in danger of igniting.

Low Cylinder Compression Pressure

There are a number of possible causes of low cylinder compression. These are usually mechanical problems that prevent the cylinder from sealing properly. The procedure for checking cylinder compression pressures is outlined later in this chapter, but this type of test is seldom performed today due to the speed and accuracy of electronic cylinder balance tests.

Low CN Fuel

This problem is more likely to be experienced by operators that bulk-purchase fuel in large volumes and then store it for prolonged periods. Diesel fuel cetane number (CN) is defined by its most volatile fractions, and it is these that are most likely to boil off when exposed to high temperatures. Low CN fuel may produce white smoke emission; this appears as a haze in the exhaust gas stream when fueling a warm engine. Test the fuel specific gravity using a fuel hydrometer and compare the reading to the fuel supplier's specification. Consult the fuel supplier as to the correct additive and proportions to correct a CN deficiency in a storage tank. This is seldom a problem in North America, but when refueling in remote locations, ensure that the fuel is purchased from reputable suppliers with a good volume of turnover.

Air Pumped Through the High-Pressure Injection Pump Circuit

Check the fuel subsystem, because this is usually the source of the air, depending on the type of system. This condition is normally accompanied by rough engine operation. Using a diagnostic sight glass can help diagnose the problem and locate it. A diagnostic sight glass is usually a section of optically clear Perspex tube coupled into a dash-6, dash-8, or dash-10 hydraulic hose: The sight glass is coupled in series into the circuit to be tested. Some current engines have sensors in the fuel subsystem that can detect air intrusion into the fuel circuit and log a DTC; depending on the engine, this can sometimes indicate where in the circuit the air is being drawn in.

Coolant Leakage to Cylinders

Confirm that the emission truly is coolant. Engine coolant has an acrid, bittersweet odor that is very noticeable. Locate the source. Some possibilities are injector cup failure, head gasket (fire ring) failure, cracked cylinder head, cracked wet liner flange, or **cavitation** perforation of wet liner. Coolant leakage may be difficult to locate; if the failure is not immediately evident, drop the oil pan, pressurize the cooling system, and observe. If necessary, place clean cardboard under the engine with the cooling system pressurized and leave for a while to attempt to identify the source; this may save an unnecessary engine disassembly. It is often easier to identify an internal coolant leak with the engine intact rather than disassembled, so explore all the options with the engine assembled first.

Low Combustion Temperatures

Low combustion temperatures may be the result of extreme low temperature conditions or a fault in the cooling system management system, such as a defective thermostat, fan drive mechanism, or shutters.

BLUE SMOKE

Blue smoke is usually caused by lube oil getting involved in the combustion process. Some possible causes are turbocharger seal failure, pullover of lube oil from oil bath air cleaner sump, worn valve guides, ring failure, glazed cylinder liners, high oil sump level, excessive big-end bearing oil throw-off, low-grade fuel, fuel contaminated with automatic transmission fluid (ATF), or engine lube placed in fuel tanks as an additive.

SMOKE EMISSION MEASUREMENT

For a number of years, several state and provincial jurisdictions have set exhaust stack maximum smoke density standards. Most of these standards are based on SAE J1667 opacity tests. An opacity test is performed using a light extinction test instrument called an *opacity meter* or *opacimeter. Smoke opacity* is defined as that percentage of light transmitted from a source that is prevented from reaching a sensor. Opacity is expressed as a percentage value. This type of emission testing applies to the aftermarket only, that is, field inspections performed by enforcement agencies. Some jurisdictions in the United States and Canada choose to enforce these standards with heavy fines. Smoke emission testing is covered in Chapter 48.

TROUBLESHOOTING GUIDELINES

As a general rule when troubleshooting a system complaint, investigate the possible causes that can be eliminated easily (and inexpensively) before proceeding to those that require more time. Component disassembly should generally be avoided until all other investigative options have been pursued. This practice will help avoid presenting a customer with an inflated bill for diagnosing a simple complaint. It makes sense to develop some guidelines for troubleshooting engine problems in a service facility. A set of guidelines will help the technician to strategize the troubleshooting procedure. Engine OEMs produce some excellent troubleshooting charts for their own products; **Figure 50–1** reproduces a diagnostic chart that relates to engines fueled by this OEM's hydraulically actuated electronic unit injector (HEUI) system.

The troubleshooting strategy that the technician uses will depend on whether the engine is hydromechanically or electronically managed and on the engine OEM. As we said before, the troubleshooting procedure required of most electronically managed engines is structured and sequential; it must be adhered to. Warranty may be denied by an engine OEM if its diagnostic procedures are not followed, and often it requires the submitting of online forms. The subject of electronic troubleshooting is dealt with in detail in the third section of this textbook. What we are attempting to do here is outline some typical engine problems that are mechanical in origin, along with possible causes and solutions.

FIGURE 50–1 International Truck engine troubleshooting strategy chart.

INTERNATIONAL	DT–466E AND THE INTERNATIONAL 530E HARD START / NO START & PERFORMANCE ENGINE DIAGNOSTICS	Date	Miles	Hours	Technician
		Eng. S/N	VIN		Unit #
		Eng. HP	Ambient Temp.	Coolant Temp.	

◄ HARD START / NO START DIAGNOSTICS ►

1. SUFFICIENT CLEAN FUEL
- Free of Water–Icing and clouding
- Correct grade of fuel

Method	Check
Visual	

2. VISUAL INSPECTION
- Inspect for leaks
- Inspect for loose connections, etc.

Fuel Oil Coolant Electrical Air	
Method	Check
Visual	

3. CHECK ENGINE OIL LEVEL
- Check engine crankcase oil level
- Check for contaminants (fuel, coolant)
- Correct Grade/Viscosity
- Miles/Hours on oil, correct level
- Check oil pressure on dash gauge

Method	Check
Visual	

4. INTAKE/EXHAUST RESTRICTION
- Inspect hoses and piping
- Check filter minder
- Inspect exhaust system

Method	Check
Visual	

Perform Test 7 if EST is not available or inoperative

5. EST TOOL – FAULT CODES
- Install Electronic Service Tool

Active	
Inactive	

◾ See Electronic Diagnostic Form for codes

6a. EST – ENGINE OFF TESTS
- Select "Engine Off" test from diagnostic test menu

Faults Found	

◾ Repair fault codes before continuing

6b. EST–INJECTOR "BUZZ TEST"

NOTE: "Engine Off Test" must be performed first, in order to gain access to the Injector "BUZZ TEST"

- Select "Injector Test" from "The Engine Off Tests" menu

Faults Found	

◾ See Electronic Diagnostic Form for codes

Perform Test 7 if EST is not available or inoperative

7. STI BUTTON – FLASH CODES
- Depress and hold "Engine Diagnostics" switch, then turn the ignition switch to the "ON" position.

Faults Found	

◾ Refer to Electronic Diagnostic form, if fault code(s) set

8. EST TOOL – DATA LIST
- Select and enter the following data as the first 3 lines in a custom data list
- Monitor the data while cranking the engine for 20 seconds minimum

Data	Spec	Actual
Bat. Voltage	7 Volts min.	
Eng. RPM	150 RPM min.	
ICP Pressure	800 PSI min.	

◾ If voltage is low, refer to ECM diagnostics
◾ If no RPM is noted, recheck fault codes
◾ If ICP pressure is low, refer to Test 10

Perform Test 9 if EST is not available or inoperative

9a. ECM VOLTAGE
- Check while cranking the engine
- Measure with DVOM
- Breakout box pins 57+ & 40–

Instrument	Spec	Actual
DVOM 57+ & 40–	7 Volts minimum	

◾ If voltage is low, refer to ECM diagnostics

9b. ENGINE CRANKING RPM
- Minimum 150 RPM engine cranking speed for 20 seconds
- Breakout box pins 34+ & 46– with Fluke 88

Instrument	Spec	Actual
Fluke 88 34+ & 46–	150 RPM minimum	

◾ If no RPM is noted, recheck fault codes

9c. INJECTION CONTROL PRESSURE
- Minimum 150 RPM engine cranking speed for 20 seconds
- Measure with breakout box: pins 27+ & 46– or breakout "Tee" signal (green) & ground (black)

Instrument	Spec	Actual
DVOM 27+ & 46–	1 Volt Minimum	

◾ If ICP pressure is low, refer to Test 10

10. LOW ICP PRESSURE TEST

NOTE: Perform this test if ICP Pressure was low in Test 8 or 9C.

- Remove EOT sensor and check for oil in reservoir and reinstall EOT
- Remove high pressure hose from oil manifold
- Attach adapter and ICP sensor to hose
- Monitor pressure while cranking the engine

Instrument	Spec	Actual
EST	800 PSI min.	
DVOM	1 Volt min.	

◾ If pressure is within specifications, check for high pressure oil leakage. Refer to EGES–145 Sec. 2.2
◾ If pressure is still low, verify that pump is rotating
◾ If pressure is still low, replace IPR and retest

11. FUEL PUMP PRESSURE
- Measure at bleeder valve on filter header
- Minimum 150 RPM cranking speed for 30 seconds

Instrument	Spec	Actual
0–160 PSI Gauge	20 PSI minimum	

◾ If pressure is low, replace fuel filter, clean fuel strainer and retest.

◾ If pressure is still low, perform Transfer Pump Restriction Test 2B (of Performance Diagnostics)

(Continued)

FIGURE 50–1 (*Continued*)

Injector P/N		Turbocharger P/N	
Engine Family Rating Code			
Complaint			

← PERFORMANCE DIAGNOSTICS →

ALL TESTS SHOULD BE PERFORMED WITH ENGINE AT OPERATING TEMPERATURE

1. CHECK ENGINE OIL LEVEL
- Check engine crankcase oil level
- Check for contaminants (fuel, coolant)
- Correct Grade/Viscosity

Method	Check
Visual	

2. SUFFICIENT FUEL/PRESSURE
- Drain sample from tank(s)
- Inspect fuel for contamination
- Measure fuel pressure at fuel filter bleeder
- Measure pressure at high idle

Instrument	Spec	Actual
0–160 PSI Gauge	20 PSI minimum @ High idle	

- ■ If pressure is low, replace fuel filter, clean fuel strainer and retest.
- ■ If pressure still low, proceed with step 2B.

2b. TRANSFER PUMP RESTRICTION

NOTE: Perform this test only if fuel pressure is low.

- Measure at fuel filter inlet @ High idle.

Instrument	Spec	Actual
0–30" Vacuum Gauge	Less than 8 " Hg.	

- ■ If restriction is high, check for blockage between pump and fuel tank
- ■ If restriction < 8 " Hg., refer to EGES–145 Sec. 2.3 for additional diagnostics.

3. EST TOOL – FAULT CODES
- Install Electronic Service Tool

Active	
Inactive	

- ■ See Electronic Diagnostic Form for codes

4a. EST – ENGINE OFF TESTS
- Select "Engine Off Test" from diagnostic test menu

Faults Found	

- ■ Repair fault codes, before continuing

4b. EST–INJECTOR "BUZZ TEST"

NOTE: "Engine Off Test" must be performed first, in order to gain access to the Injector "BUZZ TEST"

- Select "Injector Test" from "The Engine Off Tests" menu

Faults Found	

- ■ See Electronic Diagnostic Form for codes

Perform Test 5 if EST is not available or inoperative

5. STI BUTTON – FLASH CODES
- Depress and hold "Engine Diagnostics" switch, then turn the ignition switch to the "ON" position.

Faults Found	

- ■ Refer to Electronic Diagnostic form if fault code(s) set

6. INTAKE RESTRICTION
- Measure at high idle and no load
- Use manometer or magnehelic gauge

Instrument	Spec	Actual
Manometer or Magnehelic Gauge	12.5" H$_2$O	

7a. EST–ENGINE RUNNING TEST
- Select "Engine Running" test from the diagnostic test menu

Faults Found	

- ■ Refer to Electronic Diagnostic form if fault code(s) set

7b. EST TOOL–INJECTOR TEST
(CYLINDER CONTRIBUTION)

NOTE: "Engine RUNNING Test" must be performed first, in order to gain access to the "INJECTOR TEST"

- Select "Injector Test" from "Engine Running" test menu

Faults Found	

- ■ Refer to Electronic Diagnostic form if fault code(s) set

Tests 8, 9 & 10 to be performed at Full load

8. FUEL PRESSURE (FULL LOAD)
- Measure fuel pressure at fuel filter bleeder.
- Measure pressure at full load rated speed.

Instrument	Spec	Actual
0–160 PSI Gauge	20 PSI minimum	

- ■ If pressure is low, replace fuel filter, clean fuel strainer & retest
- ■ If pressure is still low, perform Test 2B.

---

9. ICP PRESSURE
- Monitor ICP pressure and engine RPM with the EST tool in data list mode
  Or use breakout "TEE" and DVOM
- Refer to EGES–145 for specifications

Data	Spec	Actual
Low Idle	PSI/Volts	
High Idle	PSI/Volts	
Full Load	PSI/Volts	

- ■ If pressure is low or unstable, disconnect ICP sensor and retest
- ■ If problem is resolved, refer to ICP diagnostics
- ■ If pressure is still low or unstable, replace IPR and retest

10. BOOST PRESSURE
- Monitor boost pressure and engine RPM with the EST tool in data list mode
  Or use dash tach and 0–30 PSI gauge and "T", if EST tool is not available
- Measure pressure at full load rated speed
- Refer to EGES–145 for specifications

Spec	Actual
PSI @ RPM	

11. CRANKCASE PRESSURE
- Measure at road draft tube with orifice tool (ZTSE–4039)
- Measure at High Idle no load RPM

Instrument	Spec	Actual
0 to 60 H20 Magnehelic Gauge	< 6" H$_2$O	

STOP

IF GUIDELINE DATA WAS OBTAINED DURING THE FIRST 11 TESTS, ENGINE OPERATION IS SATISFACTORY. NO FURTHER TESTING IS REQUIRED

12. WASTEGATE ACTUATOR TEST
- Apply regulated air to actuator
- Inspect for leakage
- Inspect actuator for movement

Instrument	Spec	Actual
0 to 60 PSI Gauge	28–32 PSI	

13. EXHAUST RESTRICTION
- Visually inspect exhaust system for damage
- Measure at a point 3 to 6 inches after turbo outlet
- Measure at full load and rated speed

Instrument	Spec	Actual
Manometer or Magnehelic Gauge	0–35" H$_2$O	

14. VALVE CLEARANCE
- Engine off: Hot or Cold

Instrument	Spec	Actual
Feeler Gauge		

Courtesy of Navistar International Corp.

LOW OIL PRESSURE

Verify the problem:

1. Check the oil sump level.
2. Install a **master gauge** (an accurate, fluid-filled gauge).
3. Warm the engine to operating temperature and check oil psi.
4. Investigate oil consumption history.
5. Determine the cause.

   Some possible causes and suggested solutions:

- Restricted oil filter or oil cooler bundle. Change the oil and filter(s). If the problem persists, clean or replace the oil cooler bundle (core), and check or clean the filter and oil cooler bypass valves.
- Contaminated lube (fuel). Detect by oil analysis or by odor. Engine lube contaminated with fuel can have a darker appearance and feel thin to the touch. If the cause is fuel, locate the source. This may be difficult; the procedure varies with the type of fuel system and the routing of the fuel to the injector. Pressure-testing of the fuel delivery components may be required. Porosity in the cylinder head casting, failed injector O-ring seals, leaking fuel jumper pipes, and cracked cylinder head galleries are some possible causes. Perform repairs as required, then service the oil and filters.
- Excessive crankshaft bearing clearance. Inspect the bearings to determine the cause. Visually check the crank journals to determine whether removal is required. Replace the bearings, ensuring that the clearance of the new bearings is checked.
- Excessive camshaft or rocker shaft bearing clearance. Replace the bearings.
- Pump relief valve spring stuck open or fatigued. Clean the valve and housing, replacing parts as necessary. Check the bypass/diverter valves in the oil cooler and filter mounting pad.
- Oil pump defect. Recondition or replace the oil pump.
- Oil suction pipe defect. Replace the oil suction pipe.
- Defective oil pressure gauge or sending unit. Replace the oil pressure gauge or sending unit.
- Broken-down (chemically degraded) lube oil. Change the oil and filters.

HIGH OIL CONSUMPTION

Verify the condition by monitoring oil consumption and analyzing exhaust smoke. Some possible causes and suggested solutions:

- Excess cylinder wall lubrication. High oil sump level, excessive connecting rod and big-end bearing oil throw-off, plugged oil control/wiper rings, oil pressure too high, or oil diluted with fuel. This type of problem usually requires engine disassembly to diagnose and repair. The condition can often destroy exhaust aftertreatment hardware.
- External oil leaks. Steam- or pressure-wash the engine, then load on a chassis dynamometer or road test to determine the source.
- High oil temperatures. Malfunctioning boost air heat exchanger, lug down engine loading, overfueling, incorrect fuel injection timing, or problem with the oil cooler or engine cooling system.
- Worn piston ring fit abnormality. Replace the rings.
- Piston ring failure. Determine the cause. Check for other damage, then replace the rings.
- Turbocharger seal failure. Recondition the turbocharger (recore or replace).
- High oil sump level. This causes aeration. Determine the cause of high oil level. Check for operator or service error first, then for the presence of fuel and engine coolant in oil.
- Glazed cylinder liners or sleeves. Caused by improper break-in procedure or prolonged engine idling. Replace cylinder liners/sleeves or use a glaze-buster to reestablish crosshatch.
- Worn cylinder head valve guides or seals. Measure to specification and recondition the cylinder head if required.
- Improper dipstick marking. Drain the oil, fill the sump to OEM specification, then check/alter dipstick markings.

HIGH OIL TEMPERATURE

Some possible causes and suggested solutions:

- Insufficient oil in circulation. Check the sump level, pump pressure, and lubrication circuit restrictions. Repair as required.
- High water jacket temperatures. Test cooling system performance.

- Plugged/failed oil cooler. Disassemble and inspect galleries, bundle, and bypass valve for restrictions and scaling. Service the cooling system afterward to prevent a recurrence.
- Oil badly contaminated. Submit a sample for analysis and repair cause.
- Engine lugdown. Provide some driver training and identify the transmission shift points. Drivers familiar with older engines may not have been adequately retrained to operate today's fuel-efficient engines, which may be programmed with short torque rise windows.

COOLING SYSTEM PROBLEMS

Cooling system problems can be grouped into the following categories:

- Overheating
- Overcooling
- Loss of coolant
- Defective radiator cap
- Defective thermostat

From the troubleshooting perspective, we can study these problems by looking at the performance problems they produce:

- High coolant temperatures
- Low coolant temperatures

High Coolant Temperature

Accurately verify the condition:

1. Check coolant level in the radiator.
2. Install a master gauge to verify the problem.
3. Observe exhaust pyrometer readings and compare to specification.

Some possible causes and solutions:

- Incorrect mixture. The correct mixture for ethylene glycol (EG) is usually an equal proportion of water and antifreeze with somewhere between 3% and 6% coolant conditioner. Increasing the antifreeze proportion with both EG and propylene glycol (PG) reduces cooling efficiency, but when high concentrations of PG are used for arctic operation, you may have no choice.
- Aerated coolant. Usually caused by combustion gases entering the cooling circuit through a defective cylinder head or failed fire ring/cylinder head gasket. Heat is not transferred efficiently through a gas. Verify the condition: Check for bubbles at the water manifold.

- Fan clutch. Test fanstat/thermal fan operation using a master gauge and loading the engine until it reaches the temperature required to cycle the fan.
- Radiator. Check for internal and external flow restrictions. Clean externally. Internal restrictions usually require removal of the radiator and either recoring or the use of specialized reconditioning equipment.
- System does not seal. This permits the coolant to boil at a lower temperature and cause boilover. Test with a cooling system pressure tester. Check and repair/replace the defective radiator cap and/or pressure relief valves.
- Improper airflow. Incorrectly sized fan or missing/damaged radiator shroud may significantly reduce flow through the radiator and engine compartment.
- Loose pump and fan drive belts. This will cause a reduction in coolant and/or airflow. Check visually and with a belt tension gauge.
- Coolant hoses. Coolant hoses should be changed every couple of years. They often fail internally while appearing sound externally. A collapsed hose may cause a significant flow restriction.
- Restricted air intake. May cause high engine temperatures. Test inlet restriction with a water manometer. Typical maximum specifications are 15-inch (380-mm) H_2O for naturally aspirated engines and 25-inch (635-mm) H_2O for boosted engines.
- Exhaust restriction. Causes high engine temperatures. Uncouple the exhaust piping from the turbo or remove the exhaust manifold to see if the condition is corrected. Check the exhaust silencer and, if so equipped, the catalytic converter for internal collapse.
- Shunt line failure. A restriction in the shunt line from the radiator top tank to the water pump inlet may cause a boil condition at the inlet, reducing coolant flow and causing overheating.
- Thermostat. Test out of engine for opening value and full open position using a boiler and a thermometer.
- Water pump. Remove and check for a loose or damaged impeller and check the impeller-to-housing clearance to specification. Rebuild or replace as required.
- Boost air heat exchanger. An airflow or internal restriction will cause a rise in engine temperatures. Test airflow through the engine compartment. Winter grille covers impede airflow through the heat exchangers and may unevenly load the fan.

- High-altitude operation. Cooling system efficiency diminishes as altitude increases. Therefore, larger cooling system capacity is required for high-altitude operation.
- Lugging. Operating an engine at high loads and lower speeds means high temperatures and reduced coolant flow. Driver training is required.
- Overfueling. This raises the amount of rejected heat and may exceed the cooling system's ability to handle it. Recalibrate engine fueling to specification.
- Fuel injection timing. Depending on the type of fuel system, both retarding and advancing fuel injection timing may result in engine overheating. Fuel injection timing may be mechanically tampered with in older engines; set timing to OEM specification. Tampering with injection timing is more complex in electronic engines because it involves defeating the OEM fuel map programming. Despite being illegal, it is done: The practice is more common in small-bore diesels that are privately owned, but technicians should be aware when confronted with a challenging emissions problem that a possible cause is fuel map tampering. Greatly diminished engine life is the consequence of minor injection timing adjustments, whereas major component failure is the consequence of more aggressive adjustments.

TECH TIP:

Diesel engine operating temperatures that run higher than expected in extreme cold may be due to the use of high-concentration PG coolant. High-concentration PG solutions do provide increased antifreeze protection, but also lower cooling efficiency, resulting in noticeably higher operating temperatures.

Low Coolant Temperature

Accurately verify the condition:

1. Check cooling system temperature management components such as shutter and fan operation.
2. Install a master gauge to verify the problem.
3. Observe exhaust pyrometer readings and compare to specification.

Some possible causes and solutions:

- Thermostat. A thermostat that is stuck in the open position will cause the engine to run cool and produce higher hydrocarbon (HC)

emissions that can result in frequent DPF regen cycles. Remove the thermostat and check its start to open and fully open temperature specifications.
- Air vent valve. If stuck in the open position, this may cause low coolant temperatures when the engine is under light loads.
- Prolonged idle or light-load operation. When little fuel is being used by the engine, there is less rejected heat for the cooling system to handle, and operating temperatures may be lower.
- Fan clutch. Test fanstat/thermal fan operation using a master gauge and loading of the engine until it reaches the temperature required to cycle the fan. Ensure that this occurs at the specified temperature and not a lower value.
- Improper airflow. Incorrectly sized fan or missing/damaged radiator shroud may result in overcooling by creating irregular flow through the engine compartment.

CYLINDER COMPRESSION PROBLEMS

Overall low or unbalanced cylinder compression can create problems of excessive blow-by, low power, and vibration. In electronically managed engines, a cylinder balance test (aka *cylinder contribution test*) will usually rapidly identify cylinder compression problems, and this is the preferred method of testing. Cylinder pressures may also be checked using a compression tester, but this is labor intensive and should usually be avoided on newer engines.

To perform a compression test, the engine should be close to operating temperature before you shut it down and remove all of the injectors. Fit the compression test gauge to the injector bore in one of the cylinders, and then crank through five rotations. The batteries should be fully charged during this test. Test each cylinder sequentially and match the test results to specifications. The results should be within the engine OEM cylinder compression parameters and normally within 10% of each other. Compression testing will locate which cylinder(s) is/are at fault, but not the cause of the problem.

A cylinder leakage or air test kit sometimes stands a better chance of identifying the cause of a problem. The cylinder leak test consists of a pressure regulator and couplings that fit to the injector bores. Ideally, the engine should be close to its operating temperature at the beginning of the test, but this is often not possible. The test is performed with the piston in the cylinder to be tested at TDC when regulated air pressure is delivered to the cylinder. The test may indicate valve seal leaks, head gasket leaks, leaks to the water jacket, leaking piston rings, and defective pistons. The **cylinder leakage test** regulator delivers air at a controlled volume and pressure, and then measures the percentage of leakage.

HIGH EXHAUST TEMPERATURE READINGS

When diagnosing high exhaust temperatures on highway diesel engines equipped with catalytic converters and DPFs, always use the engine OEM's recommended procedure. Until the universal adoption of DPFs in 2007, a pyrometer (thermocouple) was primarily a driver assist. Troubleshooting and failure analysis of exhaust aftertreatment systems is dealt with in some detail in Chapter 48 and in a later section of this chapter.

When pyrometer readings were dash-displayed in pre-2007 engines, the purpose was to alert the driver to downshift; a pyrometer was often spec'd into trucks hauling heavy loads through mountainous terrain. In post-2007 diesel engines, thermocouple-type pyrometers are used in some DPFs to help manage regeneration cycles. In pre-2007 trucks with high exhaust temperatures, first verify the condition:

1. Install a **master pyrometer** (do not rely solely on the vehicle pyrometer).
2. Do a chassis **dynamometer** test using a full instrumentation readout. See Chapter 16 on engine testing.

> **TECH TIP:**
>
> Transient (temporary) high exhaust temperatures are normal on post-2007 trucks equipped with oxidation catalysts, dosed reduction catalysts, and DPFs. During DPF regenerative cycles, transient high exhaust temperatures are normal (may cause a visible glow at night) and can be ignored unless they log a fault code.

Some possible causes of and solutions for high exhaust temperatures are:

- Air inlet restriction. Test inlet restriction value to specification using a manometer.
- Flow-restricted boost air heat exchanger. Check airflow through the hood intake grille.

A winter grille cover can limit airflow through the heat exchangers located at the front of the chassis. Check the operation of a *tip turbine* if the vehicle is so equipped.
- High-engine-load, low airflow operation. Engines using air-to-air boost air cooling *require* airflow through the heat exchanger. A dump truck with air-to-air boost cooling operating in a pit under extreme temperatures may produce high pyrometer readings even when operated skillfully.
- Fuel injection timing. Check to specification.
- Overfueling. Look for other indicators of an overfueling condition and check fuel settings to specification.

SUDDEN ENGINE SHUTDOWN

Sudden engine shutdown can result from a number of conditions. First, try to determine whether the check engine lamp (CEL) or stop engine lamp (SEL) was illuminated. If this was the case, connect to the chassis data bus, and access the engine SA to route a path to the fault mode indicator (FMI). Some possible causes and solutions:

- Electrical failure. Use the appropriate electrical circuit troubleshooting to locate the problem. Check the most obvious causes first.
- No fuel. Refuel tanks and use an appropriate priming method to get the engine running again.
- Air in fuel system. Air may be pulled into the fuel subsystem from any of a number of locations; common causes are the fuel filter sealing gaskets, double gaskets (caused by failure to remove a used gasket during servicing), and a failed filter mounting pad assembly.
- Water in fuel system. Most current secondary filters will plug on small quantities of water. Locate the source of the water. Replace and prime the filters.
- Plugged fuel line. Sequentially work through the fuel subsystem circuit to locate the failed component. An internally failed fuel hose can be difficult to locate because an internal flap may require moving fuel through the circuit to block flow. Similarly, something simple (such as a small decal floating in the fuel tank) can plug a fuel pickup line and shut down the engine, after which it floats away.
- Lubrication failure. Caused by a failed lubrication circuit component. A lubrication

circuit failure will rapidly develop into a seized engine. Attempt to manually bar the engine over. A lubrication failure often necessitates a complete engine disassembly.

ENGINE RUNS ROUGH

"Running rough" describes a condition in which the engine produces an inconsistent rpm roll (nonrhythmic), hunting (rhythmic), cylinder misfire, or surging at a specific rpm or throughout the engine-operating range.

Some possible causes and solutions:

- Air in fuel system. Often accompanied by white smoke emission. Locate the source of the air, checking the suction side of the fuel subsystem first.
- Problems in the engine breathing circuit. This includes heat exchangers, EGR and CGI coolers, venturii, control valves, VGT turbos, and DPFs.
- Leak or restriction on the charge side of the fuel subsystem. Repair a leak if evident. Use a pressure gauge to check charging pressure to specification.
- Injection nozzle, injector actuator failure, or improperly programmed injector calibration code. This results in a cylinder misfire or imbalance condition. Locate the affected cylinder using the electronically driven diagnostics, and never mechanically short out an injector.
- CN value of fuel is too low. This occurs when fuel is stored for prolonged periods, either in the vehicle or in base storage tanks, and the fuel deteriorates chemically or biochemically.
- Fuel cloud point is high. When fuel begins to wax, it can restrict filters and pumping apparatus. Analyze the fuel and add an approved cloud point depressant as required.
- Advanced injection timing. A common tampering problem in older hydromechanical engines. It may be a problem in some EUI-fueled engines that have been intentionally advance-timed by stepping a timing gauge. Check injection timing and reset to specification if required.
- Unbalanced cylinder fueling. Produces a hunting condition. In older engines, balance the fuel racks according to the OEM procedure (check the injector fuel codes). Check injector calibration code programming in electronically managed engines.
- Bent or broken EUI pushrod. Usually a cylinder misfire accompanied by mechanical clatter. Replace defective injector train components.

- Maladjusted valves. Perform an overhead adjustment.
- Cylinder leakage. Caused by a failed fire ring(s), a crack in the cylinder head/block, or valve leakage. Perform a cylinder leakage test appropriate for the engine.

ENGINE BLOW-BY

Because rings create the seal of a piston in a cylinder bore, some blow-by is inevitable due to the end-gap requirement. Normally, blow-by is a specification determined by the OEM. Remember, piston rings seal most efficiently when cylinder pressures are highest, and engine rpm is high when there is less time for gas blow-by.

Some causes and solutions of excessive engine blow-by are:

- Cracked head or piston. Diagnose the cause and recondition the engine.
- Worn, stuck, or broken piston rings. Diagnose the cause and recondition the engine.
- Glazed liner/sleeve inside wall (due to improper break-in practice or prolonged idling). Diagnose the cause and recondition the engine.
- Poor-quality or degraded engine lube. Change the oil and filters.

High crankcase pressures can also be caused by:

- Air compressor (plugged discharge line, worn rings, air pumped through oil return line). Test air compressor operation.
- Turbocharger (seal failure allows the impeller housing to leak pressurized air through to the turbine shaft and back through the oil return piping). Test turbocharger operation and recondition or replace as required.

ENGINE WILL NOT CRANK

Determine whether the problem is related to the cranking circuit (electrical or pneumatic problem) or a mechanical engine condition. Focus on the cranking circuit first and eliminate any obvious causes; in most cases, the cause of a failure-to-crank condition will be found here. Attempt to bar the engine over by hand. If it cannot be turned over, check the engine externally and both the transmission and power takeoff (PTO). If engine seizure is suspected, remove all the injectors and again attempt to bar the engine over by hand before beginning to disassemble it. If disassembly is required, carefully remove and label components so that the cause of the failure can be determined.

LACK OF POWER

"Lack of power" probably appears more frequently on shop work orders than any other problem. In many cases, the lack of power is more closely associated with driver expectations than a genuine engine problem. A chassis dynamometer with a data printout is usually required to convince a skeptical truck driver that the equipment is functioning properly. Although the technician can eliminate many causes of low power, realistically, when performing this work for a customer, it is essential to test that the engine performs to specification on a chassis dynamometer when the work is completed.

It makes a lot of economic sense for shops that frequently work on low-power complaints to prepare a strategy check sheet that addresses the specific equipment worked on; this ensures that the work is performed sequentially (eliminating obvious/quick-to-perform tasks first) and enables each technician to pursue the steps in more or less the same manner. A successful method of developing a "lack of power checklist" is to devote a technicians' shop meeting to brainstorming troubleshooting strategies and sequences for specific engine/fuel systems. Apart from the fact that the resulting checklist will incorporate the input of the entire workshop team, this exercise will have the added benefit of "educating" the less-experienced technicians. In short, the time devoted to the meeting will be paid for many times over by the time saved by avoiding inconsistent and inaccurate troubleshooting practices. Never forget the value of monitoring critical engine pressure values using a set of master gauges, as shown in **Figure 50–2**.

There are too many variables based on engine manufacturer and fuel system type to provide definitive troubleshooting strategies for lack-of-power complaints. The following is a general list of some causes of low power and their solutions:

- Restricted fuel filters. Replace the filters. Check the vehicle fuel tanks for contamination.

FIGURE 50–2 Typical set of engine testing pressure gauges.

- Restricted air inlet system. Test the inlet restriction value using a manometer. Remember, air filter elements are best tested without removal from the canister—do *not* replace unless they fail an inlet restriction test or have exceeded the in-service time limit.
- Leaks in the boost air circuit. Test for leakage using an OEM-approved method, such as direct application of a soap solution with the engine under load, ether spray at idle, or others. Small leaks in charge air cooler cores can be difficult to locate and may require removal and pressure testing. When testing with a dynamometer, always fit instrumentation to read manifold boost.
- Low manifold boost—turbocharger problem. Visually inspect the turbocharger, checking radial play and endplay; check for rotation drag caused by carbon deposits (coking).
- Restricted exhaust system. This condition is usually accompanied by poor engine response. Check piping, engine muffler(s), DPFs, and catalytic converters when so equipped. Mufflers can fail internally when

baffles and resonator walls collapse; test backpressure value to specification.

- Low fuel subsystem charging pressure. Fit a pressure gauge and test fuel pressure at idle and high-idle speeds, referencing the specifications.
- Valve lash maladjustment. Often accompanied by smoking and top end/valve clatter. Adjust valves to specification.
- Defective boost pressure sensing and fuel control devices. All current engines use either variable capacitance or piezoresistive turbo-boost sensors that seldom malfunction. Older engines used different types of aneroid devices, which were also known as puff limiters, LDAs (Bosch), AFC (air-fuel control) valves, air ratio control (ARC), and FARC (fuel-air ratio control) valves. The devices used on hydromechanical engines were not only more likely to malfunction, they could easily be tampered with. Most aneroids had a set trigger specification (predetermined manifold boost value), and their function was to limit fueling until there was enough air in the cylinders to properly combust the fuel. Some aneroids permitted a graduated increase of fueling, proportional to increase in manifold boost, whereas others simply switched at a predetermined boost value, limiting fueling until that value was achieved. Replacing a properly functioning boost fueling control device with one of lower trigger value will not cure a low-power complaint or increase engine power, although it will cause puff smoking at shifting, waste fuel, and contaminate the atmosphere. Use the OEM method of testing the device, and ensure that the correct one is fitted. Some use an intake manifold sensor and system air pressure to actuate a governor-located pilot plunger; these must be precisely set to specification.
- Governor maladjusted. Usually a result of repeated tampering with components that should only be adjusted on a pump comparator bench. Performance-test the engine on a dynamometer and reset the governor, removing the fuel injection pump assembly, if required, if the governor is integral.
- Contaminated fuel. Fuel is abused unknowingly by both drivers and technicians whenever they add any substance to vehicle fuel tanks other than diesel fuel. Some of these additives may create conditions that result

in lack-of-power complaints. There are certainly seasonal conditions that mandate the addition of alcohols to fuel tanks (crossover pipe freeze-up), but drivers and technicians should be educated to understand that dumping additives into fuel tanks, especially aftermarket additives of dubious chemistry, should be avoided. Purchasing #1D fuel is much cheaper than purchasing inexpensive, summer-grade #2D fuel and paying for the problems it creates when operating equipment in extreme winter conditions.

- Defective fuel. Not a major problem in North America, and difficult to diagnose without the use of specialized equipment. Check with the fuel supplier. Testing specific gravity may identify a fuel in which the lighter fractions have boiled off, lowering the CN, but the exact original values must be known. Defective fuel problems are usually the consequence of storing a fuel for prolonged periods or use of fuels outside the season in which they were purchased.

TECH TIP:

When evaluating actual engine temperature and pressure readings by comparing them to specifications, do not be too hasty to condemn a reading that is close to the *minimum* or *maximum* parameter but nevertheless within specification as the root cause of a problem. For instance, when troubleshooting a low-power complaint and the air filter minder reads 22 in H_2O restriction where the maximum spec is 25 in H_2O, it is unlikely that the air cleaner is the root cause, so do not change it until the root cause has been sourced.

ENGINE VIBRATION

While driveline vibrations are not uncommon, true engine vibrations are not often a problem. When investigating a vibration complaint, the technician should eliminate all possible causes in the driveline behind the engine first. In doing this, it should be remembered that the clutch may disengage the driveline from the transmission and beyond from the engine, but that most of the mass of the clutch is rotated with the engine engaged and disengaged.

- Cylinder misfire: See section "Engine Runs Rough."

- Loose vibration damper: Check bolts for shear damage and damper fastener holes for elongation. Visually inspect damper for other damage. Retorque and test operation.
- Defective vibration damper: Viscous-type dampers should be replaced at each engine overhaul but seldom are; visually inspect them. The slightest external defect is reason to replace the unit. To dynamically test a vibration damper, a lathe and dynamic balance apparatus are required—a procedure beyond the scope of most shops. Visually inspect rubber drive ring dampers.
- Defective external driven component: Every driven engine accessory is capable of unbalancing the engine. Most air compressors marketed today are balanced units and do not require timing; however, some single-cylinder compressors must be timed to the engine.

Some common accessories that may cause an unbalanced engine condition when they or their bearings fail are the fan assembly (broken/damaged blades, failed bearings), water pump, accessory drive bearings, idler pulley bearings, alternator, and others.

SOOT IN INLET MANIFOLD

Some soot in the intake manifold is normal in most diesel engines; it usually indicates an engine operated at low loads and speeds for prolonged periods in engines manufactured prior to 2004. In such operating conditions, the valve overlap duration is at a maximum in real-time values and manifold boost is minimal or nonexistent. Excessive soot in the intake manifold may be an indication of imminent turbocharger failure, an injection timing problem, or a problem related to the EGR circuit in post-2004 diesels. We take a brief look at EGR circuit troubleshooting in the next section.

EGR CIRCUIT MALFUNCTIONS

When the EGR circuit fails, in most cases at least one fault code is logged because the circuit is so thoroughly monitored. When a fault code is logged, make sure you adhere to the OEM software-driven diagnostic routine. Typical diagnostic fault codes that relate to the EGR circuit are:

- Short to ground
- Dead short
- EGR valve position circuit fault

A typical OEM diagnostic routine to verify EGR PWM-actuated valve function would appear as follows:

- Check for multiple codes. When other engine codes are logged, these should be solved first.
- Disconnect the EGR valve electrical connector. Check for pin damage and corrosion and repair as necessary.
- Reconnect the EGR valve electrical connector. Key-*on*, engine-*off* (KOEO): Use the OEM software to monitor EGR valve actual position.
- If it reads less than the specified KOEO position (usually expressed as %). Command EGR pulse width (PW) to step to 50%. If it fails to move to within 5% of the input 50%, the EGR valve is defective and should be replaced. If it moves within 5% of the requested 50%, next command it to move to 100% PW. In this position, actual valve position should be at 95% or higher. If not, replace the valve. If it is:
  - Remove the EGR valve and check for physical damage and carbon/sludge buildup. Either condition requires the valve to be replaced, but in the case of carbon/sludge buildup, check the EGR cooler for internal failure.

MANIFOLD BOOST PROBLEMS

When manifold boost is either too high or too low, engine performance complaints result. Common causes of lower than specified manifold boost are:

- Air system restriction upstream or downstream from turbocharger impeller
- Air leakage downstream from turbocharger impeller
- Low fuel delivery
- Mismatched turbocharger

Common causes of higher than specified manifold boost are as follows:

- Mismatched turbocharger
- Sticking vane ring on VGT turbos
- Excessively high inlet air temperatures
- Deposits on turbine volute or nozzle
- Overfueling caused by governor or by calibration programming
- Advanced fuel injection timing

DPF MALFUNCTIONS

DPF malfunctions are characterized by one or more of the following:

- Black smoke emission
- DPF collects excessive soot

- DPF is restricted
- DPF temperatures are high

Begin troubleshooting a DPF malfunction by inspecting it externally for indications of dents or cracks. Remove the DPF and check for indications of fuel or engine oil. Check the core substrate for visible damage. If fuel is present, perform a cylinder balance test to identify a defective injector. If oil is present, check the turbocharger(s) for oil leakage. Note that any problem upstream in the engine breathing circuit can produce excessive soot loads and black smoke: Pay special attention to the venturi for the EGR or CGI systems, EGR mixing valves, and the aftercooler.

DPF Restriction

In most cases, the engine management electronics are designed to respond to DPF restriction caused by excessive soot dump by logging fault codes and engaging power derate strategies. This type of malfunction can be caused by operating the vehicle for prolonged periods when passive regeneration cycles are either inhibited by the operator or by the mode of operation. Most have a threshold that, once exceeded, requires an active regeneration cycle to be commanded. In some cases, when the soot load threshold has been exceeded by a considerable margin (say, 200%), a factory password may have to be downloaded to clear the code and re-rate to specified power.

DPF Differential Pressure Problems

DPF high differential pressure problems are usually caused by a buildup of soot or ash in the particulate trap. The appropriate repair strategy is to command an active regeneration cycle if this is still possible. If not, the unit must either be laundered on-chassis or removed and replaced, depending on the OEM. Low differential pressure is usually caused by a failure of the tubing between the particulate trap and the pressure differential sensor. Check this circuit and replace components as necessary.

High DPF Intake Temperatures

High DPF intake temperatures can be caused by a range of engine circuits upstream from the DPF, including:

- Restricted boost air heat exchanger
- Air inlet restriction
- Exhaust restriction

- High altitude operation
- Overfueling
- Low coolant level

In every case, to troubleshoot high DPF intake temperatures, check for any active and historical codes: In most cases, high DPF intake temperatures are not sourced in the DPF, although an exhaust restriction downstream from the aftertreatment canister could cause this condition.

MECHANICAL ENGINE KNOCK

- Bottom end knock: Produces an easily recognizable low-frequency thump. The cause is big-end or connecting rod journal bearing failure, which is a condition that rapidly develops into a crankshaft failure if not attended to. Replace the bearings and thoroughly inspect and measure the throw journals.
- Failed crankshaft: Diagnose the problem in-chassis by visual inspection of journals and their bearings and the critical crankshaft stress points.
- Damaged gears: Often identified by a high-frequency whine. Remove the timing gear cover and replace failed components, remembering that debris from the failure may have been pumped through the entire lubrication circuit.
- Failure of feedback circuit component: Check rocker trains and camshaft. Repair components as required, once again remembering that debris from the failure may have been pumped through the entire lubrication circuit.

COMBUSTION KNOCK

Combustion knock is sometimes known as *diesel knock.* If the noise is rhythmic, it may be that it is being produced from one engine cylinder, which may be verified by comparing cylinder temperatures with an infrared thermometer. Some causes and solutions are:

- Fuel injection timing. Usually produces erratic knock, amplified at higher loads and rpm. Check fuel injection timing to specification.
- Air in fuel. Usually accompanied by white smoke emission. Check for air admission on the suction side of the fuel subsystem.
- Low-grade fuel. Fuel with a low CN (caused by additive contamination, prolonged storage, nonhighway ASTM grade, etc.) will extend the ignition lag phase. This results in excess fuel in the cylinder at the time of ignition, rapid pressure rise, and detonation. Analyze

the fuel quality using the fuel supplier/refiner's recommended procedure.

- Injectors out of balance. A single injector delivering excess fuel can produce combustion knock. Check overhead adjustment and injector calibration code programming. Run a cylinder balance (contribution) test using an EST.

FUEL PUMP/INJECTOR SCUFFING

Fuel injector pump plunger scuffing has become a problem in recent years in part due to the lower lubricity of LS and the more recent ULS diesel fuels and excessive addition of alcohol into fuel. Surface scuffing of the pump plungers can be difficult to diagnose, especially when the surface scuffing is minor. This type of failure is not common, but when it appears it is usually found on PLN, EUI, HEUI, and EUP high-pressure pump plungers. Its causes are water in the fuel (usually in solution with methyl hydrate alcohols, allowing it to pass through separators) or low-lubricity fuel. To overcome the problem, some OEMs coat both the plunger and barrel assembly of high-pressure fuel injectors with tungsten carbide. The symptoms of fuel injector scuffing are:

- Low power. Results from severe scuffing.
- Slight engine miss. Most notable at low-load operation.
- Misfire. Again, most notable under low-load operation.
- Smoking. Some high-load hazing evident when multiple injectors are affected.

An electronic cylinder balance (a.k.a. cylinder contribution test [CCT]) can sometimes identify an injector scuffing condition before

it sets fault codes, especially when using diagnostic software capable of graphing displays. Severe cases are more likely in older electronic and hydromechanical diesel engines that lack the diagnostic software capable of identifying the condition.

TECH TIP:

Caution truck drivers against adding excessive quantities of methyl hydrate and diesel fuel conditioners to fuel tanks. Both form a solution with any water present in the fuel tank, and the solution can bypass water separators to enter the high-pressure fuel injection circuit where it causes the scuffing damage.

QUICK REFERENCE DIAGNOSTIC CHARTS

The following sets of diagnostic charts (**Table 50–1** through **Table 50–17**) repeat some of the information already outlined and are intended as guidelines to diagnose some typical problems. As much as possible, the approach is generic, but where it is not, the specific engine or fuel system is referenced.

TECH TIP:

When a sensor logs an active fault code, try disconnecting the sensor and observing whether the FMI changes. If there is no change, it suggests that the fault lies in the wiring circuit. If the FMI changes, it suggests that the problem lies in the sensor.

TABLE 50–1 Symptom: Engine Will Not Crank

Possible Cause	Action
Discharged or dead batteries	Test the batteries. Charge or replace as required.
Loose or corroded terminals	Identify the location using voltage drop (VD) testing. Clean, tighten, or replace terminals.
High resistance in cranking circuit cables	VD test cables: (1) Switch to starter. (2) Battery to starter motor. Replace as required.
Defective starter motor or starter solenoid	Check operation using a DMM. Repair as required.
Defective key switch	Test and repair as indicated by electronic troubleshooting. Replacement switch may require reprogramming.
Seized engine	Attempt to bar engine over through two revolutions. Diagnose cause of seizure.

TABLE 50–2 Symptom: Engine Cranks, Will Not Start

Possible Cause	Action
Slow crank	Reference Table 50–1: Engine Will Not Crank.
Check fault codes	Codes logged: Use software diagnostics. No codes logged: Continue using this chart.
No fuel to engine	(1) Check fuel tank level. (2) Check for restriction in the fuel subsystem lines and filters. Replace as required.
Defective fuel transfer pump	(1) Check fuel charging pressure to spec. (2) Check for air in fuel. Repair or replace.
Degraded fuel, water in fuel	Drain fuel from the tank. Replace fuel and fuel filters. Flush new fuel through the system before cranking.
Incorrect oil viscosity (cold weather condition)	Replace the engine oil and filters when possible: 15W-40 engine lube gels in cold weather and cannot be drained.
Low compression	Perform a cylinder compression test: Use Table 50–14 to troubleshoot.
Defective charge pressure regulator	Remove the charging pressure regulator and inspect: Replace if required.
Defective electrical connections	Perform wiggle wire tests at the ECM and critical engine sensors.

TABLE 50–3 Symptom: Engine Misfire

Possible Cause	Action
Codes logged	Run diagnostic routines. Check the ECM audit trails.
Degraded or contaminated fuel	Drain the fuel tanks and replace filters.
Low charging pressure	Check fuel tank level. Sequentially check the fuel subsystem for restrictions or air ingestion. Use an Hg manometer in the primary circuit, a pressure gauge in the secondary circuit. Check the charging pressure regulator valve or restrictor fitting.
Valve lash adjustment	Perform top end adjustment.
Failed camshaft	Adjust valve lash. Run the engine hard, preferably on a dyno for 30 minutes. Recheck valve lash. Check cam lift to specification. Replace the camshaft if required.
Valves not seating	Remove the cylinder head(s). Recondition valves and seats.
Defective fuel injector or pump	Condition should be identified by codes in all current engines: If the problem is intermittent, wiggle wires, examine audit trails, and perform an electronic cylinder balance test.
Air in fuel	Locate the source of air ingestion. Check the filter pads on the primary circuit first. Use an inline diagnostic sight glass to locate the source.
Blown cylinder head gasket	Locate the source of the leak by external visual inspection. Compression test each cylinder to check for blown fire rings. Check the coolant and oil for contamination.
Leakage at high-pressure pipes	Check for trace leakage. Check the pipe nut torque on high-pressure pipes. Identify the source of the leak and check all other high-pressure pipes on PLN, EUP, and CR fuel systems.

TABLE 50–4 Symptom: Engine Stalls

Possible Cause	Action
Codes logged	Run diagnostic routines. Check audit trails. If no active codes, road or dyno test using EST snapshot mode: Set the trigger to collect data beginning at the code log event.
Idle speed set low	Reset or reprogram idle speed.
High parasitic load cut-in events	Check the air compressor and alternator, especially on city and highway buses.
Fuel tank vent circuit plugged or restricted	Check the vent or filter. Tank vent filters can rapidly plug in construction and agricultural operations. Clean/replace the vent/filters.
Fuel starvation	Check the fuel tank pickup tube(s). Check the fuel tank for foreign matter: A decal or piece of paper over the pickup tube inlet can shut the system down. Check the fuel lines for internal restriction such as a rubber flap. Replace the lines as required.
Low fuel supply operating on rough terrain	Check the fuel tank level and replenish if necessary.
Defective injector nozzle(s)	Identify the affected injector(s) and replace. Identify the cause of nozzle failure and remedy: If caused by water, identify the source.
Defective injection pump(s)	This condition should produce codes in current engines. In older engines, use the OEM service literature.

TABLE 50–5 Symptom: Irregular Engine rpm

Possible Cause	Action
Air ingested into the primary side of the fuel subsystem: results in erratic engine rpm roll	Locate the air source and repair: Check the primary fuel filter pad and fuel tank pickup tube first.
Fractured fuel transfer pump, pulsation damper: results in erratic engine rpm roll	Test the charging pressure in the secondary fuel circuit. Replace the pulsation dampening disc.
Unbalanced fueling: results in rhythmic engine rpm fluctuation known as hunting	Perform a cylinder balance test.
Cylinder leakage	Perform a cylinder balance test on electronically managed engines. Cylinder leakage can be caused by a blown fire ring (head gasket), cylinder valves, or piston rings.

TABLE 50–6 Symptom: Lack of Power (LOP)

Possible Cause	Action
Codes logged	Run diagnostic routines and check the audit trails before doing anything else.
EGR mixing chamber problem	Inspect the mixing gate door and leakage. Repair as needed.
Boost side leak	Check for leaks downstream from the turbocharger impeller housing. Test the charge air cooler for leaks.
Plugged or restricted fuel tank vent(s) or filters	Clean the vents and replace the filters if necessary.
Plugged air filter	Check filter restriction using a water-filled manometer. Replace if outside of specification.
Degraded fuel	Determine the cause of fuel degradation, especially when biodiesel is used. Drain the fuel and replace the fuel filters. Refuel with fresh fuel.
Low fuel charging pressure	(1) Check the fuel tank level. (2) Check fuel filter restriction. (3) Check for air ingestion. (4) Check the charging pressure fuel pressure regulator. Fill the fuel tank and replace defective components.
Defective injector nozzle(s)	Identify the affected injector(s) and replace. Identify the cause of nozzle failure and remedy: If caused by water, identify the source.
Valve lash adjustment	Perform a valve adjustment.
Turbocharger malfunction	Remove flow piping: Inspect radial play at the turbine and impeller. Check for contact or lube leakage on both sides. Replace or recore the turbo.
Exhaust restriction	Check for restriction in the exhaust piping and DPF canister. In vehicles with low horizontal exhausts, check the exit piping from the DPF/muffler canister.
Externally or internally plugged charge air cooler (CAC)	Visually check for external plugging of exchanger fins (results in insufficient cooling). Remove the CAC and perform flow and leakage tests.
Restricted boost side ducts and pipes	Remove and visually inspect: Replace if defective.

Note: Caused by many factors. If possible, verify the lack of power complaint by chassis dyno testing. Never act on a driver's word alone: Over 50% of LOP complaints prove to be baseless.

TABLE 50–7 Symptom: Poor Fuel Mileage

Possible Cause	Action
Codes logged	Run diagnostic routines and check the audit trails before doing anything else.
Restricted air intake circuit	Use an H_2O manometer (upstream from the impeller housing) and pressure gauges (downstream from the impeller housing) to identify the location. Repair/replace as required.
Fuel leakage	Check for evidence of external fuel leakage and repair.
Defective fuel injectors	Dribbling nozzles may not trip a fault code in some systems. Usually accompanied by more frequent DPF regen cycles. Test older hydromechanical nozzles and repair/replace.
Internal engine wear	Identify the root cause. You may find that an electronic cylinder balance test helps. Worn rings may also produce other symptoms such as plugging of pressure control valve (PCV) filters and more frequent DPF regen cycles. Repair the engine as required.

TABLE 50–8 Symptom: Excessive Oil Consumption

Possible Cause	Action
External oil leaks	Check the engine for obvious external leakage. Check all seals and gaskets. Add ultraviolet (UV) dye to the oil then pressure wash if the source of the leakage is difficult to locate.
Turbocharger oil leakage to manifold	Check for oil in the turbocharger inlet and soot in the exhaust outlet. Check for high inlet restriction (plugged air filter). Perform repairs as necessary.
Leakage at EGR valve piston shaft	Inspect the EGR circuit for oil loss. Replace the EGR valve if necessary.
Front and rear main seal leakage	Check for oil tracking at both seals. Check the seal races on the crankshaft. Replace and realign the main seals and install wear sleeves if necessary.
Air compressor passing oil	Check the air supply circuit downstream from the air compressor. Remove the compressor and check the drain-back ports for plugging. Replace the compressor flange gasket and/or compressor.
Plugged crankcase breather or PCV circuit	Identify the cause of clogging and clean or replace components.
High exhaust backpressure	Check the exhaust backpressure. Check the exhaust circuit for internal restrictions such as collapsed resonator baffles.
Worn valve guides and seals	Check the valve guide bore size to specification and seal integrity. Repair/replace components as necessary.
Worn piston rings	You may identify this condition by running a cylinder balance test if you are familiar with the duty cycle results produced by a healthy engine. Perform a cylinder leakage test in nonelectronic engines. Rebuild the engine.
Leakage from HEUI oil actuation circuit to the fuel supply gallery	Condition is usually caused by rolled or failed center O-rings in the HEUI injector assembly.

TABLE 50–9 Symptom: Engine Overheating

Possible Cause	Action
Low coolant level	Locate the cause. Visually inspect for external leaks and pressure test the circuit. Repair and replenish the coolant.
Loose or worn fan/water pump drive belts	Adjust the belt tension or replace the drive belts.
EGR heat exchanger leak	Replace the EGR cooler: Do not attempt to repair it.
Restricted airflow through the radiator	Carefully clean bugs and road dirt from the rad cooling fins using a low-pressure hose. Test after cleaning.
Defective radiator cap	Dynamic pressure test the rad cap to ensure it seals to specified pressure. Replace if necessary.
Defective thermostat(s)	Test the thermostat opening temperature: Also check the temperature sensor accuracy. Replace components as necessary.
Defective fan cycle controls	Check the viscous fan operation by running the engine to the specified fan temperature. With on/off fan controls, check the means used to disengage/engage the fan, electric and pneumatic.
Combustion gas in coolant	Check for evidence of cylinder head gasket and injector sleeve failure. Repair as necessary.
Defective water pump	Check the water pump drive. Remove the water pump and check the impeller to shaft integrity. Repair or replace the water pump and reinstall.
Plugged oil cooler	Usually produces higher than specified oil temperatures along with normal range coolant temperatures. Remove the oil cooler and disassemble to clean/remove the restriction.
Winterfront not opened, or insufficiently open	Check the winterfront and advise the owner that winterfronts are not recommended by OEMs.
Defective shutterstat	Remove the shutterstat and test the pilot temperature and on/off cycles: Shutters should default to the open position.
Improper driver shifting practices	Check the engine audit trail if available. Refer operator to driver trainer.

TABLE 50–10 Symptom: High Exhaust Temperature

Possible Cause	Action
Codes logged	Run diagnostic routines to identify the root cause. Where separate DPF module (noncatalyzed type) is used, check for DPF codes.
Improper driver shifting practices (high load and steep terrain operation)	Check the engine audit trail if possible. Refer operator to driver trainer.
High EGR temperatures	EGR flow rate is too high or ineffective EGR heat exchanger. Check the EGR mixing gate operation and EGR heat exchanger for clogging.
Restricted air intake	Use an H_2O manometer to check for inlet restriction and repair the cause.
Leak in air intake circuit	Check hose clamps, pipes, and ducts. Repair as required.
Exhaust leak upstream from turbine housing	Check for external leaks under load. Replace gaskets and manifold coupling seals as necessary.
Exhaust restrictions	Check for exhaust circuit restrictions, including the cylinder head exhaust tract insulation, loose baffles, plugged catalytic converters, and DPFs. Replace or repair as necessary.
Overfueling or advanced timing	More common in hydromechanical engines: Check the audit trail for fuel injection system related events; run a cylinder balance test. Perform a tune-up on nonelectronic engines, verifying base injection timing.
High load operation with insufficient ram air	High load operating a ram air-cooled CAC when the vehicle is moving at low velocity can produce overheat. Review the type of operation the engine has been spec'd for with the owner.

TABLE 50–11 Symptom: Low Oil Pressure

Possible Cause	Action
Low oil level	Add oil and check for oil leaks or an oil burning condition.
Incorrect oil viscosity	Drain the oil and replace the filters. Replenish with oil, meeting the OEM-specified viscosity for the temperature conditions.
Defective oil pressure gauge or sensor	Check the operation of the oil pressure sensor first then the pressure gauge. Replace components as necessary.
Restricted full flow oil filter	Plugged full flow filters trip the bypass valve on the oil filter flange and may, or may not, cause low oil pressure. Replace the oil and filters.
Engine oil diluted with fuel	Check for fuel system leaks: This varies according to the type of fuel system used. Check the O-rings on the fuel injectors and EUPs. Repair and replace as necessary.
Oil pump failure	Check the mounting arrangement. When the oil pump is remote mounted, carefully check the pickup plumbing for air ingestion. Replace or repair components as necessary.
Oil filter and filter mounting pad problems	Remove the filter(s) and visually inspect the gaskets. Check for possible restrictions to the in/out ports of the oil filter. Repair, clean, or replace components as necessary.
Excessive clearance between crankshaft journals and bearings	Perform a bearing roll-in. Note that this is not a common problem today as friction-bearing technology has advanced significantly.
EGR valve leaking excessively	Check EGR valve operation and repair as necessary.
Degraded engine oil	Low-quality engine oils, especially those with high detergent loads, can break down and thin, resulting in low oil pressure. Replace the engine oil and filters with those specified by the OEM.

TABLE 50-12 Symptom: Oil in Coolant

Possible Cause	Action
Defective oil cooler core or bundle O-rings	Remove and disassemble the oil cooler. Test the bundle or plate stack. Replace if defective. Rolled or failed bundle O-rings can also cause this condition. Replace as necessary. Clean out the entire cooling system using detergent.
Failed head gasket	Replace the cylinder head gasket. In cases where nonintegral grommets are used, take special care in placing these.
Cylinder head or cylinder block porosity	Identify the location of the failure and replace as necessary.

TABLE 50-13 Symptom: Coolant in Engine Oil

Possible Cause	Action
Cracked cylinder head	Disassemble and repair the oil cooler: This is a less common outcome of an oil cooler failure than oil in coolant.
Head gasket failure	Pressure test the cooling system and replace the cylinder head gasket.
Injector cup seal failure	Hydrostatically test the cylinder head and replace the injector cups as required.
Cylinder wet liner failure	Pressure test the system and replace the defective components as required.
Defective oil cooler core	Hydrostatically test the cylinder head to locate the failure and replace the cylinder head.

TABLE 50-14 Symptom: Low Compression

Possible Cause	Action
Incorrect valve lash adjustment	Perform a complete overhead tune up, making sure the valves are set to spec.
Blown fire ring(s) in the head gasket	Replace the head gasket.
Broken or fatigued valve springs	Check and replace as required: In the case of fatigued valve springs, it makes sense to replace them all.
Valves not seating	Remove the cylinder head and check the valve seat faces. Replace the valves and valve seats.
Piston ring failure	Rings may be stuck, worn, broken, or glazed. Determine the root cause of failure and replace the ring sets.
Failed camshaft and/or lifters	Determine the root cause and replace failed components, being sure to check every component in the valve train.

TABLE 50-15 Symptom: Fuel in Lube

Possible Cause	Action
Excessive idling in cold weather (cylinder washdown)	Program optimized idle, install auxiliary cold weather assists, and instruct the driver how to handle the truck in cold weather.
Injector nozzle malfunction	Mostly a condition on older hydromechanical engines. Remove and test the injectors. Replace the nozzle valves and reassemble the injectors.
Injector O-ring failure	Pull the injector assembly and inspect for worn, torn, or rolled O-rings. Replace all O-rings whether observed to be defective or not.
HEUI injection actuation pressure (IAP) circuit failures	Check the HEUIs, jumper pipes if used, and the cylinder oil and fuel manifolds. Replace components as required.

TABLE 50–16 Symptom: EGR System Malfunctions

Possible Cause	Action
Excessive idling—especially in cold weather, it causes carbon coking in the EGR heat exchanger that chokes down on flow	Program optimized idle and instruct the driver how to handle the vehicle in cold weather. Equip the vehicle with auxiliary power for cold weather hotel loads.
High EGR temperature	Indicates a failed EGR heat exchanger. Replace the heat exchanger or heat exchanger core.
EGR valve housing cracked	Inspect the EGR housing and replace if necessary.
EGR gate valve sticking	Check oil supply to the valve. Check for oil coking or corrosion around the actuator bushing. Also check electrical connections to the actuator. Clean, repair, and replace components as required.
EGR valve not functioning properly due to low oil pressure	Troubleshoot the low oil pressure condition using Table 50–11.
Turbo VGT actuator does not respond	Determine whether the problem is mechanical, pneumatic, or electrical (depending on the OEM). Check for codes. If none, focus on a mechanical cause at the turbo VGT actuator or within the turbocharger.

TABLE 50–17 Symptom: High or Low Crankcase Oil Level

Possible Cause	Action
Coolant in oil	Check for internal cooling systems leaks: pressure check on hot and cold engine progressively disassembling it until the leak is sourced. May be sourced to oil cooler but this is not common as the condition usually pumps oil into coolant circuit.
Fuel in oil	Check engine locations where fuel comes into close contact with oil, for instance HEUI injectors. May also be caused by unintended siphoning of fuel into oil sump while removing Injectors or EUPs.
Aerated oil	Allow oil to settle and check crankcase level. The condition may be caused by excessively high or low oil sump level. Use of an inappropriate engine oil can also aerate oil.
Refill abuse	Correct the oil level, then check again after an 8-hour work shift. This problem occurs frequently. Odor (fuel) and milky appearance (coolant) should eliminate these as causes.

TECHNICAL SUPPORT

It is in the business interest of every engine OEM to ensure that breakdowns occur as little as possible. It is also in their interest that when breakdowns do occur, they are repaired in a timely manner and steps are taken to avoid a recurrence. For this reason, all the OEMs provide technical support for their products. It is usually called something like Service Operations Department. In most cases, OEM service operations divide up territory geographically and provide a district service manager (DSM) for each area. While dealership managers will often contact DSMs for warranty approval, this is only one responsibility of a DSM. A more important DSM role is that of providing product technical support.

DSM ROLE

If you are routinely working on engine diagnostic routines, it is inevitable that you will be working "outside of the box" from time to time. For this reason, you should have the contact information of the DSM pasted into your shop e-mail address book and the phone number on your toolbox. The DSM is one of the first to take training on a new OEM engine series, because it then becomes a DSM responsibility to provide

TABLE 50–18 J1939 Documents Pertaining to HD-OBD: the fields shown in italics are those required to be open-access under HD-OBD

Document	Document Title
J1939	*RP for serial control and communications vehicle network*
J1939-01	Truck and bus specific
J1939-02	*Construction and Agriculture Specific (same as ISO 11783-1)*
J1939-03	Onboard Diagnostics Implementation Guide
J1939-05	OBD for marine SI engines (stern drive and inboard)
J1939-11	Physical layer—shielded twisted pair with drain
J1939-12	Physical layer—twisted quad, active terminators (ISO 11783-2)
J1939-13	Diagnostic connector: 9-pin
J1939-15	Physical layer—twisted pair
J1939-21	Data link layer
J1939-31	Network layer
J1939-71	*Applications layer—multiplexing, info sharing, proprietary data*
J1939-73	*Application layer diagnostics—multiplexing diagnostics*
J1939-74	Application configurable messaging
J1939-81	Network management
J1939-84	*OBD communications compliance test cases for HD vehicles*

product support. A good DSM collates questions and feedback and can usually provide answers to questions before they appear in online TSBs and SIS amendments.

HD-OBD

HD-OBD was launched in 2010, with each of the major OEMs being required to produce one chassis line that was compliant. The next phase of HD-OBD implementation was scheduled for the first day of 2014, but this was not effected. At the time of writing (2015), although many OEM chassis lines are compliant, full compliance continues to be on hold. When the HD-OBD initiative is fully in effect, all engine OEMs will be required to open up data bus access to allow generic ESTs to communicate with J1939 to a repair level for any emissions-related problem. HD-OBD implementation has been a complex process, and the final details are still being worked out, but ultimately the system in the United States will sync in with EURO VI requirements.

HD-OBD will level the playing field when it comes to emissions-related diagnostics in the truck repair industry. Small independent service facilities will be able to invest in repair tooling that can route them through diagnostics, repairs, replacement, and software programming of engine emissions systems. **Table 50–18** shows, in *italics,* the J1939 fields that must be opened for access. The end result of HD-OBD is that troubleshooting using generic diagnostic ESTs should be greatly simplified. In addition to code analysis, an electronic breakout box such as that shown in **Figure 50–3** can assist in locating engine electronic problems.

J1939-84 covers the scan tool protocols and details that have yet to be finalized. **Figure 50–4** shows the structure of a HD-OBD data packet (see Chapter 37 for a full explanation of packet messaging) that generic ESTs will work with.

FIGURE 50–3 Breakout box designed for testing DD15 engine electronics.

FIGURE 50-4 HD-OBD data packet structure.

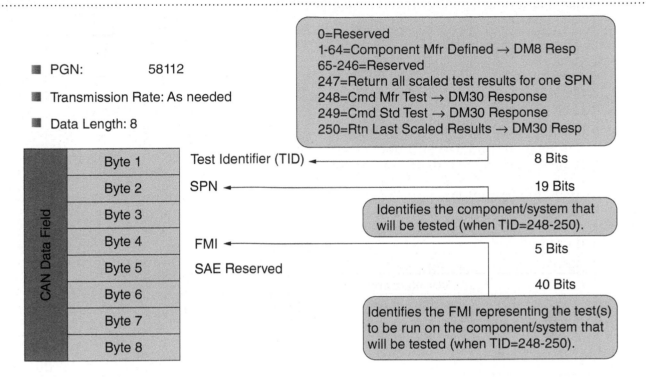

SUMMARY

- The term *troubleshooting* describes a systematic procedure used to diagnose an engine or fuel system complaint.
- All troubleshooting of electronically managed engines should be guided by the OEM-recommended EST and online SIS.
- Software-driven troubleshooting maps must be adhered to because it has been proven to significantly reduce the time to diagnose the root cause of a complaint.
- *Thinking inside the box* means accepting software-guided troubleshooting sequences and problem-solving paths.
- Only when an engine problem falls outside of the OEM diagnostic routines should the technician resort to *thinking outside the box.*
- The diesel technician should be able to analyze exhaust smoke emission and use this knowledge to help diagnose engine and fuel system malfunctions.
- White exhaust smoke indicates the presence of condensing liquid in the exhaust gas.
- Black exhaust smoke indicates the presence of particulate in the exhaust gas.
- Blue smoke emission is generally associated with an engine oil-burning condition.

- An opacity meter is a light extinction test instrument used by transportation regulation enforcement agencies to test exhaust smoke density to J1667 standards.
- Work methodically through sequential troubleshooting procedures. *Never* skip a step on the basis of an assumption.
- Engine malfunctions have some common root causes regardless of the engine OEM. Learn some of the typical causes of everyday engine complaints.
- The implementation of the final phase of HD-OBD is imminent. When finally enacted, all engine OEMs will be required to open up bus access to all emissions-related fields to generic ESTs.
- A component of HD-OBD is that independent service facilities will be able to take emissions-related problems through diagnosis to a final repair level.
- The HD-OBD final rule will bring emissions diagnostic profiles into line with EURO VI protocols.
- Keep an open mind. Fully research challenging problems. When seeking advice, seek the advice of an expert.

REVIEW QUESTIONS

1. Which of the following instruments would check dry air filter restriction with the highest accuracy?
   a. Pyrometer
   b. Trouble light
   c. H_2O manometer
   d. Dash restriction gauge

2. A typical maximum inlet restriction specification on a turbo-boosted diesel engine would be:
   a. 25-inch (635-mm) H_2O.
   b. 25-inch (635-mm) Hg.
   c. 25 psi (172 kPa).
   d. 250 kPa (36 psi).

3. Which of the following conditions would be *least* likely to cause black smoke emission?
   a. Restricted air filter
   b. Retarded injection timing
   c. Restricted diesel particulate filter
   d. Excessive use of cetane improver

4. Technician A states that excessive idling can result in plugging of the EGR heat exchanger. Technician B states that low oil pressure can cause some types of EGR gate valves to stick. Who is correct?
   a. Technician A only
   b. Technician B only
   c. Both A and B
   d. Neither A nor B

5. Operating an engine without a coolant thermostat would most likely result in an increase of which noxious emission?
   a. HC
   b. NO_x
   c. SO_2
   d. CO_2

6. Which of the following should be done first when investigating a complaint of poor fuel mileage?
   a. Overhaul the engine
   b. Change the air filter
   c. Run a lab test on the fuel
   d. Connect an EST and check for codes

7. Technician A states that an excessive amount of oil in the crankcase can produce a low oil pressure problem in a diesel engine. Technician B states that the first thing to check when oil pressures fluctuate is the crankcase oil level. Who is correct?
   a. Technician A only
   b. Technician B only
   c. Both A and B
   d. Neither A nor B

8. Technician A states that a small dent in a viscous-type vibration damper is not a concern unless there is visible leakage. Technician B states that some compressors have to be timed to the engine or a vibration will result. Who is correct?
   a. Technician A only
   b. Technician B only
   c. Both A and B
   d. Neither A nor B

9. There is evidence of soot in the intake manifold of a boosted truck diesel engine. Which of the following conditions would be most likely to contribute to this condition?
   a. Engine lugdown
   b. High-idle operation
   c. Rated speed operation
   d. Running at low speed with low loads

10. Technician A states that white smoke emission can be caused by air starvation to the engine. Technician B states that blue smoke is associated with an engine that is burning oil in its cylinders. Who is correct?
    a. Technician A only
    b. Technician B only
    c. Both A and B
    d. Neither A nor B

11. Technician A says that incorrect valve lash can cause low cylinder compression. Technician B says that a failed camshaft can result in low cylinder compression. Who is correct?
    a. Technician A only
    b. Technician B only
    c. Both A and B
    d. Neither A nor B

12. Technician A says that excessive idling in cold weather can result in fuel contamination of engine lube. Technician B says that a blown exhaust manifold gasket can result in fuel contamination of engine lube. Who is correct?
    a. Technician A only
    b. Technician B only
    c. Both A and B
    d. Neither A nor B

13. Technician A says that the first thing that should be done when troubleshooting an engine miss is to perform an overhead adjustment (valves and injectors). Technician B says that the first thing that should be done when troubleshooting an engine miss is to connect an EST and check for any logged codes. Who is correct?
    a. Technician A only
    b. Technician B only
    c. Both A and B
    d. Neither A nor B

14. Technician A says that an engine that stalls at periodic intervals can be the result of fuel starvation. Technician B says that an engine can stall when operated with a fuel with a high CN value. Who is correct?
    a. Technician A only
    b. Technician B only
    c. Both A and B
    d. Neither A nor B

15. Technician A says that a fuel-in-oil condition can be recognized because the lube oil turns a chocolate-milk color. Technician B says that high crankcase oil level can produce low or fluctuating oil pressure readings. Who is correct?
    a. Technician A only
    b. Technician B only
    c. Both A and B
    d. Neither A nor B

GLOSSARY

abrasive wear occurs when hard particles get between two moving surfaces, cutting or scratching the surfaces. In the case of lubed mating components, the particles have to be thicker than the lubricant film for abrasive wear to take place.

absolute maximum power the highest power an engine can develop at sea level with no limitations on speed, fuel-air ratio, or fuel quantity.

absolute pressure a pressure scale with its zero point at absolute vacuum, expressed as pounds per square inch absolute (psia).

accumulator device for storing energy. The term is often used to describe the high-pressure chamber or common rail used in some electronically controlled fuel injection systems.

ACERT Caterpillar combustion management technology that uses a four-phase emissions reduction strategy to meet 2004, 2007, and 2010 EPA standards. It was used on all Caterpillar on-highway and most off-highway engines. Critical ACERT components include series turbocharging, variable valve timing, CR fueling, MEUI and HEUI injectors, and exhaust gas aftertreatment.

acronym a word formed by the initial letters of other words.

active code an electronically monitored system circuit, condition, or component that is malfunctioning and logs an ECM code, which may be displayed or read with an EST.

active DPF system a diesel particulate filter that actively generates the heat required to regenerate (burn off soot) the device. Heat is usually derived by injecting diesel fuel or from a heat grid.

actively pressurized cooling system (APCS) a means of increasing diesel engine cooling capacity by pressurizing the cooling system using boost air to raise the boiling point of the antifreeze mixture.

active regeneration term used to describe diesel particulate filter regeneration aided by fuel dosing, sometimes in combination with spark ignition.

actuator hardware that puts the results of computer processing into action. Examples of actuators are the injector drivers in a diesel EUI or EHI system.

adaptive when used as a prefix, such as in *adaptive cruise control*, means electronically managed with *soft* parameters.

adaptive trim ECM software that evaluates fuel flow performance of electrohydraulic injectors and EUIs at set engine-operating hour intervals and makes corrections to ensure fueling balance. It is sometimes abbreviated to *A-trim*.

AdBlue a Daimler term for diesel exhaust fluid (DEF), an aqueous urea solution of 67.5% water and 32.5% urea used for selective catalytic reduction (SCR)-type catalytic converters. AdBlue sold in DD and Freightliner outlets is identical to DEF.

ADEM see *advanced diesel engine management*.

ADEPT (not an acronym) the Cummins ISX software and hardware package for MY 2017; it is designed to work in conjunction with AMTs.

adhesive wear occurs when moving surfaces make contact without adequate lubrication, producing heat through friction and elevating surface temperatures to melting point; this can result in the surfaces adhering to each other. It is the fastest progressing wear characteristic.

adsorption a chemical term best defined as *adhesion*. When a substance is adsorbed, it does not undergo any significant chemical change.

advanced combustion and emissions reduction technology (ACERT) see *ACERT*.

advanced diesel engine management (ADEM) Caterpillar acronym used to describe its management electronics and associated hardware.

aeolipile a reaction turbine invented and built by Hero, a Greek, around AD 60. It was the first heat engine and forerunner of the modern jet turbine.

AFC circuit the turbo-boost sensing and fuel management components on a Cummins PTC-AFC pump used on hydromechanical engines.

AFR see *air-fuel ratio*.

afterburn term that can be used to describe the normal combustion of fuel in a diesel engine cylinder after injector nozzle closure or random ignitions of fuel pockets after primary flame quench in an engine cylinder.

afterburn injection see *dosing injection*.

after top dead center (ATDC) any engine position during piston downstroke.

aftertreatment control module (ACM) an aftertreatment device electronic controller (SA 61) bussed to the engine controller either by J1939 or by a proprietary bus.

aftertreatment module (ATM) a double or single canister device containing a DPF, SCR, and other catalytic converters. Managed by a dedicated controller using a proprietary bus or by a module on J1939 using a SA 61 source address.

air box term used to describe the chamber charged by a Roots blower in an older DDC two-stroke cycle engine. The air box supplies the engine cylinders with the scavenging air charge.

air conditioning (A/C) the cooling circuit in an HVAC climate control system.

air-fuel control (AFC) usually refers to turbo-boost and/or altitude compensation fuel management in diesel engines.

air-fuel ratio (AFR) the mass ratio of an air-to-fuel mixture.

air-to-air after cooling (ATAAC) turbo-boost air cooling by heat exchanger in which the cooling medium is ram air; better known as a *charge air cooler (CAC)*.

alcohol a hydrocarbon oxygenate produced by distillation of organic matter.

algorithm software term that describes the processing sequence and logic map required to produce a computed outcome.

alloy the mixing of a molten base metal with metallic or nonmetallic elements to alter the metallurgical characteristics of a metal.

all speed governor a British term for *variable speed governor;* used by Bosch.

alpha data data represented by letters of the alphabet.

alternating current (AC) current flow that cyclically alternates in direction; usually produced by rotating a coil within a magnetic field.

altitude compensator device used on older diesel fuel injection systems containing a barometric capsule; used to measure atmospheric pressure and derate fueling at altitude to prevent smoking.

altitude deration the engine fuel delivery cutback that is managed to occur on the basis of increase in altitude, to prevent engine overfueling as the air charge becomes less oxygen dense. Power deration is typically 4% per 1,000 feet of altitude in boosted engines.

amber the Greek word for "electron"; a translucent, yellowish substance derived from fossilized trees.

American Petroleum Institute (API) classifies lubricants and sets standards in the petroleum-refining industry.

American Society for Testing Materials (ASTM) industry-driven industrial standards agency used to define benchmarks for fuels and materials in the automotive industry such as lube oils. Standards are set by accord and influence both recommended practice and legislated standards.

American Standard Code for Information Interchange (ASCII) widely used data coding system found on PCs.

American Trucking Association (ATA) organization with a broad spectrum of representation, responsible for setting standards in the U.S. trucking industry.

ampere unit of electrical current flow equivalent to 6.28 × 1,018 electrons passing a given point in a circuit per second.

ampere-turns (At) the basic unit of measurement of magnetomotive force.

amplification term used to describe what happens in electronic circuits when very small currents are used to switch much larger ones using transistors.

amplified common rail system (ACRS) term currently used by DDC to describe its version of Bosch amplified CR, in which pressures in the electrohydraulic injector are more than doubled for injection.

amplified pressure common rail (APCR) another term used to describe *ACRS* or *FARC.*

amplifier piston hydraulically actuated piston that pumps fuel to injection pressure values in a Cat/International HEUI and ACRS EHIs; also known as *intensifier piston.*

anaerobic sealant paste-like sealant that cures (hardens) without exposure to air.

analog the use of physical variables, such as voltage or length, to represent values.

analog signal a communication line signal consisting of a continuous electrical wave.

AND gate an electronic switch in which all the inputs must be in the *on* state before the output is in the *on* state.

aneroid a device used to sense light pressure conditions; usually consist of a diaphragm, spring, and fuel-limiting mechanism. The term is used to describe manifold boost sensors that limit fueling until there is sufficient boost air to combust the fuel.

annular ring shaped.

annuli plural of annulus.

annulus a ring.

anode positive electrode; the electrode toward which electrons flow.

anodizing oxide coating on the surface of a metal formed by an electrolytic process.

antifreeze a liquid solution added to water to blend the engine coolant solution that raises the boil point and lowers the freeze point. Ethylene glycol (EG), propylene glycol (PG), extended life coolants (ELCs), and waterless engine coolants (WECs) are currently used.

antinodes portion of a wave below the zero, mean, or neutral point in a waveband.

antithrust face term for the minor thrust face of a piston; the outboard side of the piston as its throw rotates off the crankshaft centerline through the power stroke.

antithrust side piston term meaning minor thrust side.

APCS see *actively pressurized cooling system.*

API gravity measure of how the weight of a petroleum liquid compares to the weight of water; measured with a hydrometer. If API gravity is specified as greater than 10, the petroleum-based liquid is lighter than water, so it would float. If the API gravity specification is less than 10, the liquid is heavier than water and would sink. API gravity is used to compare the relative densities of petroleum liquids and is important if the technician is doing performance testing on engine dynamometers.

app widely used short form for (computer) application.

application software programs that direct computer processing operations.

aqueous urea the reducing agent used in SCR systems, commonly known as *diesel exhaust fluid (DEF)* and less commonly as *AdBlue.* Aqueous urea is a solution of 32% urea and distilled water.

arcing bearing or gear failure caused by electric arcing.

articulating piston a two-piece piston with separate crown and skirt assemblies, linked by the piston wrist pin and afforded a degree of independent movement. The wrist pin is usually full floating or bolted directly to the conn rod, in which case it is known as a crosshead piston.

ash 1. the powdery/particulate residues of a combustion reaction. 2. solid residues found in crude oils. Ash is present in trace quantities in engine lubricating oils and diesel fuels.

assembly line data link (ALDL) the standard light-duty (automotive) vehicle data link; the current OBD II data link and also used by Volvo-Mack Trucks in post-2014 trucks. A 16-pin connector also known as an *SAE J1962 connector.*

Association of Diesel Specialists (ADS) organization to which fuel injection specialty shops belong and which monitors industry standards of practice and education.

ASTM see *American Society for Testing Materials.*

ASTM #1D fuel fuel recommended for use in high-speed, on-highway diesel engines required to operate under variable load and variable speeds. Minimum CN must be above 40. In theory, the ideal fuel for highway truck and bus diesel engines, but in practice it is not used as often as #2D fuel because it has less heat energy by weight, making it less economical.

ASTM #2D fuel fuel recommended for use in high-speed, on-highway diesel engines required to operate under constant loads and speeds. Like #1D fuel, the minimum CN is required to be above 40. It is widely used in highway truck operations because it produces better fuel economy than #1D fuel due to its higher calorific value, albeit at the expense of slightly inferior performance.

ASTM 975 standard to which all petroleum-based diesel fuels must conform.

ASTM 6751 standard to which pure biodiesel-based diesel fuels must conform.

asynchronous transfer mode (ATM) a method of transmission and switching that can handle vast amounts of data at high speed.

ATA connector see *ATA data link*.

ATA data link a legacy term used to describe a J1708 data bus connector (six-pin Deutsch), but used by some to reference either the J1708 or J1939 data link.

ATDC see *after top dead center*.

Atkinson cycle variation on the Otto cycle. By connecting the piston to the crankshaft with a double pivot linkage, it enables the four-piston strokes of the Otto cycle to take place in one crankshaft revolution. It also permits a longer power stroke than compression stroke, promising theoretically higher efficiencies than the Otto cycle.

atm a unit of atmospheric pressure equivalent to 14.7 psi (101.3 kPa). It is used as a unit of measurement in the United States and United Kingdom, especially on fuel calibration instruments; an atm is close but not exactly equivalent to the European unit *bar*.

atom the smallest part of a chemical element that can take part in a chemical reaction; composed of electrons, protons, and neutrons.

atomization the process of breaking liquid fuel into small droplets by pumping it at high pressure through a minute flow area.

atomized droplets the liquid droplets emitted from an injector nozzle.

A-trim see *adaptive trim*.

audit trail a means of electronically tracking electronically monitored problems in an engine management system. It may be discreet, that is, not read by some diagnostic ESTs and programs; also known as *tattletale*.

auto baud detect capable (ABDC) requirement for post-2014 ESTs connecting to the J1939 data bus. A non-ABDC EST can take down the bus.

AUTOEXEC.BAT a batch file loaded into the DOS kernel that governs boot-up protocol.

automated manual transmission (AMT) a standard mechanical transmission platform designed or adapted for computer-controlled shifting.

automotive governor a term sometimes used to describe a limiting speed, mechanical governor.

auxiliary power unit (APU) power supply unit used on many trucks to provide electrical power when the engine is not running; gasoline, diesel, or fuel cell sourced.

Aware Navistar telematics system capable of vehicle tracking, data mining, and mapping.

axial power turbine (APT) term used by DDC to describe its compounded turbocharger that imparts drive torque directly to the engine powertrain.

axis the point about which a body rotates; the center point of a circle. Plural: axes.

B5 standard petroleum-based diesel fuel cut with 5% biodiesel.

B20 standard petroleum-based diesel fuel cut with 20% biodiesel.

B100 term used to describe pure biodiesel fuel meeting the ASTM standard D6751.

backbone data bus consisting of a twisted wire pair.

backfire ignition/combustion of the fuel in an oxyacetylene torch in the torch tip; causes a popping and squealing noise.

background computations computer operating responses of lower priority than foreground operations that, while important, do not require immediate response; monitoring of engine fluid temperatures would be classified as a background computation.

back leakage term used to describe leakage past a nozzle valve. The leakage is routed to a leak-off or return circuit.

back leakage test an injector bench fixture test in which nozzle-valve-to-nozzle-body leakage is measured.

balanced atom an atom in which the number of electrons and protons are equal.

bandwidth volume or capacity of a data transmission medium; the number of packets that can be pumped down a channel or multiplex backbone.

bar a metric unit of pressure of 105 newtons per square meter; approximately, but not exactly, equal to 1 unit of atmosphere or 1 atm.

barometric capsule a barometer device used on some hydromechanical injection pumps to limit high-altitude fueling.

barometric pressure sensor (BARO) an electronic barometric pressure-sensing device.

barrel the stationary member of a reciprocating plunger pump element.

base circle (BC) the smallest radial dimension of an eccentric. It is used to describe cam geometry; the train that the cam is responsible for actuating would be unloaded on the cam base circle. Also known as *inner base circle* or *IBC*.

basic input/output system (BIOS) chip that supplies instructions to the CPU, when a computer is booted, on how to interface between the disk operating system and the system hardware.

baud times per second that a data communications signal changes and permits one bit of data to be transmitted.

baud rate the speed of a data transmission.

bay a vacant location in the computer housing/system designed to accommodate system upgrades.

beach marks patterned succession of ripple marks observed in a fatigue fracture indicating the progression of a crack front.

bearing shell a half segment of a friction bearing such as would be used as a crankshaft main bearing.

bedplate replaces a set of engine main bearing caps with a single casting plate that bolts to the cylinder block. It enables a lighter cylinder block to withstand high resistance to torsional forces.

before top dead center (BTDC) a piston location in the cycle before full piston travel.

beginning of energizing (BOE) moment that an EHI, EUI, or EUP is electrically energized.

beginning of injection (BOI) in engine management, a specific point at which injection begins.

bell crank a single-arm lever with its fulcrum at the apex of a shaft; often used as a mechanical relay. The word originates from medieval church bell-ringing mechanisms.

benzene hydrocarbon fuel fraction obtainable from coal or petroleum; known to be a *carcinogen*.

big end the crankshaft throw end of a connecting rod.

binary system a two-digit arithmetic, numeric system commonly used in computer electronics.

biocide bacteria-killing agent that can be added to stored diesel fuel or biodiesel that is under attack by bacteria colonies.

biodiesel fuel derived from farm products with a vegetable and alcohol base; when used in current diesel engines, it should meet ASTM standard D6751.

biomethane organic methane gas produced by the rotting of vegetable matter (sometimes from landfill sites) in the absence of oxygen. Can be commercially produced using anaerobic digesters with the appropriate organic matter. When biomethanes are permitted to vent to atmosphere, they have global warming potential that is more than 20 times greater than CO_2, so they are rated as a negative GWP fuel. Volvo-Mack DME is biomethane based.

bipolar transistor a three-terminal transistor that functions as a sort of switched diode.

bit a binary digit that can represent one of two values: on or off; presence of voltage or no voltage; the smallest piece of data that a computer can manipulate. There are 8 bits to a byte.

bits per second (BPS) a measure of the speed at which data can be transferred.

black smoke smoke that appears black to the observer. Caused by particulate (solids) emission in the exhaust gas stream; light is blocked by the particulate, making it appear black.

blended torque transmission the CVT transmission used in HEV buses that allows drive torque input from either the diesel engine powerplant or the electric motor/generator, or both, simultaneously providing infinitely variable output torque.

B-life OEM-generated ratings that project the percentages of engines in a series that will fail at various mileage intervals. A B10-life correlated to a mileage value means that 10% of that engine family has failed at that mileage.

blink codes fault codes blinked out using diagnostic lights; also known as *flash codes*.

blotter test an inaccurate and generally obsolete method of testing used engine oil for viscosity and contamination.

blue smoke usually associated with engine oil combusted in the engine cylinder; caused by the mixture of condensing droplets and particulate emitted when oil is burned in an engine.

BlueTec a term used by Daimler to describe any engines equipped with SCR technology. For this reason, Detroit Diesel uses the term to describe SCR on its post-2010 DD family of engines.

Bluetooth a wireless network suited to applications where lower volumes of data have to be transferred; used primarily for phones, headsets, and tablets.

boil point the temperature at which a liquid vaporizes.

bomb calorimeter test a test used to calculate the heating value of a fuel, in which a known quantity of the substance is combusted and the heat released is calculated.

boom hoist in a truck or engine shop, usually refers to a portable crane on rollers; commonly used to remove engines from truck chassis. Often referred to by the slang term *cherry picker*.

boosted engine any turbocharged engine; turbo-boosted.

boot the process of loading an operating system into RAM or main memory.

boot-up to load an operating system into RAM, electronically reload a system program, or reset a computer.

bore an aperture; the internal diameter of a pump or engine cylinder or the act of machining a cylindrical aperture.

bottom dead center (BDC) lowest point of travel of a piston in an engine cylinder during its cycle.

boundary lubrication thin film lubrication characteristics of an oil.

Boyle's law states that for a given, confined quantity of gas, pressure is inversely related to volume, so as one value goes up, the other goes down. In compressing gas in an engine cylinder during piston upstroke, cylinder volume is reduced, so cylinder pressure accordingly is increased.

brake fade a vehicle braking characteristic caused by excessive heat that can expand brake foundation components, such as drums, and lower the coefficient of friction of the critical friction surfaces.

brake horsepower (BHP) standard expression for brake power, commonly used in the truck industry. See *brake power*.

brake power power developed by an engine measured at the flywheel by a dynamometer or brake; factored by torque and rpm.

BrakeSaver™ a Caterpillar engine-mounted, hydraulic retarder optioned in older engines.

brake specific fuel consumption (BSFC) a measure of the fuel required to perform a unit of work; used in graphs of engine data designed to show fuel efficiency at specific engine loads and rpm.

breakout box a diagnostic device fitted with coded sockets that accesses an electrical or electronic circuit by teeing into it; used in conjunction with a DMM.

breakout T term used to describe a breakout box or (in some cases) a diagnostic device that tees into two- or three-wire circuits to enable diagnoses by DMM of a single component such as a sensor.

bridge the software and/or hardware used to make electronic connections, such as that used to connect nodes in a network.

British thermal unit (Btu) the amount of heat required to raise the temperature of 1 pound of water 1 degree Fahrenheit at 60°F; the standard unit of heat energy measurement.

brittle describes the property of a material that is unable to sustain any plastic deformation without fracturing; a china coffee cup could be described as being brittle.

Brix refractometer tool designed to measure the sugar content in liquids, but also used to measure WEC freeze protection.

broach a boring bit used for final, accurate bore sizing.

broker term commonly used to describe a private owner-operator (O/O) of a truck; most brokers own their tractor and haul fleet-owned trailers.

bubble collapse the condition caused by wet liner combustion pressure impulses acting on the coolant, resulting in vapor bubbles that implode and cause cavitation.

buffers memory locations used to store processed data before it is sent to output devices.

bundle multiple arrangement of cooling tubes that form the core of a heat exchanger.

buret see *vial*.

bus 1. a transit vehicle. 2. an electronic connection; transit lines that connect the CPU, memory, and input/output devices of a computer; increasingly used to mean "connected."

bushing any of a number of types of friction bearings designed to support shafts.

bus systems term used to describe data highways.

bus topology multiplexing geometry arranged so that no single controller (SA/MID) networked to the bus has more status than another. If one SA/MID module on the bus fails, the remainder can function unaffected.

buttress an additional/auxiliary support device such as a gusset.

buttress screws transverse bolts used in addition to vertical plain, main bearing cap screws; used in engines such as Mack Trucks E7 to help control cylinder block torque twist.

butt splice the joining of two pieces in a series connection.

bypass filter a filter assembly plumbed in parallel with the lubrication circuit, usually capable of high filtering efficiencies.

bypass valve a diverter valve fitted to full flow filter (series) mounting pads; designed to reroute lubricant around a plugged filter element to prevent a major engine failure.

byte unit of measure of computer data, comprised of 8 bits; used to quantify computer data memory.

cab-over-engine (COE) truck chassis in which the engine compartment is located directly underneath the driver cab, eliminating the hood.

cache high-speed RAM located between the CPU and main memory; used to increase processing efficiency.

calibrating orifice see *balance orifice*.

calibration adjusting performance specifications to a standard. Fuel trimming of diesel fuel injection components is known as *calibration*.

calibration code the rating of hydraulic fuel flow of individual injectors during bench testing; required to program electronic injectors to the ECM to balance cylinder fueling.

calibration correlate a set of readings with a standard or the process of adjusting to a standard.

calibration parameters the specific values required when setting performance to specification.

California Air Resources Board (CARB) The state of California agency responsible for driving emissions legislation and enforcement. By establishing standards that exceed federal standards and effecting them earlier, CARB has led the emissions control initiative throughout North America.

calipers comparative measuring instrument used for measuring od or id.

calorific value the heating value of a fuel measured in Btu, calories, or joules.

cam an eccentric; an eccentric portion of a shaft, often used to convert rotary motion into reciprocating motion.

cambox the lower portion of a port-helix metering injection pump in which the actuating camshaft is mounted and the lubricating oil sump is located.

cam geometry the shaping of a cam profile and the effect it produces on the train it actuates.

cam ground trunk-type pistons that are machined slightly eccentrically. Because of the greater mass of material required at the wrist pin boss, this area will expand proportionally more when heated. Cam ground pistons are designed to assume a true circular shape at operating temperatures.

cam heel the point on a cam profile that is exactly (diametrically) opposite the toe or center point of the highest point on the cam.

cam nose the portion of the cam profile with the largest radial dimension; its center point would be the cam toe. It is that portion of the cam profile that is OBC.

cam plate the input shaft driven, rotating-reciprocating member used to actuate the distributor plunger in a Bosch-type, sleeve-metering, rotary distributor injection pump such as the VE.

cam profile the cam geometry; simply, the shape of the cam.

camshaft a crankshaft-driven shaft, machined with eccentrics (cams) designed to actuate trains positioned to ride the cam profiles; the engine feedback assembly actuator responsible for timing/actuating cylinder valves and fuel injection apparatus. Driven at half engine speed on four-stroke cycle engines and at engine speed on two-stroke cycle engines.

camshaft position sensor (CPS) any of a number of types of engine position sensors using either an inductive pulse generator or Hall-effect electrical principle.

CAN 2.0 high-speed data bus architecture and protocols developed jointly by Bosch and Intel; the basis of heavy-duty J1939 and light-duty CAN-C data buses. Also known as a *class C bus*. Current versions function at maximum speeds up to 1 Mb/s, with 500 kb/s being typical.

CAN-C the light-duty version of a CAN 2.0 data bus used in most post-2010 automobiles and light trucks.

canister a cylindrical container.

capacitance measure of how much electrical charge can be stored for a given voltage potential; measured in farads.

capacitive discharge ignition (CDI) spark ignition system in which electrical energy is stored in a capacitor and switched by thyristor into the high-tension circuit.

capacitor an electrical device that can store an electrical charge or block AC and pass DC; also known as *condenser*.

carbon (C) an element found in various forms including diamonds, charcoal, and coal. It is the primary constituent element in hydrocarbon fuels. Its atomic number is 6.

carbon dioxide (CO_2) the product of combusting carbon in the oxidation reaction of an HC fuel. It is an odorless, tasteless gas that is nontoxic and not classified as a noxious engine emission, but that contributes to greenhouse gases that concern environmentalists.

carbon monoxide (CO) a colorless, odorless, and poisonous gas that is produced when carbon is not completely oxidized in combustion.

carcinogen a cancer-causing agent.

Carnot cycle relates to the ratio of work output to heat input, which should equal the difference between the temperatures of the heat source and rejected heat combined, divided by the temperature of the heat source.

cartridge a removable container; used to describe the housing that encloses a filter.

cassette architecture term used to describe the stacking of batteries, ultracapacitors, and hydraulic accumulators in banks. Used in hybrid electric, electric vehicle, and hydraulic hybrid powertrain technology.

catalyst a substance that stimulates, accelerates, or enables a chemical reaction without itself undergoing any change.

catalytic converter   an exhaust system device that enables oxidation and reduction reactions.

Caterpillar Engine Company   a major diesel engine manufacturer. Corporate center is in Peoria, Illinois.

Caterpillar Fleet Information Software (FIS)   program that permits data, tracked and stored in the ADEM software, to be downloaded to a PC for analysis.

Caterpillar information display (Cat ID)   the Caterpillar digital dash display that provides the driver with ECM feedback data such as fuel economy and engine parameters.

cathode   negative electrode; the electrode from which electrons flow.

Cat Messenger   an advancement on the Cat ID driver display unit providing feedback on engine operating conditions, maintenance tracking, theft deterrence, and chassis performance.

cavitation   describes metal erosion caused by the formation and subsequent collapse of vapor pockets (bubbles) produced by physical pulsing into a liquid, such as that of a wet liner against the wall of coolant that surrounds it. Bubble collapse causes high unit pressures and can rapidly erode wet liners when the protective properties of the coolant diminish.

CD-ROM   an optically encoded data disk that is read by a laser in the same way an audio CD is read; designed for read-only data.

C-EGR   see *cooled exhaust gas recirculation.*

CELECT   term used for *Cummins Electronics,* the management system for Cummins's EUI-fueled N14 and M11 engines.

CELECT injector   a Cummins EUI.

CELECT Plus   term for the second generation of CELECT EUI management used on Cummins N14 and M11 engines.

CENTINEL   Cummins onboard engine oil management system that claimed to extend engine oil change intervals up to 300,000 miles (483,000 km) by using monitoring electronics and a makeup oil tank; currently illegal.

central gateway   a module that acts as a transducer (translator) for data networks using different communication protocols.

central processing unit (CPU)   computer subcomponent that executes program instructions and performs arithmetic and logic computations.

centrifugal filter   a filter that uses a centrifuge consisting of a rotating cylinder charged with pressurized fluid and canted jets to drive it; centrifugal filters often have high efficiencies and are often of the bypass type.

centrifugal force   the force acting outward on a rotating body.

centrifuge   a device that uses centrifugal propulsion or a centrifugal force principle of operation.

cetane improvers   see *ignition accelerators.*

cetane number (CN)   the standard rating of a diesel fuel's ignition quality. It is a comparative rating method that measures the ignition quality of a diesel fuel versus that of a mixture of cetane (good ignition characteristics) and heptamethylnonane (poor ignition characteristics). A mixture of 45% cetane and 55% heptamethylnonane would have a CN of 45. Diesel fuels refined for use on North American highways are classified by the ASTM as #1D and #2D and must have a minimum CN of 40.

chain hoist   a mechanical or power-operated ratcheting lifting device consisting of an actuating block, lift chains, and hook.

charge air cooler (CAC)   the heat exchanger that cools turbo-boosted air before it is delivered to the engine cylinders; in truck engines, this is usually ram air assisted.

charge air cooling   the cooling of turbo-boost air by means of ram air or coolant medium heat exchangers.

charge differential   electrical pressure usually described as potential difference and measured in voltage.

charging circuit   the portion of the fuel subsystem that begins with the charging or transfer pump and is responsible for delivering fuel to the injection pumping/metering apparatus.

charging pressure   a term used to describe the pressure on the charge side of the transfer pump in a fuel subsystem. Charging pressure parameters are defined by the cycle speed of the charging pump, the flow area the pump unloads to, and the regulating valve.

charging pump   the pump responsible for moving fuel through the fuel subsystem. Plunger, gear, and (less commonly) vane-type pumps are used.

Charles's law   states that the volume occupied by a fixed quantity of gas is directly proportional to its temperature if the pressure remains constant.

chassis dynamometer   a test bed that measures brake power delivered to the vehicle wheels by having them drive roller(s) to which torque resistance is applied and accurately measured.

chassis-mounted charge air cooling (CMAC)   method of cooling turbo-boost air using a ram air heat exchanger; effective in highway applications, but less so in off-road service.

chatter   a nozzle bench test characteristic in which a nozzle valve rapidly opens and closes; caused by the slow rate of pressure rise when testing nozzle valves.

check engine light (CEL)   a dash warning light that is often used as a first-level alert to the driver; usually related to maintenance.

check valve   usually spring-loaded, two-position valve.

chemical bonding   the force holding atoms together in a molecule or a crystal.

cherry picker   commonly used slang term for *boom hoist.*

chief executive officer (CEO)   the head of an organization.

chip   a complete electronic circuit that has been photo-infused to a semiconductor material such as silicon; also known as *I/C (integrated circuit), microchip.*

chopper wheel   the rotating disc that cuts a magnetic field to produce rotational speed or rotational position data to an ECM, either by producing an AC voltage value or by pulse width modulation.

clad   see *cladded processes.*

cladding   see *cladded processes.*

cladded processes   a means of surface-coating one metal with another, usually by using high temperatures to produce a molecular bond between the cladding and base metal. The *plasma transfer wire arc (PTWA)* is an example of a cladded (cladding) process.

Class C bus   see *CAN 2.0.*

clean gas induction (CGI)   a Caterpillar exhaust gas recirculation strategy that sources dead gas downstream from the exhaust aftertreatment circuit; hence the term "clean."

clearance volume   the volume in an engine cylinder when the piston is at top dead center.

clevis   a yoke that is often used in conjunction with a clevis pin and a lever to convert rotary motion to linear or vice versa.

client   anything in a computer-processing cycle or multiplex data transaction that can be described as having a need.

clipboard temporary storage location in a computer for data during cut, paste, and program transfer operations.

clip points locations on a data bus onto which ESTs can be physically connected to communicate with the bus.

clock speed the measure of how fast a CPU can process data; measured in MHz (megahertz) or millions of cycles per second.

clockwise (CW) right-hand rotation.

closed circuit an electrical circuit through which current is flowing.

closed circuit voltage (CCV) voltage measured in an energized circuit.

closed crankcase ventilation (CCV) an EPA requirement for diesel engine crankcases beginning in 2007 (off-highway 2008). Diesel engine OEMs have adopted positive or centrifugal-type filtration of crankcase vapors prior to rerouting them to the intake upstream from the turbocharger impeller; equivalent to the automotive *positive crankcase ventilation (CCV)*.

cloud point the temperature at which wax crystals present in all diesel fuels become large enough to make the fuel appear hazy. It is also the point at which plugging of fuel filters becomes a possibility. The cloud point is usually 5°F (3°C) above the fuel's pour point.

cluster the smallest data storage unit on a digital memory device.

cluster heartbeat an SOH check between the engine ECM and the cluster communications: Typically tests every second upon key-on operation and logs a fault code if a malfunction is detected.

CMP sensor camshaft position sensor.

coalesce to combine to form a single whole.

coaxial cable type of wiring used to transmit signals; has almost unlimited bandwidth, but is unable to carry two-way signals.

coder/decoder (codec) device that converts analog voice and data signals to digital signals and vice versa.

coefficient of friction a means of rating the aggressiveness of friction materials; alters with temperature and the presence of any kind of lubricant.

coefficient of thermal expansion the manner in which a material behaves as it is heated and cooled. For instance, aluminum has a higher coefficient of thermal expansion than steel, meaning that when a similar mass of each material is subjected to an identical amount of heat, the aluminum will expand more.

coil-on-plug ignition (CPI) system used in the Cummins Westport ISX 12G in which one coil per cylinder is used. The coil is contained in a single molded block with multiple high-tension terminals. A single unit is commonly referred to as a *coil-pack*.

coil-pack see *coil-on-plug ignition (CPI) system*.

coils electromagnetic devices used as the basis of solenoids, transformers, and motors; and in electronics, to shape voltage waves.

coincidental damage in failure analysis, a term used to refer to secondary component or system failures created by the *root cause* failure.

cold soak cycle typically stated as an 8-hour key-off cycle, but varies by OEM; after a cold soak cycle, IAT and ECT should be equal.

cold-start strategy a programmed startup sequence in an electronic management system in which the timing, fuel quantity, and engine-operating parameters are managed on the basis of ambient and engine fluid temperatures. During this process, other inputs such as throttle position may be ignored by the ECM.

collateral damage in military parlance, destruction beyond the intended target. In failure analysis, the term is used to describe coincidental damage.

combustion the act of burning a substance; an oxidation reaction.

combustion pressure usually refers to peak cylinder pressure during the power stroke.

command circuit used to describe input sensors such as the throttle position sensor (TPS) that commands (requests) an output from the ECM.

commercial mobile radio service (CMRS) the open and low-security radio communication frequencies functioning at 6.25, 25, and 100 Hz.

Commercial Vehicle Integration and Infrastructure (CVII) a New York state telematic initiative to track driver ID and perform wireless vehicle safety inspections; a model used for other I2V communications.

common platform a term created to describe what happens when two major OEMs merge and proceed to develop common technology, but for purposes of brand identification, badge and market the technology under different names. This has been the case for Volvo and Mack and Detroit Diesel and Mercedes-Benz engine development.

common powertrain controller (CPC) Detroit Diesel DDEC VI and 10 term for their engine ECM with a source address SA of 00 on the powertrain bus.

common rail (CR) the high-pressure accumulator pipe that supplies the electrohydraulic injectors (EHIs) in a CR fuel system.

common rail system (CRS) fuel injection system in which injection pressures are created by a pump that then supplies fuel to an accumulator or common rail connected to fuel injectors. The fuel injectors are then electrically or electrohydraulically actuated by the ECM.

communications adapter (CA) the serial communications adapter required to connect (handshake) PC software with the chassis data bus.

compact disk (CD) optically encoded digital data storage.

compacted graphite iron (CGI) a new-generation cylinder block casting composite used because of its high strength, resistance to torque twist, and light weight. One example of CGI is known as *GJV-450*.

companion cylinders term used to describe pistons paired by their respective crank throws to rotate together through the engine cycle, such as #1 and #6 in an inline, six-cylinder engine.

comparative measuring use of instruments that gauge a dimension but require another instrument to produce an actual value. For example, dividers would require a tape measure to convert the dimension measured to a value.

comparator anything used to compare one value to another.

comparator bench a fuel injection pump test fixture used to compare the performance and output values of an injection pump with a set of master specifications. Usually consists of a means of driving the injection pump (as if it were being driven by the engine it is designed to fuel), a drive turret equipped with a protractor (for phasing), and graduated vials (means of measuring fuel quantity injected). The term can also be used to describe the test fixtures used to set up mechanical injectors and EUIs, HEUIs, and EHIs.

composite steel trunk piston a trunk-type piston in which the crown and skirt sections are manufactured separately and then screwed together using a proprietary process by Mahle; see *Monocomp piston*.

compound 1. (noun) a substance consisting of two or more elements held together by chemical force and not necessarily retaining any characteristics of the composite elements. 2. (verb) the process of increasing the force acting on a plunger or piston by using both mechanical and fluid forces.

compound turbocharging a turbocharger circuit in which the turbine connects to a reduction gearing coupling with an output shaft indirectly connected to the engine crankshaft. This allows the turbocharger to directly transmit torque to the engine drivetrain. An example is the 2010 DD *axial power turbine* (APT).

compressed air the means of powering shop tools and truck chassis equipment in many applications. It is usually pressurized to between 90 and 150 psi, plumbed throughout a shop or vehicle chassis.

compressed natural gas (CNG) pressurized natural gas used for commercial and automotive vehicles; consists largely of methane.

compressed natural gas direct injection (CNG-DI) Westport electronic fuel injector used in Cummins Westport NG engines.

compressional load a force that attempts to compress or squeeze from diametrically opposite directions to a common point in the component under load.

compression ignition (CI) an engine in which the air-fuel mixture is ignited by the heat of compression.

compression pressure the actual cylinder pressure developed on the compression stroke.

compression ratio the ratio of piston swept volume to total cylinder volume with the piston at bottom dead center; a volumetric ratio, not a pressure ratio.

compression ring the ring(s) designed to seal cylinder gas pressure located in the upper ring belt.

compressor housing the section of a turbocharger responsible for compressing the intake air and feeding it into the intake circuit; also known as *impeller housing*.

Compulink The Cummins CELECT EST.

computer-assisted design (CAD) the commonly used industrial component design tool.

computer-assisted machining (CAM) programmable, computer-managed machining.

concentric circles having a common center.

concept gear a two-piece assembly found in some diesel engine timing geartrains that uses coaxial springs between the hub and outer toothed ring to maintain zero lash tooth contact between gears in contact with each other; aka *scissor gear*.

condensation the changing of a vapor to a liquid by cooling.

condenser see *capacitor*.

conductance the ability of a material to carry an electrical current.

conduction heat transmission through solid matter.

conductor material that readily permits the flow of electrons from atom to atom; usually metallic elements that have fewer than four electrons in their outer shells.

connecting rod the rigid mechanical link between the piston wrist pin and the crankshaft throw.

consolidated engine controller (CEC) an ECM that houses the microcomputer and output switching such as injector drivers. The term is specifically used by Navistar.

constant geometry (CG) usually used to describe a turbocharger in which all the exhaust gas is routed through the turbine housing, which has no internal or external controls.

constant horsepower sometimes used to describe a high-torque rise engine.

constant volume sampling (CVS) an exhaust gas measurement procedure used before certification.

contact stress fatigue occurs when two surfaces slide or roll against each other, developing high stress, surface movement, and fatigue cracks in one or both surfaces.

Contamination Control a Caterpillar program started in 1999 aimed at minimizing mechanical damage caused by wear; extends to lube quality and handling plus shop floor maintenance practices.

continuity an unbroken circuit; term used to describe a continuous electrical circuit. A continuity test would determine if a circuit or circuit component was capable of current flow.

continuously open throttle valve (CTV) brake Mercedes-Benz variation on the internal engine compression brake using small valves (the CTVs), fitted into the engine cylinder head, that allow some cylinder leakage to the exhaust during both the compression and exhaust strokes under braking.

continuously variable transmission (CVT) describes any transmission capable of infinite output ratios. Can be achieved by use of drive belts/chains and tapered input/output rotors or by using planetary gearsets.

control cartridge term used to describe the control actuator and valve assembly on an EUI, EUP, HEUI, or EHI injector.

controller area network (CAN) data bus architecture developed by Robert Bosch and Intel for vehicle applications. CAN is a serial data transmission network used as the basis for CAN-C (automotive) and SAE J1939 (truck and heavy equipment) data backbones.

control rack the fuel control mechanism on an MUI or multicylinder port-helix metering pump that, when moved linearly, rotates the pumping plunger(s) in unison.

control sleeve the component that is tooth meshed to the port-helix pump control rack and connects to the plungers by means of slots used to rotate the plungers in the barrels.

control strategy the manner in which an ECM has been programmed to manage the engine, especially in the event of an electronically monitored problem.

control unit the part of a computer CPU responsible for fetching, decoding, executing, and storing.

convection heat transfer by currents of gas or liquids.

conventional memory the first data logged into RAM upon boot-up; used primarily to retain the operating system.

conventional theory (of current flow) asserts that current flows from a positive source to a negative source. Despite the fact that it is fundamentally incorrect, it is nevertheless widely accepted and used. See *electron theory*.

cooled exhaust gas recirculation (C-EGR) introduced in 2002 to address EPA 2004 diesel emissions standards. Dead (unreactive) end gas is first cooled, then rerouted into the intake system to dilute the intake charge and lower temperatures, reducing NO_x emission.

CoPilot Mack Trucks V-MAC digital monitor and driver display unit.

coprocessor a chip or CPU enhancement designed for specific tasks such as mathematical calculation.

cordierite ceramic material used for honeycomb flow-through substrates on diesel particulate filters and catalytic converters; not in itself a catalyst.

corrosion chemical change and deterioration of metal surfaces caused by acidic, alkaline, or electrolytic conditions.

corrosive alkaline or acidic substance that dissolves metals and skin tissue.

coulomb a measure of current volume, 1 coulomb is equal to $6.28 \times 1,018$ electrons.

counterclockwise (CCW) left-hand rotation.

counterflow radiator a double-pass radiator in which coolant is cycled through U column tubes from (usually) a bottom-located intake tank to a bottom-located output tank; has higher cooling efficiency than other radiator designs.

covalent bonding the atomic condition that occurs when electrons are shared by two atoms.

covert term that means "undercover"; commonly used in vehicle electronics to describe the logging of data that cannot be read using commonly available diagnostic software. Events such as engine overspeed conditions that could affect the system warranty are often written covertly to an electronic system.

cracked rod connecting rod manufactured and machined in one piece, following which the big end is separated by a precisely defined fracture. This ensures a cap-to-rod fit of the highest precision.

crank angle a location in an engine cycle noted by rotational degrees through the cycle.

crank axis center point about which a crankshaft rotates.

crankcase the lower portion of the engine cylinder block in which the crankshaft is mounted and under which is the lubrication oil sump.

crankshaft a shaft with offset throws designed to convert the reciprocating movement of pistons into torque.

crank throw the offset journal on a crankshaft to which a connecting rod is connected.

creep describes the independent movement of two components clamped by fasteners when they have different coefficients of thermal expansion or have different mass, which means their expansion and contraction rates do not concur. A function of a gasket is to accommodate component creep while maintaining an effective seal.

crimping pliers pliers designed to crimp a terminal to a wire without crushing or damaging the terminal.

critical flow venturi (CFV) one type of MAF sensor, sometimes known as a pressure differential flow sensor. Its operating principle is based on the relationship between inlet pressure and flow rate through a venturi, so it uses an inlet and outlet pressure sensor on either side of a venturi; this enables the ECM to calculate flow mass.

critical pollutants pollutants identified by the United States EPA that include six airborne pollutants: ozone, lead, carbon monoxide, sulfur dioxide, nitrogen dioxide, and respirable particulate matter.

crossflow radiator a usually low-profile design of radiator (used with aerodynamic hood/nose) in which the entry and output tanks are located at either end and coolant flow is horizontal.

crossflow valve configuration a cylinder head valve configuration in which the intake and exhaust valves are located in series in the cylinder head, meaning that gas flow from the inboard valve differs from (and may interfere with) that of the outboard valve.

crosshead piston an articulating piston with separate crown and skirt assemblies in which the connecting rod is bolted directly to the wrist pin.

crossover a pipe that connects a pair of fuel tanks mounted on either side of a truck frame at the sump level, enabling fuel to be drawn from one tank while enabling equal fuel load in each tank.

crown the leading edge face of a piston or, in articulating pistons, the upper section of the piston assembly. Crown geometry (shape) plays a large role in defining the cylinder gas dynamic.

crown valve a now obsolete DDC MUI nozzle valve.

crown valve nozzle an obsolete DDC hydraulic injector nozzle integral with early version MUIs.

crude oil the organic fossil fuel pumped from the ground from which diesel fuel, gasoline, and many other petroleum products are refined; raw petroleum.

cryogenic term used to describe the storage of ambiently gaseous fuels in liquid state at extreme low temperatures. The term is also used to describe reefer thermodynamics that use cryo media and motors.

cryogenics the branch of technology that deals with very low temperatures and their effects.

CTV brake see *continuously open throttle valve (CTV) brake*.

Cummins Accumulator Pump System (CAPS) a Cummins variation of common rail fueling with full authority electronic management that was used on ISC and ISL engines until 2004.

Cummins electronic engine control (CELECT) computer subcomponent that executes program instructions and performs arithmetic and logic computations.

Cummins Engine Company a major manufacturer of truck diesel engines. Corporate center is in Columbus, Indiana.

Cummins ISB Interact System B series; inline 4.4-liter (four-cylinder) and 6.7-liter (six-cylinder) engines in post-2007 versions.

Cummins ISC Interact System C series; inline 8.3-liter, six-cylinder engine.

Cummins ISL Interact System L series; inline 8.9-liter, six-cylinder engine.

Cummins ISM Interact System M series; inline 11-liter, six-cylinder engine.

Cummins ISX Interact System X series; inline 15-and 11.9-liter, six-cylinder engines.

current the flow of electrons in a closed electrical circuit.

current transformer a DMM accessory that permits high electrical current flow values to be transduced and read.

cursor the underline character or arrow that indicates the working location on a computer screen display.

cybernetics the science of automated (computer) control of machines, systems, and nature. Diesel engine controllers or ECMs are cybernetic devices.

cycle 1. a sequence of events that recurs, such as those of the diesel cycle. 2. one complete reversal of an alternating current from positive to negative.

cycling circuit breaker an SAE #1 circuit protection device. When tripped by current overload, it opens only until the element cools, after which it closes. This cycle can be repeated indefinitely.

cylinder block the main frame of any engine to which all the other components are attached.

cylinder gas dynamics engine cylinder gas movement during the cycle. High turbulence was an objective in many older diesel engines, whereas lower turbulence or quiescent dynamics are used in many newer diesels with high injection pressures.

cylinder head the component clamped to a cylinder block containing the engine breathing and fueling control mechanisms.

cylinder leakage test procedure used to test cylinder leakage by applying regulated air to the cylinder at a controlled volume and pressure and producing a percentage of leakage specification.

cylinder volume total volume in an engine cylinder with the piston at BDC; the sum of swept volume and clearance volume.

DAF vehicle information electronics (DAVIE) the online SIS used by Paccar (Kenworth and Peterbilt) trucks. A subscription service.

Darlington pair two transistors arranged to form an amplifier that permits a very small current to switch a large one.

dash display unit (DDU) dash-mounted, LED driver display screen.

data raw (unprocessed) information.

database a data storage location or program.

data bus multiplex backbone consisting of a twisted wire pair.

data bus communications networked messaging transactions between vehicle controllers networked by multiplexing. Current trucks, buses, and heavy equipment use J1587 and J1939 buses along with proprietary buses for non-powertrain communications.

data communications link (DCL) term used to describe what is more commonly referred to as a *data link connector (DLC)*.

data compression a means of reducing the physical storage space needed for data by coding the data.

data connector (DC) see *data link connector*.

data frame a data tag consisting of 100–150 bits for transmission to the bus. Each tag codes a message for sequencing transmission to the data bus and also serves to limit the time transmission consumes on the bus.

data hub the center (hub) of a network system. Used by most truck engine OEMs to log data such as warranty status, repair history, and proprietary programming of onboard controllers.

data link the connection point or path for data transmission in networked devices.

data link connector (DLC) the means of connecting ESTs to a chassis data bus for purposes of reading or programming. Current DLCs are 6-pin (J1587/1708) or 9-pin (J1939), or 16-pin (J1962).

data logging the tracking of computer data for later analysis.

DataMax Mack Trucks' onboard data logger and driver display system. Used in conjunction with InfoMax, it can enable downloading of vehicle performance data for analysis.

data mining the collecting of data for analysis; in trucking, used for such things as prognostics, warranty claims, and condition-based maintenance.

data processing the production and manipulation of data by a computer.

DAVIE see *DAF vehicle information electronics*.

DDEC 10 version of DDEC engine management electronics introduced for DD MY 2010 engines.

dead volume fuel fuel that is statically retained for a portion of the cycle; usually refers to the fuel retained at residual line pressure in a high-pressure injection pipe that connects injection pump elements with injectors in a PLN system.

decoding a CPU control unit operation that translates program instructions.

dedicated short-range communications (DSRC) the current IEEE 802.11 protocol used for state I2V geofence communications.

default preselected option in computer processing outcomes that kicks in when a failure occurs outside the programmed algorithm; failure strategy that permits limited functionality when a critical input is lost; revert to basics; limp-home mode.

delivery valve a combination check and pressure management valve that is used on many hydromechanical diesel fuel injection systems.

Delphi common rail see *high-pressure heavy-duty diesel common rail (HPHDDCR)*.

Delphi E3 injector a two-actuator EUI used by Caterpillar, DD, Volvo, and Mack Trucks beginning in 2007. From MY 2010 onward, only Caterpillar and Volvo-Mack use E3 injectors. The E3 features a smart nozzle directly controlled by the ECM.

Denoxtronic Bosch NO_x reduction hardware and software system.

Departronic Bosch diesel particulate filtration system.

desktop a computer term that either describes a nonportable, desk-based PC system or the screen display at any given moment of PC operation.

detonation combustion in an engine cylinder occurring at an explosive rate, accelerated by more than one flame front; caused by a number of different conditions, but in diesel engines often by prolonged ignition lag when ambient temperatures are low, when it is known as *diesel knock*.

Detroit Diesel (DD) a major diesel engine manufacturer, part of Daimler Trucks North America (DTNA); formerly known as Detroit Diesel Corporation (DDC). Corporate center is in Dearborn, Michigan.

Detroit Diesel Customer Support Network (DDCSN) DDC's online service information system.

Detroit Diesel Data Summaries (DDDS) software used by DD to enable the downloading of engine data to a database for analysis.

Detroit Diesel Diagnostic Link (DDDL) DD's PC-driven diagnostic software that works in tandem with DD's online service information system known as *DDCSN*.

Detroit Diesel Electronic Controls (DDEC) DDEC I was introduced in 1985 and marketed in 1987. It was the first full authority engine management system available on a North American engine. DDEC evolved through a number of versions using Roman numerals until DDEC VI (2007). In 2010, this changed; the current version is known as DDEC10, consistent with the EPA model year.

Detroit Diesel Reprogramming Station (DDRS) DDEC10 DD-Series software required to diagnose and reprogram post-2010 engines.

Deutsch connector a widely used, weatherproof, proprietary electrical and electronic connector.

device drivers software used to control input and output devices.

Dexcool a brand of EG-based antifreeze.

Diagnostic Link a DDEC PC-based troubleshooting software package driven from MS Windows, designed to guide the technician through troubleshooting sequences, customer data programming, DDEC programming, and data analysis.

diagnostic link connector (DLC)   the means of connecting ESTs to a chassis data bus for purposes of reading or programming. Current DLCs are 6-pin (J1587/1708), 9-pin (J1939), or 16-pin (J1962). Another name for *data link connector (DLC)*.

diagnostic pressure sensor   Cummins HPI-TP sensor located downstream from the rail actuator in each bank.

diagnostic sight glass   a section of optically clear Perspex tube coupled into #6, #8, or #10 hydraulic hose; used to troubleshoot air admission into fuel and hydraulic circuits. The sight glass is coupled in series into the circuit to be tested.

diagnostic trouble code (DTC)   means of classifying logged codes either numerically or in text on J1587 and J1939.

dial bore gauge   an instrument designed to facilitate rapid bore comparative measurements; much used by the diesel engine rebuilder.

dial indicator   an instrument designed to measure movement, travel, or precise relative dimensions; consists of a dial face, needle, and spring-loaded plunger. It can measure values down to one hundred-thousandth of an inch or thousandths of a millimeter.

diamond dowels   diamond-shaped alignment dowels used on flywheel housings that are less inclined to deformation than cylindrical dowels.

Diamond Logic   Navistar International engine and chassis management system; accessed using Navistar EZ-Tech.

Diamond Logic Builder   Navistar International engine and chassis access software; a free Web download.

Diamond Plus   term used by Navistar International to describe one generation of Diamond Logic.

diatomic   a molecule consisting of two atoms of the same element.

dielectric   insulator substance, such as the separation plates used between the conductor plates in a typical capacitor.

diesel coolant additive (DCA)   proprietary supplemental coolant additive.

diesel cycle   the four-stroke, compression ignition cycle patented by Rudolf Diesel in 1892. Though the term *diesel* can be used to describe some two-stroke cycle CI engines, the diesel cycle is necessarily a four-stroke cycle.

diesel engine   an internal combustion engine in which the cylinder fuel air charge is ignited by the heat of compression.

diesel exhaust fluid (DEF)   the term used in the United States and Canada for the aqueous urea solution used in post-2010 SCR systems. Consists of 32% urea and 68% distilled water. DEF is known as AdBlue in Europe and by Daimler/DD.

diesel fuel   a simple hydrocarbon fuel obtained from crude petroleum by means of fractioning; usually contains both residual and distillate fractions.

diesel gallon equivalent (DGE)   a means of rating the performance of alternate fuels versus a diesel fuel equivalent. Although CNG is rated by GEG in CA, LNG is rated in DGE: the DGE of LNG is 6.06 pounds.

diesel knock   a detonation condition caused by prolonged ignition lag.

diesel multistage filter (DMF)   a combination DPF, oxidation catalytic converter, and muffler assembly used on some post-2007 highway diesel engines.

diesel oxidation catalyst (DOC)   single-stage oxidation catalyst that has been used on highway diesel engines since the mid-1990s.

diesel particulate filter (DPF)   a diesel soot scrubber that physically traps particulate from the exhaust gas, then burns it off during regeneration cycles. Most are ECM managed to regenerate under passive (preferred) and active cycles that require fuel dosing and a heat source. Heat is usually derived from upstream injection of diesel fuel or from a heat grid. It is required in most highway and off-highway post-2007 diesel engines.

diffuser   the device in a turbocharger compressor housing that converts air velocity into air pressure.

digital   the representing of data in form of digits or other discrete symbols.

digital audiotape (DAT)   high-density data storage tape written to by a helical scan head.

digital calipers   a precise id and od measuring instrument with the appearance of Vernier calipers, the accuracy of a micrometer, and the ability to convert from the standard to the metric system at the push of a button.

digital computer   a calculating and computing device capable of processing data using coded digital formats.

digital dash display (DDD)   one of many terms used to describe a dash-located driver information display screen; usually LED-based.

digital diagnostic reader (DDR)   DDC term for an EST.

digital diagnostic tool (DDT)   term used to describe a handheld EST.

digital micrometer   a micrometer that displays dimensional readings digitally.

digital multimeter (DMM)   An instrument that reads voltage, resistance (ohms), and current (amperes).

digital signals   data interchange/retention signals limited to two discernible states; combinations of ones and zeros into which data, video, or human voice must be coded for transmission/storage and subsequently reconstructed.

digital video disk (DVD)   an optical data storage medium with read-only or read/write/erase capability.

digitizing   the process used to convert data to digital format.

dimethyl ether (DME)   a methane-based fuel derived from decomposing vegetation (sometimes garbage). Used in Asia and Europe and currently being introduced in California in systems manufactured by Volvo-Mack.

direct current (DC)   current flow through a circuit in one direction only.

direct-fire ignition (DFI)   another term for coil-on-plug spark ignition.

direct injection (DI)   describes any engine in which fuel is injected directly into the engine cylinder and not to any kind of external prechamber. Most current diesel engines are direct injected.

direct-operated check (DOC)   the actuator on a 4-terminal Caterpillar C3 MEUI (Delphi E3) that controls the electrohydraulic nozzle and permits soft (ECM-controlled) NOPs.

discrete   in computer technology, this means *coded*. For instance, coding analog values into binary and hexadecimal values is expressing those values in a *discrete* format.

disk-operating system (DOS)   The set of software commands that govern computer operations and enable functional software programs to be run.

displacement on demand (DOD)   term used to describe the emission reduction and fuel consumption strategy of shutting down (by not fueling) engine cylinders; used on diesel engines since the early 1990s.

distillate any of a wide range of distilled fractions of crude petroleum, some of which would be constituents of a diesel fuel; refers to the more volatile fractions in a fuel. It is sometimes used to refer to diesel fuels generally.

distributor head section of a Bosch-type, sleeve-metering, rotary distributor pump in which the plunger moves; contains delivery passages, an electric fuel shutdown, screw plug with vent screw, and delivery valves.

distributor plunger center- and cross-drilled plunger used in rotary distributor pumps to feed injection fuel to the hydraulic head or distributor head supply passages.

distributor rotor driveshaft-driven rotor on an inlet-metering, opposed plunger distributor pump that connects the pump chamber with the supply passages in the hydraulic head for fuel delivery to the injectors.

dividers a comparative-type measuring compass, usually with an adjusting screw for setting precise dimensions.

doping the process of adding small quantities of impurities to semiconductor crystals to provide them with either a P or an N electrical characteristic.

doser block pressure regulator (DBPR) Detroit Diesel's DD-Series regulator for its aftertreatment dosing circuit.

dosing the process of injecting fuel (usually from the fuel subsystem) into the exhaust for purposes of regenerating a diesel particulate filter or for activating an NO_x adsorber catalyst.

dosing control module (DCM) a module that manages DPF and DEF dosing cycles. May be networked to the engine ECM by either J1939 or by a proprietary bus.

dosing injection describes injection of fuel into an engine cylinder late in the power stroke that is not intended to be combusted in the cylinder, or downstream in the exhaust system for purposes of regenerating DPF and NAC aftertreatment devices.

double helix a port-helix plunger design with both upper and lower helix characteristics that results in a variable beginning and ending of the pump effective stroke.

double overhead camshaft (DOHC) an engine with a pair of overhead camshafts, cradle-mounted on the cylinder head. An example is the pre-2010 family of Cummins ISX engines.

double pass radiator a counterflow radiator in which the coolant is routed to make two passes, therefore entering and exiting from separate tanks both located either at the top or the bottom of the radiator; a high-efficiency radiator.

downflow radiator a typical radiator in which hot coolant from the engine enters at the top tank, flows downward, and exits through a bottom tank.

downlink the transmission signal from a communications satellite to an earth receiver or the receiver itself.

download data transfer from one computer system to another; often used to describe proprietary data transfer when reprogramming vehicle ECMs.

DPF delete software required to enable a post-2007 diesel engine to run after the DPF has been illegally removed. This not-uncommon practice results in costly engine damage and heavy EPA fines.

DPF pulse cleaner one type of off-vehicle DPF cleaning device. It uses high-volume, low-pressure air pulses to remove contaminants.

drayage truck specialized truck that hauls loads short distances within ports, and from ports to linehaul hub terminals. Known for producing high emissions because of stop–start operation, and thus the subject of many CARB dictates for trucks operating in California ports.

driver another name for a *power transistor*; a transistor capable of switching high-current loads. May also refer to the software that manages computer output signals.

driver information display (DID) a digital dash monitor used for chassis data bus and telematics.

DriveWyze subscription-based telematics software than can be run from a smartphone or tablet; enables weigh and inspection station bypass in some states.

droop an engine governor term denoting a transient speed variation that occurs when engine loading suddenly changes.

droop curve a required hydromechanical governor characteristic in which fueling drops off an even curve as engine speed increases from the rated power value to high idle.

dry liners liners that are fitted either with fractional looseness or fractional interference that dissipate cylinder heat to the cylinder block bore and have no direct contact with the water jacket.

dry sump an engine that uses a remotely located oil sump; not often seen on highway diesel applications, but used in some bus engines to reduce the profile of the engine. Commonly used in off-highway construction equipment.

dual helices a commonly used plunger geometric design with identical helices machined diametrically opposite each other on the plunger; helps prevent side loading of the plunger at high-pressure spill.

ductile describes materials (usually steels) that are malleable or flexible, and thus capable of temporary plastic deformation without fracturing when a load is applied.

dumb node a network node with no independent processing or data retention capability.

Duramax Isuzu-built, GM diesel engines available in 6600 and 7800 versions.

Durathon a GE sodium metal hydride ($NaNiCl_2$) battery used in tandem with lithium-ion batteries to increase on-vehicle energy storage capacity.

duty cycle usually refers to the percentage of *on* time of a component: In the case of fuel injectors, duty cycle is usually expressed in milliseconds or crank angle degrees.

dynamic RAM (DRAM) RAM with high-access speed.

dynamometer a testing device that loads an engine by applying a resistance to turning effort (torque) and factors this against time to produce brake power values. Often used to performance-test or break in engines after reconditioning.

Dynatard Mack internal engine compression brake; not used in Mack engines after 1996.

dyno short form for dynamometer.

E-3 injector see *Delphi E-3 injector.*

E-7 Mack Trucks inline, six-cylinder, 12-liter engine.

E7-EUP Mack Trucks V-MAC III-managed, inline, six-cylinder, 12-liter engine.

E-9 Mack Trucks V-8 engine.

earth British and Australian term for the electrical ground circuit; see *ground.*

eccentric not circular; having axes that are not common.

Echeck Cummins EST.

Ecoboost a single-canister DPF and SCR module manufactured by Cummins; aimed to address EPA 2017 fuel economy and reduced GHG requirements by significantly reducing weight and increasing NO_x reduction efficiency.

Econovance Mack Trucks mechanical or electronic variable timing device for port-helix metering injection pumps.

eddy-current dynamometer   an electromotive dynamometer that applies resistance to turning effort of the MUT by acting like an electric motor attempting to turn in reverse.

EEPROM   electronically erasable, programmable read-only memory. Vehicle computer memory category that can be rewritten or flashed with customer or proprietary reprogramming; includes an ECM write-to-self capability.

effective stroke   describes that portion of a constant travel plunger or piston stroke used to actually pump fluid.

ELAB   Bosch fuel shutoff solenoid used on early V-MAC I PE7100 injection pumps.

Electrical Information System (EIS)   Mack Trucks online SIS.

electricity   a form of energy that results from charged particles—specifically electrons and protons—either statically (accumulated charge) or dynamically, such as current flow in a circuit.

electric-only vehicle (EOV)   a vehicle powered by electric motors with onboard energy stored in battery banks and ultracapacitor cassettes. Stationary charging is by connection to a grid electrical power source, whereas mobile charging is by regenerative braking.

electric shock resistant (ESR) footwear   protective boots required for working on hybrid diesel electric powertrains; designated by an orange omega on a white rectangle.

electrohydraulic injector (EHI)   an ECM-switched injector used on CR and EUP injection systems. Opening and closing values are soft, being controlled by the ECM.

electrohydraulic pintle nozzle (EPN)   A category of low-pressure injection nozzle used for dosing injectors in diesel applications. EPNs are used extensively in gasoline fuel injection systems.

electrolysis   a chemical change produced in an electrolyte by an electrical current, often resulting in decomposition.

electrolyte   a solution capable of conducting electrical current.

electromagnetic interference (EMI)   low-level radiation (such as emitted from electrical power lines, vehicle radar, etc.) that can interfere with signals on data buses unless suppressed.

electromagnetism   describes any magnetic field created by current flow through a conductor.

electromechanical injector (EMI)   a pintle-type injector in which the pintle nozzle is integral with an armature. When the EMI is energized, the nozzle opens. Used in GFI and as a dosing injector in diesel DPFs.

electromechanical switch   any switch in which output status is controlled manually or by automatically switching electrical circuits on and off; differentiated from *smart* or *ladder* switches.

electromotive force (EMF)   voltage or charge differential.

electron   a negatively charged component of an atom.

electronically erasable, programmable read-only memory   see *EEPROM*.

electronic control analyzer programmer (ECAP)   now-obsolete Caterpillar PC-based programming and diagnostic instrument.

electronic control module (ECM)   see *engine control module (ECM)*.

electronic control unit (ECU)   SAE-recommended term to refer to a system controller (computer) that manages an electronic system other than the engine; however, some OEMs use the term to refer engine controllers.

electronic data recorder (EDR)   any vehicle data storage device capable of capturing real-time data and storing it after shutdown. The term is generally used to refer to data that is pertinent following an accident or engine/chassis problem event.

Electronic Diesel Control (EDC)   Bosch term for its engine management electronics.

electronic digital calipers (EDC)   an electronic version of what used to be known as Vernier calipers; consists of a set of jaws that can measure id or od and has a digital display.

electronic distributor unit (EDU)   DD term for injector drivers that are ECM-located in all generations of DDEC after DDEC I. In the most recent versions of DDEC, the EDU is located in the MCM.

electronic/engine control module (ECM)   refers to the computer and integral switching apparatus in an electronically controlled vehicle system. The SAE-recommended term for describing the engine controller electronics using the SA 00 address on the chassis data bus; most engine OEMs adhere to this recommendation, but not all. See *engine control module*.

electronic engine control unit (EECU)   term used by Volvo and Mack to describe the engine controller occupying the SA 00 address on the chassis data bus.

electronic engine management   computerized engine control.

electronic foot-pedal assembly (EFPA)   mechanical pedal assembly containing a TPS and IVS.

electronic governor   any kind of governing using computer controls.

electronic logging device (ELD)   any of a variety of modules capable of capturing, storing, and sometimes broadcasting (V2I) engine and chassis running data.

electronic management system (EMS)   management by computer or computers.

electronic onboard [data] recorder (EOBR)   data and ID tracker currently mandatory for truckers penalized with a greater than 10% HOS infraction by the FMCSA—but the FMCSA has scheduled to make EOBRs mandatory for all linehaul trucks for 2016.

electronics   branch of electricity concerned with the movement of electrons through hard wire, semiconductor, gas, optical, and vacuum circuits.

electronic pump   see *electronic unit pump*.

electronic screening (E-Screen)   telematics-based screening of trucks within a geofenced area for purposes of bypassing weigh stations and driver/vehicle inspections.

electronic service tool (EST)   term that covers a range of instruments, including DMMs, diagnostic lights, generic and proprietary handheld reader-programmers, and PCs.

electronic smart power (ESP)   (Cummins) an ECM programming option that can be used to improve vehicle drivability and fuel economy.

Electronic Technician (ET)   Caterpillar PC-based software that enables the technician to diagnose system problems, reprogram ECMs, and access system data for analysis to produce fuel mileage figures and driver performance profiles.

electronic unit injector (EUI)   The cam-actuated, electronically controlled pumping mechanism used to fuel most of the first generation of electronically controlled truck diesel engines; also known by the acronym MEUI.

electronic unit pump (EUP) a cam-actuated, ECM-controlled pumping and metering unit that supplies a common rail, hydraulic or electrohydraulic injector by means of a high-pressure line.

electron theory the theory which asserts that current flow through a circuit is by electron movement from a negatively charged point to a positively charged one. See *conventional theory.*

electrostatic oil separator (EOS) a crankcase emissions control device that uses static electricity to separate oil from crankcase vapors.

electrostatics the force field that surrounds an object with an electrical charge.

element 1. any of more than 100 substances (most naturally occurring, some manmade) that cannot be chemically resolved into simpler substances. 2. a component part of something, such as a pump element.

emissions control device (ECD) term used to describe emission control hardware.

emulsify to disperse one liquid into another or to suspend a fine particulate in a solution.

emulsion the dispersion of one liquid into another, such as water in the form of fine droplets into diesel fuel.

end gas the gas that results from combusting fuel in engine cylinders; usually refers to the gases present at flame quench (that is, before any exhaust gas treatment): a mixture of CO_2, H_2O, and whatever noxious gases are present.

ending of energizing (EOE) denotes the end of the switched duty cycle of an EUI.

ending of injection (EOI) the instant at which fuel injection ceases.

end of line (EOL) usually used in reference to terminating a programming procedure or data packet message.

energized-to-run (ETR) any of a group of solenoids that must be electrically energized to remain in *on* status; a nonlatching-type solenoid.

energy best expressed as stored potential. Its unit is kilowatt/ hours (kW/h) or horsepower/hours (hp/h). In technology we more commonly use the term *potential energy.*

engine a machine that converts one form of energy to another.

engine brake any type of engine retarder. The term usually describes an internal engine compression brake, but may also refer to an exhaust compression brake or an engine-mounted hydraulic retarder.

engine control module (ECM) SAE-recommended term to refer to a system controller (computer) that manages an engine; however, some OEMs use the term to refer to any electronic controller.

engine displacement the sum of the swept volume of all the engine cylinders.

engine dynamometer a dynamometer used for testing the engine on a test bed outside of the chassis.

engine/electronic control module (ECM) see *engine control module.*

engine/electronic control unit (ECU) according to the SAE, the preferred use of this term is *electronic control unit* and references system controllers other than the engine controller: However, the term is used by some OEMs to reference their engine controller. See *electronic control module; engine control module.*

engine family rating code (EFRC) engine series ratings (Caterpillar).

engine hours a means of comparing engine service hours to highway mileage. Most engine OEMs equate 1 engine hour to 50 highway linehaul miles (80 km), so a service interval of 10,000 miles (16,000 km) would equal 200 engine hours. The term *service hours* is also used.

engine longevity the engine life span. For highway diesel engines, it is usually reckoned in miles; for off-highway applications, in hours.

engine management diagnostics (EMD) diesel engine diagnostic fields that relate to emissions controls covered by HD-OBD that should be accessible to generic ESTs.

engine management system (EMS) refers to OEM computerized engine controls and sometimes the controller software.

Engine Manufacturers Association (EMA) association of engine manufacturers that by consensus work with the ASTM, SAE, and TMC to recommend industry standard practices.

engine position sensor (EPS) shaft position sensor using a reluctor pulse generator or Hall-effect principle.

engine silencer a muffler that uses sound absorption and resonation principles to change the frequency of engine noise.

Environmental Protection Agency (EPA) federal regulating body that sets and monitors noxious emissions standards, among other functions.

EPS see *engine position sensor.*

erosion the process of gradually wearing away material by abrasives or high-pressure liquid or gas.

E-Screen a telematics-driven, wireless monitoring and inspection system used to enable wireless roadside inspections (WRIs).

etching bearing or other component failure caused by chemical action.

E-Tech Mack Trucks V-MAC III, electronic unit pump (EUP) fueled, E-7 engine manufactured up until 2007.

ethanol a colorless, liquid, volatile alcohol, fermented from hexose sugars. The type of alcohol found in safe-to-consume alcoholic drinks. Chemically known as: C_2H_2OH. May also be used as fuel, either in its pure state or cut into petrochemicals.

ethylene glycol (EG) an antifreeze of higher toxicity that the EPA hopes to phase out, but as yet is commonly used.

E-Trim Caterpillar EUI fuel flow specification required to be programmed to the ADEM ECM whenever an EUI is removed and replaced. E-Trim data is important because it enables the ECM to balance fueling to each cylinder.

EURO VI the current European Union equivalent of our EPA Highway Rule for engine emissions. EURO V1 is theoretically as rigorous as the U.S. EPA MY 2013 standards, but there are many loopholes that reduce its effect.

execute effect an operation or procedure.

executive the resident portion of a computer or program operating system.

exhaust blowdown the first part of the cylinder exhaust process that occurs at the moment the exhaust valves open.

exhaust brake an external engine compression brake that operates by choking down the exhaust gas flow area; sometimes used in conjunction with an internal engine compression brake, meaning that the piston contributes to retarding effort on both its upward strokes.

exhaust gas recirculation (EGR) a means of routing "dead" end gas back into the intake to dilute the intake charge of oxygen, reducing combustion heat and therefore NO$_x$ production. In most truck diesel engines' EGR, exhaust gas is cooled by a heat exchanger before being rerouted to the intake.

exhaust manifold   the cast-iron or steel component bolted to the cylinder exhaust tracts responsible for delivering end gases to the turbocharger and the exhaust system.

exhaust pressure governor (EPG)   a combination exhaust engine brake and engine warmup device used on Volvo engines. When exhaust flow is partially choked off downstream from the turbocharger, it creates high back-pressure to warm the engine when cold and provide engine braking when warm.

exhaust throttle valve   device located at the turbine exit of some turbochargers used to choke down exhaust gas flow during engine warmup. This holds combustion heat within the engine and speeds warmup to operating temperature. Used by John Deere.

expansion board   a circuit board added to a computer system to increase its capability.

explosion   an oxidation reaction that takes place rapidly; high-speed combustion.

extended life coolant (ELC)   coolant premix that claims a service life of up to 6 years with almost no maintenance. When ELC is not premixed, its service life is dependent on the quality of the water it is mixed with.

external compression brake   an engine exhaust brake.

Extreme Pressure Injection (XPI)   the Cummins in-house engineered common rail fuel system used on post-2010 ISX15, ISX11.9, and ISL engines.

EZ-Tech   International Navistar PC to chassis data bus software and hardware. An EZ-Tech notebook (usually a Panasonic Toughbook) connects to the chassis data bus by means of a Navistar CA and J1939 data port (nine-pin Deutsch).

failure analysis   diagnosis of a failed component, usually out of engine.

failure mode indicator (FMI)   see *fault mode indicator (FMI)*.

failure strategy   a software-driven response to a failure event; may be OEM- or customer-programmed. For instance, an engine can be programmed to shut down in the event of a loss of oil pressure.

fanstat   a combination temperature sensor and switch (usually pneumatic) used to control the engine fan cycle; primarily used in engines prior to the electronic age.

farad   a measure of capacitance. One farad is the ability to store $6.28 \times 1,018$ electrons at a 1 V charge differential.

FARC valve   Caterpillar turbo aneroid.

fault mode indicator (FMI)   defines a component or circuit failure to an EST by assigning a numeric failure or imminent failure mode (SAE).

Federal Motor Carrier Safety Alliance (FMCSA)   body responsible for setting on-highway safety regulations.

feedback assembly   the engine's mechanical, self-management components consisting of a geartrain, camshaft, valvetrains, MUI and EUI actuating trains, fuel injection pumping apparatus, and valves.

Ferrotherm™ piston   a Mahle trademark for two-piece articulating piston assemblies consisting of a forged steel crown and aluminum skirt; used by most commercial vehicle diesel OEMs from the early 1990s until the introduction of single-piece, forged or composite steel trunk pistons for the 2004 emissions year.

ferrous metals   metals that are composed primarily of iron and usually attracted by a magnet.

fetching   CPU function that involves obtaining data from memory.

fiber optics   the transmission of laser light waves through thin strands of fiber; used to digitally pulse data more economically and at much higher speeds than are possible with copper wire.

FIC module   fuel injection control module; usually a slave module connected by a proprietary CAN bus to the engine ECM, responsible for controlling injection pumps (such as on V-MAC I), electronic unit injectors, or electronic unit pumps.

field effect transistor (FET)   group of transistors used to switch or amplify within a circuit.

fields   specific items of (electronic) information.

field service bulletin (FSB)   one OEM's term for *technical service bulletin (TSB)*.

field service tips (FSTs)   one OEM's term for *technical service bulletin (TSB)*.

file   a collection of related data.

filter minder   a negative pressure sensing device designed to indicate air filter restriction; mounted on the air filter canister or on the dash.

filter monitor   a pressure-sensing device that monitors DPF or aftertreatment device backpressure and alerts the vehicle data bus when a plug-up condition is imminent. Some are also capable of signaling temperature.

fire point   the temperature at which a combustible produces enough flammable vapor for a continuous burn; always a higher temperature than flash point.

fire ring   normally used to refer to the fixed ring that may be integral with the cylinder head gasket responsible for sealing the cylinder. Sometimes used to refer to the top compression ring, but this usage is uncommon.

FireWire   a digital audio/video serial bus interface standard offering high-speed communications that can be used to network with vehicle data buses.

fixed disk   a data storage device used in PCs and mainframe computers consisting of a spindle and multiple stacked data retention platters.

flame front   during flame propagation, the leading edge of the flame in an engine cylinder.

flame propagation   the flame pattern from ignition to quench during a power stroke in an engine cylinder.

flame quench   the moment that the flame ceases to propagate or extinguishes in an internal combustion engine.

flammable   describes any substance that can be combusted.

flash   term used to describe the downloading of new software to EEPROM.

flashback   a highly dangerous condition that can occur during operation of oxyacetylene equipment, in which the flame may travel behind the mixing chamber in the torch and explode the acetylene tank using the system oxygen. Most current oxyacetylene torches are equipped with flashback arresters.

flash codes   the ECM-generated fault codes that are usually displayed by means of diagnostic lights and alert the driver or technician as to the nature of an electronically monitored malfunction; also known as *fault codes, blink codes*.

flash memory   nonvolatile computer memory that can be electrically erased and reprogrammed. It is primarily used in memory cards and USB flash drives (thumb drives, jump drives) and as data retention on vehicle ECM personality modules.

flash point   the temperature at which a combustible produces enough flammable vapor for momentary ignition.

flash programming   term that has come to mean any reprogramming procedure.

flash RAM   nonvolatile RAM; NV-RAM.

flow area   the most restricted portion of a fluid circuit; for instance, a water tap sets a flow area and as the tap is opened, the flow area increases, thereby increasing the volume flow of water.

flow control   refers to any device that can proportionly control flow through a circuit. A thumb over the end of a hose is a flow control device.

fluid   any substance that has fluidity. Both liquids and gases are fluids. Fluid power incorporates both hydraulics and pneumatics.

fluid friction   the friction of dynamic fluids, always less than solid friction.

fluidity   a state that permits a substance to conform to the shape of the vessel in which it is contained. Both liquids and gases possess fluidity.

fluid power   term used to describe both hydraulics and pneumatics.

flutes   protruding lands with grooves in between.

flywheel   an energy and momentum storage device usually bolted directly to the crankshaft.

flywheel housing concentricity   a critical specification which ensures that the relationship of the flywheel and anything connected to it is concentric.

FMVSS 304   regulation that covers compressed natural gas (CNG) mobile vehicle fuel systems and container integrity.

follower   used to describe a variety of devices that ride a cam profile and transmit the effects of the cam geometry to the train to be actuated; also known as *tappet*.

font   typeface size and appearance.

force   the action of one body attempting to change the state of motion of another. The application of force does not necessarily result in any work being accomplished.

foreground computations   computer-operating responses that are prioritized, such as the response to a critical command input. An example is the throttle position sensor (TPS), the signal from which must be acted on immediately to generate the appropriate outcome.

foreground processing   computer processing cycle transactions of high priority, such as response to accelerator position. Foreground processing instructions are often retained in cache to enable superfast response times.

forged steel trunk piston   a trunk-type piston assembly with an partial skirt manufactured by Mahle under the trade name *Monotherm*. First appeared for the 2004 model year, but rapidly have become the piston of choice in medium- and large-bore truck diesel engines.

format   1. To alter the appearance or character of a program or document. 2. To prepare data retention media, such as diskettes, to receive data by defining tracks, cylinders, and sectors, which is a process that removes any previously logged data.

forward leakage   an injector bench fixture test that tests the nozzle seat sealing integrity.

fossil fuel   unrenewable, organically derived fuels such as petroleum and coal.

four-terminal EUI   a more recently introduced, dual-actuator EUI. Operates on the same principles as a two-terminal EUI, but has an ECM-controlled, electrohydraulic nozzle that allows soft (as opposed to fixed-value) NOPs.

four-terminal MEUI   the Caterpillar term used to describe the twin-actuator Delphi E3 injector. The acronym is *mechanically actuated, electronically controlled unit injector (MEUI)*. Replaced the two-terminal MEUI in post-2007 Caterpillar engines.

fractions   refers to separate compounds of crude petroleums separated by distillation and other fractioning methods such as catalytic and hydrocracking and classified by their volatility.

fractured rod   a conn rod manufacturing process; see *cracked rod*.

freight efficiency   term that is replacing "fuel efficiency" by fleet operations managers; best defined as fuel consumed per ton of freight hauled.

Freightliner Corporation   currently the truck chassis manufacturer with the largest market share; owned by Daimler Trucks North American (DTNA). Corporate center is in Portland, Oregon.

fretting   occurs when two parts that fit tightly are allowed to move slightly against each other, sometimes resulting in microwelding, creating small surface irregularities. It can result from a head gasket that fails to allow thermal creep as the cylinder head and block pass through heat and cool cycles.

friction   the resistance that an object or fluid encounters in moving over or through another.

friction bearing   a shaft-supporting bearing in which the rotating member can directly contact the bearing face or race.

fuel   substance that can be used as a source of heat energy.

fuel-air ratio   term used to describe the mass ratios between fuel and air in diesel engines; used in preference to the automotive *air-fuel ratio* because the first word listed is the control variable in the ratio.

fuel-amplified common rail (FACR) system   an evolution of CR used in Detroit Diesel's DD series of engines. The EHIs used in FACR systems use intensifiers to produce injection pressures that more than double the rail pressure. DD uses the acronym ACRS to describe FACR.

fuel conditioner   usually unknown quantities of cetane improver and pour point depressants suspended in an alcohol base.

fuel control actuator   any of a number of electronically controlled devices used as fuel control mechanisms.

fuel demand command signal (FDCS)   International HEUI output driver signal.

fuel efficiency   relates to the cost per ton, per mile hauled by a commercial vehicle and measured as *load specific fuel consumption (LSFC)*. A measure of the productivity of trucks.

fuel filter   device for filtering sediment from fuel; rated by entrapment capability.

fuel filter module (FFM)   a hub to which fuel filter pads, water separator, fuel heat exchanger, and sensors are integrated.

fuel heater   a heat exchanger device used in extreme cold to prevent diesel fuel from waxing in the fuel subsystem.

fueling actuator   Cummins HPI-TP metering control solenoid; also known as the rail actuator.

fueling algorithm   the set of ECM programmed rules and procedures designed to produce the desired performance and emissions from an engine at any given moment of operation.

fueling chamber   the lower chamber in the Cummins TP injector that forms the injector pumping chamber. Also known as cup.

fuel injection control (FIC) module   a fuel management module separate from the ECM and connected to it by a proprietary bus.

fuel map   a diagram or graph used to indicate fueling through the entire performance range of an engine; also used to describe the ECM fuel algorithm.

fuel pressure sensor (FPS)   a pressure-sensing mechanism, usually of the variable capacitance type, that measures the charging pressure in the fuel subsystem and signals its value to the ECM.

fuel rate   actual rate of fuel pumped through an injector to an engine cylinder; factored by cam geometry and engine rpm.

fuel rate test   a HEUI diagnostic test that may identify a marginally defective injector and sometimes one with intermittent performance. Test results are reported in gal/p-hr and the objective is to identify deviance.

fuel ratio control (FRC)   Caterpillar aneroid mechanism for limiting fueling in low boost conditions.

fuel subsystem   the fuel circuit used to pump fuel from the vehicle fuel tank and deliver it to the fuel metering/injection apparatus. The fuel subsystem typically comprises a fuel tank, water separator, primary filter, transfer or charge pump, secondary filter, and the interconnecting plumbing.

fuel tank   the fuel storage reservoir on a vehicle.

full authority   refers to the extent to which an electronic controller can manage a system. Early computer control systems adapted hydromechanical hardware for electronic management and were known as *partial authority*; most current engine and other truck systems are engineered for computerized management and have *full authority*.

full flow filter   a filter plumbed in series on the charge side of the pump that feeds a circuit.

full range governor (FRG)   a Caterpillar term for *variable speed governor*.

function keys   numerical keys prefixed by the letter *F* that act as program commands and shortcuts.

fuzzy logic   an ECM or computer processing outcome that depends on multiple inputs, operating conditions, and operating system commands; differentiated from closed loop, in which the processing outcome is primarily mastered by a single sensor.

gallons per hour (gph)   the means of rating liquid flow in a hydraulic circuit.

galvanometer   a meter used to measure small electrical currents.

gas analyzer   a test instrument for measuring and identifying exhaust gas content.

gas dynamics   the manner in which gases behave during the compression and combustion strokes and the processes of engine breathing.

gasket   a physical seal between a pair of clamped mating faces. It must sustain a seal and accommodate component creep.

gasket yield point   the moment that a malleable gasket is crushed to its desired shape to conform to the required shape between two clamped components to provide optimum sealing.

gasoline   a hydrocarbon fuel composed of volatile petroleum fractions from the aromatic and paraffin ranges.

gasoline-equivalent-gallon (GEG)   the way in which CNG is sold (and taxed in the state of California) and possibly nationwide in the near future. A GEG of CNG is 126.67 cubic feet or 5.66 pounds.

gate   a routing switch with either digital or mechanical actuation.

gateway module   a module that enables communications between two or more data buses by "translating" bus protocols. A gateway module may be stand-alone or integrated into another module. For instance, the instrument cluster unit (ICU) acts as a gateway in some multiplexing systems.

gear pump   a positive displacement pump, consisting of intermeshing gears, that uses the spaces between the teeth to move fluid through a circuit.

genset   a complete electricity generating unit consisting of an internal combustion engine and an electricity generator.

geofence   the use of wireless technologies in conjunction with GPS and telematics to interact with vehicle data buses to perform a range of tasks, from toll collection to wireless HOS and safety inspections. With two-way communication capability, fleet and DOT instructions can be relayed to the vehicle operator, and may provide features such as vehicle immobilization in the case of suspected theft.

geosynchronous orbit   the "park" orbit of communications satellites 22,300 miles (35,400 km) from the earth's equator.

gerotor   a type of gear pump that uses an internal crescent gear pumping principle.

gigabyte   a billion bytes; a measurement of digital memory capacity.

glazing   the process of abrasive polishing of a surface to a mirror finish. The term is used to describe a type of wear in a cylinder liner that results in a failure of rings to seal because the crosshatch is destroyed.

glazing friction   wearing of a component to a mirror finish.

global parameter group number (GPGN),   a global PGN, a J1939 message packet that is broadcast over the bus to any rather than a specific controller on the bus.

global positioning satellite (GPS)   telecommunications satellite; currently used for vehicle tracking, navigation, and data exchange.

global warming potential (GWP)   a rating applied to fuels and refrigerants that classifies their environmental damage potential.

governing algorithm   the processing cycle map built on input circuit sensor status signals and programmed software instructions that manage fuel injector duty cycles.

governing map   see *governing algorithm*.

governor   a component that manages engine fueling on the basis of fuel demand (accelerator) and engine rpm; may be hydromechanical or electronic.

governor differential lever   a double-bell, crank-type, lever device that pivots on a fulcrum.

governor map   ECM software that determines exactly how an engine is managed as conditions such as fuel request, altitude, and engine rpm change.

governor spring   the force, usually variable, that opposes centrifugal force in mechanical governors; often amplified or set by accelerator pedal travel.

governor weight forks   a means of jamming governor centrifugal weights in their outermost position for purposes of tuning an engine.

graduate   see *vial*.

graphical user interface (GUI)   software such as MS Windows that is icon and menu driven.

gray scaling   used by monochrome monitors and scanners to code color to black, white, and shades of gray.

greenhouse gases (GHGs) gases that absorb and emit radiation. GHGs include CO_2, methane, water vapor, nitrous oxide, and ozone. The burning of fossil fuels since the Industrial Revolution has greatly increased GHGs in the Earth's atmosphere.

grid electrification term used to describe the provision of electrical shore power in truck stops.

gross power expression of raw engine power with all potential parasitic loads and emissions controls removed. (There is an SAE formula for gross power—J1995.) See *net power*.

ground describes the point or region of lowest voltage potential in a circuit; the portion of a vehicle electrical circuit serving multiple system loads by providing a return path for the current drawn by the load. It is used in vehicle systems using 48 V or less and ideal for the commonly used 12-V vehicle systems. Known as *earth* in Australia and Britain.

ground strap a conductive strap, usually braided wire, that extends a common ground electrical system.

groupware software that allows multiple users to work together by sharing information.

gumming a term used to describe unburned fuel and lubrication oil residues when they sludge in piston ring grooves and other areas of the engine.

gusset a triangular bracket used to strengthen two perpendicularly joined beams.

H₂O manometer a water-filled manometer.

Hall-effect probe a means of signaling high-current values to a DMM using a reckoning method not noted for accuracy.

Hall-effect sensor device for accurately sensing rotational or linear position and speed; normally used to produce a digital signal, but may be configured to produce an analog signal using a DAC. A moving metallic shutter alternately blocks and exposes a magnetic field from a semiconductor sensor.

handheld (HH) the acronym is used to describe devices such as ESTs that are portable and can be carried in the hand.

handheld electronic service tools (HH-ESTs) any of a number of different portable electronic service tools designed to access, read, and reprogram chassis computer systems.

handshake establishment of a communications connection, especially between two electronic systems. The communication protocols must be compatible.

hard in electronics, a value that should not or cannot be changed. The term has evolved to reference anything in computer technology that can be physically touched. An example is printed service literature: service literature might be accessed online, in which case it would be called *soft* format; or printed out, in which case it would be converted to a *hard* format.

hard copy computer-generated data that is printed to a page rather than retained on disk.

hard cruise closed-loop cruise control in which set road speed controls fueling, meaning that the road speed sensor is the closed-loop driver. Not often used in current trucks, because it results in wasted fuel compared to *soft cruise* or *smart cruise*.

hard disk see *fixed disk; hard drive*.

hard drive a data storage device used in PCs and mainframe computers. They can consists of a spindle and multiple stacked data retention platters (mechanical) or be digital solid-state devices.

hard parameter a fixed value that cannot or should not be altered or rewritten. Maximum engine rpm is an example of a hard parameter.

hardware computer equipment excluding software.

Hazard Communication Regulation federal rules from OSHA that incorporate the Right-to-Know clauses pertaining to workplace hazards.

HD-OBD see *heavy-duty onboard diagnostics*.

head crash occurs when a computer disk head collides with the hard disk surface, causing loss of memory.

headers the manifold deck to which the coolant tubes are attached in a heat exchanger bundle, or the term used to describe low gas restriction, individual cylinder exhaust pipes that converge at a point calculated to maximize pulse effect.

headland the area above the uppermost compression ring and below the leading edge of the piston.

headland piston term used to describe a piston design that has minimized the headland volume.

headland volume the headland gas volume in a cylinder.

Health Effects Institute (HEI) an independent, non-profit corporation that specializes in researching the effects of air pollution; headquartered in Boston.

heat energy an expression of the energy potential a substance possesses. It is actually the amount of kinetic energy at the molecular level in an element or compound.

heat engine a mechanism that converts thermal energy into mechanical work.

heat exchanger any of a number of devices used to transfer heat from one fluid to another where there is a temperature difference using the principles of conduction and radiation.

heating value the potential heat energy of a fuel; also known as calorific value.

heating, ventilating, and air conditioning (HVAC) used to describe the climate control system, which is usually integrated on current trucks.

heavy-duty onboard diagnostics (HD-OBD) legislation that requires OEMs to provide open access to any emissions-related commercial vehicle systems weighing more than 14,000 lb (6,350 kg). Phased implementation of HB-OBD began in 2010 (OEMs required to produce one engine family meeting the standard) and was originally scheduled for full adoption in MY 2013, but at the time of writing, implementation was still not finalized.

helical gear a gear with spiral-cut teeth.

helical scan technology used to write data at high density on tape helically as opposed to longitudinally.

helices plural of helix.

helix a spiral groove or scroll. The helical cut recesses in some injection pumping plungers that are used to meter fuel delivery. Plural: helices.

hexadecimal message code the 16-member numeric code system used by J1939. Numbers 0 through 9 are represented by the usual numeric digits and numbers 10 through 15 by the letters A to F.

Hg manometer a mercury (Hg)-filled manometer.

high-idle speed the highest no-load speed of an engine.

high-intensity kaizen event (HIKE) cooperate organizational and customer service efficiency improvement system used by Cummins, Kenworth, and a number of truck fleets to provide increased service efficiency.

high-pressure direct injectors (HPDIs) Westport NG piezo-actuated CR injectors used in dual fuel engines in which diesel fuel is used to pilot-ignite the gaseous charge.

high-pressure heavy-duty diesel common rail (HPHDDCR) the Delphi term for its F2R CR fuel system used on post-2013 PACCAR MX-Series engines; a CR diesel fuel system that uses either two or three engine camshaft-actuated EUPs to develop rail pressures.

high-pressure injection-time pressure (HPI-TP) Cummins's electronically controlled open nozzle common rail system using ECM-controlled metering and timing actuators to manage fuel injection. Used on ISX engines up to MY 2010.

high-pressure pipe a steel alloy pipe or line that delivers fuel from an injection pump element to the injector nozzle.

high-pressure washer a high-pressure water pump used to clean equipment and components before repair and inspection that has generally replaced steam cleaners.

high spring injector a type of hydraulic injector nozzle that locates the injector spring high in the injector/nozzle holder body. NOP is usually adjusted by an adjusting screw that acts directly on the spring.

high-temperature, low-shear (HTLS) the fluid dynamics required for diesel engine lubricating oils meeting MY 2017 standards.

Highway Diesel Rule (HDR) regulation launched by the EPA in MY 2000 and regularly updated since; regulates emissions for highway diesel-powered commercial vehicles.

Highway Master Caterpillar remote communications technology that enables remote programming of vehicles; used in conjunction with Caterpillar Fleet Information software.

histogram a graphic display in which data is represented by rectangular columns used for comparative analysis.

historic codes fault codes that are no longer active but are retained in ECM memory (and displayed) for purposes of diagnosis until they are erased; also known as *inactive codes*.

hone any of a number of types of abrasive stones used for finishing metals. Rotary hones are electrically or pneumatically driven and are used for sizing and surface-finishing cylinder liner bores.

horsepower the standard unit of power measurement used in North America, defined as a work rate of 33,000 lb-ft. per minute; equal to 0.746 kW.

host computer a main computer that is networked to other computers or nodes.

hotel loads the auxiliary loads and resulting costs a truck requires while in transit and parked. Includes bunk/cab/engine temperature management and any comfort apparatus (TV/refrigerator/computer, etc.) in the cab.

hotspot the geographical area over which a WiFi client device can effectively network.

hours of service (HOS) logged actual driving time of a truck driver; per FMCSA regulations, required to be rigorously tracked on paper or by EOBR.

HPI-PT electronically managed, common rail, open nozzle fuel system used to fuel earlier Cummins K-19 engines (off-highway) in which pressure is the control variable.

hunting rhythmic fluctuation of engine rpm, usually caused by unbalanced cylinder fueling but may be caused by a defective injector.

hunting gears an intermeshing gear relationship in which after timing, the gears may have to be turned through a large number of rotations before the timing indices realign.

hybrid electric vehicle (HEV) any of a number of different diesel-electric (or NG-electric) drivetrains that typically can use all engine, all electric, or any proportions of both power sources to power a vehicle.

hybrid organic acid technology (HOAT) an extended-life coolant (ELC) said to be universal but generally not recommended in heavy-duty applications. Dexcool (GM) is one example. HOAT antifreeze is usually but not always colored with an orange dye.

hydraulically actuated electronic unit injector (HEUI) Caterpillar oil pressure actuated, high-pressure fuel pumping/injecting element.

hydraulically amplified diesel injector (HADI) the electrohydraulic amplifier injector used by ACRS injection.

hydraulic governor, nonservo a hydraulic governor that uses fuel pressure, unloaded into a defined flow area by a positive displacement pump, as the basis for determining rpm; not used on any current truck engines.

hydraulic governor, servo type a hydraulic governor that uses centrifugal weights to sense rpm but where the force responsible for actually moving the fuel control mechanism is hydraulic, either engine oil or fuel pressure.

hydraulic head stationary member of an inlet-metering, opposed plunger rotary distributor pump within which the distributor rotor rotates. As the distributor rotor turns, it is brought in and out of register with each discharge port connecting the pump with the fuel injectors.

hydraulic hybrid, advanced materials and multifuel engine research (HAMMER) joint Eaton and United States Army parallel hybrid technology aimed at reducing fuel consumption in military ground vehicles; evolved into the Eaton civilian hydraulic parallel hybrid technology that became known as *hydraulic launch assist*.

hydraulic hybrid vehicle (HHV) diesel- or NG-powered, parallel drive (dual-drive input) and series drive (hydrostatic drive only) systems used to enable small-bore engines to provide hydraulic motive power to the wheels of a vehicle that would normally require a more powerful engine.

hydraulic injector any of a group of injectors that are opened and closed hydraulically as opposed to electronically; this includes the nozzle assemblies used in many EUI and HEUI units. One OEM uses the term *mechanical injector* in place of *hydraulic injector*.

hydraulic launch assist (HLA) Eaton-developed, hydraulic parallel hybrid technology used in intra-city courier vans and small shuttle buses.

hydraulics the science and practice of confining and pressurizing liquids in circuits to provide mechanical power; control and actuator circuits that use confined liquids under pressure. The science of fluid power circuits.

hydrocarbon (HC) substance primarily composed of elemental carbon and hydrogen. Fossil fuels and alcohols are both hydrocarbon fuels.

hydrocarbon injector one OEM's term for a DPF dosing injector.

hydrodynamic suspension the principle used to float a rotating shaft on a bed of constantly changing pressurized lubricant.

hydrogen (H) the simplest, most abundant element in the known universe, occurring in water and all organic matter. It is colorless, odorless, tasteless, and explosive. Its atomic number is 1.

hydromechanical engine management any engine that is managed and fueled without the use of computers; today used primarily in engines of 70 HP (52 kW) or less.

hydromechanical governing engine governing without the use of a computer; requires a means of sensing engine speed (centrifugal force exacted by flyweights/fuel pressure) and a means of limiting fuel.

hydromechanical management all engines managed without computers.

hydrometer an instrument designed to measure the specific gravity of liquids, usually battery electrolyte and coolant mixtures. It is not recommended for measuring either substance in truck engine applications, where a refractometer is the appropriate instrument due to greater accuracy.

hypermedia a multimedia presentation tool that permits rapid movement between screens to display graphics, video, and sound.

hypertext link the highlighting and bolding of a text word/phrase to enable Web page or program selection by mouse/click; increases user friendliness of the Internet and many other programs.

hypothesis a reasoned supposition, not necessarily required to be true.

hysteresis 1. in governor terminology, a response lag. 2. molecular friction caused by the lag between the formation of magnetic flux behind the magnetomotive force that creates it.

icons pictorial/graphical representations of program menu options displayed onscreen.

idle speed the lowest speed at which an engine can be run; usually managed by the governor. Highway engines will default to idle speed when the accelerator pedal is at a zero angle.

idle speed balance (ISB) test a DDEC diagnostic routine that displays the extent of idle speed compensation fueling for each EHI in DD-Series ACRS.

idle speed compensation (ISC) a DDEC VI and DDEC10 feature used on DD-Series engines that monitors crankshaft velocity through each sector of rotation at idle and compensates EHI fueling to balance the engine.

IEEE 802.11 wireless communications standard that conforms to Institute of Electrical and Electronics Engineers (IEEE) protocol 802.11; uses the 2.4, 3.6, and 5.0 GHz bands. WiFi/WLAN communications standard used in North America.

I-EGR internal exhaust gas recirculation. A crude form of EGR in which the valvetrain is managed so that some of the end gas remains in the engine cylinder as "dead" gas for the next cycle.

ignition accelerators volatile fuel fractions that are added to a fuel to decrease ignition delay. They increase CN.

ignition lag the period between the entry of the first droplets of fuel into the engine cylinder and the moment of ignition; based on the fuel chemistry and the actual temperatures of the engine components and the air charge.

IMPACT Volvo online SIS.

impeller 1. the driven member of a turbocharger responsible for compressing the air charge. 2. the power input member of a pump, such as on a torque converter or hydraulic retarder.

inactive codes fault codes that are no longer active but are retained in ECM memory (and displayed) for purposes of diagnosis until they are erased; also known as *historic codes*.

indicated power (ip) expression of gross engine power usually determined by calculation and, in the United States, expressed as indicated horsepower.

indirect injection (IDI) any of a number of methods of injecting fuel to an engine outside the cylinder. This may be to an intake tract in the intake manifold or to a cell adjacent to the cylinder, such as a precombustion chamber.

induction circuit refers to the engine air intake circuit, but more appropriately describes air intake on naturally aspirated engines than on boosted engines.

Industrial Fastener Institute (IFI) regulatory body for setting fastener standards. Manufacturers of fasteners are required to be registered with the IFI.

inert chemically unreactive; any substance that is unlikely to participate in a chemical reaction.

inertia in physics, the tendency of a body at rest or in motion to continue in that state unless influenced by an external force.

inflammable a substance capable of being *inflamed* or combusted; describes anything that can be oxidized in a redox reaction.

InfoMax vehicle-to-land station data transfer system that uses WiFi short-range wireless technology. It permits download of vehicle and driver performance data and upload of customer data programming.

INFORM Cummins PC-based data management system.

information technology (IT) the science of networking and the software and hardware that enables it.

infrared the wavelength just greater than the red end of the visible light spectrum, but below the radio wave frequency.

infrared thermometer accurate heat measuring instrument that can be used for checking cylinder fueling balance.

infrastructure-to-vehicle (I2V) telematics communication from land-based control center or data hub to a vehicle while mobile.

inhibitor something that slows or prevents a chemical or physical reaction.

injection actuation pressure (IAP) Caterpillar's HEUI actuation oil pressure.

injection control pressure (ICP) actuation oil pressure in HEUI fuel systems.

injection control valve an ECM-controlled, electrohydraulic valve used in the Cummins CAPS fuel system.

injection lag a diesel fuel injection term describing the time lag between port closure in a pumping element and the actual opening of the injector.

injection pressure regulator (IPR) ECM-controlled device that manages HEUI-actuating oil pressure.

injection quantity calibration data fuel flow specification code assigned to EUIs, EUPs, and electrohydraulic injectors. A code that must be programmed to the ECM. Also known by terms such as *QR, IQCC,* and *E-Trim programming.*

injection quantity compensation code (IQCC) term used to rate injector fuel flow; in DD-series engines, a six-digit code that must be programmed to the engine electronics (MCM).

injection rate a diesel fuel injection term defined as the fuel quantity pumped into an engine cylinder per crank angle degree. In systems except for the HEUI, common rail (CR), and post-2007 EUP/EUI systems, injection rate is determined by the pump actuating cam profile geometry.

injector a term broadly used to describe the holder of a hydraulic nozzle assembly. It may also be used to describe PT, TP, MUI, EUI, HEUI, and EHI assemblies.

injector driver module (IDM) separate injector driver unit used in International's versions of HEUI up to 1997.

IDM functions are integrated in a single ECM in current applications.

injector drivers the ECM-controlled components that electrically switch EUI and HEUI assemblies. Injector drivers may be integral with the main ECM housing or contained in a separate module or housing.

injector quantity compensation coding (IQCC) general term used to rate injector fuel flow; an alphanumeric code that must be programmed to the ECM so that cylinder fueling is balanced.

injector response time (IRT) time in ms between the ECM injector drive signal and the moment of EUI control valve closure.

Injector Verification Test (IVT) Caterpillar ADEM software that complements E-Trim by evaluating injector performance every 125 hours of engine operation to balance injector fueling.

inlet metering describes any injection pump that meters fuel quantity admitted to the pump chamber. For instance, in an inlet-metering, opposed plunger injection pump, all of the fuel admitted to the high-pressure pump chamber is injected each time the plungers are actuated.

inlet restriction a measure of the pressure value below atmospheric, which is developed on the pull side of a pumping mechanism. Air inlet restriction and fuel inlet restriction are common specifications used by the diesel technician.

inlet restriction gauge instrument that measures (usually air) inlet restriction; often on-chassis.

inner base circle (IBC) in cam geometry, the portion of the cam profile with the smallest radial dimension; also known as base circle/BC. When the train riding the cam profile is on IBC, it is unloaded.

input the process of entering data into a computer system.

input devices the hardware responsible for signaling/switching data to a computer system, such as a keyboard on a PC or sensors on a vehicle system.

inside diameter (id) diametrical measurement across a bore.

inside micrometer standard or metric micrometer consisting of a spindle and thimble but no anvil; used for making internal and bore measurements.

INSITE Cummins PC software.

INSPEC Cummins Windows-driven PC vehicle ECM diagnostics and programming software.

insulator material that either prevents or inhibits the flow of electrons; usually nonmetallic substances that contain more than four electrons in their outer shell.

intake circuit the series of components used to route ambient air into engine cylinders. In a diesel engine, it includes filter(s), piping, turbo compressor housing, charge air cooler, EGR mixer, and intake manifold.

intake manifold the piping that is responsible for directing intake air into the engine cylinders; clamped to the intake tract flange faces.

intake module assembly of air guide components used in some post-2004 and most 2007/2010 diesel engines consisting of intake manifold(s), EGR mixing chambers, and a heat exchanger.

Intebrake internal engine compression brake used on Cummins ISX Series engines that is capable of multiple-stage progressive braking.

integrated circuit (I/C) an electronic circuit constructed on a semiconductor chip, such as silicon, that can replace many separate electrical components and circuits.

integrated fuel system module (IFSM) module containing the fuel management hardware for Cummins HPI-TP managed engines such as ISX.

intensifier piston Caterpillar HEUI hydraulically actuated piston that pumps fuel to injection pressure values; also known as *amplifier piston.*

Interact System (IS) Cummins term used to describe its integrated electronic engine management systems with the ability to connect with fleet management and analysis software. Acronym is used ahead of the engine series letter.

Interact System B (ISB) series Cummins inline six-cylinder 6.7-liter engine.

Interact System C (ISC) series Cummins inline six-cylinder 8.3-liter engine.

Interact System L (ISL) series Cummins inline six-cylinder 8.9-liter engine.

Interact System M (ISM) series Cummins inline six-cylinder 11-liter engine.

Interact System X (ISX) Cummins inline, six-cylinder, 12- or 15-liter engine.

interface the point or device where an electronic interaction occurs. In older chassis electronics with no common bus, separate vehicle system controllers sometimes required interface hardware and software.

interference angle used to provide aggressive valve to valve seat bite. This is achieved by machining a valve seat at ½ or 1 degree less than the cylinder head mating seat. It is seldom used when valve rotators are used; therefore, it is not common in diesel engines.

interference fit the fitting of two components so that the od of the inner component fractionally exceeds the id of the outer component. Liners are sometimes interference fit to cylinder bores. Interference fitting requires the use of a press, chilling, heating, or other forceful means.

internal cam ring the means of actuating the pumping plungers in an opposed plunger, inlet-metering rotary injection pump. Cam profiles are machined inside the cam ring and as the plunger rollers rotate within it, they are forced inboard to effect a pump stroke (see Chapter 23 for a full explanation).

internal combustion engine a heat engine in which the combustion of fuel is contained within a cylinder; differentiated from a steam engine in which the fuel is combusted outside of the *engine.*

internal compression brake any of a number of engine brakes that use the principle of making the piston perform its usual work through the compression stroke and then negate the power stroke by releasing the compression air to the exhaust system at TDC on completion of the compression stroke.

internal exhaust gas recirculation (I-EGR) introduced by Mack Trucks in smaller vocational diesels in 2002 to achieve EGR within the cylinder head using cylinder head valve timing.

International Service Information System (ISIS) A service system designed to interact with Master Diagnostics/ServiceMaxx and Diamond Plus/Diamond Logic data bus management electronics.

International Truck & Engine see *Navistar.*

Internet the global computer multimedia network communications system; a network of networks.

intranet an internal computer network designed for organizational communications using Internet protocols; also known as a LAN (local area network).

ion an atom with either an excess or deficiency of electrons; that is, an unbalanced atom.

iron (Fe) the primary constituent of steel.

ISIS see *International Service Information System*.

ISO 9141 International standards that define control module interconnectivity and data protocols between SAs and MIDs connected to a CAN 2.0 data bus.

ISO 15765 International standards that define control module interconnectivity and data protocols between SAs connected to a CAN 2.0 data bus.

isochronous governor a zero droop governor or one that accommodates no change in rpm on the engine it manages as engine load varies. In electronically managed truck engines, the term is sometimes used to describe engine operation in PTO mode.

ISX-TP fuel system used by Cummins in ISX engines until MY 2010. Known as a time-pressure system in which *time* was the control variable managed by the ECM, and *pressure* was held relatively constant.

J1587/J1708 the first-generation powertrain serial data bus used in heavy-duty trucks and equipment; still used for some chassis and trailer component networking.

J1667 SAE standards for emission testing of highway diesel engines manufactured before 1991 EPA standards; currently used by many jurisdictions for field enforcement of opacity emissions standards.

J1850 data backbone hardware and protocols used in light-duty CAN multiplexing systems that preceded CAN-C.

J1939 data backbone hardware and protocols used in heavy-duty CAN powertrain multiplexing systems. Based on CAN 2.0 architecture and protocols. Current maximum rated speed is 1 Mb/s and average speed is 500 kb/s.

Jacobs brake see *Jacobs retarders*.

Jacobs C-Brake a Jacobs internal engine compression brake designed for certain Cummins engines.

Jacobs retarders Jacobs is known mainly for its internal engine compression brakes, but also manufactures driveline retarders used primarily in off-road mobile equipment.

Jake brake widely used slang term for an internal engine compression brake.

joule unit of energy that describes the work done when an electrical current of 1 ampere flows through a resistance of 1 ohm in 1 second; or, in mechanical terms, the work that results when a force of 1 newton moves the point of application 1 meter.

jumper pipes a term used to describe the pipes that connect the charge and return galleries with DDC MUIs or with each other in multicylinder heads.

kaizen Japanese word meaning "continuous improvement." It has become a catchword in industry and is often linked with the practice of TQM.

KAMPWR electrical circuit that powers KAM (Navistar).

Karman vortex flow MAF sensors see *vortex flow MAF sensors*.

keep-alive memory (KAM) nonvolatile RAM.

keeper split lock fitted to a peripheral groove at the top of a cylinder valve stem; holds the spring retainer in position.

Kenworth truck OEM owned by Paccar DAF.

kernel the resident portion of a disk or program operating system.

kerosene a petroleum-derived fuel with a lower volatility than gasoline and fewer residual oils than diesel fuel.

keyboard the data entry device used on EST and computer systems enabling alpha, numeric, and command switching.

keystone the trapezoidal shape that gets its name from the trapezoidal stones used in a classic Roman arch bridge.

keystone ring a trapezoidally shaped piston ring commonly used in diesel engine compression ring design.

keystone rod a connecting rod with a trapezoidal eye (small end) to increase the loaded sectional area.

kilobyte a quantitative unit of data consisting of 1,024 bytes.

kilowatt (kW) a unit of power measurement equivalent to 1,000 watts. It is equal to 1.34 BHP.

kinetic relating to motion or movement.

kinetic energy the energy of motion.

kinetic molecular theory states that all matter consists of molecules that are constantly in motion and that the extent of motion will increase at higher temperatures.

Kirchhoff's first law states that the current flowing into a point or component in an electrical circuit must equal the current flowing out of it.

Kirchhoff's second law states that voltage will drop in exact proportion to the resistance in a circuit component and that the sum of the voltage drops must equal the voltage applied to the circuit; also known as *Kirchhoff's law of voltage drops*.

kPa kilopascal; metric unit of pressure measurement. Atmospheric pressure is equivalent to 101.3 kPa.

L-10 Cummins inline, six-cylinder, 10-liter engine produced in versions for PT and CELECT management.

lacquering the process of baking a hard skin on engine components, usually caused by high-sulfur fuels or engine oil contamination.

ladder switch a "smart" switch so named because it contains a ladder of resistors, usually five per switch, known as a ladder bridge. The processor that receives data from the ladder switches on the data bus has a library of resistor values that enables it to identify switch status and its commands.

lambda the Greek letter *l* used as a symbol to indicate stoichiometric combustion. See *stoichiometric*.

lambda sensor an exhaust gas sensor used on electronically managed, SI gasoline-fueled engines to signal the oxygen content in the exhaust gas to the ECM.

lamina a thin layer, plate, or film.

lands the raised areas between grooves, especially on the ring belt of a piston.

laptop computer a portable PC.

large bore in the trucking industry, describes diesel engines with displacements between 12 and 16 liters.

laser any of many devices that generate an intense light beam by emitting photons from a stimulated source. It is used in computer technology to read and write optically.

laser printer a common PC printer device that aims a laser beam at a photosensitive drum to produce text or images on paper.

latching solenoid a solenoid that locks to a position when actuated and usually remains in that position until the system is shut down/de-energized.

latent heat thermal energy that is absorbed by a substance undergoing a change of state (such as melting or vaporization) at a constant temperature.

leak-off lines/pipes the low-pressure return circuit used in most current diesel fuel injection systems.

lean NO_x catalyst (LNC) a catalytic converter designed to reduce NO_x under conditions of excessive oxygen; usually ECM managed and requires HC injection to enable the reduction process, which uses a rhodium catalyst.

lever a rigid bar that pivots on a fulcrum and can be used to provide a mechanical advantage.

lifters components that ride a cam profile and convert rotary motion of the camshaft into linear motion or lift. Lifters used in truck diesel engines are generally solid or roller types.

light-emitting diode (LED) diode that converts electrical current directly into light (photons) and therefore is highly efficient, as there are no heat losses.

limiting speed governor (LSG) a standard automotive governor that defines the idle and high idle fuel quantities and leaves the intermediate fueling to be managed by the operator within the limitations of the fuel system.

limp-home a default strategy that enables partial operation of a system, usually for a limited time period; see *default*.

linear magnet a proportional solenoid used for precise positioning; an ECM output.

linehaul terminal-to-terminal operation of a truck, meaning that most of the mileage is highway mileage.

liners the normally replaceable inserts into the cylinder block bores of most diesel engines that permit easy engine overhaul service and greatly extended cylinder block longevity.

liquefied natural gas (LNG) NG refrigerated into a liquid state and contained as such under pressure; used as a fuel in vehicle technology.

liquefied petroleum gas (LPG) another term used to describe *propane*, a petroleum-derived gas consisting of boil-off vapors of crude oil.

liquid crystal display (LCD) flat panel display consisting of liquid crystals sandwiched between two layers of polarizing material. When a wire circuit below is energized, the liquid crystal medium is aligned to block light transmission from a light source, producing a low-quality screen image.

lithium ion (Li-ion) battery a battery in which lithium ions move from the cathode to the anode during discharge and in reverse during charge cycles. Various types are in widespread use, including by the military, transit, and hybrid electric applications, because of their high power and good energy density.

load ratio of power developed versus rated peak power at the same rpm.

load specific fuel consumption (LSFC) a measure of the *fuel efficiency* of a truck. Relates to hauling productivity rather than the more abstract *fuel economy*.

local area network (LAN) also known as an *intranet*; a usually private computer network used for communications and data tracking within a company or institution.

local bus an expansion bus that connects directly to the CPU.

locking tang a tab on a component, such as a bearing, that may help position and lock it.

logic a widely used (and abused) term referring to anything to do with computers.

logical processing data comparison and mapping operations by a computer's CPU.

log on an access code or procedure used in network systems (such as truck OEM data hubs); used for security and identification.

longevity long life or life span.

lower helix the standard helix milled into most port-helix plungers used in truck diesel applications. These produce a constant beginning, variable delivery characteristic when no external variable timing mechanism is used.

low spring injector an injector design that locates the spring directly over the nozzle valve, thereby reducing the mass of moving components compared to a high spring model. Injector spring tension is usually defined by shims.

low sulfur (LS) fuel containing a maximum of 0.05% sulfur; required for on-highway use between 1993 and October 2006 but no longer legal.

low-temperature filter (LTF) a type of DPF designed to remove entrapped diesel particulate emissions from applications that run at low loads. Collected ash has to be removed periodically. LTFs are designed for applications in which *average* exhaust temperatures are less than 437°F (225°C) but generally exceed 392°F (200°C).

LS fuel see *low-sulfur*.

lubricity literally, the oiliness of a substance.

lugging term used to describe an engine that is run at speeds lower than the base of the torque rise profile (peak torque) under high loads, that is, high cylinder pressures.

M-11 Cummins inline, six-cylinder, 11-liter engine managed by CELECT Plus or Interact System (IS) electronics; ceased production in 2010.

machine cycle the four steps that make up the CPU processing cycle: fetch, decode, execute, and store.

machine-under-test (MUT) term used to refer to an engine or transmission being tested on a dynamometer.

Mack Trucks E-3 inline, six-cylinder light-duty diesel engine using Bosch CR fuel management; ceased production in 2007.

Mack Trucks Inc. a major manufacturer of medium- and heavy-duty trucks and engines. Corporate center is in Greensboro, North Carolina.

magnetic flux test magnetic flux crack detection procedure used to identify defects in crankshafts, connecting rods, cylinder heads, and other parts. An electric current is flowed through the component being tested and iron particles suspended in liquid are then sprayed over the surface. The particles will concentrate where the magnetic flux lines are broken up by cracks.

magnetism the phenomenon that includes the physical attraction for iron observed in lodestone and associated with electric current flow. It is characterized by fields of force, which can exert a mechanical and electrical influence on anything within the boundaries of that field.

magneto an electric generator using permanent magnets and capable of producing high voltages.

magnetomotive force (mmf) the magnetizing force created by flowing current through a coil.

Magnum Monosteel™ piston a Federal Mogul steel trunk piston introduced in 2007 to compete with Mahle Monotherm pistons.

mainframe large computers that can process and file vast quantities of data. In the transportation industry, the data hubs to which dealerships and depots are networked are usually mainframe computers.

main memory RAM; electronically retained data pipelined to the CPU. Data must be loaded to RAM to be processed by a computer.

major thrust side when cylinder gas pressure acts on a piston, it tends to pivot off a vertical centerline; the major thrust side is the inboard side of the piston as its throw rotates through the cycle.

malfunction indicator light (MIL) a dash warning light that indicates a problem in the engine exhaust emissions management system.

malleable possessing the ability to be deformed without breaking or cracking.

manifold boost turbo-boost.

manometer a tubular, U-shaped column mounted on a calibration scale and filled with water or mercury to balance at 0 on the scale. The instrument is used to measure light pressure or vacuum conditions in fluid circuits.

mapping term used in place of *algorithm*, describing the steps required to produce a computed outcome.

mass the quantity of matter a body contains; weight.

mass airflow (MAF) sensor means of measuring the mass of air entering the intake circuit of an engine. Uses either a hot wire or Delta pressure sensing system.

master bar a test bar used to check the align bore in engine cylinder blocks.

master control module a Freightliner multiplexing module used to monitor hardwired switches on the steering wheel, column stalk, and headlight controls. The master control module is CAN bussed to the *central gateway* to communicate with the powertrain networks.

Master Diagnostics (MD) Navistar International EZ-Tech driven software designed to troubleshoot Navistar engines and chassis components up to MY 2007. Replaced by *ServiceMaxx (SM)*.

master gauge a diagnostic gauge of higher quality used to corroborate readings from an in-vehicle gauge.

master program the resident portion of an operating system. In a vehicle ECM, the master program for system management would be retained in ROM.

master pyrometer an accurate thermocouple pyrometer used when performing dynamometer testing.

material safety data sheet (MSDS) a data information sheet on any known hazardous substance that must be displayed or provided on request; mandated by WHMIS.

matter physical substance; anything that has mass and occupies space.

MBE-900 Mercedes-Benz 6.4-liter, I-6 engine.

MBE-4000 Mercedes-Benz 12.8-liter, I-6 engine; ceased production in 2010.

mean average.

mean effective pressure (MEP) average pressure acting on a piston through its complete cycle, the net gain of which converts to work potential. It is usually calculated by disregarding the intake and exhaust strokes and subtracting the mean compression pressure from the mean combustion pressure.

mechanical advantage the ratio of applied force to the resultant work in any machine or arrangement of levers.

mechanical efficiency a measure of how effectively indicated horsepower is converted into brake power; factors in pumping and friction losses.

mechanical governor a governor in which the centrifugal force developed by the rotating flyweights used to sense rpm is the force used to move/limit the fuel control mechanism.

mechanical injector one OEM's term for hydraulic injector.

mechanically actuated, electronically controlled unit injector (MEUI) Caterpillar term for an EUI; see *electronic unit injector*.

mechanical unit injector (MUI) cam-actuated, governor-controlled unit injector used by DDC and Caterpillar.

medium bore in the trucking industry, describes diesel engines with displacements between 8 and 12 liters.

megabyte one million bytes; a quantitative measure of data; often abbreviated to "meg."

megahertz a measure of frequency; 1 million cycles per second. The system clock of a computer is speed-rated in megahertz.

megapascal (MPa) One million pascals; metric pressure measurement unit.

memory address the location of a byte in computer memory.

menu a screen display of program or processing options.

message identifier (MID) the SAE term used to identify a controller (module) with an address on a J1587/1708 powertrain bus. Each controller on the bus is assigned a numeric code; the engine ECM uses a MID 128 address.

metallurgy the science of the production, properties, and application of metals and their alloys.

metals any of a group of chemical elements such as iron, aluminum, gold, silver, tin, and copper that are usually good conductors of heat and electricity and can usually form basic oxides.

metering the process of precisely controlling fuel quantity.

metering actuator one of two ECM-controlled electro-hydraulic solenoids used to manage injected fuel quantity on Cummins common rail and HPI-TP fueled engines. Duration of energization determines injected fuel quantity delivered to the engine cylinder by the injector.

metering chamber the lower chamber in a Cummins TP injector located under the TP pump (lower) plunger.

metering recesses the milled recesses in port-helix plungers that are used to vary the fuel quantity and timing during pumping.

meter resolution a measure of the power and accuracy of a DMM.

methane the main component of *natural gas (NG)*. A simple alkane with a chemical symbol of CH_4.

methanol also known as wood alcohol; used as fuel in racing and some commercial vehicles. Produces better thermal efficiency and power than gasoline-fueled engines, but combusts at a stoichiometric ratio of 6.5:1, so fuel consumption is high.

Metri-Pack connector a type of commonly used, sealed electrical/electronic connector.

MEUI-C injector Caterpillar term for its Delphi E3 injector used in post-2007 engines.

Mexican hat piston crown a piston design in which the center of the crown peaks in the fashion of a sombrero; commonly used in DI diesel engines.

micrometer a precise measuring instrument consisting of a thimble, barrel, and anvil; used to make accurate id, od, and thickness measurements.

micron (µ) one-millionth of a meter; equivalent to 0.000039 inch. The Greek letter mu is used to represent micron.

microorganism growth a condition that may result from water contamination in fuel storage tanks.

microprocessor a small processor; sometimes used to describe a complete computer unit.

microwaves radio waves used to transmit voice, data, and video; limited to line-of-sight transmission to distances not exceeding 30 km.

Miller cycle variation on the Otto cycle engine that uses a supercharger and holds open the intake valves for the first part of the compression stroke, providing higher efficiencies.

millions of instructions per second (MIPS) rating of processing speed.

min-max governor British term for *limiting speed governor*; used by Bosch.

minor thrust face the outboard side of the piston as its throw rotates away from the crankshaft centerline on the power stroke. See *thrust face*.

minor thrust side when cylinder gas pressure acts on a piston, it tends to pivot off a vertical centerline. The minor thrust side is the outboard side of the piston as its throw rotates through the cycle.

mixture the random distribution of one substance with another without any chemical reaction or bonding taking place. Air is a mixture of nitrogen and oxygen.

model year (MY) usually refers to the EPA emissions designation of a truck engine and its emissions rating, but OEMs commonly use the term simply to mean year of manufacture.

modem a communications device that converts digital output from a computer to the analog signal required by the phone system.

modular switch field (MSF) a subcomponent of a Freightliner SAM that incorporates a system of multiplexed switches consisting of a master control module and one or more slave modules and sub-bus switches.

modulation in electronics, the altering of amplitude or frequency of a wave for purposes of signaling data.

module a housing that contains a microprocessor and switching apparatus or either of each.

module identifier (MID) a widely used variation of the SAE J1587/1708 term *message identifier* because it better describes its function as a controller. Each controller on the powertrain bus is assigned a numeric MID; the ECM uses a MID 128 address.

monatomic a molecule consisting of a single atom.

monitor the common output screen display used by a computer system; usually an LCD.

Monocomp™ piston a Mahle trademark for a trunk-type piston in which the crown and skirt sections are manufactured separately. The two separate sections are then screwed together using a proprietary process. The piston crown section is manufactured from high-temperature steel, then threaded into the steel skirt assembly.

Monotherm™ piston a Mahle trademark for forged steel, trunk-type piston assemblies with an open skirt. Monotherm pistons first appeared on the 2004 Cummins ISX and have more recently become the piston of choice for 2007 and later emissions-compliant medium- and large-bore truck diesel engines.

motherboard the primary circuit board in a computer housing to which the other components are connected.

motive power automotive, transportation, marine, and aircraft.

motor control module (MCM) DD term for the fuel and engine system proprietary bus-connected module driven by DDEC electronics.

motoring running a vehicle at 0 throttle with chassis momentum driving the engine.

muffler an engine silencer that uses sound absorption and resonation principles to alter the frequency of engine noise.

multimedia the combining of sound, graphics, and video in computer programs.

multi-orifii nozzle a typical hydraulic injector nozzle whose function is to switch and atomize the fuel injected to an engine cylinder. Hydromechanical versions consist of a nozzle body machined with the orifii, a nozzle valve, and a spring; they are used in engines using port-helix injection pumps, MUIs, EUIs, EUPs, and HEUIs. Electronic or smart nozzles are also multi-orifii but are switched by an ECM-controlled actuator.

multiple splice an electrical connection that joins a number of wires at a single junction.

multiplexing name for the connecting of two or more electronic system controllers on a data backbone to synergize system operation and reduce the number of common components and hard wiring.

multipulse injection a feature of most current diesel fuel injection systems, in which a fueling pulse can be divided into up to seven separate injection events within a single cycle.

multitasking the ability of a computer to simultaneously process multiple data streams.

MX-Series engines Paccar (Kenworth and Peterbilt) engines using EUP fuel systems and SMART injectors (MY 2010 to 2013) and Delphi CR (MY 2013 and later).

N 14 Cummins evolution of the 855 cu. in. engine produced for PT, CELECT, and CELECT Plus management—an inline, six-cylinder engine.

Nalcool a brand of antifreeze coolant solution supplemental additive.

nanosecond one-billionth of a second.

National Automotive Technicians Education Foundation (NATEF) organization dedicated to setting certification standards for educational programs teaching auto and truck technicians.

National Institute for Automotive Service Excellence (NIASE, ASE) organization dedicated to setting certification standards for auto and truck technicians and administering nationwide certification testing.

natural gas (NG) naturally occurring subterranean organic gas (gaseous crude petroleum) composed largely of methane.

naturally aspirated (NA) describes any engine in which intake air is induced into the cylinder by the lower-than-atmospheric pressure created on the downstroke of the piston and receives no assist from boost devices such as turbochargers.

Navistar a major manufacturer of truck chassis and engines. Previously International Harvester and often referred to by the slang term *binder* (sourced from the strong agricultural heritage of the company). Corporate center is in Chicago, Illinois.

Navistar Service Information (NSI) dealership and bodybuilder replacement SIS for the former ISIS.

needle-motion sensor nozzle valve movement detector used in Bosch pintle nozzles. It consists of a coil and reluctor: At NOP, valve movement induces a voltage.

needle valve nozzle another way of describing a multi-orifii, hydraulic injector nozzle (DDC).

negative temperature coefficient (NTC) the electrical characteristic of a conductor in which resistance to current flow decreases as temperature increases. Most engine temperature sensors use a reference voltage and NTC conductor to signal temperature.

net power an SAE formula to calculate actual engine power by running it with all potential parasitic loads and emissions controls activated. SAE net power formula is specified in J1349.

network a series of connected computers designed to share data, programs, and resources.

network access point (NAP) wireless data transfer module used for data transfer from vehicle to land station.

networking the act of communicating using computers.

neural network term for the main multiplexing bus to which system controllers (SAs) are attached in J1939 architecture.

neutron a component part of an atom with the same mass as a proton, but with no electrical charge. Present in all atoms except the simplest form of hydrogen.

new scroll pump a Caterpillar port-helix metering injection pump.

new technology diesel exhaust (NTDE) term used by HEI to describe EPA 2010 and later diesel engines.

newton unit of mechanical force defined as the force required to accelerate a mass of 1 kilogram through 1 meter in 1 second.

nibble 4 bits of data or half a byte.

nickel metal hydride (NiMH) battery A common HEV battery; uses an aqueous solution of potassium hydroxide as electrolyte and nickel oxide (positive) and a metal hydride (negative) electrodes.

Ni-ResistTM insert a high-strength, nickel alloy piston ring support insert in an aluminum trunk-type piston with a coefficient of heat expansion similar to that of aluminum.

nitrogen (N) a colorless, tasteless, and odorless gas found elementally in air at a proportion of 76% by mass and 79% by volume. Its atomic number is 7.

nitrogen dioxide (NO_2) one of the oxides of nitrogen produced in vehicle engines and a significant contributor in the formation of photochemical smog.

node 1. dumb terminal (limited processing capability) or PC connected to a network. 2. portion of a wave signal above a zero, mean, or neutral point in the band.

noise in electronics, unwanted pulse or wave form interference that can scramble signals.

noncycling circuit breaker circuit protection device classified as SAE #2. When tripped by current overload, it remains open until the circuit is de-energized and the breaker cools. May be electromechanical or *virtual*.

normal rated power the highest power specified for continuous operation of an engine.

notebook computer briefcase-sized PC designed for portability.

NOT gate any circuit whose outcome is in the *on* (or one) state until the gate switch is in the *on* state, at which point the outcome is in the *off* (or zero) state.

NO_x adsorber catalyst (NAC) a two-stage exhaust aftertreatment system that uses base metal oxides to initially adsorb (store) NO_x compounds, followed by the use of a rhodium reduction catalyst and fuel *dosing*-induced combustion to reduce NO_x back to N_2.

noxious emissions engine end gases that are classified as harmful. Includes NO_x and HC but does not include CO_2 and tailpipe-emitted H_2O (both greenhouse gases).

NO_x sensor measures exhaust gas NO_x by essentially electrolytically reducing the compound and comparing the "reduced O_2" with the O_2 in the atmosphere. See Chapter 34 for a full explanation.

nozzle the component of most hydraulic and electronic injector assemblies responsible for switching and atomizing fuel for injection.

nozzle check see *nozzle valve*.

nozzle closing pressure (NCP) the specific pressure at which a hydraulic injector nozzle closes; always lower than NOP due to nozzle differential ratio. Also known as *valve closing pressure*.

nozzle control valve (NCV) actuator the actuator on a Delphi E3 EUI that controls the opening and closing of the injector nozzle on an ECM command signal.

nozzle differential ratio the ratio of nozzle valve seat to nozzle valve shank sectional areas. This ratio defines the pressure difference between NOP and nozzle closure values.

nozzle opening pressure (NOP) the trigger pressure value of a hydraulic injector nozzle.

nozzle seat the seat in an injector nozzle body sealed by the nozzle valve in its closed position.

nozzle valve the open-close moving component of a nozzle assembly.

nozzle valve motion sensor (NVMS) motion sensor used to detect nozzle valve movement (at NOP) by inducing a signal voltage proportional to nozzle valve speed of motion.

nucleus the center of an atom, which incorporates most of its mass and is usually made up of neutrons and protons.

numeric data represented by number digits.

numeric keypad microprocessor-based instrument with numeric-only input keys, such as on first-generation ProLink ESTs.

Occupational Safety and Health Administration (OSHA) U.S. federal agency responsible for administering safety in the workplace.

octane rating denotes the ignition and combustion behavior/rate of a fuel, usually gasoline. As the octane number increases, the fuel's antiknock characteristics increase and the burn rate slows.

offset camshaft key timing a Cummins method of timing engine position with cam-actuated injector pump mechanisms.

ohm a unit for quantifying electrical resistance in a circuit.

Ohm's law the formula used to calculate electrical circuit performance. It asserts that it requires 1 V of potential to pump 1 A of current through a circuit resistance of 1; named for Georg Ohm (1787–1854).

oil cooler a heat exchanger designed to cool oil, usually using engine coolant as its medium.

oil pan the oil sump, normally flange-mounted directly under the engine cylinder block.

oil window the portion of the upper strata of the earth's crust in which crude petroleum is formed.

onboard diagnostics II (OBD II) troubleshooting fields that relate specifically to emissions control on light-duty vehicles that must be accessible on the data bus by generic ESTs; a requirement on light-duty vehicles since 1995.

OnCommand an online Navistar service information and fleet data tracking system that incorporates SIS, vehicle service records, and technician training in a single subscription package.

opacimeter see *opacity meter*.

opacity meter a light extinction means of testing exhaust gas particulate and liquid emission that rates density of exhaust smoke based on the percentage of emitted light that does not reach the sensor; the higher the percentage reading, the more dense the exhaust smoke.

open circuit any electrical circuit through which no current is flowing, whether intentional or not.

open circuit voltage (OCV) voltage measured in a device or circuit through which there is no current flow.

open nozzle refers to an injector that is sealed by its pump plunger, such as the Cummins HPI-TP used in the pre-2010 ISX series engines.

opens an electrical term referring to open circuits/no continuity in a circuit, portion of the circuit, or a component.

operand machine-language directive that channels data and its location.

operating environment defines the monitor display character and the graphical user interface (GUI), consisting of icons and other symbols, to increase user friendliness.

operating system (OS) core software programs that manage the operation of computer hardware and make a computer capable of running functional programs.

opposed plungers reciprocating members of an inlet-metering, opposed plunger rotary distributor pump. Usually a pair of opposed plungers are used, but some pumps use two pairs. The plungers are forced outward as fuel is metered into the pump chamber. When the plunger actuating rollers contact the internal cam profiles, they are driven inboard (toward each other), simultaneously pressurizing the fuel in the pump chamber.

optical character recognition (OCR) process by which certain scanners read type by shape and convert it to a corresponding computer code.

optical codes graphic codes that represent data for purposes of scanning, such as bar codes.

optical disks digital data storage media consisting of rigid plastic disks on which lasers have burned microscopic holes. The disk can then be optically scanned (read) by a low-power laser.

optical memory cards digital data storage media the size of a credit card, capable of retaining the equivalent of 1,600 pages of text.

Organization of Petroleum Producing Countries (OPEC) a cartel of oil-producing countries that regulates oil supplies to maintain pricing.

OR gate a multiple input circuit whose output is in the *on* or one state when any of the inputs is in the *on* state.

orifice a hole or aperture.

orifice nozzle a hydraulic injector nozzle that uses a single orifice (unusual) or a number of orifii through which high-pressure fuel is pumped and atomized during injection.

orifii plural of orifice.

original equipment manufacturer (OEM) term used to describe the manufacturer of an original product, distinct from an aftermarket manufacturer (replacement product).

oscilloscope an instrument designed to graphically display electrical waveforms on a display monitor.

Otto cycle the four-stroke, spark-ignited engine cycle patented by Nicolas Otto in 1876. The four strokes of the cycle are induction, compression, power, and exhaust.

outer base circle (OBC) the portion of a cam profile with the largest radial diameter.

output the result of any processing operation.

output devices components controlled by a computer that effect the results of processing. The LCD monitor and printer on a PC system and the injector drivers on a diesel engine are examples of output devices.

outside diameter (od) outside measurement of a shaft or cylindrical component; can also be used to mean any outside dimension.

outside micrometer a standard micrometer designed to precisely measure od or thickness. Consists of an anvil, spindle, thimble, barrel, and calibration scales.

overhead adjustment term used to refer to setting cylinder head valves and timing injectors; also known as a *tune-up*.

overhead camshaft (OHC) an engine with a camshaft cradle-mounted on the cylinder head.

overspeed a governor condition in which the engine speed, for whatever reasons, exceeds the set high-idle speed or top engine limit.

oversquare engine an engine in which the cylinder bore diameter is larger than the stroke dimension.

owner-operator a private for-hire trucker who owns the vehicle and usually hauls fleet-owned trailers; often known as a *broker*.

oxidation the act of oxidizing a material; can mean combusting or burning a substance.

oxidation catalyst a catalyst that enables an oxidation reaction. In the oxidation stage of a catalytic converter, the catalysts platinum and palladium are used.

oxidation stability describes the resistance of a substance to being oxidized. It is a desirable for an engine lubrication oil to resist oxidation, so one of its specifications would be its oxidation stability.

oxides of nitrogen (NO$_x$) any of a number of nitrogen-oxygen compounds that may result from the combustion process: They are referred to collectively as NO$_x$. When combined with HC and sunlight, they react to form photoelectric smog.

oxyacetylene a commonly used cutting, heating, and welding process that uses pure compressed oxygen in conjunction with acetylene fuel.

oxygen colorless, tasteless, odorless gas; the most abundant element on Earth; occurs elementally in air and in many compounds, including water.

ozone an oxygen molecule consisting of three oxygen atoms (triatomic). It exists naturally in the Earth's ozonosphere (6 to 30 miles altitude) where it absorbs ultraviolet light, but can be produced by lightning and by photochemical reactions between NO$_x$ and HC. Ozone is explosive and toxic.

Paccar MX-Series see *MX-Series engines*.

PACE/PACER Cummins partial authority, electronic PT fuel system management; not used after MY 1997.

packet a data message delivered to the data bus when a ladder switch resistance changes, indicating a change in switch status.

palladium an oxidation catalyst often used in catalytic converters.

pallet the "bearing" end of a rocker that directly contacts a valve stem or yoke pad.

parallel circuit electrical circuit that permits more than a single path for current flow.

parallel hybrid (PH) term usually used to describe a powertrain in which a diesel engine drives a genset and a mechanical drivetrain options either direct or electric drive.

parallel hydraulic drive (PHD) a vehicle in which torque can be delivered to the drive wheels by an internal combustion engine alone, by a hydraulic motor alone, or any ratio of combinations of both.

parallel hydraulic hybrid (PHH) an Eaton Corporation parallel drive system in which a conventional diesel-driven drivetrain is assisted by a hydraulic system consisting of a reversible piston pump and motor coupled to the drive shaft by a clutch, accumulators, plumbing, and a control circuit.

parallel ports peripheral connection ports for computer devices that require large-volume data transmission such as printers and scanners.

parallel port valve configuration engine cylinder valve arrangement that locates multiple valves parallel to the crank centerline, permitting equal gas flow through each (assuming identical lift).

parameter a value, specification, or limit.

parameter group (PG) see *parameter group number*.

parameter group number (PGN) code for components and some subcircuits on the J1939 data bus. The general equivalent of J1939 to the PID on the older J1587.

parameter identifier (PID) coded components within a J1587/1708 controller system.

parasite a creature that lives off another; a flea is an example. The term is adapted to describe leech loads in power circuits.

parasitics energy losses in an engine due to factors that do not directly result in production of power. Friction losses and auxiliary devices can be considered parasitic losses. One way of reducing engine parasitics is to lower rpm, which is why many modern engines are governed at lower rpms.

parent bore term used to describe an engine with integral cylinder bores machined directly into the cylinder block. It is not often used in diesel engines, and when used the bore surface area may be induction hardened to provide improved longevity.

parity the even or odd quality of the number of 0s (zeros) and 1s (ones); a value that may have to be set to handshake (connect) two pieces of electronic equipment.

partial authority term widely used in truck technology to describe a hydromechanical system that has been adapted for management by computer. A good example is the port-helix metering injection pump that was adapted for electronic management in early Caterpillar, Mack, and John Deere engines.

particulate matter (PM) solid matter; often refers to minute solids formed by incompletely combusted fuel and emitted in the exhaust gas.

passive DPF a catalyzed DPF that uses latent diesel exhaust heat to burn off collected particulate (soot) from a wall flow-type filter.

passive DPF mode the primary regeneration cycle of a DPF capable of active and passive modes. It uses latent diesel exhaust heat to burn off collected particulate (soot).

passive regeneration usually the primary generation mode of a diesel particulate filter in which latent exhaust heat and engine-out NO_x are used to oxidize (combust) accumulated soot. The result of a passive regeneration reaction in a DPF is nitrogen, CO_2, and ash.

password an alpha, numeric, or alphanumeric value that either identifies a user to a system or enables access to data fields for purposes of download or reprogramming.

peak pressure the highest pressure attained in a hydraulic system.

peak torque maximum torque. In an internal combustion engine, peak torque always occurs at peak cylinder pressure, and in most cases this will be achieved at a lower speed than rated power rpm.

Peltier effect a heat exchanger principle used in some exhaust gas analyzers to drop a test sample below the dew point to remove water.

pencil injector nozzle a slim pencil-shaped hydraulic injector; often uses an internal accumulator that eliminates the need for a leak-off circuit. It is nearly obsolete.

Pencool a supplemental coolant additive (SCA) that balances diesel engine coolant chemistry and provides cavitation protection.

peripherals input and output devices that support the basic computer system, such as the monitor and the printer.

periphery in cam geometry, the entire outer boundary of the cam; cam profile.

peristaltic pump a pump used in some exhaust gas analyzers to remove water from a test sample while allowing the gas to have minimal contact with the water.

Perkins Diesel Engine a British engine manufacturer, a wholly owned subsidiary of Caterpillar. Many Caterpillar-marketed, small-bore engines are rebadged Perkins.

personal computer (PC) any of a variety of computers designed for full function in isolation from other units but which may be used to network with other systems. The term is generally used to describe computers running an MS Windows operating environment.

personality module Caterpillar and Navistar PROM/EEPROM component.

personality ratings term used by Caterpillar and Navistar to describe PROM and EEPROM functions.

personal protective equipment (PPE) clothing and equipment designed to minimize the risk of injuries in the workplace.

Peterbilt truck OEM owned by Paccar-DAF.

petroleum any of a number of organic fossilized fuels found in the upper strata of the Earth's crust that can be refined into diesel fuel and gasoline, among other fuels.

pH used to evaluate the acidity or alkalinity of a substance. Derived from a logarithm of the reciprocal of the hydrogen ion concentration in a solution in moles per liter: p = power, H = hydrogen.

phasing the precise sequencing of events; often used in the context of phasing the pumping activity of individual elements in a multicylinder injection pump.

photochemical reaction a chemical reaction caused by radiant light energy acting on a substance.

photochemical smog smog formed from airborne HC and NO_x exposed to sunlight; also known as *photoelectric smog* or photosynthetic smog.

photoelectric smog see *photochemical smog*.

photonic semiconductor semiconductor that emits or detects photons or light.

photons a quantum of electromagnetic radiation energy; when visible, known as light.

photovoltaic the characteristic of producing a voltage from light energy.

physical layer term used for the hardware used in a data bus: for instance, the yellow and green coded twisted wire pair used in J1939 is referenced as the physical layer.

pickup tube a suction tube or pipe in a fuel tank or oil sump.

piezo actuator see *piezo injector*.

piezoelectricity some crystals become electrified when subjected to direct pressure, producing a voltage increasing with pressure rise. In piezoelectricity, the direction of polarization reverses if the direction of applied stress changes, that is, from compression to tension. Piezo effect is therefore reversible, and this reversibility is the principle used in piezo actuators.

piezo injector diesel fuel injector that is switched by a piezo actuator located in a control circuit or integrated directly into the injector valve shaft. A piezo actuator is constructed of several hundred piezo crystals; mechanical movement occurs almost instantly when the wafer stack has voltage applied to it. A piezo injector has a faster response time than a solenoid-actuated injector.

pilot ignition a means of igniting a fuel charge that might normally require a spark by injecting a short pulse of diesel fuel into a cylinder to ignite a premixed charge of gaseous fuel and air.

pilot injection the injection of a short-duration pulse of diesel fuel, followed by a pause to await ignition, followed by the resumption of the fuel pulse. Used as a cold-start strategy in some systems to eliminate diesel knock. Can also be used as the ignition means in applications using an alternative fuel that does not readily compression-ignite. In such instances, a short pulse of diesel fuel is injected to act as the ignition means for the primary fuel.

pin boss the wrist pin support bore in a piston assembly.

pintle nozzle a type of hydraulic injector nozzle used in some IDI automobile, small-bore diesel engines until recently.

pipelining rapid sequencing of functions by the CPU to enable high-speed processing.

pipette a glass or plastic tube used to draw liquid samples for spectrographic or refractometer analysis.

piston the reciprocating plug in an engine cylinder bore that seals and transmits the effects of cylinder gas pressure to the crankshaft.

piston pin a *wrist pin* that links the piston assembly to the connecting rod eye.

piston speed the distance traveled by one piston in an engine per unit of time.

pitting a wear pattern that results in small pockmarks or holes.

pixels picture elements. A measure of screen display resolution—each dot that can be illuminated is called a pixel.

plain old telephone service (POTS) telecommunications using the telephone system for part or all of the transaction; still the backbone of most telecommunications.

plasma a gas of positive ions and free electrons with an approximately equal positive and negative charge.

plasma transfer wire arc (PTWA) surface coating of cylinder bores used in diesel engine remanufacturing (Caterpillar) and by diesel engines using aluminum cylinder block with parent bores. The procedure superheats steel alloy and sprays atomized droplets into a compressed air stream to create a laminate structure in the bore of around 150 microns thickness.

Plastigage™ a shaft-to-friction bearing clearance measuring system consisting of nylon cord that deforms to conform with the clearance dimension so it can be measured against a coded scale on the packaging envelope.

platinum an oxidation catalyst often used in catalytic converters.

platinum resistance thermometer (PRT) measures the change in the electrical resistance of gases that takes place with temperature change. Used in place of thermocouple pyrometers where temperatures do not exceed 1,100°F (600°C). Also known as *resistance temperature detector (RTD)*.

PLD module term used to describe the engine controller module on Mercedes-Benz diesel engines; a German acronym meaning ECM.

plunger the reciprocating member of a plunger pump element.

plunger geometry term used to describe the shape of the metering recesses/helices in a pumping plunger and therefore the pump timing and delivery characteristics.

plunger leading edge the point on a pumping plunger closest to the pump chamber.

plunger pump any pump that uses a reciprocating piston or plunger and, in most cases, is hydraulically classified as positive displacement.

pneumatics the science of the mechanical properties of gases, especially in confined circuits designed to provide motive power.

policy adjustment a polite way of describing a shop floor error that requires a service facility to write off time on a repair invoice.

polymer a compound composed of one or more large molecules, which are formed by chains of smaller molecules.

polyswitch circuit protection device that uses a positive temperature coefficient (PTC) principle to protect electrical circuits; they automatically reset as the device cools. Built into some SAM chassis modules to handle certain kinds of intermittent faults.

poppet nozzle a forward opening nozzle valve used in older IDI diesel engines.

popping pressure see *nozzle opening pressure*.

pop test the testing of NOP on a hydraulic injector nozzle using a bench or pop tester.

port 1. an aperture or opening. 2. a computer connection socket used to link a computer with input and output devices.

port closure the beginning of effective stroke in a plunger and barrel pumping element, occurring when the plunger leading edge closes off the spill/fill port(s).

port opening the ending of effective stroke in a plunger and barrel pumping element, occurring when the fill/spill ports are exposed to the chamber.

positive crankcase ventilation (PCV) an EPA requirement for diesel engine crankcases beginning in 2007 (off-highway 2008). Diesel engine OEMs have adopted positive or centrifugal-type or electrostatic filtration of crankcase vapors prior to rerouting them to the intake upstream from the turbocharger impeller. It is usually called *closed crankcase ventilation (CCV)* in diesels.

positive displacement describes a pumping principle in which the quantity of fuel pumped (displaced) per cycle does not vary, so the volume pumped depends on the rate of cycles per minute. When a positive displacement pump unloads to a defined flow area, pressure rise will increase in proportion to rpm or cycles per minute.

positive filtration a filter in which all of the fluid (gas or liquid) to be filtered is forced through the filtering medium. Most air, fuel, coolant, and oil filters used today employ a positive filtration principle.

positive temperature coefficient (PTC) the electrical characteristic of a conductor in which resistance to current flow increases as temperature rises. Copper wire can be said to possess a PTC characteristic.

POST power-on self-test. A BIOS test run at boot-up of a computer or controller module to ensure that all components are operational.

potential difference electrical charge differential measured in voltage.

potential energy any of a number of different means of storing energy. A charged battery, compressed air, or unburned fuel can all be said to possess potential energy.

potentiometer a three-terminal variable resistor or voltage divider used to vary the voltage potential of a circuit; commonly used as a throttle position sensor.

pour point a means of evaluating a fuel or lubricant's low-temperature flow characteristics. The pour point of a fuel is slightly higher in temperature than its gel point.

powdered metal technology see *sinter*; refers to sintering production processes, which may include certain types of alumina ceramics.

power the rate of accomplishing work; it is necessarily factored by time.

power distribution module (PDM) the core of the engine and/or vehicle electrical system(s). PDMs may have some processing capacity and usually house circuit protection devices for the subcircuits they feed.

power line carrier (PLC) term used to describe communication transactions delivered through a power line. Digital signals are converted to analog radio frequencies for the transaction and subsequently decoded by the receiver ECM. An example is the power line carrier use of the auxiliary (blue) wire in a standard seven-pin trailer connector for trailer-to-tractor ABS communications.

Power Service Literature (PSL) the DD online technical service literature site located within the DDCSN portal. Subscription required.

PowerStroke International-built, HEUI-fueled V-8 engine used by Ford up until 2011. It was available in 7.3-liter (until 2004) and 6.0-liter (until 2011) displacement versions.

power takeoff (PTO) an engine or transmission located device used to provide auxiliary power. It can also mean the primary coupling between the engine and powertrain, so in a truck engine this would be the flywheel.

powertrain the components of a system directly responsible for transmitting power to the output mechanisms. In an engine, the powertrain components are the piston assemblies, connecting rods, crankshaft, and flywheel.

power transistor a transistor used as the final switch in an electronic circuit to control a solenoid or other output; sometimes known as a *driver*.

pre-delivery inspection (PDI) an inspection on a vehicle prior to its being put into service; usually undertaken by the OEM dealership, although some fleets perform their own PDIs, believing them to be more exacting.

predictive repair logic the use of software maps (usually logged in OEM data hubs, but catching on in major fleets) to anticipate imminent failure of components or systems before an over-the-road breakdown.

prefix a syllable or letter(s) or numbers added at the beginning of a word or acronym.

pre-injection metering (PRIME) a Caterpillar term for the mechanical pilot injection concept used in its HEUI injectors.

prelubricator a pump used to charge the lubrication circuit on a rebuilt engine before startup.

Premium Tech Tool (PTT) MS Windows–driven, three-app diagnostic software used by Volvo and Mack Trucks. See *Tech Tool™*.

pressure limiting valve (PLV) a safety valve built into many types of hydraulic systems; often just a simple spring and ball check.

pressure-time (PT) Cummins common rail hydromechanical fuel system used in highway applications until 1994. An electronic version known as HPI-PT was used on K-Series engines until replaced by CR fueling.

pressurizing the process of raising the pressure in a circuit.

preventive maintenance (PM) routine scheduled maintenance on vehicles.

primary filter usually describes a filter on the suction side of a fuel subsystem, whereas the term *secondary filter* describes the filter on the charge side of the transfer pump.

prime mover an initial source of power: For instance, the prime mover of a genset is the diesel engine that drives the generator.

processing the procedure required to compute information in a computer system. Input data is processed according to program instructions, and outputs are plotted.

ProDriver Detroit Diesel-DDEC driver digital display.

program set of detailed instructions that organize processing activity.

programmable electronic engine control (PEEC) describes an electronically managed Caterpillar 3406B engine.

programmable logic controller (PLC) small computer that performs switching functions in much the same way as a relay.

programmable read-only memory (PROM) a chip or chips used to qualify ROM data to a specific chassis application. In early vehicle computers, this was usually the only method of reprogramming data to an ECM; this PROM function has now been superseded by the EEPROM capability found in most ECMs.

Pro-Link 9000 a first-generation generic handheld EST capable of scanning the controllers with addresses on a CAN bus, including J1939. Capable of diagnostic and limited programming operations on some systems. Software cartridges or multiprotocol data cards were used to read each OEM system.

Pro-Link iQ a current generic handheld (HH) EST capable of scan, reprogram, and diagnostic functions using both hardwire and wireless technology.

PROM see *programmable read-only memory*.

ProManager Detroit Diesel-DDEC software that permits ECM data to be downloaded to a PC for analysis.

propagate to breed, transmit, or multiply. The word is often used to describe the combustion process in an engine cylinder, such as in flame propagation.

propane a petroleum-derived gas consisting of boil-off vapors; often known as *liquefied petroleum gas (LPG)*.

proportional solenoid a solenoid whose armature will be positioned according to how much current is flowed through its coil. It is often an ECM-actuated output. Proportional solenoids may be linear, such as the V-MAC rack actuator; or rotary, such as the Caterpillar BTM.

proposed category (PC) term used by the API to classify a replacement engine lubricating oil before it achieves consensus approval.

proprietary bus an OEM bus network outside of the powertrain bus (J1939) that supports cab and chassis electronics. Multiple proprietary buses can be used on trucks, buses, and heavy off-road equipment; to interface with the powertrain bus, a gateway module is used.

proprietary OS operating system that is privately owned and specific to a manufacturer or operator.

propylene glycol (PG) A glycol-based antifreeze solution that is less toxic than ethylene glycol (EG). PG mixture strength must be tested with a refractometer that has a PG scale and must not be mixed with EG.

protocols sets of rules and regulations; often used to define communication language.

proton positively charged component of an atom located within its nucleus.

proton exchange membrane (PEM) fuel cells fuel cells using solid polymer membranes (a thin plastic film) as the electrolyte; used in most current motive power applications of fuel cell technology.

psi pounds per square inch; standard unit of pressure measurement.

PT (pump) control module (PTCM) the controller used by Cummins in its now-obsolete PACE/PACER partial authority, electronic management system.

pulsation damper used on a Cummins gear-type supply pump to smooth the pressure waves caused as it discharges fuel into its outlet.

pulse exhaust a tuned exhaust system used to optimize the gas dynamics of exhaust gas delivered to the turbocharger.

pulse wheel the rotating disc used to produce rpm or rotational position data to an ECM. The term is most often applied to the rotating member of a Hall-effect sensor, but at least one manufacturer uses the term to describe an AC reluctor wheel.

pulse width (PW) usually refers to EUI duty cycle, measured in milliseconds.

pulse width modulation (PWM) constant-frequency digital signal in which on/off time can be varied to modulate duty cycle.

pump drive gear the gear responsible for imparting drive force to a pump.

pump-line-nozzle (PLN) the hydromechanical or electronically managed injection pump to line to nozzle fuel injection principle used in most diesel fuel systems until the introduction of EUI engines. The term can be, but is not usually, applied to some more recent systems, such as the Mack E-Tech, Mercedes-Benz, and first-generation Paccar MX EUP systems.

pushrods solid cylindrical rods located between a follower and a rocker assembly that transmit the effects of cam profile to action at the rocker arm.

push tubes hollow cylindrical tubes located between a follower and a rocker assembly that transmit the effects of cam profile to action at the rocker arm.

PX-Series medium-duty Paccar engines that are really rebadged Cummins engines. The two currently available are PX6 (6.7-liter Cummins ISB) and PX8 (8.3-liter Cummins ISC).

pyrometer a thermocouple-type, high-temperature sensing device used to signal exhaust temperature. It consists of two dissimilar wires (pure iron and constantan) joined at the hot end with a millivoltmeter at the "read" end. Increase in temperature will cause a small current to flow, which is read at the voltmeter as a temperature value.

Qualcomm transfer PC-based, remote communications technology that enables wireless data downloads for analysis for data programming uploads. It is used in conjunction with proprietary Fleet Information Software, Highway Master, and other data management packages.

quantity control valve (QCV) Detroit Diesel's MCM-controlled fuel metering valve to the ACRS high-pressure pump elements; used to manage rail pressure.

quantum a defined quantity of energy proportional to the frequency of radiation it emits.

Quantum System (QS) Cummins off-road electronic engine management system.

quick response (QR) code Type of a matrix barcode in a machine-readable optical format. Also, Denso electrohydraulic injector fuel flow calibration data specification that must be programmed to the ECM, which allows the ECM to precisely balance fueling to the engine cylinders.

QuickServe OnLine (QSOL) Cummins online engine and electronics server for repair, troubleshooting, and service bulletins.

quiescent a term used to describe any low-turbulence engine cylinder dynamic. Its root is from the word "quiet."

rack actuator a proportional solenoid (Bosch) or hydraulic servo (Cat) responsible for moving the rack in a computer-controlled, port-helix metering injection pump; an ECM output.

rack actuator housing the housing at the rear of a computer-controlled port-helix metering injection pump that contains sensors and the rack actuating mechanism. It is located in place of the governor on a hydromechanical engine.

rack position sensor an electromagnetic sensor used to signal rack position data to the ECM on electronically controlled, port-helix metering injection pumps.

radial piston pump means of creating injection pressures in some current common rail diesel fuel injection systems. Multicam profiles actuate reciprocating plungers that unload to an accumulator or rail.

radial vector the radial angle of a reference point, say TDC, in a crankshaft that indicates the mechanical advantage of a throw in its relationship with the crankshaft centerline.

radiation the transfer of heat or energy by rays not requiring matter such as a liquid or a gas.

radiator a heat exchanger used in liquid-cooled engines; designed to dissipate some of the engine's rejected heat to atmosphere.

radioactive any substance or set of physical conditions capable of emitting radioactivity. Exposure to high-level radioactivity can be life threatening; low-level radioactivity (such as electrical or radar waves) represents a debatable hazard.

rail a manifold that acts as a high-pressure accumulator used to supply CR injectors.

rail actuator see *fueling actuator*.

rail pressure control valve (RPCV) a linear proportioning solenoid with integral spool valve used as an ECM output in a common rail injection system; its function is to precisely manage rail pressure. In ECM processing, it is looped with the rail pressure sensor (inputs actual rail pressure) to attempt to maintain "desired" rail pressure.

rail pressure sensor (RPS) V-Ref supplied, variable capacitance-type or piezoresistive-type pressure sensor that signals *actual* rail pressure (CR) to the ECM at any given moment of operation.

RAM see *random access memory*.

ram air air fed into engine compartment, cooling, and intake circuits by the velocity of a moving vehicle; increases proportionally with vehicle speed.

ramps in cam geometry, the shaping of the cam profile between the IBC and the OBC. The ramp geometry defines the actuation/unload characteristics of the train that rides its profile.

random access memory (RAM) electronically retained "main memory" of a computer system.

RAPIDO the Paccar-DAF online service information system consisting of ServiceXpert and Parts-RAPIDO.

rapid start shutoff valve Cummins common rail fuel system electric (solenoid) shutoff valve that traps fuel in the rail on shutdown to enable an almost instant restart.

rated power the peak horsepower power produced by a diesel engine; often expressed as *rated speed* because it is always correlated to a specific rpm.

rated speed the rpm at which an engine produces peak power.

rate shaping a fuel injection term that describes the ability of a fuel system to control fuel delivery to the cylinder independent of the hard limitations of cam geometry and engine rpm. HEUI injectors (actuated hydraulically with actuation pressure controlled by the ECM) were the first to be capable of rate shaping. All current CR diesel fuel systems are rate-shape capable.

ratio quantitative relationship between two values expressed by the number of times one contains the other.

reaction turbine an aeolipile, the first heat engine.

reactive describes substances that can interact chemically if they come into contact with other materials, resulting in toxic fumes, combustion, or explosion.

reader-programmer a generic or OEM electronic service tool (EST) designed to scan, reprogram, and perform some diagnostics on an electronic system.

read-only memory (ROM) data that is retained either magnetically or by optical coding and designed to be both permanent and read only.

ream the machining process of accurately enlarging an orifice using a steel boring bit with straight or spiral-fluted cutting edges.

Recommended Practice (RP) a TMC standard practice published in TMC *RP Manuals* (available on DVD and published annually) that sets technical standards in the trucking industry. RPs are consensually agreed to by industry and may or may not be backed up by legislation.

recording density number of bits that can be written to a digital storage device.

rectifier device used to convert AC into DC.

reductant a substance that chemically reduces a compound back to its elemental state. Aqueous urea (DEF) is a reductant that "reduces" NO_x back to elemental oxygen and nitrogen.

reference coil Mack Trucks PLN rack position sensor magnetic field temperature reference; validates input from the rack position sensor.

reference voltage (V-Ref) the ECM-controlled output to onboard sensors.

refraction the extent to which a light ray is deflected (bent) when it passes through media such as water, coolant, or fog.

refractive index the ratio of the speed of light in a vacuum versus the speed of light through a specified medium; in practice, the term is used to express natural light, refractometer readings in coolant, or battery electrolyte.

refractometer an instrument that uses light to measure the refractive index of liquids. It is regarded as a more reliable means of testing battery electrolyte and antifreeze protection.

regeneration cycle the burn-off cycle of a diesel particulate filter in which accumulated soot is combusted.

regeneration system (RS) the *diesel particulate filter (DPF)* self-cleaning management system: The means used to manage and burn off accumulated DPF soot.

regenerative braking vehicle retarding effort achieved in a parallel hybrid drive unit when the drive electric motor magnetic field is reversed, both applying retarding torque and generating electricity that can be used to charge the batteries.

register alignment or track point of two components.

registers 1. temporary storage locations in a CPU; 2. a not-so-common means of describing comparator bench *vials.*

rejected heat that portion of the potential heat energy of a fuel not converted into useful kinetic energy.

relay any of a number of different means of using a low-energy circuit to switch to a higher-energy circuit. In electrical circuits, a low-current control circuit switches a high-current actuator circuit.

relief valve a valve, commonly used in hydraulic circuits (such as fuel subsystem and lubrication circuits), that defines maximum circuit pressure. The simplest type consists of a ball check, which is loaded by a spring to seal a return line. When circuit pressure is sufficient to unseat the ball check, circuit fluid is diverted from the main circuit to the return.

reluctance resistance to the movement of magnetic lines of force.

reluctor term used to describe a number of devices that use magnetism and motion to produce an AC voltage.

remote data interface (RDI) DDEC communications link between the vehicle electronics and a fleet's PC or PC network.

reprogram general term used to cover a range of rewrite and overwrite procedures in computer technology.

residual line pressure the pressure that dead volume fuel is retained at in a high-pressure pipe in a PLN fuel system that uses delivery valves at the injection pump; usually around two-thirds of the NOP value.

resistance opposition to electrical current flow in a circuit.

resistance temperature detector (RTD) resistive thermal device used to measure the change in the electrical resistance of gases that takes place with temperature change. Used in place of thermocouple pyrometers where temperatures do not exceed 1,100°F (600°C). Also known as *platinum temperature detector (PTD)* depending on the OEM.

resolution the smallest interval measurable by an instrument. In computer terminology, it usually describes the image clarity of a CRT display in pixels. It also defines range in a DMM.

resolver a rotor angular position and direction sensor that functions by analysis of magnetic fields: used in hybrid electric powertrains.

resonation a noise-reducing principle used in engine silencers that scrambles sonic nodes and antinodes by reflecting sound back toward its source, thereby altering the frequency.

Resource Conservation and Recovery Act (RCRA) U.S. federal legislation that regulates the disposal of hazardous materials.

restriction gauge device used to measure hydraulic restriction in a fluid power or fuel injection circuit.

retarder generally refers to braking action, that is, the retarding of vehicle movement.

retraction collar/piston the component on a delivery valve core that is designed to seal before it seats and therefore helps define the residual line pressure value.

retraction spring any spring in any component that causes an assembly to mechanically withdraw or retract.

reversible fan engine compartment variable pitch cooling fan using a thermatic principle to determine blade pitch. In cleaning mode, a blade pitch effectively reverses the underhood air movement, allowing the fan to blow dirt and debris from heat exchangers.

rhodium a hard white metal occurring naturally in platinum ores and used as an NO_x reduction catalyst in gasoline-fueled engines.

Right-to-Know legislation a provision of the U.S. Federal Hazard Communications law that imposes on employers the duty of fully revealing the potential dangers of hazardous materials to which their employees may be exposed.

Right-to-Repair legislation law enacted in Massachusetts in 2013, with similar initiatives pending in many other states; requires that OEMs make available to independent repair facilities anything they make available to their dealership networks at fair cost.

ring belt the area of the piston in which the piston ring grooves are machined.

ring groove a recess in the wall of a piston into which a piston ring is inserted.

RoadRelay a digital dash display feature available with current Cummins engines; can display any critical engine running data while also maintaining a downloadable audit trail.

road speed governing (RSG) the managing of engine output on the basis of a specific road speed. It can also be used to mean the maximum programmed road speed limit.

road speed limit (RSL) usually the maximum programmed road speed value programmed to a vehicle management system, meaning that the vehicle should not travel faster than this speed. However, some OEMs permit maximum cruise speeds to be programmed above RSL to encourage drivers to use cruise control, so this is not always true.

road speed sensor a sensor, usually of the pulse generator type, located at the transmission tailshaft or a wheel assembly that signals the ECM with road speed data.

rocker shaft-mounted, pivoting lever that transmits the effects of cam profile to valves and injection pumping apparatus.

rocker arm see *rocker*.

rocker assemblies the entire rocker assembly consisting of rockers, rocker shaft, and pedestals.

rocker claw/lever mechanical injector hold-down or short-out tool; should not be used on EUIs.

rocker pallet the end of a rocker that contacts the injection pumping tappet, the valve stem, or the valve bridge.

rod eye the upper portion of a connecting rod that connects to the piston wrist pin; also known as *small end*.

ROM see *read-only memory*.

root cause in failure analysis, the original source of a failure. It should be differentiated from *coincidental damage* that can often mislead in the troubleshooting process.

root mean square (rms) a term used to describe averaging when performing machining operations; also used to describe AC voltage measurement by ascribing to it an equivalent DC value.

Roots blower a positive displacement air pump consisting of two gear-driven, intermeshing spiral-fluted rotors in a housing; used to scavenge DD two-stroke cycle engines.

router connection between two networked computers or two vehicle ECMs.

RP see *Recommended Practice*.

RP146 a TMC Recommended Practice that advises the adoption of SAE standard wiring colors and codes as outlined by SAE J2191 for all heavy-duty highway trucks.

RP1210 the *communications adapter (CA)* standard that manufacturers are supposed to adhere to. Some OEM CAs are only tested on that OEM's systems and may not communicate with competitor electronics, so generic CAs are recommended.

RPM/TDC sensor a means of providing signal shaft speed and position to the ECM. An inductive pulse generator or Hall-effect principle is used.

RS-232 port a serial communications port (often Com 1) in a computer system that accepts a standard phone jack. Some handheld ESTs are equipped with an RS-232 port, which can drive a printer or PC data display.

run-in usually describes the engine break-in procedure following a rebuild outlined by the OEM.

sac a spherical cavity. It refers to the chamber in some multi-orifii injector nozzles beyond the seat and from which the exit orifii extend.

SAE horsepower a structured formula used to calculate brake power data that can be used for comparison purposes.

SAE J1587 electronic data protocols used for data exchange on the older serial J1587 bus. J1587 protocols are still used by some bus devices, though they are not supported by all post-2010 engine OEMs; in these cases, a gateway module must be used to allow bus-to-bus networking.

SAE J1667 standards for tailpipe emissions testing.

SAE J1708 hardware compatibility protocols between micro-computer systems on the older J1587 data bus. Its data link is a six-pin Deutsch connector.

SAE J1939 the set of high-speed multiplexing standards used on the current heavy-duty CAN 2.0 platform serial data bus, categorized as a Class C bus. Both software and hardware protocols and compatibilities are covered by J1939, which is updated by simply adding a suffix. The standard SAE, nine-pin Deutsch connector is referred to as a J1939 data link connector (DLC). Transaction speeds max out at 1 Mb/s but currently average around 500 kb/s.

SAE J1962 the standard light-duty (automotive) vehicle data link that is also used by Volvo-Mack in its post-2014 trucks. A 16-pin connector also known as an *ALDL*.

SAE J2191 standardized wiring colors and codes for heavy-duty highway trucks as covered by RP146.

SAE J standards standards developed by SAE industry committees and generally agreed to, usually (but not always) without any statutory obligation.

SAE power an engine power output matrix using rigid guidelines to ensure reliability in making performance comparisons for different engines.

SAE viscosity grades the industry standard for grading lubricating oil viscosity.

sampling the process a computer system uses to monitor noncommand-type input data from the sensors in a system. Inputs from oil pressure, ambient temperature, coolant temperature, and so on would be monitored by the ECM by sampling.

saturation condition of an electromagnet in which a current increase results in no increase in the magnetic flux field.

Saybolt universal seconds (SUS) a measure of lubricant kinematic viscosity used to compare flow dynamics;

specifically, the time required to flow 60 cm³ through a calibrated tube at 100°F (38°C).

scavenge   term used generally to describe the process used to expel end gases from an engine cylinder and specifically to describe: 1. the final stage of the exhaust process in a four-stroke cycle engine that occurs at valve overlap. 2. cylinder breathing on a two-stroke cycle diesel engine.

scavenging pump   usually refers to a secondary oil pump in an engine lube circuit that provides redundancy in the event the primary pump sucks air. It is often spec'd to vehicles designed to operate on steep inclines.

scissor jack   an air-actuated floor jack with a pair of clevises that lock to the truck frame rails and can lift one end of the chassis well clear off the floor.

scopemeter   handheld or PC-based electrical circuit display reader that can perform most of the functions of an oscilloscope. The PC-based Pico-Scope is often used to display such things as injector PW and verify bus communications status.

scraper ring   piston ring below the top compression ring that plays a role in sealing cylinder gas as well as managing the oil film on the cylinder wall.

screen   any computer output display from LCDs through CRTs.

scroll   a helical shape. Term used by Caterpillar to describe a helix.

scrolling   the moving of lines of data up or down on a computer display screen.

SCSI controller   controller that can support multiple disc drives and enable high data transfer rates.

SCSI port   a type of parallel port that can support multiple different devices to a single port.

scuffing   a damage mode that involves superficial scraping of metal against metal.

search engine   software that when provided with a key word(s) scans and retrieves data from memory or off the web.

secondary filter   usually refers to a filter downstream from the transfer or charge pump in a typical fuel subsystem. It is in most cases under pressure and capable of much finer filtration than a *primary filter*, which is usually under suction.

section modulus   relates the shape of a beam, cylinder, or sphere to section and stiffness; the greater the section modulus, the higher the rigidity and resistance to deflection. It is a factor of RBM or resist bending moment.

sector   in computer terminology, a wedge-shaped section of a disk or section of track.

selective catalytic reduction (SCR)   term that describes NO$_x$ reduction converters for truck applications using *aqueous urea* (commonly known as DEF or AdBlue) injection. On injection, the urea vaporizes to gaseous ammonia that reacts with NO$_x$ compounds to reduce them back to elemental nitrogen and water.

self-regeneration   term used to describe onboard regeneration (cleaning) cycles of a *diesel particulate filter (DPF)*. Essentially, it refers to the combustion of accumulated soot during normal vehicle operation.

self-test input (STI)   international HEUI diagnostic scan initiated by depressing a dash STI button.

semiconductor   materials that neither conduct well nor insulate; they have four electrons in their outermost shell.

sending unit   a variable resistor and float assembly that signals the liquid level in a tank to a gauge and/or ECM.

sensor   a term that covers a wide range of command and monitoring input signal devices to ECMs/ECUs.

Sentry   Volvo-Mack telematics system capable of vehicle tracking, data mining, and remote trouble code reporting.

sequential storage   storage of data on media such as magnetic tape, where data is read and written sequentially.

sequential troubleshooting chart   procedure map commonly used by engine OEMs to structure electronic troubleshooting. The technician routes the troubleshooting path through the chart on the basis of test results in each step.

serial port   port connection that transfers data one bit at a time and therefore more slowly than a parallel port. A mouse is connected to a serial port.

Series 50   DDEC-controlled, EUI-fueled, DDC inline, four-cylinder engine.

Series 55   obsolete DDC 12-liter, inline, six-cylinder engine managed by DDEC III with EUP fueling.

Series 60   an inline six-cylinder Detroit Diesel engine using EUI fueling; manufactured up to 2010. Available displacements were 11.1, 12.7, and 14 liters.

Series 92   DDC 6-/8-cylinder, V-configuration engine available with DDEC; common transit vehicle engine. Obsolete, but some remain in service today.

series circuit   a circuit with a single path for electrical current flow.

series hydraulic hybrid (SHH)   a drivetrain arrangement in which the propulsion means is exclusively hydraulic: A diesel engine drives a hydraulic pump, which in turn powers a hydraulic motor. When an accumulator is added, so is regenerative braking capability.

server   in the computer processing cycle or multiplex transaction, the unit that fulfills a client need.

service hours   a means of comparing engine service hours to highway mileage. Most engine OEMs equate 1 engine hour to 50 highway linehaul miles (80 km), so a service interval of 10,000 miles (16,000 km) would equal 200 engine hours. The term *engine hours* is also used.

service information system (SIS)   term OEMs use to describe their service instructions, procedures, and specifications; in most cases, SISs are published online because of the ease of updating, correcting, and tagging information with TSBs.

service literature   general term used to cover OEM service information regardless of whether it is hard (paper) copy, disk based, or online sourced. Most truck OEMs use online service information systems today.

ServiceMaxx (SM)   Navistar service diagnostic software released for post-2007 MaxxForce engines. ServiceMaxx replaces Master Diagnostics (MD), but is designed to work with pre-2007 Navistar electronics.

ServiceNet (SN)   Paccar's subscription-based, online SIS. Accessed through webECAT and run with DAVIE software.

seventh injector   term used by one OEM to describe a fuel dosing injector located in the exhaust system and used for DPF regeneration.

shear   the stress produced in a substance or fluid when its layers are laterally shifted in relation to one another. *Viscosity* describes a fluid's resistance to shear.

shell   term used to describe the concentric orbital paths of electrons in atomic structure.

shorepower   term used to refer to standard AC supply off the grid.

Shorepower Truck Electrification Project (STEP) a *grid electrification* project that was implemented in truck stops beginning in 2013. STEP truck stops now exist in many interstate and provincial highways across the United States and Canada. They provide shore-power AC for parked trucks to eliminate idling.

shutdown solenoid an ETR or latching solenoid that functions to no-fuel the engine to shut it down.

shutters slatted ram air management devices that are pneumatically or ECM controlled to run between fully open, fully closed, or anything in between. The default is usually fully open, which results in lower-than-specified engine operating temperatures.

shutterstat a temperature-sensing pneumatic switch used to manage air shutter operation.

sight glass see *diagnostic sight glass.*

signal-detect and actuation module (SAM) a Freight-liner term for its proprietary bus controllers used for non-powertrain chassis requirements; a clumsy way of saying ECU.

signals codes, signs, or symbols used to convey information.

Signature Series first version of the inline, six-cylinder ISX engine manufactured by Cummins; a 15-liter engine using HPI-TP fueling and specified with 600 BHP and 2000 lb-ft. of torque.

silicon a nonmetallic element found naturally in silica; silicon dioxide in the form of quartz.

silicon carbide (SiC) conductive material used to make wall-flow DPFs. SiC has some advantages over cordierite because it conducts heat away from hot spots and usually has longer service life.

silicon-controlled rectifier (SCR) similar to a bipolar transistor but with a fourth semiconductor layer added. See full explanation in Chapter 32. It is extensively used to switch DC in vehicle electronic and ignition systems.

silicone any of a number of polymeric organic compounds of the element silicon associated with good insulating and sealing characteristics.

single overhead camshaft (SOHC) an engine with a single, overhead camshaft cradle-mounted on the cylinder head.

single pass describes a heat exchanger in which the target fluid is channeled through a single path. See *single pass radiator.*

single pass radiator any radiator through which flow is unidirectional.

single speed control (SSC) Mack Trucks isochronous PTO governing.

sinter a means of alloying metals in which the constituent materials are mixed in powdered form and then coalesced by subjecting them to heat and pressure. It produces more uniform metallurgical characteristics than alloying which is undertaken in a molten state.

sintered steel a steel produced by a sintering process; used in certain engine and fuel system components to produce especially tough and durable material characteristics.

Six Sigma a production improvement methodology developed by Motorola Corporation as a corporate means of eliminating defects and improving customer service.

sleeve-metering a means of varying the effective stroke in injection pumps by using a movable (by the governor) control sleeve. It is used in a number of obsolete injection pumps, such as the American Bosch M-100, but more recently only in the Bosch sleeve-metering, rotary injection pumps such as the VE.

sleeves see *liners.*

small bore in the trucking industry, describes diesel engines with displacements between 5.9 and 8 liters.

small end the connecting rod eye.

smart general—and some would say slang—term used to describe computer controls; see *smart logic.*

smart actuators devices with processing capability controlled directly off a chassis data bus.

smart cruise see *soft cruise.*

smart dosing actuator sensor/processing/actuator device used in emission control systems where it monitors gas emissions and doses accordingly.

SMART injector term used by Paccar, MB, and DDC to describe an *electrohydraulic injector (EHI).*

smart logic term for computed outcomes that use a broad range of input and memory factors to produce "soft" outcomes rather than adhere to hard values. For instance, *smart* cruise control learns road terrain patterns and permits some latitude around the programmed road speed value to improve fuel economy, and may "reward" drivers for exceeding fuel economy target thresholds. The term is also used to describe computer peripherals that possess some processing capability.

Smart Roadside Initiative (SRI) FMCSA-orchestrated endeavor to use telematics to enable wireless mobile safety inspections.

smart switch so named because it contains a ladder of resistors, usually five per switch, known as a ladder bridge; the processor mastering the multiplex can determine switch status by using a programmed resistance library that identifies the switch and its status.

smog a word formed by combining the words "smoke" and "fog"; a haze produced by suspended airborne particulates. Two major types exist: sulfurous smog produced by combusting sulfur-laden fuels, such as coal and heavy oils; and photochemical smog, a primary cause of which is vehicle emissions.

snapshot test a diagnostic test performed on a PC or ProLink that captures frames of running data before and after an event that can be identified by either an automatic (such as a fault code) or manual trigger.

soak tank a tank, usually heated, that is filled with a detergent or alkaline solution; used to clean engine components.

Society of Automotive Engineers (SAE) organization responsible for setting many of the manufacturing standards and protocols of the motive power industries and dedicated to educating and informing its members.

Society of Automotive Engineers (SAE) power see *SAE power.*

sodium metal hydride ($NaNiCl_2$) battery a high energy density battery used in conjunction with lithium-ion batteries in some EVs to boost vehicle travel range.

soft term used in electronics to indicate a flexible value. It has evolved to reference anything in electronic/computer technology that cannot be physically touched. An example is service literature: This might be accessed online, in which case it would be called *soft* format; or printed out, in which case it would be converted to a *hard* format.

soft copy data that is retained electronically or on disk, as opposed to being on paper.

soft cruise   a cruise control mode programmed into some vehicle/engine management electronics in which the road speed is managed within a window extending both above and below the set speed. Soft cruise can increase fuel economy and is often used in conjunction with vehicle maximum speed programming below maximum cruise speed. Also known as *smart cruise*.

soft parameter   a value that varies and depends on input and processing variables (see *fuzzy logic*). The term is often used to describe current cruise control systems that permit a cushion both above and below the set value. See *soft cruise*.

software   the programmed instructions that a computer requires to organize its activity to produce outcomes.

solar cells   PN or NP silicon semiconductor junctions capable of producing up to 0.5 V when exposed to direct sunlight.

solenoid   an electromagnet with a movable armature.

solid state   components that use the electronic properties of solids such as semiconductors to replace the electrical functions of valves.

solid state storage   volatile storage of data in RAM chips.

sound absorption   a means of converting sound waves to friction and then heat, which is then dissipated to atmosphere; used in engine silencers/mufflers.

sound card   multimedia card capable of capturing and reproducing sound.

source address (SA)   a controller with an address on the powertrain (J1939) or CAN bus. An SA identifies a unique address on the bus and is assigned a numeric code; the engine controller is assigned a SA 00. An SA is the equivalent of a MID on J1587.

spalling   surface fatigue that occurs when chips, scales, or flakes of two surfaces in contact with each other separate because of fatigue rather than wear; also known as *contact stress fatigue*.

spark ignited (SI)   any gasoline-fueled, spark-ignited engine, usually using an Otto-cycle principle.

spark ignition (SI)   the ignition means used for internal combustion engine fuels that do not autoignite under cylinder compression. NG-fueled engines often use SI systems.

special field notification (SFN)   a type of TSB that usually outlines a mandatory fix.

specific fuel consumption (SFC)   fuel consumed per unit of work performed.

specific gravity   the weight of a liquid or solid versus that of the same volume of water.

specific PGN   a J1939 message packet that targets a specific program group (PG) field within a controller.

spectrographic testing   a low-level radiation test that can accurately identify trace quantities of matter in a fluid; used to analyze engine oils.

spike   an electrical (voltage) or hydraulic pressure surge.

spill circuit   the return fuel circuit used in diesel fuel systems, most of which circulate more fuel than is required to fuel the engine.

spill timing   term used to describe port closure timing of a port-helix metering injection pump to the engine it fuels and when establishing injection pump bench phasing.

spill valve (SV) actuator   the control cartridge actuator in a Delphi E3 EUI; when switched by ECM drivers, it manages EUI plunger effective stroke. It works in conjunction with the nozzle control actuator, which manages nozzle opening and closing.

spill valve solenoid (SVS)   solenoid on a Caterpillar 4-terminal MEUI that either spills or traps (when energized) fuel in the MEUI plunger pump chamber.

spindle   an intermediary, responsible for transmitting force. In a hydraulic injector, it relays spring force to the nozzle valve.

splice   to join.

split lock   the keeper fitted to a peripheral groove at the top of a cylinder valve stem that holds the spring retainer in position.

split-shot injection   term used to describe pilot injection especially in first-generation EUI fuel systems; diesel fuel injection intentionally broken into more than one pulse during a single injection cycle to one engine cylinder.

spreader bar   a rigid lifting aid permitting an engine to be raised on a single-point chain hoist using two, three, or four lift points on the engine.

spreadsheet   software that enables numeric data organization and calculation.

spur gear   a gear with radial teeth.

square engine   an engine in which the bore and stroke dimensions are the same or nearly the same.

stanchion   a vertical bracket bolted to the chassis, used to mount exhaust aftertreatment canisters, stack(s), and other equipment; usually reinforced with gussets and cross-struts.

star network   network set up to operate from a central hub computer.

starpoint   a junction block used in Freightliner multiplexing that acts as a router and provides an electrical termination point for the cab CAN bus.

start of injection (SOI)   describes the moment atomized fuel exits nozzle orifii, an event that always occurs.

state of health (SOH)   a common ECM test for any sensor, actuator, or subcircuit. SOH checks may be run before startup or during system operation.

static electricity   accumulated electrical charge not flowing in a circuit.

static friction   the characteristic of a body at rest to attempt to stay that way. See *inertia*.

static RAM   a RAM chip with a medium- to large-volume memory retention and high-access speed.

static timing   term used to describe port closure timing of a fuel injection pump to an engine.

steel   an alloy of iron produced by the addition of a small percentage of carbon.

Sterling   now-defunct truck brand owned by DTNA and before that by Ford. Ceased production in 2010.

stiction   stationary friction; an example is thread contact friction during fastener torquing.

stoichiometric   in a chemical reaction, describes having the exact quantity of reactants (for example, fuel and air in a combustion reaction) to complete the reaction. See *stoichiometric ratio*.

stoichiometric ratio   an air-fuel ratio (AFR) term meaning that at ignition, the engine cylinder has the exact quantity of air (oxygen) present to combust the fuel charge. If more air is present, the AFR mixture is lean; if less air is present, it is rich.

stoichiometry   the science of determining the ratio of reactants required to complete a chemical or physical reaction.

stop bits   in a multiplexing packet, the packet content that signals the end of a message.

stop engine light (SEL)   a level III driver alert indicating that the driver should shut down the engine; or, if programmed to do so, the management system will shut down the engine. Usually illuminated 30 to 60 seconds before shutdown.

stop engine override (SEO or STEO) a driver-actuated button that can override an ECM-initiated shutdown for a preprogrammed period such as 30 or 60 seconds; designed to temporarily defeat a failure strategy shutdown. SEO events are logged into an audit trail and may be used to deny warranty.

storage media any nonvolatile data retention device; data chips, CD-ROM, DVDs, and USB jump drives are examples.

strategy action plan. In computer technology, it relates to how a series of processing outcomes is put together: For instance, startup strategy deals with how the sequence of events is switched by the ECM to result in the engine being cranked and started.

stress raiser a feature in either the shape (section modulus) or composition (metallurgical) of a component that causes a localized increase in stress. This can initiate a failure.

stroke linear travel of a piston or plunger from BDC to TDC. In an engine, piston stroke is defined by the crank throw dimension.

sublimation the process of converting a solid directly to a vapor by heating it; may also mean "refinement."

substrate 1. the supporting material on which an electric/electronic circuit is constructed/infused. 2. thermally stable, inert material on which active catalysts are embedded on a vehicle catalytic converter or diesel particulate filter.

subsystem identifier (SID) branch circuit within a controller (SA or MID address) off the data bus used for diagnostic reporting.

suction circuit the portion of a lubrication or fuel subsystem that is on the "pull" side of the transfer pump.

suffix a syllable or letter(s) or numbers added at the end of a word or acronym.

sulfur an element present in most crude petroleums but refined out of most current highway fuels. During combustion, it is oxidized to sulfur dioxide. It is classified as a noxious emission.

sulfur dioxide (SO_2) the compound formed when sulfur is oxidized that is the primary contributor to sulfurous-type smog. Vehicles today contribute little to sulfurous smog problems due to the use of low-sulfur fuels.

sump the lubricating oil storage device on an engine; more commonly referred to as an *oil pan*.

supercapacitor (SC) high-density capacitor; usually stacked using cassette architecture and used in some hybrid electrical drive systems and cranking-assist modules.

supercharger technically, any device capable of providing manifold boost, but in practice used to refer to gear-driven blowers such as the Roots blower.

supplemental coolant (system) additive (SCA) conditioning chemical added to antifreeze mixtures.

suspect parameter group (SPG) for purposes of troubleshooting on J1939, a label assigned to either a status condition or a component when an abnormal controller condition is identified.

suspect parameter number (SPN) a label or signal broadcast by a bus message to identify the source controller when an SPG is assigned to an abnormal controller condition on the J1939 bus. The SPN translates PGNs and identifies the DTC and FMIs.

swash plate angled plate used to actuate pistons in a rotating barrel. The plate angle may be controlled, providing variable displacement pumping capability.

swash plate pump a pump that uses a rotating barrel of cylinders loaded with multiple pistons. An angled circular plate (the swash plate) set obliquely on a shaft acts as a cam to convert rotary motion into reciprocating movement to actuate pistons or plungers; also known as a *wobble plate pump*.

swept volume volume displaced by a piston as it travels from BDC to TDC.

synchronous reference sensor (SRS) DDEC engine position sensor triggered by the cam gear of DD engines that inputs an analog voltage signal to the ECM.

synergize the act of creating synergy.

synergy any process in which the sum of a group of sub-components exceeds the sum of their individual roles; used to describe somewhat independent vehicle systems that share hardware and software to cut down on duplicated components and increase overall effectiveness or processing speeds.

synthetic oil petroleum-based and other elemental oils that have been chemically compounded by polymerization and other laboratory processes.

system board see *motherboard*.

system clock device that generates pulses at a fixed rate to time/synchronize computer operations.

system-detect and actuation module (SAM) Freightliner's new name for the ECUs that occupy the body and chassis controller addresses on its chassis network.

system pressure regulator a usually hydromechanical device responsible for maintaining a consistent line pressure; located downstream from a pump.

system unit the main computer housing and its internal components.

tablet a portable, microprocessor-driven computer that may have significant processing power and storage capacity.

tang release tool a lock release tool required to service the sealed connector blocks on electronic engines.

tappet used to describe a variety of devices that ride a cam profile and transmit the effects of the cam geometry to the train to be actuated; also known as *follower*.

tattletale an audit trail that may be discreetly written to ECM data retention; the recording of electronic events for subsequent analysis.

Tech Central International Trucks' central data hub.

technical service bulletin (TSB) the more common term used to describe up-to-date amendments and corrections to a service procedure or product recall.

Technology and Maintenance Council (TMC) division of the ATA that sets and recommends safety and operating standards.

Tech Tool™ (TT) Volvo Trucks three-app software replacing the pre-2007 diagnostic software. The three-facet package has PC-based software that interacts with the chassis data bus, along with online access to the corporate data hub, and a DVD database.

telecommunications any distance communication regardless of transmission medium.

teleconferencing audio/video communication using computers, a camera, and modem linkages.

telematics information technology required for wireless networking of computers, especially in mobile equipment such as trucks, buses, agricultural and construction equipment. For instance, telematics are used by fleets to network a truck chassis data bus with communications hubs

telematics diagnostic connector (TDC) standardized hardwire and wireless connector protocols (in the process of being determined) for a universal telematics interface.

telemetry the processes of obtaining and transmitting data from sensors for processing or display. For instance, the telemetry of a typical drive-by-wire, analog-type TPS requires a V-Ref supply, potentiometer, and chassis ground, plus the connection wiring to connect the device to the ECM that requires the signal.

teleprocessing networked station-to-station data exchange and processing.

telescoping gauge spring-loaded T-gauge used to make internal dimension measurements. This is a secondary measurement instrument, because after making and setting the dimension, another instrument such as a microm-eter is required to convert the dimension to a measurement.

Tempilstick™ a heat-sensing crayon used for precise determination of high temperatures.

template torque procedure used on torque-to-yield fas-teners that usually involves torquing to a specified value with a torque wrench followed by turning the fastener through an arc of a specified number of degrees mea-sured by a protractor or template. It produces more con-sistent clamping pressures than torque-only methods.

tensile strength unit force required to physically sepa-rate a material. In steels, tensile strength exceeds yield strength by around 10%.

terabyte a trillion bytes.

terminal 1. a computer station or network node. 2. an electrical connection point.

terminating resistor used to insulate either end of a data bus twisted wire pair from radiation interference.

thermal efficiency measure of how efficiently an engine converts the potential heat energy of a fuel into usable mechanical energy; usually expressed as a percentage.

thermal failure a failure related to overheating.

thermatic fan a fan with an integral temperature-sensing mechanism that controls its effective cycle.

thermistor a commonly used temperature sensor that is supplied with a reference voltage and, by using a temper-ature-sensitive variable resistor, signals back to the ECM a portion of that voltage.

thermocouple a device made of two dissimilar metals, joined at the "hot" end and capable of producing a small voltage when heated. Operates on the principle used in pyrometers that monitor DPF and engine exhaust temperatures.

thermostat the low-temperature regulator of an engine cooling system; a self-contained, temperature-sensing/coolant flow modulating device used to manage coolant flow within the engine cooling system.

thermo-syphoning procedure that protects water-cooled turbocharger shaft and bearing housings against overheating when a hot shutdown occurs. The turbo-charger cooling circuit uses convection and a loop to cycle coolant through the turbo bearing circuit until the temperature reaches parity with the mean coolant temperature.

thick film lubrication lubrication of components where clearance factors tend to be large and unit pressures low.

Think Big a Caterpillar-sponsored associate degree pro-gram for technicians.

Think Bigger a Caterpillar-sponsored bachelor degree program for technicians.

three-way splice the uniting of three wires at junction.

threshold value outside limit or parameter.

throttle in SI gasoline and diesel engines with pneumatic governors, a mechanism that controls airflow to the intake manifold. The term is commonly used to describe the speed control/accelerator/fuel control mechanism in a diesel engine.

throttle delay a mechanical device used to create a lag between accelerator demand and fuel delivered, usually to cut down on smoke emission.

throttle position sensor (TPS) device for signaling accelerator pedal angle to the TPS. One common type is designed to receive a V-Ref input delivered to a potentiometer, which returns a portion of that voltage as a signal to the ECM that correlates with accelerator pedal angle. More recently, Hall-effect type TPSs have been introduced.

throttle snap a momentary full-fuel request (flooring the accelerator) to test the fuel system response. J1667 emis-sions testing requires throttle snaps.

thrust linear force.

thrust bearing a bearing that defines the longitudinal or end play of a shaft.

thrust collar in a mechanical governor, the intermediary between the centrifugal force exacted by the flyweights and the spring forces that oppose it. The thrust collar in a governor is usually connected to the fuel control mechanism.

thrust face a term used to describe loading of surface area generally, but most often of pistons. When the piston is subject to cylinder gas pressure, there is a tendency for it to cock (pivot off a vertical centerline) and load the con-tact faces off its axis on the pin.

thrust washer see *thrust bearing*.

thyristor three-terminal solid-state switch.

timing the manner in which events or actions are sequenced. The term is used in many applications in engines relating to valves, injection, ignition, and others.

timing actuator one of two ECM-controlled electrohy-draulic solenoids used to manage timing on Cummins common rail, HPI-TP–fueled engines. Duration of energi-zation determines fuel quantity delivered into the timing chamber of an HPI-TP injector, defining start of injection.

timing advance unit a hydromechanical or electronically controlled timing advance mechanism used with port-helix metering pumps.

timing bolt means of locking a component or engine to position for purposes of timing.

timing chamber term used by Cummins to describe the upper chamber in its two-stage injector units, such as CELECT and TP injectors.

timing check valve device found in Cummins two-stage injector units that traps fuel in the timing chamber dur-ing downstroke.

timing dimension term used to describe the setting of injector height in EUIs and MUIs.

timing dimension tool a tune-up tool used to set the tappet height on MUIs and EUIs.

timing event marker (TEM) Mack Trucks Bosch engine position sensor located in the rack actuator housing of an electronic PLN injection pump.

timing reference sensor (TRS) crankshaft position sensor. The acronym was originally used by DDC, and current versions of DDEC use a 36-tooth *tone wheel*.

tip turbine a charge air cooler fan device driven by turbo-boosted air, designed to blow filtered air through the heat exchanger and increase boost air cooling efficiencies.

tone wheel the rotating disc used to produce rpm and rotational position data to an ECM. The term is most often applied to the rotating member of a Hall-effect sensor, but at least one manufacturer uses the term to describe an AC reluctor wheel.

top dead center (TDC) outboard extremity of travel of a piston or plunger in a cylinder.

top engine limit (TEL) a Caterpillar term meaning *high idle*.

topology the configuration of a computer network; a network schematic.

torched piston a piston that has been overheated to the extent that meaningful analysis of cause is usually not possible.

torque twisting effort or force. Torque does not necessarily result in accomplishing work.

torque rise the increase in torque potential designed to occur in a diesel engine as it is lugged down from the rated power rpm to the peak torque rpm, during which the power curve remains relatively flat. High torque rise engines are sometimes described as constant horsepower engines.

torque rise profile diagrammatic representation of torque rise on a graph or fuel map.

torque-to-yield bolts with metallurgical properties that allow them to stretch to their yield point as they are tightened; used where more precise clamping loads are required, such as on cylinder heads and connecting rods.

torque twist effect one way of describing the twist forces a cylinder block must sustain as engine torque is transferred to the drivetrain; increases as engine torque increases.

torsion twisting force.

torsionals term for the uneven twisting forces to which a shaft or drivelines are subjected.

torsional stress twisting stresses. A crankshaft is subject to torsional stress because a throw through its compression stroke will travel at a speed fractionally lower than mean crank speed, whereas a throw through its power stroke will accelerate to a speed fractionally higher than mean crank speed. These occur at high frequencies.

total base number (TBN) measure of lube oil acidity reported in lab lube oil analysis; will increase as low ash oils such as CJ-4 become commonplace.

total dissolved solids (TDSs) dissolved minerals measured in a coolant by testing the conductivity with a current probe (TDS tester). High TDS counts mean that use of the coolant can damage moving components in the cooling system, such as water pumps.

total indicated runout (TIR) a measure of eccentricity of a shaft or bore; usually measured by a dial indicator.

total quality management (TQM) a customer service philosophy which maintains that customer service is the core of all business activity and that every employee in an organization should be made to feel part of a team with a common objective.

toxic describes materials that may cause death or illness if consumed, inhaled, or absorbed through the skin.

train a sequence of components with a common actuator. See *valvetrain*.

transducer an input circuit device that converts temperature, pressure, linear, and other mechanical signals into electrical signals to be sent to an ECM. A transducer may produce either analog or digital signals to be sent to control modules.

transducer module (Caterpillar) component responsible for transducing all engine pressure values (such as oil/turbo-boost, etc.) to electrical signals for ECM input.

transfer pump the fuel subsystem pump used to pull fuel from the fuel tank and deliver it to the injection pumping/metering apparatus.

transformer an electrical device consisting of electromagnetic coils, used to increase/decrease voltage/current values or isolate subcircuits.

transient short-lived, temporary; often refers to an electrical spike or hydraulic pressure surge.

transistor any of a large group of semiconductor devices capable of amplifying or switching circuits.

transmission control protocol/Internet protocol (TCP/IP) a standard for data communications that permits seamless connections between dissimilar networks.

transorb diode used to protect sensitive electronic circuits (such as an ECM) from the inductive kick that can be created by solenoids when their magnetic field collapses.

transponder a ground-based satellite uplink; can be either mobile or stationary.

transposition error a data entry mistake.

trapezoid a quadrilateral with one pair of parallel sides.

trapezoidal ring see *keystone ring*.

trapezoidal rod a connecting rod with a trapezoidal small end or rod eye, designed to maximize the sectional area of the rod subject to compressive pressures; more commonly referred to as a *keystone rod*.

trapped volume spill (TVS) used on HPI-TP injectors; provides an escape route for fuel just as the lower plunger bottoms into the cup, bringing an abrupt closure to the injection pulse.

triage preliminary assessment. Cummins has introduced triage bays into some of its dealerships: these are placed where a rapid assessment is made by a technician so that the truck can be directed into the correct area (and technician) for service or repair. Triage processing usually requires connecting to the chassis data bus and scanning audit trails.

triangulation see *trilateration*.

triatomic describes a molecule consisting of three atoms of the same element. Ozone is triatomic oxygen.

tribology the study of friction, wear, and lubrication.

trilateration the locating of a common intersection by using three circles each with different centers; the mathematical basis of GPS technology.

trim code another way of saying injector *calibration code*. Measures injector flow on a test bench and assigns it a code which then must be programmed to the ECM.

TRIZ a Russian acronym that translated means "theory of inventive problem solving"; a catchphrase used in the workplace that may result in someone paying attention to employee input into the suggestion box.

troubleshooting the procedures involved in diagnosing problems.

Truck Intellidrive Freight Mobility Initiative an FMCSA-orchestrated initiative to mandate telematics access to all trucks for purposes of HOS and OOS enforcement.

trunk-type piston in diesel engine applications, a single-piece piston assembly machined from aluminum or steel alloys.

truth table a table constructed to represent the output of a multiswitch circuit, based on the switch status within the circuit.

tuned exhaust an exhaust system that times the unloading of each pulsed slug from the engine cylinder so that it is unloaded into the tailstream of the slug that preceded it. In diesel technology, it specifically relates to how exhaust gas is routed into the turbine housing to maximize breathing efficiency while minimizing heat losses.

tune-up term for the setting of valves and timing injectors in diesel engines; more commonly known as *overhead adjustment.*

turbine a rotary motor driven by fluid flow such as water, oil, or gas.

turbo commonly used short form of *turbocharger.*

turbo-boost sensor (TBS) a device used to signal manifold boost values to the ECM. An aneroid is used in hydromechanical engines and either a piezoresistive or variable capacitance device is used in electronically controlled engines.

turbocharger an exhaust gas driven, centrifugal air pump used on most truck diesel engines to provide manifold boost. It consists of a turbine housing, within which a turbine is driven by exhaust gas; and a compressor housing, within which an impeller charges the air supply to the intake manifold.

twisted wire pair used as the physical data backbone in multiplex systems. The wires are twisted to minimize EMI. In a J1939 data backbone, the busline dominant Hi wire is color-coded yellow and the dominant Lo wire is color-coded green.

two-stage filtering any filtering process that takes place in separate stages.

two-stage valve a fuel system valve used to manage pressure overloads in the fuel subsystem.

two-terminal EUI an older-style EUI (pre-2007) with a single actuator or control cartridge. This generation of EUIs was equipped with hydraulic injector nozzles, with a fixed-value NOP.

two-terminal MEUIs term used to describe the single-actuator EUIs used up until 2007 EPA emissions regulations.

typeface the design appearance of alpha characters.

ultracapacitor (UC) functions like two capacitors in series; used as storage-assist device in HEV applications.

ultra high-pressure heavy-duty common rail fuel injection (UPCRI) Paccar term for the Delphi FR2 common rail fuel system used on its MY 2013 and later MX-Series engines.

ultra-low sulfur (ULS) fuel formulation introduced in most jurisdictions after October 2006 and adopted as the national standard in 2010. ULS has a maximum sulfur content of 0.0015% (15 ppm) and is required for DPF-equipped engines meeting Tier IV (2010) emissions standards.

ultra-low sulfur diesel (ULSD) see *ultra-low sulfur (ULS).*

ultrasonic sound waves and vibrations with a frequency above the normal range of human hearing (higher than 15–20 kHz); used as a means of cleaning components.

ultrasonic bath a vessel filled with liquid (fuel/water/alkaline solution) through which ultrasonic sound waves are transmitted. Effective at loosening carbon, coke, and other crystalline deposits from components such as injectors and EGR heat exchangers.

ultraviolet (UV) radiation radiation having a wavelength just beyond the violet end of the visible light spectrum; emitted by the sun, but much of it is filtered out by the ozone shield in the Earth's stratosphere.

undercrown the reverse side of a piston crown. In most current diesels, a lube oil cooling jet is targeted at a specific location on the undercrown.

undersquare engine an engine in which the bore dimension is smaller than its stroke dimension; refers to high-compression engines. Most diesel engines are undersquare.

unit injection system (UIS) Bosch term for its EUI diesel fuel system.

unit injector a combined pumping, metering, and atomizing device.

unit pump system (UPS) Bosch term for its EUP diesel fuel system.

units of atmosphere (atms) a standard pressure measurement based on actual atmospheric pressure. One atm is equivalent to 14.7 psi or 101.3 kPa. Less used today, as industry tends to engineer products using the metric system.

universal coolant (UC) a premix antifreeze that can be blended with any EG- or PG-based product supposedly without any negative impact on its performance properties.

universal product code (UPC) the commonly used commercial bar code designed for optical scanners.

universal serial bus (USB) a means of connecting peripherals (external devices) to a PC or network system.

uplink signal transmission from a stationary or mobile ground station to a telecommunications satellite.

upload the act of transferring data from one medium or computer system to another.

upper helix a helix milled into the upper portion of a pumping plunger; gives the characteristic of a variable beginning of pump effective stroke.

urban canyon location where telematic, cell, and radio signals are blocked by large buildings.

urea crystallized nitrogen-base compounds in solution with distilled water. Aqueous urea is injected into SCR-type reduction catalytic converters.

USB flash drives memory data storage devices integrated with a universal serial bus (USB) interface. They are small, portable, very lightweight, and rewritable by flashing.

user ID a password used for security and identification on multiuser computer systems.

vacuum restriction a restriction on the suction side of a fluid circuit; for instance, a plugged filter.

valence number of shared electron bonds an element can make when it combines chemically to form compounds. A valence electron is one in the outer shell of an atom.

validation 1. data confirmation/corroboration. 2. the third and final stage of a vehicle ECM reprogramming sequence in which a successful data transfer is confirmed to a central data hub.

valve any device that controls fluid flow through a circuit.

valve bridge a means of actuating a pair of cylinder valves with a single rocker; also known as *valve yoke.*

valve closes orifice (VCO) (nozzle) a sacless hydraulic injector nozzle tip in which each orifice extends from the seat.

valve closing pressure (VCP) the specific pressure at which a hydraulic injector nozzle closes, which is always lower than NOP due to nozzle differential ratio; also known as *nozzle closing pressure*.

valve float a condition caused by running an engine at higher-than-specified rpm, in which valve spring tension becomes insufficient, causing asynchronous (out of time) valve closing.

valve margin dimension between the valve seat and the flat face of the valve mushroom; critical valve machining specification.

valve pockets recesses machined into the crown of a piston designed to accommodate cylinder valve protrusion when the piston is at TDC.

valve polar diagram a valve mapping exercise that makes use of circles or a spiral configuration to map the valve closing and opening event during the engine cycle.

valvetrain all the components between the cam and the valve; typically includes followers/tappets, push tubes/rods, rocker assemblies, and valve bridges/yokes.

valve yoke see *valve bridge*.

vaporization changing the state of a liquid to a gas.

variable geometry (VG) term usually applied to turbochargers that have either external (wastegate) or internal means of managing the way in which exhaust gas acts on the turbine.

variable nozzle (VN) one type of VG turbocharger that uses an ECM-controlled actuator to vary the turbine volute flow to determine turbo efficiencies.

variable speed control (VSC) Mack Trucks electronic setting of rpm using cruise switches.

variable speed governor (VSG) a governor in which the speed control/throttle mechanism inputs an engine speed value and the governor attempts to maintain that speed as the engine load changes.

variable speed limit (VSL) rpm limiting on a moving vehicle for PTO operation.

variable valve actuator (VVA) electronically controlled and hydraulically (engine lube) actuated, variable valve timing; can delay intake valve closure, reducing the compression charge and ratio.

variable valve timing (VVT) used by diesel engine OEMs to optimize power while minimizing emissions; ECM controlled and hydraulically actuated (engine lube) when used. Examples are the Caterpillar ACERT C13 and C15 engine families.

VCADS Volvo computer-assisted diagnostic system; the software required to troubleshoot Volvo Trucks electronics.

VD16D a Volvo inline six-cylinder, 16.1-liter displacement engine.

vector a straight line between two points in space; a line that extends from the axis of a circle to a point on its periphery.

VECTRO Volvo electronic engine management.

VED-12 Volvo VECTRO-managed, inline 12-liter, six-cylinder engine.

vehicle communication interface (VCI) a Paccar *communication adapter (CA)* required to connect to its MX-Series engines. At the time of writing, the Paccar VCI is not RP1210-compliant, so a generic CA cannot be substituted.

vehicle computer-assisted diagnostics (VCADS) see *VCADS*.

vehicle control center (VCC) vehicle-based communications and control center that organizes telematics, communications, and navigation. VCC is networked to the J1939 data bus and controls connections to the outside world using technologies such as GPS, Bluetooth, and two-way satellite communications.

vehicle control unit (VCU) a vehicle management module on the older J1587/1708 bus using the MID 144 address on the chassis data bus; used by some OEMs to optimize powertrain and chassis operations.

vehicle data link (VDL) the means of connecting an EST to a chassis data bus; currently a J1939 (heavy-duty) or J1962 (light-duty) connector.

vehicle electronic programming system (VEPS) Caterpillar and International initial ECM proprietary programming, which is usually performed on the assembly line.

vehicle identification number (VIN) a 17-character alphanumeric identification code that identifies every major chassis subsystem, including such things as date of manufacture, manufacturing plant, and key options.

vehicle interface connector (VIC) the physical connector that networks the engine electronics to the chassis electronics.

vehicle management and control (V-MAC) Mack Trucks chassis management electronics; currently in version IV.

vehicle management and control IV (V-MAC IV) see *V-MAC IV*.

vehicle personality module (VPM) (Caterpillar/Navistar) term used to describe the PROM and EEPROM components in a chassis management module.

vehicle speed sensor (VSS) an inductive pulse generator sensor, usually located in the tailshaft of the transmission; a standardized sensor whose accuracy depends on the correct programming of drive tire rolling radii and final drive ratios.

vehicle-to-infrastructure (V2I) telematics communication between a vehicle and a land-based control center or data hub.

vehicle-to-vehicle (V2V) telematics communication between two or more mobile vehicles.

venting the act of "breathing" an enclosed vessel or circuit to atmosphere to moderate or equalize pressure.

vial calibrated cylindrical glass vessel (test tube) used for precise measurement of fuel delivery on a fuel injection pump calibration bench; also known as *graduate* or *buret*.

video display terminal (VDT) an LED monitor or CRT.

videographics array (VGA) the quality category of a video display monitor.

virtual a commonly used computing term describing what occurs when a physical condition is simulated by processing logic. A good example is a computer game that portrays a *virtual* world on a screen, such as a car navigating a racetrack controlled by a joystick. A foursome of onboard truck cameras can show a *virtual* overhead view of a truck to the driver as it is navigated into a parking place.

virtual protection device an electrical circuit protection strategy used by chassis computers, capable of electronically opening the circuit when excessive current draw is detected. Virtual fuses/breakers may be cycling or noncycling, depending on the type of circuit being protected. A technician and an EST may be required to reset a noncycling virtual fuse even after a prolonged shutdown.

Virtual Technician (VT) DD and Freightliner telematics capable of remote troubleshooting and running data mining.

viscosity   often used to describe the fluidity of lubricant, but correctly defined it is a fluid's resistance to *shear.*

Visibility Package (VP)   an optional fleet management add-on to DD Virtual Technician software; provides operational and tracking data to a data hub for analysis.

visible image area (VIA)   the means of assessing the actual size of a video display monitor by measuring diagonally across the screen. A nominal 15-inch monitor may actually measure only 13.5 inches.

V-MAC   see *vehicle management and control (V-MAC).*

V-MAC III   Mack Trucks generation III module used with EUP fuel systems up to MY 2007.

V-MAC IV   Mack Trucks generation IV module used with post-2007 EUI fuel systems.

V-MAC module   Mack Trucks chassis (and engine) management module.

volatile memory   RAM data that is retained only when a circuit is switched on.

volatile organic compounds (VOCs)   the boiled-off, more volatile fractions of hydrocarbon fuels. Evaporation to atmosphere occurs during production, pumping, and refueling procedures.

volatility   the ability of a liquid to evaporate. Gasoline has greater volatility than diesel fuel.

volt   a unit of electrical potential; named after Alessandro Volta (1745–1827).

voltage   electrical pressure; a measure of charge differential.

voltage drop   voltage reduction that occurs in exact proportion to the resistance in a component or circuit. A voltage drop calculation is made to analyze component and circuit conditions.

volumetric efficiency   the cyclical fill efficiency of a vessel. In engine breathing, this refers to the actual quantity of air in the engine cylinder during operation compared to what it would contain at atmospheric pressure.

volute   a snail-shaped diminishing sectional area such as used in turbocharger geometry.

Volvo electronic controls   see *VECTRO.*

Volvo electronics III (VECTRO III)   Volvo Trucks chassis management electronics generation III; used with its EUI fueling.

Volvo (vehicle) computer-assisted diagnostics (VCADS)   see *VCADS.*

Volvo Trucks   manufacturer of trucks and engines. Corporate centers are in Sweden and Allentown, Pennsylvania.

vortex flow MAF sensors   MAF sensor with an obstruction in the airflow that causes air passing around the obstruction to generate a stream of vortices (similar to mini-tornadoes). These increase with airflow velocity, so by locating an ultrasonic speaker and pickup (microphone) across the stream of vortices, which spin off in opposing directions, a frequency-modulated shift can be signaled to the ECM. The frequency increases in proportion to air velocity.

VP-44   one type of radial piston-type pump manufactured by Bosch for fuel injection systems.

wall flow filter   an extruded ceramic or SiC DPF filter with hundreds of square channels per square inch through which exhaust gas is routed. The objective is to entrap soot.

waste-spark system   device used in spark ignition systems in which a plug is fired on both compression and exhaust strokes; helps minimize HC emissions.

water detection paste   a commercially available substance, such as Gasoila WF25, used to test fuel tanks for the presence of water. The paste is applied to a probe, and changes color when in contact with water.

water-in-fuel (WIF) sensor   usually located in the filter/water separator sump; it signals an alert when covered with water.

waterless engine coolant (WEC)   an EG and additive coolant/antifreeze premix designed to last the life of the engine with little or no maintenance; achievable if the solution is never contaminated with water or other types of antifreeze.

water separator   a canister, located in a fuel subsystem, used to separate water from fuel and prevent it from being pumped through the injection circuit.

watt   a unit of power commonly used to measure mechanical and electrical power; named after James Watt (1736–1819).

wavelength   frequency or the distance between the nodes and antinodes of a radiated or otherwise transmitted wave.

WeatherPack connector   a commonly used, proprietary, sealed electric and electronic circuit connector system; used in many electronically managed circuits.

web ECAT   the online Paccar parts catalog launched within the DAVIE portal.

W. Edwards Deming   the inventor of TQM, a customer service-driven corporate structure.

weep hole   bleed hole used in engine water pumps to permit trace coolant discharge.

Western Star   manufacturer of trucks owned by DTNA. Corporate center is in Portland, Oregon.

Westport Innovations   company that specializes in supplying alternate fuel adaptations of diesel engines to the commercial truck and bus industries. Offers CNG, LNG, and hydrogen fuel systems.

Westport MonoInjector   an electronically controlled injector capable of delivering NG or hydrogen fuel to engine cylinders.

wet liners   cylinder block liners that have direct contact with the water jacket and therefore must support cylinder combustion pressures and seal the coolant to which they are exposed.

wet service   a slang term for a full diesel engine service including an oil and filter change.

white smoke   caused by liquid condensing into droplets in the exhaust gas stream. Light reflects or refracts from the droplets, making them appear white to the observer.

wide-open throttle (WOT)   term usually used in the context of SI gasoline-fueled engines to mean full fuel request. It is used by one diesel OEM to describe high-idle speed.

WiFi   see *wireless fidelity.*

Windows   the Microsoft Corporation graphical user interface program manager widely used in PC systems.

wireless   denotes the use of radio frequencies to transmit analog or digital signals.

wireless fidelity (WiFi)   wireless communications that conform to Institute of Electrical and Electronics Engineers (IEEE) protocol 802.11; the WiFi communications standard used in North America.

wireless inspection processing (WIP)   telematics processing software or means of referring to the procedure; see *wireless inspection processing system.*

wireless inspection processing system (WIPS)   telematics processing system run by a jurisdiction within a geofence. Used to enable WRIs.

wireless roadside inspection (WRI)   a telematics-enabled wireless inspection system currently offered by 28 states on vehicles that have appropriate software activated. The goal is to make WRI mandatory throughout the United States and Canada.

wireless vehicle link 2 (WVL2)   a Nexiq wireless CA using IEEE 802.11 protocols (WiFi).

wobble plate pump   slang term for a *swash plate pump*.

word processing   using a computer system to produce mainly text in documents and files.

word size   the number of bits that a CPU can process simultaneously; a measure of processing speed. The larger the word size, the faster the CPU.

work   name for what is accomplished when force produces a measurable result.

Workplace Hazardous Materials Information System (WHMIS)   the section of the Hazard Communications legislation that deals with tracking and labeling of hazardous workplace materials.

World Wide Web   the network of networks that is key for the information age we live in today; usually referred to as *the Web*.

wrist pin   the pin that links the connecting rod eye to the piston pin boss; also known as *piston pin*.

write once, read many (WORM)   optical disk that can be written to once (permanently) and read many times.

yield point   the force a beam or component can sustain before it begins to deflect.

yield strength   unit force required to permanently deform a material: In steels, yield strength is approximately 10% less than tensile strength.

zener diode   a diode that will block reverse bias current until a specific breakdown voltage is achieved.

A	ampere
ABDC	auto-baud detect capable (post-2014 J1939)
ABS	antilock brake system
AC	alternating current
A/C	air conditioning
ACC	adaptive cruise control
ACERT	Advanced Combustion and Emissions Reduction Technology
ACM	aftertreatment control module
ACRS	amplified common rail system
ADEM	advanced diesel engine management (system)
ADS	Association of Diesel Specialists
AFC	air-fuel control
AFR	air-fuel ratio
ALCL	assembly line communications link
ALDL	assembly line data (diagnostic) link
ALU	arithmetic and logic unit
AMT	automated manual transmission
AMU	air manifold unit
ANSI	American National Standards Institute
APCR	amplified pressure common rail (system)
APCS	actively pressurized cooling system
API	American Petroleum Institute
APS	ambient pressure sensor
APT	American pipe thread
APT	axial power turbine
APU	auxiliary power unit
AQI	air quality index
AR	active regeneration
ASCII	American Standard Code for Information Interchange
ASE	(National Institute for) Automotive Service Excellence
ASME	American Society of Mechanical Engineers
ASTM	American Society for Testing and Materials
ASVR	Australia Vehicle Standards Rules (NTC)
At	ampere-turns
ATA	American Trucking Association
ATAAC	air-to-air aftercooling
ATC	automatic traction control
ATD	aftertreatment device
ATDC	after top dead center
ATF	automatic transmission fluid
atm	atmosphere (unit of pressure equivalent to 1 unit of atmospheric pressure)
ATM	asynchronous transfer mode
AWG	American wire gauge
BARO	barometric pressure sensor
BC	base circle
BDC	bottom dead center
BHM	bulkhead module
BHP	brake horsepower
BIOS	basic input/output system
BMEP	brake mean effective pressure
BOE	beginning of energizing
BOI	beginning of injection
BP	brake power
BPS	bits per second
BPS	boost pressure sensor
BSFC	brake specific fuel consumption
BTDC	before top dead center
BTM	brushless torque motor
Btu	British thermal unit
C	carbon
C7	Caterpillar 7.2-liter, ACERT engine
C9	Caterpillar 9.3-liter, ACERT engine
C-10	Caterpillar 10.2-liter engine
C11	Caterpillar 11.1-liter, ACERT engine
C-12	Caterpillar 12-liter engine
C13	Caterpillar 12.5-liter, ACERT engine
C-15	Caterpillar 14.6-liter engine
C15	Caterpillar 15.2-liter ACERT engine
C-16	Caterpillar 15.8-liter engine

CA	communications adapter	codec	coder/decoder
CAA	Clean Air Act	COE	cab-over-engine (truck chassis)
CAC	charge air cooling	CPC	common platform controller
CAD	computer-assisted design	CPC	common powertrain controller
CAFE	corporate average fuel economy	CPL	control parts list (Cummins parts #)
CAM	computer-assisted machining/ manufacturing	CPS	camshaft position sensor
CAN	controller area network	CPS	characters per second
CAPS	Cummins Accumulator Pump System	cps	cycles per second
		CPU	central processing unit
CARB	California Air Resources Board	CR	common rail
CAT-ID	Caterpillar information display	CRC	cyclic redundancy check
CBM	condition-based maintenance	CRS	Cat Regeneration System
cc	cubic centimeter	CRS	common rail system
CCA	cold cranking amps	CRT	cathode ray tube
CCV	closed circuit voltage	CSA	Canadian Safety Association
CCV	closed crankcase ventilation	CSC	customer support center
CCW	counterclockwise (left-hand rotation)	CTA	Chicago Transportation Authority
CD	compact disk	CTS	coolant temperature sensor
CDI	capacitive discharge ignition	CTV	continuously open throttle valve
CD-ROM	compact disk–read-only memory	CVS	constant volume sampling
CEC	consolidated engine controller	CVSA	Commercial Vehicle Safety Association
C-EGR	cooled exhaust gas recirculation	CVT	continuously variable torque
CEL	check engine light		
CELECT	Cummins electronic engine controls	CW	clockwise
		CWS	collision warning system
CEO	chief executive officer	DAT	digital audiotape
CFO	chief financial officer	DBPR	doser block pressure regulator
cfm	cubic feet (per) minute	DC	direct current
CFR	ceramic fiber reinforced	DCA	diesel coolant additives
CFV	critical flow venturi	DCL	data communication link
CG	constant geometry	DCM	dosing control module
CGI	clean gas induction	DCU	dosing control unit
CGI	compacted graphite iron	DD	Detroit Diesel (division DTNA)
CGW	central gateway (module)	DD11	Detroit Diesel 10.6-liter engine
CHM	chassis module	DD13	Detroit Diesel 12.8-liter engine
CI	compression ignition	DD15	Detroit Diesel 14.8-liter engine
cid	cubic inch displacement	DD16	Detroit Diesel 15.6-liter engine
CLS	coolant level sensor	DDC	Detroit Diesel Corporation
CMAC	chassis-mounted charge air cooling	DDCSN	Detroit Diesel Customer Support Network
CMC	cluster message center	DDD	digital dash display
CMOS	complementary metal oxide semiconductor	DDDL	Detroit Diesel Diagnostic Link
		DDDS	Detroit Diesel Data Summaries
CMP	camshaft position	DDEC	Detroit Diesel electronic controls
CMRS	commercial mobile radio service		
CMVSS	Canadian Motor Vehicle Safety Standard	DDL	diagnostic data link
		DDR	digital diagnostic reader
CN	cetane number	DDRS	Detroit Diesel Reprogramming Station (DDEC10)
CNG	compressed natural gas		
CNG-DI	compressed natural gas direct injection	DDS	driveline disengagement switch
		DDT	digital diagnostic tool
CO	carbon monoxide	DDU	dash display unit
CO_2	carbon dioxide	DEF	diesel exhaust fluid

DFI	direct-fire ignition	EFPA	electronic foot-pedal assembly
DGE	diesel gallon equivalent	EFRC	engine family rating code
DI	direct injection; direct-injected	EG	ethylene glycol
DID	driver information display	EGR	exhaust gas recirculation
DIMM	double inline memory module	EHI	electrohydraulic injector
DIP	dual in-line package (chip)	EIA	Electronics Industries Association
DLC	data link connector	EIS	Electrical Information System
DLC	diagnostic link connector	ELC	extended life coolant
DME	dimethyl ether	EMA	Engine Manufacturers Association
DMF	diesel multistage filter	EMF	electromotive force
DMM	digital multimeter	EMI	electromagnetic interference
DOC	diesel oxidation catalyst	EMM	extended memory manager (ECMs)
DOC	direct-operated check	EMS	engine management system
DOE	U.S. Department of Energy	ENIAC	electronic numeric integrator and calculator
DOHC	double overhead camshaft	EOBR	electronic onboard recorder (HOS tracker)
DOS	disk operating system	EOE	ending of energizing
DOT	Department of Transportation	EOF	end of frame (multiplexing packet)
DPF	diesel particulate filter	EOI	ending of injection
DRAM	dynamic RAM	EOL	end of line (programming)
DSM	district service manager	EOS	electrostatic oil separator
DSRC	dedicated short-range communications	EPA	Environmental Protection Agency
DTC	diagnostic trouble code	EPN	electrohydraulic pintle nozzle
DTNA	Daimler Trucks North America	EPS	engine position sensor
DVD-ROM	digital video disk–read-only memory	ESP	electronic smart power (Cummins)
DVOM	digital volt ohmmeter	ESS	engine speed sensor
DW	double weight (DDC governor)	EST	electronic service tool
E-7	Mack Trucks inline, 6-cylinder, 12-liter engine	ET	Electronic Technician
E7-EUP	Mack Trucks V-MAC III-managed, inline, 6-cylinder, 12-liter engine	E-Tech	Mack Trucks V-MAC III, EUP 12-liter
E-9	Mack Trucks V8 engine	ETR	energized-to-run
ECAP	electronic control analyzer programmer (Caterpillar EST)	EUI	electronic unit injector
ECB	electronic circuit breaker	EUP	electronic unit pump
ECI	electronically controlled injection	EV	electric-only vehicle
ECM	electronic/engine control module	FACR	fuel-amplified common rail (system)
ECS	evaporative (emission) control system	FARC	fuel-air ratio control (Caterpillar)
ECT	engine coolant temperature	FDCS	fuel demand command signal (Navistar)
ECU	electronic control unit	Fe	iron
EDC	Electronic Diesel Control (Bosch)	FET	field effect transistor
EDCs	electronic digital calipers	FFM	fuel filter module
EDR	electronic data recorders	FIC	fuel injection controller
EDU	electronic distributor unit (DDEC)	FID	flame ionization detection
EEC	electronic engine control	FIS	Fleet Information Software (Caterpillar)
EECU	electronic engine control unit	FM	frequency modulation
EEPROM	electronically erasable, programmable read-only memory		

FMCSA	Federal Motor Carrier Safety Alliance		HPI-TP	high-pressure injection-time pressure
FMI	failure/fault mode indicator (SAE)		HRC	Rockwell "C" hardness
FMVSS	Federal Motor Vehicle Safety Standard		HTHS	high-temperature, high-shear (engine lube)
FPS	fuel pressure sensor		HVAC	heating, ventilating, and air-conditioning
FRC	fuel ratio control		HVER	heavy vehicle event recorder
GCM	governor control module		I2V	infrastructure-to-vehicle
GE	grid electrification		IAP	injection actuation pressure
GEG	gasoline equivalent gallon		IAT	intake ambient temperature
GFI	gasoline fuel injector		IBC	inner base circle
GHG	greenhouse gas		I/C	integrated circuit
GM	General Motors (Corporation)		ICM	individual clutch modulation
gnd	ground		ICP	injection control pressure (Navistar)
gph	gallons per hour		ICU	instrument control unit
GPS	global positioning satellite		id	inside diameter
GUI	graphical user interface		ID	identify
GWP	global warming potential		IDI	indirect injection/injected
H	hydrogen		IDM	injector driver module (Navistar)
H_2O	water		IEEE	Institute of Electrical and Electronics Engineers
HADI	hydraulically amplified diesel injector		I-EGR	internal exhaust gas recirculation
HAMMER	hydraulic hybrid, advanced materials and multifuel engine research		IFI	Industrial Fastener Institute
HC	hydrocarbon		IFSM	integrated fuel system module (Cummins)
HCCI	homogenous charge compression ignition		IHP	indicated horsepower
HDEO	heavy-duty engine oil		IMEP	indicated mean effective pressure
HD-OBD	heavy-duty onboard diagnostics		IMT	intake manifold temperature
HE	hydroerosive (machining technology)		INFORM	Cummins data analysis software
HEI	Health Effects Institute		INSITE	Cummins PC software
HEST	high exhaust system temperature		INSPEC	Cummins data analysis software
HEUI	hydraulically actuated electronic unit injector		ip	indicated power
HEV	hybrid electric vehicle		IPR	injection pressure regulator (Navistar)
Hg	mercury		IQCC	injection/injection quantity calibration code
HH-EST	handheld electronic service tool		IRIS	infrared information system
HHV	hydraulic hybrid vehicle		IRT	injector response time
HIKE	high-intensity kaizen event		IS	Interact System
HLA	hydraulic launch assist		ISB	idle speed balance (DDEC test)
HOAT	hybrid organic acid technology (Dodge antifreeze)		ISB	Interact System B series (Cummins) 6.7-liter engine
HOS	hours of service		ISC	idle speed compensation (DDEC)
HPDI	high-pressure direct injection/injector		ISC	Interact System C series (Cummins) 8.2-liter engine
HPHDDCR	high-pressure heavy-duty diesel common rail (Delphi)		ISIS	International Service Information System
HPI	high-pressure injection (Cummins)		ISL	Interact System L series (Cummins) 8.9-liter engine
HPI-PT	high-pressure injection pressure time (off-highway system)			

ISM	Interact System M series (Cummins) 11-liter engine
ISO	International Standards Organization
ISX	Interact System X series— Cummins 15- or 12-liter engine
IT	information technology
IVS	idle validation switch
IVT	injector verification test
K-19	Cummins inline, 6-cylinder, 19-liter engine
KAM	keep-alive memory
KAMPWR	electrical circuit that powers KAM (Navistar)
km	kilometer
KOEO	key-on, engine-off
kPa	kilopascals
L-10	Cummins inline, 6-cylinder, 10-liter engine
LAN	local area network
LCD	liquid crystal display
LDS	load disconnect switch
LED	light-emitting diode
Li-ion	lithium ion (battery)
LiMePo	lithium metal polymer
Li-Po	lithium polymer
LNG	liquefied natural gas
LPG	liquid petroleum gas
LRR	low rolling resistance (LRR)
LS	limiting speed
LS	low sulfur
LSFC	load specific fuel consumption
LSG	limiting speed governing/ governor
LTF	low-temperature filter
m	meter
M-11	Cummins inline, 6-cylinder, 11-liter engine
MAF	mass airflow
MAP	manifold actual pressure
MB-906	Mercedes-Benz 6.4-liter engine
MB-4000	Mercedes-Benz 12.8-liter engine
MCM	motor control module (DD)
MD	Master Diagnostics (Navistar)
MEP	mean effective pressure
MEUI	mechanically actuated, electronically controlled electronic unit injector
MHz	megahertz
MID	message identifier (J1587)
MID	module identifier
MIL	malfunction indicator lamp/ light

MIPS	millions of instructions per second
mm	millimeter
mmf	magnetomotive force
MON	motor octane number
MOSFET	metal oxide semiconductor field effect transformer
MP-7	Mack Trucks 11-liter engine
MP-8	Mack Trucks 13-liter engine
MP-10	Mack Trucks 16-liter engine
MPa	megapascals
MPC	multiprotocol cartridge/card (ProLink)
MPP	massively parallel processors
MSDS	material safety data sheet
MSF	modular switch field
MTA	Metropolitan Transportation Authority (NYC)
MTSO	mobile telephone switching office
MUI	mechanical unit injector
MUT	machine under test
MX-Series	Paccar DAF engines
N	nitrogen
N-14	Cummins I-6, 14-liter engine
NA	naturally aspirated
NAC	NO_x adsorber catalyst
NAFTA	North American Free Trade Agreement
$NaNiCl_2$	sodium metal hydride
NAP	network access point (wireless data transfer module)
NBF	German acronym for needle motion sensor (Bosch)
NG	natural gas
NHTSA	National Highway Transportation Safety Association
NIASE	National Institute for Automotive Service Excellence
NiMH	nickel metal hydride (battery)
N•m	Newton-meter
NO_2	nitrogen dioxide
NOP	nozzle opening pressure
NO_x	oxides of nitrogen
NPGs	nonaqueous propylene glycols
NPN	negative-positive-negative (semiconductor)
NSI	Navistar Service Information
NTC	negative temperature coefficient
NTC	National Transport Commission (Australia)
NTDE	new technology diesel exhaust
NVMS	nozzle valve motion sensor

NV-RAM	nonvolatile random access memory		PH	parallel hybrid
O	oxygen		PHC	partially burned hydrocarbon
OAT	organic acid technology (antifreeze)		PHH	parallel hydraulic hybrid
			PID	parameter identifier (J1587)
OBC	outer base circle		PLC	power line carrier (multiplexing)
OBD	onboard diagnostics		PLC	programmable logic controller (smart relay)
OC	occurrence count			
OCR	optical character recognition		PLD	German acronym meaning ECM (MB engines)
OCV	open circuit voltage			
od	outside diameter		PLN	pump-line-nozzle (diesel fuel injection)
OEM	original equipment manufacturer			
			PLV	pressure limiting valve
OHC	overhead camshaft		PM	particulate matter
OI	optimized idle		PM	preventive maintenance
O/O	owner operator		PMI	preventive maintenance inspection
OOS	out of service			
OPEC	Organization of Petroleum Exporting Countries		PN	positive-negative (junction semiconductor)
			PNP	positive-negative-positive (semiconductor)
OPS	oil pressure sensor			
OS	operating system		POST	power-on self-test
OSHA	Occupational Safety and Health Administration		POTS	plain old telephone service
			ppb	parts per billion
OTS	oil temperature sensor		PPDM	powertrain power distribution module
Pa	Pascal (unit of pressure)			
PACE/PACER	Cummins partial authority, electronic PT fuel system management		ppm	parts per million
			PRIME	pre-injection metering (Caterpillar HEUI)
			PRT	platinum resistance thermometer
Pb	lead			
PC	personal computer		PSL	Power Service Literature (DDC)
PC	port closure (spill timing)		PT	pressure-time (Cummins)
PC	proposed category (engine lube)		PTC	positive temperature coefficient
PCM	powertrain control module		PTCM	PT (pump) control module
PCM	pulse code modulation		PTG	pressure-time governor controlled (Cummins)
PCMCIA	Personal Computer Card International Association			
			PTO	power takeoff
PCU	powertrain control module		PTT	Premium Tech Tool
PCV	positive crankcase ventilation		PTWA	plasma transfer wire arc
PDI	pre-delivery inspection		PW	pulse width
PDM	power distribution module		PWM	pulse width modulation/ modulated
PE	pump (injection) enclosed (actuation—integral camshaft)			
			PX-6	Paccar 6.7-liter engine
PEEC	programmable electronic engine control (Caterpillar)		PX-8	Paccar 8.2-liter engine
			QCV	quantity control valve (DDC)
PEM	proton exchange membrane (fuel cell)		QR	quick response (code)
			QS	Quantum System
PF	pump (injection) foreign (actuation—external camshaft)		QSOL	QuickServe Online (Cummins)
			R	resistance
			RAM	random access memory
PG	parameter group (J1939)		RCRA	Resource Conservation and Recovery Act
PG	propylene glycol			
PGN	parameter group number (J1939)		R&D	research and development
pH	power hydrogen (measure of acidity/alkalinity)		RDI	remote data interface
			RE	Bosch rack actuator

RF	radio frequency		SO_2	sulfur dioxide
rms	root mean square		SOF	soluble organic fraction
RODS	Records of Duty Standards (FMCSA)		SOH	state of health
			SOHC	single overhead camshaft
ROI	return on investment		SOI	start of injection
ROM	read-only memory		SOM	start-of-message
RON	research octane number		SPG	suspect parameter group
RP	recommended practice		SPL	smoke puff limiter
RPCV	rail pressure control valve		SRAM	static random access memory
rpm	revolutions per minute		SRS	synchronous reference sensor (DDEC)
RPMC	rail pressure management control		SSC	single speed control
RPS	rail pressure sensor		SSU	seconds Saybolt universal (fluidity rating)
RQV	Bosch VS governor			
RS	regeneration system (DPF)		STC	step timing control (Cummins)
RS-232	port standard telephone jack		STEO	stop engine override
RSG	road speed governing		STEP	Shorepower Truck Electrification Project
RSL	road speed limit			
RSV	Bosch VS governor		STI	self-test input
RTD	resistance temperature detector		STOP	stop engine light
S	sulfur		SVGA	super video graphics array
SA	source address (J1939)		SVA	spill valve solenoid
SAE	Society of Automotive Engineers		TBN	total base number
SAE J1587	data bus software protocols		TBS	turbo-boost sensor
SAE J1667	emission testing standards		TCP	transmission control protocol
SAE J1708	data bus hardware protocols		TCU	transmission control unit
SAE J1930	recommended acronyms/ terminology		TDC	telematics diagnostic connector
			TDC	top dead center
SAE J1939	data bus hardware/software protocols		TDS	total dissolved solids
			TEL	tetraethyl lead (gasoline)
SAE J1962	the light-duty ALDL		TEL	top engine limit (Cat: high idle)
SAM	signal-detect and actuation module		TEM	timing event marker
			TIG	tungsten inert gas (welding)
SC	supercapacitor		TIR	total indicated runout
SCA	supplemental coolant additive		TMC	Technology and Maintenance Council
SCFR	squeeze cast, fiber reinforced			
SCR	selective catalytic reduction		TML	tetramethyl lead (gasoline)
SCR	silicone-controlled rectifier		TP	throttle position
SCSI	small computer system interface		TP	time pressure (Cummins)
SEL	stop engine light		tpi	teeth per inch
SEO	stop engine override		tpi	threads per inch
Series 50	DDC I-4, DDEC engine		TPS	throttle position sensor
Series 55	DDC I-6 EUP, DDEC engine		TQM	total quality management
Series 60	DDC I-6, DDEC engine		TRS	timing reference sensor (DDEC)
Series 92	DDC two-stroke cycle engine			
SFC	specific fuel consumption		TSB	technical service bulletin
SHH	series hydraulic hybrid		TT	tailored torque (DDC)
SI	spark-ignited		TT	Tech Tool™
SI	Système International (metric system)		TTS	transmission tailshaft speed
			TTY	torque-to-yield
SID	subsystem identifier (J1939)		TVS	trapped volume spill
SIMM	single inline memory module		UC	ultracapacitor
SIS	service information system		UC	universal coolant
SM	ServiceMaxx (Navistar diagnostic software)		UFS	unintended fueling sensor
			UHC	unburned hydrocarbon

UIS	unit injection system (Bosch EUI fuel system)	VIA	visible image area
ULEV	ultra-low emissions vehicle	VIN	vehicle identification number
ULS	ultra-low sulfur (fuel)	VIP	vehicle interface program
ULSD	ultra-low sulfur diesel	V-MAC	vehicle management and control
UNC	unified (thread) coarse (United National Coarse)	VMRS	vehicle maintenance reporting standards
UNF	unified (thread) fine (United National Fine)	VOC	volatile organic compound
UPC	universal product code	VP	visibility package (DD)
UPCRI	ultra high-pressure heavy-duty common rail fuel injection	VPM	vehicle personality module (Caterpillar/Navistar)
UPS	unit pump system (Bosch)	VR	voltage regulator
USB	universal serial bus	V-Ref	reference voltage (almost always ±5 V-DC)
UV	ultraviolet	VS	variable speed
V	volt	VSC	variable speed control
V21	vehicle-to-infrastructure (telematics)	VSC	vehicle stability control
V2V	vehicle-to-vehicle (telematics)	VSG	variable speed governor/governing
VAT	volts-amps tester	VSL	variable speed limit
V-Bat	battery system voltage	VSL	vehicle speed limit
VCAD	Volvo (vehicle) computer assisted diagnostics	VSS	vehicle speed sensor
VCC	vehicle control center	VT	Virtual Technician
VCI	vehicle communication interface	VVA	variable valve actuator
VCO	valve closes orifice (nozzle)	VVT	variable valve timing
VCP	valve closing pressure	W	watt
VCU	vehicle control unit	WEC	waterless engine coolant
VD-12	Volvo 12-liter engine	WHMIS	Workplace Hazardous Materials Information System
VDL	vehicle data link	WIF	water in fuel (sensor)
VDT	video display terminal	WiFi	wireless fidelity
VECTRO	Volvo electronic controls	WIP	wireless inspection processing (telematics)
VED-11	Volvo Trucks 11-liter engine	WIPS	wireless inspection processing system
VED-13	Volvo Trucks 13-liter engine		
VED-16	Volvo Trucks 16-liter engine	WORM	write once, read many
VEPS	vehicle electronics programming system	WOT	wide-open throttle
VG	variable geometry	WRI	wireless roadside inspection
VGA	video graphics array	WT	World Transmission (Allison)
VGT	variable-geometry turbocharging	WVL2	wireless vehicle link 2
VI	viscosity index	XPI	extreme pressure injection (Cummins CR)

INDEX